Inquiry into
BIOLOGY

Authors

Helen Colbourne
Forest Lawn High School
Calgary, Alberta

Bob Constantin
Writer/Educator
Formerly of Bishop McNally High School
Calgary, Alberta

Darcy Dobell
Professional Writer/Educator
Tofino, British Columbia

Claudia Fehres
William Aberhart High School
Calgary, Alberta

Deborah MacFadyen
Jack James High School
Calgary, Alberta

Adrienne Mason
Professional Writer
Tofino, British Columbia

George Thomson
Crescent Heights High School
Medicine Hat, Alberta

Alexandra Venter
Professional Writer
Calgary, Alberta

Contributing Authors

Jonathan Bocknek
Educational Writer
Vallican, British Columbia

Jenna Dunlop
Educational Writer
Toronto, Ontario

Glen Hutton
Educational Writer
Vulcan, Alberta

Christine Weber
Educational Writer
Chilliwack, British Columbia

McGraw-Hill Ryerson

Toronto   Montréal   Boston   Burr Ridge, IL   Dubuque, IA   Madison, WI   New York   San Francisco
St. Louis   Bangkok   Bogotá   Caracas   Kuala Lumpur   Lisbon   London   Madrid   Mexico City
Milan   New Delhi   Santiago   Seoul   Singapore   Sydney   Taipei

*COPIES OF THIS BOOK
MAY BE OBTAINED BY
CONTACTING:*
McGraw-Hill Ryerson Ltd.

WEB SITE:
http://www.mcgrawhill.ca

E-MAIL:
orders@mcgrawhill.ca

TOLL-FREE FAX:
1-800-463-5885

TOLL-FREE CALL:
1-800-565-5758

OR BY MAILING
YOUR ORDER TO:
McGraw-Hill Ryerson
Order Department
300 Water Street
Whitby, ON L1N 9B6

Please quote the ISBN and
title when placing your order.

The McGraw·Hill Companies

McGraw-Hill Ryerson
Inquiry Into Biology

The information and activities in this textbook have been carefully developed and
reviewed by professionals to ensure safety and accuracy. However, the publisher shall
not be liable for any damages resulting, in whole or in part, from the reader's use of
the material. Although appropriate safety procedures are discussed and highlighted
throughout the textbook, the safety of students remains the responsibility of the
classroom teacher, the principal, and the school board district.

ISBN-13 978-0-07-096052-7
ISBN-10 0-07-096052-6

www.mcgrawhill.ca

5 6 7 8 9 TCP 1 9 8 7 6 5 4 3 2 1

Printed and bound in Canada

Care has been taken to trace ownership of copyright material contained in this text.
The publishers will gladly accept any information that will enable them to rectify
any reference or credit in subsequent printings.

SCIENCE PUBLISHER: Keith Owen Richards
PROJECT MANAGER: Susan Girvan
SENIOR DEVELOPMENTAL EDITOR: Jonathan Bocknek
DEVELOPMENTAL EDITORS: Glynn Gomes, Leslie Macumber, Alexandra Venter
SUPERVISING EDITOR: Crystal Shortt
PHOTO RESEARCH & PERMISSIONS: Pronk&Associates
EDITORIAL ASSISTANTS: Erin Hartley, Michelle Malda
MANAGER, PRODUCTION SERVICES: Yolanda Pigden
PRODUCTION COORDINATOR: Andree Davis
SET-UP PHOTOGRAPHY: Dave Starrett/Pronk&Associates
COVER DESIGN: Pronk&Associates
ART DIRECTION: Pronk&Associates
ELECTRONIC PAGE MAKE-UP: Pronk&Associates
COVER IMAGE: (background), © CHARLES McDOWELL/Grant Heilman Photography;
(large inset), © Reino Hanninen/Alamy; (medium inset), © Eric Crichton/CORBIS;
(small inset), © Dr Jeremy Burgess/SPL/PUBLIPHOTO

Acknowledgements

Producing a textbook of high quality is a true team effort, requiring the input and expertise of a very large number of people. The authors, editorial team, and publishers of this book would like to convey our sincere thanks to the reviewers listed below who provided crucial analyses of our draft manuscript, and often provided reviews of designed pages. Their assistance was invaluable in helping us develop a text that we hope you will find completely appropriate for your teaching and your students' learning. In addition, the comments from those teachers (and their students!) who took part in the field testing of this material were very helpful and much appreciated. We realize that tackling a new curriculum with a text-in-progress is a big challenge, and we thank you for being up to the task.

We also thank the following writers who researched and prepared the Special Features in *Inquiry into Biology*: Kirsten Craven, Jenna Dunlop, Susan Girvan, Eric Grace, Barbara Hehner, Ann Heide, Lynne Kailan, Denyse O'Leary, George Thomson, and Alexandra Venter. Finally, we thank the talented and dedicated members of the team at Pronk&Associates who did their best no matter what challenges they faced.

Reviewers

Susan Barker
University of Alberta
Edmonton, Alberta

Agnieszka Barwacz-Riou
Strathmore High School
Strathmore, Alberta

Erich Berndt
Sir Winston Churchill High School
Calgary, Alberta

Dean Brown
Crescent Heights High School
Medicine Hat, Alberta

Stephen Brown
Lord Beaverbrook High School
Calgary, Alberta

Duncan Buchanan
St. Francis Xavier High School
Edmonton, Alberta

Tanya Buhlmann
Queen Elizabeth High School
Edmonton, Alberta

Jenai Christensen
Ross Sheppard High School
Edmonton, Alberta

Maureen Cimino
Jasper Place High School
Edmonton, Alberta

Roger Cowan
Brooks Composite High School
Brooks, Alberta

Michael Craig
William Aberhart High School
Calgary, Alberta

Jane Dyke
Ross Sheppard High School
Edmonton, Alberta

Ken Ealey
St. Jerome, A Science Academy
Edmonton Catholic Schools
Edmonton, Alberta

Rhonda Elser
Calgary Catholic Separate
School Board
Calgary, Alberta

Claudia Fehres
William Aberhart High School
Calgary, Alberta

Eulalia Fernandez
William Aberhart High School
Calgary, Alberta

Evelyn Fray
Ross Sheppard High School
Edmonton, Alberta

Julianne Hafer
Ross Sheppard Senior High
Edmonton, Alberta

Gary Hanna
Memorial Composite High School
Stoney Plain, Alberta

Natasha Heron
Henry Wise Wood High School
Calgary, Alberta

Robert C. Hicks
Lord Beaverbrook Senior
High School
Calgary, Alberta

Gord Jasper
Dr. E.P. Scarlett Senior High School
Calgary, Alberta

Stephen Jeans
University of Calgary
Calgary, Alberta

Christina Kang
Notre Dame High School
Calgary, Alberta

Mark Ladd
Peace River High School
Peace River, Alberta

Kathryn Lowther
Western Canada High School
Calgary, Alberta

Ann Lukey
Ecole Secondaire Beaumont
Composite High School
Beaumont, Alberta

William MacLean
Forest Lawn High School
Calgary, Alberta

Contents

UNIT 1

ENERGY AND MATTER EXCHANGE IN THE BIOSPHERE

UNIT 2

ECOSYSTEMS AND POPULATION CHANGE 72

UNIT 5

UNIT 6

UNIT 7

UNIT 8

POPULATION AND
COMMUNITY DYNAMICS

Safety in Your Biology Laboratory

Scientific investigations are integrated throughout this textbook. Keep in mind at all times that working in a biology laboratory can involve some risks. *Therefore, become familiar with all facets of laboratory safety, especially for performing investigations safely.* To make the investigations and activities in *Inquiry into Biology* safe and enjoyable for you and others who share a common working environment:

- become familiar with and use the following safety rules and procedures,
- follow any special instructions from your teacher, and
- *always read* over the safety notes before beginning each lab activity. Your teacher will tell you about any additional safety rules that are in place at your school.

General Rules

1. Inform your teacher if you have any allergies, medical conditions, or physical problems (including a hearing impairment) that could affect your work in the laboratory.
2. Inform your teacher if you wear contact lenses. If possible, wear eyeglasses instead of contact lenses, but remember that eyeglasses are not a substitute for proper eye protection.
3. Read through all of the steps in the investigation before beginning. Be sure to read and understand the *Cautions* and safety symbols at the beginning of each Investigation or Launch Lab.
4. Listen carefully to any special instructions your teacher provides. Get your teacher's approval before beginning any investigation that you have designed yourself.
5. *Never* eat, drink, or taste any substances in the lab. Never pipette with your mouth. If you are asked to smell a substance, do not hold it directly under your nose. Keep the object at least 20 cm away, and waft the fumes toward your nostrils with your hand.

Safety Equipment and First Aid

6. When you are directed to do so, wear safety goggles and protective equipment in the laboratory. Be sure you understand all safety labels on materials and pieces of equipment. Familiarize yourself with the safety symbols used in this textbook, and with the WHMIS symbols found on the following page.
7. Know the location and proper use of the nearest fire extinguisher, fire blanket, fire alarm, first-aid kit, and eye-wash station (if available).
8. Never use water to fight an electrical equipment fire. Severe electrical shock may result. Use a carbon dioxide or dry chemical fire extinguisher. Report any damaged equipment or frayed cords to your teacher.

9. Cuts, scratches, or any other injuries in the laboratory should receive immediate medical attention, no matter how minor they seem. If any part of your body comes in contact with a potentially dangerous substance, wash the area immediately and thoroughly with water.
10. If you get any material in your eyes, do not touch them. Wash your eyes immediately and continuously for 15 minutes, and make sure your teacher is informed. If you wear contact lenses, take your lenses out immediately if you get material in your eyes. Failing to do so may result in material being trapped behind the contact lenses. Flush your eyes continuously with water for 15 minutes, as above.

Lab Precautions

11. Make sure your work area is clean, dry, and well-organized.
12. Wear heat-resistant safety gloves and any other safety equipment that your teacher or the Safety Precautions suggest, when heating any item. Be especially careful with a hot plate that may look as though it has cooled down. If you do receive a burn, apply cold water to the burned area immediately. Make sure your teacher is notified.
13. Make sure the work area, the area of the socket, and your hands are dry when touching electrical cords, plugs, sockets, or equipment such as hot plates and microscopes. Ensure the cords on your equipment are placed neatly where they will not be a tripping hazard. Turn OFF all electrical equipment before connecting to or disconnecting from a power supply. When unplugging electrical equipment, do not pull the cord—grasp the plug firmly at the socket and pull gently.
14. When using a scalpel or knife, cut away from yourself and others. Always keep the pointed end of any sharp objects directed away from yourself and others when carrying such objects.
15. When you are heating a test tube, always slant it so the mouth points away from you and others.

Safety for Animal Dissections

16. Ensure your work area is well ventilated.
17. Always wear appropriate protective equipment for your skin, clothing, and eyes. This will prevent preservatives from harming you in any way.
18. If your scalpel blade breaks, do not replace it yourself. Your teacher will do this for you.
19. Make sure you are familiar with the proper use of all dissecting equipment. Whenever possible, use a probe or your gloved fingers to explore a specimen. Scalpels are not appropriate for this. They can damage the structures you are examining.

Laboratory Clean-up

20. Wipe up all spills immediately, and always inform your teacher. Acid or base spills on clothing or skin should be diluted and rinsed with water. Small spills of acid solutions can be neutralized with sodium hydrogen carbonate (baking soda). Small spills of basic solutions can be neutralized with sodium hydrogen sulfate or citric acid.

21. Never use your hands to pick up broken glass. Use a broom and dustpan. Dispose of broken glass and solid substances in the proper containers, as directed by your teacher.

22. Dispose of all specimens, materials, chemicals, and other wastes as instructed by your teacher. Do not dispose of materials in a sink or drain unless directed to do so.

23. Clean equipment before putting it away, according to your teacher's instructions. Turn off the water and gas. Disconnect electrical devices. Wash your hands thoroughly after all laboratory investigations.

Working with Living Organisms

24. When in the field, be careful and observant at all times to avoid injury, such as tripping, being poked by branches, etc., or coming into contact with poisonous plants.

25. On a field trip, try not to disturb the area any more than is absolutely necessary. If you must move anything, do so carefully. If you are asked to remove plant material, do so gently. Take as little as possible.

26. In the classroom, remember to treat living organisms with respect. Make sure all living organisms receive humane treatment while they are in your care. If it is possible, return living organisms to their natural environment when your work is done.
    NOTE: Some schools do not permit labs that involve bacteria. Your teacher will inform you of your school board's policy in this regard.

27. When working with micro-organisms, observe your results through the clear lid of the petri dish. Do not open the cover. Make sure that you do not touch your eyes, mouth, or any other part of your face during these investigations.

28. When handling live bacterial cultures, always wear gloves and eye protection. Be careful not to spill the cultures. Wash your hands thoroughly with soap immediately after handling any bacterial culture.

29. Carefully clean and disinfect your work area after handling bacterial cultures and other living organisms.

30. Follow your teacher's instructions about disposal of your swabs, petri dishes containing your cultures, and any other disposable materials used in the lab.

31. Your teacher will autoclave cultures before discarding them, if an autoclave is available. If an autoclave is not available, the culture surface should be sprayed with a 10% solution of chlorine bleach. (Your school may have other disposal techniques.)

Safety Symbols

	Disposal Alert This symbol appears when care must be taken to dispose of materials properly.
	Biological Hazard This symbol appears when there is danger involving bacteria, fungi, or protists.
	Thermal Safety This symbol appears as a reminder to be careful when handling hot objects.
	Sharp Object Safety This symbol appears when there is danger of cuts or punctures caused by the use of sharp objects.
	Fume Safety This symbol appears when chemicals or chemical reactions could cause dangerous fumes.
	Electrical Safety This symbol appears as a reminder to be careful when using electrical equipment.
	Skin Protection Safety This symbol appears when the use of caustic chemicals might irritate the skin or when contact with micro-organisms might transmit infection.
	Clothing Protection Safety A lab apron should be worn when this symbol appears.
	Fire Safety This symbol appears as a reminder to be careful around open flames.
	Eye Safety This symbol appears when there is danger to the eyes and safety glasses should be worn.
	Poison Safety This symbol appears when poisonous substances are used.
	Chemical Safety This symbol appears when chemicals could cause burns or are poisonous if absorbed through the skin.
	Animal Safety This symbol appears when live animals are studied and the safety of the animals and the students must be ensured.

WHMIS Symbols for Hazardous Materials

Compressed Gas	Flammable and Combustible Material
Oxidizing Material	Corrosive Material
Poisonous and Infectious Material Causing Immediate and Serious Toxic Effects	Poisonous and Infectious Material Causing Other Toxic Effects
Biohazardous Infectious Material	Dangerously Reactive Material

Safety in Your Online Activities

The Internet is like any other resource you use for research—you should confirm the source of the information and the credentials of those supplying it to make sure the information is credible before you use it in your work.

Unlike other resources, however, the Internet has some unique pitfalls you should be aware of, and practices you should follow.

- It's easy to waste a lot of time following links that "look interesting" long after you've found the information you need. Take advantage of the online links provided at *www.albertabiology.ca* to use your Internet research time efficiently. Develop your Internet discipline early: focus on what you need to know, find it, and log off.

- Online content is constantly changing. If you find some useful information once, there's no guarantee that it will be there when you go back to look for it. You may want to print it in order to have a permanent record. Always include the source and date of the information you're saving.

- When you copy or save something from the Internet, you could be saving more than information. Be aware that information you pick up could also include hidden, malicious software code (known as "worms" or "Trojans") that could damage your system or destroy data.

- It's easy to find your way into sites that are considered to be "off limits" by teachers and parents. Why are they judged this way? They are off-limits because they contain material that is disturbing, illegal, harmful, and/or was created by exploiting others. There are rules about what is acceptable in print and on the airwaves; they apply to Internet material as well. Also be aware that these site visits can come back to "haunt" you if you pick up "cookies" (electronic tags), that identify your computer as a target for more of the same.

- *Never, ever* give out personal information online. This includes your name, your age, your gender, your email address, street address, phone number, or your picture. Protect your privacy, even if it means not registering to use a site that looks helpful. Discuss ways to use the site while protecting your privacy with your teacher. There may be a way to access it through the school or the school library.

- Report any online content or activity that you suspect is illegal to your teacher. This can include online hate, harassment, cyberstalking, cyberbullying, or attempts to lure you into a face-to-face meeting with a stranger; dangerous activities concerning terrorism or illegal weapons; or physical threats. Discuss ways to deal with such material with your teacher; report it to the Internet Supervisor at your school, and find out what the school policy is for dealing with such material.

With your teacher and fellow students, discuss ways to apply critical thinking to online research and develop safe Internet practices.

Introducing *Inquiry into Biology*

Biology—the study of the living world—has long been a part of your science education. *Inquiry into Biology* will take you to a deeper level of understanding, helping you build on your knowledge of living systems, energy, matter, and the cycles and pathways that unite them as an interconnected whole.

Introducing Your Inquiry

Start with the **Unit Opener** to get a sense of the topics you are about to investigate. Try to answer the **Focussing Questions** based on what you know now. Before you begin a unit, log on to *www.albertabiology.ca* to take the **Unit Prequiz**. You can use the quiz to find out what you recall from earlier science studies—results are available at the click of a button. If you need to refresh your memory, turn to the **Unit Preparation** feature.

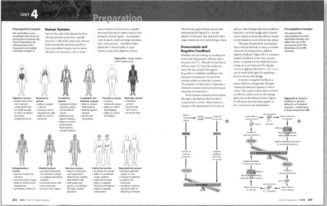

Using *Inquiry into Biology*

Each chapter opens with a list of **Chapter Concepts**, giving you an overview of key points and how they relate to one another. The opening text and photograph will give you the context, and you will use the **Launch Lab** to do or discuss an idea that will be explored further in the chapter.

Each section opens with Section Outcomes that outline the knowledge and skills you will develop in each section. The list of **Key Terms** highlights biology vocabulary you will be using. Each key term appears in boldface type in the section, where it is explained in context, and it is defined again in the **Glossary** at the back of the book.

Watch for the **BiologyFile** feature in the margins of many pages. **FYI** gives you instant facts and fascinating tidbits. **Try This** challenges you to test an idea. **Web Link** connects you to the McGraw-Hill Alberta Biology web site, where you can inquire further about a topic of interest.

The variety of **Investigations** presented may be directing you to conduct an inquiry to confirm results of experiments done by others, design a procedure to conduct your own investigation, or hone your skills in decision-making by gathering data and evaluating evidence in order to make decisions and solve practical problems. **Thought Labs** guide you in analyzing data or researching information to look for patterns, form opinions, and evaluate points of view.

Check out the back of the book for **Appendices** that detail basic scientific practices and procedures—from using measurement and microscopes to a quick review of related chemistry and tips for writing Diploma Exams.

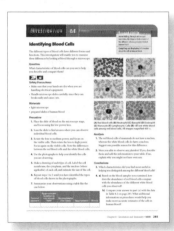
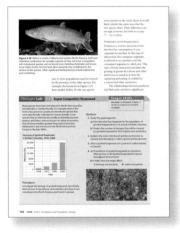

Real-world Applications

The **Connections** feature in each chapter spotlights a specific idea, technology, or issue that touches your life. Find out, for example, how Albertans are linked to a hippopotamus population in Ghana, making money (and energy) from manure, using traditional healing technologies, and reintroducing an endangered species to its traditional homeland among the Blackfeet Nation in the United States.

The **Career Focus** at the end of each unit features an interview with someone whose work in a particular field of biology may inspire your own career aspirations. You will also find a sampling of related careers that draw upon other fields within and beyond those of biology.

Assessing Your Learning

Use the following opportunities to pause and reflect on your learning.

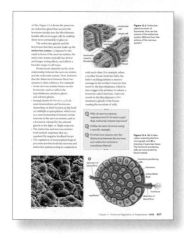

- **Questions for Comprehension** ("Q questions") check basic understanding of concepts.

- The **Section Summary** lists key points.

- The **Section Review** helps you gauge your understanding of essential knowledge and applications.

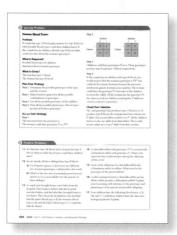

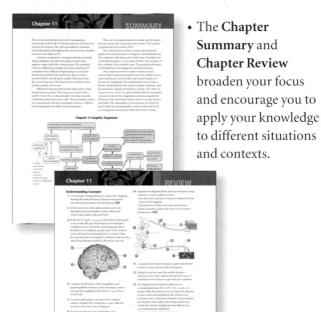

- **Sample Problems** model techniques related to your study of genetics, and **Practice Problems** provide opportunities for you to develop and assess your ability to solve these problems.

- The **Chapter Summary** and **Chapter Review** broaden your focus and encourage you to apply your knowledge to different situations and contexts.

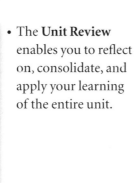

- The **Unit Review** enables you to reflect on, consolidate, and apply your learning of the entire unit.

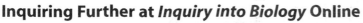

Inquiring Further at *Inquiry into Biology* Online

In addition to the Unit Prequizzes and Web Links, *Inquiry into Biology* Online at *www.albertabiology.ca* highlights and reinforces key points from each chapter. The Electronic Study Partner aids and reinforces your understanding of key concepts and skills. Your web resource is also packed with study tips, strategies, research tools, and opportunities to extend your learning in many new directions

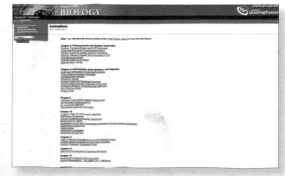

Energy and Matter Exchange in the Biosphere

General Outcomes

In this unit, you will

- explain the constant transfer of energy through the biosphere and its ecosystems

- explain the cycling of matter through the biosphere

- describe energy and matter exchange in the biosphere as an open system and explain how this maintains equilibrium

Unit Contents

Focussing Questions

1 Why can matter be recycled in the biosphere, while energy must be supplied constantly?

2 What roles do photosynthesis and cellular respiration play in the transfer of energy and the availability of matter in the biosphere?

3 How do human activities and technologies affect the quality and availability of energy and matter in the biosphere?

Unit PreQuiz ?

www.albertabiology.ca

As 2004 drew to a close, two astronauts onboard the International Space Station (ISS) waited—perhaps a little nervously—for the arrival of a vital care package. In early December, they had been placed on a restricted diet to conserve their dwindling food supply. On December 24, the Russian Space Agency launched an emergency shuttle, which reached the station two days later. The shuttle's precious cargo included fuel, oxygen, water, and the welcome addition of fresh food. Had the mission failed, the astronauts would have been faced with only two options: abandon the station or starve.

In the future, astronauts will not face food shortages. They will benefit from technologies that reuse and recycle all solid, liquid, and gaseous materials—including wastes. Such systems are now being developed and tested. The ISS is already outfitted with solar arrays to capture and store the Sun's energy for use in lighting, heating, and powering machinery.

To be fully self-sufficient, the ISS must be able to maintain all life onboard, as well as provide all of the matter and energy needed to support its mechanical systems. This is the most ambitious project ever attempted—a self-sustaining, life-supporting system beyond the boundaries and influence of Earth. What lessons might the ISS offer, in return, to the citizens of the planet that conceived it?

Prerequisite Concepts

This unit builds on your knowledge of the hydrologic cycle.

The Study of Ecology

In 1866, a German biologist and philosopher named Ernst Haeckel invented the term ecology. The word ecology comes from a Greek word that means house or home. At the time, the term was used to describe the observations made and the work done by scientists who studied the nature and history of plants and animals. As more scientists began to ask questions about and explore the interactions of plants and animals, the definition of ecology became broader.

Ecology is the study of the relationships between living things (organisms) and their non-living surroundings, the environment. Ecologists may be found studying events as varied as the cellular processes of microscopic bacteria and the flow of carbon atoms from air, to land, to water throughout the entire planet. Their work

may be performed on a mountainside, in a canoe, on a park lawn, in a laboratory, and on computers.

Ecology involves observations, insights, and innovations from many areas of study, within science as well as outside it. Figure P1.1 outlines the connections between these areas of study.

The Biosphere— Earth's Life System

A system is an object or a group of objects that a scientist chooses to study. Everything other than the system is referred to as the surroundings. Systems are separated from their surroundings by a boundary, which may be real or arbitrary. For example, a pond has a distinct boundary that separates the pond from its surroundings. A grassland, on the other hand, may gradually merge with a neighbouring forested region.

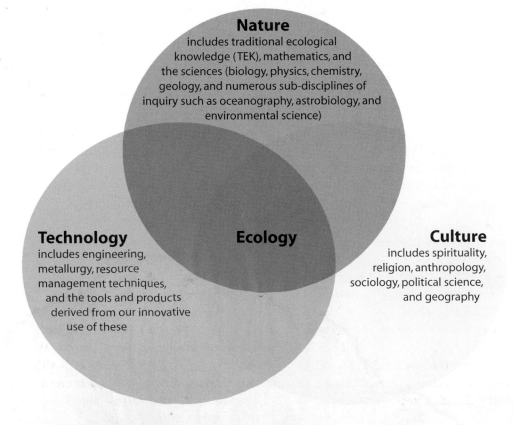

Figure P1.1 Ecology links natural, cultural, and technological dimensions of inquiry. Many areas within and outside of science contribute to our understanding, use, and management of the environment.

Nature
includes traditional ecological knowledge (TEK), mathematics, and the sciences (biology, physics, chemistry, geology, and numerous sub-disciplines of inquiry such as oceanography, astrobiology, and environmental science)

Technology
includes engineering, metallurgy, resource management techniques, and the tools and products derived from our innovative use of these

Ecology

Culture
includes spirituality, religion, anthropology, sociology, political science, and geography

Biosphere: all of the areas on Earth that are inhabited by and that support life

Atmosphere: the gaseous part of Earth, concentrated mainly within 10 km of Earth's surface, but also extending hundreds of kilometers higher

Geosphere: the solid, mainly rocky part of Earth (also called the lithosphere)

Hydrosphere: all of the water (solid as well as liquid) that exists and moves through the geosphere

Figure P1.2 Organisms may be found on land, in water, several kilometres into the atmosphere, and several metres into the soil. All organisms and their non-living environment make up the biosphere.

In such a case, the boundary of the grassland would be identified by an observer whose boundary might differ from that of another observer.

Systems may be classified into two types according to their interactions with their surroundings.

- An open system is one that allows energy and matter to cross the system's boundary—to enter and leave it.
- A closed system is one that allows only energy (but not matter) to cross the boundary.

In terms of matter, Earth is essentially a closed system. All the matter that is already here remains here. In terms of energy, Earth is an open system. The Sun's energy enters the atmosphere, where some of it is reflected back into space and some is absorbed by the atmosphere. The remaining energy passes on to Earth's liquid and solid surfaces, where some is reflected and some is absorbed. Eventually and ultimately, all of the energy absorbed by the atmosphere and the surface is radiated back into space as heat.

In Unit 1, you will investigate the interactions of matter and energy with the components of the biosphere—the thin layer of air, land, and water on and in which all life on Earth is found.

Energy Transfer in the Biosphere

Chapter Concepts

1.1 How Energy Enters the Biosphere

- Producers (autotrophs) capture energy and store it by photosynthesis or chemosynthesis.

- Consumers (heterotrophs) and decomposers consume autotrophs and other heterotrophs.

- Matter is cycled in the biosphere, but energy follows a one-way path.

1.2 How Energy Is Transferred in the Biosphere

- Food chains and food webs are models that describe feeding relationships and energy transfer between organisms in trophic levels.

- Ecological pyramids are models that describe relationships between trophic levels quantitatively.

- Because all organisms are connected, changes that affect one trophic level affect other trophic levels.

When the United Nations named Sheila Watt-Cloutier one of 2004's seven Champions of the Earth, the Canadian Inuit leader used the occasion to stress her message. "Our elders and hunters have intimate knowledge of the land, sea ice, and have observed disturbing changes to the Arctic climate and environment," she has said. "Our observations are confirmed by western science in the Arctic Climate Impact Assessment." This report—the work of both scientists and indigenous people—highlights the impacts of global warming, which most scientists agree is linked to increased carbon dioxide concentrations in the atmosphere. This increase is due mainly to the burning of carbon-based energy resources.

All organisms need energy to grow and maintain their lives. In this chapter, you will explore how energy is transferred to organisms and to the environment that supports them.

Considering Connections

In September 2004, Sheila Watt-Cloutier was invited to speak to a committee of United States senators. Her aim was to encourage the United States to reverse its position on the Kyoto Protocol, which came into effect in February 2005. The Kyoto Protocol is an agreement to reduce contributions of gaseous emissions that cause global warming. It was signed by 141 countries.

Procedure

Near the end of her testimony, Watt-Cloutier asked the Senate committee members to consider how the Arctic region, its peoples, and its wildlife are connected to the rest of the world. Read her statement below, and then answer the Analysis questions that follow.

"Use what is happening in the Arctic—the Inuit Story—as a vehicle to re-connect us all, so that we may understand that the planet and its people are one. The Inuit hunter who falls through the depleting and unpredictable sea ice is connected to the cars we drive, the industries we rely upon, and the disposable world we have become."
(*Testimony of Sheila Watt-Cloutier, Chair, Inuit Circumpolar Conference to the Senate Committee on Commerce, Science and Transportation, Washington DC, September 15, 2004.*)

Analysis

1. In what ways could an Inuit hunter falling through the sea ice be connected to the activities of people who live south of the Arctic?

2. Aboriginal peoples often talk about how all living things are connected to, and depend on, one another. What does "being connected" mean to you?

3. Do you think you are connected to everyone and everything in the world? Can you prove that you are *not*? Explain your ideas to a partner, and share them with the class.

On Earth Day 2005, hundreds of people joined to form this shape of an Inuit drum dancer to send a message to the world.

How Energy Enters the Biosphere

Section Outcomes

In this section, you will
- **explain** how energy enters the biosphere through the processes of photosynthesis and chemosynthesis
- **describe** how energy is transferred in the biosphere through the activity of producers (autotrophs) and consumers (heterotrophs)
- **perform** an investigation to demonstrate the storage of light energy in the form of the chemical energy of starch in green plants

Key Terms

cellular respiration
photosynthesis
producers
consumers
albedo
chemosynthesis
primary consumers
secondary consumers
tertiary consumers
decomposers

Figure 1.1 The fast-moving ruby-throated hummingbird is a common site in much of Canada, from Alberta to Nova Scotia. Each summer, the tiny birds begin a migration trek that takes them as far south as Mexico.

The ruby-throated hummingbird (*Archilochus colubris*) is one of Canada's smallest birds. Ranging in size from 7.5 cm to 9 cm, the hummingbird flaps its wings between 55 and 75 times each second. In flight it can reach speeds of nearly 100 km/h. The "hummer" is barely a blur as it darts from flower to flower in search of sweet nectar. Not surprisingly, the ruby-throated hummingbird expends, and therefore needs, a great deal of energy to stay alive. It gets this energy by eating insects caught in flight, as well as from the nectar sipped from the flowers of plants.

The Need for Energy

All organisms need energy to stay alive. They use this energy to grow, maintain body processes, and reproduce. Many kinds of organisms require energy to move, as well. Energy to support these activities is released in the bodies of organisms from carbohydrates and other energy-rich organic molecules. In animals, plants, and most other species (kinds) of organisms, the process that releases this energy is **cellular respiration**. (For a small number of species that live in environments without oxygen, the energy-releasing process is fermentation.) The word equation and chemical equation below summarize the process of cellular respiration.

How is energy stored in energy-rich molecules in the first place? It is stored through the process of photosynthesis. Through **photosynthesis**, plants, algae, and some kinds of bacteria use the Sun's light energy to chemically convert carbon into carbohydrates such as sugars and starches. The word equation and chemical equation below summarize the process of photosynthesis.

cellular respiration	$C_6H_{12}O_6(s)$ + $6O_2(g)$ → $6CO_2(g)$ + $6H_2O(\ell)$ + energy carbohydrates + oxygen → carbon dioxide + water + energy (sugars and starches)
photosynthesis	$6CO_2(g)$ + $6H_2O(\ell)$ + light energy → $C_6H_{12}O_6(s)$ + $6O_2(g)$ carbon dioxide + water + light energy → carbohydrates + oxygen (sugars and starches)

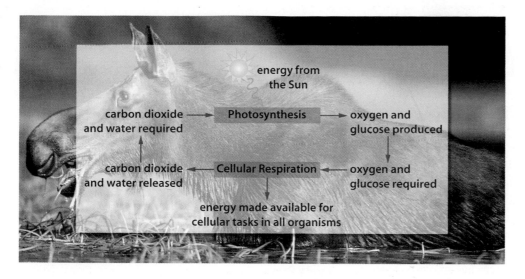

energy from
the Sun

carbon dioxide
and water required → **Photosynthesis** → oxygen and
glucose produced

carbon dioxide
and water released ← **Cellular Respiration** ← oxygen and
glucose required

energy made available for
cellular tasks in all organisms

Figure 1.2 Energy from the Sun is captured by photosynthetic organisms (producers). These organisms convert this energy to glucose and other energy-rich compounds such as starches, proteins, and fats. These compounds provide energy and matter for the producers themselves, as well as for consumers of the producers. Notice that photosynthesis and cellular respiration are almost the reverse of each other. Both processes use the same matter, but the form of energy used and released is different.

Organisms that are able to use the Sun's energy to produce food for themselves in this way are called **producers**. Producers are also known as autotrophs, which means "self-feeders."

The ruby-throated hummingbird and other animals are not able to make the energy-rich molecules they need to fuel their life processes. Instead, they must obtain these molecules by consuming other organisms (or absorbing nutrients from them). Thus, animals and some other kinds of organisms are *heterotrophs*, which means "other-feeders." Heterotrophs that consume other heterotrophs or autotrophs are called **consumers**. (You will look at consumers and producers in greater detail later in this section as well as in Section 1.2.) Figure 1.2 outlines how producers and consumers are linked through the processes of photosynthesis and cellular respiration.

• • •

Q1 What is cellular respiration?

Q2 What is photosynthesis?

Q3 In what way does the energy involved with photosynthesis differ from the energy involved with cellular respiration?

Q4 What is the connection between organisms that are producers and organisms that are consumers?

• • •

A Closer Look at Producers

The Sun is the source of energy for all producers that grow on Earth's surface or that float on or near the surface of the ocean and other bodies of water (see Figure 1.3). About 10^{22} J (joules) of the Sun's radiant energy reaches Earth each day.

A Boreal forests occur in most of Canada, in Russia, and Scandinavia. Dominated by coniferous trees, boreal forests make up about one-third of all the forest area on Earth.

Magnification: 21 ×

B A single millilitre of ocean water may contain thousands of microscopic producers (phytoplankton) called diatoms.

Figure 1.3 From low-growing mosses to towering trees, much of Earth's land surface supports the growth of green plants, which help nourish land-dwelling consumers. In the open ocean, producers float freely near or on the water surface, where the Sun's energy is able to reach them.

Target Skills

Performing an experiment to investigate variables related to the storage of solar energy in plants

Ensuring the safe and responsible handling of equipment and materials, both personally and with regard to the welfare of others in the class

Storing Solar Energy in Plants

As photosynthesis takes place in the leaves of a plant, carbohydrates are produced. Some of the first carbohydrates that are synthesized are simple sugars such as glucose. Some of this glucose is converted to starch. Starch is a higher-energy molecule than glucose, and it is stored for later use by the plant. Starch turns a brownish-purple colour when it is stained with iodine solution. In this investigation, you will test the hypothesis that plants need light energy to carry out photosynthesis and, thus, convert and store this energy in the form of starch.

Question

Do plants need sunlight to make food for themselves through photosynthesis?

Hypothesis

If plants need sunlight to perform photosynthesis and make starch, then the leaves of plants that are exposed to sunlight should show the presence of starch and the leaves of plants that have been denied sunlight should not.

Prediction

Re-read the introduction to this investigation, as well as the whole procedure. In your notebook, record a prediction about the results you would expect to see if the hypothesis is correct.

Materials

- small test tube
- stopper or stirring rod
- water
- 5 g of cornstarch
- 400 mL beaker of boiling water
- 150 mL beaker with 50 mL of hot ethanol in a hot water bath
- Lugol's iodine solution (in a dropper or spray bottle)
- plants with solid green leaves such as geranium (*Pelargonium*) or ivy (*Hedera*)—one plant grown for 4 days exposed to sunlight or under grow lights, and one plant placed in the dark for 4 days
- plants with variegated leaves such as *Coleus*, variegated geranium (*Pelargonium*), or spider plant (*Chlorophytum*)—one plant grown for 4 days exposed to sunlight or under grow lights, and one plant placed in the dark for 4 days

Safety Precautions

Ethanol ignites easily and iodine stains skin and clothing. Handle all chemicals with great care.

Procedure

1. Confirm the colour change that occurs when iodine solution is applied to starch. Place 10 mL of warm water in a test tube. Add cornstarch to the water until it no longer dissolves. Mix with a stirring rod or stopper and shake the test tube. Now add one drop of iodine solution to the mixture, then mix once again.

2. You will test for starch in the leaves of four plants. Two of the plants have variegated leaves, and the other two have solid green leaves. (A variegated leaf has streaks or patches of white.) One of the variegated plants and one of the solid green plants were grown in the light for four days. The other two plants, one of each type, were placed in darkness for four days.

3. Take a leaf from each plant. Mark the leaves from plants grown in the light with a notch so you can identify them later. Using tweezers, place each leaf in boiling water for about 10 min. This will soften the cell membranes and remove some of the water-soluble pigments (colouring) in the leaf.

4. Use the tweezers to place each leaf in hot ethanol for about 10 min to remove all the pigment colourings.

5. Use the tweezers to place each leaf in a dry Petri dish. Add a few drops of iodine solution to each leaf (or spray the leaves carefully with the solution). Cover the Petri dishes to prevent ethanol and iodine vapours from escaping.

6. When the investigation is finished, clean up your work area and dispose of all materials as directed by your teacher.

Analysis

1. Which of the leaves you tested showed the presence of starch? Explain how you know.

2. Draw an outline of each leaf. Use shading or a different coloured pen or pencil to indicate where starch was detected.

3. What is the relationship between the pattern in the variegated leaves and the presence of starch?

4. How accurate were your predictions?

5. How valid was the hypothesis?

Conclusions

6. Write a conclusion about the effect of light on the formation of starch in green leaves.

7. What, if any, other factors could have affected the results of this investigation? Explain how you could minimize these factors or their effects.

Extension

8. State a hypothesis and prediction based on the following scenario: Your teacher covers some of the leaves of a solid green plant with aluminium foil. The rest of the leaves are left uncovered. The plant is grown in sunlight for several days. You are then asked to test one covered leaf and one uncovered leaf for the presence of starch. With your teacher's permission, test your hypothesis and prediction.

9. Predict what would happen if you covered the leaf of a solid green plant with a picture-film negative, exposed the plant to sunlight for several days, and then performed the starch test. With your teacher's permission, test your prediction.

As summarized by Figure 1.4, there are three outcomes for this radiant energy.

1. About 30 percent of the energy is reflected from clouds, particles in the atmosphere, or from land or the surface of the ocean back into space. **Albedo** is a term used to describe the amount of reflected energy. Earth's albedo varies from place to place, but the average is about 30 percent. Light-coloured, reflective surfaces and thick cloud cover have high albedos of 80 percent to 90 percent. Dark surfaces such as forest canopies (treetops) and water have lower albedos of 25 percent or less.

2. About 19 percent of the energy is absorbed by gases such as water vapour and carbon dioxide in the atmosphere. Some of this energy will heat the atmosphere, and some will radiate back into space.

3. About 51 percent of the energy reaches Earth's surface. Energy absorbed by the land and oceans warms the planet's surface. Some of the heat from the warmed surface radiates upward into the atmosphere and out into space.

Figure 1.4 Scientists estimate that one to two percent of all the energy that reaches Earth from the Sun is captured by producers and converted to chemical energy through photosynthesis. About half of the incoming energy is absorbed by the atmosphere or reflected back into space without ever reaching Earth's surface.

Of the energy that reaches the ground, only a small fraction reaches producers. Of this, only a portion is used for photosynthesis. The result is that only one to two percent of the total radiant energy that reaches Earth is converted into chemical energy through photosynthesis. (The amount varies from place to place, depending on factors such as the type of organisms present and the intensity of the light.)

Even though the fraction of the Sun's energy that reaches producers is very small, the role of these organisms is significant. Producers generate about 150 billion tonnes to 200 billion tonnes of organic (carbon-containing) matter each year. This amount of life-sustaining matter supports most life on Earth.

• • •

5 What percentage of the Sun's energy is absorbed by Earth's land and ocean surfaces?

6 How does the amount of energy from the Sun that reaches producers compare with the amount of energy from the Sun that first reaches Earth's atmosphere?

• • •

Figure 1.5 This deep-sea vent community, clustered near a black smoker, was discovered on the ocean floor off the Galápagos Islands. Here, giant tubeworms (*Riftia pachyptila*) several metres in height sway in the steam-heated water. Blind shrimp, clams, mussels, crabs, fishes, and even octopuses are other common members of the vent communities.

Energy for Life in the Deep Ocean

In 1977, a group of geologists were exploring volcanic deep-sea vents near the Galápagos Islands off the west coast of South America. Housed in a small submarine, the geologists had descended to a depth of about 2500 m to study the vents. Sometimes referred to as "black smokers", many deep-sea vents spew out hydrogen sulfide-containing water that looks like clouds of dark smoke. Drawing closer to these vents, the scientists encountered the last thing they were expecting: life. Here in this otherwise barren, Moon-like environment, far below the deepest penetration of the Sun's rays, they found a wealth of species, most of which were new to science (Figure 1.5).

Chemosynthetic Producers

The unusual deep-sea vent organisms live near what is often scalding-hot, acidic water. (Heated by geothermal activity, the water surrounding deep-sea vents can reach 350 °C.) Because light does not penetrate to the depths of the ocean floor, these heat-resistant vent organisms cannot rely on photosynthesis to support producers. Instead, bacteria dwell within the tissues of tube worms that live on and near the black smokers. These micro-organisms are able to split the hydrogen sulfide molecules spewing from the deep-sea vents. The bacteria then capture the energy stored in the chemical bonds of the molecules. Unlike photosynthesis, which produces oxygen, sulfuric acid is produced as a byproduct of this process, which is called **chemosynthesis**.

The discovery of chemosynthetic bacterial producers living in the extreme conditions of deep-sea vents inspired scientists to investigate other extreme environments. A variety of species have since been discovered in colder regions of the ocean floor (called cold-water seeps), in hot springs, in intensely salty lakes, and in deep caves. Chemosynthetic producers are also found in places far less extreme than these. For example, beneath the soil you walk on live types of chemosynthetic bacteria. They convert ammonia in the soil to other nitrogen compounds that are used by different kinds of plants and micro-organisms. These nitrifying bacteria, as they are called, play an important role in the nitrogen cycle, which you will explore in Chapter 2.

• • •

7 How is chemosynthesis similar to and different from photosynthesis?

• • •

A Closer Look at Consumers

Only producers are able to capture energy from the Sun (or inorganic molecules). Thus, all other organisms directly or indirectly depend on producers to meet their needs for energy. As noted earlier, these dependent organisms must consume organic matter (other organisms) as a source of energy, so they are called consumers. Consumers can be classified into groups based on how they obtain their food.

Herbivores are organisms that eat plants. Herbivores are termed **primary consumers**, because they are the first (primary) eaters of plants and other producers. On land, insects, snails, grazing mammals, and birds and mammals that eat seeds and fruits are the most common primary consumers. In water, some species of fish, small invertebrate animals such as clams, and some aquatic insects are common primary consumers. In the deep-ocean vents, tubeworms and mussels are common primary consumers.

Carnivores are animals that eat other animals. Carnivores that eat mainly herbivores are **secondary consumers**. Spiders, frogs, and insect-eating birds are examples of secondary consumers. Often, secondary consumers are themselves consumed by other carnivores, which are called **tertiary consumers** (the third set of eaters). In the deep-ocean vents, giant crabs and blind fish are secondary and tertiary consumers. There may also be higher levels of consumers above these.

The members of another consumer group, **decomposers**, obtain their energy-rich molecules by eating or absorbing leftover or waste matter (Figure 1.6). This waste matter includes the feces of living organisms, dead bodies, or body parts of other organisms. Decomposers include certain kinds of fungi, bacteria, earthworms, and insects. Decomposers are important to the biosphere because they return organic and inorganic matter to the soil, air, and water. These materials can then be used again by producers to make new energy-rich organic molecules. Decomposers are the matter recyclers of the biosphere. They ensure that the matter needed by all organisms is always available.

• • •

8 Why are herbivores classified as primary consumers?

9 What are secondary and tertiary consumers?

10 Why are decomposers heterotrophic organisms and not producer organisms?

• • •

Biology File

Web Link
Canada is at the forefront of deep-sea research and technology. In fact, the first black-smoker-releasing chimneys from the ocean floor were brought to the surface with the aid of a remotely operated submersible vehicle, called ROPOS, and a Canadian Coast Guard research vessel. What is Canadian deep-sea research centred on, what is being investigated, and how does Canada contribute to our understanding of deep-sea biology and geology?

www.albertabiology.ca
WWW

Figure 1.6 In most cases, decomposers can be classified as more than one type of consumer, depending on their food source. For instance, the beetle *Tenebrio molitor* larvae ("mealworms") shown here eat decaying plant material as well as dead insects and feces.

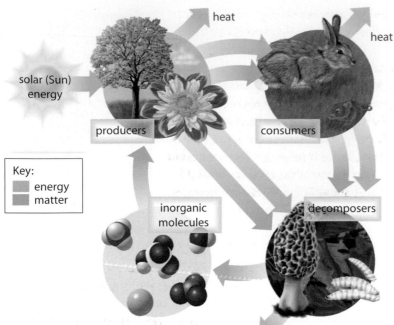

solar (Sun) energy

heat

producers

heat

consumers

Key:
energy
matter

inorganic molecules

decomposers

heat

Figure 1.7 Matter cycles within the biosphere, but energy passes through it. As chemical energy is transferred from producers to consumers to decomposers, all the energy eventually dissipates into the environment as heat.

The Fate of Energy in the Biosphere

Earth is a closed system to matter. With the exception of meteorites that reach the surface and satellites and space probes that we launch into space, no matter enters or leaves the biosphere. In other words, Earth has the same supply of matter today that it has had for the billions of years of its history. Atoms and molecules are cycled—used and reused endlessly—in the biosphere.

Energy does not and cannot cycle as matter does. Energy follows a one-way path through the biosphere (Figure 1.7). Why should this be? Recall from previous studies that energy cannot be created or destroyed. It can only be converted from one form to another or transferred from one object to another. This idea is known as the *first law of thermodynamics*. For example, radiant energy from the Sun may be converted into the chemical energy stored in the bonds of carbohydrate molecules. That chemical energy may be converted into motion (kinetic energy) and heat. The total amount of energy in all these conversions does not change.

No process of energy conversion is 100 percent efficient, however. With each conversion of energy, there is less energy available to do useful work. This idea is known as the *second law of thermodynamics*. For example, when you ride in a car, the chemical energy of the fuel is transformed into kinetic energy, sound energy, and (ultimately) heat that randomly disperses into the environment. The same is true of energy released by cells during cellular respiration. This dispersed energy is "lost" for any use by living systems. It cannot be recaptured to support life.

The second law of thermodynamics has important consequences for living systems. Each time a cell uses energy to perform a function, some of that energy is dispersed ("lost") as unusable heat. If additional energy is not supplied to the cell, it will eventually cease to function—it will die. A constant supply of energy, therefore, is necessary to sustain life. This is why producers are essential to life on Earth. Producers are the means by which all organisms are connected to each other through the transfer of energy. You will examine this interrelationship in greater detail in the next section.

• • •

11 In what ways do the laws of thermodynamics apply to the processes that take place in and between organisms?

• • •

Section 1.1 Summary

- For most organisms, energy enters the biosphere through the process of photosynthesis. For organisms that live in the deep ocean and (mainly) in other extreme environments, energy enters their part of the biosphere through the process of chemosynthesis.
- The energy-releasing process of cellular respiration and the energy-storing processes of photosynthesis (and chemosynthesis) are related to each other, providing organisms with the energy and matter they need to survive. Photosynthetic producers capture the

BiologyFile

FYI

All organisms transfer energy to the environment as heat as they carry out cellular respiration and other energy-related activities. While sleeping, a person produces about as much heat as a 100 W light bulb!

Sun's energy and convert it to chemical energy in the form of high-energy carbohydrate molecules. Chemosynthetic producers capture the chemical energy stored in chemical bonds and convert it to chemical energy in the form of high-energy carbohydrate molecules.

- Consumers (heterotrophs) must eat other organisms for the energy they need. Primary consumers eat autotrophs. Secondary and tertiary consumers eat other heterotrophs. Decomposers consume dead organic material.

- According to the laws of thermodynamics, energy cannot be created or destroyed, only transformed from one form to another. No energy transformation is completely efficient. Therefore, as energy is transferred from one organism to another, much of it is lost as unusable heat to the environment.

Section 1.1 Review

1. Compare the general chemical reaction for photosynthesis to the general chemical reaction for cellular respiration.

2. Describe, using specific examples, the main similarities and differences between photosynthesis and chemosynthesis.

3. Herbivores eat plants and carry out cellular respiration to access the energy stored in carbohydrates, such as glucose. Explain how plants access the energy stored in glucose.

4. Explain why only a fraction of the energy from the Sun that reaches the biosphere is available for use by photosynthetic organisms.

5. Distinguish among producers, primary consumers, secondary consumers, and tertiary consumers in terms of energy.

6. Summarize the two laws of thermodynamics introduced in this section.

Use the following information to answer the next question.

Albedo

The table below lists the albedos of several of Earth's natural features.

Albedo of Natural Features

Features	Albedo
thick clouds	90 percent
thin clouds	40 percent
fresh snow	80–90 percent
sand	30–35 percent
forest	7–18 percent
grass	18–25 percent

7. If global warming is occurring, as most scientists accept it is, and if the Arctic is experiencing losses of snow and ice cover, as satellite evidence and resident Inuit observers report it is, describe how incoming radiant energy from the Sun could be affected as a result of changes in albedo.

8. Skunk cabbage (*Symplocarpus foetidus*), shown in the photograph, is a woodlands and wetlands plant that grows in eastern North America as well as in northeastern Asia. It is one of the first wetland plants to bloom in the spring. Inside the spike-like structure that pushes out of the ground is a cluster of tiny flowers that produce enough heat to raise the temperature within this structure to between 16 °C and 24 °C. In the photograph, the snow has melted in a ring surrounding the emerging plant. Explain what has happened to produce this result.

Eastern skunk cabbage (*Symplocarpus foetidus*)

How Energy Is Transferred in the Biosphere

In the biosphere, an ecological system, or *ecosystem*, is made up of all the organisms that live in an area and the physical environment of that area. The physical environment includes water, inorganic substances (minerals), and sunlight—that is, non-living things. Organisms, their products (wastes and remains), and the effects they have on their environment are living components of an ecosystem. Together, the interacting living and non-living components form a self-regulating system through which energy and matter are transferred. Describing and understanding how these transfers occur is a major theme of ecology. (You will examine ecosystems in greater detail in Unit 2.)

Trophic Levels Describe Feeding Relationships in Ecosystems

The modified flowchart in Figure 1.8 summarizes three ways to represent feeding relationships in ecosystems. Organisms in an ecosystem can be identified by how they obtain their food and the kind of food they eat. For example, organisms can be classified as producers, herbivores, carnivores, and decomposers. Organisms also can be identified by the type of food-maker or food-consumer they are. For example, organisms could be classified as producers, primary consumers, secondary consumers, and tertiary consumers.

Another, related way to think about feeding relationships among organisms uses the concept of a trophic level. The word trophic comes from a Greek word that means "food." So a **trophic level** in an ecosystem is a feeding level through which energy and matter are transferred. The first trophic level in any ecosystem provides all the chemical energy required to fuel the other trophic levels. Thus, the first trophic level consists of producers. All remaining trophic levels in any given ecosystem consist of consumers. Notice in Figure 1.8 that decomposers may feed at any of the trophic levels.

- - -

12 In terms of feeding relationships, in what ways can organisms in an ecosystem be identified?

13 What is a trophic level?

14 Which trophic level or levels contain producers and which contain consumers?

- - -

Food Chains and Food Webs

In the 1920s, a young ecologist named Charles Elton set out from Oxford University in England to study the organisms on a desolate island in the frigid Arctic waters off the northern coast of Norway. Together with another ecologist, Victor Summerhayes, Elton was interested in documenting the feeding relationships in this remote place, called Bear Island. It was here that

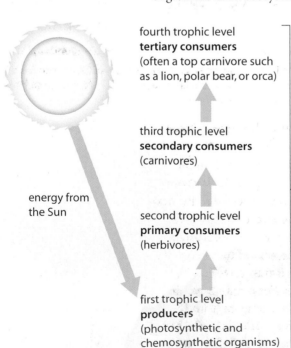

fourth trophic level
tertiary consumers
(often a top carnivore such as a lion, polar bear, or orca)

third trophic level
secondary consumers
(carnivores)

second trophic level
primary consumers
(herbivores)

first trophic level
producers
(photosynthetic and chemosynthetic organisms)

energy from the Sun

Consumers that feed at all trophic levels:
decomposers

Figure 1.8 Organisms in an ecosystem may be identified by how they obtain their food, or by consumer level, or by trophic level.

Elton first introduced the concept of food chains and the related concept of food webs.

A **food chain** is a model that shows the linear pathways through which food is transferred from producers to primary consumers and to higher trophic levels. Figure 1.9 compares a food chain in a terrestrial (land) ecosystem with one in a marine (ocean) ecosystem.

Elton quickly found that simple food chains could not adequately describe the tangled web of feeding relationships that he observed. Thus, he developed the concept of a food web. A **food web** is a model of food (energy) transfer in an ecosystem that shows the connections among food chains. Figure 1.10 on the next page compares food webs for a woodland-lake ecosystem and an Arctic ecosystem. Use the Try This exercise in the margin to examine these food webs.

Energy Transfer and Trophic Levels

Food chains generally have only a few trophic levels, usually somewhere between three and six. The length of a food chain has limits because the laws of thermodynamics limit the amount of energy that can be transferred from one trophic level to another. As energy is transferred from producers and consumers, only some of that energy is passed along at each step. Consider what it would be like to be in a contest where each team of players had to toss a bucket of water from one person to another until it reaches the last player in the line. There would be only a little water left over for the last player, because some of the water would be spilled each time the bucket was tossed to the next person. Similarly, each time energy is transferred in a food chain, some of the energy is transformed into unusable heat.

How Much Energy Is Transferred from One Trophic Level to Another?

The efficiency with which energy is transferred from one trophic level to the next varies among different kinds

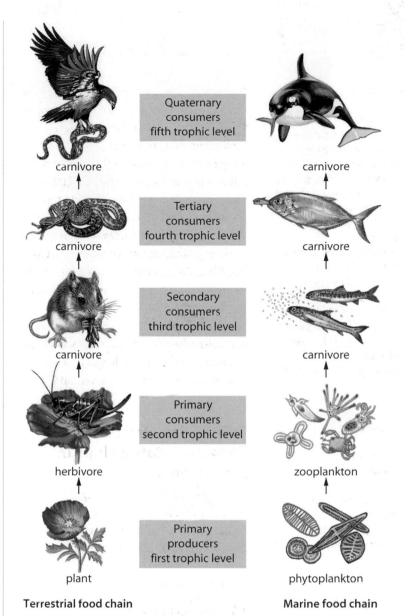

	Quaternary consumers fifth trophic level	
carnivore		carnivore
	Tertiary consumers fourth trophic level	
carnivore		carnivore
	Secondary consumers third trophic level	
carnivore		carnivore
	Primary consumers second trophic level	
herbivore		zooplankton
	Primary producers first trophic level	
plant		phytoplankton

Terrestrial food chain   **Marine food chain**

Figure 1.9 Terrestrial and aquatic ecosystems contain different species of organisms but can have the same overall structure of feeding relationships, as shown in these food chains.

of organisms. It usually ranges between 5 percent and 20 percent. In other words, about 80 percent to 95 percent of the chemical energy that is available at one trophic level is *not* transferred to the next one. Figure 1.11 on page 18 shows why.

For convenience, ecologists often assume that 10 percent of the energy at one trophic level is transferred to the next trophic level. For example, assume that 3500 kJ of the energy captured by grain plants such as barley is available to a cow that eats the plants. Following the assumption of 10 percent energy transfer, only 350 kJ of the energy in the cow

A

would be available to a person who eats some beef. This 10 percent assumption is referred to as the "rule of 10." (You may also see it called the 10 percent rule or the 10 percent law, but it is not a scientific law.) The rule of 10 makes energy calculations easier, but it is an oversimplification. Thought Lab 1.1 will give you some practice working with energy values. In Investigation 1.B, you will consider how much energy from the Sun is available to you through your diet.

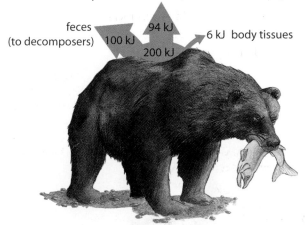

cellular respiration and heat (to the environment)

feces (to decomposers) 100 kJ   94 kJ   6 kJ body tissues

200 kJ

Figure 1.11 A grizzly bear transfers energy to waste products and to the environment, as heat, during cellular respiration. Although the energy values are estimates, very little energy (6 kJ) is transferred to the bear for growth and maintenance. Cellular respiration enables the bear to access the energy content in food so that it can roam, hunt, gather berries, stay warm, reproduce, and survive the winter.

15 Why is less energy transferred from one trophic level to the next in an ecosystem?

16 Explain why there is a limit to the length of food chains.

Modelling Feeding Relationships through Ecological Pyramids

The high visibility of organisms on the barren tundra enabled Charles Elton to observe the number and size of organisms found at each trophic level in the arctic ecosystem that he studied. Through these studies, Elton recognized a pattern in the distribution of the energy and the numbers of organisms among trophic levels. Figure 1.12 shows the pattern that results by sequencing producers and consumers in order of the amount of energy available at each trophic level. Elton was the first to suggest the pyramid-shaped pattern shown in Figure 1.12. Initially called "Eltonian pyramids", these models of feeding relationships are now referred to as *ecological pyramids*. There are three types: pyramids of numbers, pyramids of biomass, and pyramids of energy.

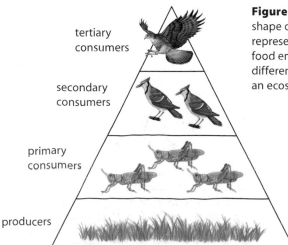

Pyramids of Numbers

In many ecosystems, animals at higher trophic levels are fewer in number than organisms at lower trophic levels. For instance, in Figure 1.12, there are fewer secondary consumers than there are primary consumers. And there are fewer primary consumers than there are producers. The pattern that results is called a **pyramid of numbers**, and it is usually depicted with a shape like that shown in Figure 1.13 on page 20. Each bar of a pyramid of numbers represents a different trophic level and its width represents the relative numbers of organisms at that level.

Counting the numbers of organisms in an ecosystem can be a useful (but time-consuming) way to estimate the amount of energy in each trophic level. However, pyramids of numbers do not always take the upright shape shown in Figure 1.13. Consider a forest ecosystem. Sunlight filters through the forest canopy and is captured through photosynthesis. The trees are producers at the first trophic level, but there are very few trees compared with the number of other forest organisms. There are, for example, thousands and thousands of plant-eating insects at the second trophic level. At the

higher trophic levels, large numbers of carnivorous insects and woodland birds consume the plant-eating insects. A pyramid of numbers for this woodland ecosystem has an inverted shape such as the one shown in Figure 1.14 on page 21.

• • •

 Explain why a pyramid of numbers can be upright or inverted.

• • •

Pyramids of Biomass

One limitation of a pyramid of numbers is that it does not take into account the size of individual organisms. Many

BiologyFile

Try This
Compare the two food webs in Figure 1.10. How do the lengths (number of trophic levels) of food chains within these food webs compare? How does the overall complexity of these food webs compare? How might the overall complexity of food webs in a tropical rainforest ecosystem compare? Explain your reasoning in all your answers.

Figure 1.12 The pyramid shape of this diagram represents the amount of food energy available at different trophic levels of an ecosystem.

tertiary
consumers

secondary
consumers

primary
consumers

producers

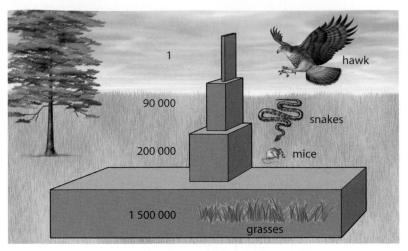

Figure 1.13 This pyramid of numbers for a grassland ecosystem represents the relative numbers of organisms at each link in a food chain (and, thus, at each of several trophic levels).

organisms tend to be larger than the food they eat. Thus, birds tend to be larger than the seeds or insects they consume, and wild cats such as the cougar (*Puma concolor*) tend to be larger than the prey that they catch. There are exceptions, however. A cougar may successfully bring down a moose or an elk. Beetles that dine on a tree are clearly much smaller than their food.

To overcome this limitation, ecologists began to use an alternative measure of energy transfer within an ecosystem: biomass. **Biomass** is the dry mass of living, or once-living, organisms per unit area. Biomass measurements

Thought Lab 1.1 Analyzing Energy Transfers

Target Skills

Analyzing data on energy transfer from producers to consumers

Procedure

1. Recall that only a very small fraction of the Sun's radiant energy is absorbed by and incorporated into plant material. For ease of calculation, assume that the amount of energy captured by plants and contained in their tissues is two percent of the total energy available from sunlight. Also assume that 10 percent of the energy at one trophic level is transferred to the next level. (Remember, though, that the 10 percent value is an oversimplification.) Based on this information, answer the Analysis questions.

Analysis

1. The three food chains shown here represent typical food chains for people with different diets. Study the food chains and determine the percentage of the Sun's energy available to humans at the end of each chain.

2. About 80 percent of the world's population eat mostly grain-based foods. Why do you think this is the case?

3. How might diet influence the number of humans that Earth can ultimately support?

4. One square metre of land that is planted with rice produces about 5200 kJ of energy per year. A chicken farm produces about 800 kJ/m^2 of potential food energy per year. Assume that a human must consume 2400 kJ per day to survive. Although it is an oversimplification to imply that a person could survive by eating only one type of food, calculate the total area of land needed to support the student population of your school for year on a diet of (a) rice and (b) chicken.

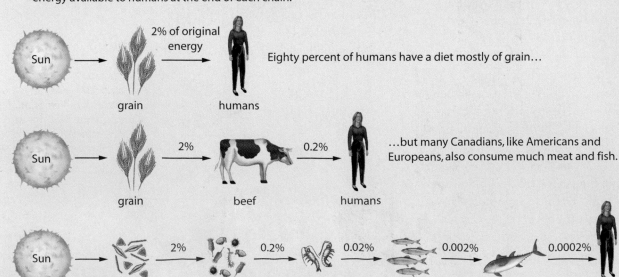

of a population of organisms are an excellent indicator of the amount of energy present in the living tissue of an ecosystem. From these measurements (usually given in g/m²), a **pyramid of biomass**, such as the one in Figure 1.15, can be constructed.

Each level of a pyramid of biomass represents a trophic level. The pyramid demonstrates how the amount of biomass changes as energy is transferred from one trophic level to the next. One complication with pyramids of biomass arises because scientists define biomass in different ways. Some scientists include only living materials in their calculation of biomass. Other scientists also include once-living materials, such as dead trees, shrubs, and grasses. There are also exceptions to the upright pyramid shape, as there is with pyramids of numbers. For example, in an ocean ecosystem, at any moment in time, the biomass of the producers (microscopic floating organisms called phytoplankton) may be much less than the biomass of zooplankton, the floating organisms that feed upon them. The result is an inverted pyramid of biomass such as the one shown in Figure 1.16 on page 22.

How can there be fewer producers than consumers in an ocean ecosystem? The phytoplankton producers grow and reproduce at a rate that far exceeds that of the zooplankton. The number of producers doubles in size every few days,

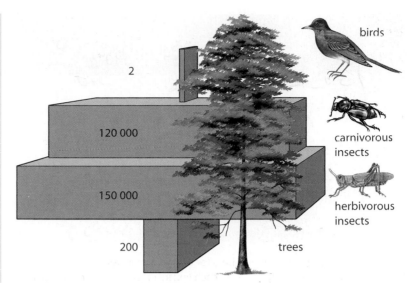

Figure 1.14 In this reversed pyramid of numbers for a woodland ecosystem, a single tree at the first trophic level may feed thousands of plant-eating insects at higher trophic levels.

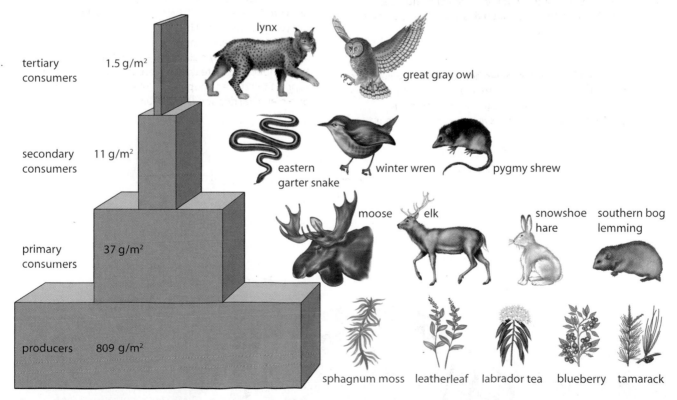

Figure 1.15 This pyramid of biomass shows the relative dry mass, in grams per square metre, of organisms in a bog ecosystem. Some examples of organisms at each trophic level are included. (Diagrams are not to scale.)

Weave Your Own Food Web

Like all organisms on the planet, humans are part of food webs. In this investigation, you will draw a food web based on a record of your food consumption over three days, illustrating the specific feeding relationships and patterns of energy transfer in your ecosystem. You will follow the path of solar energy as it is transferred through various trophic levels to you at the top of each food chain. Using the rule of 10, you will calculate the percentage of the Sun's energy that is available to you through your diet, based on the food choices you make.

Procedure

1. For three days, keep a full record of the food and beverages you eat. Design a chart to record your food and beverage intake. Be sure to include both the type and amount of food or drink consumed, other than water. Be as accurate as you can. For instance, if you eat a slice of pizza, you should record all the items and approximate amounts of each (i.e. the dough, as well as all the toppings) separately. You may have to rely on your own judgment at times, as not all food will fall into a neat category.

2. Using the nutritional information from food labels, the Internet, and/or the library, look up the amount of energy in each food or beverage item you consumed and record the values in kilojoules (kJ). Since the food energy recorded on most food labels show kilocalories (kcal), rather than kilojoules, you will need to convert all kilocalorie values to kilojoules. One kilocalorie is equal to 4.2 kilojoules (1 kcal = 4.2 kJ). (Note that the "calories" shown on food labels are actually kilocalories. Sometimes they are capitalized to indicate this. Thus, 1000 calories = 1 Calorie = 1 kilocalorie.) Try to be as accurate as you can. **ICT**

3. Calculate the total number of kilojoules of food energy you ate over the entire three days. Then calculate your average daily consumption by dividing this total by three.

4. Organize the food and beverages you consumed over the three days into the following categories:

   Producers (First Trophic Level): Includes all plant-based food such as grains, vegetables, fruit, and all sweeteners.

   Primary Consumers (Second Trophic Level): Includes plant-eating organisms (herbivores) such as most livestock (cattle, chicken, lamb) and some wild game (deer, moose, bison), plus eggs and dairy. Also includes aquatic herbivores such as tilapia, carp, and catfish, as well as shellfish.

   Secondary Consumers (Third Trophic Level): Includes flesh-eating (carnivorous) fish such as salmon, sardines, and trout. Because pigs eat both plant and animal tissue, include pork in this category as well.

   Tertiary Consumers (Fourth Trophic Level): Includes higher-level carnivores such as tuna and sharks, which feed on many fish and sea animals. Tertiary consumers are higher on the food chain than secondary consumers.

   If you are unsure which category a food or beverage falls into, research it on the Internet or in the library. If that fails to provide an answer, make an educated guess.

5. Using the food record you kept, calculate the number of kilojoules contained in the food you consumed in each category. Once you have calculated these totals, divide each total by three to get the average number of kilojoules you consumed each day from each trophic level.

6. Next, divide each daily average by the average number of kilojoules you consumed daily (calculated in Step 3). This will give you the percentage of your diet that comes from each trophic level. For instance, imagine that you get 5862 kJ from the first trophic level and that your total consumption of food energy per day is 8373 kJ. To calculate the percentage of your diet from the first trophic level:

$$\frac{5862 \text{ kJ}}{8373 \text{ kJ}} \times 100 = 70 \text{ percent}$$

This means that 70 percent of the energy in your diet comes from producers. Similarly, if you consume 1674 kJ from the second trophic level and 837 kJ from the third trophic level, 20 percent of the energy in your diet comes from primary consumers and 10 percent comes from secondary consumers.

7. Create a food web that illustrates the food you consumed over the three-day period. Place yourself in the highest trophic level and use arrows to show the path that energy follows through the food web.

Analysis

1. What percentage of your food comes from comes from producers? From primary consumers? From secondary consumers? From tertiary consumers?

2. Using the rule of 10 and the assumption that the producers transform about 2% of the Sun's energy through photosynthesis, determine the percentage of the Sun's energy assimilated through your current diet. You may want to draw food chains to help you visualize how much energy is transferred between trophic levels. Refer to the food chains in Thought Lab 1.1 as a guide. For example:

Step 1: If 70% of the energy in your diet comes from producers, the percentage of the Sun's energy represented by this portion of your diet is calculated as follows:

$$0.70 \times 0.02 = 0.0014 = 0.14\%$$

(What do these values mean? 0.70 is equivalent to 70%; it is the percentage of energy from producers in your diet. 0.02 is equivalent to 2%. It is the percentage of the Sun's energy captured by producers during photosynthesis.)

Step 2: If 20% of the energy in your diet comes from primary consumers, the percentage of the Sun's energy represented by this portion of your diet is:

$$0.20 \times 0.02 \times 0.10 \times 0.10 = 0.00004 = 0.0040\%$$

Step 3: If 10% of the energy in your diet comes from secondary consumers, the percentage of the Sun's energy represented by this portion of your diet is:

$$0.10 \times 0.02 \times 0.10 \times 0.10 \times 0.10 = 0.000002$$
$$= 0.00020\%$$

Step 4: Therefore, the total percentage of the Sun's energy assimilated is:

$$0.14\% + 0.0040\% + 0.00020\% = 0.1460\% = 0.15\%$$

3. Compare your results with those of your classmates. Who assimilated the largest percentage of the Sun's energy through their diet? Who assimilated the least? Determine what percentage of these students' food came from which trophic levels. From what trophic level did the person who assimilated the highest percentage of the Sun's energy consume the most food? What about the person who assimilated the least?

4. How many trophic levels are represented in the longest food chains in your food web? Do you think you would assimilate more of the Sun's energy if your food chains were longer? What if they were shorter?

Extension

5. It requires seven times more land to sustain a meat-based diet than a plant-based diet. In other words, the same amount of land required to feed one meat-eater can grow enough crops to feed seven vegetarians. Similarly, the world's cattle eat the same amount of food that would feed 8.7 billion people if humans consumed it directly. Finally, it is estimated to take about 43 000 L of water to produce about half a kilogram of ground beef (Dr. David Pimentel, professor of ecology and agricultural sciences at Cornell University, 1997). Based on these facts, what would be the benefits of vegetarianism in overcrowded or densely populated nations?

but this is not reflected in their biomass because they are eaten as quickly as they reproduce. Thus, enough energy is being transferred to the zooplankton to keep the ecosystem from collapsing. A similar inverted relationship often exists between the zooplankton and the fish that consume them.

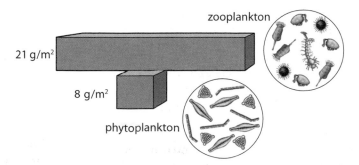

Figure 1.16 In this inverted pyramid of biomass for an ocean ecosystem, the mass of zooplankton (in grams per square metre) in the second trophic level is greater than the mass at the first trophic level of the phytoplankton on which they feed.

Pyramids of Energy

A third type of ecological pyramid may be used to remove the exceptions of the other two types. A **pyramid of energy** shows the total amount of energy that is transferred through each trophic level (Figure 1.17). A pyramid of energy is always upright, because there can never be less energy in a lower trophic level than in a higher one. Thus, even though phytoplankton have less biomass, more energy flows through the first trophic level than the second trophic level (zooplankton), and the pyramid of energy for the ocean ecosystem remains upright. A pyramid of energy also clearly shows how little energy is left at the highest trophic level. This is why food chains are restricted in size.

• • •

18 Describe two ways that a pyramid of energy is different from a pyramid of numbers and a pyramid of biomass.

• • •

Energy Transfer and Stability in Ecosystems

According to the Inuit in the northern regions of Canada, Alaska, and Eurasia, weather patterns in the Arctic are changing. Inuit elders have observed and described how the sea ice is unusually thin in areas and that the spring melt season is starting earlier in the year. The weather, they say, has become *uggianaqtuq* (pronounced OOG-gi-a-nak-took), an Inuktitut word meaning "to behave in an unusual way."

These observations are increasingly supported by qualitative and quantitative observations from western scientists. Changes that affect climate, numbers and distribution of organisms, and their diversity are being described throughout the world. Ecologists have learned that the stability of feeding relationships in ecosystems decreases with a decrease in the number of species (that is, biodiversity)—especially the number and variety of producers. Understanding food web interactions is important for predicting how biodiversity may increase or decrease in ecosystems, whether in the Arctic, the boreal forest, or the prairie grasslands. In Investigation 1.C, you will explore this idea further as you research the role that certain species play in the food web of an ecosystem that is unstable—an endangered grassland ecosystem.

Section 1.2 Summary

- A food chain is a model that shows the linear pathway through which food is transferred from producers to primary consumers and to progressively higher feeding levels. A food web is a more

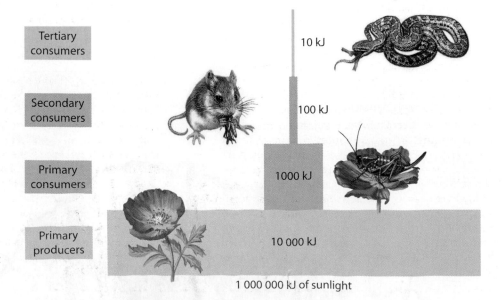

Figure 1.17 This pyramid of energy transfer shows 10 percent efficiency in energy transfer from one trophic level to the next. The rate of efficiency can vary from 5 to 20 percent. This assumes that 1 percent of solar energy is captured by primary producers.

Tertiary consumers — 10 kJ

Secondary consumers — 100 kJ

Primary consumers — 1000 kJ

Primary producers — 10 000 kJ

1 000 000 kJ of sunlight

complex model of energy transfer that shows the connections among several food chains. Both are based on the common concept of trophic (feeding) levels.

- Only part of the available energy from one trophic level can be transferred to the next trophic level. As a result, food chains are limited in length. On average, it is assumed that only 10 percent of energy available at a particular trophic level is transferred to the next trophic level.

- Ecological pyramids are used to describe quantitative relationships between trophic levels. A pyramid of numbers is based on the number of organisms in each trophic level. A pyramid of biomass is based on the biomass of organisms in each trophic level. A pyramid of energy is based on the total amount of energy in each trophic level and cannot be inverted.

- Changes within one trophic level may result in changes to a higher or lower trophic level, as well as energy transfer through an ecosystem. These changes may affect ecosystem biodiversity and stability.

Thought Lab 1.2 Energy Fluctuation in an Ecosystem

Target Skills

Analyzing food source data from an aquatic community to understand variables that may be causing a change in population size of a certain species

Due to the numerous links back and forth between trophic levels, and the fact that some organisms can occupy more than one trophic level at a time, species survival tends to be linked to the status of other trophic levels. In this activity, you will consider the effect changes in the numbers of Pacific herring (*Clupea pallas*) have on other species in an Arctic ocean ecosystem: the steller sea lion (*Eumetopias jubatus*).

The numbers of steller sea lions in Alaska and Canada have been shrinking. Between the late 1970s and early 2000s, the body size of the sea lion has also been shrinking, as has the number of pups born each year. The sea lion is a protected species in both the United States and Canada, so scientists have been puzzled as to why its numbers keep decreasing. The decrease in body length and mass might suggest that the sea lions are not getting enough to eat. Coincidently, there has also been a decrease in number of Pacific herring in the region due to over-fishing, food shortages, and possibly changing water temperatures. Pacific herring have been a major food source for the sea lions in the past, but scientists believe that sea lions are now consuming larger amounts of walleye pollock (*Theragra chalcogramma*), which has been increasing in number in the Arctic. Could this change in the feeding patterns of the sea lions be the reason for their decline?

Procedure

Examine the following table and answer the Analysis questions that follow.

Available Energy in Two Types of Fish

Type of fish	Fatty or non-fatty?	Available energy (kJ/g)
Pacific herring (*Clupea pallas*)	fatty	4.4–11.7
walleye pollock (*Theragra chulcogramma*)	non-fatty	3.2–5.9

Analysis

1. How might the change in energy content of the sea lions' prey affect the body size of the sea lions?

2. How might the body size of sea lions relate to their overall population numbers?

3. Suggest two reasons why the number of sea lion pups might be decreasing each year.

4. You are an ecologist who has recently discovered a decrease in the numbers of kelp (a type of seaweed) in the same Arctic ecosystem. You have also found an increase in the numbers of sea urchins that feed off of the kelp and a decrease in the number of sea otters (*Enhydra lutris*) feeding on the sea urchins. You know that there are no longer enough sea lions in the area to support the orcas ("killer whales"), *Orcinus orca*, but the numbers of the whales remains stable. Draw a food web to explain the feeding relationships in this ecosystem. Using your food web, explain how a change in the diet of the sea lions could result in a decline in the numbers of kelp. (**Hint:** What dietary change have the killer whales most likely made?)

Target Skills

Working co-operatively to research, synthesize, and analyze information about the ecology and trophic levels of a threatened species and an endangered ecosystem

Drawing a food web to depict feeding relationships between the threatened species and other species

Analyzing information to assess how ecological variables may affect the threatened species and its ecosystem

Presenting the result of an investigation to a group

Ecology of an Endangered Prairie Ecosystem

While most people are concerned about endangered species, few realize that these species are often members of an ecosystem that is also endangered. Endangered ecosystems, such as the tropical rainforest, have the highest rate of species loss on the planet. How does the health of an endangered ecosystem affect the livelihood of an endangered species, and vice versa? Loss of an endangered species may change the feeding relationships and energy transfer within its food web. Such changes may be difficult for an endangered ecosystem to recover from. Similarly, environmental changes that affect the ecosystem may also affect the endangered species, which may also be susceptible to these stressors. In this investigation, you will investigate an endangered species living in one of the most threatened ecosystems in the world—the North American prairie.

Procedure

1. With your group, research the ecology of the prairie ecosystem and one of the eight endangered species listed below that are found in this ecosystem. Use Internet or library resources, or contact an ecologist. Find out about your species' role in its food web and possible explanations for its threatened existence, as well as factors that may be endangering the prairie ecosystem. Consider and collect information you may need to answer the Analysis questions. **ICT**

   - Burrowing owl (*Athene cunicularia*)
   - Swift fox (*Vulpes velox*)
   - Prairie rattlesnake (*Crotalis viridis*)
   - Sage Grouse (*Centrocercus urophasianus*)
   - Sprague's Pipit (*Anthus spraguen*)
   - Long-billed curlew (*Numenius americanus*)
   - Loggerhead shrike (*Lanius ludovicianus*)
   - Ord's kangaroo rat (*Dipodomys odrii*)

2. As a group, list the different trophic levels and links in the food web that your species belongs to.

3. On your own, draw a food web to depict your species' feeding relationships with other species. (Share your food web with your other group members for feedback and possible modification.)

4. Present your research findings in a presentation to your class.

Analysis

1. List the main factors threatening the existence of your species, as well as the existence of the prairie ecosystem. Do any of these factors overlap? If so, which ones?

2. How would the extinction of your species affect the feeding relationships and energy transfer in its food web?

3. Describe the connection between energy transfer and ecosystem stability. How might changes to the food web hypothesized in question 2 affect the stability of the endangered prairie ecosystem?

4. Make a future prediction concerning the survival of your species and the prairie ecosystem based on your research findings.

Extension

5. Create an action plan that could help preserve the species you investigated and/or the prairie ecosystem.

1. Explain why a food web cannot exist without producers.

2. Describe the role(s) of fungi in a food web.

3. Use word processing or graphics software to draw a food chain that includes tuna. Your food chain can include either the names of the organisms or both the names and an illustration of the organisms. **ICT**

4. Use word processing or graphics software to draw a food web of a deep-sea vent community. Your food chain can include either the names of the organisms or both the names and illustrations of the organisms. **ICT**

5. A major volcanic eruption ejects millions of tonnes of ash into the atmosphere. Explain how this eruption could indirectly affect the size of a population of herbivorous fish living in a pond thousands of kilometres from the volcano.

6. a) Use graphics or word processing software to draw a pyramid of numbers to represent a hypothetical aquatic community in which 4×10^9 phytoplankton support 11 herbivorous fish which, in turn, can feed one carnivorous fish. **ICT**

   b) Use graphics or word processing software to draw a pyramid of biomass for the aquatic community described in part (a) of this question. You do not have to use exact values. **ICT**

7. A pyramid of biomass shows the relative biomass per unit area for each trophic level. Explain why it is important to include the unit area in a biomass comparison.

8. a) Explain how changes to a lower trophic level (for example, a decrease in the number of producers) affect higher trophic levels.

   b) Explain how changes to higher trophic levels (for example, an increase in the number of secondary or tertiary consumers) affect lower trophic levels.

9. Identify situations in which the first trophic level (primary) consumers can have a significant influence on the amount of photosynthetic activity in a community.

Use the following information to answer the next question.

Energy Transfer

Assume that a one square kilometre field produces 300 t/km^2 of grain in one year. The grain that is grown in the field contains 14 190 kJ/kg of energy. One beef cow, with an average mass of 500 kg, needs 7.7 kg of grain every day. Assume that an average person needs 2400 kJ of energy per day to survive and beef contains 13 900 kJ/kg.

---

10. a) Calculate how many cattle, in theory, this 1 km^2 field could support for one year.

    b) Calculate the number of people, in theory, that this 1 km^2 field could support for one year if the people ate only the grain. (Keep in mind that this is an over-simplification. A person could not survive by eating only one type of food.)

    c) Calculate the number of people the field could support for a year, if the people ate only beef. (Keep in mind that this is an oversimplification. A person could not survive by eating only one type of food.)

    d) Compare the numbers of people that the field could support in parts (b) and (c). What do the results suggest about the most efficient use of farmland (rangeland for cattle or cropland for growing grain) to feed the most people. Include the disadvantages or limitations of this approach.

Biomagnification: A Fish Story

Fish are an excellent source of energy and nutrients—in fact, they have been called the perfect food. In recent years, however, many scientists have reported finding toxic chemicals in fish. Methylmercury (a toxic form of mercury) is one such chemical. Chronic exposure to methylmercury damages the kidneys, liver, and nervous system. In pregnant women, it interferes with the brain development of the fetus.

Some chemical compounds break down more readily than others—some in a matter of days or weeks, but others not for years. Chemicals such as mercury are persistent—that is, they resist decomposition by micro-organisms and environmental conditions. As a result, these chemicals or their derivatives can remain in the environment for decades.

Mercury occurs naturally in rocks, and natural processes release mercury into the soil and water. The major sources of mercury in the environment, however, result from human activities. Improper disposal of batteries and fluorescent lamps, burning hospital waste, and burning coal for fuel release significant amounts of mercury into the environment. Some micro-organisms in aquatic systems convert elemental mercury to methylmercury, which plants and animals more easily absorb. Over time, the methylmercury accumulates in the tissues of the aquatic organisms. The concentration of methylmercury increases at successively higher trophic levels—a process known as biomagnification.

What's for Dinner?

Health Canada has set an allowable limit of 0.5 ppm (parts per million) of methylmercury in commercial fish, such as salmon and canned tuna. This limit does not apply to large predatory fish, such as shark, however.

Concentration of Methylmercury in Aquatic Organisms

Organism		Concentration (ppm)
Plankton	phytoplankton	0.0109 to 0.176
	zooplankton	0.0110 to 0.376
Crustaceans	shrimp	0.01
	lobster	0.31
Vegetarian fish	tilapia	0.02
	catfish	0.05
Predatory fish	sardines	0.02
	salmon	0.01
	tuna (canned)	0.12
	goldeye (fresh-water)	0.452
	shark	0.99

Note: 1 ppm = 1 mg/Kg (Concentrations vary according to location and species.)
Sources: United States Environmental Protection Agency, Alberta Fish and Wildlife

• • •

1. Sketch a possible food web for five of the saltwater organisms listed in the table above, based on the amount of methylmercury found in their tissues.

2. Calculate how much methylmercury you would ingest if you consumed 0.2 kg of
   a) shrimp   **b)** tilapia   **c)** goldeye

3. Why does Health Canada recommend that women of child-bearing age not eat shark meat more than once a month?

4. Fish make up about 25 percent of the traditional diet of many Aboriginal peoples in Alberta. How might fish consumption advisories take this into account?

5. What actions could you take to reduce levels of methylmercury in the environment?

Producers (autotrophic, or self-feeder, organisms) are the basis of all food chains. Producers include photosynthetic organisms (plants, algae, and some kinds of bacteria) and, in select ecosystems, chemosynthetic micro-organisms (certain kinds of bacteria and archaea). Through photosynthesis, producers transform the Sun's radiant energy into energy-rich carbohydrate molecules such as glucose. Through cellular respiration, plants, animals, and most other kinds of organisms use the energy from these molecules to support and sustain their lives.

Consumers (heterotrophic, or other-feeder, organisms) obtain energy by consuming producers and/or other consumers. Primary consumers eat producers, secondary and tertiary consumers eat other consumers, and decomposers consume all kinds of organisms.

Food chains are simple models of energy transfer from one trophic level to another. Food webs are more complex models of energy transfer that show the ways in which organisms in different food chains can interact. Food chains rarely extend beyond four trophic levels because only a small percentage of the energy from one trophic level is transferred to the next level. Ecological pyramids of numbers, biomass, and energy are quantitative models that describe the connections among organisms at different trophic levels.

Because interactions of organisms in ecosystems are so interrelated, changes at any trophic level, or changes to the environment that supports the organisms, can destabilize ecosystems. As a result, the numbers and kinds of organisms can decrease.

Chapter 1 Graphic Organizer

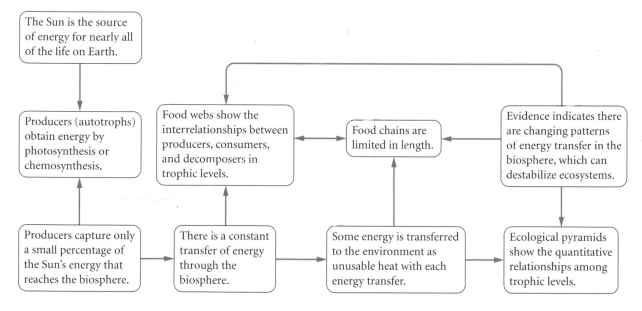

Understanding Concepts

1. Explain why decomposers, such as mushrooms, are classified as heterotrophs, not as autotrophs.

2. Explain how producer organisms living in deep-sea vent communities are able to survive without using photosynthesis to manufacture food molecules.

3. Describe why there is a limit to the number of organisms in a food chain.

4. a) Identify the assumption many ecologists often make about the amount of energy that is transferred from one trophic level to the next trophic level.
   b) How useful is this assumption? Justify your response.

5. List two pieces of evidence, based on traditional knowledge, that energy transfer in the Arctic region is changing.

6. Provide three reasons why solar energy is not completely converted to chemical energy by primary consumers.

7. Select the type of model—a food chain, a food web, pyramid of numbers, or pyramid of biomass—that would be the most informative to show energy transfer between trophic levels in the Arctic Tundra. Justify your selection.

Use the following information to answer the next question.

Ocean Ecosystems

Some transient orcas (*Orcinus orca*), also commonly called killer whales, feed on sea otters (*Enhydra lutris*). (Unlike resident orcas, which live in groups of about 40 individuals and stay in the same area for most of their lives, transient orcas are those that live in very small groups and travel widely in search of food.) Sea otters eat sea urchins, which feed on kelp. Researchers have noted that because killer whales have reduced sea otter population, the size of kelp forests has decreased.

8. Explain how the transient orcas could be having an indirect effect on kelp.

9. a) Explain how the same species can occupy more than one trophic level within the same food web.
   b) Explain how this type of interaction can enhance the stability of a food web.

10. Explain why autotrophs (producers) rather than decomposers occupy the lowest level of a food chain.

11. a) Explain why models showing the relationships among trophic levels in an ecosystem may be shown in the shape of pyramids.
    b) Describe the difference between the information depicted in a pyramid of numbers, a pyramid of energy, and a pyramid of biomass.

Applying Concepts

12. Identify the factors that might cause annual fluctuations in the photosynthetic activity of producer organisms in a grassland ecosystem in southern Alberta.

13. Explain why the energy transfer from a snowshoe hare (*Lepus americanus*) to a carnivorous lynx (*Lynx rufus*) is less efficient than energy transfer from grass to a snowshoe hare.

Use the following information to answer the next question.

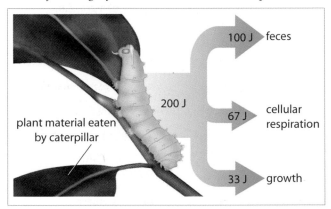

plant material eaten by caterpillar — 200 J — 100 J feces — 67 J cellular respiration — 33 J growth

14. Use the diagram above to explain why approximately 80 to 95 percent of the potential energy available at one trophic level is not transferred to the next level.

Use the following information to answer the next question.

Pyramid of Biomass

Typically, the shape of a biomass pyramid is similar to that of a pyramid of energy. In some aquatic ecosystems, a relatively low biomass of producers (called phytoplankton) supports a higher biomass of primary consumers (zooplankton). For example, this is a pyramid of biomass based on data obtained through study of the English Channel ecosystem.

Dry weight (g/m²)

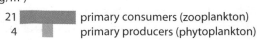

21 — primary consumers (zooplankton)
4 — primary producers (phytoplankton)

15. Explain why the pyramid of biomass in the English Channel is inverted.

Use the following information to answer the next question.

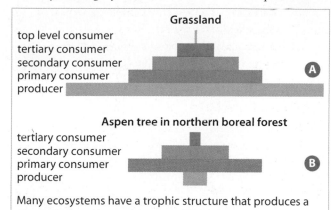

Grassland

top level consumer
tertiary consumer
secondary consumer
primary consumer
producer

(A)

Aspen tree in northern boreal forest

tertiary consumer
secondary consumer
primary consumer
producer

(B)

Many ecosystems have a trophic structure that produces a pyramid of numbers with a broad base. In some ecosystems, however, there can be fewer producers than primary consumers.

16. Explain why the trophic structure of a grassland ecosystem results in an upright pyramid of numbers while the trophic structure of an aspen tree in the northern boreal forest is inverted.

Use the following information to answer the next question.

Ecological pyramid data for two ecosystems

Ecosystem A			Ecosystem B	
Trophic level	Dry weight (g/m²)	Relative number of organisms	Trophic level	Dry weight (g/m²)
primary producers	809	4×10^9	primary producers (phyto-plankton)	4
primary consumers	37	11	primary consumers (zoo-plankton)	21
secondary consumers	11	1		
tertiary consumers	1.5	0		
decomposers	5	millions and millions		

17. a) Use word processing or graphics software to create three separate graphs of the data on this chart. You should end up with two pyramids of biomass and one pyramid of numbers. Clearly label each graph. (**Hint:** see Figure 1.14 on page 21) **ICT**
b) Describe the advantages and disadvantages of using a pyramid of biomass rather than a pyramid of numbers for Ecosystem A.

18. Suppose that you are investigating possible changes of energy transfer in the taiga (boreal forest) of northern Canada. Explain how traditional knowledge of First Nation, Metis, and Inuit inhabitants of this region could help you with your research.

19. a) You eat a strawberry. Calculate the amount of plant material you would have to eat to gain 1 kg of mass. (Assume the rule of 10 applies.)
b) You eat turkey meat. The turkey ate insects that, in turn, ate plant material. If you could live entirely on turkey meat, calculate the amount of plant material the insects would have to eat to feed enough turkeys so you could gain 1 kg of mass. (Assume the rule of 10 applies.)

Making Connections

Use the following information to answer the next question.

Human Diet

You have seen that there are fewer carnivores than herbivores in ecosystems because of the inefficiency of energy transfer between trophic levels, and that the world could support more people if we ate only plant material. Some people feel this means that humans should switch to a vegetarian diet; others disagree.

20. a) Explain, in terms of energy transfer, why some people believe humans should eat only plant material. Include simple food chains to support your answer.
b) Identify two reasons, in ecological terms, why switching the entire human population to a vegetarian diet might not work.

Use the following information to answer the next question.

Orcas

From 1995 to 2001 the population size of the southern resident population of orcas (*Orcinus orca*) has decreased from a high of 98 individuals to a low of 79 animals, which is a reduction of 20% of the entire population in only 6 years (pers. obs. 2002, Bain 2002). While at this point we do not understand the entire web of causation for this decline, several contributing factors have been reported, such as prey availability and the decrease in salmon stocks, the exposure to toxic chemicals and in particular PCB's (Ross 2001, Dahlheim et al. 2000), as well as the increase in commercial and private vessels mostly for whale watching over the last 10 years (Bain 2002).
[Source: Kriete, *Bioenergetic Changes from 1986 to 2001 in the Southern Resident Killer Whale Population*, Orcinus Orca, 2002.]

21. Explain why this top carnivore is becoming endangered. Focus your argument on the transfer of energy in the marine ecosystem.

CHAPTER 2

Cycles of Matter

Chapter Concepts

2.1 The Role of Water in Cycles of Matter

- There is a finite amount of water, which is re-used through the hydrologic cycle.

- Water is a universal solvent of polar molecules.

- Water is essential to humans and ecosystems.

- The hydrologic cycle plays a central role in nutrient cycles (biogeochemical cycles).

2.2 Biogeochemical Cycles

- Carbon, oxygen, sulfur, and nitrogen are found in living organisms and in the land, atmosphere, and water. They are recycled through biotic and abiotic processes.

- Phosphorus is found in living organisms and in the land and water. It is recycled through biotic and abiotic processes.

- Disruptions in one biogeochemical cycle can affect another.

2.3 The Balance of the Matter and Energy Exchange

- Biotic and abiotic processes maintain the balance of matter and energy exchange in the biosphere.

- Natural processes and human activities can affect the transfer of energy and the cycling of matter through the biosphere.

Like all plants, trees of the Pacific Northwest coastal rainforest need nitrogen from the soil to grow. New evidence from the University of British Columbia shows that, unlike most plants, coastal rainforest trees rely on the Pacific Ocean as their source of nitrogen. The urine and feces of bears and scavengers that feast on Pacific salmon are the main source of about 60 million kg of nitrogen-containing salmon tissue that "feeds" the forest soil.

Salmon need healthy forests and streams to reproduce, and forests and bears need abundant salmon. Streams need standing trees to retain soil and provide shade. So healthy streams depend on fish, and the fish depend on the streams. In this chapter, you will explore how the movement of matter in the biosphere connects organisms and ecosystems in a life-sustaining relationship.

Whose Planet?

Salmon stocks are dwindling throughout the Pacific Northwest. Because of the newly discovered close relationship between salmon and the trees, some biologists have urged that forest, wildlife, and fish management must be integrated. This seems reasonable, given that each population—rainforest trees, bears, inland salmon, and ocean-going salmon—affects the health and stability of the others. Some people go further, suggesting that human rights, such as the basic right to exist without interference from others, should be extended to all living things. Other people suggest that natural entities such as streams, oceans, and forests should have legal standing in courts in order to provide some protection from human decisions and actions.

Procedure

1. Consider this proposal by applying your current knowledge and feelings about biosphere connections to one of the following scenarios. Discuss your views and ideas with a partner or in a small group.

   • People wanting to enjoy the quiet and beauty of nature build homes in "wild" areas that are habitat for other species. Should one species (humans) be allowed to "own" the habitat of other species?

   • Loggers working to support their families and communities are often hampered by laws protecting organisms such as endangered owls and old-growth trees. Should these other organisms have rights that encroach on a person's right to make a living?

   • Tourist operators and their clients now have the technology and financial resources to venture almost anywhere in Canada. This includes using helicopters to take mountain bikers and skiers into delicate alpine terrain and taking motor boats through sensitive wetlands. Should people be allowed to go anywhere they wish for whatever purpose?

Analysis

1. In your opinion, should other organisms have the same rights as humans? Should those rights apply only to some organisms? How would you choose?

2. Is it justifiable to extend rights and laws to natural entities such as a mountain? Is it practical? Does that matter? Defend your opinions.

As salmon decompose, nutrients such as nitrogen are released to the soil. Tree ring studies show that when salmon are abundant, trees grow up to three times faster than when salmon are scarce.

The Role of Water in Cycles of Matter

Section Outcomes

In this section, you will
- **explain** water's primary role in the biogeochemical cycles as a result of its chemical and physical properties
- **analyze** data on water consumption and loss in plants and animals
- **evaluate** the use of water by society

Key Terms

biogeochemical cycles
hydrologic cycle
polar
hydrogen bond
cohesion
adhesion

Figure 2.1 Water is constantly being recycled in the hydrologic cycle. As a result, this athlete could be drinking water molecules that were once consumed or respired by a dinosaur.

On a hot day, you might find your skin covered with perspiration. Where did the water in this perspiration come from?

The human body loses and must replace approximately three percent of its total water volume daily. There is a limited amount of water in the biosphere, but water is naturally recycled, which makes it available to living organisms. Part of the water in your body may have come from a distant rainforest. When rain fell on this rainforest, some of it may have gone into the soil, where it was drawn up by a tree's roots and transpired (lost through pores in its leaves, called stomata, that are used for gas exchange) to the atmosphere. Other rain may have fallen on rocks and evaporated back into the atmosphere. The combined transpiration and evaporation from a terrestrial area is called evapotranspiration.

Water is a product of cellular respiration. During cellular respiration, the chemical breakdown of glucose results in the production of water as a byproduct. All the chemical reactions that occur within an organism make up the organism's metabolism. The water

that is produced by cellular respiration is therefore known as metabolic water.

The hydrogen and oxygen atoms that make up metabolic water actually come from glucose and atmospheric oxygen gas. Thus, plants, animals, and all other organisms that conduct cellular respiration also release water that makes its way into the atmosphere. Wind currents could have carried some of the water to the Rocky Mountains, where the water molecules would have condensed and fallen as precipitation (rain and snow).

The water molecules might then have joined water molecules from other sources in a river. From there, they might have been drawn into a local water treatment facility and entered the tap water you drank. Your body would have used some of these water molecules in cellular processes and perhaps stored the rest, later secreting them as the perspiration that evaporated and cooled you down (Figure 2.1).

The routes that water and other chemical nutrients take through the biotic and abiotic components of the biosphere are known as **biogeochemical**

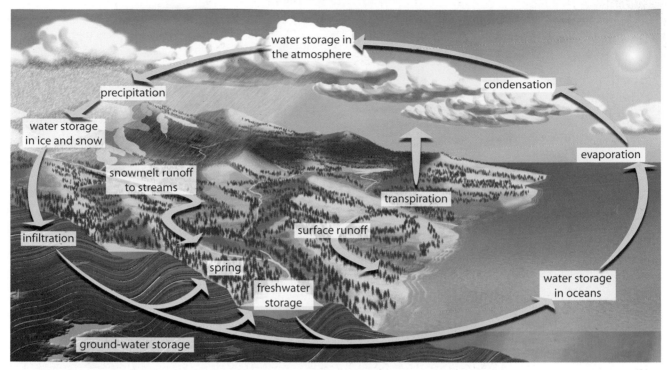

Figure 2.2 As water cycles through the environment, it can transport many other materials along with it.

cycles. You have seen how the water cycle, or **hydrologic cycle**, can connect ecosystems separated by great distances. The hydrologic cycle involves all phases of water (Figure 2.2). More than 97 percent of the water in the biosphere exists in liquid form. This is due, in part, to water's relatively high boiling point compared with the boiling points of other liquids. Water also exists as ice and gas in Earth's atmosphere. The water in the atmosphere results from evaporation, including evapotranspiration. About 86 percent of the global evaporation of water is from the oceans.

Water vapour is a greenhouse gas. It not only traps heat in the atmosphere, but also transfers heat. Where large amounts of sunlight reach Earth, such as in the tropics, the radiant energy heats the ground and causes evaporation. As the water vapour rises, it moves toward the Poles and releases heat as it expands and cools. This process in the atmosphere distributes heat away from the equator.

Heat is also transferred by liquid water. Ocean currents, for example, transfer warm water from hotter to cooler regions. The warm water can heat the air, moderating the temperature over nearby land.

Water has several properties that make it an excellent carrier of dissolved minerals and other materials and an effective medium for transferring energy.
- Water is a universal solvent.
- Water has a relatively high boiling point and melting point.
- Water has special adhesive and cohesive properties.
- Water has a high heat capacity.

The Universal Solvent

As water moves from place to place and changes from one physical state to another, it carries a variety of other substances. Water in the soil, for example, contains nutrients such as nitrogen and phosphorus. Water can also carry toxic compounds, such as methylmercury.

A water molecule consists of two hydrogen atoms that are covalently bonded to one oxygen atom. The hydrogen end of the molecule has a slightly positive charge and the oxygen end has a slightly negative charge, making water a **polar** molecule (Figure 2.3). This polarity allows a water molecule

slight negative charge at this end

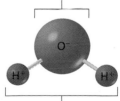

slight positive charge at this end

Figure 2.3 The partial positive charges and partial negative charge make this water molecule polar.

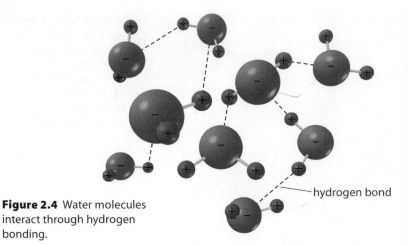

Figure 2.4 Water molecules interact through hydrogen bonding.

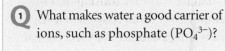
hydrogen bond

to make a weak attraction, called a **hydrogen bond**, between the hydrogen of one molecule and the oxygen of a nearby molecule (Figure 2.4). The structure of water, which includes its polarity and its ability to form hydrogen bonds, enables it to dissolve a wide variety of substances, including molecular compounds such as carbon dioxide and ionic compounds such as sodium chloride (table salt).

• • •

Q 1 What makes water a good carrier of ions, such as phosphate (PO_4^{3-})?

• • •

Hydrogen Bonding Affects Water in Different Phases

Hydrogen bonding explains why water remains liquid over a large temperature range and why water can continue to dissolve and transport substances over this temperature range.

An individual hydrogen bond is relatively weak. As a result, hydrogen bonds between water molecules form, break, and re-form frequently. Many hydrogen bonds together are quite strong, however. A large amount of energy is needed to break the many hydrogen bonds in a volume of water. Only when its hydrogen bonds are broken can water start to boil and undergo a phase change from a liquid to a gas. Therefore, water has a relatively high boiling point (100 °C) when compared with other liquids that do not

have hydrogen bonding. Similarly, frozen water (ice) has a relatively high melting point (0 °C), compared with substances that do not have hydrogen bonds.

Hydrogen bonding also explains the density of liquid water. Unlike the solid and liquid phases of most other substances, frozen water is less dense than liquid water. When water freezes, it expands because hydrogen bonds hold the water molecules in an open crystal structure (Figure 2.5). When ice melts at 0 °C, its solid, crystalline structure begins to break down. The loosened molecules pack more closely together and fill in spaces in the collapsing solid structure. This increases the density of water, until water reaches its greatest density (1 kg/L) at 4 °C. As the temperature continues to rise, water becomes less dense because of thermal expansion.

Water's density characteristics have key consequences for life and the cycling of nutrients. In the spring, as water is melting, it becomes more dense as it warms until it reaches 4 °C. The denser water sinks below the less dense and cooler water, leaving the cooler water at the top to warm and subsequently sink. Similarly, as winter approaches and the water temperature cools towards 4 °C, the cooler water becomes more dense and sinks below the warmer water. When the warmer water cools, it sinks until it reaches its maximum density at 4 °C.

As water sinks and rises, nutrients and dissolved oxygen are cycled with it. Water that percolates into spaces in rocks expands when it freezes, weathering the rocks to help create sand and soil and unlocking nutrients in the process. Because ice is less dense and therefore floats on water, it insulates the deep water in a lake during the winter, preventing the water from freezing and providing a refuge for aquatic life.

Hydrogen bonding causes **cohesion**, the attraction of water molecules to each other. Cohesion is responsible for surface tension, the reason why many insects can walk on water (Figure 2.6). Surface

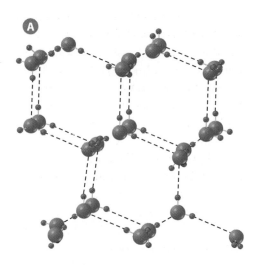

Figure 2.5 (A) Hydrogen bonds prevent the water molecules in ice from getting as close to each other as they do in liquid water. **(B)** Ice floats on water because ice has a lower density than water.

tension also keeps organic debris on the water surface, where it provides nutrients for aquatic organisms.

Adhesion is the attraction of water molecules to molecules of other substances, such as the inner surface of a glass tube or the cell wall of a tree's xylem (water-conducting tissue). Adhesion provides an upward force on water and counteracts the pull of gravity. The water molecules in xylem are also cohesively attracted. So, when transpiration removes water molecules from the xylem, the remaining water in the xylem is pulled up to replace these lost molecules. Together cohesion and adhesion explain how, in transpiration, water can travel from the roots of a tree up to its leaves against the force of gravity.

• • •

2. Explain the role of hydrogen bonding in

a) transporting nutrients over a large temperature range

b) nutrient cycling in lakes

c) transpiration

• • •

Water Stores Heat

Because of hydrogen bonding, water has a very high heat capacity compared with other substances. *Heat capacity* is a measure of the amount of heat a substance can absorb or release for a given change

in temperature. Substances with a high heat capacity, such as water, require the transfer of large amounts of energy to effect small changes in temperature. Thus, water heats up more slowly than almost any other compound and holds its temperature longer when the input of energy stops. This property enables organisms, which have a high concentration of water in their tissues, to maintain a fairly constant internal temperature. At an ecosystem level, water's high heat capacity means that bodies of water such as oceans and lakes have a moderation effect on the air temperatures of nearby land. At a global level, water's heat capacity and its ability to hold heat make it possible for surface currents to distribute heat from warm equatorial regions to higher latitudes.

Figure 2.6 Surface tension prevents the legs of this water strider (*Gerris remigis*) from penetrating the surface of the water.

Water World

Living organisms depend on the hydrologic cycle and are an essential part of it. By mass, water comprises more than 50 percent of all plant and animal tissue. The adult human body is composed of about 70 percent water, and a radish is composed of 95 percent water. Dormant forms of life, such as fungal spores, bacterial spores, and plant seeds contain much smaller percentages of water.

For actively metabolizing organisms, water consumption, retention, and loss are part of the daily routine. Animals obtain water directly by eating, drinking, and absorbing water through the surface of their skin. Animals also obtain water through cellular respiration. They lose water through breathing and sweating,

---

Thought Lab 2.1 Water Gains and Losses

Animals must strictly balance water gains and losses to live. The Ord's kangaroo rat (*Dipodomys ordii*) is a small, nocturnal (active at night) rodent that is found in southern Alberta and Saskatchewan, the United States, and Mexico. Like other kangaroo rats, the Ord's kangaroo rat lives in sand dunes and semi-arid (fairly dry) grasslands where there are few to no sources of surface water, such as ponds and streams. Although it rarely drinks water, the Ord's kangaroo rat is able to obtain most of the water it needs by metabolizing the food it eats. As well, it is very efficient at conserving water.

Procedure

1. A water budget quantifies the amount of water an organism gains and loses through various activities. The data table below compares the daily water budget for a human and an Ord's kangaroo rat.

2. Calculate the percentage of the total water gain from (a) metabolic water and (b) absorbed water for a human and an Ord's kangaroo rat.

3. Calculate the percentage of the total water loss from (a) urine and (b) evaporation for each organism.

Analysis

1. What are the similarities between the two water budgets?

2. What is the relative importance of metabolic water for the Ord's kangaroo rat, compared with a human?

3. **a)** In what part of the water budget is an Ord's kangaroo rat more efficient at conserving water than a human?

   b) Suggest one physiological strategy that the kangaroo rat uses to conserve water.

4. Compare the percentages of total water lost through evaporation for a human and an Ord's kangaroo rat. How might the Ord's kangaroo rat's nocturnal behaviour be related to its water budget?

5. The cellular respiration of different foods produces different amounts of water:
   - 1.0 g of glucose (carbohydrate) results in 0.6 g of water.
   - 1.0 g of fat results in 1.07 g of water.
   - 1.0 g of protein produces 0.4 g of water.

   a) Assume that grain is two percent fat, 62 percent carbohydrate, 11 percent protein, and 10.4 percent free water. For how many days could the kangaroo rat's water needs be met by 1 kg of grain?

   b) Assume that a cooked beef steak is seven percent fat, 27 percent protein, and 65.6 percent free water. For how many days could a human's water needs be met by 1 kg of beef?

Water Budgets for a Human and an Ord's Kangaroo Rat

Water budget for a human			
Water gains (mL)		**Water losses (mL)**	
metabolic water	190	urine	900
absorbed (drinking)	1045	feces	200
absorbed (eating)	665	evaporation (including 350 mL from breathing)	800
Total water gain	1900	Total water loss	1900

Water budget for an Ord's kangaroo rat			
Water gains (mL)		**Water losses (mL)**	
metabolic water	54.0	urine	13.5
absorbed water total	6.0	feces	2.6
		evaporation (including breathing)	43.9
Total water gain	60.0	Total water loss	60.0

Source: Bodil Schmidt-Nielsen and Knut Schmidt-Nielsen. 1951. A complete account of the water metabolism in kangaroo rats and an experimental verification. *Journal of Cellular and Comparative Physiology* Volume 38, Issue 2, Pages 165–181.

and in urine and feces. Plants obtain water through their roots but lose vast amounts by transpiration.

• • •

Q3 What is metabolic water?

Q4 How do organisms gain water?

Q5 How do organisms lose water?

• • •

Water—An Essential Service

People, like other organisms, depend on their environment for food, water, and clean air to breathe. Natural features, such as an underground river that is tapped for drinking water, are sometimes called ecosystem services to reflect the fact that these features provide for human needs. Fresh water provides an essential ecosystem service.

The two largest natural disasters in Canada were droughts in the prairie provinces. North America experienced two regional- to continental-scale droughts in the twentieth century, during the 1930s and the 1980s. The impact of the drought in the 1980s was less severe, however, due to improved farming practices since the 1930s. There is evidence from Moon Lake, North Dakota, United States, that extreme droughts were more frequent before about 1200 C.E. These droughts had greater intensity and duration (from decades to a century) than the drought in the 1930s.

Alberta has experienced droughts many times in the past and will continue to do so in the future. If global temperatures rise, the rate of evaporation of water from land, lakes, and plants may increase, potentially making Alberta even drier. Currently, Alberta has rich supplies of freshwater from rivers, lakes, wetlands, and underground sources. Population growth, however, combined with agricultural and industrial use, has increased the demand for water in the province.

Water quality is another issue that affects the amount of water that is available for drinking, washing, and other uses. Water that cannot be cleaned of toxic chemicals and pathogens is no longer useful. If it is released into the environment, it can cause great harm to ecosystems. Water is considered to be a renewable resource, but only if it is used wisely. How do human activities affect water quality in your community? Examine this question further in Investigation 2.A on page 41.

Water and Ecosystems

A 4000 m^2 cornfield can transpire 16 000 L of water in a day. When water is scarce, plants respond by closing their stomata, which reduces transpiration. When the stomata are closed, however, plants cannot take in carbon dioxide. As a result, photosynthetic activity in plants drops if there is insufficient water.

To test the effect of a drought on an entire forest, researchers working in the Amazon shielded a group of more than 500 trees (the trial group) from rain using plastic panels (Figure 2.7). A group of uncovered trees was used as a control. Throughout the five-year drought simulation, scientists checked for changes

BiologyFile

Web Link
University of Alberta ecology professor, Dr. David Schindler, has received numerous awards and honours for his untiring work in the study of water, aquatic ecosystems, and the effects of pollutants and overindulgent human use on both. In what ways has Dr. Schindler been recognized by the Canadian and international community, and for what reasons?

www.albertabiology.ca
WWW

Figure 2.7 In 1998, the Woods Hole Research Center of the United States began testing the effects of a simulated drought on trees in an Amazon rainforest. The researchers used plastic panels to prevent rainwater from reaching the forest floor. After five years in drought conditions, many of the larger, older, trees died.

in the trees. At the end of the simulation, the roots of many of the covered trees had grown deeper into the soil, where they could access water. As well, the rate of growth of the tree trunks had slowed. Many of the largest trees, which were hundreds of years old, had died.

The experimental results led the researchers to pose a number of questions, which scientists continue to examine. For example, if there was a severe drought in the tropics, would the rain forests take in significantly less carbon dioxide for photosynthesis? If the rain forests absorbed less carbon dioxide, which is a greenhouse gas, how might this affect the global climate? How would limited plant growth affect biogeochemical cycles other than the hydrologic cycle?

The hydrologic cycle is linked to all the other cycles of matter. Therefore, a change in the hydrologic cycle will affect the other cycles of matter. How can such changes affect ecosystems? You will investigate possible answers to this question in the next section.

Section 2.1 Summary

- There is a limited (finite) amount of water in the biosphere. It is re-used, however, in the hydrological cycle and exists as a solid, a liquid, and a gas in the environment.
- Water is able to dissolve a wide variety of substances. Hydrogen bonding plays a key role in determining the properties and uses of water, such as its ability to dissolve and transport materials.
- Water provides an essential service for humans and ecosystems. Drought and poor water quality can affect water availability and impact humans and the environment.
- The hydrologic cycle plays a central role in nutrient cycles (biogeochemical cycles).

| Section 2.1 | Review |

1. a) Use graphics or word processing software to illustrate the hydrologic cycle. **ICT**

b) Use this cycle to make an operational definition of the term "biogeochemical cycle."

2. Explain the role that water vapour plays in maintaining global temperatures.

3. a) Use graphics or other software to draw a model of a water molecule. Label your diagram. **ICT**

b) Use graphics or other software to draw a model of water molecules interacting though hydrogen bonding. Label your diagram. **ICT**

4. Describe the relationship between the structure of the water molecule and the fact that many call water a "universal solvent."

5. Explain how the cohesion of water molecules allows the insect shown opposite to walk on the surface of liquid water.

6. State three reasons why water is important to life.

7. Explain how animals cope with the constant loss of water.

8. Identify five major uses of water in Alberta.

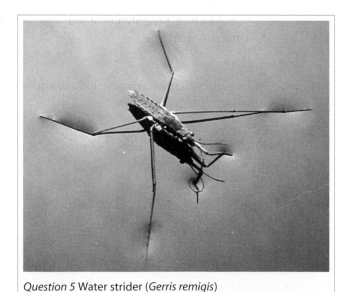

Question 5 Water strider (*Gerris remigis*)

9. Define the term "water quality." Explain why it is important for:

a) society

b) ecosystems

Societal Uses of Water

Issue

About 97.5 percent of the water that is consumed in Alberta comes from surface water, such as the water in lakes and rivers. The rest of the water that is consumed comes from ground water, which collects when rain or melted snow filters down through the ground and accumulates underground in large gaps in the rocks.

Gathering Data and Information

1. In a group, choose one of the categories of water use in Alberta that is shown in the pie graphs. Answer the following questions:

   - How much water (in L) is used for this purpose?
   - What are some ways (if any) to reduce the use of water for this purpose?
   - Is water quality affected? If so, what can be done to restore water quality?
   - What are the benefits of using water for this purpose?

Organizing Findings

2. As a group, make a brief presentation of your findings to the rest of the class.

Opinions and Recommendations

1. Which use of water in Alberta do you think should be decreased? Justify your response.

2. What are some possible ways to decrease water use in the category you chose in question 1?

3. Do you think water use is a basic human right that people should not have to pay for? Or do you think people should pay *more* for water than they do, in order to encourage water conservation?

4. One solution to meeting the demand for irrigation in drier regions of Alberta is to use pipelines to divert water from other parts of the province. Evaluate the arguments for and against doing this:

Benefits:	Costs:
• The diversion would allow for the growth of economically important crops.	• The removal of large amounts of water from a particular source (bulk water removal) would be permanent.
• The diversion would allow for the growth of important food crops.	• Ecosystems that depend on the source of the diverted water could be negatively affected.
• Rural communities could use the diverted water in their homes and town buildings.	• Diversion could introduce species, such as parasites, from the water source into ecosystems in the other region.

a) With your classmates, discuss whether the risks of diversion outweigh its benefits.

b) What questions would you pursue to evaluate, more thoroughly, the risks and benefits of a diversion strategy for a specific rural area?

Alberta's surface-water consumption uses

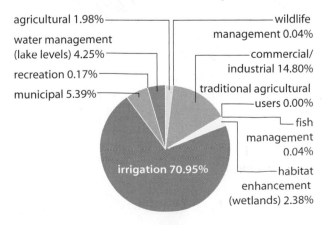

agricultural 1.98%
water management (lake levels) 4.25%
recreation 0.17%
municipal 5.39%
wildlife management 0.04%
commercial/industrial 14.80%
traditional agricultural users 0.00%
fish management 0.04%
irrigation 70.95%
habitat enhancement (wetlands) 2.38%

Alberta's ground-water consumption uses

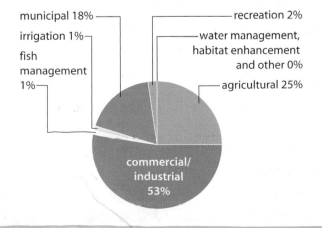

municipal 18%
irrigation 1%
fish management 1%
recreation 2%
water management, habitat enhancement and other 0%
agricultural 25%
commercial/industrial 53%

Biogeochemical Cycles

Figure 2.8 The pea plant on the right has been well watered and has received ample sunlight. Why does it look so unhealthy compared to the plant on the left?

Because autotrophs produce their own food, it might seem reasonable to think that they could live independently of heterotrophs. How are primary producers, such as plants, connected to heterotrophic organisms? Plants, like all organisms, require matter to build cell structures and provide energy. In order to survive and grow, organisms must obtain nutrients that serve as sources of energy or chemical building blocks, or both. For example, the pea plants in Figure 2.8 can only survive if they have access to nutrients, such as compounds that contain sulfur, nitrogen, and phosphorus. These compounds must be in forms that the pea plants can use. Heterotrophs convert many nutrients into forms that plants can access and use. Fertilizers provide another source of accessible plant nutrients (see Figure 2.9).

The recycling of matter through the biotic and abiotic parts of ecosystems allows all organisms, including plants, to obtain essential nutrients.

At each step in a biogeochemical cycle, substances are temporarily stored in nutrient reservoirs, such as organisms, soil, air, and water. All biogeochemical cycles involve some substances that are being stored in these reservoirs for various amounts of time and some substances that are moving through the environment, from reservoir to reservoir. Substances can cycle between nutrient reservoirs relatively quickly. When this happens, they are said to be part of the **rapid cycling** of nutrients. For example, carbon moves from producer to consumer to decomposer, and back to the atmosphere through rapid cycling.

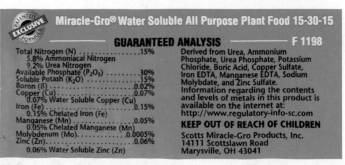

Figure 2.9 Fertilizers contain essential nutrients required by plants.

Substances also accumulate and are stored for long periods of time in nutrient reservoirs. Fossil fuel deposits, such as coal and oil, are carbon reservoirs formed over millions of years as organic matter built up without fully decomposing. Deep underground, the organic matter was subjected to intense pressure. When substances accumulate and are unavailable to organisms they are said to be part of the **slow cycling** of nutrients. It can take millions of years for these substances to again become available as nutrients for living organisms. Figure 2.10 illustrates the connections between the rapid cycling of substances (on the left) and the slow cycling of substances (on the right).

Some elements, such as oxygen (O), carbon (C), nitrogen (N), and sulfur (S), form compounds that easily travel in both water and air. As a result, these elements can literally travel around the

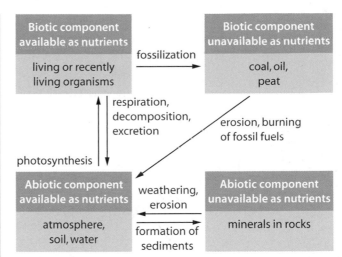

world. Other elements, such as iron (Fe) and phosphorus (P) are found in soil and water, but generally do not enter the atmosphere.

The Carbon and Oxygen Cycles

Plants consume billions of tonnes of carbon in the form of carbon dioxide (CO_2) each year—much more carbon than animals and plants release from cellular respiration. As Figure 2.11 shows, much of the carbon that is released back into the atmosphere as carbon dioxide comes from forest fires and the breakdown of organic matter, such as plant materials, by decomposers.

Figure 2.10 The four nutrient reservoirs are categorized with respect to whether they involve biotic or abiotic components of the ecosystem and whether the nutrients they contain are directly available to living things.

Figure 2.11 The carbon and oxygen cycles. How are these cycles interconnected?

Q 6 What is a nutrient reservoir?

Q 7 Explain the connections between the slow cycling and rapid cycling of nutrients.

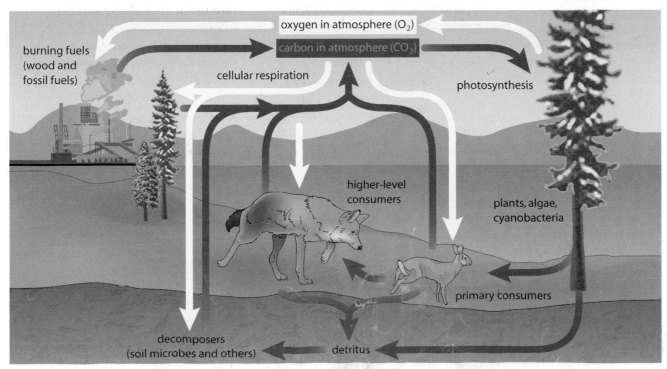

Web Link
How much carbon dioxide do you and your family generate in your daily activities? Compare the results of at least two online carbon dioxide calculators.

www.albertabiology.ca
www

Thus, plants, animals, and decomposers play an important role in the rapid cycling of carbon.

Plants, animals, and decomposers also play an important role in the rapid cycling of oxygen. As the following diagram shows, photosynthesis produces oxygen gas (O_2), which is needed for cellular respiration.

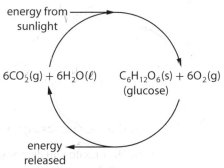

Photosynthesis

energy from sunlight

$6CO_2(g) + 6H_2O(\ell)$　　$C_6H_{12}O_6(s) + 6O_2(g)$
　　　　　　　　　　　　　　(glucose)

energy released
Cellular Respiration

Although the processes are very different, the overall equations for photosynthesis and cellular respiration are complementary. As well, both photosynthesis and cellular respiration contribute to the rapid cycling of carbon and oxygen.

Explore the connection between photosynthesis and respiration in the investigation that follows.

Q 8 How are (a) plants and (b) animals involved in the rapid cycling of carbon?

The Slow Cycling of Carbon

As you have learned, living organisms play an important role in the rapid cycling of carbon. Living organisms also play an important role in the slow cycling of carbon. Photosynthetic organisms remove carbon dioxide from the atmosphere and incorporate carbon into organic matter. The trees in forests act as carbon sinks (reservoirs that absorb more carbon than they emit to the environment). The trees store large amounts of carbon, most of which is only released when they die and decompose or are combusted by forest fires. Deforestation accounts for the return of about 2 gigatonnes (Gt) of carbon to the atmosphere per year. In addition, photosynthetic organisms in

---

INVESTIGATION 2.B

Target Skills

Designing an investigation to compare carbon dioxide production by a plant and an animal

Gathering data to measure the rate of carbon dioxide production by a plant

Stating a conclusion based on the analysis of collected and provided data

Carbon Dioxide Production in Plants and Animals

Plants and animals both use glucose as an energy source and as a source of carbon to build cell structures. Therefore, like animal cells, plant cells carry out cellular respiration. The amount of carbon dioxide that plants produce by cellular respiration is very small, however, compared with the amount of carbon dioxide that plants take in during photosynthesis. In this investigation, you will research and design a procedure to measure the rate of carbon dioxide production by a plant. You will then use the data you collected to compare carbon dioxide production by a plant with carbon dioxide production by an animal (data is provided for the latter).

Question

How does carbon dioxide production compare in plants and animals?

Hypothesis

In your group, generate a hypothesis about the rate of carbon dioxide production in plants compared with that of animals.

Prediction

Make a prediction about the outcome of this investigation.

Safety Precaution

Your teacher will inform you about safety precautions appropriate to your experimental design.

Materials

As per your experimental design.

Experimental Plan

1. Research (using the Internet or library) and design a procedure to measure the rate of carbon dioxide production by a plant. The following questions can help guide your research and design decisions. ICT

   • What is a respirometer and how can you build one?

   • How could you use carbon dioxide sensors (if they are available) and an appropriate interface such as a computer, calculator, or handheld device?

   • How could you use pH?

2. In your experimental design, be sure to consider the following factors:

   • controlled, manipulated, and responding variables

   • materials (for example, germinating seeds could work well; they generate carbon dioxide through cellular respiration but do not yet absorb carbon dioxide through photosynthesis, a factor that will affect your results if you use mature plants.)

   • data collection (for example, what measurements will you take? How often will you take them? How will you record your data?)

   • safety

   Note: The rate of carbon dioxide production in mL/min from respiration is approximately equal to the rate of oxygen consumption in mL/min.

3. Review your procedure with your teacher.

Data and Observations

4. Record your data as per your experimental design. Be sure to note all observations you make.

Analysis

1. **a)** The rate of carbon dioxide production for a Chilean cricket, *Hophlosphyrum griseus*, at 27 °C is, on average, 2.856×10^{-6} mL/min. Calculate the amount of carbon dioxide that an average Chilean cricket would produce in 15 minutes.

   b) Would a larger cricket produce more or less carbon dioxide than the average cricket? Explain your reasoning.

   c) Would an active cricket or a resting cricket respire at a higher rate? Explain your reasoning.

2. **a)** At what rate did the plants in your experiment produce carbon dioxide?

   b) An average Chilean cricket has a mass of 36.2 mg. Calculate and compare the amount of carbon dioxide produced, per gram, for the plants you studied and the crickets.

3. **a)** Which variables did you control?

   b) Discuss how using controlled variables helps you interpret the results of this investigation.

Conclusions

4. Did your results support your hypothesis? Explain.

5. How could you demonstrate that photosynthesis and cellular respiration are complementary processes?

6. Up to a point, cellular reactions increase as temperature increases.

   a) Predict how increasing the temperature in this investigation would affect your results.

   b) Predict how increasing environmental temperatures might affect the rapid cycling of carbon.

Extension

7. Many other factors affect the rate at which plants respire. Choose two of the following factors and hypothesize how a change in each factor may influence the rate of carbon dioxide production:

   • light levels

   • maturation of tissues (i.e., germinating seed versus mature plant)

   • availability of nutrients

   • species of plant

Rapid cycling of carbon

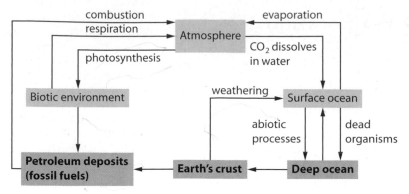

Slow cycling of carbon

Figure 2.12 The rapid cycling of carbon is shown in green, and the slow cycling of carbon is shown in purple.

Biology File

FYI
Human activities, such as deforestation and burning fossil fuels, add about 8 billion tonnes of carbon dioxide to the atmosphere each year. Only about 3.2 billion tonnes of this carbon dioxide remains in the atmosphere, however; 4.8 billion tonnes are unaccounted for. The missing carbon dioxide is called the *missing carbon sink*. Some scientists speculate that part of the missing carbon dioxide gets absorbed by the oceans. Other scientists speculate that terrestrial vegetation, somewhere in the northern hemisphere, is absorbing carbon dioxide at a higher rate than previously thought. Many scientists around the world are involved in trying to find the missing carbon sink.

the ocean, such as phytoplankton and algae, reproduce rapidly, producing large amounts of biomass and incorporating carbon into their structures. Much of this biomass is consumed by zooplankton, fish, whales, and other heterotrophs. A small percentage of the biomass of autotrophs and heterotrophs drifts to the ocean floor. Over millions of years, organic matter that is not fully broken down by decomposers may become incorporated into rocks or contribute to petroleum (fossil fuel) deposits.

The ocean itself is the largest carbon sink. It contains 38 000 Gt of carbon in the form of dissolved carbon dioxide. Another 11 000 Gt of carbon lies on the ocean floor, trapped in methane hydrates, compounds that are complexes of methane (CH_4) and water. Figure 2.12 summarizes the rapid and slow cycling of carbon in the biosphere.

Natural processes that return carbon to rapid cycling can occur quickly (such as in forest fires) or extremely slowly (such as in weathering). Limestone rock contains carbon. It is formed from calcium carbonate ($CaCO_3$), which comes from the shells of aquatic organisms (Figure 2.13) or may precipitate from dissolved calcium carbonate in water. As limestone weathers over time, small amounts of carbon are released back into the soil, air, and water.

Human activities influence the slow cycling of carbon in a number of ways. In particular, the combustion of petroleum

deposits quickly releases carbon back into the atmosphere. Since the industrial revolution (around the late eighteenth and early nineteenth centuries), levels of atmospheric carbon dioxide have increased by about 30 percent.

⑨ List the major carbon sinks on the Earth.

⑩ Explain how each of the following human activities can affect carbon cycling:
   a) deforestation
   b) burning of fossil fuels
   c) agriculture

The Sulfur Cycle

All organisms require sulfur because it is an important part of proteins and vitamins. Plants and algae use sulfur in the form of sulfate (SO_4^{2-}), which dissolves readily in water. They incorporate the sulfur into their cells and tissues. When they die, decomposers quickly return much of the sulfur to the soil or atmosphere. The distinctive sulfurous smell, like the smell of rotten eggs, from a muddy pond or wetland is hydrogen sulfide (H_2S). It indicates that decomposers are hard at work. Figure 2.14 shows how sulfur is converted to different forms in the sulfur cycle.

Figure 2.13 Why are seashells a source of slow-cycling carbon?

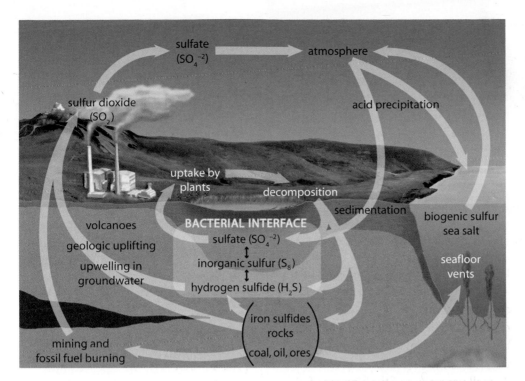

Figure 2.14 Sulfur compounds do not stay in the atmosphere long. When there is rain or snow, sulfur is returned to Earth's surface, where it is eventually used by plants, algae, and bacteria. The decomposition of organic matter, as well as volcanoes and human activities, distributes sulfur into air, soil, and water.

Various bacteria use sulfur-containing compounds in photosynthesis or in types of cellular respiration. In fact, bacteria are an essential part of the sulfur cycle. Different types of bacteria have different roles. Figure 2.15 shows a mini-ecosystem that contains different types of bacteria, each type capable of converting one form of sulfur to another. Sulfate reducers convert sulfate to sulfide, while sulfur oxidizers convert sulfide to elemental sulfur and sulfate. As the diagram below shows, the waste that is generated by one type of bacteria is a required material for a different type of bacteria.

Acid Deposition

Some sulfur is taken out of rapid cycling when bacteria convert the sulfur to forms that are layered down as sediments, eventually becoming part of rocks. Fossil fuel deposits, such as oil, coal, and natural gas, also contain sulfur. Coal that is mined in Alberta is considered to be high grade because it has a lower sulfur content than coal that is mined in other areas of the world. Weathering releases some of the sulfur that is trapped in rocks. Volcanic activity also releases some of the trapped sulfur into the atmosphere as sulfur dioxide (SO_2).

Sulfur dioxide reacts with oxygen and water vapour in the atmosphere to form sulfurous acid (H_2SO_3) and

BiologyFile

Web Link

The Winogradsky column is an artificial ecosystem that represents a natural pond-mud ecosystem. What accounts for the different layers in a Winogradsky column?

www.albertabiology.ca
WWW

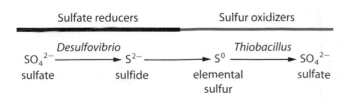

Figure 2.15 This mini-ecosystem, called a Winogradsky column after its inventor, Sergei Winogradsky, contains several types of bacteria. The black layer at the bottom is composed of iron sulfide, a by-product of bacteria using sulfate in their metabolism.

BiologyFile

sulfuric acid (H_2SO_4). These reactions result in **acid deposition** (such as acidified rain, snow, or sleet), which returns sulfur to the oceans and soils. Although acid deposition is a natural part of the sulfur cycle, large amounts of acid deposition can damage plants, acidify lakes, and leach nutrients from the soil.

When people burn fossil fuels such as oil, coal, and natural gas, sulfur (as sulfur dioxide) is released into the atmosphere. The production of sour gas (natural gas that contains hydrogen sulfide), such as that found in the foothills of the Rocky Mountains in Alberta, is another significant source of sulfur emissions. The amount of sulfur that is released to the atmosphere due to human activities is far greater than the amount that is released by natural processes.

• • •

11 How can acid deposition affect ecosystems?

12 What is the general role of bacteria in the sulfur cycle?

• • •

Explore another connection between the sulfur and carbon cycles in the next Thought Lab.

The Nitrogen Cycle

Nitrogen gas ($N_2(g)$) makes up 78.1 percent of Earth's atmosphere by volume. In contrast, oxygen makes up 20.9 percent of Earth's atmosphere, and carbon dioxide and other trace gases make up only one percent. Nitrogen is an essential part of the proteins found in organisms and the genetic material (DNA) found in cells. Most organisms, however, cannot use atmospheric nitrogen. Some bacteria can convert nitrogen gas into ammonium (NH_4^+) in a process called **nitrogen fixation** (Figure 2.16). The lumpy nodules on the roots of legume plants, such as clover, contain nitrogen-fixing bacteria that live in a mutually beneficial relationship with the plants (Figure 2.17). These bacteria fix (convert) nitrogen into ammonium, which is shared with the plants. The plants provide the bacteria with sugars produced in photosynthesis.

Thought Lab 2.2 Carbon, Sulfur, and Iron

Target Skills

Explaining how coal mining can damage the environment and disrupt biogeochemical cycles

Coal mining exposes otherwise buried deposits of sulfur compounds. Pyrite (iron sulfide, FeS) is known as "fool's gold" because of its shiny, golden appearance. Pyrite slowly breaks down once it is exposed to oxygen, converting the sulfide to sulfuric acid. This process is accelerated when *Thiobacillus* bacteria use the pyrite for energy.

Analysis

1. Abandoned coal mines are sometimes surrounded by areas in which all the trees and other plants have died. Hypothesize as to what might have caused this situation.

2. **a)** Much of Alberta's coal is now mined in large pit mines that have significant impact on the surrounding environment. What problems do you think these mines create?

   b) In what ways do you think your views about controlling these mines would be different, depending on whether you live nearby one of these mines?

3. Explain how mining might affect:

   a) the sulfur cycle

   b) the carbon cycle

4. Iron cycles between two ionic forms, Fe^{2+} and Fe^{3+}. In the presence of oxygen or by the action of bacteria, Fe^{2+} is changed to Fe^{3+}. Soils, sediments, and water contain both forms of iron, and organisms contain Fe^{3+} compounds. Pyrite contains Fe^{2+}. How might coal mining affect the iron cycle?

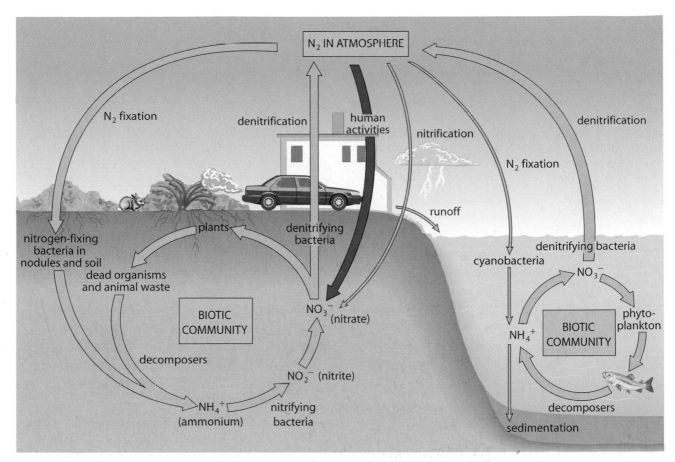

Figure 2.16 Bacterial communities in the soil and ocean play an important role in the nitrogen cycle. As well, lightning can convert atmospheric molecular nitrogen (N_2) to nitrate, a form of nitrogen that plants can use.

Ammonium is also produced when decomposers break down organic matter in a process is called **ammonification**. Some types of soil bacteria convert the ammonium into nitrite (NO_2^-) and then into nitrate (NO_3^-). Plants can use the nitrate as a nitrogen source.

Denitrifying bacteria complete the cycle by converting nitrite or nitrate back into nitrogen gas. As Figure 2.16 shows, this process, called **denitrification**, occurs in environments where there is very little oxygen.

The nutrient-deficient plant shown in Figure 2.8 on page 42 would have been healthier if it had been fertilized or grown with nitrogen-fixing bacteria. A common farming method is to grow legumes (such as alfalfa and clover) one growing season and crops (such as corn) the following season. This method, called crop rotation, helps to maintain a high nitrogen content in the soil.

• • •

13. What are two sources of fixed nitrogen that plants can use?

14. Draw a flow chart or diagram to illustrate the conversion of atmospheric nitrogen to nitrate, nitrite, and ammonium.

• • •

The Phosphorus Cycle

Phosphorus is an essential nutrient, but it is often available in only limited quantities in the environment. Phosphorus is concentrated in living organisms, however. Phosphorus is a part of cellular DNA and ATP (the energy carrier essential to all cells) and is a major component of bones and teeth.

Unlike carbon, nitrogen, and sulfur, phosphorus does not cycle through the atmosphere. Phosphorus is found in soil and water, and weathering gradually releases the phosphorus trapped in rocks. (See Figure 2.18 on the next page.)

Magnification: 88 ×

Figure 2.17 Nitrogen-fixing bacteria live in the round nodules on the roots of legume plants such as this one.

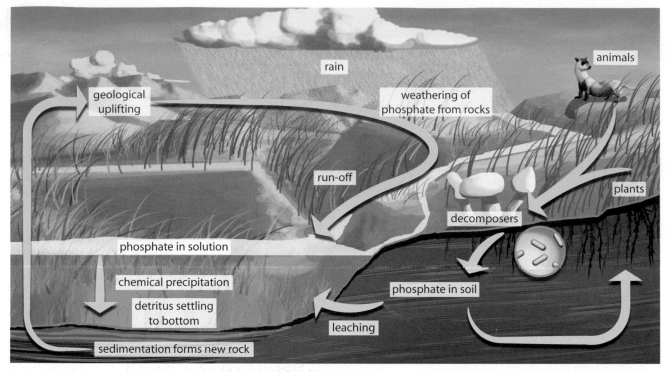

Figure 2.18 The phosphorus cycle

Animals obtain phosphorus by consuming foods such as milk, grain, and meat. Producers, such as plants and algae, can only use phosphorus if it is in the form of phosphate (PO_4^{3-}), which dissolves in water. The scarcity of phosphorus keeps the growth of producers in balance, but it can also limit the growth of crops. How might increased availability of phosphorus affect an aquatic ecosystem?

The growth of algae in aquatic ecosystems is limited by the amount of available nutrients. The overgrowth of algae, called an **algal bloom**, produces large amounts of organic matter. As decomposers break down the organic matter, they use up the oxygen in the water, resulting in the death of fish and other aquatic life.

In the 1970s, scientists debated whether algal blooms were caused by excess nitrogen or phosphorus. Figure 2.19 shows an experimental lake in Ontario, which was divided by a plastic barrier. Researchers added nitrogen to one side of the lake and nitrogen and phosphorus to the other side.

As a result of the research at the Experimental Lakes Area, Canadian scientists were able to convince the federal government to ban the use of phosphates in soaps and laundry detergents.

> **15** Why do organisms need phosphorus?
>
> **16** How is phosphorus transported through the biosphere?
>
> **17** What are the effects of increased amounts of phosphorus on aquatic environments?

Figure 2.19 Experimental Lake 226, near Kenora, Ontario, in 1973. One side of the lake is bright green due to an algal bloom due to excess phosphorus.

BiologyFile

FYI
The build-up of excess nutrients in aquatic systems is called eutrophication. If eutrophication occurs in an ecosystem, algal overgrowth can block sunlight so that plants below the surface can no longer photosynthesize. When these plants die, the decomposer population grows quickly, depleting oxygen levels in the water so organisms requiring oxygen can no longer survive.

What's in the Water?

Both human activities and natural processes affect water quality. Scientists monitor water quality by testing for chemical and biological contaminants and for pH (a measure of acidity or alkalinity).

Question

How do human activities affect local water quality?

Hypothesis

With your lab partner, write a hypothesis about water quality in two similar but contrasting areas, such as:

- upstream of a city vs. downstream of the city

- upstream of an animal farm vs. downstream of the animal farm

- run-off from a freshly watered plant vs. run-off from a freshly watered and fertilized plant

Prediction

Based on your hypothesis, predict how water samples from the two areas will differ with respect to pH and concentrations of sulfate (or iron), nitrate, and phosphate.

Materials

- water sample from each area
- Probeware or colourimetric assay kit for sulfate (or iron), nitrate, phosphate, and pH
- 8 to 10 test tubes (10 mL)
- pipette bulb
- 2 pipettes (2 mL)
- 2 sample jars and lids
- metal scoopula

Safety Precautions

Read and follow the safety instructions that come with the assay kit. Wear gloves and wash your hands after completing the investigation.

Procedure

1. Make a data table in which to record your results.

2. Obtain water samples from the two contrasting areas.

3. If you and your lab partner are using a colourimetric assay kit, first label each set of test tubes with the field site and the test (for example, nitrate). Use the pipette bulb and a pipette to dispense water from each water sample into the labelled test tubes. Use the colourimetric assay kit to test the samples in the test tubes, and record the data.

4. If you are using Probeware, test the samples directly from the sample jars and record the data.

Analysis

1. Draw a bar graph to compare the results of each test for the two water samples.

2. Explain any differences between the two samples.

3. Compare your results with the amounts of sulfate (or iron), nitrate, phosphate, and pH in Calgary tap water, given below.

Calgary Tap Water Parameters

Water quality parameter	Units	Calgary tap water
sulfate	mg/L	30.4–43.6
iron	mg/L	< 0.1
nitrate (as total nitrogen)	mg/L	0.052–0.124
phosphate	mg/L	0.001–0.004
pH		6.98–8.18

Conclusions

4. Based on your results, suggest how human activities are affecting local water quality.

5. How might problems with local water quality affect the natural environment?

Extension

6. In August 2005, a train derailment caused 730 000 L of fuel oil and wood preservative to empty into Wabamun Lake, west of Edmonton. Since then, the Paul Band has been active in the cleanup effort of what is, to them, a sacred resource. Which chemicals contaminated the lake? Where were the immediate effects? What is the status of the lake now?

The Flow of Matter and Transfer of Energy are Linked

Each biogeochemical cycle is unique. Carbon, oxygen, sulfur, nitrogen, and phosphorus each take a different path through the biosphere. All of these cycles, however, and the hydrologic cycle are similar and interrelated. All six cycles involve both the abiotic and biotic environment. When living organisms take nutrients from their surroundings, for example, the nutrients become, at least temporarily, a part of the biotic environment. Therefore, effects on the transfer of energy from producer to consumer to decomposer also affect the biogeochemical cycling of matter. As Section 2.3 describes, natural processes and human activities can influence the transfer of energy and matter through the biosphere in various ways.

Section 2.2 Summary

- Carbon, oxygen, sulfur, and nitrogen are found in living organisms and in the land, atmosphere, and water.
- Phosphorus is found in living organisms and in the land and water.
- All of these nutrients are recycled through biotic and abiotic processes. They are stored in nutrient reservoirs for short to longer periods of time. They cycle among these reservoirs at different rates.
- Biogeochemical cycles are similar and interrelated. Disruptions in one biogeochemical cycle can affect another biogeochemical cycle. Human activities impact the biogeochemical cycles.

Section 2.2 Review

1. a) Explain why carbon moving from producer to consumer to decomposer and back to the atmosphere is an example of the rapid cycling of matter.

b) Explain why the formation of a fossil fuel such as coal is an example of the slow cycling of matter.

2. Describe the essential differences between the biogeochemical cycles for elements such as nitrogen or oxygen and for elements such as phosphorus and calcium.

3. Describe the role(s) of bacteria in:

a) the sulfur cycle

b) the nitrogen cycle

4. Identify three features that biogeochemical cycles have in common.

5. Explain why green plants need:

a) nitrogen

b) sulfur

c) phosphorus

6. a) Use word processing or graphics software to create a flow chart or other graphic organizer illustrating the nitrogen cycle. **ICT**

b) Describe the role of nitrogen fixation in supplying essential nutrients to the species found at higher levels in a food chain.

7. a) Use word processing or graphics software to create a flow chart or other graphic organizer illustrating the sulfur cycle. **ICT**

b) Explain the role that the burning of fossil fuels plays in the sulfur cycle and, in particular, acid deposition.

8. a) Use word processing or graphics software to create a flow chart or other graphic organizer illustrating the phosphorus cycle. **ICT**

b) In terms of the phosphorus cycle and environmental damage, explain why laundry detergents today are no longer made with phosphates.

The Balance of the Matter and Energy Exchange

Section Outcomes

In this section, you will
- **explain** how energy, matter, and the productivity of ecosystems are interrelated
- **explain** the influence on atmospheric composition of the equilibrium between the exchange of oxygen and carbon dioxide in photosynthesis and cellular respiration
- **describe** evidence and scientific explanations for changes in the composition of Earth's atmosphere from past to present, and **describe** the significance of these to current states of equilibrium in the biosphere
- **outline**, **explain**, and **evaluate** the influence of human activities on the biosphere
- **design** and **evaluate** a model of a closed biological system

Key Terms

productivity
stromatolites

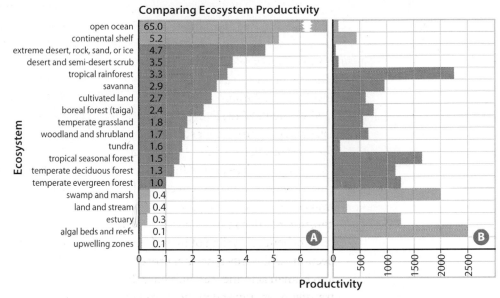

Figure 2.20 Comparing productivity of ecosystems in terms of **(A)** the percentage of Earth's surface and **(B)** average net productivity. Net productivity here is the total amount of radiant energy that is transformed to chemical energy by producers, minus the amount used by the producers during cellular respiration.

The biosphere is not a closed system. Although the biosphere does not exchange significant amounts of matter with its surroundings (outer space), there is a constant input of energy into the biosphere from the Sun and a constant output of radiant energy (heat) to space. The amount of sunlight that is received by an ecosystem affects the amount and type of productivity in the ecosystem. **Productivity** is the rate at which an ecosystem's producers capture and store energy within organic compounds over a certain length of time. It is commonly measured in terms of energy per area, per year ($J/m^2/a$). It can also be expressed in terms of biomass of vegetation added to an ecosystem per area, per year ($g/m^2/a$).

Productivity is the rate at which organisms produce new biomass. (In other words, productivity does not refer to the total mass of all producers in an area at any one time.) For example, a forest has a very large biomass. The mass of its vegetation is greater than that of a grassland of equal size. But productivity of a grassland ecosystem may actually be

higher during the growing season, because animals are constantly eating the plants and new ones are constantly being produced. Thus, new mass accumulates in a grassland ecosystem at a higher rate than in the forest.

Figure 2.20 shows that productivity varies among ecosystems. The rate of productivity depends on many variables. These include the number of producers present in the ecosystem, the amount of light and heat available, and the amount of rainfall the system receives.

Productivity in the ocean is determined by the available nutrients and sunlight. The ocean receives nutrients at the mouths of large rivers and at upwelling zones on the west side of continents. As well, nutrients are released during the seasonal melting of ice. Nutrients promote the growth of algae.

In general, the amount of solar radiation limits a region's productivity. Can too much solar radiation affect productivity? Explore this question in the following Thought Lab.

Approximately six percent of the sunlight that reaches Earth's surface is ultraviolet radiation (UVR). UVR transfers much more energy than visible light. As a result, UVR can inhibit photosynthesis and harm cells by damaging their DNA. DNA damage, in turn, can lead to cancer.

Organisms that live in sunny regions are adapted to resist the harmful effects of UVR. As well, environmental factors can protect organisms. For example, the alpine lakes of the Canadian Rockies are at a high elevation, but studies show that dissolved organic matter in these alpine lakes can shield aquatic organisms from UVR.

Atmospheric gases also shield the biosphere from some incoming UVR. Ozone (O_3) in the lower atmosphere (troposphere) pollutes the air, but ozone in the upper atmosphere (stratosphere) absorbs UVR. The stratospheric ozone layer is thinning, however. From the 1950s through the 1990s, chlorofluorocarbons (CFCs) were used as propellants in spray cans and coolants in refrigerators. They were also used in the manufacture of plastics. In the 1970s, scientists discovered that CFCs, decomposed by UVR, were destroying the ozone layer. In 1985, a springtime depletion of stratospheric ozone was discovered over the South Pole. (This is often referred to as the Antarctic ozone hole.)

In 1987, 27 countries signed a global environmental agreement called the Montréal Protocol to Reduce Substances that Deplete the Ozone Layer. Its London Amendment (1990) called for the production of CFCs to end by 2000. The production of CFCs has been banned in many countries. There are other human-generated chemicals that are contributing to ozone thinning, however. For example, hydrochlorofluorocarbons (HCFCs) are one alternative to CFCs and are considered to be less harmful to the ozone layer. The Copenhagen Amendment (1992) to the Montréal Protocol calls for a ban on the production of HCFCs by 2030.

Procedure

Working in a group, use the information presented below to answer the Analysis questions.

Analysis

1. What might be the effects of increasing amounts of UVR on productivity?

2. What direct effects does increasing UVR have on animals?

3. What indirect effects might increasing UVR have on animals?

4. Suggest an approach to counteract increased levels of UVR in ecosystems. What would you need to find out to ensure that your approach is a wise one?

Effects of UVR on Different Organisms

Type of organism	Overall effect of increasing amounts of UVR	Adaptations for protection against UVR	Environmental features that protect against UVR
algae or phytoplankton	• can inhibit photosynthesis	• UVR-absorbing compounds	• dissolved material in water can act as a shield
plants	• in general, inhibits photosynthesis • reduces leaf size and decreases growth of many plants	• pigmentation • UVR-absorbing compounds • DNA repair processes	• shade can protect plants
bacteria	• depending on species, may be killed or highly resistant	• DNA repair processes	• amount of Sun exposure is limited
protozoa	• varies; damages cells in some species	• DNA repair processes in some protozoa	• protozoa living in deeper waters are shielded from UVR
zooplankton	• can be damaging or kill depending on age and other factors	• pigmentation • UVR-absorbing compounds • DNA repair	• zooplankton are shielded from UVR when they swim to deeper waters
fish	• damaging • can kill fish	• pigmentation • DNA repair in fish eggs	• deeper, cooler waters protect developing fish
amphibians	• causes developmental damage • can kill some amphibians • possibly reduces amphibians' ability to fight disease	• pigmentation • DNA repair processes	• dissolved materials in water can act as a shield • some amphibians are nocturnal
humans	• causes skin deterioration, skin cancer, and eye problems (cataracts)	• pigmentation (melanin in skin) • DNA repair processes	• shade, clothing, and sunscreen can protect against UVR

Productivity Depends on Available Moisture

The deserts and tropical forests of Africa both receive considerable sunlight but, as Figure 2.21 shows, deserts are too dry for most of the year to support very much productivity. Likewise, the tundra receives less than 25 cm of precipitation per year, and water is mostly trapped in snow and permafrost.

• • •

18 Explain how increased amounts of sunlight can have both positive and negative effects on productivity.

19 What are two major factors (other than available nutrients) that limit productivity?

• • •

The Biosphere in Balance

To live, an organism must maintain its internal conditions within certain limits in spite of changing external conditions. In a grizzly bear's body, for example, the pH and the levels of sugars and ions in the blood fluctuate on a daily basis but remain within narrow limits. Maintaining a state of balance, or *equilibrium*, is called homeostasis. To help maintain homeostasis, the cells of a grizzly bear's body must convert ingested food into usable energy and rid the body of wastes.

Figure 2.21 Satellite image of the amount of vegetation in Africa. Regions that are closer to the equator and coast are more humid and have the most vegetation.

In 1979, ecologist James Lovelock proposed the Gaia Hypothesis, which considers homeostasis on a global level. According to the Gaia Hypothesis, the biosphere acts like an organism that regulates itself, maintaining environmental conditions within certain limits. The biosphere needs a constant input of energy and the cycling of nutrients to maintain its internal balance.

Life itself plays a role in maintaining the conditions of the biosphere that allow organisms to survive. Scientists speculate that if life had never existed on Earth, atmospheric levels of carbon dioxide and oxygen would be very different (see Table 2.1).

Table 2.1 Composition of Earth's Atmosphere and Oceans

	Substance	Percent current composition	Percent hypothetical composition, with no life
Atmosphere	carbon dioxide	0.03	98
	nitrogen	78	1
	oxygen	21	0
	argon	1	1
Oceans	water	96	85
	salt	3.5	13

Source: James Lovelock, *Gaia, A New Look at Life on Earth*, 2000.

Deposits of ancient micro-organisms hold clues about the composition of Earth's atmosphere and oceans from 3.8 to 2.5 billion years ago. In the ancient past, the atmosphere lacked free oxygen (it was anoxic) and bacteria and bacteria-like organisms grew, forming thick mounds in shallow seas, lagoons, and lakes. As the micro-organisms died, the cells piled up, trapping or precipitating sediments and eventually forming sedimentary rocks, called **stromatolites** (Figure 2.22). Some stromatolites show bands of iron oxides, which formed when iron ions combined with dissolved oxygen in the oceans. Most stromatolites with these distinctive black iron bands are an estimated 2.5 billion years old or more. They suggest that, around this time, the level of oxygen in the oceans had started to increase.

BiologyFile

Web Link
Not all scientists agree with Lovelock, that Earth acts like an organism. How is the Gaia Hypothesis accepted in the scientific community?

www.albertabiology.ca
WWW

BiologyFile

FYI
When tropical rainforests are clear-cut, all vegetation is removed and available nutrients diminish. Areas once shaded by trees become too sunny and hot for transpiration to occur, rain washes away any remaining soil, and water evaporates more quickly into the atmosphere. Eventually, rainfall decreases over the clear-cut area and drought may occur. This disruption of the water cycle can cause climate change.

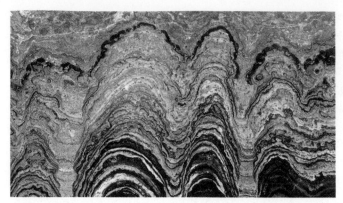

Figure 2.22 The iron banding pattern in this stromatolite formation developed when there was dissolved oxygen in the oceans, but little or no oxygen in the atmosphere.

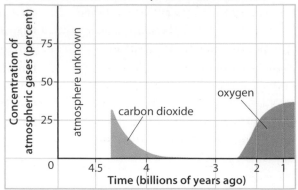

Figure 2.23 Atmospheric oxygen concentrations in the biosphere over time

Stromatolites that are less than 1.8 billion years old do not have black bands of iron oxides. Scientists speculate that, at this time, most of the iron ions in the oceans were already bound in iron oxides. With the ocean's store of iron ions used up, the oxygen produced by photosynthesis was free to build up as oxygen gas and eventually to escape into Earth's atmosphere.

Scientists think that the sudden increase in atmospheric oxygen about 2.5 billion years ago was mostly due to the activity of photosynthetic micro-organisms, such as cyanobacteria (see Figure 2.23). Over time, species that were well-adapted to life in the oxygen-rich biosphere evolved. Today, most life on Earth could not survive without oxygen. The interchange between photosynthetic organisms and consumers maintains levels of oxygen that are suitable for life as we know it.

Replicating Earth's Biosphere

Scientists have tried to replicate the self-regulating conditions of the biosphere in artificial environments. Biosphere 2 was a large-scale biosphere experiment in which engineers constructed a closed system, much like a massive domed greenhouse, in Arizona, United States (Figure 2.24). Plants in the system provided a source of oxygen and food, and human and animal wastes were filtered to recycle water. Researchers were able to live continuously and virtually independently in Biosphere 2 for several months, until oxygen levels dropped and carbon dioxide levels rose to unsafe levels.

The difficulties that Biosphere 2 researchers faced showed that the balance of energy and matter exchange in Earth's biosphere depends on an extremely complex system. Nevertheless, in order to support space colonies someday, scientists continue to investigate designs for a self-regulating closed system.

NASA has designed a program called the Advanced Life Support (ALS) program to research how plants may be grown in a space colony for food and oxygen regeneration. ALS also enables scientists to investigate how chemical and biological methods can be used to convert waste into usable resources. NASA has also conducted several experiments where humans have spent several

Figure 2.24 Inside Biosphere 2, a research facility designed to be a closed system for 100 years. The system was never completely closed for more than two years. However, the facility is still used for ecosystems research.

months in self-sustaining environments at the Johnson Space Centre to test their research. In addition, the space agency also sponsors an international field project on Devon Island in the Canadian Arctic that models a hypothetical colony on Mars. The NASA Haughton-Mars Project is situated in the Arctic because the geology and biology of this region mirrors the Martian lithosphere better than anywhere else on Earth. New technologies are being tested in this Mars-like environment, providing useful information for future Mars colonists. The colony includes living and research facilities, as well as a fully enclosed greenhouse.

INVESTIGATION 2.D

Biosphere in a Bottle

What are the essential abiotic components of an ecosystem? What are the essential biotic components of an ecosystem? In this investigation, you will design a model biosphere in a bottle.

Question

How can you design a model ecosystem that can survive as a self-regulating system?

Materials

- 2 L (or larger) clear bottle with lid
- bottom sediment
- pond or river water
- small aquatic plants (such as floating duckweed and various submerged plants)
- small aquatic invertebrates (such as snails, flatworms, shrimps, and insects)
- thermometer (alcohol or digital)
- Parafilm™ or sealing wax
- 10 mL test tube

Procedure

1. With your group, design a model biosphere using the suggested materials. Your model biosphere must be completely sealed, using the Parafilm™ or sealing wax. It will require an outside light source, however, and a method for monitoring temperature. Record initial and any subsequent changes in water level, and note any condensation on the inside of the bottle.

   Note: Consider the ethical treatment of animals in your design.

2. Create a table to use to record, over time, observations such as temperature, water level, species present, changes to species composition or abundance, clarity of the water, and other variables that you feel may be important.

3. Set up your model biosphere, and make initial observations.

4. Make daily observations of your model biosphere for two weeks or longer.

Analysis

1. Identify the producers, consumers, and decomposers in your model biosphere.

2. Which biogeochemical cycles were represented in your model biosphere?

3. Why did you use a clear bottle, rather than an opaque bottle, for your model biosphere?

4. How did the temperature in the model biosphere change over the trial period?

5. How did you recognize the cycling of water in your model biosphere?

6. How well did your model biosphere function as a self-regulating system?

7. Compare your model biosphere with another group's model biosphere. Are there any differences? If so, what may have caused these differences?

Conclusions

8. Predict the effect of decreasing the amount of light available to the model biosphere.

9. Predict the effect of a significant reduction in productivity in Earth's biosphere on levels of:

   a) atmospheric oxygen

   b) atmospheric carbon dioxide

Figure 2.25 This satellite image reveals the path of nutrient-rich sediments from Ontario and the United States into Lake Erie. The excess nutrients cause algal blooms, which have created a dead zone in the lake.

Human Activities and the Natural Balance

Dead zones are regions of lakes or oceans in which aquatic life has suffocated due to algal blooms. There are approximately 150 dead zones in the oceans, ranging in area from 2.6 km² to more than 100 000 km². Algal blooms can occur seasonally in response to the turnover of nutrient-rich waters in warmer temperatures. As you learned in Section 2.2, however, various types of pollution can also contribute to algal blooms:

- Nutrients in the soil exposed by deforestation can be washed into rivers by rain.
- Sewage (particularly if inadequately treated) that is discharged into bodies of water carries significant amounts of phosphate and nitrate, which promote the growth of algae.
- Surface run-off and snowmelt carrying manure from livestock operations can add phosphate and nitrate to streams and rivers.
- Run-off from fertilized agricultural fields and lawns can enter rivers and oceans.

Figure 2.25 shows the path of nutrient-rich run-off into Lake Erie, which sits on the Ontario, Canada-United States border. Scientists are concerned about a dead zone in the central basin of Lake Erie during the late summer and early fall. Dead zones are just one example of how human activities can affect the balance of matter and energy exchange in the biosphere.

Solutions to environmental problems are often discovered in the biosphere itself. Wetlands, such as bogs, marshes, and swamps, are environments where soil is permanently saturated with water, either from ground water or surface

Thought Lab 2.4 Evaluating Water Treatments

Target Skills

Analyzing data on water quality to evaluate the effectiveness of using grasses to treat agricultural run-off

Haynes Creek is a tributary of the Red Deer River, located east of Lacombe, Alberta. Haynes Creek runs through agricultural areas with heavy pesticide and fertilizer use, and through cattle farms. In the past, water from Haynes Creek has not met drinking water quality guidelines or standards for the preservation of aquatic life.

Scientists hypothesized that one way to improve water quality in Haynes Creek, and to slow erosion from the creek bed, would be to plant grass in drainage ditches around the creek. They did this, and then tested the creek water upstream and downstream of the grass "filter." Their results are shown in this graph.

Analysis

1. What effect did the grass "filter" in the creek have on the creek's water quality?

2. How could the findings of this experiment be applied to prevent farmland run-off from negatively affecting the water quality in nearby streams?

Nitrogen & phosphorus losses from cultivated fields

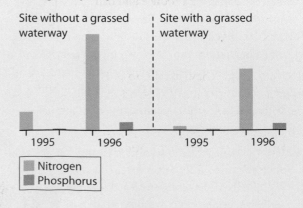

Figure 2.26 Many plants, animals, and other organisms inhabit wetlands. About 20 percent of Alberta, by area, is made up of wetlands. Most of these wetlands are located in northern Alberta. Animals such as the great blue heron and the endangered whooping crane depend on wetlands for survival. Some of the numerous ecosystem services that are provided by wetlands include water purification, water storage, biodiversity preservation, and flood control.

BiologyFile

FYI
Like nutrients, many human-made contaminants cycle through the environment. Other contaminants, such as the pesticide dichlorodi-phenyltrichloroethane (DDT) and polychlorinated biphenyls (PCBs; used in electrical equipment and other specialized uses), can also biomagnify. Such contaminants, known as persistent organic pollutants (POPs), can also travel thousands, or tens of thousands, of kilometres in the atmosphere and be deposited in the Arctic. POPs have been found in Arctic wildlife and Aboriginal people who traditionally hunt and eat these animals. For example, scientists have found high levels of PCBs in nursing Inuit mothers in Nunavut.

water (Figure 2.26). As a result, they act as large water filters. Unfortunately, many wetlands around the world have been drained in order to make room for agricultural land or urban growth.

The people of Calcutta, India have built a vast network of canals and wetlands to treat sewage coming out of the city. Calcutta is one of the most populated cities in the world, and it produces tonnes of sewage every day. Algae and bacteria in the wetlands feed on the organic material. Fish have been added to feed on the algae, in order to prevent algal blooms. Many people have been able to support themselves by growing vegetables or fishing in the wetlands, and selling the produce and fish.

Preserving the Natural Balance

Many communities have chosen to change the way they meet their food, water, and energy needs to preserve the natural working order of the biosphere. For example, the Piikani First Nation of southern Alberta (a member of the Blackfoot Confederacy) operates a wind turbine, called Weather Dancer 1, to generate electricity (Figure 2.27). The turbine generates energy for 450 homes

and produces no carbon dioxide emissions. Powering the same number of homes by burning fossil fuels would release approximately 2500 tonnes of carbon dioxide gas per year, as well as other pollutants. Technologies such as Weather Dancer 1 are helping to preserve fossil fuel reservoirs and do not contribute to excessive carbon dioxide generation and carbon release in the

Figure 2.27 "Green power" produced by the Weather Dancer 1 wind turbine is distributed to homes on Alberta's electricity grid system.

rapid cycling of carbon. This reduces the production of a greenhouse gas. Also, since fossil fuels are not used, this eliminates a source of sulfur and the resulting acid deposition.

Like many First Nations peoples, the Piikani traditionally see themselves as part of the natural environment. They consider harm done to the natural environment as harm done to themselves. For the Piikani, using a non-polluting and renewable energy system makes sense in terms of their cultural beliefs.

Communities everywhere are facing the challenge of meeting their needs while preserving the integrity, or natural balance, of the biosphere. Fortunately, humans have developed many tools that can help us preserve the natural balance.

Far-Reaching Consequences

Ecologists are discovering that biogeochemical cycles are linked in unexpected ways. Similarly, the transfer of matter through the biosphere is closely linked to the transfer of energy through the biosphere. Local tap water may contain water molecules that were once transpired by a tree in a tropical rainforest. Fertilizers applied to a local

---

Thought Lab 2.5 — Design a Self-Sustaining Mars Colony

Target Skills

Evaluating the technological requirements for a self-sustaining, Earth-like system

Evaluating the potential benefits to humanity and the possible environmental consequences of implementing such technology

If humans were to colonize another planet, such as Mars, they would have to find a way to create an ecosystem that can sustain itself in a manner similar to Earth's biosphere. Except for energy, such a colony would recycle and re-use all its components. In this Thought Lab, you will consider the requirements for a self-sustaining colony on Mars. (Contact with Earth is impractical due to the amount of time it takes to travel between the two planets using current technology.)

Procedure

1. In a group, design a self-sustaining Mars colony. Begin by brainstorming the requirements of such a colony. How would water, oxygen, and carbon dioxide be exchanged? How would nutrients be recycled? How would you address the issue of food production and waste disposal? How would energy be generated?

2. Make a list of what colonists would need to survive on Mars. Create a table of "inputs" the colony would require in order to obtain these things, and "outputs" that could be recycled to obtain them. What cycles would exist as a result of this recycling? How might the colony be affected if one of these cycles were to become disrupted?

Analysis

1. On Mars, large quantities of water are frozen in the polar ice caps and under the planet's surface. How could these resources be incorporated into a self-sustaining ecosystem?

2. Scientists have suggested that, like the International Space Station, a Mars colony could be powered by collecting the Sun's energy with solar panels. However, because of its distance form the Sun, Mars only receives half of the solar radiation that Earth does. Extensive atmospheric dust also reflects incoming sunlight. Suggest ways in which a self-sustaining Mars colony could address these issues. Do you think solar panels are a viable means of supplying power to a Mars colony? Why or why not? Can you provide a feasible alternative?

3. Mars has only a third of Earth's gravity. What sorts of problems might this present to a Mars colony and how would you address them?

4. The soil on Mars is very corrosive. Colonists may be able to grow crops in greenhouses using hydroponics (using nutrient-rich water instead of soil). Suggest a way that nutrients required for plant growth (such as nitrogen and phosphorus) might be recycled within the greenhouse.

5. The thin Martian atmosphere is about 95 percent carbon dioxide. However, Mars experiences only a very slight greenhouse effect. As part of the plans for colonizing Mars, some scientists have suggested the need to create a greenhouse effect for Mars—called a "runaway greenhouse effect." What do you think might be necessary to engineer this effect? What are some possible consequences of doing so?

6. Some people find the idea of terra-forming another planet or moon (making it Earth-like for human habitation) disagreeable. They point to the current condition of Earth as evidence that we have not yet learned how to live in balance with our home planet. On the other hand, some people find the idea of terra-forming inspiring—an opportunity to have a fresh start, to "get things right" based on the knowledge we have developed about the biosphere and its interconnected systems. What is your opinion? Provide reasons to support it.

---

green space may find their way into distant waterways, resulting in aquatic dead zones.

The effects that disruptions in one part of the biosphere may have on other parts of the biosphere can be difficult to predict. Satellite data and computer modelling are helping scientists understand the interactions between different biogeochemical cycles and the transfer of energy in the biosphere. By studying the steps in the biogeochemical cycles, and by standing back and looking at the biosphere as a whole, scientists can better understand what keeps the transfer of energy and the cycles of matter in balance, and what keeps the biosphere hospitable to life.

Section 2.3 Summary

- Biotic and abiotic processes maintain the balance of matter and energy exchange in the biosphere. Productivity is influenced by environmental factors such as sunlight and nutrient (including water) availability.
- Natural processes and human activities can affect the transfer of energy and the cycling of matter through the biosphere.
- Nutrient run-off can cause algal blooms and dead zones.
- Wetlands can clean polluted water and provide other ecosystem services.

Section 2.3 Review

1. Explain why the biosphere is considered to be an open system.

2. Define the term "productivity."

3. Explain why, during the summer, the productivity of a grassland ecosystem may be greater than the productivity in a forest.

4. Identify four variables that determine the productivity in a terrestrial ecosystem and explain how each affects production of new biomass.

5. Identify the two variables that determine the productivity in the oceans.

6. Briefly describe the Gaia Hypothesis.

7. Explain how scientists have used stromatolites to predict the oxygen levels in the atmosphere early in Earth's history.

Use the following information to answer the next question.

Algal Blooms
Algae are the producers in most aquatic ecosystem and are vital to the survival of other organisms in this environment. Algal blooms, however, can result in dead zones in lakes.

8. a) Describe why algal blooms occur and identify four human activities that can lead to their formation.

   b) Explain why algal blooms create dead zones in many lakes during the late summer and early fall.

Use the following information to answer the next question.

Hydrogen Sulfide
Hydrogen sulfide ($H_2S(g)$) is a colourless, flammable gas that can be deadly when inhaled. It can form when bacteria in swamps or even sewers break down organic matter in the absence of oxygen. It produces a foul odour that is described as the smell produced by rotting eggs. In the summer, when the temperature is warmer, bacteria in wetlands, mud, and soil are more active and produce more hydrogen sulfide gas than they do in cooler weather.

9. Suppose that global climate change had a similar effect and the annual emissions of hydrogen sulfide increased. Explain how this might affect:

   a) the sulfur cycle

   b) the productivity of temperate deciduous forest ecosystems

Phytoremediation

Petrochemical spills release toxic hydrocarbons into the environment. Some of these hydrocarbons can make their way into underground or surface waters and end up contaminating drinking water. One approach to treating hydrocarbon pollution is phytoremediation, which makes use of the natural ability of plants and micro-organisms to degrade or remove contaminants from soil and water. Researchers have found that prairie ecosystems have an important role to play in this approach.

It Takes Teamwork

Together, plants and micro-organisms can remove toxic hydrocarbons from soil and water, and even convert some of these contaminants into less harmful compounds. As in the nitrogen cycle, different types of bacteria either work independently or in an integrated manner to convert one form of hydrocarbon to another. Some bacteria produce non-toxic compounds, such as carbon dioxide and methane.

Plants produce compounds (root exudates) that stimulate bacterial metabolism. So, a combination of plants and bacteria can work well to clean up hydrocarbons. As shown in the diagram below, plants with fibrous roots, such as prairie grasses, are very good at adsorbing (attracting to their surface) hydrocarbons. Plants take up contaminated water when they take up hydrocarbons. This keeps the hydrocarbons out of the ground water and may allow the contaminants to collect in plant tissues. Plants can break down some of the hydrocarbons, and transpiration gradually transfers volatile hydrocarbons from the ground to the atmosphere.

The Right Solution to Pollution

Petrochemicals are widely used in manufacturing and as fuel, and accidental spills can occur during extraction, transportation, or use. Some clean-up methods are more effective than others, depending on the amount and type of petrochemicals spilled and the condition of the contaminated environment. Scientists need to consider whether the contamination poses an immediate risk to people or wildlife. One option is to treat the contamination on site (*in situ*), as in phytoremediation. Another option is to remove the contaminated soil or water to clean it using chemical or biological methods (*ex situ*).

• • •

1. Where might you look for plants that could be useful in phytoremediation?

2. Sometimes, bacteria convert hydrocarbons into more toxic products. Because of this risk, should phytoremediation be abandoned as a solution to hydrocarbon pollution? Explain.

3. Why might scientists be concerned about animals feeding on plants that are being used for phytoremediation?

4. Suppose that there is a large petrochemical spill that could quickly contaminate ground water. Would phytoremediation be an appropriate choice to deal with the spill? Explain your reasoning.

5. What makes phytoremediation a relatively economical solution for treating hydrocarbon contamination?

6. How would a phytoremediation method for treating heavy metal contamination be different from a phytoremediation method for treating hydrocarbon contamination?

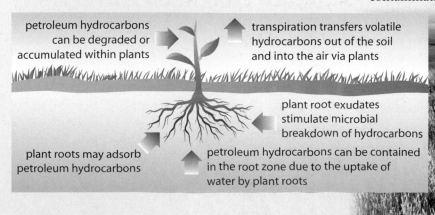

petroleum hydrocarbons can be degraded or accumulated within plants

transpiration transfers volatile hydrocarbons out of the soil and into the air via plants

plant root exudates stimulate microbial breakdown of hydrocarbons

plant roots may adsorb petroleum hydrocarbons

petroleum hydrocarbons can be contained in the root zone due to the uptake of water by plant roots

There is a limited (finite) amount of water in the biosphere. It is re-used, however, in the hydrologic cycle. Water is able to dissolve a wide variety of substances. Hydrogen bonding plays a key role in determining the properties and uses of water, such as its ability to dissolve and transport materials. Water provides an essential service for humans and ecosystems. Drought and poor water quality can affect water availability and impact humans and the environment.

Carbon, oxygen, sulfur, and nitrogen are some of the main nutrients (chemical elements) found in living organisms and in the land, atmosphere, and water. Phosphorus is found in living organisms and in the land and water, but is rarely found in the atmosphere. Biogeochemical (nutrient) cycles make these chemical elements available continuously. Nutrients are recycled through biotic and abiotic processes in the environment. They are stored in nutrient reservoirs for short to longer periods of time, and they cycle among these reservoirs at different rates.

Natural processes and human activities can affect the transfer of energy and the cycling of matter through the biosphere. Disruptions in one biogeochemical cycle can affect another cycle. For example, excess sulfur and nitrogen in the environment can result in acid deposition, which can harm both terrestrial and aquatic ecosystems. Excess nitrogen and phosphorus can run off into aquatic ecosystems where it can cause eutrophication and algal blooms.

Chapter 2 Graphic Organizer

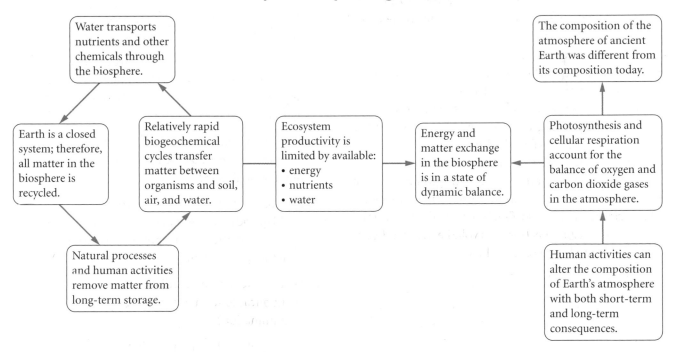

Understanding Concepts

1. Use word processing or graphics software to illustrate the relationship between the carbon and oxygen cycles. **ICT**

2. Identify the properties of water that make it an excellent transporter of dissolved materials, and briefly describe each.

3. Describe the role of plants and animals in:
   a) the rapid cycling of carbon
   b) the slow cycling of carbon

4. Explain how animals lose and replace water from their bodies.

5. Explain, with reference to the molecular structure of water:
   a) why ice floats
   b) why water is called the universal solvent
   c) why water has special adhesive and cohesive properties

6. Explain why each of the following is a reservoir for nitrogen:
   a) living organisms
   b) soil
   c) water
   d) atmosphere

7. Identify which of the following elements cycle through Earth's atmosphere: carbon, phosphorus, sulfur, oxygen, and nitrogen.

8. Explain how excess phosphate can affect aquatic ecosystems.

9. a) Identify the process that led to the increase in the amount of oxygen in Earth's atmosphere to current levels.
   b) Describe one way scientists have been able to assess the historical composition of Earth's atmosphere.

10. Describe the reason why farmers apply fertilizers to many of their crops.

11. a) Identify the useable form(s) of nitrogen that are available for green plants in a terrestrial ecosystem.
    b) Explain the role of bacteria in supplying these usable forms of nitrogen to plants.
    c) Describe how other bacteria actually remove these useable forms of nitrogen from the soil.

12. a) Describe acid deposition and explain how human activities have contributed to increased levels of acid deposition in eastern Canada.
    b) Name two biogeochemical cycles that are involved in acid deposition.

13. Compare and contrast the phosphorus and nitrogen cycles in terms of the role that the lithosphere plays in each cycle.

14. Define, using an example, the meaning of "ecosystem services."

Use the following information to answer the next question.

Nutrient Upwelling

As shown in this illustration, nutrient-rich water rises from deeper levels to replace the surface water that has drifted away. These nutrients are responsible for supporting the large fish populations commonly found in these areas.

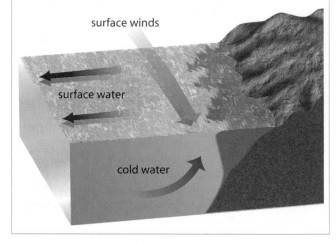

15. Explain why, in general, there is less productivity deep in the oceans, compared with productivity of water closer to coastal areas.

16. Explain the importance of wetlands.

17. Use word processing and/or graphics software to illustrate the main stages in the nitrogen cycle in a terrestrial ecosystem. **ICT**

18. Summarize how the properties of water are essential for life as we know it.

Applying Concepts

19. A researcher hypothesizes that increasing global temperatures will make it harder for algae to resist damage due to ultraviolet radiation (UVR). Another researcher suspects the opposite. Outline an experimental procedure that could be used to test this hypothesis in laboratory conditions.

Use the following information to answer the next question.

Deforestation

In order to study the effects of deforestation on biogeochemical cycles, scientists cut down an area of forest in the Hubbard Brook Experimental Forest in a mountainous region of New Hampshire, United States. Pesticides were used to prevent any vegetation from regrowing in this part of the valley. Following deforestation, the amount of water flowing out of the area increased by 40 percent. Scientists also measured the amount of nitrate in stream water in the forested and deforested areas. Their results are shown in the following graph.

The Concentration of Nitrate in Streams Leaving Forested and Deforested Areas over Time

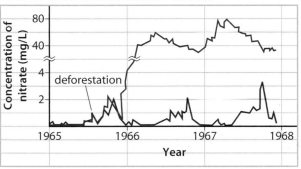

The Hubbard Brook Experiment. The red line indicates the amount of nitrate in streams leaving deforested area. The blue line indicates the amount of nitrate in streams leaving intact nearby forests.

20. a) Explain how the results of this experiment might be used to explain flooding in areas downstream of a forest that has been cleared of trees.
   b) Predict how large-scale deforestation around the world might affect the hydrologic cycle.
   c) Describe the results of the graph. Explain the impact of deforestation on the amount of nitrate retained in the soil.
   d) Explain, in general terms, how deforestation affects the nitrogen cycle.
   e) Assuming no pesticides were being used, identify two other factors that might limit the growth of new vegetation in a previously deforested area.

21. Ground water comes from precipitation that has filtered down through soil and spaces between rocks. Explain how the careless dumping of pesticides into a land fill could impair ground-water quality.

Use the following information to answer the next question.

Walkerton, Ontario

In Walkerton, Ontario, seven people died and thousands became ill after pathogenic bacteria (*E. coli* 0157:H7) contaminated the town's water supply in 2000. Although the town's water supply was chlorinated, there was insufficient chlorine in the water to kill the bacteria. The source of the bacteria was later traced to an area near one of the town wells, a farmer's field that had recently been spread with manure. Prior to the *E. coli* outbreak, the region had received heavy rains.

22. a) Describe, in terms of the hydrologic cycle, how Walkerton's water supply might have become contaminated.
   b) Suggest two actions that a municipality could take in order to safeguard the quality of drinking water supplies.

Making Connections

23. Use word processing and/or graphics software to show the relationship between the hydrologic and phosphorus cycles. **ICT**

24. Do wild animals produce garbage and/or pollution? Explain your answer.

Use the following information to answer the next question.

Acid Deposition

Some of the molecules that are released by burning fossil fuels include sulfur dioxide and nitrogen oxides. These molecules react with oxygen and water vapour in the air to produce acid deposition, which can damage plants and leach nutrients from the soil.

25. a) Use word processing and/or graphics software to illustrate the formation of acid deposition as the result of driving a car that burns gasoline. **ICT**
   b) Explain how driving a car in Alberta can affect an ecosystem elsewhere in the country.

Career Focus: **Ask a Sustainability Expert**

There is no job description for what Professor Tang Lee does, but everything he does relates to sustaining the health of the planet and its inhabitants. He is an architect and a Professor of Environmental Design at the University of Calgary, where he teaches and conducts research into topics such as indoor air quality and sustainable building design. He is often called on to give expert testimony in court and to be interviewed on radio and television. As well, he is also a co-owner and operator of a tilapia (*Oreochromis niloticus*) fish farm, which supplies fish to stores in Calgary and Edmonton.

Q What is sustainability?

It can be as simple as conducting our lives so that we don't adversely affect future generations. There are many different definitions. You can sustain health, energy resources, food. To my mind, it is all of the above.

Q Why do you run a fish farm?

I look at the oceans being over-fished, and it's destroying water ecosystems. And there's so much pollution being dumped into the ocean—heavy metals, like mercury, cadmium, and lead. ... I worry about the health of my children and grandchildren. To make a long story short, I decided to raise fish in a way that does not deplete the oceans—in a way that does not use chemicals, and hormones, and antibiotics, which of course go up the food chain.

Q How do you operate your fish farm?

Lots of fish farms have what's called a flow-through system, which means they take water out of the river and put it through the tank. Waste from the fish and uneaten fish food gets discharged (untreated) into the river. We don't do that. We have a greenhouse, and so the wastewater is put in a hydroponics system as well as soil culture. To make the soil culture we grind up any dead fish and mix this into the soil. We have beautiful compost that we donate to the garden clubs!

We only bring in about 10 percent of the water we use to replace water lost to evaporation, spillage, and so forth. And because of this, we don't discharge large amounts of nutrients downstream. We have

equipment and the hydroponics system to filter the water. We also have a constructed wetland on our site, which does the final polishing. After the water goes through the wetland, it's completely clear. Nature is incredible in terms of how it can purify, as long as we don't overload the system.

Q You also design solar-powered buildings. What motivates you to do this?

We live in a privileged period of civilization in which we have fossil fuels to consume. The future is going to be different. ... We're not going to be able to use, in the same way, fossil fuels for heating, cooling, and powering our buildings, or for transportation.

Q What keeps you in a positive frame of mind?

I'm hopeful because there are people who are working toward renewable energies, like solar and wind, different types of planning systems, and new types of vehicles. ... We see a lot of what we call *ecovillages* springing up, in which communities are trying to be as self-sufficient as possible.

Q How else does architecture relate to sustainability?

It's more than just designing a building that's very energy efficient. We have to rethink what beautiful is. For example, do we really need imported marble in our homes? There's other beauty, such as Rocky Mountain stone, that we have right here in Alberta. We have to challenge the assumptions of our ways.

Other Careers Related to Sustainability

Environmental Technologist Environmental consulting firms, petrochemical companies, government agencies, and research centres employ technicians to collect and analyze environmental samples. Environmental technologists need a solid understanding of environmental regulations. Either a two-year technical diploma or a Bachelor of Science degree is required for an entry-level position.

Horticulturalist Trained gardeners maintain green spaces and cultivate crops for human consumption. A Bachelor of Applied Science degree, or a two-year college diploma combined with an apprenticeship, prepares gardeners to work in greenhouses, nurseries, and production fields. Horticulturalists can also specialize in agribusiness, or golf or landscape management.

Environmental Planner City or regional planners work with architects, land developers, transportation specialists, and others to plan how urban centres should grow. Environmental planners need to consider environmental, economic, and social aspects of city life. An undergraduate degree in planning or environmental studies is needed to start working in this field.

Professor of Environmental Design Environmental design is a broad field of study that looks at how human intervention impacts the environment in positive and negative ways. Professors with doctorate degrees or equivalent experience conduct and lead research on environmental design issues, teach at universities, and may consult for government or private companies.

Environmental Communications Specialist Freelance journalists and staff reporters cover environmental stories for media outlets. Public relations specialists help universities, governments, and companies communicate with the general public through brochures, newsletters, and advertisements. A communications specialist may have a college diploma or an undergraduate degree in communications, journalism, or science, combined with a work-practicum or relevant volunteer experience.

Environmental Lawyer Certified lawyers with additional expertise in environmental science mediate or represent clients in legal disputes, such as cases of illegal waste disposal. Environmental lawyers also advise industrial and real-estate companies of their rights and responsibilities according to environmental regulations.

Go Further...

1. Indoor environments affect outdoor environments, and vice versa. Research one aspect of building construction or interior design that affects the outside environment.

2. It is important for buildings to be designed to bring in fresh air. When carbon dioxide levels are too high, buildings get stuffy and people get headaches and feel sleepy. How do outdoor carbon dioxide levels affect the amount of fresh air that people need to bring into buildings?

3. In what ways are food quality and food safety global issues?

Understanding Concepts

1. Explain how energy is transferred in a terrestrial environment.

2. At one time fungi, such as mushrooms, were classified in the same kingdom as green plants. Explain, in terms of their trophic level, why fungi are no longer placed in the same kingdom as green plants.

3. Explain how energy is transferred in a thermal vent community.

4. Use word processing or graphics software to construct a flow chart that illustrates the conversion of animal wastes to a form of nitrogen that green plants can use. **ICT**

5. Describe how phosphorus is utilized in plants and animals.

6. Predict what would happen to the levels of carbon dioxide and oxygen in the atmosphere if global productivity decreased.

Use the following illustration to answer the next question.

7. **a)** Identify the population(s) that would likely increase if the squid population increased.

   b) Use word processing and/or graphics software to illustrate a food chain in which sea birds are the top predators. Identify the producers, primary consumer, secondary consumer, and tertiary consumer in your food chain. **ICT**

   c) Assume that only 10 percent of the energy available at one tropic level is passed on to the next trophic level. If the phytoplankton provided 25 000 kJ of energy to the zooplankton, calculate the amount of energy available to the fish.

Use the following information to answer the next question.

> **Pyramid of Numbers**
> The following is a pyramid of numbers for a deciduous forest ecosystem.
>
> **Deciduous forest**
>
> tertiary consumer ———
> secondary consumer ———
> primary consumer ——
> producer ———————

8. Use word processing or graphics software to illustrate a pyramid of biomass for this same ecosystem. **ICT**

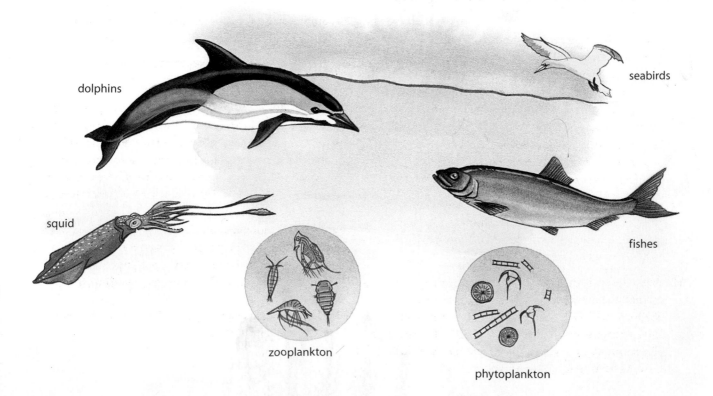

dolphins

seabirds

squid

fishes

zooplankton

phytoplankton

9. From the energy that a potato beetle gains from its food, the beetle uses 17 percent for growth and loses 33 percent by cellular respiration and 50 percent through feces (wastes). If the potato beetle consumes 750 J of energy, calculate how much of this energy is available to the next trophic level.

10. Identify four properties of water that make it vital to living organisms.

11. a) Identify the biogeochemical cycles that are involved in acid deposition, and explain how it forms.
    b) Describe the impact of acid deposition on a deciduous forest ecosystem.

12. Compare and contrast the relative amount of productivity in:
    a) the Arctic and a tropical rainforest;
    b) the coastal waters of British Columbia and a geologically inactive region of the sea floor; and
    c) a geologically inactive region of the sea floor and a region of the sea floor near a deep sea vent.

13. Explain how the current composition of the atmosphere compares with the composition of the atmosphere three billion years ago.

14. Explain the term metabolic water.

15. Compare the rapid cycling of carbon to the slow cycling of carbon.

16. Living cells capture a tiny amount of available solar radiation. This small amount is enough to support almost all life on Earth.
    a) Predict the consequences if photosynthetic organisms were able to capture twice as much solar energy. Explain.
    b) Predict the consequences if photosynthetic organisms were only able to capture half as much solar energy. Explain.

17. a) Describe dead zones in aquatic ecosystems.
    b) Explain, in terms of the phosphorus cycle, how human activities contribute to the formation of dead zones in lakes.

18. Antarctic krill (*Euphausia superba*) are shrimp-like animals that are abundant in the Southern Ocean. Krill are used as a feed supplement in the aquaculture industry. Some people suggest that krill be harvested for direct human use. What effects might increased krill farming have on Antarctic ecosystems?

19. a) Identify the roles that Alberta's wetlands play in the environment.
    b) Explain how wetlands can help to protect water quality.

Applying Concepts

Use the following information to answer the next question.

Exploring Distant Planets

Suppose that space scientists launch a robotic explorer to a distant planet that is similar to Earth 3.5 billion years ago. The robot reveals that there is liquid water on this planet, and water vapour in the atmosphere surrounding it, but no oxygen. There are many underwater volcanoes, which emit hydrogen gas and hydrogen sulfide gas. Using a special microscope, the robotic explorer also finds communities of bacteria coated with a black precipitate, which are thriving in the warm mineral-rich water.

20. a) As a scientist on the research team, describe how you think the newly discovered bacteria survive.
    b) Do you think this planet could support other forms of life? Explain.

21. Using the rule of 10 as a guide, calculate how much of 2500 J captured by 1.25 kg of a plant shrub would be passed on to a cougar that ate 1.00 kg of deer meat. (Assume that the deer ate 1.25 kg of the shrub.)

22. Summarize one major line of evidence suggesting that Earth's atmosphere was once free of oxygen.

Use the following information to answer the next question.

Space Station

Suppose that you have been asked to help design a space station in which astronauts will live for several years. The astronauts will have no access to outside food and will not be able to remove any waste from the space station during the mission. Water is a limited and expensive resource on board the space station. The reason for this is that there is limited storage space for water and there is no continuous water supply. However, some water can be produced when the fuel cells on board the space station combine oxygen and hydrogen to make electricity. Water may also be recovered from urine and feces from the astronauts.

23. Identify the key features you will include in the space station, and justify your choices.

Use the following information to answer the next question.

Algae and Cyanobacteria

Algae and cyanobacteria use photosynthesis to produce large quantities of oxygen. Both algae and cyanobacteria occur naturally in surface waters. Although their individual size is usually microscopic, when conditions are ideal, both can undergo a phenomenon known as a "bloom." This results when the algae reproduce rapidly and the individuals form clumps visible to the naked eye. It is difficult to predict when a bloom will occur. However, all blooms require light, nutrients, and oxygen. Some species bloom only in spring, others more frequently in the fall. These organisms can bloom in flowing or standing water. Blooms may even occur under ice in the middle of winter. Large, nuisance blooms commonly form following periods of hot, calm weather when the water is warm. They are also more likely to occur when water nutrient levels, and in particular phosphorus, are high.

Most algae do not produce substances that are toxic to humans or animals. In contrast, some cyanobacteria produce substances that are extremely toxic, and are capable of causing serious illness or even death if consumed. These substances are called cyanotoxins.

[Source: Agriculture and Agri-Food Canada; *Algae, Cyanobacteria and Water Quality*; March 2002]

---

24. a) Explain why it is a problem when algae and cyanobacteria reproduce in large numbers. Why are cyanobacterial blooms even more dangerous than algal blooms?

  b) Identify the nutrient that causes them to reproduce in large numbers.

  c) Although algal and cyanobacterial blooms occur naturally, many human activities contribute to this problem. Describe three human activities that contribute to blooms in aquatic ecosystems.

25. Use word processing and/or graphics software to illustrate a pyramid of biomass using the following population data from a coral reef: producers, 700 g/m^2; primary consumers, 132 g/m^2; secondary consumers, 11 g/m^2. **ICT**

26. Some scientists compare the biosphere to a living organism (Gaia Hypothesis). Explain this hypothesis and discuss the transfer of energy and matter through the biosphere.

27. Use word processing or graphics software to construct a flow chart that illustrates the slow cycling of carbon through the biosphere. **ICT**

28. a) Identify two biogeochemical cycles that are significantly influenced by human activities.

  b) Identify the biogeochemical cycles in which bacteria play an important role.

  c) Use word processing or graphics software to illustrate one of the biogeochemical cycles identified in "b" above. **ICT**

Use the following information to answer the next question.

Landfills

Landfill is the major method for waste disposal. Landfills are holes in the ground where the waste is placed, perhaps the site of a disused quarry or pit, or they may be purposefully excavated. Almost everyone uses and discards batteries into the waste stream. Although waste batteries are a small amount of the solid waste stream, they are a concentrated source of some types of heavy metals. The main constituents of concern for human health and the environment include cadmium, lead, and mercury.

---

29. Explain, in terms of biogeochemical cycles, what might happen to the chemicals in batteries that are put in landfills.

30. On Earth, matter cycles and energy "flows."

  a) To make this statement clearer, explain how the concept of matter is different from that of energy in matter and energy exchange in the biosphere.

  b) Use graphics software to draw a diagram to illustrate the given statement. **ICT**

31. Hydrogen sulfide gas reacts with metals, resulting in the precipitation of metal sulfides. Which organisms might you consider using to help clean up aquatic environments contaminated with heavy metals, such as mercury? Explain.

32. Use graphics software to draw a diagram showing how photosynthesis and cellular respiration form a cycle of connected reactions. **ICT**

Making Connections

Use the following information to answer the next question.

> ### The Real Dirt on No-Till Soil
> ### Jill Clapperton
>
> Soils are formed from a stew of geological ingredients or parent materials (rocks and minerals), water, and billions of organisms. The interactions between climate, parent material, organisms, landscape, and time affect all major ecosystem processes which lead to the development of soil properties that are unique to that soil type and climate. The activities of, and chemicals produced by, soil micro-organisms, and the chemicals leached from plant residues and roots can further influence the weathering of parent materials changing the mineral nutrient content and structure of soil. Thus, farm management practices such as crop rotations, tillage, fallow, irrigation, and nutrient inputs can all affect the population and diversity of soil organisms, and in turn, soil quality.
>
> There are three soil properties that define soil quality: chemical, physical and biological. The chemical properties of a soil are usually related to soil fertility such as available nitrogen (N), phosphorus (P), potassium (K), micronutrient uptake of Cu, Zn, Mn, and etc, as well as [soil] organic matter content (SOM) and pH. Soil structural characteristics such as aggregate formation and stability, tilth, and texture are physical properties. The biological properties of a soil unite the soil physical and chemical properties. For instance, fungi and bacteria recycle all the carbon, nitrogen, phosphorus, sulphur and other nutrients in SOM, including animal residues, into the mineral forms that can be used by plants. By breaking down the complex carbon compounds that make up SOM into simpler compounds, soil organisms acquire their energy.
>
> [Source: Jill Clapperton, "Managing the Soil as a Habitat," *FarmTech* 2004, pp. 38–42]
>
> **Note:** A soil with good tilth has large pore spaces for adequate air infiltration and water movement. Roots only grow where the soil tilth allows for adequate soil oxygen levels. It also holds a reasonable supply of water and nutrients.

33. a) Explain, in terms of biogeochemical cycles, how the overapplication of insecticides and herbicides could have an impact on the soil structural characteristics.

b) Explain why many farmers apply synthetic fertilizers containing nitrogen and phosphorus to their land before planting their crops in the spring.

Use the following information to answer the next question.

> ### Snow Geese
>
> Since the 1960s, the number of snow geese in Canada has increased from an estimated half a million to three million. For much of the year, the snow geese have easy access to croplands in the United States. In the late spring, the snow geese migrate to their breeding grounds in the Arctic. Some people consider these birds to be a nuisance and a threat to the tundra ecosystem, and feel that the snow geese population should be reduced by culling (killing a portion of the population).

34. Do you think culling the snow geese would help protect the tundra ecosystem? Explain.

Use the following information to answer the next question.

> Human activities around the world can affect you here in Canada. Toxic chemicals that are dumped in an ocean might end up in fish you eat for dinner. If you are an Aboriginal hunter in the Arctic, you might ingest traces of the pesticide DDT, sprayed in 2003 by a local health official in Morocco to kill malaria-carrying mosquitoes.

35. Infer how human activities in other countries might affect the environment in Canada, and vice versa.

Use the following information to answer the next question.

> ### Alberta Floods
>
> In June 2005, many regions in Alberta experienced heavy rainfall and floods. During this period, Albertans were asked to restrict their use of water.

36. a) Explain why communities would need to restrict water use during a flood.

b) Given the heavy rains in 2005, explain why many scientists are concerned about water shortages in the future in Alberta.

37. Assuming that ecosystems are self-sustaining and self-regulating, explain why each of the following should or should not be considered an ecosystem:

a) a pond
b) a fish aquarium
c) a wheat farm
d) the city of Edmonton
e) Earth

General Outcomes

In this unit, you will

- explain that the biosphere is composed of ecosystems, each with distinctive biotic and abiotic components

- explain the mechanisms involved in the change of populations with the passage of time

Unit Contents

Focussing Questions

1 What components make up the environment of a population of lawn dandelions in southern Alberta? How do these components compare with those that make up the environment of a population of lawn dandelions in northern Alberta?

2 Which factors could influence the rise and fall of populations of lawn dandelions in any environment?

3 How can changes in populations over thousands and millions of years be explained scientifically?

Unit PreQuiz ?
www.albertabiology.ca

For outdoor enthusiasts, the St. Mary Reservoir near Cardston in southern Alberta is a popular destination. For scientists, this reservoir is a gold mine for hiking into Alberta's past. University of Calgary archaeologist, Brian Kooyman, calls this site "one of the best preserved areas of ancient animal tracks in North America—possibly the world." Here, more than 10 000 years ago, as the ice sheets that covered much of Alberta receded, ancient animals— many of them now extinct—roamed. Mammoths, bison, camels, wolves, and pony-sized horses have left evidence of their existence, mainly in the form of fossilized bones and footprints. Scientists once thought that the North American horse (*Equus conversidens*) became extinct due to its inability to adjust to climate changes. They now have a different hypothesis, as a result of laboratory techniques used to identify blood proteins found on spear points: another animal— humans—hunted the horses, perhaps to extinction.

In this unit, you will learn how populations of plants, animals, and other organisms interact with one another and with their environment. You will also consider how changes in a population of organisms, as well as in a specific environment, occur with the passage of time.

Prerequisite Concepts

This unit builds on your knowledge of interactions of organisms within ecosystems from Unit 1, and it draws upon your knowledge of biological diversity and energy transfer in global systems from previous studies.

The Need for Reproduction

All species of organisms grow and produce offspring and, in so doing, pass on their hereditary information to succeeding generations. Thus, reproduction is essential to the survival of a species.

In order for multicellular organisms to grow, repair themselves, and reproduce, their cells undergo division. While many cells in your body, for instance, are growing and dividing, some are wearing out and dying. Cells reproduce through a continuous sequence of growth and division known as the cell cycle. The cell cycle consists of two main stages, the growth stage and the division stage. There are two types of cell division: *mitosis* and *meiosis*.

Mitosis

In mitosis, body cells (but not reproductive cells) divide to form two new cells, which are identical to the parent cell. Before a cell divides, the chromosomes first replicate (make copies of themselves). The cell then divides. The resulting two cells have the same number of chromosomes as the parent cell. (Chromosomes consist of DNA, the genetic information of a cell.) So, if a body cell has 46 chromosomes (as human cells do) after mitosis, the "daughter cells" also have 46 chromosomes.

Meiosis

Meiosis is a special type of cell division that occurs only in reproductive cells (sperm cells and egg cells). Meiosis

Table P2.1 Comparing Mitosis and Meiosis

Mitosis	Meiosis
one division	two divisions
two daughter cells	four daughter cells
daughter cells are genetically identical	daughter cells are genetically different
chromosome number in daughter cells same as in parent cell	chromosome number in daughter cells half that in parent cell
occurs in somatic (body) cells	occurs in reproductive cells (sperm and egg cells)
used for growth and repair of body cells (and in asexual reproduction in some organisms)	used for sexual reproduction, producing new genetic combinations in offspring from one generation to the next

produces reproductive cells called gametes. During meiosis, the nucleus of a gamete divides twice. The gametes, either egg or sperm, contain only one copy of each type of chromosome that the parent cell contains. So, in humans for example, the gametes from each parent contain only 23 chromosomes. Meiosis ensures that when a sperm fertilizes an egg, the resulting cell has the correct number of chromosomes. In humans, this is 46. (If the gametes did not go through meiosis before fertilization, there would be 92 chromosomes in humans.) Table P2.1 and Figure P2.1 compare meiosis with mitosis.

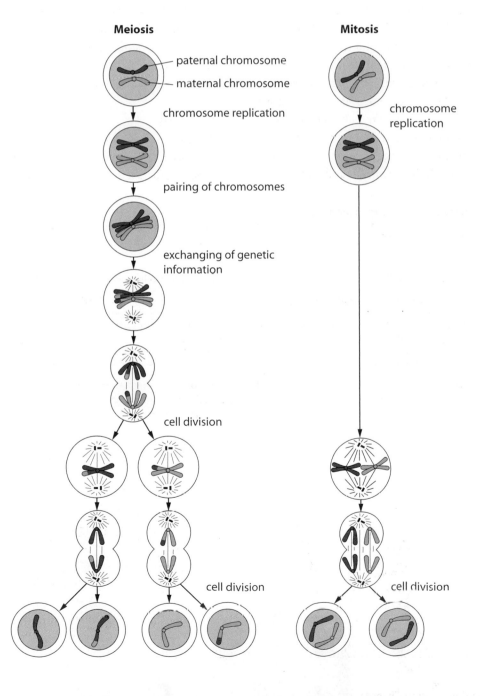

Figure P2.1 Meiosis involves two divisions of the nucleus with no replication of genetic material between them. Thus, it produces four daughter cells, each with half the original number of chromosomes. Mitosis involves a single division of the nucleus after chromosome replication. Thus, it produces two daughter cells, each containing the original number of chromosomes.

Ecosystems and Their Diversity

Chapter Concepts

3.1 Individuals, Populations, and Communities in Ecosystems

- The distribution and abundance of organisms depend on interactions among organisms, and between individuals and their environments.

- An organism's environment includes abiotic and biotic components.

- Interactions between organisms and their environment can be categorized based on: individuals, populations, communities, and ecosystems.

3.2 Classifying and Naming Organisms

- Organisms are organized into groups (such as kingdoms), depending on shared biological characteristics.

- Internationally, scientists use a biological system of binomial nomenclature (two-word naming systems).

- Dichotomous keys are used to identify the two-word scientific name for individuals of a species.

3.3 Studying Organisms in Ecosystems

- Each biome has a particular mix of organisms that are adapted to living in its environmental conditions.

- Organisms have habitats, ranges, and ecological niches in ecosystems.

- Limiting factors influence the distribution, range, and abundance of organisms.

- Scientists take random samples to estimate population sizes.

- Sampling techniques include censuses, transects, and quadrats.

A healthy ecosystem is thick with populations of diverse organisms. The ecosystem shown here is characterized by some unhealthy populations. In the southern interior of British Columbia, one species—the mountain pine beetle—has been destroying large tracts of lodgepole pine, with consequences for all other organisms in the area. The mountain pine beetle infestation is an example of the failure of mechanisms that ensure the health of an ecosystem.

In this chapter you will see how organisms interact with their environment and other organisms, study the mechanisms that keep organisms and ecosystems healthy, and learn how scientists identify organisms and measure and record diversity. You'll practice using scientific tools to distinguish organisms and track and estimate populations of organisms within a local ecosystem.

The Mountain Pine Beetle vs an Ecosystem

The lodgepole pine grows in the North American west, as far north as the Yukon. It tolerates most soil conditions; cold, wet winters; and warm, dry summers. Seed cones can withstand freezing temperatures and most insects. The trees have fairly thin bark and a shallow root system, making them susceptible to damage by fire and insects; however, the high temperatures of fires release the seeds to quickly regenerate trees after a forest fire. During the last hundred years, forest fires have been controlled and suppressed.

The mountain pine beetle is a common parasite of the lodgepole pine. Adult beetles bore through the thin bark to lay eggs and deposit a fungus carried on their bodies. The larvae live in and feed on the bark during the winter, as does the fungus. The bark damage usually kills the host tree, although sustained temperatures of −25 °C during the early fall or late spring or temperatures of −40 °C during winter can kill the larvae. Infestations usually last 5 to 7 years and happen in 20- to 40-year cycles.

The pine beetle infestation began in British Columbia in 1993, and over a decade later residents in affected areas are reporting:

- small mammals such as squirrels have disappeared
- song birds have left the area
- trap lines are increasingly empty
- cougars are coming to settled areas and preying on family pets
- devil's club, a plant used for Aboriginal medicine, is increasingly hard to find

Analysis

1. What biotic and abiotic components of the environment affect the life cycle of the lodgepole pine? What biotic and abiotic components of the environment affect the life cycle of the mountain pine beetle?

2. Can you suggest reasons why the current mountain pine beetle infestation has lasted longer than the usual 5 to 7 years?

3. What can you infer from the local reports about the impact of the loss of the trees on other organisms?

Extension

4. Choose one of the following roles and write or present a short paragraph on how the pine beetle infestation affects you as:
   a) a local elder
   b) a logger
   c) a planner for the department of forests
   d) a wilderness tour operator

The mountain pine beetle (*Dendroctonus ponderosae*) has devastated pine forests in British Columbia, and lodgepole pine trees (*Pinus contorta*) in Kakwa Wildland and Willmore Wilderness Parks in western Alberta have been treated for infestations. (Adult size 4 to 7.5 mm.)

Individuals, Populations, and Communities in Ecosystems

Section Outcomes

In this section, you will
- **define** and **explain** the interrelationship among individual organisms, populations, communities, and ecosystems
- **recognize** different aspects of ecosystems that ecologists might study
- **plan** and **design** an investigation to study a local ecosystem

Key Terms

biotic
abiotic
species
population
community
ecosystem
biosphere

Figure 3.1 Pronghorn (*Antilocapra americana*) are found in southern Alberta. This is the northern extent of their distribution in North America. At one time, there were herds of close to 40 000 000 pronghorn in North America. Now there are fewer than 30 000. What factors might affect their distribution and abundance?

Among North American mammals, the pronghorn, shown in Figure 3.1 and once thought to be a North American relative of the African antelope because of its physical resemblance, is the swiftest, with a speed of up to 80 km/h. This speed, and the pronghorn's ability to sustain it over long distances, indicate that the pronghorn is well-adapted to living in the open plains environment. How does the pronghorn interact with its environment? What does the pronghorn eat, and what eats it? What physical and behavioural characteristics make the pronghorn well-suited for life in its environment? Why has the pronghorn survived on the open plain, while other organisms have not?

Organisms and Their Environment

The term "environment" refers to everything that affects an organism throughout its life, as well as everything that the organism affects. Throughout a pronghorn's life, it will come in contact with many different organisms: other pronghorns, insects, bacteria, foods such

as grasses, other mammals it can co-exist with, and predators such as coyotes. These are what ecologists call the living—**biotic**—components of its environment. As well, a pronghorn will drink large amounts of water, breathe even larger quantities of air, and roam in hundreds of hectares of soil throughout the four seasons. Ecologists call these components of the environment, such as sunlight, water, and minerals, **abiotic**, or non-living.

Every organism on Earth—including you—affects, is affected by, and therefore interacts with the biotic and abiotic components of its environment.

- - -

Q 1 Identify three biotic components and three abiotic components of a pronghorn's environment.

Q 2 Identify three biotic components and three abiotic components of your environment.

Q 3 Identify three biotic and three abiotic components of a starfish's environment.

- - -

BiologyFile

FYI

Western science has divided the physical world into living and non-living components in order to describe and explain organisms and their interactions. Other cultures do not make the same distinction. For example, Aboriginal people in North America consider all elements of the world to be living.

Figure 3.2 The starfish is an individual organism; it is shown here among a population of sea urchins. These organisms are living in a community of other organisms, or biotic components. The community is part of an ecosystem, which is also shown here. The ecosystem includes the biotic and abiotic elements *plus* their interactions.

Ecologists—scientists who study the interactions of organisms with one another and their environment—usually focus on a specific level of an environment, ranging from the smallest component to a more inclusive and complex picture. As highlighted in Figure 3.2, these levels include individual organisms, populations, communities, and ecosystems.

Individual Organisms

Ecologists who study individual organisms want to learn how the abiotic environment in which an individual lives affects its behaviour or physical features. For example, an ecologist might investigate the physical features of a species of alpine plant that allow it to live in an environment that is cold, dry, and windy. Another ecologist might study why a particular species of snail, the Banff Springs snail shown in Figure 3.3, only lives in seven thermal springs in Banff National Park and nowhere else in the

world. Investigations like these help to explain the distribution of organisms— that is, why organisms are only present in certain locations. Abiotic conditions affect the distribution of organisms.

In the investigation on the next page, you will measure how the *morphology* (physical appearance) of an organism can change when abiotic conditions change.

Populations

Organisms that are able to breed with one another and produce fertile offspring are known collectively as a **species**. The concept of species is related to the next level of ecological organization: population. A **population** is a group of individuals of the same species living in a specific area at the same time. Population ecologists describe changes in the size of a population, its abundance, as time passes. For example, they may study how the population of lilies in the Bugaboo Mountains, shown in Figure 3.4 on the next page, increases, decreases, or remains the same during a period of time. They might also study the rate at which a population changes in size, and what factors determine the relative numbers of males and females (or young and old) in a population.

Population ecologists from Alberta are studying how populations of collared pika (see Figure 3.5A on page 81.) are changing. Pikas, which are related to rabbits, live among boulders in alpine

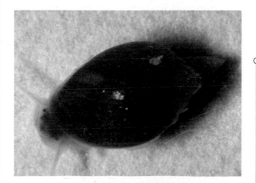

Figure 3.3 The adult Banff Springs snail (*Physella johnsoni*) has a shell length of about 5 mm. It is found in only a small number of hot springs in Banff National Park. What abiotic and biotic components allow it to live in water as hot as 36 °C?

Biology File

FYI
Antilocapra americana is often called an antelope, because it resembles animals that live in Africa and Asia. In fact, the pronghorn is the only modern, surviving member of a family called *Antilocapridae*, found only in North America. You will review the classification of organisms later in this chapter, in Section 3.2.

Figure 3.4 Each of these glacier lilies (*Erythronium grandiflorum*) is part of a population. How would you define this population? Can you identify its edges or boundaries? Why do you think it's a boundary?

pikas are particularly vulnerable to changes in temperatures. After a series of warmer winters, starting in 1998, populations in one study area declined markedly, as shown in Figure 3.5B. The researchers hypothesize that rising temperatures associated with global warming have resulted in changes in vegetation, so the pikas have less to eat. As well, the lack of snow pack during warm winters may reduce the amount of snow that usually covers the pikas' rock-tunnel homes. Consequently, during cold spells, there may not be enough snow to provide the "insulative blanket" the pikas need to survive.

regions. They forage on grasses and flowers, which they hoard in small "haystacks" in their tunnels for use in the winter. Studies, such as those carried out by ecologist Dr. David Hik of the University of Alberta, have shown that

Communities

In nature, populations are rarely isolated. Instead, populations of different species interact with one another as part of a community. A **community** consists of all

---

INVESTIGATION 3.A

Target Skills

Measuring biotic characteristics of ecosystems and speculating on their relationship to abiotic characteristics

Working cooperatively to gather and share data

Observing Leaves

Changes in abiotic conditions, such as the amount of moisture or salt in soil or the amount of available sunlight, can result in changes in the morphology of a plant. In this investigation, the class will measure the leaves of a plant in two locations with different abiotic conditions to see how the different conditions affect a plant's morphology.

Materials

- ruler
- materials for recording data

Procedure

1. With your teacher, determine an area to study. You will be measuring the leaves of a plant species in two locations that have different abiotic conditions. For example, you could measure the leaves of a tree near a stream and a tree of the same species some distance away from the stream, dandelions in a field that is regularly mowed and dandelions in a field that is

"wild," or a plant near a roadway and a plant of the same species in a nearby forested area.

2. Predict if there will be any differences in measurements for the plants in the two locations.

3. Working in pairs, measure the length at least 25 leaves on plants in each location and record the data. (If you are measuring leaves on a tree or shrub, use a larger sample size, such as 100 leaves. Take care not to endanger yourself or the plant during this activity.) Determine the average leaf length in each study area.

Analysis

1. Describe how the abiotic conditions in the two locations differ.

2. Was there a difference in average leaf size in the two locations?

3. If there was a difference, hypothesize why, making reference to abiotic conditions.

Figure 3.5A Yukon populations of collared pika (*Ochotona collaris*) declined dramatically between 1998 and 2000. Researchers acknowledge that they have much to learn about this species, but they hypothesize that rising global temperatures may be linked to the pika's decline.

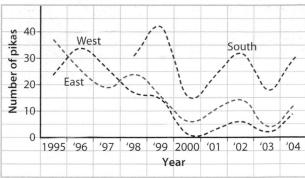

Relative Abundance of Collared Pikas from 1995 to 2004

Figure 3.5B This graph shows how the number of collared pikas changed during a nine-year period on three slopes (east, west, and south) in the southwest Yukon study area of Ruby Range.

of the individuals in all of the interacting populations in a given area. Community ecologists typically study the interactions among the members of different populations. For example, they may be interested in why some communities are made up of many different species, while other communities contain only a few. In one study in Saskatchewan, for example, community ecologists compared the number of species of birds within sections of intact forest to the number of species in "forest fragments" (small stands of forest surrounded by agricultural land). They found that species that preferred to be in the interior of forests were more common in the larger, intact forests. Species that preferred the "edges" of forests, such as predatory birds, were more common in the smaller forest fragments.

Interactions that might influence the structure of a community include competition between individuals of the same species in different populations, as well as the relationship between predator and prey populations. Abiotic factors (such as how much moisture is present or the number of hours of sunlight) also have a strong influence on which and how many species live in a community. So, for example, a community ecologist might study how bird species compete for nesting habitat, or how prolonged droughts change the composition of plant species growing in a particular area.

Environments Change Over Time

Most communities are dynamic; they continue to change as abiotic conditions in the environment change (see Figure 3.6 on the next page). As the population level of one organism fluctuates, this affects the population levels of other organisms that may consume or be consumed by the organism. As well, as populations in a community interact with one another, they can modify the environment so that it becomes more suitable for other species. These other species then gradually take over and form a new community. For example, after a disturbance such as fire, an open area is created in a forest. The first organisms to establish themselves in this open area are members of species that do well in open, disturbed habitats. As these first organisms inhabit the area, they create shade, alter the soil, and, in various other ways, make the habitat less suitable for species like themselves and more suitable for other species.

Similar changes in communities occur whenever new habitat is available to support life. New habitat may be available after a rockslide, flood, or volcanic eruption, or after a glacier recedes. A century or more after ice has melted, a lush meadow (such as the one in Figure 3.6 on the next page) will grow,

Figure 3.6 Communities that inhabit an area can change as time passes. When glacial ice first melted, populations of lichens and mosses were some of the first species to establish themselves in the area shown here. Eventually, soil was created and new plants began to grow. How might this meadow look in 200 years?

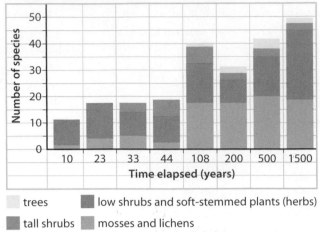

Change in Abundance of Species Over Time

trees
tall shrubs
low shrubs and soft-stemmed plants (herbs)
mosses and lichens

Figure 3.7 As time passed in this community, the number and type of species changed, growing on till that was exposed by a melting glacier. Why would you not expect to find evidence of trees growing until 100 years or more had passed?

with willows, wild flowers, grasses, and heathers. Several centuries later, a forest might cover this meadow. Figure 3.7 shows changes in a community as time passed after a glacier retreated in Glacier Bay, Alaska, United States.

Q 4 Describe an interaction that could occur between two organisms in a community.

Ecosystems

A community of populations, together with the abiotic factors that surround and affect it, is called an **ecosystem**. An ecosystem includes all of the non-living parts of the environment in a particular area and all the living organisms, as well as the interactions among them.

Although people often think of ecosystems as being quite large, they can be very small. In fact, the size of an ecosystem depends on what you are studying. There are small ecosystems within large ecosystems, which are within even larger ecosystems. For example, the lichen-covered boulder in Figure 3.8 could be considered an entire ecosystem. It contains a community of

living things, together with abiotic components such as air, water, and minerals. This ecosystem interacts with, and is part of, a larger ecosystem that contains the community of organisms living in the scree slope, or avalanche chute, where the boulder might be found. Both of these ecosystems are part of an even larger ecosystem, which extends beyond the boundaries of the

Figure 3.8 This boulder ecosystem is part of the larger ecosystem of organisms on the avalanche path. What bar of the graph shown in Figure 3.7 does it most closely resemble?

BiologyFile

Try This
Draw a diagram (either by hand or on a computer), or use a variety of coins or other small items you can manipulate, to compare and contrast the following ecological levels of organization: individuals, populations, communities, and ecosystems.

photograph. To prepare for your final investigation in this chapter, you will think about local ecosystems in the next Thought Lab.

The Bigger Picture: Earth's Biosphere

All the ecosystems in the world and their interactions make up the **biosphere**. You can think of the biosphere as the largest possible ecosystem. The biosphere includes all parts of Earth that are inhabitable by some type of life (in other words, all the land surfaces and bodies of water on Earth) and extends several kilometres into the atmosphere and several metres into the soil. All living things that inhabit these environments, as well as the abiotic components with which they interact, are part of the biosphere.

Populations are not randomly scattered throughout the biosphere, however. Each species has its own "place" in the biosphere. For example, mountain goats live in specific places in Canada, as shown by the range map in Figure 3.9.

They do not live across the entire country. As you now know, the distribution of a species is related to the ways the biotic and abiotic components of an environment affect individual organisms and their ability to survive. In order to study distribution, however, ecologists must first be able to accurately identify the organisms they encounter. You will learn how to do this in Section 3.2.

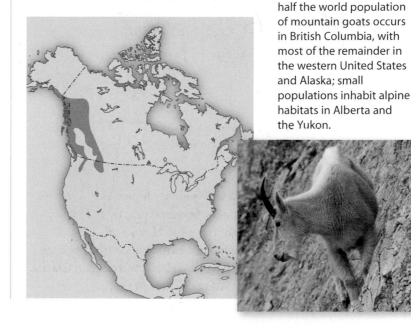

Figure 3.9 With their dense, insulative fur, powerful shoulder muscles, dexterous toes, and adhesive-like hoof pads, mountain goats (*Oreamnos americanus*) are able to live in the high mountain regions of western North America—the only places these animals are found naturally on Earth. About half the world population of mountain goats occurs in British Columbia, with most of the remainder in the western United States and Alaska; small populations inhabit alpine habitats in Alberta and the Yukon.

Thought Lab 3.1 Planning for Your Field Study

When Dr. David Hik set out to study the collared pika, he planned and carried out a field study. When staff at Alberta's Ministry of Sustainable Resources Development wanted to monitor the mountain pine beetle in Alberta's pine forests, they planned and carried out field studies. At the end of this chapter, you will take part in a field study to investigate and compare two ecosystems. Throughout this chapter, you and your group will be preparing for your field study. Here, you will begin your preparations by considering individuals, populations, and communities within two ecosystems.

Target Skills

Planning a field study to compare biotic and abiotic components of two ecosystems

Working cooperatively to gather and begin organizing data for a field study

Selecting and **using** appropriate technologies to aid in effective communication

Procedure

1. Read Investigation 3.D on page 106 so you can see what you will be doing in your field study.

2. As a group, brainstorm a list of possible local ecosystems that you could use as the focus for your field study. Recall that ecosystems can vary in size. Choose two ecosystems from your list. They should be similar types of ecosystems but in different locations. For example, one ecosystem could be a small pond in a forested area, and the other ecosystem could be a nearby water-filled ditch. Or one ecosystem could be a regularly mowed field, and the other ecosystem could be a nearby area that is not regularly mowed.

3. Decide on a method you will use to store and organize the information you gather during your field study. For example, you might use an electronic filing system.

4. Individually, choose one species that lives in both ecosystems you plan to study. From your experiences and observations, or after completing research, write a paragraph that explains how this species interacts with the abiotic and biotic components of its environment. For example, what eats this species, and what does it eat? What are its nutrient requirements?

Analysis

Describe the typical (a) population, (b) community, and (c) ecosystem of the species you chose in step 4.

Section 3.1 Summary

- An environment includes biotic and abiotic components.
- Ecologists divide the interactions between organisms and their environment into four levels: individual organisms, populations, communities, and ecosystems.
- Ecologists tend to specialize and focus on one level of an environment. They could be population ecologists, community ecologists, or they could spend their time studying an individual organism or an entire ecosystem.
- The study of an individual organism includes the effect of abiotic elements of its environment on physical features or behaviour.
- The study of a population includes all the members of the same species living in a specific area, plus their interactions with and the effects of the abiotic elements of their environment.
- The study of a community includes all individuals of all interacting populations in a specific area, and the effects of the abiotic elements of the environment.
- The study of an ecosystem includes all biotic and abiotic elements and their interactions.
- Most communities change over time because the abiotic elements change over time. Changing abiotic elements affect organisms and their interactions on all levels.

| Section 3.1 | Review |

1. In ecological terms, describe the difference between a population and a community.

2. Define the term ecosystem and explain how a fallen tree in a forest could be regarded as an entire ecosystem.

Use the following information to answer the next question.

Limber Pine (*Pinus flexilis*)
The limber pine is described as a small, scrubby mountain tree with short twisted limbs, that usually grows to a height of only 5 m to 10 m. Its bark is silvery-grey on young trees, becoming very rough and almost black at maturity. The limber pine is an alpine tree that grows on high mountain slopes where it is cold, dry, and very windy.

3. Explain how the limber pine's physical characteristics can be a result of the abiotic conditions in its ecosystem.

Use the following information to answer the next questions.

Coyotes
Several families of coyote (*Canis latrans*) were found to be living within the boundaries of Waterton Lakes National Park in June 2006.

4. a) Identify the three components of a population as defined by ecologists.

   b) Describe why all of the coyotes in this park might be considered a single population.

   c) Describe why all of the coyotes in this park might not be considered a single population.

   d) Choose the argument from part (b) or part (c) that you think is more reasonable, and justify your choice.

Use the following information to answer the next question.

Northern Pike
The earliest fish to spawn in spring, northern pike (or Jackfish) inhabit Great Slave Lake. They have long, spotted, greenish brown bodies, and prominent snouts. Average weights for these fish run from 2 to 7 kg, but pike weighing 13 to 18 kg have been caught by people fishing in these waters.

5. In ecological terms, explain how the northern pike found in Great Slave Lake is not only part of a population but also part of a community and part of an ecosystem.

6. An ecologist is studying the plants that are eaten by Rocky Mountain bighorn sheep. Explain why the ecologist might measure soil nutrients, such as nitrates, as part of the study.

7. Identify at least four things that affect the pattern of distribution and the range of living things.

8. Describe the biosphere.

Classifying and Naming Organisms

Section Outcomes

In this section, you will
- **explain** how organisms are classified in domains and kingdoms
- **explain** how organisms are named using a two-name system called binomial nomenclature
- **identify** species using a dichotomous key

Key Terms

taxonomy
kingdom
domain
binomial nomenclature
dichotomous key

Figure 3.10 When forestry officials such as this one go into areas to check for pests like the mountain pine beetle (*Dendroctonus ponderosae*) how do they communicate their findings to the scientific community? A simple system for identifying and naming organisms has been in development since the 1700s. It is flexible enough to accommodate the discovery of new species and is still used by biologists all over the world.

Ecologists looking for the effects of the mountain pine beetle on the lodgepole pine community, as shown in Figure 3.10, need to be able to correctly identify the trees and the insects. They also need to be able to share information about their findings with colleagues elsewhere in the province, the country, and possibly around the world. Knowledge and practices developed in one part of the world to deal with a species can be more easily communicated to others if everyone can quickly agree on the identity of the organisms under discussion. Scientists can then pool their information to learn from each other's studies and more easily adapt and adopt successful practices.

The Classification of Organisms

The challenge of identifying, classifying, and naming the organisms that make up the diversity of life on Earth has existed since humans first began to observe the environment around them. The total number of species in the world is now estimated to be somewhere between 10 and 100 *million*.

Taxonomy is the practice of classifying living things. The continual development of more sophisticated tools for observation and analysis and resulting discovery of new species or reassessment of known ones means that taxonomy remains a practice in development. As you will see, the system is changing now and will continue to do so.

Early Classification Systems

One of the earliest attempts to classify life was made by the Greek philosopher Aristotle more than 2000 years ago. At that time, people had identified about 1000 different kinds of organisms. Aristotle put these organisms into two large groups: plants and animals. He called each group a **kingdom**, and the kingdoms later became known as Kingdom Plantae and Kingdom Animalia. Aristotle further categorized the animals based on their size and the way they moved on land, in water, and in air. He divided the plants into three categories based on differences in their stems.

Aristotle's classification system had its limitations, and over time it was changed. A student of Aristotle's, for example, grouped plants according to physical characteristics such as

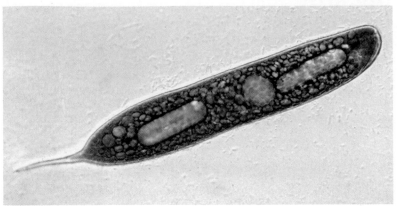

Magnification: 1220 ×

Figure 3.11 The micro-organism *Euglena* can photosynthesize like plants do, but it can also move like animals do. How would you classify this organism?

BiologyFile

FYI
Within Domain Eukarya, the greatest diversity occurs in Kingdom Protista. Protists have lived on Earth for a much longer time than plants and animals, which has given them more opportunity to diversify. Many scientists feel that Kingdom Protista should be further divided into as many as seven different kingdoms.

reproductive structures and other types of external tissues. For the most part, however, this two-category system was used until the invention of rudimentary microscopes. The discovery of micro-organisms and cells forced scientists to reconsider their criteria for classification. Some micro-organisms have methods of locomotion and consume food like animals do. Others carry out photosynthesis like plants do. Still others, such as the *Euglena* in Figure 3.11, have characteristics of both plants *and* animals. *Euglena* is just one organism that scientists were having difficulty categorizing as either a plant or an animal. The German biologist Ernst Haeckel solved this problem, at least temporarily, in 1866. He proposed classifying micro-organisms that were neither animals nor plants in a third kingdom, which he named Protista.

Classification in Transition

Discoveries after Haeckel's time led to agreement that six kingdoms should be used to sort, organize, and identify organisms. However, the scientific community is once again debating the organization of organisms and is shifting to a grouping of a number of kingdoms within three domains.

The Six Kingdoms of Life

The six kingdoms of life are Archaea, Bacteria, Protista, Fungi, Plantae, and Animalia. Both Kingdom Archaea (or Archaebacteria) and Kingdom Bacteria (or Eubacteria) consist of single-celled

organisms that lack a nucleus. The micro-organisms in Kingdom Bacteria are very diverse and can exist in a wide range of habitats. There is a special group of organisms, however, the Archaebacteria, that are capable of living in extreme environments, such as salt lakes, hot springs, and underwater thermal hot vents. As a result of advances in genetic analyses, which showed distinct differences between these species and other species of bacteria at the molecular level, biologists created a new kingdom to classify these micro-organisms during the 1990s.

All the organisms in Kingdoms Animalia, Plantae, Fungi, and Protista have cells that have nuclei and are called *eukaryotes*. These organisms can be unicellular or multicellular.

Organisms in Kingdom Protista, called protists, include both unicellular and multicellular organisms. Some protists photosynthesize (the autotrophs), while others (the heterotrophs) ingest their food. Still others obtain nutrients by decomposing and then absorbing their food much like fungi do. Protists include algae and protozoans such as *Euglena*.

Organisms in Kingdom Fungi obtain their food by secreting digestive enzymes onto their food source and then absorbing the molecules that are released by the enzymes. Fungi were once considered to be plants because they are *sessile* (do not move). Fungi do not have chloroplasts in their cells, however, and thus do not photosynthesize. There are both multicellular and unicellular fungi. Mushrooms, moulds, and yeasts are included in this kingdom.

Kingdom Plantae includes organisms that photosynthesize to make their own food. Most plants are sessile and multicellular, with relatively complex and specialized cells. Plants include mosses, ferns, coniferous trees, and flowering plants.

Organisms in Kingdom Animalia ingest their food, and most are motile. Like plants, they have complex and specialized cells. Animals include insects (such as the mountain pine beetle), mammals (such as humans), and birds.

> ⑤ Explain why fungi are placed in a different kingdom than plants.

The Three Domains of Life

Dividing living things into strict categories and groups is often very difficult, particularly as new understanding of organisms emerges. The six-kingdom system is being amended to better explain the life forms modern research has been able to distinguish. There is now a level of classification above kingdoms, called **domains**, in common use. As shown in Figure 3.12, there are three domains: Bacteria, Archaea, and Eukarya.

These domains are based on the cellular composition of organisms. As mentioned previously, bacteria and archaea are the smallest and simplest types of cells, those without a nucleus. Their two former kingdoms are now the domains Bacteria and Archaea and contain the unicellular *prokaryotes* (*pro* means before, and *karya* means nucleus). When details of the molecular biology of these organisms were compared in 1996, it was clear that there were many striking differences. In fact, these two groups of organisms are as different from one another as they are from eukaryotes (protists, fungi, animals, and plants). As a result, archaea and bacteria were distinct enough from other another to warrant their own separate domains.

This domain-based classification system allows for an expanding list of kingdoms as research continues.

The Levels of Classification

A domain is the broadest category of classification. Scientists group organisms in a domain in a hierarchical fashion, through increasingly narrow, more precise categories, down to species. All animals, for example, belong to Kingdom Animalia, but there are many different types of animals. A bird, for example is more like a bat than a dragonfly, even though they all fly. (Both birds and bats have backbones; dragonflies do not.) As well, a bat is more like a whale than a bird. (Bats and whales are both mammals.)

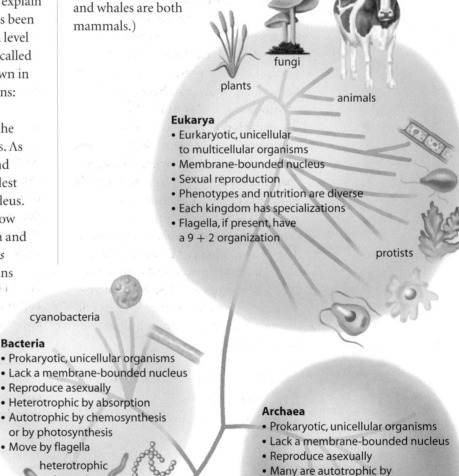

eukaryotes

fungi

plants

animals

Eukarya
- Eurkaryotic, unicellular to multicellular organisms
- Membrane-bounded nucleus
- Sexual reproduction
- Phenotypes and nutrition are diverse
- Each kingdom has specializations
- Flagella, if present, have a 9 + 2 organization

protists

cyanobacteria

Bacteria
- Prokaryotic, unicellular organisms
- Lack a membrane-bounded nucleus
- Reproduce asexually
- Heterotrophic by absorption
- Autotrophic by chemosynthesis or by photosynthesis
- Move by flagella

heterotrophic bacteria

Archaea
- Prokaryotic, unicellular organisms
- Lack a membrane-bounded nucleus
- Reproduce asexually
- Many are autotrophic by chemosynthesis; some are heterotrophic by absorption
- Unique rRNA base sequence
- Distinctive plasma membrane and cell wall chemistry

prokaryotes

common ancestor

Figure 3.12 Adoption of the three-domain system of classification has given scientists even greater flexibility when it comes to classifying Earth's diversity. The former kingdoms of Archaea and Bacteria are now each in their own domain. The kingdoms Protista, Fungi, Plantae, and Animalia are grouped in the domain of Eukarya.

Table 3.1 Hierarchical Classification for the Bobcat, *Lynx rufus*

Group	Bobcat's classification	Organisms that can be included in this group
domain	Eukarya	euglena, mushrooms, lodgepole pines, earthworm, starfish, bee, shark, horse, oyster, frog, dog, cougar, lynx, house cat, bobcat
kingdom	Animalia	earthworm, starfish, bee, shark, horse, oyster, frog, dog, cougar, lynx, house cat, bobcat
phylum	Chordata	shark, horse, frog, dog, cougar, lynx, house cat, bobcat
class	Mammalia	horse, dog, cougar, lynx, house cat, bobcat
order	Carnivora	dog, cougar, lynx, house cat, bobcat
family	Felidae	cougar, lynx, house cat, bobcat
genus	*Lynx*	lynx, bobcat
species	*rufus*	bobcat

To distinguish among groups that have similarities, Swedish biologist Carolus Linnaeus (1707–1778) subdivided each kingdom into smaller and smaller groups of more and more similar organisms by using simple physical characteristics to categorize and describe organisms. After kingdom come phylum (plural "phyla"), class, order, family, genus (plural "genera"), and species. At each level, there are more similarities among members of the group. Table 3.1 illustrates the hierarchy and the increasingly narrow groupings, using the classification for the bobcat.

Naming Systems

The scientific names of organisms are based on their classification. Early scholars also grouped similar organisms and gave each group a Latin name. For example, they called bees *Apis*. Later, when they wanted to describe a particular species, they added a series of descriptive words. A variety of naming systems were tested. In one, the European honeybee had a name with 12 descriptive words! Linnaeus used his classification system to develop a much simpler naming system. He suggested a two-name, or binomial, naming system based on the last two categories of his classification system. The first word of an organism's scientific name is the genus, and the second word

is the species. (In scientific naming, the first letter of the genus is always capitalized, but the species name is all lower case. Both the genus and species names are italicized, or when handwritten, underlined.) So, in Linaeus's system, the honeybee was *Apis mellifera*. (*Mellifera* means honey maker.)

Today, scientists still use the binomial system, called **binomial nomenclature**, devised by Linnaeus. To make the system universal, scientists agreed to use a language that is spoken by no country but forms the basis of many languages—Latin. When scientists discover and classify a new species, they give it a two-part Latin name based on its classification. (Greek root words are also often used.)

Using these two-part scientific names allows scientists from all around the world to be sure they are talking about the same species when they are communicating, regardless of whether they speak English, Spanish, or Chinese. Common names of organisms can vary from language to language, and even from region to region in a country. For example, a robin in England is an entirely different bird from a robin in Canada. In North America, the names "cougar," "panther," "puma," and "mountain lion" are all used for the same species of animal, *Puma concolor*. While the use of common names can be confusing, scientific names are universal.

Keep in mind, however, that scientific names can still change, particularly when new information is discovered. New technologies, such as DNA analysis, often lead to a more specific understanding of how various species are related. Skunks, for example, were previously categorized in a family with weasels, the Mustelidae. (*Mustela* is Latin for "weasel.") However, recent DNA analysis has shown that skunks are distinctive enough from weasels to be placed in their own family, the Mephitidae, with two species of Asian stink badger. (*Mephitis* is Latin for "foul odour.")

BiologyFile

FYI

Homo sapiens is the scientific name for human beings. The name is based on the following classification:

domain	Eukarya
kingdom	Animalia
phylum	Chordata
class	Mammalia
order	Primates
family	Hominidae
genus	Homo
species	sapiens

Dichotomous Keys

Identification keys use observable characteristics to identify organisms. **Dichotomous keys** are arranged in steps, with two statements at each step. For example, if you are trying to identify a mite, such as the one in Figure 3.13, the first step in a dichotomous key gives two choices: red and not red (see Table 3.2). To use a dichotomous key, you always begin by choosing from the first pair of descriptions and then follow through the key from there. Since this mite is red, you would then proceed to step 2 and answer the questions there. This mite is the red velvet mite in the genus *Trombidium*.

Table 3.2 A Portion of a Key to Mites and Ticks of North America

1a. body colour red, go to 2

1b. body colour not red, go to 3

2a. body without hair; body globular and somewhat elongated; red freshwater mite, *Limnochares Americana*

2b. body with dense velvety hair; body oval to rounded rectangle; velvet mite, *Trombidium* genus

3a. body length 0.5 mm or less; two-spotted spider mite, *Tetranychus uriticae*

3b. body length more than 0.5 mm, go to 4

4a. etc.

The stepped comparisons in the keys can be very detailed, as shown in these examples from a key for identifying certain insects, or, more specifically, arthropods with six legs and well-developed wings. Therefore, the

Figure 3.13 This mite is less than 1 mm in size. It has been magnified to make identification easier. What characteristics could you use to identify the genus or species of this mite?

organism in question has already been described in a general way and placed in a phylum before an attempt is made to identify the class or order, as follows:

11a. Wings held flat over abdomen when at rest, last abdominal segment not enlarged, usually found in colonies: *Isoptera* (termites)

11b. Wings not held flat over abdomen when at rest, males with the last abdominal segment enlarged like a scorpion's stinger and held over the body, not found in colonies: *Mecoptera* (scorpion flies)

14a. Sucking mouthparts in the form of a rigid beak, front wings with clear tips, overlapping at rest, revealing a triangular panel on the back: *Heteroptera* (true bugs)

14b. Chewing mouthparts, front wings without clear tips. See step 15

Detailed dichotomous keys such as this one can fill several pages, and you may need a microscope to make some of the distinctions required to make an identification. Most important, you need to be a very keen observer and be able to sketch or photograph details to assist you in the process. Having a specimen on hand to help with identification is not always possible or desirable, depending on the type of organism, its habitat, and its abundance.

In the next investigation, you will create and use your own dichotomous key.

Creating a Dichotomous Key

If you find a plant you have never seen before, how could you discover its identity? Many field guides help you match the characteristics of your specimen with those of similar organisms using a dichotomous key. As you have learned, a dichotomous key uses a series of paired comparisons to sort organisms into smaller and smaller groups. In this investigation, you will learn how to make your own dichotomous key.

Materials
- paper
- pencil
- sample dichotomous keys
- leaves and catkins or needles and cones of Alberta tree species (optional)

Procedure

1. Use this blank dichotomous key diagram as a model for your own dichotomous key. Note that your final key may not look exactly the same.

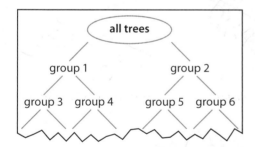

2. Study the 10 trees shown on the next page. (As an alternative, you could collect 10 or more plants from one or both of the ecosystems you chose for your field study.)

3. Select one characteristic. Sort the trees into two groups, based on whether they have this characteristic.

4. List each tree's number under either Group 1 or Group 2 on your key diagram.

5. Record the characteristic that identifies each group.

6. Select another characteristic for each subgroup, and repeat steps 4 and 5 for the next level down on your diagram.

7. Continue to subdivide the groups until you have 12 groups with one tree in each.

8. Using the characteristics in your diagram, construct a dichotomous key that someone could use to identify any tree in the given group. To do this, create a series of numbered steps, with the first step showing the first characteristic you used. At each step, offer two choices for classifying the tree based on a *single* characteristic. For example, you may have used the characteristics "have needles" as your first dividing characteristic. The first numbered step in your key would be
1a. have needles
1b. do not have needles
Use the sample keys provided by your teacher to help you.

9. Exchange keys with a partner. Use your partner's key to classify a tree, and record all the characteristics of the species you chose.

Analysis

1. Is your partner's dichotomous key identical to yours? Explain why or why not.

2. **a)** Was your partner able to use your key successfully?

   b) How could you improve your key?

3. Which characteristics of trees were not useful for creating your key? Explain why not.

Conclusion

4. Why does a key offer only two choices at each step?

Extension

5. Non-native, invasive plants in Alberta, such as spotted knapweed (*Centaurea biebersteinii*), jeopardize ecosystems by out-competing native plant species. Examples of several other invasive plant species that pose problems in Alberta are purple loosestrife (*Lythrum salicaria*), creeping bellflower (*Campanula rapunculoides*), common tansy (*Tanacetum vulgare*), reed canary grass (*Phalaris arundinacea*), and common soapwort (*Saponaria officinalis*). Research the names of other invasive plant species in the province. Choose at least five of the species you researched, and design a key to identify them.

whitebark pine (*Pinus Albicaulis*)

jack pine (*Pinus banksiana*)

lodgepole pine (*Pinus contorta*)

tamarack (*Larix laricina*)

white spruce (*Picea glauca*)

black spruce (*Picea mariana*)

subalpine fir (*Abies lasiocarpa*)

trembling aspen (*Populus tremuloides*)

balsam fir (*Abies balsamea*)

white birch (*Betula papyrifera*)

Section 3.2 Summary

- Organisms are sorted into a hierarchical system, starting with the broadest categories, domain and kingdom, and ending with the most specific category, species. The common classification levels are domain, kingdom, phylum, class, order, family, genus, and species.
- The classification system that is most commonly used today has three domains and a number of kingdoms. This system has been different in the past and may be different in the future.
- The three domains used to classify organisms are: Bacteria, Archaea, and Eukarya.
- The four kingdoms within the domain of Eukarya are: Protista, Fungi, Plantae, and Animalia.
- Scientists use binomial nomenclature to name organisms. The two-part scientific names use mostly Latin words and include the organism's genus and species.
- A dichotomous key is a branched or stepped process that can be used to identify organisms.

Section 3.2 Review

1. Explain why the categories into which organisms are grouped have changed over the past 2000 years, and why they will likely continue to change in the future.

2. Define the term taxonomy.

Use the following information to answer the next question.

3. Early scientists may have grouped the three animals shown above into a category called "flying animals." Use these three animals to explain why this category would not be particularly useful to biologists.

4. Use spreadsheet software to create a chart summarizing the main characteristics of the kingdoms of life identified in this textbook. Be sure to include an example of an organism found in each kingdom. **ICT**

5. a) Use the information in the dichotomous key shown opposite to classify the seven organisms pictured.

   b) List the steps that you used in this key to explain how you determined that the lamprey eel is classified in the Class Agnatha.

6. Why is it useful and logical for all scientists to use the same system of classification?

Use the following information to answer the previous question.

Dichotomous Key to Classes of the Subphylum Vertebrata

Squirrel   Tufted Puffin   Lamprey Eel

Trout   Shark

Snake   Frog

1a.	Hair present . . . . Class Mammalia
1b.	Hair absent . . . . go to 2
2a.	Feathers present . . . . Class Aves
2b.	Feathers absent . . . . go to 3
3a.	Jaws present . . . . go to 4
3b.	Jaws absent . . . . Class Agnatha
4a.	Paired fins present . . . . go to 5
4b.	Paired fins absent . . . . go to 6
5a.	Skeleton bony . . . . Class Osteichthyes
5b.	Skeleton cartilagenous . . . . Class Chondrichthyes
6a.	Skin scales present . . . . Class Reptilia
6b.	Skin scales absent . . . . Class Amphibia

Studying Organisms in Ecosystems

Section Outcomes

In this section, you will
- **identify** abiotic and biotic characteristics, and **explain** how they affect ecosystems
- **explain** how ecosystems support a diversity of organisms because of a variety of niches and habitats
- **explain** how limiting factors can affect the distribution and size of a population of organisms
- **design** an investigation to study a local ecosystem
- **research** the impacts of an introduced species in western Canada
- **explain** the use of sampling techniques, such as quadrats and transects
- **investigate** and **study** a local ecosystem

Key Terms

climate
biome
habitat
range
ecological niche
biodiversity
limiting factor
samples
transect
quadrat
density

Figure 3.14 How do you think the variety of life in the Badlands of Alberta compares with the variety of life in a tropical rainforest? Life is not uniformly distributed throughout the biosphere. Abiotic factors, such as temperature and the availability of water, can result in a "patchy" distribution of organisms.

At first glance, the Alberta Badlands seem to be an inhospitable environment (see Figure 3.14). What could possibly live there? Yet this environment is home to many populations, including eagles, hawks, ground squirrels, rattlesnakes, scorpions, and hardy plants, such as cactus, that can thrive in the dry conditions and the extremes in temperature from hot, dry days to cold, clear nights. The diversity of life in the Badlands differs from the diversity in nearby river valleys and from the diversity in northern Alberta spruce forests.

Life on Earth is not evenly distributed. As noted in Section 3.1, the patterns of distribution of life are, in large part, due to abiotic factors. Most organisms either directly or indirectly obtain their energy from sunlight. As well, each requires certain levels of abiotic conditions such as temperature, humidity, salinity (saltiness), and moisture. Organisms can tolerate fluctuations in these levels but only within a range, and there is always a level that is best for the organism. It is the abiotic factors that affect the distribution of Earth's organisms.

Climate and Biomes

You learned in your previous science courses that **climate** refers to the average weather conditions in a particular region over a period of time, usually 30 years or more. Climate is determined by temperature and rainfall, which, in turn, result from the unequal heating of Earth and other factors, such as local geography, snow and ice cover, and the proximity of large bodies of water.

You may recall that the unequal heating of Earth's atmosphere, shown in Figure 3.15, causes Earth's major climate zones from the tropics near the equator, through the temperate zones, to the cold

Figure 3.15 Because Earth is spherical, sunlight strikes it unevenly. The most intense rays strike near the equator. The sunlight that reaches the Poles is spread over a wider area (and, thus, is more diffuse).

Terrestrial Biomes According to Temperature and Precipitation

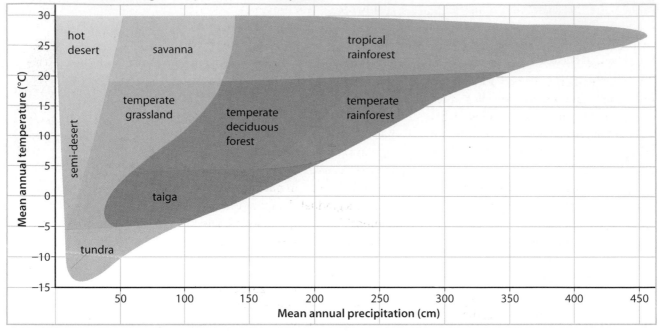

Figure 3.16 Distinctive patterns become apparent when terrestrial biomes are plotted according to mean annual temperature and precipitation. How could you use this graph to predict the distribution of Earth's biomes?

regions near the North and South Poles. The unequal heating of the atmosphere sets up conditions that produce global air and water movements (trade winds and ocean currents) that interact with physical features (mountains, islands, and lakes) to produce various patterns of rainfall. As a result, some areas of the world are quite dry, while others are very wet.

The pattern of precipitation influences the type of soil that forms in different regions. These two factors in combination with other factors, such as topography, altitude, latitude, and temperature, determine the types and abundance of plants and other photosynthetic organisms that can

survive. The photosynthetic organisms, in turn, determine the variety and population sizes of animals, fungi, and other non-photosynthetic species that inhabit the area.

It is possible to identify some very general types of large ecosystems, or groups of ecosystems, called **biomes** in specific regions on Earth. A biome, as you may recall from previous studies, has a particular mix of plants, animals, and other organisms that are adapted to living under certain environmental conditions.

When terrestrial biomes are plotted according to their mean annual temperature and mean annual precipitation, as in Figure 3.16, you can

Figure 3.17 Latitude **(A)** affects the distribution of biomes on Earth. Altitude (elevation) **(B)** has a similar effect in a more local area.

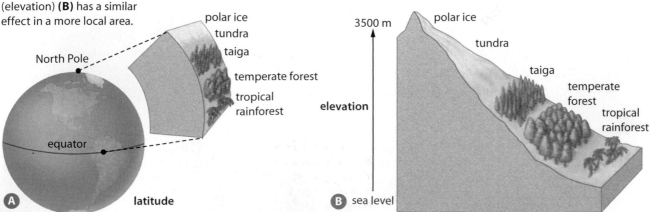

see that particular patterns result. Most notably, the abundance of terrestrial life increases as the temperature and amount of precipitation increase. An increase in temperature *or* precipitation will usually also result in increased abundance of organisms but not to the same degree as an increase in both factors (and not when it becomes too hot). Thus, the distribution of organisms is directly related to abiotic conditions in the biome.

Since changes in temperature vary not only with latitude but also with altitude (elevation), you might anticipate distinctive regional biome patterns similar to those in Figure 3.17A. However, because precipitation, which can be affected by a mountain, plays such a vital role in determining the characteristics of an area, you often find a grassland region at the base of a mountain, rather than a forest as shown in Figure 3.17B.

Figure 3.18 shows the distribution of Earth's terrestrial biomes by latitude and includes some finer distinctions than those shown in Figure 3.16. Each terrestrial biome is characterized by communities of species with similar adaptations to that particular combination of physical conditions. There are also aquatic biomes, which include lakes, rivers, estuaries (where rivers flow into an ocean), coral reefs, intertidal zones (where an ocean meets the land), open ocean, and deep sea. It is important to note that at the edges of biomes, there is a gradual transition from one biome to the next. So, for example, where the taiga meets the tundra in northern Canada, there is a gradual change in the composition of plants and animals, not an abrupt change.

• • •

7 On the map in Figure 3.18, identify the biome(s) found in Alberta. What are the limitations of dividing Earth into broad biomes?

• • •

Habitats

Within a biome, there can be a tremendous amount of variation. For example, the taiga biome (also referred

BiologyFile

Web Link
Choose one biome to investigate further. What are the distinctive features of its climate, geography, and soil? Which plants and animals are present in this biome that would be absent from other biomes? Why?

www.albertabiology.ca
WWW

Figure 3.18 The distribution of Earth's major biomes. The same type of biome can occur in different regions in the world, but usually at similar latitudes.

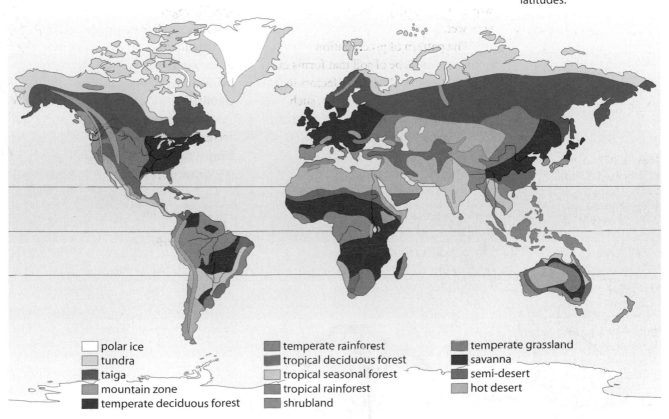

polar ice
tundra
taiga
mountain zone
temperate deciduous forest

temperate rainforest
tropical deciduous forest
tropical seasonal forest
tropical rainforest
shrubland

temperate grassland
savanna
semi-desert
hot desert

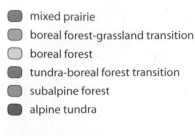
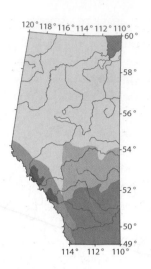

Figure 3.19 Different types of soil and other abiotic features, such as temperature, result in different vegetation zones in Alberta latitudes.

to as the northern coniferous forest or the boreal forest) covers a major part of central and northern Canada, Europe, and Asia. The taiga can vary widely, however, from north to south and from east to west. So, even though these areas are all considered to be part of the taiga, the density of the forests and the types of trees within these forests can vary. Figure 3.19, for example, shows the vegetation zones within Alberta. Even though most of the province is broadly identified as taiga in Figure 3.18, vegetation zones in the province may be further classified into the zones shown in Figure 3.19.

Within biomes and vegetation zones are different habitats, each with its own set of organisms and abiotic conditions. A **habitat** is a place or area with a particular set of characteristics, both biotic and abiotic. Each species is found in the specific habitat that its physical, physiological,

and behavioural adaptations equip it to survive and reproduce in.

Sometimes, all members of a species live in the same general type of habitat. The habitat may be spread over a single large area or be found in a number of separate locations. Hoary marmots (see Figure 3.20), for example, live in the alpine and subalpine areas of mountains in western Canada. There may be groups of marmots separated by large distances, but all members of this species live in similar habitats.

The **range** of a population or species is defined as the geographical area where the population or species is found. The limit of a species' range is generally determined by its habitat requirements. The species will only be found where its habitat is present. This is determined by environmental variables, including both abiotic factors (such as temperature and rainfall) and biotic factors (such as type of food). The range of the hoary marmot is shown in Figure 3.21. Note that the hoary marmot does not live *throughout* this range, but only in its particular habitat *within* this range.

• • •

Q 8 Distinguish between a species' habitat and range.

• • •

Figure 3.20 The habitat of the hoary marmot (*Marmota caligata*) is the alpine and subalpine areas of northwestern North America. Its diet includes grasses, wildflowers, and other plants found in high-altitude meadows.

Figure 3.21 The range of the hoary marmot: Identify three reasons why the hoary marmot is not found outside this range.

Ecological Niche

Members of different species can share the same range and even the same habitat, or at least show considerable overlap in the types of habitats they prefer. This is possible because they have different ecological niches. The **ecological niche** of a species is the role that its members play in a community and the total range of biotic and abiotic requirements that its members need in order to survive. For example, the ecological niche of the northern long-eared bat shown in Figure 3.22 includes the temperature range it tolerates, the type of boreal forest trees on which it roosts, and the size and type of insects it eats.

You could think of a population's habitat as its street address, and its ecological niche as its job in the community. Two species can share the same habitat because they have different ecological niches. The bat in question, or even two species of warbler, for instance, can co-exist within a habitat because they may nest in different types of trees or feed on different insects. Trouble arises, as in the case of a mountain pine beetle infestation, when one species' niche affects (in this case, destroys) the habitat of others.

• • •

9 Assume that a species of animal has a very restricted diet; it eats only two species of plants. Using the word "niche" in your answer, explain why this species may have a higher probability of becoming endangered than a species that eats ten species of plants.

• • •

Habitats and Niches within Ecosystems

Within an ecosystem, differing biotic and abiotic characteristics result in a variety of habitats and niches. In an aquatic ecosystem such as a lake, for example, there is vertical stratification, or layering, of water caused by different physical and chemical conditions, such as different amounts of light and nutrients. In the upper layers of a lake, there is sufficient light for photosynthesis. Water temperatures also vary within layers of a lake. Generally, the upper layers are warmer due to solar radiation, while the deeper layers are colder.

Each species in a lake occupies a niche that it requires for its survival. The individuals that photosynthesize and absorb nutrients from the water, as some algae do, inhabit the warmer, brighter surface water, as do the organisms that consume them. Other photosynthetic aquatic species may need to be rooted into the bottom sediments in the zone that is closest to the shore. Animals may swim through the water or crawl along the bottom sediments. Figure 3.23 on the next page shows the different zones in a lake, and how they differ depending on the depth of water (thus, light penetration and temperature) and their distance from shore (thus, habitat for organisms that can float or swim and those that are bottom-dwellers).

A similar diversity of habitat and niches occurs in terrestrial communities. In a forest, for example, soils with differing mineral and moisture content support different plants. These plants, in turn, provide food and habitat for different animals. The variety of habitats and niches, and thus the variety, or

Figure 3.22 The range of the northern long-eared bat (*Myotis septentrionalis*) extends across much of Canada. Alberta's populations of this species are found mainly in boreal forest, from Edmonton to Wood Buffalo National Park in the extreme north of the province.

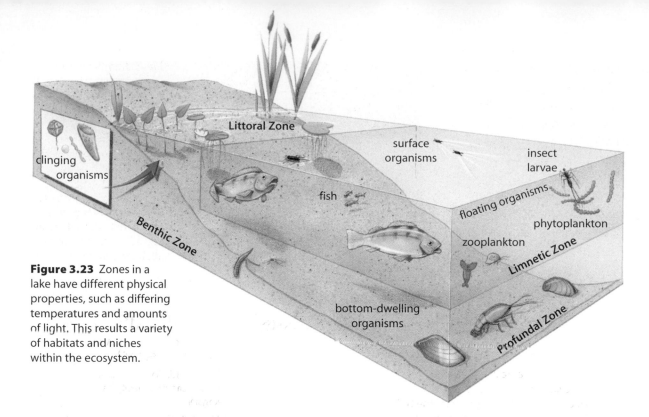

Figure 3.23 Zones in a lake have different physical properties, such as differing temperatures and amounts of light. This results a variety of habitats and niches within the ecosystem.

Labels in figure: Littoral Zone, clinging organisms, Benthic Zone, fish, surface organisms, insect larvae, floating organisms, phytoplankton, zooplankton, Limnetic Zone, bottom-dwelling organisms, Profundal Zone

BiologyFile

Web Link
Alberta has been divided into *ecoregions*, which are determined by abiotic and biotic components, such as climate, geography, vegetation, soil type, and fauna. In which ecoregion do you live? What are its main abiotic and biotic characteristics?

www.albertabiology.ca
WWW

biodiversity, of species, can vary widely in different areas depending on the specific abiotic and biotic components. Examine the photographs in Figure 3.24. Figure 3.24A shows a forest that has been harvested and replanted with only one species of tree, the white spruce (*Picea glauca*). Figure 3.24B is a mixed forest, with a greater diversity of tree species. The diversity of species results in a diversity of habitats and niches as well. In the Thought Lab opposite, you will analyze data that compare the diversity of bird species in a forest dominated by one tree species with a mixed forest.

Factors Limiting Growth in Ecosystems

Trembling aspen, such as those in Figure 3.25, are fast growing. Their range includes much of Canada, yet they do not live everywhere. There are places with large stands of trembling aspen, places where trembling aspen grow more sparsely, interspersed with other plants, and places where trembling aspen are absent. The bacteria in Figure 3.26 on page 100 could, in theory, reproduce exponentially without limits. If this were possible, after 20 hours there would be

Figure 3.24 How would the variety of habitats and niches differ between a forest that has been harvested and replanted with a single species of tree, known as a monoculture **(A)**, and a forest with a variety of tree species **(B)**?

1.1×10^{12} individuals. Within four days, the mass of the bacterial population would be greater than the mass of Earth! Clearly this does not happen. There are no bacterial populations that large on Earth, despite the fact that both the growth rate and the generation time in this example are plausible. Populations cannot grow in an unlimited fashion for a sustained period of time. (Some can for a shorter period of time, however.) The growth, survival, and distribution of

Figure 3.25 Trembling aspen (*Populus tremuloides*) reproduce fairly quickly through a process called vegetative reproduction. The shoots that spread widely from the trees' roots produce new trees that are essentially clones of the parent tree. If these plants are so fast-growing, why are they not everywhere in Alberta? What conditions limit their growth?

Thought Lab | 3.2 | Forest Habitat and Bird Biodiversity

Target Skills

Analyzing data to look for patterns between and among variables

Evaluating the impact of human activities on the biodiversity of an ecosystem

How will communities of birds vary between a forest dominated by one tree species (a pure stand) and a forest with a variety of tree species (a mixed stand)? This is a question that two biologists—Erin Bayne from the University of Alberta and Keith Hobson from the University of Saskatchewan—examined in a study in Saskatchewan. What they learned can be used to predict how future changes to boreal forests, particularly logging practices, might impact species of birds.

In their study, Bayne and Hobson set up "count stations" in stands of black spruce, jack pine, aspen, and white spruce. They had stations in pure stands and in mixed stands. For example, for black spruce, they had study areas where over 75% of the canopy (the "top" of the forest) was dominated by black spruce (pure stands) and study areas where more than 25% of the canopy was dominated by black spruce and one or two other tree species (mixed stands). They used the following protocols (procedural rules) in their study:

- All count stations were at least 250 m apart.
- All count stations were at least 100 m from the "edge" of the study area.
- All birds that were heard or seen during a 10 min early-morning count were recorded.
- Observers were tested beforehand to ensure that they had similar levels of expertise at identifying birds.
- Counts were taken twice, in early and late June.
- Observers counted at each station only once; for the second survey, a different observer was used.

In this Thought Lab, you will interpret some of Bayne and Hobson's results, given in the following table.

Procedure

Examine the data in the table. Compare species richness and abundance in the eight sample sites. *Species richness* is the number of species. *Abundance* is the actual number of individual birds.

Analysis

1. In this study, what did the researchers find out about the species richness and abundance of bird communities when they compared stands of trees with just a single tree species (pure stands) with stands with a variety of tree species (mixed stands)?

2. Based on your understanding of habitats and niches, explain the researchers' results.

3. Choose three of the protocols that the researchers used. Explain why each protocol resulted in a more accurate survey.

4. How might a study such as this be helpful when planning how and where to harvest trees and what to replant?

5. When fire burns through a forest on a regular basis, it burns in patches, rather than in a devastating way that destroys the entire forest. How does this type of periodic forest fire result in a diversity of habitats in a forest?

Comparing Species Richness and Abundance in Pure and Mixed Stands of Trees

Species of tree	black spruce		jack pine		trembling aspen		white spruce	
Type of stand	pure	mixed	pure	mixed	pure	mixed	pure	mixed
Species richness	13	15	11	18	18	24	20	23
Abundance	56	60	39	90	76	91	71	94

(Adapted from: Hobson and Bayne, 2000, Breeding Bird Communities in Boreal Forests of Western Canada)

populations are controlled by **limiting factors**—abiotic and biotic conditions that limit the number of individuals in a population.

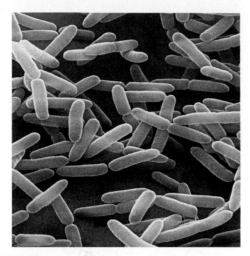

Figure 3.26 Populations of microscopic bacteria such as those shown in this micrograph grow very quickly. What finally causes a population to stop growing?

Abiotic Limiting Factors

The abiotic components of an ecosystem limit the distribution and size of the populations that live there. Plants, for example, have an optimum set of abiotic requirements, including soil type, moisture and humidity levels, and temperature range. Their populations are controlled by these abiotic requirements. Gardeners, farmers, and foresters must keep in mind the abiotic factors that limit plant growth. They must ensure that their plants have the proper soil conditions, as well as the appropriate temperature and moisture for optimum growth. If conditions change, resulting in severe hot or cold, drought or flood, or

---

INVESTIGATION 3.C

Target Skills

Defining and **delimiting** ideas to assist in planning a field study

Gathering and **recording** data and information

Preparing for Your Field Study

In this investigation, you will continue to prepare for your field study at the end of this chapter. You will determine some of the abiotic components of the ecosystems you chose for your field study. Your team will select the tools you will need for your field study. The group will also begin to assign tasks required to prepare for the field study.

Materials

Library resources or Internet access (optional)

Procedure

1. Using print or Internet resources, research some of the abiotic components of the ecosystems you will be investigating, such as climate, soil types, topography, hours of sunlight, and annual temperature and precipitation. **ICT**

2. As a group, brainstorm three abiotic features of your ecosystems and tools you might use to measure them. For example, what tools will you need to measure soil and air temperature, moisture content in soil, or the depth that light penetrates into a pond? What other tools might aid in your study? (**Hint:** How will the team identify the organisms found in your field study? How will the team record what you see and the data you obtain?)

Analysis

1. **a)** How do the tools you use to gather information about an ecosystem affect the accuracy or precision of your measurements? For example, how does gathering information on soil moisture content from an Internet database or map compare with completing the measurements yourself? (Refer to Appendix A to review the distinction between scientific accuracy and precision.)

   b) What are two advantages and two disadvantages of each tool?

2. Is it precise enough to measure an abiotic factor at only one location in an ecosystem? Explain your answer.

3. How will you obtain the tools you have selected? Which members of the team will be responsible for using the various tools?

Extension

4. Contact a field biologist at a local university or forestry department office to find out what tools they use when conducting a field study.

---

depletion of nutrients, then plant growth will be compromised.

Figure 3.27 shows cottonwoods that grow along the banks of the Oldman River in southwestern Alberta. Periodic flooding of the riverbanks is a natural feature of the cottonwood's environment. These trees are adapted to survive flooded conditions for one to two months. The increased moisture, timed with the growth of young cottonwood seedlings, is a critical part of the life cycle of this tree. Cottonwood populations are now suffering poor growth, and in some cases no growth, because of changes in water levels and flow patterns in rivers that have been dammed.

• • •

 10 Describe two abiotic limiting factors that could limit the growth of a greenhouse full of tomatoes.

• • •

Biotic Limiting Factors

A population may grow rapidly, then level off—it no longer increases in size but remains fairly constant. (Births roughly equal deaths in the population.) What factors cause the growth of a population to slow? Several biotic factors, including competition for resources, predators, and parasites, play a role.

Competition Limits Populations

The size of a population can be limited by the availability of resources, such as food. For example, when a population reaches a point where there is no longer an abundance of food for each member of the population, the members must compete with each other for the limited food supply. At this point, the number of births decreases or the number of deaths increases (or both), and population growth slows. In this type of competition, called *intraspecific competition*, members of the same population compete with each other for the limited resource.

Members of a population may not only compete for food, however. They may also compete for other resources, including water, sunlight, soil nutrients, shelter, mates, and breeding sites. Regardless of the resource, the result of the competition is always the same—a reduction in the population's growth rate.

Competition can also occur between two or more populations. For example, two species with similar niches may compete with each other for food, water, or other resources found in the habitat. In some cases, one species will eventually out-compete the other, and the "losing" species will disappear from the area. A result like this may indicate that the interacting species had very similar ecological niches, although other factors are often involved. The bull trout (see Figure 3.28 on the next page) has been out-competed, throughout much of its range in Alberta, by other trout species, including brook and brown trout, which were introduced into habitats where they do not commonly occur. Learn more about the effects of introduced species in the next Thought Lab.

Sometimes, two species may have similar, but not completely overlapping, niches. Both species can live in a particular area, although the density of

Figure 3.27 Periodic flooding is necessary to sustain cottonwood populations that grow on the banks of the Oldman River. Dams on the river have changed river levels and have interrupted the seasonal flooding, which is needed for the survival of cottonwood seedlings.

BiologyFile

FYI
The loss of cottonwood forests affects abiotic and biotic parts of the riparian (riverside) habitat. Cottonwood trees moderate water temperatures and supply carbon and other nutrients to the river habitat as their leaves and branches decompose. They provide a habitat for a variety of insects, birds, and small mammals. As well, their roots anchor the soil and reduce erosion during floods. Fallen trees provide a river habitat for trout and food for aquatic insects. Even standing dead trees provide an important habitat. These snags, as the dead trees are called, are used by birds that nest in holes or cavities.

Figure 3.28 Native to much of Alberta and western North America, bull trout (*Salvelinus confluentus*) are actually a species of char, not trout. Competition with introduced species, such as brook trout (*Salvelinus fontinalis*) and brown trout (*Salmo trutta*), for food and other resources has contributed to the decline of this species. Other significant limiting factors include habitat loss and overfishing.

one or more populations may be lowered by the presence of the other species. For example, the barnacles in Figure 3.29 have similar niches. If only one species

were present on the rocky shore, it would likely inhabit the entire area that the two species share. Their differences are enough, however, for both to occupy the same habitat.

Predators Limit Populations

Predation is a biotic interaction that involves the consumption of one organism by another. In this type of interaction, the consumer organism is referred to as a predator and the consumed organism is called prey. This type of biotic interaction includes the grazing of grasses by a horse and other herbivores as much as it does the capturing and eating of a rabbit by a coyote and other carnivores.

The relationships between predators and their prey can have a significant

---

Thought Lab 3.3 Super Competitor: Knapweed

Many species have been introduced to North America, either intentionally or unintentionally. For example, most of the food crops grown in Canada are introduced species that were intentionally cultivated for human benefit. Some species that are introduced, usually accidentally, become invasive and have a serious impact on native ecosystems. One of these invaders, spotted knapweed (*Centaurea biebersteinii*), was introduced into North America from Europe in the late 1800s.

Hectares of spotted knapweed in British Columbia, 1958–2000

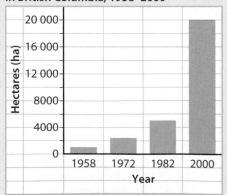

Procedure

Investigate the biology of spotted knapweed. Specifically, find out how it reproduces, what animals eat it, how it was introduced into North America, and how it is spread.

Analysis

1. Study the graph opposite.

   a) Describe what has happened to the population of spotted knapweed since its arrival in British Columbia.

   b) Predict the number of hectares that will be covered by spotted knapweed in 2020. Explain your prediction.

2. Explain why some introduced species can become so invasive and damaging to native species and ecosystems.

3. Why is spotted knapweed not a pest in its native habitat in Europe?

4. **a)** Populations of spotted knapweed are present in Alberta. How could spotted knapweed be spread throughout the province?

   b) Predict how this might affect:

   i) farming and ranching   **ii)** native ecosystems

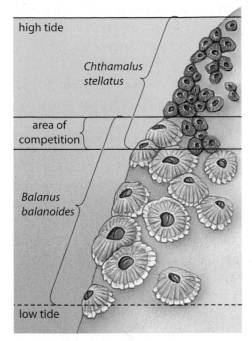

Figure 3.29 The two species of ocean barnacles, *Chthamalus stellatus* and *Balanus balanoides*, have similar niches. Although they compete for space and other resources, there are sufficient differences in their ecological niches for both to establish viable populations at different depths of the rocky shore.

impact on communities. A striking example occurred in the Aleutian Islands, a chain of volcanic islands west of Alaska. In the mid-1700s, fur traders introduced Arctic foxes to nearly 200 islands. (See Figure 3.30.) Native populations of seabirds, many of which nested on the ground, were easy targets for the invading predators. Within 50 years, Aleut (Aboriginal people of the Aleutians) hunters reported a noticeable decline in seabird populations. By the early 1900s, populations of the Aleutian Canada goose were so reduced that the bird was on the brink of extinction.

The ecological impact of the foxes, however, was not limited to this loss. Prior to the introduction of the foxes, the islands supported the growth of dense grasslands. Seabird droppings (guano) fertilized the otherwise nutrient-poor volcanic soils of the islands, allowing for this lush growth. As the numbers of birds dwindled, so did the supply of guano. By the early 1900s, fox-inhabited islands had become transformed from grassland to tundra. With the removal of foxes from many of the islands, which occurred during the latter-half of the twentieth century, seabird populations—including those of the Aleutian Canada goose—are recovering, as are their grassland habitats.

• • •

11 Identify and explain the limiting effects of introducing Arctic foxes to the Aleutian islands.

• • •

Parasites Limit Populations

Parasitism is an interaction in which one organism (the *parasite*) derives its nourishment from another organism (the *host*), which is harmed in some way. Parasitism is similar to predation because one organism benefits from the interaction and the other organism does not. In parasitism, however, the host is not always permanently harmed or entirely consumed.

An increase in the density of the host population makes it possible for the parasites to increase in number. The increased number of parasites decreases the hosts' ability to survive or reproduce, and may lead to a decrease in the density of the host population. This can result in fluctuations of parasite and host, similar to the cycles of predator and prey.

Figure 3.30 Although Arctic foxes (*Alopex lagopus*) commonly inhabit northern Canada and regions of the Arctic Circle, their residence on the Aleutian islands near Alaska occurred as a result of human, rather than natural, action.

The Smeetons and the Swift Fox

Things were not looking good for the swift fox (*Vulpes velox*) in 1978. Once a common resident of the short- and mixed-grass prairie, ranging north to south from central Alberta to northern Texas, it had just been declared extirpated by the Canadian government. (An extirpated species is extinct in one geographical area but may be present elsewhere.) Habitat fragmentation, due to conversion of native prairie into agricultural land, had contributed to its decline. Luckily for North America's smallest canid, Miles and Beryl Smeeton were on its side.

A Not-So-Swift but Steady Recovery

In 1971, Miles and Beryl Smeeton, renowned outdoor adventurers and authors, founded the Wildlife Reserve of Western Canada, now the Cochrane Ecological Institute (CEI). A year later, they established the world's first and only captive breeding colony of swift fox, bred solely for re-introduction into their historic range in Canada. After starting out with six pairs of foxes imported from the United States, the Smeetons signed an agreement with the University of Calgary to develop and initiate a re-introduction program. The Smeetons were promised help, as well, from the Canadian Wildlife Service and the Calgary Zoo.

The first captive-reared foxes were released in southern Alberta in 1983. Initially, the "soft release" method was used: pairs of foxes were penned and fed over the winter, allowing them to become oriented to their release area, and then released in the spring. Later, the "hard" method was also used: foxes were dispersed directly into the wild with minimal holding time. Between 1983 and 1997, over 800 captive-bred foxes were re-introduced in Alberta and Saskatchewan.

Despite continued threats of coyote predation and habitat fragmentation, researchers now estimate the population of swift fox in Alberta and Saskatchewan to be about 656 foxes, based on a census taken in 2000−2001. This is almost triple the estimate since the last census taken in 1996−1997, and a sign that a self-sustaining wild population has gained a foothold. In 1998, the swift fox was downlisted from extirpated to endangered in Canada.

The Return of the Senopah

In 1998, with a proven record in swift fox re-introduction, the CEI embarked on a five-year partnership with the Blackfeet Nation in Montana to re-introduce the swift fox, or "Senopah" as it is known to the Blackfeet. The Senopah has great spiritual significance for the Blackfeet, but it had been declared extirpated in Montana in 1969.

The CEI, now run by Miles and Beryl's daughter Clio, provided the foxes for the re-introduction. The Blackfeet Tribal Fish and Wildlife Department provided the land and assisted with the re-introduction, along with help from the conservation group Defenders of Wildlife.

In the first year, 30 captive-bred juveniles were released, with annual translocations to follow. By 2002, 10 dens with kits had been documented, and the population has continued toward the goal of self-sustainability. A similar re-introduction of swift foxes onto Blood (Kainai) tribal lands in southwestern Alberta began in 2005.

• • •

1. Evaluate the following point of view: "Why should we worry about preserving endangered species? After all, extinction is natural—species have been dying out for millions of years."

2. In addition to the swift fox, Alberta's Wildlife Act lists 12 other species as being threatened or endangered in Alberta. What are the species? What are the penalties for hunting, trapping, or trafficking in endangered species?

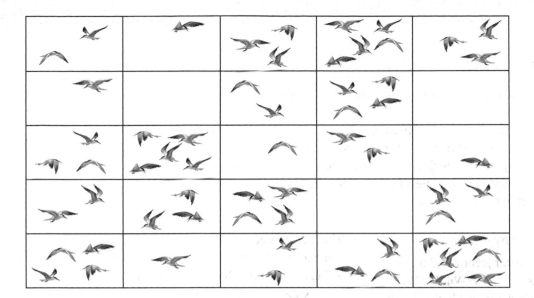

Figure 3.31 Examine a random sample of five of these 25 quadrats. Based on your sample, what is the average number of birds per quadrat? How many birds do you estimate are in this flock?

Sampling Populations in Ecosystems

If you were asked to sample a population of insects, or plants, or salamanders in an ecosystem in order to determine population size, how would you go about it? Some populations may be small enough for you to count every individual. This technique is not easy and it is not commonly done, although governments regularly conduct a count, or census, of their human populations.

Usually, however, a census is too time-consuming, expensive, or impractical to conduct. Instead, ecologists estimate the size of a population. There are a variety of ways to do this. The most common way is to count or estimate the number of individuals in a number of **samples** (small portions or subsets of the entire population) and then calculate the average. The results are then applied, or extrapolated, to the entire area occupied by the population, as shown in Figure 3.31.

Estimating Numbers Using Transects or Quadrats

In some sample areas, organisms are sampled along a **transect**, which is a very long rectangle. In transect sampling, a starting point and direction are randomly chosen, and a line of a certain length (for example, 100 m) is marked out. The occurrence of any individual within a certain distance of the line is recorded. The distance from the line might be 1 m if plants are being sampled, or perhaps 50 m if mobile organisms (such as birds or mammals) are being studied. A sample transect is shown in Figure 3.32.

For plants and other organisms that tend to stay in one spot all their lives (such as marine life growing on a rocky shoreline), ecologists generally use **quadrats** to sample a given population. First, several locations are randomly chosen within the study area, and at every location a quadrat of the same size (for example, 1 m^2) is marked out. Next, the number of individuals of a species within the quadrat is counted, or the number of individuals of each of several species is counted if more than one population is being studied.

Figure 3.32 In this study area, you would count individuals of one species within 5 m of a 100 m long transect.

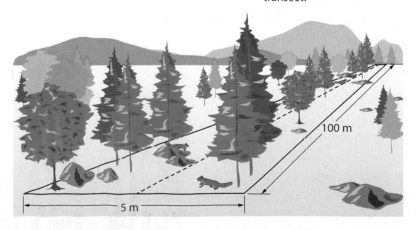

100 m

5 m

The **density** (the number of individuals per unit of volume or area) of the population is determined by calculating the average number of individuals per quadrat, and then dividing by the size of the quadrat. The size of the population can then be estimated by extrapolating from the density (for example, 2.5 individuals per m^2) to the entire study area. For example, if the study area is 1000 m^2, then the population size is roughly 2500 individuals.

This kind of information is collected by groups such as the staff at the Canadian Forest Services, who record data about species in particular areas. Information includes where and when the species are found and how they interact with the rest of the habitat and is used to identify areas that could be unique, as well as to monitor change in ecosystems over time.

Similar methods are used in studies of aquatic ecosystems to estimate the sizes of various populations. Often, water columns, samples of a known volume of water, are collected. The water is then passed through a net or sieve, and the number of organisms in each sample is counted. As with quadrats, the average density (number of individuals per unit volume) can be used to estimate the size of the population contained in the entire body of water.

When using any sampling technique, it is important to take *random* samples—that is, samples in which all of the individuals in the population have an equal chance of being represented. In Investigation 3.D, you will try one, or both, of these techniques to sample populations in your ecosystem field study.

INVESTIGATION | 3.D

Target Skills

Performing a field study to observe and measure abiotic and biotic characteristics of ecosystems

Applying classification and binomial nomenclature in a practical context

Analyzing the interactions and connections of abiotic and biotic characteristics within investigated ecosystems

Evaluating the accuracy and reliability of measuring instruments used, and identifying the degree of error they introduce

Working cooperatively to collect and share data and ideas

An Ecosystem Field Study

You have been preparing for your field study throughout this chapter. In this investigation, you will sample and compare study sites from the two similar ecosystems you chose in Thought Lab 3.1. You will use the tools you chose in Investigation 3.C to help you gather information about the biotic and abiotic components of these ecosystems.

Question

How can you determine, qualitatively and quantitatively, the interrelationships between the abiotic and biotic components of ecosystems?

Safety Precautions

- Wear gloves if you are handling soil or water samples.
- Wash your hands thoroughly after your field study.

- Minimize your impact on organisms and their habitat as much as possible. Collect representative sample specimens of plants and animals only if absolutely necessary for identification. Use sketches or digital photos, if possible.

- If you disturb a habitat (by digging a hole, for example), return the habitat as close as possible to its original condition.

Materials

- tent pegs
- string
- Hula Hoops™ (optional)
- selected tools and materials approved by your teacher
- field guides

Experimental Plan

1. With your group, and using the suggested materials as a starting point, develop a plan for investigating the two study sites you chose in Thought Lab 3.1. Half of your group should study one site, and the other half should study the second site. You want to be able to compare the diversity of life in the two sites. Use the string and tent pegs (or Hula Hoops™) for transects or quadrats. In your study, you must:

   - include information about the abiotic features of your study site
   - determine the two or three dominant plant(s) of your study site
   - provide an overview of the species present in your study site, including an estimation of the number of species and their populations. (If necessary, in order to identify the species of each organism, plan to draw a sketch or take a photo of Plant 1, Plant 2, Animal 1, Animal 2, and so on, and use library or Internet resources to identify them when you come back from the field.) **ICT**
   - use classification systems and naming systems
   - take a sample (or samples) to estimate the populations of the organisms in your study site

2. Develop a data table that you will use to collect data at your study site.

3. Develop a plan to ensure the safety of your group as well as the safety of the organisms in your study area.

4. Have your plan approved by your teacher.

Data and Observations

Conduct your field study and record your results.

Analysis

1. Prepare a report detailing the abiotic and biotic components of your ecosystem. Include the following information:

   - location and size of your study area
   - the history of the area (for example, how long it has remained undisturbed or how recently it was developed)
   - the methods and tools you used in your field study
   - the abiotic components of your study area, including both qualitative and quantitative observations
   - the biotic components of your study area, including plant and animal species (common and scientific names) and, for at least two species, a description of their ecological niche in this ecosystem

Conclusions

2. Why was it important to choose sample areas randomly?

3. Why was it important to sample more than one area in your field study?

4. What are some limiting factors that might affect species in your study site?

5. a) Write a description comparing the diversity and abundance of species in the two study sites.

   b) Describe how the ecosystems of the two study sites are similar.

   c) Describe how they are different.

6. How have humans changed either of the ecosystems of the sites you studied?

7. Describe the tools and materials your team chose in terms of usefulness, accuracy, and reliability.

8. What are some ways you could improve your investigation techniques in future field studies?

Section 3.3 Summary

- Organisms are not distributed evenly across Earth. Patterns of distribution of life are largely due to abiotic factors such as climate, latitude, and elevation, and the ability of organisms to tolerate ranges of temperature, humidity, salinity, moisture, and light.
- A habitat is a place or area, within a biome or ecosystem, with a particular set of abiotic and biotic characteristics.
- An organism's range is the geographical area where the organism is found.
- The ecological niche of a population is the role that its members play in an ecosystem.
- The variety of niches and habitats within an ecosystem allow it to support a diversity of organisms.
- A limiting factor is any abiotic or biotic factor that controls the number of individuals in a population. Biotic limiting factors include competition, predation, and parasites.
- Organisms can be sampled using transects or quadrats, situated randomly in a study area. From these samples, the density of a population can be extrapolated.

Section 3.3 | Review

1. Use an example to help you explain how the concept of niche differs from the concept of habitat.

Use the following information to answer the next question.

Terrestrial Biomes According to Temperature and Precipitation

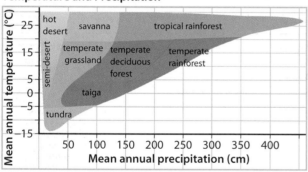

Distinctive patterns become apparent when terrestrial biomes are plotted according to mean annual temperature and precipitation.

2. Explain how you could use this graph to predict why much of southern Alberta is in the grassland biome while much of northern Alberta is in the taiga (boreal forest) biome.

3. Identify the abiotic conditions that might affect the size of a population of mosquitoes in Alberta throughout the year.

Use the following information to answer the next question.

Boreal Forest
In Alberta, the boreal is located in the northern half of the province and is characterized by mixed wood forests comprised of both coniferous (spruce and pine) and deciduous (poplar and birch) tree species.

4. Describe how these species of trees would compete for the same resources.

Use the following information to answer the next question.

Red-backed Voles
(*Clethrionomys rutilus*)
Populations of red-backed voles, found throughout much of Canada's boreal forest, fluctuate in cycles. Populations peak every two to five years and then decline  sharply before building up again. In one study, researchers measured a density of 398 voles per hectare, which later fell to a density of 27 voles per hectare. Red-backed voles live in a variety of habitats but prefer moist, dense grassland with high soil moisture. They feed on fungi, lichens, seeds, berries, bark, flowers, and other parts of plants. Their predators include owls, hawks, and mammals such as coyotes.

5. Identify the factors that might lead to regular population cycles of the red-backed voles and explain how each factor can limit the population of this mammal.

An individual organism's environment includes biotic and abiotic components. Individual organisms affect and are affected by the biotic and abiotic components in the environment as they interact with them. Organisms are part of a population, a community, ecosystem(s), and Earth's biosphere. The distribution of an organism is determined by the abiotic components of environments in the biosphere.

In order to study organisms, biologists had to develop systems for logically organizing and naming them. They use a hierarchical system to group organisms in increasingly specific categories. The broadest categories are domain and kingdom, through phylum, class, order, family, genus, to the most specific category, species. The categories have often been revised to accommodate new discoveries. It is a universal, Latin-based system, and individual organisms are identified by a two-word system of naming, called binomial nomenclature. An organism's scientific name is its genus and species names.

To identify organisms, biologists use dichotomous keys, which are arranged in steps. Each step has two statements, with answer choices as true or not true. Biologists work their way through each step until the species of the organism has been identified.

The unequal heating of Earth creates different climates in different parts of the world. This affects the organisms that live in particular places and results in distinct biomes, or groups of ecosystems, with similar abiotic conditions. Within biomes and ecosystems, there is a great deal of variation in habitats and niches.

The growth of a particular population in a particular habitat is limited by abiotic factors (such as climate and soil type) and biotic factors (such as competition for resources, predation, and parasitism).

Biologists use sampling techniques, such as transects and quadrats to sample populations in large ecosystems. Transects are often used to sample mobile populations over larger areas. Quadrats are often used to sample plants and other organisms that do not move. (Both methods can be used together.)

Chapter 3 Graphic Organizer

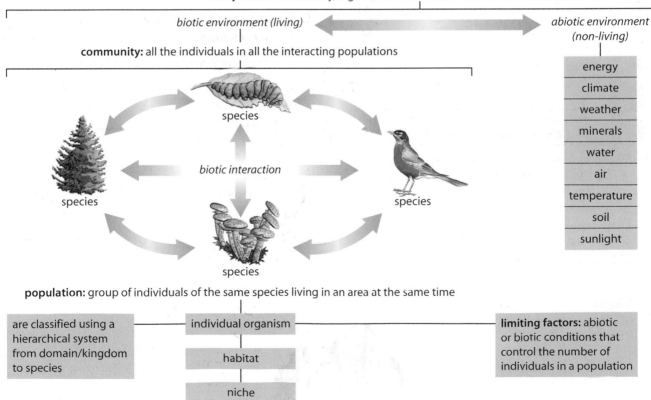

ecosystem: a community, together with the abiotic factors that surround and affect it

biotic environment (living)

abiotic environment (non-living)

community: all the individuals in all the interacting populations

species

species

biotic interaction

species

species

energy
climate
weather
minerals
water
air
temperature
soil
sunlight

population: group of individuals of the same species living in an area at the same time

are classified using a hierarchical system from domain/kingdom to species

individual organism

habitat

niche

limiting factors: abiotic or biotic conditions that control the number of individuals in a population

Understanding Concepts

1. Predict five abiotic and five biotic factors in the ecosystem shown above.

2. Explain how an animal's habitat relates to its niche.

Use the following information to answer the next question.

The freshwater leech shown feeds on the blood of fish, frogs, turtles, and mammals.

3. Explain why the freshwater leech is an example of a parasite.

4. Compare an ecosystem to a biome.

Use the following information to answer the next question (5).

Coral reefs are considered to be ecosystems.

5. Explain how the physical nature of a coral reef provides habitats and niches for other organisms.

6. The tree swallow (*Iridioprocne bicolour*) and the little brown bat (*Myotis lucifugus*) breed in similar habitats. Both feed on insects they catch while in flight. Explain why these organisms do not occupy exactly the same ecological niche.

7. Use a forest fire as an example to explain how an ecosystem can change over time.

8. Explain how the trees in a coniferous forest might compete with each other.

9. Identify the kingdom in which you would place a single-celled, eukaryotic organism that makes its own food.

10. Identify three resources you could use to determine the scientific name of an organism.

11. Explain why an introduced species usually causes the population of a native species to decline.

12. The term "multidisciplinary" refers to a subject that requires understanding of many disciplines such as chemistry, geology, meteorology (weather), geography, archeology, and biology. Explain why ecology is a multidisciplinary subject.

13. List the three domains of life identified in this text, and provide an example of each domain.

14. a) Explain how interspecific competition, intraspecific competition, predation, and parasitism can control the size of a population.
   b) Explain, using examples, how abiotic factors can also limit the size of a population.

Applying Concepts

Use the following information to answer the next question.

Classifications for six species

Organism	house cat	dog	coyote	striped skunk	brown bat	praying mantis
Kingdom	Animalia	Animalia	Animalia	Animalia	Animalia	Animalia
Phylum	Chordata	Chordata	Chordata	Chordata	Chordata	Arthropoda
Class	Mammalia	Mammalia	Mammalia	Mammalia	Mammalia	Insecta
Order	Carnivora	Carnivora	Carnivora	Carnivora	Chiroptera	Mantodea
Family	Felidae	Canidae	Canidae	Mephistidae	Vespertilionidae	Manitidae
Genus	*Felis*	*Canis*	*Canis*	*Mephitis*	*Myotis*	*Stagmomantis*
Species	*domesticus*	*familiaris*	*latrans*	*mephitis*	*lucifugus*	*carolina*

15. a) Identify the two animals in the table that are most closely related. Explain your answer.

b) Identify the animal that is not closely related to the other five animals. Explain your answer.

c) Use the scientific name of one of the animals in this chart to explain binomial nomenclature.

d) Predict the family of a wolf and a lion. Explain why you selected these names.

e) Infer why scientists would classify cats, dogs, coyotes, and skunks in the Order Carnivora.

f) Use graphics or word processing software to create a flow chart or concept map illustrating the relationship between the mammals in this chart. **ICT**

Use the following information to answer the next question.

Suppose that you have discovered an unknown organism while on a field trip. When you examine the organism under a microscope, you can see that it is multicellular and its cells have no chloroplasts to carry out photosynthesis.

16. a) Identify the kingdom that you would place this organism in.

b) Explain why there are other possibilities, as well.

17. Use graphics software to draw a diagram explaining why biodiversity will differ between a lawn that is regularly mowed with an adjacent lawn that has been left to go "wild." Write a short paragraph contrasting the abiotic conditions on both lawns. In addition, write a paragraph contrasting the habitats and niches in each lawn. **ICT**

Use the following information to answer the next questions.

Grizzly Bear

The scientific name of an organism often describes one or more characteristics of the organism. Take, for example, the grizzly bear. The scientific name of the grizzly bear is *Ursus arctos horribilis*. When taxonomists first encountered grizzlies during the 19th century, the bear's size and aggressiveness no doubt inspired this name. The common name *Ursus arctos* came later, when taxonomists recognized that grizzlies were the same as brown bears. *Ursus* is a genus in the family Ursidae (bears) that includes the widely distributed brown bears, black bears, and the polar bear.

Grizzly bears in the Central Rockies Ecosystem (CRE), the area in and near Banff National Park and Kananaskis Country, exist within a few hours drive of about 1 000 000 people. This is one of the most developed and used landscapes in North America where grizzly bears still survive. It is a critical link in the Yellowstone to Yukon landscape because here habitat available for large carnivores is relatively restricted.

18. a) Explain why scientists use Latin as the language of taxonomy.

b) Study the species name of the grizzly. Infer why taxonomists might have used the name "arctos" to describe brown bears.

c) Identify two so-called natural factors that may limit the population of grizzly bears in Alberta.

d) Describe how human activities have likely impacted the population of grizzly bears in Alberta.

19. Use graphics or word processing software to make a concept organizer that includes the following terms: cell, nucleus, no nucleus, eukaryote, prokaryote, plants, animals, archaebacteria, bacteria, fungi, Protista, Animalia, and Plantae. **ICT**

Making Connections

20. Identify a change in an ecosystem that has been caused by an action of people. Explain how you think this change might affect the diversity of the ecosystem.

21. Identify the things you do every day that can affect the ecosystem you live in.

Use the following information to answer the next question.

There is a growing concern worldwide about the numbers of species that are going extinct. Conservation organizations work to protect endangered species, but there may be disagreement about what exactly a "species" is.

22. a) Describe how naming an organism might influence our attitudes about the organism. For example, is a fish more likely to be protected if it is an endangered species or if it is newly discovered and different from all known species of fish?

b) Describe how naming an organism such as the grizzly bear (*Ursus arctos horribilis*) might influence our feelings about the organism.

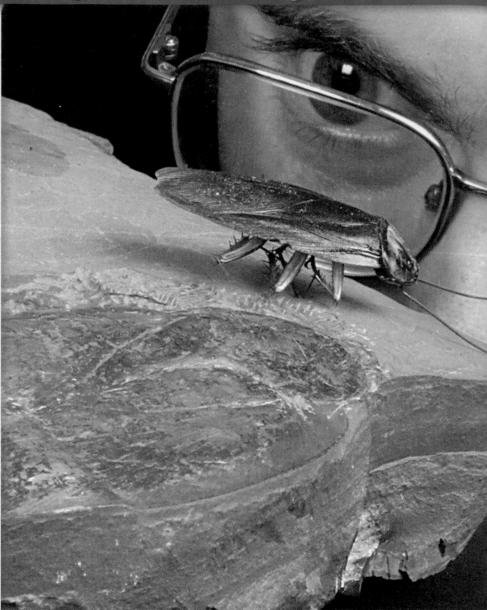

CHAPTER 4

Mechanisms of Population Change

Chapter Concepts

4.1 Adaptation, Variation, and Natural Selection

- Sexual reproduction and inherited mutations contribute to variation among individuals in populations.

- Individuals in a population have a selective advantage over other individuals if their mutations allow them to better survive and reproduce under selective pressures.

4.2 Developing a Theory to Explain Change

- Fossil evidence shows that species change over time and that species eventually become extinct.

- To develop the theory of natural selection, which explains evolutionary change, scientists have gathered and organized many pieces of evidence.

- There is evidence that modern species evolved from ancestral forms.

4.3 How Species Form

- A species consists of reproductively compatible populations.

- New species can form when populations become reproductively or geographically isolated from each other.

- The process of adaptive radiation occurs when a common ancestor diversifies into a variety of species.

- Two models for the pace of evolution are gradualism and punctuated equilibrium.

There are about 4000 cockroach species worldwide. The fossil in this photograph shows a 9 cm-long cockroach (*Arthropleura pustulatus*) that lived 300 million years ago. It was more than twice the size of the American cockroach (*Periplaneta americana*), a species common today. It was preserved so well that its mouthparts and antennae, and even the veins in its wings, are visible. When this cockroach was alive, there was a *greater* diversity of life forms than there is today. Fossils have helped to shape our current ideas about the process by which organisms that are living today descended from ancient forms of life and changed with the passing of time. Using fossil evidence, observations of species, experimentation with laboratory populations, and modern techniques, such as genetic analysis, scientists are adding to our understanding of life on Earth.

Could Cockroaches Rule Earth?

Procedure

1. Read the paragraph below, and answer the questions that follow.

Cockroaches live in many different habitats throughout the world. They are particularly hardy. They are able to survive without food for several weeks and have a varied diet, which can include unusual items such as wallpaper paste and paint. The females can reproduce several times a month, once they are reproductively mature. (Female American cockroaches live for about 14 months and lay their first egg capsule at about one year of age.)

Analysis

1. One female American cockroach can lay an egg capsule containing 16 eggs every five days. If a female is reproductive for two months, approximately how many offspring will she produce?

2. a) If half of the cockroach's offspring are female, and all of them reproduce, how many offspring will they produce? (Show your calculations.)

   b) Do you think this is a realistic situation? Explain.

3. While some cockroach species are abundant in certain areas, cockroaches are not "taking over the world." With a partner, discuss what you think might limit their populations. (**Hint:** Review what you learned in Chapter 3 about the factors that limit populations.)

4. People often use insecticides to kill cockroaches. In some cases, however, using insecticides can result in populations of insects that are resistant to—not harmed by—the very insecticide they are exposed to. Then, the insecticide is no longer able to control the insect populations by killing individuals. How do you think insecticide-resistance in a population might happen?

This reconstruction of an ancient tropical forest shows the type of habitat in which cockroaches, and many other insect species, first appeared over 300 million years ago.

Adaptation, Variation, and Natural Selection

Section Outcomes

In this section, you will
- **describe** how sexual reproduction and changes in genetic information result in variation within populations
- **design** an investigation to measure variations in a population
- **describe** how some mutations may improve an individual organism's chance for survival and reproduction
- **define** natural selection

Key Terms

variation
biological species
mutation
selective advantage
natural selection
selective pressure

Figure 4.1 No two organisms, even within the same species, are identical. Some differences, such as colour and size, are visible in the Rocky Mountain bighorn sheep (*Ovis canadensis*) shown above. Other differences, such as resistance to a particular parasite or bacterial infection, are not visible, but all differences are examples of the variations among individuals in a population.

Organisms, such as the bighorn sheep in Figure 4.1, constantly face environmental challenges that limit populations. Severe weather, drought, famine, and competition for food, space, and mates are all challenges that organisms may or may not be able to overcome. Organisms that survive long enough to reproduce have the opportunity to pass along to their offspring the genetic information that helped them survive. In this section, you will learn how variation within species, and organisms' interactions with their environment, help to explain changes in populations from one generation to another.

Adaptations and Survival

The American bittern, Figure 4.2, is found in marshes and fields in Alberta, where it lives among grasses and reeds. The colouring of its plumage helps to camouflage the bittern so that it blends in with its environment. As with other species, the bittern's adaptations make it well-suited to its habitat. An adaptation is a structure, behaviour, or physiological process that helps an organism survive and reproduce in a particular environment. Camouflage is one such adaptation.

Another adaptation is the biochemical and body processes of a Richardson's ground squirrel in hibernation (for example, physiology such as reduced heart and breathing rate). The needle-sharp talons and excellent vision of an owl are structural adaptations that make owls excellent predators in their environment. The thick, leathery leaves of the buffaloberry are also structural adaptations. They help to reduce water loss on hot summer days, which are an abiotic feature of their environment.

Figure 4.2 The American bittern (*Botaurus lentiginosus*) is well-camouflaged among plants in its habitat. How could the colouration of *individuals* help the survival of a *population*?

BiologyFile

FYI
The American bittern's ability to conceal itself extends to its behaviour, as well. It stands so that the lines on its plumage match the reeds surrounding it. If the reeds are swaying in the breeze, the bittern also sways, mimicking the movement of the reeds.

Figure 4.3 In sexual reproduction, the genes from two parents combine to produce offspring with visible and non-visible variations in their charactertistics. The kittens (*Felis domesticus*) in this litter have different fur colour and patterns, partly because each kitten inherited a different combination of genetic information from its parents.

How do these adaptations develop? Adaptations are the result of a gradual change in the characteristics of members of a population over time. A **variation**—a visible or invisible difference—that helps an individual in a population survive is likely to be passed on from survivor to survivor. Through generations of survivors, this variation will become more common, perhaps so common that it is considered to be a characteristic, or trait, of the population. Not all variations become adaptations. A variation in an individual can be an advantage or disadvantage, or have no effect on the individuals as they live and interact in their environment.

- - -

1 Sharks have an excellent sense of smell. Is this an adaptation? Explain your answer.

- - -

Variation within a Species

A **biological species** is a group of reproductively compatible populations. This means that members of these populations can interbreed and produce offspring that are healthy and are themselves able to reproduce successfully.

You and your classmates are all the same species, but clearly there is a great deal of variety among the individuals in your class. Why? How does this variation arise? Offspring have a combination of genetic material from both parents. Through sexual reproduction, parents pass on distinct units of hereditary information (genes) to their offspring.

The number of possible combinations of genes that offspring can inherit from their parents results in great genetic variation among individuals within a population. The kittens in Figure 4.3, for example, are all from the same litter, yet each has different fur colour and markings. The kittens look different because, through sexual reproduction, each kitten has inherited a different combination of genetic information from its parents. Some of this genetic information is expressed in each kitten's physical appearance and behaviour. Other genetic information has no visible effect but remains part of each kitten's genetic make-up and can be passed on to the next generation.

Genetic variation in a *population* is due to the variety of genetic information in all *individuals* of the population. In the next investigation, you will measure variation within a population.

- - -

2 How does sexual reproduction lead to variation among individuals in a population?

- - -

Mutations Lead to Genetic Variation

Mutations are changes in the genetic material of an organism. Mutations happen continuously in the DNA of any living organism. They can occur spontaneously, when DNA is copied before a cell divides. For example, your own DNA has about 175 mutations, compared with your parents' DNA, because of mistakes that occur as your

Variations Great and Small

Target Skills

Designing an investigation to describe an inherited variation in a population

Gathering and **recording** data to demonstrate variation

Stating a conclusion based on analysis of collected data

Diversity (variations) within a species can help populations survive environmental changes. Diversity within a species can be monitored genetically, or it can be demonstrated by measuring individuals within a population. Most traits in a population vary in a continuous way from one extreme to the other. A plot of the distribution of the trait in a population often produces a bell-shaped curve. In this investigation, you will design an experiment to measure a particular characteristic in two populations—plant seeds and humans.

Question

Are there measurable differences in size among individuals of the same species?

Hypothesis

Make and record a hypothesis about how a particular characteristic might be distributed throughout a population. (For example, would it be evenly distributed?)

Materials

- ruler
- electronic balance
- bean seeds or peas
- graph paper

Experimental Plan

1. With your group, design an investigation to determine the variation in the mass of plant seeds and a second investigation to determine the variation in the length of the human thumb or the width of the human hand.

2. State and record a hypothesis for each investigation.

3. As a group, decide how you will make the appropriate measurements and how many samples you will need. Also decide whether to pool your data with other groups. (Keep in mind that the larger the sample size, the more reliable the results are.)

4. Design a table similar to the one shown in the sample to record data for each investigation.

5. Identify the variables that you will control to ensure that your data are reliable.

6. Show your experimental plan to your teacher before beginning your investigation.

Data and Observations

1. Conduct your investigations, and record your results.

2. Group the data into meaningful categories.

3. Pool data from other groups if required to produce meaningful results.

4. A frequency histogram is a representation of a frequency distribution by means of rectangles whose widths represent class intervals and whose areas are proportional to the corresponding frequencies. Use a computer and spreadsheet software to construct a frequency histogram of data collected. **ICT**

Sample Data Table and Histogram

Data Range (mm)	Frequency
0–10	1
10–20	3
20–30	6
30–40	3
40–50	2

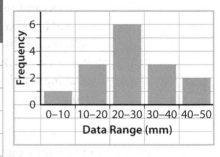

Analysis

1. Identify the range of the data that you collected for each investigation.

Conclusions

2. What can you conclude about the variations within a population? Is there a "typical" length or mass? Or is the frequency the same for each data range?

3. Would you get a greater or smaller variation in the range of data if all of the individuals sampled came from the same parents—for example, if all of the seeds you measured originated from the same plant?

4. What advantage would size (either large size or small size) have to the population studied? (For example, what advantage would large size have to a seed?)

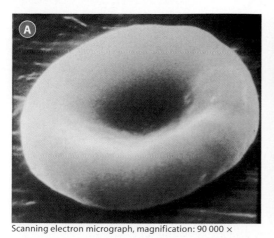

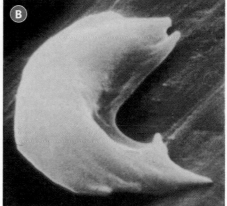

Scanning electron micrograph, magnification: 90 000 ×   Scanning electron micrograph, magnification: 90 000 ×

Figure 4.4 Normal, healthy red blood cells are round and smooth. They pass easily through blood vessels. Sickled cells can stick in the blood vessels, resulting in blood clots and reduced blood flow to vital organs. People who inherit the mutated gene for sickled cells from both of their parents have a condition called sickle cell disease.

DNA is copied. Mutagens, such as UV radiation, are environmental agents that can cause mutations in DNA, as well.

When DNA mutates, a cell may exhibit new characteristics. You can see an example of this in Figure 4.4, which shows a healthy blood cell (A) and an abnormal, sickle-shaped red blood cell (B). Other possible results include the cell dying, malfunctioning, or multiplying more than it should, resulting in a cluster of cells that form a tumour. Some mutations will not appear to have any effect on a cell. Whatever the result, if the mutation occurs in a body (somatic) cell, the mutation disappears when the organism dies. If, however, the mutation alters the DNA in a gamete (reproductive cell), the mutation may be passed on to succeeding generations. For example, if the kittens in Figure 4.3 have mutations in their egg or sperm cells, these mutations could be passed on to their offspring. These mutations were not present in their parents' DNA. Thus, mutations are a significant source of genetic variation in populations.

Mutations Can Provide a Selective Advantage

Mutations that significantly alter proteins in DNA often adversely affect the well-being of an organism and can be harmful. In some instances, however, a mutation enables an organism to survive its environment better, which, in turn, means that the organism is more likely to survive and reproduce. This situation is more common when an organism's environment is changing. Mutations that once were no advantage, or perhaps were even a disadvantage, may become favourable in a new environment. In this situation, the mutation provides a **selective advantage** in the new environment.

As an example, there is a mutation in houseflies that makes them resistant to the insecticide DDT. This mutation also reduces the flies' growth rate. So, before the introduction of DDT to their environment, having this mutation would have been a disadvantage to the flies. When DDT was introduced, however, this mutation enabled the individuals that possessed it to survive. These flies had a selective advantage in the population. They were more likely to survive and reproduce, thus potentially passing on this now-helpful mutation to their offspring.

In another study, researchers found that populations of California ground squirrels that overlap the range of northern Pacific rattlesnakes have a factor in their blood that makes them better able to combat the rattlesnakes' venom. Ground squirrels with this factor are likely to be the ones that will survive

BiologyFile

FYI
Mutated genes can cause or contribute to some diseases, such as diabetes, heart disease, Huntington's, cancer, and Alzheimer's. Hereditary conditions can occur because a parent with the mutation can pass it to children. There are tests available and more being developed that can help doctors pinpoint the mutation and the disease. The goal of the research is to improve the ability to treat patients and prevent unwanted mutations from passing on to future generations.

FYI

A person who receives the gene for sickled cells from both parents inherits sickle cell disease, which is harmful and can be life-threatening. A person who receives the gene from only one parent, however, can benefit from it. This is because people with a single copy of this gene are more resistant to malaria, an insect-borne disease that is one of the leading causes of illness and death in Africa.

BiologyFile

FYI

In natural selection, the environment selects for certain characteristics in a population. For centuries, however, people have been selecting organisms for particular traits. This is called *artificial selection*. Early indigenous peoples of Central America—ancestors of the peoples who would develop great cities such as those of the Olmec and Maya—developed the ancestral versions of the corn that we are familiar with today from one or more ancient grasses, including *teosinte*.

Modern corn kernel compared with *teosinte*

and reproduce, thus passing on the genes for this factor to their offspring. (In other words, the mutation that provided ground squirrels with the protection against snake venom gave those individuals a selective advantage.) As a result, in the future, a high proportion of the population will have the genetic make-up that allows them to withstand rattlesnake venom.

In populations that reproduce quickly, such as bacteria, viruses, and many insects, a rapidly changing environment can result in populations that also become adapted fairly quickly. If the environment changes, the mutated form of a gene that was previously insignificant in the population may provide a selective advantage to some individuals. As a result, the organisms that have the mutant form survive, and the genetic information is passed on to the next generation. In time, the gene that provided the selective advantage becomes more prevalent in the population. The once neutral or even negative mutation can, in some cases, mean the survival of a population.

For instance, populations of cockroaches can become adapted to new environments, such as those where they are sprayed with insecticides, relatively quickly. The cockroaches with a mutation that allows them to survive the insecticide can potentially pass this mutation onto their offspring. In the next generation, this mutation becomes more common in the population and more individuals in the population are resistant to the insecticide. Figure 4.5 shows another species that can quickly become adapted to new environments because it reproduces so quickly.

• • •

Q **3** Using a suitable example, distinguish between a mutation that provides a selective advantage and a mutation that provides a selective disadvantage.

• • •

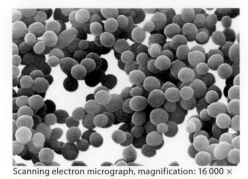

Scanning electron micrograph, magnification: 16 000 ×

Figure 4.5 These *Staphylococcus aureus* cells appear to be identical, but some may have a mutation that makes them resistant to antibiotics.

Investigate this type of organism and its ability to adapt in the next Thought Lab.

Natural Selection

Natural selection is a process that results when the characteristics of a *population* of organisms change because *individuals* with certain inherited traits survive specific local environmental conditions and, through reproduction, pass on their traits to their offspring. For natural selection to occur, there must be variety or diversity within a species. This is clearly what caused the antibiotic-resistant *Staphylococcus aureus* you will study in Thought Lab 4.1.

In this population of bacteria, the bacteria that survived were *selected for* by their environment. They survived the change in the environment around them, which was the application of an antibiotic, and thus could reproduce and pass on the genetic information that coded for resistance to that particular antibiotic. *Individuals* did not change during their lifetime; rather, with the passage of time, the *population* changed in its ability to resist certain antibiotics. In other words, populations change, not individuals. An abiotic environmental condition can be said to select *for* certain characteristics in some individuals and select *against* different characteristics in other individuals. In this way, the environment exerts **selective pressure** on a population.

For example, in a population of finches, some of the birds may have wider beaks than others. If there is an environmental change that makes having a wide beak an advantage, these wide-beaked finches will be more likely to survive and pass on the genes for wide beaks to their offspring. In native grasses such as rough fescue, shown in Figure 4.6, individuals that have the ability to withstand drought will survive during conditions of sustained dry conditions. They will then pass on the trait for drought resistance to their offspring. In the next generation, the abundance of the trait for drought resistance will increase in the population, because more of the drought-resistant individuals survive to reproduce. Should there be a big increase in the moisture in the population of

Figure 4.6 Three species of rough fescue, Foothills (*Festuca campestris*), Plains (*Festuca hallii*), and Northern (*Festuca scabrella*), cover approximately two thirds of Alberta. In fact, Alberta is the only place in North America where all three species grow naturally. In 2001, more than 2000 Albertans voted rough fescue as their favourite grass for a provincial emblem. The main reason given was its role as winter food for bighorn sheep, deer, elk, and bison.

Thought Lab 4.1 Evolving "Superbugs"

Target Skills

Analyzing data and **applying** a conceptual model to show how antibiotic resistance could occur in a population of *Staphylococcus aureus*

Gathering and **recording** information about the rise of antibiotic resistance in bacteria

Staphylococcus aureus bacteria, shown in Figure 4.5 on the previous page, can cause painful ear infections in children and life-threatening infections in the wounds of surgery patients. Like many other micro-organisms, *S. aureus* bacteria reproduce quickly. They reproduce asexually by dividing as frequently as every 20 min. This can result in a single cell having close to a billion descendants in about 6 h. Because of these astounding reproductive rates, beneficial mutations in the population may increase in frequency very quickly. This phenomenally rapid asexual cloning of individuals that are resistant to the new environment (for example, to the antibacterial action of an antibiotic) makes it challenging for scientists to develop effective antibiotics.

Procedure

1. Review the data shown in the table. Based on the data, when is bacterial resistance to a particular antibiotic likely to occur in *Staphylococcus aureus*?

2. Using different-coloured playing chips, model how a population of *Staphylococcus aureus* could become resistant to an antibiotic. (**Hint:** Use one colour of chip for bacteria that are resistant to an antibiotic.)

Analysis

1. Explain how the following situation might lead to antibiotic resistance of *Staphylococcus aureus* in patients.

   A patient is prescribed the antibiotic erythromycin for an infected cut. The prescription instructs the patient to take the antibiotic for two weeks. After one week, however, the cut seems to have cleared up and the patient stops taking the antibiotic.

2. With a partner, choose one of the following questions to research. Prepare a written, oral, or computer presentation to share your findings. **ICT**

   - How can the overuse of antibiotics lead to antibiotic resistance in bacteria?

   - Why do some agricultural practices contribute to antibiotic resistance in some bacteria species, and how can this contribute to antibiotic resistance in bacteria that cause diseases in humans?

Historical Progression of Antibiotic Resistance of *Staphylococcus aureus*

Antibiotic	Year introduced	First reports of resistance in patients
penicillin	1941	1945–1946
streptomycin	1944	1945
tetracycline	1948	1955
erythromycin	1952	1950s
methicillin	1961	1961
gentamicin	1964	1976
ciprofloxacin	1988	1990
vancomycin	1956	1997

rough fescue's environment, the trait for drought resistance will no longer be an advantage. In fact, if no individuals in the population can withstand extremely moist conditions, the population may not survive in that environment.

Natural selection does not anticipate change in the environment. Instead, natural selection is situational. A trait that at one time seems to have no particular relevance to survival becomes the trait that later helps individuals in a population survive and reproduce in a changed environment. This trait then persists within a population, because it is inherited by the offspring of the survivors. Adaptations that are beneficial in one

situation may be useless or detrimental in another situation. Complete the next Thought Lab to see how changing environmental conditions affected a finch population over several years.

• • •

4 Identify two examples, mentioned in this section, that show variation in a species being caused by a mutation.

5 Explain how the ability of a population of insects to withstand the effects of an insecticide is an example of natural selection.

• • •

Thought Lab | 4.2 | Analyzing Changes in Beak Depth

Rosemary and Peter Grant have been studying the medium ground finch (*Geospiza fortis*) of the Galápagos Islands for several decades. These finches use their strong beaks to crush seeds. They prefer the small seeds that are abundant during wet years. Because fewer small seeds are produced during dry years, the finches also have to eat larger seeds, which are harder to crush. For several years, the Grants have been measuring the depth (dimension from top to bottom) of the finches' beaks.

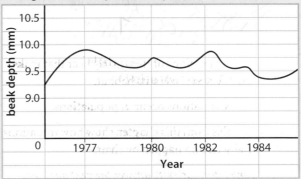

Changes in beak depth of *Geospiza fortis*, 1977–1984

The medium ground finch, *Geospiza fortis*

Procedure

Use the questions below to interpret the graph.

Analysis

1. 1977, 1980, and 1982 were drought years; 1984 was a wet year. What do you notice about the average beak depth in the finch population during dry years compared with wet years?

2. How do the data relate to selective pressure and natural selection?

3. An observer suggested that the finches exercised their beaks more when they ate large seeds that were tough to open, making their beaks stronger. Evaluate the plausibility of this explanation for the graphed data.

Section 4.1 Summary

- An adaptation is a physical feature, behaviour, or physiological process that helps an organism survive and reproduce in a particular environment. Examples of adaptations include camouflage, night vision, deep roots, nesting, and hibernation.
- Variety within a population and the environment in which an organism lives creates a situation in which natural selection can occur.

- Mutations and reproduction cause variations among individuals in a population.
- A mutation may provide an individual with an advantage or a disadvantage, or neither (neutral).
- Natural selection is the process by which a population of organisms changes because individuals with certain traits can better survive the local environmental conditions and pass on these traits to their offspring.

Biology File

Web Link

Health professionals and scientists worldwide are concerned about the resistance of bacteria to antibiotics. Many share information and ideas in an attempt to slow this alarming trend. What practices do health professionals recommend to reduce the spread of antibiotic-resistant bacteria?

www.albertabiology.ca
WWW

Section 4.1 | Review

1. Identify five adaptations of this grizzly bear that make it well suited for survival in its habitat.

2. Describe how variations occur in populations.

3. Using examples from this chapter, show how mutations and natural selection happen by chance.

Use the following information to answer the next question.

Pumpkins

A gardener is trying to win a competition for the largest pumpkin. Every year, she saves the seeds from the largest pumpkin in her garden. The next year, she plants only those seeds in a large plot. She finds that her pumpkins are becoming larger over the years.

4. **a)** Explain whether there is selective pressure in this pumpkin population.

   b) Is this situation an example of natural selection? Justify your answer.

5. Evaluate the following statement: "Natural selection works like a newspaper copy editor; it works only with what is already present in a population." [**Note:** Copy editors check written material, usually as the final step

before it is set into type, to correct errors in grammar, spelling, usage, and style.]

6. In a population of sparrows, most birds have a bill that is about 10 mm long. Some birds, however, have bills that are slightly longer or slightly shorter than average. Explain why this variation within a population is important when discussing natural selection.

7. Suppose that you are designing an investigation to measure variation within a population. Explain why it would not be appropriate to measure the length of 100 leaves from the same tree.

Use the following information to answer the next question.

Insect Resistant Pests

Pesticide resistance is a genetically based phenomenon. Resistance occurs when a pest population—insects, for instance—is exposed to a pesticide. When this happens, not all insects are killed. Those individuals that survive frequently have done so because they are genetically predisposed to be resistant to the pesticide.

Repeated applications and higher rates of the insecticide will kill increasing numbers of individuals, but some resistant insects will survive. The offspring of these survivors will carry the genetic makeup of their parents. These offspring, many of which will inherit the ability to survive the exposure to the insecticide, will become a greater proportion with each succeeding generation of the population.

8. Explain how some insects develop resistance to pesticides in terms of natural selection.

9. Explain what is meant by the expression "populations evolve, not individuals."

Developing a Theory to Explain Change

Scientific knowledge develops as people observe the world around them, ask questions about their observations, and seek answers to their questions. A *scientific hypothesis* is a statement that provides one possible answer to a question, or one possible explanation for an observation. Hypotheses are tested to determine their validity, mainly through experiments, observation, developing models from data, or a combination of these. Hypotheses that consistently lead to successful predictions and explanations are sometimes synthesized into a general statement that explains and makes successful predictions about a broad range of observations. Such a statement is called a *scientific theory*.

For centuries, people have been asking questions about how life developed on Earth. They have found objects (such as fossils), made observations (such as recognizing the natural variations in populations), collected and analyzed data, and formulated hypotheses to explain their observations. The resulting **theory of evolution by natural selection** is a well-supported, widely accepted explanation of how life has changed, and continues to change, during Earth's history. In this section, you will survey key events in the development of this theory, as well as scientific observations that support it.

Developing the Theory of Evolution by Natural Selection

Some ancient Greek philosophers believed that life evolved gradually. However, two of the most influential philosophers, Plato (427–347 B.C.E.) and Aristotle (384–322 B.C.E.), believed that all life existed in a perfected and unchanging form. This view of life prevailed in western culture for over 2000 years. By the sixteenth century, the predominant philosophy in western culture was that all species of organisms had been created independently of one another and had remained unchanged ever since.

Buffon's *Histoire Naturelle*

One of the first people to challenge publicly the idea that life forms are unchanging was French naturalist Georges-Louis Leclerc, Comte de Buffon (1707–1788). In 1749, he published the 44-volume *Histoire Naturelle*, which compiled his understandings of the natural world. In this work, Buffon noted the similarities between humans and apes, and speculated that they might have a common ancestor. In other writings, Buffon suggested that Earth was much older than 6000 years, as was commonly believed.

Buffon's ideas were revolutionary for his time. By 1830, however, other scholars from many areas of inquiry—paleontology, geology, geography, and biology—began to share their ideas to explain how life could change with the passage of time.

Cuvier's Fossils

French naturalist Georges Cuvier (1769–1832) is largely credited with developing the science of **paleontology**, the study of ancient life through the examination of fossils. Cuvier found that each stratum (layer of rock) is characterized by a unique group of fossil species. He also found that the deeper (older) the stratum, the more dissimilar the species are from modern life (see Figure 4.7). As Cuvier worked from stratum to stratum, he found evidence that new species appeared and others disappeared over the passage of time. This evidence showed that species could become extinct.

To explain his observations, Cuvier proposed the idea that Earth experienced many destructive natural events, such as floods and volcanic eruptions, in the past.

Figure 4.7 Deep rock strata (layers of rock) are older than strata that are closer to the surface. Different species of fossilized organisms can be found in different rock strata. This is evidence that not all life forms came into existence at the same time. (The arrangement of strata varies when mountains are formed. Often, the strata are tilted and the oldest layers are toward the inside of the mountain.)

younger stratum with more recent fossils

older stratum with older fossils

These events, which he called *revolutions*, were violent enough to have killed numerous species each time they occurred.

> **6** A geologist finds the fossil of a species of fish in one stratum but not in the next highest stratum. Infer how Cuvier might have explained this observation.

Lyell's *Principles of Geology*

Other scientists had ideas that differed from Cuvier's theory. Scottish geologist Charles Lyell (1797–1875) rejected the idea of revolutions. He proposed, instead, that geological processes operated at the same rates in the past as they do today. He reasoned that, if geological changes are slow and continuous rather than catastrophic, then Earth might be more than 6000 years old. As well, Lyell theorized that slow, subtle processes could happen over a long period of time and could result in substantial changes. The forces that build and erode mountains, for example, and the rate at which this change happens is no different today than it was in the past. Floods in the past had no greater power than floods that occur today. This idea inspired naturalist Charles Darwin and others. If Earth is slowly changing, they wondered, could slow, subtle changes also occur in populations?

> **7** How did Lyell's observations about changes in geology inspire naturalists' thoughts about changes in life on Earth?

Lamarck: The Inheritance of Acquired Characteristics

In his book *Philosophie Zoologique*, French naturalist Jean-Baptiste Lamarck (1744–1829) outlined his ideas about changes in species over time. By comparing current species of animals with fossil forms, Lamarck observed what he interpreted as a "line of descent," or progression, in which a series of fossils (from older to more recent) led to a modern species. He thought that species increased in complexity over time, until they achieved a level of perfection.

Lamarck also thought that characteristics, such as large muscles, that were acquired during an organism's lifetime could be passed on to its offspring. Following this reasoning, the large, powerful chest muscles of a horse would be passed on to its offspring, which would have the same characteristics. Lamarck called this the **inheritance of acquired characteristics**.

Lamarck provided a hypothesis for how the heredity of characteristics from one generation to the next might happen. More importantly, he noted that an organism's adaptations to the environment resulted in characteristics that could be inherited by offspring. At the time, there was little understanding of cell biology and no understanding of genetics. The idea of inheriting acquired characteristics was generally accepted to explain observations that species are not static and could change. Even Charles Darwin, who is credited with developing a comprehensive theory to explain how change in populations can occur, accepted Lamarck's idea of inheritance and acknowledged Lamarck in his writing. Lamarck's ideas were controversial to many people, though, simply because they firmly believed that species never changed.

By the end of the 1800s, as biologists learned about cells, genes, and heredity, Lamarck's mechanism for inheritance was rejected.

• • •

8 A farmer spends much of her time outdoors and, as a result, has very tanned skin. What would the hypothesis of inheritance of acquired characteristics say about the skin of her children? Why?

• • •

Darwin's Evidence

In 1831, 22-year-old Charles Darwin (1809–1882) left England on the HMS *Beagle*, a British survey ship. The primary purpose of the expedition was to map the coast of South America. As well, the journey provided Darwin with an opportunity to explore the natural history of various countries and geographical locations. Figure 4.8 outlines the *Beagle's* journey.

At first, Darwin did not always understand the significance of many of his observations. Years later, however, many of these observations (as well as ideas and observations resulting from new work by Darwin and others) became important to his theory of evolution by natural selection. Darwin's main observations, and the questions he asked about these observations, are summarized in Table 4.1.

• • •

9 Describe, using two examples, how Charles Darwin used observation of the world around him to develop his hypothesis about how species might change with the passage of time.

• • •

Figure 4.8 The five-year voyage of the HMS *Beagle* took the young Charles Darwin around much of the world. Most of his time, however, was spent exploring the coast and coastal islands of South America.

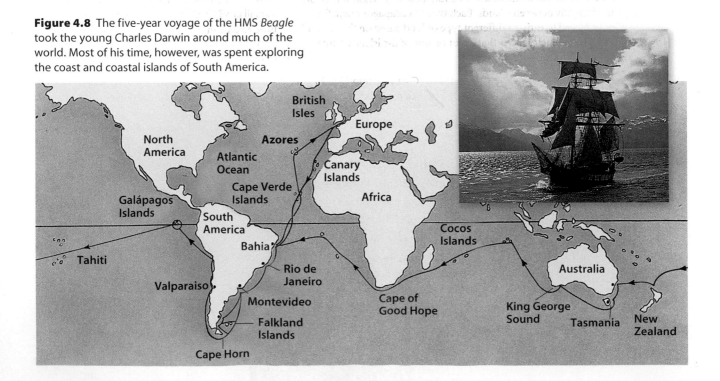

Table 4.1 Darwin's Observations and Questions Arising from Them

Observations	Questions
1. The flora and fauna of the different regions the *Beagle* visited were distinct from those Darwin had studied in England and Europe. For example, the rodents in South America were structurally similar to one another but were quite different from the rodents Darwin had observed on other continents.	If all organisms originated in their present forms during a single event, Darwin wondered, why was there a distinctive clustering of similar organisms in different regions of the world? Why were all types of organisms not randomly distributed?
2. Darwin observed fossils of extinct animals, such as the armadillo-like glyptodont, that looked very similar to living animals.  glyptodont, an ancient 4 m, 2 t animal from South America  modern armadillo from South America (1.5 m)	Why would living and fossilized organisms that looked similar be found within the same region?
3. The finches and other animals Darwin saw on the Galápagos Islands closely resembled animals he had observed on the west coast of South America. 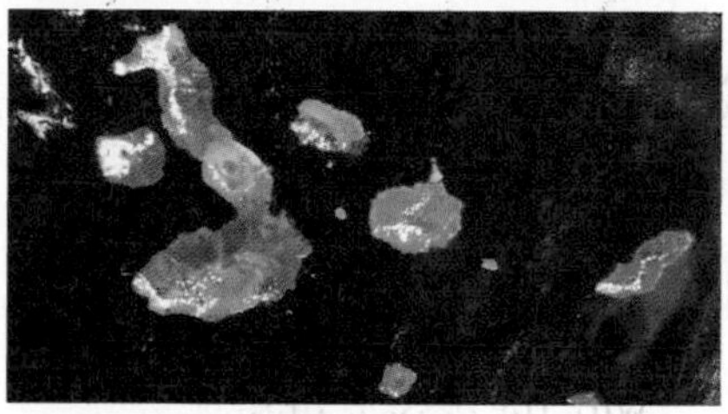 The Galápagos Islands, shown in this satellite image, include more than 20 small volcanic islands located approximately 1000 km off the coast of Ecuador.	Why did the Galápagos species so closely resemble organisms on the adjacent South American coastline?
4. Galápagos species (such as tortoises and finches) looked identical at first, but actually varied slightly between islands. Each type of Galápagos finch, for example, was adapted to eating a different type of food based on the size and shape of its beak. Ten finch species that occur on one of the islands, Santa Cruz, are shown here.  Warbler finch (*Certhidea olivacea*)  Cactus ground finch (*Geospiza scandens*)  Woodpecker finch (*Cactospiza pallida*)  Sharp-beaked ground finch (*Geospiza difficilis*)  Small insectivorous tree finch (*Camarhynchus parvulus*)  Small ground finch (*Geospiza fuliginosa*)  Large insectivorous tree finch (*Camarhynchus psittacula*)  Medium ground finch (*Geospiza fortis*)  Vegetarian tree finch (*Platyspiza crassirostris*)  Large ground finch (*Geospiza magnirostris*)	Why was there such a diversity of species in such a small area? Could these species have been modified from an ancestral form that arrived on the Galápagos Islands shortly after the islands were formed?
5. Through his experience in breeding pigeons and studying breeds of dogs and varieties of flowers, Darwin knew that it was possible for traits to be passed on from parent to offspring, and that sexual reproduction resulted in many variations within a species.	Could a process similar to artificial selection also operate in nature?

Darwin did not use the word "evolution" in the original edition of *On the Origin of Species*. ("Evolved" is used once; it is the final word in the book.) Instead, Darwin wrote about "descent with modification." One reason he did not use "evolution" is that he felt it implied progress—that each generation was improving in some way. Natural selection is different from progress. It results from an ability to survive local conditions and reproduce successfully, thereby giving the survivors the opportunity to pass on the trait that helped them survive and reproduce.

Darwin and Wallace and the Theory of Evolution by Natural Selection

Charles Darwin was not the only person to organize his and others' observations and ideas into a comprehensive theory to explain how species changed over time. Alfred Russel Wallace (1823–1913), another British naturalist, reached conclusions that were similar to Darwin's. The findings of both scientists were made public in a presentation by Charles Lyell in 1858.

Darwin and Wallace accepted that populations changed as time passed, but they were unclear *how* populations changed. An essay by economist Thomas Malthus (1766–1834), called *Essay on the Principles of Population*, provided them with a key idea. Malthus had proposed that populations produced far more offspring than their environments (for example, their food supply) could support and were eventually reduced by starvation or disease.

According to Darwin and Wallace, individuals with physical, behavioural, or other traits that helped them survive in their local environments were more likely to survive to pass on these traits to offspring. Darwin and Wallace reasoned that competition for limited resources among individuals of the same species would *select for* individuals with favourable traits—traits that increased their chances of surviving to reproduce. Thus, a growing proportion of the population would have these traits in later generations and, as time passed, the population as a whole would have them. Darwin called this process natural selection. He published his ideas in 1859 in *On the Origin of Species by Means of Natural Selection*.

• • •

 How might competition for resources lead to natural selection?

• • •

Darwin proposed two main ideas in *On the Origin of Species*:

1. Present forms of life have arisen by descent and modification from an ancestral species.

2. The mechanism for modification is natural selection working for long periods of time.

Darwin proposed that all life on Earth had descended from some unknown organism. As descendants of this organism spread out over different habitats during the millennia, they developed adaptations that helped them better survive in their local environments. Darwin's theory of natural selection showed how populations of individual species became better adapted to their local environments over time.

Compare Darwin's hypothesis to explain evolution with Lamarck's ideas about inheritance in the next Thought Lab.

Further Evidence of Evolution

In *On the Origin of Species*, Darwin assembled a group of facts that had previously seemed unrelated. Darwin certainly was not the only person to conclude that life had changed during long periods of time, but he was the first person to publish these ideas in a comprehensive manner. Darwin's ideas were developed, for the most part, by his observations of the distribution of organisms throughout the world (Table 4.1 on the previous page). Before and after publication of *On the Origin of Species*, biologists, geologists, geographers, and paleontologists provided a wealth of information that supported and strengthened what scientists now call the theory of evolution by natural selection.

The Fossil Record

Sedimentary rock with fossils provides a **fossil record** of the history of life by showing species that were alive in the past. (See Figure 4.9.) For instance, when people examined the Burgess Shale fossil

Figure 4.9 (A) The animals unearthed in the Burgess Shale lived over 500 million years ago during the Cambrian Explosion, when a stunning "explosion" of Earth's biodiversity occurred. Remarkably, even some soft parts of animals, such as gills and digestive systems, are preserved. **(B)** This 60 cm fossil of *Anomalocaris canadensis* was found in the Burgess Shale near Field, British Columbia.

| **Thought Lab** | **4.3** | **Comparing the Ideas of Lamarck and Darwin** |

Flying fish (*Exocoetus volitans*) are actually superb gliders, not flyers. To escape predators, the fish, which are about 18 cm long, aim toward the surface of the water and beat their powerful tails back and forth. When they break the surface, they continue to beat their tails, which increases their forward speed up to about 55 km/h. By spreading their side-fins, they are able to glide up from and over the surface for distances as great as 200 m!

Darwin and Lamarck both developed ideas about the inheritance of characteristics. Although Darwin read Lamarck's work and learned from his ideas, Darwin eventually proposed an alternative hypothesis that gave a different explanation for the mechanism that resulted in change. Read the following quotations from the writings of Lamarck and Darwin:

"The environment exercises a great influence over the activities of animals, and as a result of this influence the increased and sustained use or disuse of any organ are causes of modification of the organization and shape of animals and give rise to the anomalies observed in the progress of the complexity of animal organization."

—Jean-Baptiste Lamarck in *Philosophie zoologique*, 1809

"... natural selection, or the survival of the fittest, does not necessarily include progressive development—it only takes advantage of such variations as arise and are beneficial to each creature under its complex relations of life. And it may be asked what advantage, as far as we can see, would it be to an ... intestinal worm ... to be highly organised. If it were no advantage, these forms would be left, by natural selection, unimproved or but little improved, and might remain for indefinite ages in their present lowly condition."

—Charles Darwin in *On the Origin of Species*, 1859

Procedure

1. Rewrite each quotation in your own words.

2. How does Lamarck's idea of "use or disuse" differ from Darwin's idea, which was later called "descent with modification?"

Analysis

1. Flying fish use large pectoral fins to glide in air. Explain how (a) Lamarck and (b) Darwin might account for the origin of the large pectoral fins and the ability to glide.

2. Lamarck suggested that organisms arise spontaneously and then become increasingly more complex. With a partner, discuss why this idea is not supported by the theory of natural selection. (**Hint:** You might want to consider an organism such as a snake, which evolved from a population of animals that had legs.)

BiologyFile

Web Link

The Burgess Shale in British Columbia, the rich fossil beds near Drumheller, Alberta, and the Joggins Fossil Cliffs in Nova Scotia are just a few of many Canadian sites with a rich store of fossils. What have Canadian fossils contributed to our understanding of evolution?

www.albertabiology.ca
WWW

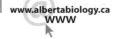

beds in British Columbia, they found fossils of animals that had lived in an ancient ocean during the Cambrian period, over 500 million years ago. Not only are micro-organisms and soft-bodied animals preserved in the Burgess Shale, but also these fossil beds contain some of the earliest animals with hard parts to be seen in the fossil record. Some of the fossilized animals found in the Burgess Shale are ancestors of animals that are common today. Others have long been extinct and are unlike anything in our modern oceans.

The fossil record provides the following evidence:

- Fossils found in young layers of rock (from recent geological periods and usually closer to the surface) are much more similar to species alive today than fossils found in deeper, older layers of rock.
- Fossils appear in chronological order in the rock layers. So, probable ancestors

Geologic Time Scale

Era	Period	Million years ago	Major evolutionary events
Cenozoic	Quaternary	5	Humans evolve
	Tertiary		First placental mammals
		65	
Mesozoic	Cretaceous		Flowering plants dominant
		144	First birds
	Jurassic		First mammals
			First flowering plants
		213	
	Triassic		First dinosaurs
		248	
Paleozoic	Permian		Cone-bearing plants dominant
		286	First reptiles
	Carboniferous		Great coal deposits form
		320	First seed plants
		360	
	Devonian		First amphibians
		408	First land plants
	Silurian		First jawed fish
		438	
	Ordovician		Algae dominant
			First vertebrates
		505	
	Cambrian		Simple invertebrates
		590	
Precambrian			Life diversifies
			Eukaryotes
			Prokaryotes
			Life evolves
		3500	

Representative organisms

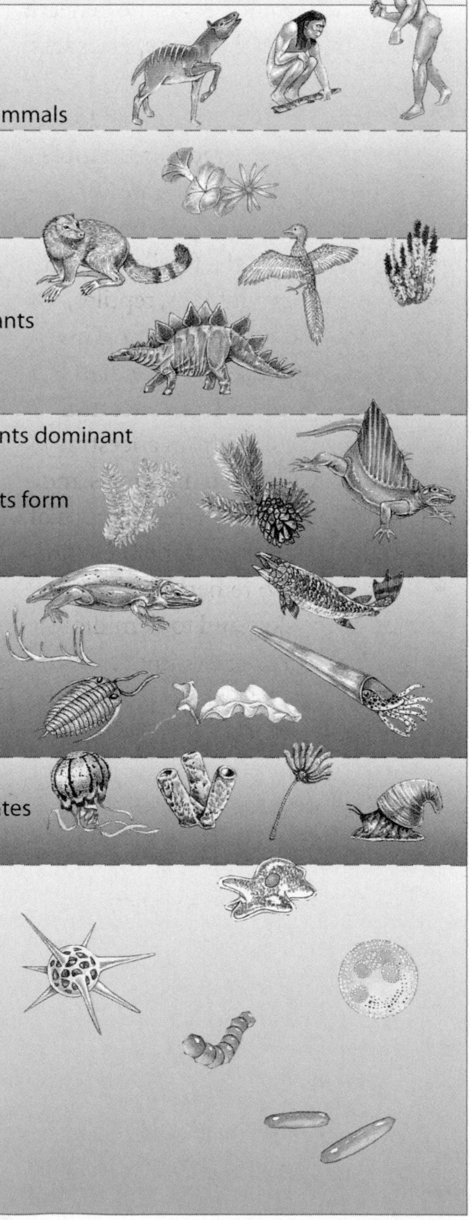

Figure 4.10 This geologic time scale shows when organisms first appear in the fossil record.

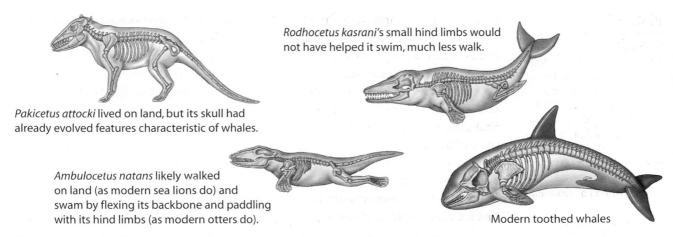

Rodhocetus kasrani's small hind limbs would not have helped it swim, much less walk.

Pakicetus attocki lived on land, but its skull had already evolved features characteristic of whales.

Ambulocetus natans likely walked on land (as modern sea lions do) and swam by flexing its backbone and paddling with its hind limbs (as modern otters do).

Modern toothed whales

Figure 4.11 Fossil evidence suggests that modern, aquatic, toothed whales evolved from a terrestrial ancestor, *Pakicetus attocki*. *Basilosaurus* and *Dorudon*, not shown in this illustration, appear more recently in the fossil record, after the appearance of *Rodhocetus*.

for a species would be found in older rocks, which would usually lie beneath the rock in which the later species was found.

- Not all organisms appear in the fossil record at the same time. For example, the fossil history of vertebrates shows that fish are the oldest vertebrates. In subsequent layers, the fossils of other vertebrates—amphibians, reptiles, mammals, and birds—appear. This reinforces scientific evidence that amphibians evolved from ancestral fish, reptiles evolved from ancestral amphibians, and both mammals and birds evolved from different groups of reptiles (mammals first, and then birds). It is important to remember that these changes were slow and took millions of years. The geological time scale in Figure 4.10 shows when organisms first appear in the fossil record.

• • •

11 List two ways that the fossil record has helped scientists understand that organisms change over time.

• • •

Transitional Fossils

The original fossil record gave only scattered "snapshots" of ancestral forms, and critics of the theory were concerned about the "gaps." The ongoing discovery

of hundreds of **transitional fossils**—fossils that show intermediary links between groups of organisms—has helped scientists better understand the process and relationships between groups of organisms. Transitional fossils link the past with the present. For example, scientists have found fossilized whales that lived 36 to 55 million years ago. These fossils link present-day whales to terrestrial ancestors. The *Basilosaurus* and *Dorudon* were ancient whales that had tiny hind limbs, but led an entirely aquatic life. *Dorudon* was about the size of a large dolphin, about 5 m long. It had a tiny pelvis (located near the end of its tail) and 10-cm legs, both of which would have been useless to an animal that lived an aquatic life. A more recently discovered transitional form, *Ambulocetus*, announced in 1994, had heavier leg bones. Scientists hypothesize that it lived both on land and in water. Figure 4.11 shows *Ambulocetus*, as well as two other ancestors of present-day whales, whose discovery has filled gaps in the fossil record of whales.

In 1995, the fossil of a previously unknown dinosaur called *Atrociraptor* ("savage robber") was discovered near Drumheller (see Figure 4.12). *Atrociraptor* was a small meat-eating dinosaur, about the size of a 10-year-old child. It is thought to be a close non-birdlike relative of *Archaeopteryx*. Fossils

Figure 4.12 Based on where *Atrociraptor* was found in the fossil record, it was alive about 70 million years ago, during the Cretaceous period.

of *Archaeopteryx* show a transitional stage in the fossil record because this species had characteristics of both reptiles (dinosaurs) and birds. *Archaeopteryx* had feathers, but, unlike any modern bird, it also had teeth, claws on its wings, and a bony tail.

In early 2005, a Canadian team of paleontologists made another amazing discovery at a fossil site in China. They found a pair of shelled eggs inside a fossilized dinosaur. The dinosaur, a kind of theropod, is considered to be an ancestor of modern birds. The shape of the eggs, the evidence at the fossil site, past fossil discoveries, and the paleontologists' understanding of the biology of birds and reptiles suggested to them that this dinosaur laid its eggs in intervals like modern-day birds, rather than all at once like reptiles do.

Patterns of Distribution

As you know from Chapter 3, organisms are not distributed evenly over Earth. **Biogeography** is the study of the past and present geographical distribution of organisms. Many of the observations that Darwin and Wallace used to develop their theories were based on biogeography. Darwin and Wallace hypothesized that species evolve in one location and then spread out to other regions.

Biogeography supports this hypothesis with examples such as the following:

- Geographically close environments (for example, desert and forest habitats in South America) are more likely to be populated by related species than are locations that are geographically separate but environmentally similar (for example, a desert in Africa and a desert in Australia). So, for instance, cacti are native only to the deserts of North, Central, and South America. They are not naturally found in other deserts in the world, such as those in Australia or Africa.
- Animals found on islands often closely resemble animals found on the closest

continent. This suggests that animals on islands have evolved from mainland migrants, with populations becoming adapted over time as they adjust to the environmental conditions of their new home. For example, the lizards found on the Canary Islands, off the northwest coast of Africa, are very similar to the lizards found in west Africa.

- Fossils of the same species can be found on the coastline of neighbouring continents. For example, fossils of the reptile *Cynognathus* have been found in Africa and South America. How can this be explained? The location of continents are not fixed; continents are slowly moving away from one another. At one time, the continents of Africa and South America were joined in one "supercontinent."
- Closely related species are almost never found in exactly the same location or habitat.

Anatomy

Vertebrate forelimbs can be used for various functions, including flying (birds and bats), running (horses and dogs), swimming (whales and seals), and swinging from tree branches (monkeys). Despite their different functions, however, all vertebrate forelimbs contain the same set of bones, organized in similar ways. How is this possible? The most plausible explanation is that the basic vertebrate forelimb originated with a common ancestor. **Homologous structures** are those that have similar structural elements and origin but may have a different function. The limbs shown in Figure 4.13 have similar structures, such as number of bones, muscles, ligaments, tendons, and blood vessels. These structural elements are arranged, however, to be best suited for different functions: walking, flying, or swimming. Homologous structures are similar because they were inherited from a common ancestor. As you can see in Figure 4.13, homologous structures differ in their anatomy based on an organism's lifestyle and environment. For example, the bones in a horse's leg are larger and heavier than the bones in a bat's wing.

Homologous structures can be similar in structure or function or both. The limbs in Figure 4.13 are structurally similar. As well, the lower limbs of the human, frog, and horse perform the same function: movement on land. Functional similarity in anatomy, however, does not necessarily mean that species are closely related. The wings of insects, birds, bats, and pterosaurs (extinct flying reptiles) are similar in function, but not in structure. (For example, bones support bird wings, whereas a tough material called chitin

makes up insect wings.) All of these organisms evolved independently of one another and did not share a common ancestor with wings.

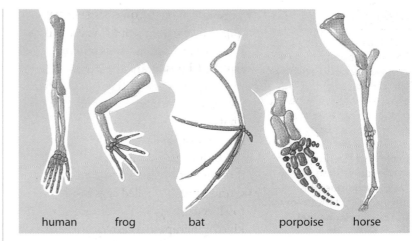

human frog bat porpoise horse

Figure 4.13 These vertebrates have the same basic arrangement of bones (as indicated by the colours), but the bones have different uses.

Thought Lab 4.4 Homologies of Hair

cuticle cortex medulla cuticular scale

pigment granules

Cross Section of a Hair

Mammals are the only animals that have hair. Among mammalian species, hair can vary in length, density, texture, and colour. The basic structure of hair, however, is the same for all mammals. Each hair has a central medulla that is surrounded by a dense cortex, which contains most of the pigment granules that give each hair its colour. The cortex is covered by a layer called the cuticle. The scales of the cuticle are specific to a particular genera or even species of mammals. Thus, mammalian hair has a common origin, yet may serve different functions. In this activity, you will investigate variations in the functions of mammalian hair.

Procedure

1. Work in small groups of three or four.

2. Each person in your group should choose a different type of mammalian hair from the following list:

   a) the stout, strong hairs of a porcupine

   b) the dense underfur, or underhairs, of a sea otter

   c) the vibrissae ("whiskers") of a cat

   d) the thick mane of a lion

   e) the long, thick hair of a woolly mammoth

   f) the horn of a rhinoceros, which is made of densely packed hair

   g) the "scales" of a pangolin, which are modified hairs

   h) the soft, fluffy qiviut (fur) of a muskox

3. Conduct research to investigate the structure of the hair you have chosen. Research how the animal's lifestyle and habitat might explain the particular function(s) of its hair.

Analysis

1. Based on the information you collected and your understanding of natural selection,

   a) hypothesize how the structure of the hair is related to abiotic conditions in an animal's environment

   b) write a hypothesis stating how the variations might have arisen from the basic hair structure of a common mammalian ancestor

2. Present your findings to the others in your group in a written or oral report, a computer presentation, or another form that is easily shared. **ICT**

3. Write a statement that describes one similarity and one difference in the adaptations of the hair studied by the members of your group.

Some structures evolved for one function and became useful for another function as time passed. For example, feathers might have evolved originally as an adaptation for insulation and later might have become useful for flight. Adaptations that were originally selected for one function but later became useful for another function are called *exaptations*. Originally, exaptations were called pre-adaptions. How could the term "pre-adaptation" lead to some misconceptions about natural selection?

Body parts that perform similar *functions*, even though the organisms do not have a common evolutionary origin, are called **analogous structures**.

• • •

12 Are bird wings and bat wings homologous structures or analogous structures? Explain your answer.

• • •

Embryology

The embryos of different organisms exhibit similar stages of embryonic development. For example, all vertebrate embryos have paired pouches, or out-pocketings of the throat. In fish and some amphibians, the pouches develop into gills. In humans, the pouches become parts of the ears and throat. At certain stages in the development of the embryo, the similarities among vertebrates are more apparent than the differences, as you can see in Figure 4.14.

The similarities among embryos in related groups (such as vertebrates) point to a common ancestral origin. It follows that related species would share both adult features (such as basic arm-bone arrangements, as discussed earlier) and embryonic features (such as the presence of paired pouches in the throat).

Figure 4.14 Similarities in the embryos of fish, reptiles, birds, and mammals provide evidence of evolution.

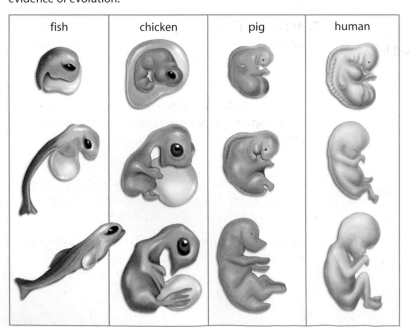

fish	chicken	pig	human

 • • •

13 How does an understanding of embryology support the idea that similar organisms, such as vertebrates, have a common ancestor?

• • •

Molecular Biology

The evolutionary relationships among species are reflected in their DNA and proteins. The field of molecular biology developed as technologies to identify molecules, such as DNA and protein molecules, developed. This field has provided evidence that helps to support the idea of common ancestry and evolution through natural selection. From molecular biology, we have learned the following information about life on Earth:

• All cells consist of membranes filled with—among other components— water, genetic material, proteins, lipids, and carbohydrates.

• Proteins called enzymes control biochemical reactions in all organisms.

• In all organisms, proteins are synthesized from amino acids.

• In all organisms, all cells that can replicate contain DNA. Since DNA carries genetic information, scientists can determine how closely related two organisms are by comparing their DNA. If two species have similar patterns in portions of their DNA, this similarity indicates that these portions of their DNA were most likely inherited from a recent common ancestor.

Genetics

The use of modern technology has led to many discoveries that support Darwin's theory. Scientists now know how species passed on their traits to their offspring, and how the blueprints (genes) for these traits could change by mutation, as you learned in section 4.1. Current evolutionary theory connects genetics with the theory of natural selection, and how natural selection operates on populations. Thus, genetic evidence and the understanding of heredity and mutations lend support to hypotheses that stem from observations of fossils, anatomy, biogeography, embryology, and molecular biology.

> **(14)** List five different fields of science that have contributed to the theory of evolution by natural selection. How has each field contributed to refining this theory?

Section 4.2 Summary

- Scientific theories explain facts and tie them together in a comprehensive way, enabling scientists to make predictions about new situations and experimental outcomes.
- The theory of evolution ties together facts to provide a logical framework that explains how life on Earth has changed and is still changing.
- Charles Darwin and Alfred Russel Wallace both developed hypotheses to explain natural selection.
- Contributions by Cuvier, Lamarck, Malthus, Lyell, and others helped to develop the hypotheses that have become the theory of evolution by natural selection.
- The fossil record, biogeography, anatomy, molecular biology, and genetics all provide evidence for evolution.
- New discoveries of fossils, called transitional fossils, help fill in the "gaps" in the fossil record.
- Homologous structures are those that have similar structural elements and origin but may have a different function. Analogous structures perform similar functions, even though the organisms do not have a common evolutionary origin.

Section 4.2 | Review

1. Describe the contributions of the following people to the understanding of evolution:

   a) Cuvier

   b) Malthus

   c) Wallace

   d) Lyell

2. Although Lamarck and Darwin proposed different explanations for how characteristics are passed from parent to offspring, their theories had some similarities. Identify and compare these similarities.

3. Is a bat more closely related to a bird or to a mouse? Explain your answer using the terms "analogous structure" and "homologous structure."

4. Much of the theory of evolution has been developed by interpreting certain observations or by making logical inferences about these observations. Outline the inferences that Darwin and other scientists made from each of the following observations.

   a) Some species found on islands are very similar to species found on neighbouring continents.

   b) No two individuals are exactly alike.

   c) Resources, such as food, are limited.

5. List three facts that support the idea of organisms sharing a common ancestor.

6. An athlete breaks her leg. Years later, she has a child who walks with a limp. Is this an example of a trait being passed from one generation to the next? Justify your answer.

7. At the site of a fossil bed, you come across fossils in a number of layers in the sediment. Which layers would have the oldest fossils, and which would have the youngest fossils? Explain your reasoning.

8. Define the term transitional fossils and explain how these help scientists to better understand relationships between groups of organisms.

9. Use word processing or spreadsheet software to create a table summarizing the differences between homologous and analagous structures. Use the following headings: structure, function, and origin. **ICT**

10. Explain how scientists can use DNA to determine the evolutionary relationship between two organisms.

Debating Science

"When I consider healthy discussions that take place in the scientific world, vigorous debate (or at least consideration) of opposing alternatives is critical for the successful development of ideas and identification of promising new areas of research. The ideas that withstand critical challenges from colleagues end up being the most robust and strongest theories."

—Brent Edwards, PhD,
Starkey Hearing Research Centre

How often have you read about a scientific "breakthrough" only to see it disputed (or completely contradicted) a few months later? What's good for you one year seems to be bad for you the next. *What is going on?*

Science is a process of constructing, refining, and revising knowledge and understanding. Individuals or small groups of scientists start the process. However, the result of their work—a new discovery, a rejected hypothesis, or a modified theory—is a collaborative process that requires feedback, discussion, and the eventual consensus of others in the scientific community.

The Role of Scientific Review

Science requires, and is founded on, the practice of peer review. In 1560, an Italian scholar, Giambattista della Porta, founded the first organization for the exchange of scientific ideas, known as The Academy of the Mysteries of Nature. Its purpose was to present scientific ideas for review and discussion. Since that time, countless societies, associations, journals, symposia, conferences, and now Internet resources have been set up to give scientists a place to communicate their ideas and findings for the evaluation of their peers.

This scrutiny is an essential part of the scientific process. Peer reviewers compare assumptions with their own knowledge, attempt to replicate or verify findings, and frequently challenge their colleagues' conclusions. This is why it is so important to document all procedures and carefully record the resulting data.

The review process has uncovered faulty experimental designs, incorrect conclusions, and—at times—deliberately fraudulent data. In many cases, however, the process of peer review and scientific debate has led to the development, refinement, and acceptance of scientific laws and theories that help shape our understanding of the world around us.

The process is not foolproof. The sheer volume of material being published today in a variety of increasingly specialized journals makes it very difficult for the field to police itself effectively. Individual publications must have strict guidelines for submissions to ensure that legitimate research is being presented for review.

In Darwin's day, 1858, he publicly reported on the studies he and Alfred Russel Wallace had done related to the origin and diversity of life to the Linnean Society in London. *On the Origin of Species* was published the next year as a book, and scientific colleagues used it to review the evidence presented and the conclusions. That review continues as more evidence is found, and more conclusions are reached, published, and debated.

Science and Society

Scientific debates are not always confined to the topics of scientific evidence and conclusions. Scientists do not exist in a vacuum; they are part of society. Their discoveries have led to inventions that have transformed the ways in which we live our lives. Some scientific discoveries go beyond practical applications to challenge assumptions that sustain social institutions.

For example, since the days of Aristotle, people in western society had believed that Earth was the centre of the universe. Theologians and political authorities had based their justification of social order on this understanding. In 1543, Nicolaus Copernicus, a Polish astronomer, challenged this Earth-centred view by publishing a new theory about Earth orbiting the Sun. In the 1600s, the astronomer and physicist Galileo Galilei (1564–1642) was imprisoned and threatened with torture for supporting Copernicus's theory. Representatives of the state felt that a Sun-centred universe was a dangerous idea that would undermine social structures and authority.

When Darwin published his book in 1859, those debating his theories and conclusions were not just scientists. Many non-scientists were alarmed by the implications of Darwin's conclusions, which were thought to challenge the idea that humans were created intentionally by God for a special purpose and that, again, this would undermine the social order.

The social debate over evolution was still raging in 1925 when the state of Tennessee passed legislation that made it "unlawful" for any teacher there to "teach any theory that denies the story of the Divine Creation of man as taught in the Bible, and to teach instead that man has descended from a lower order of animals." A high school biology teacher named John Thomas Scopes was soon charged with the offense. His trial, which became known through the media as "The Scopes Monkey Trial," was held in a packed courthouse and followed by national newspapers in the U.S. (It also was the first trial to be broadcast on national radio.)

The arguments for and against the indictment largely revolved around preserving the separation of church and state, the validity of various interpretations of the Bible, and whether a conviction created a special status for one faith. The actual science related to the theory of evolution was not the focus of the debate; the concern was about its social impact.

Some of the current debates among scientists—for example, about climate change and the importance of preserving biodiversity—have also moved beyond the sphere of science and entered the public forum. Once again, scientific conclusions are under fire, not because the science is thought to be wrong, but because there are concerns that the implications will somehow undermine social (and economic) principles and practices.

Some observers of the Scopes Monkey Trial suggested that if they had a chance to debate the issue, monkeys might have strong objections.

• • •

1. You and your colleagues at the university have discovered a protein that you believe is a major trigger for certain types of heart disease. You've rerun your tests many times and gotten consistent results. Now it's time to publish them. Choose two potential journals in which you could publish the research.

   a) Describe the readership, including the total number and their general areas of expertise.

   b) Describe the process for submitting research for review.

   c) Explain how the publication is funded.

   d) Assess and describe any potential impact the factors you've researched might have on the quality of attention and review your team's work on proteins and heart disease will receive.

2. When and why do you think members of the general public should get involved in discussions about scientific findings? Describe the best forum for holding such discussions (for example, schools, courts, newspapers, radio, television, public meetings, or the Internet) and why you think it is the most effective.

3. The peppered moth, *Biston betularia*, has been the subject of scientific study since 1848, when it was noted that the numbers of individuals of flecked and dark moth populations fluctuated over relatively short periods of time that corresponded to the amount of air pollution in the moth's habitat. Numerous studies confirm the hypothesis that natural selection is driving these population changes. However, this hypothesis has been challenged, mainly in the popular media, rather than in scientific journals. Do research to find and summarize the evidence that has been cited to challenge the hypothesis.

4. *The Journal of Negative Results in Biomedicine* is one of a handful of scientific journals devoted to communicating the negative results of failed investigations and disproved hypotheses. Some scientists suggest that all scientific journals should do a better job of providing such information. Do you agree? Justify your reasoning.

How Species Form

Figure 4.15 The Northern leopard frog (*Rana pipiens*) **(A)** and Southern leopard frog (*Rana sphenocephala*) **(B)** were once thought to be part of a single, extremely variable species. Today, scientists agree that what they thought was one species of leopard frog is at least seven different, but related, species in North America.

The two leopard frogs in Figure 4.15 look remarkably similar, but they are different species. How is a species defined? Historically, biologists defined species in terms of their physical form. Physical similarity, however, does not necessarily mean that organisms are the same species. Biologists now consider physiology, biochemistry, behaviour, and genetics, as well, when distinguishing one species from another.

What Is a Species?

As you read in Section 4.1, a biological species consists of populations that can interbreed and produce a group of viable offspring, which can also reproduce in nature. Biological species that are geographically isolated cannot interbreed. What about biological species that share the same habitat?

Biological species can also be described as being reproductively isolated from other species. Obviously, highly dissimilar species, such as elephants and frogs, cannot mate, so they are reproductively isolated. Populations that breed at different time periods, such as those that breed in the spring and those that breed in the fall, are also reproductively isolated. What about species that are similar, such as two

species of warbler? In this section, you will learn how populations remain reproductively isolated from one another and how this can lead to the formation of new species.

Forming a New Species

There are two general pathways that can lead to the formation of new species, or **speciation**. As shown in Figure 4.16A, a new species may result from accumulated changes in the population over a long period of time. A new species gradually develops as a result of mutation and adaptation to changing environmental conditions, and the old species is gradually replaced. This is known as *transformation*. The evolution of mammoths followed this pathway. The ancestral mammoth lived approximately 2.6 million to 700 000 years ago. It slowly evolved into the steppe mammoth that lived 700 000 to 500 000 years ago, and finally into the woolly mammoth that lived 350 000 to 10 000 years ago.

If this pathway were the only mechanism for the creation of new species, however, the total number and diversity of species in existence would remain virtually unchanged. In the second pathway to speciation, shown in Figure 4.16B, one or more species arise

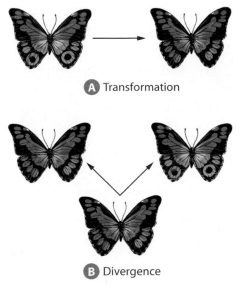

(A) Transformation

(B) Divergence

Figure 4.16 There are two pathways to speciation: **(A)** one species evolves into another species and **(B)** one or more species arise from a parent species.

from a parent species that continues to exist. This is known as *divergence*. For example, the small hoofed *Hyracotherium*, which lived approximately 50 million years ago, is thought to have been the common ancestor of modern horses, tapirs, and rhinoceroses.

Both pathways to speciation are the result of natural selection. The second pathway increases biological diversity because it increases the number of species.

• • •

 Define speciation and the two general pathways to speciation.

• • •

Keeping Populations Separate

For speciation to occur, two populations must be prevented from interbreeding. This means that the populations must become isolated from one another through geographical or biological barriers. If the populations remain isolated long enough, speciation will eventually occur because of changes accumulated in the population due to natural selection, which affects reproduction. When this happens, individuals in one population are no longer able to reproduce successfully with individuals in the other population.

Geographical Barriers

Geographical barriers, such as mountains and rivers, prevent interbreeding and result in speciation because they keep populations *physically* separated. For example, a substantial lava flow may isolate populations, changes in ocean levels may turn a peninsula into an island, or a few colonizers may reach a geographically separate habitat (such as a newly formed island). After a long period of time, speciation will occur. The separated populations will no longer be able to mate and reproduce successfully with others members of the original population.

The geographic isolation of a population does not have to be maintained forever for speciation to occur. It must be maintained long enough, however, for the population to become reproductively incompatible with the original population.

Members of the ancestral species of Galápagos finches reached one of the islands in the archipelago, possibly as a result of being blown off course in a tropical storm. Unable to return to the mainland, the ancestral species evolved differently from their mainland relative. The ancestral birds, and their successive generations, have since spread through the islands. New species developed as they evolved in response to the unique environments on individual islands.

Figure 4.17 on page 138 shows the hypothesized descent of multiple species from one common ancestor. The length of each vertical line reflects how much the DNA of each species has mutated from the group's common ancestor.

Biological Barriers

Even if the ranges of species overlap, there are many **biological barriers** that can keep the species reproductively isolated. For example, behaviour is a biological barrier that will keep

BiologyFile

Try This
Most woolly mammoths became extinct about 11 000 years ago. (A smaller form, called the dwarf woolly mammoth, survived until as recently as 3500 to 5000 years ago on an island off the coast of northern Russia.) Fossil records show that human hunting had a role to play in the extinction of the woolly mammoth, as did global warming. Many scientists are concerned about how global warming might affect populations today. (For example, changes in climate or water levels can affect food supplies or result in a loss of habitat.) With a partner, discuss ways in which global warming might affect the evolution of species by natural selection.

BiologyFile

FYI
Charles Darwin used the variations he could see and measure in the Galápagos finches to hypothesize how speciation might have happened in the Galápagos Islands. Today, DNA evidence supports Darwin's original hypothesis and adds further information to help scientists understand how the different lineages of finches could have arisen from an ancestral population.

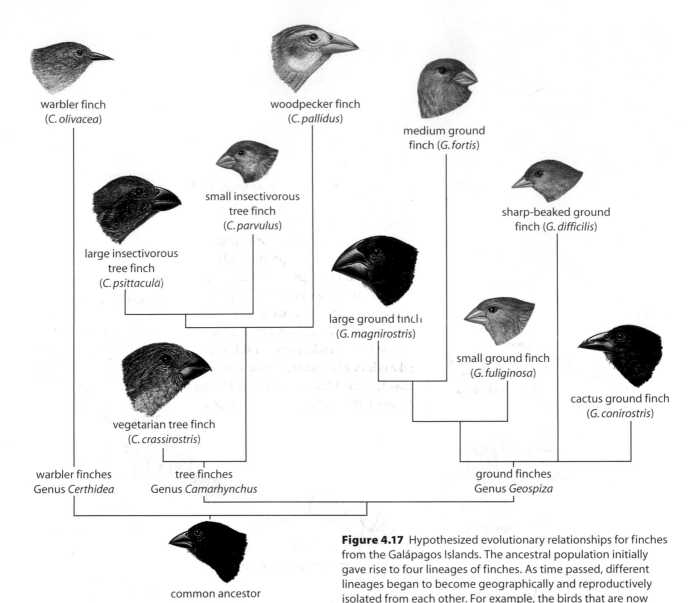

warbler finch
(*C. olivacea*)

woodpecker finch
(*C. pallidus*)

medium ground
finch (*G. fortis*)

small insectivorous
tree finch
(*C. parvulus*)

sharp-beaked ground
finch (*G. difficilis*)

large insectivorous
tree finch
(*C. psittacula*)

large ground finch
(*G. magnirostris*)

small ground finch
(*G. fuliginosa*)

cactus ground finch
(*G. conirostris*)

vegetarian tree finch
(*C. crassirostris*)

warbler finches
Genus *Certhidea*

tree finches
Genus *Camarhynchus*

ground finches
Genus *Geospiza*

common ancestor

Figure 4.17 Hypothesized evolutionary relationships for finches from the Galápagos Islands. The ancestral population initially gave rise to four lineages of finches. As time passed, different lineages began to become geographically and reproductively isolated from each other. For example, the birds that are now called warbler finches developed beaks that were more slender than the beaks of their ancestor to specialize in eating insects.

individuals separate. The courtship songs of birds are one type of behavioural barrier. Male birds use distinct calls that are recognized by other birds of the same species during their mating season. Birds that have diverged from a common ancestral species may have similar calls, but their calls are different enough from the calls of neighbouring species to provide a biological barrier to reproduction.

Species of spiders also use biological barriers. Female spiders use pheromones (chemical signals) to attract mates of the same species. Some male spiders, such as the one in Figure 4.18, use specific movements to identify themselves to the females.

Other species may live in the same general area but use different habitats, and therefore encounter each other rarely, if at all. An example is two species of garter snakes. One species usually lives near water, and the other species lives in open areas, rarely near water. This is different from a geographical barrier because there is no physical impediment keeping the populations apart.

Take a look at the behavioural barriers to reproduction in leopard frogs in the following Thought Lab.

Figure 4.18 The small (15 to 20 mm), male golden orb spider (from the Genus *Nephila*) signals his identity and intentions to the female (20 to 30 mm, shown on the left) by plucking a strand of the web. His "love song" keeps his species reproductively isolated from other spider species because the female recognizes the signals of his particular mating behaviour. This prevents him from being mistaken for an interloper and being eaten by the female.

 16 How is a bird's call a barrier to speciation?

Speciation Occurs in Reproductively Isolated Populations

When populations become reproductively isolated—even when they have not become geographically isolated—speciation has occurred. For example, animals can become reproductively isolated within the geographical range of a parent population if they begin to use resources that are not used by their parents. Lake Victoria in Africa is the largest tropical lake in the world. The lake is home to hundreds of species of closely related fishes, called cichlids (see Figure 4.19). Each species has features

Figure 4.19 At one time, more than 600 species of cichlids lived in Africa's Lake Victoria. By analyzing a specific gene in the fish, scientists have estimated that the first cichlids entered Lake Victoria 200 000 years ago.

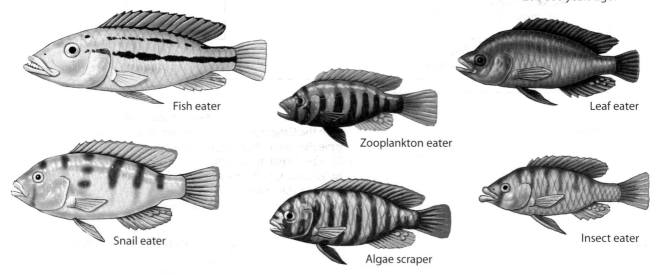

Fish eater

Zooplankton eater

Leaf eater

Snail eater

Algae scraper

Insect eater

Thought Lab | **4.5** | **Leopard Frogs: One Species or Seven?**

Target Skills

Using a range of tools to **gather** and **record** data and information about species of leopard frogs

Using appropriate modes of representation to **communicate** ideas

Procedure

How do frog calls result in keeping species separate? Listen to the calls of two different species of leopard frogs, supplied by your teacher.

Analysis

1. How is a frog call a barrier that keeps species distinct?

2. Leopard frogs in North America include the northern leopard frog (*Rana pipiens*), southern leopard frog (*Rana sphenocephala*), Rio Grande (*Rana berlandieri*), plains (*Rana blairi*), Florida (*Rana sphenocephala sphenocephala*), Ramsey Canyon (*Rana subaquavocalis*), and lowland (*Rana yavapaiensis*). Choose two of these species. Use print or electronic resources to help you describe, in point form, the differences that result in their being considered separate species. **ICT**

Biology File

FYI

In the 1950s, the Nile perch was introduced to Lake Victoria as a source of food for the local human population. This species preyed heavily on cichlids and, by 1990, more than half of the known species of Lake Victoria cichlids had vanished. Now, however, the perch is being fished heavily and some cichlid populations appear to be recovering.

that make it unique from other cichlid species in the lake, and none of these species is found anywhere else on Earth. Remarkably, these species all are descended from a single common ancestor—a species of cichlid that entered Lake Victoria from the Nile River. This incredible explosion of speciation within the same lake happened as small groups of the parent population began to exploit different food sources and habitats in the lake. The lake level has risen and fallen many times during its history, periodically isolating small groups of fish, and these fish have changed extensively because of selective pressures. Scientists studying the cichlids hypothesize that many of the species in the lake today originated after the lake dried to just a few small pools of water about 14 000 years ago. Populations were isolated in these pools of water until the water level rose again. The speciation of cichlids has produced a remarkable variety of cichlids with a fascinating diversity of teeth, jaws, mating behaviours, and coloration.

• • •

 17 How could the rise and fall of lake levels over thousands of years result in the speciation of a population of fish?

• • •

Adaptive Radiation

The diversification of a common ancestral species into a variety of species, all of which are differently adapted, is called **adaptive radiation**. The speciation of finches throughout the Galápagos Islands is an example of adaptive radiation. Another example is the fruit fly genus *Drosophila* of the Hawaiian islands. Descendents of the ancestral *Drosophila* proliferated on the first island they inhabited. Then, individuals began to disperse to other islands. The islands were ecologically different enough to have different environmental situations acting on individuals. The various

selective pressures resulted in different feeding and mating habits, as well as morphological (physical) differences of the hundreds of types of fruit flies that now inhabit the islands.

The Pace of Evolution

How fast is evolutionary change? There are currently two models that scientists have proposed for the pace of evolution: gradualism and punctuated equilibrium. Since Darwin's time, many evolutionary biologists have supported the model of **gradualism**, which says that gradual change occurs steadily, in a linear fashion. According to this model, big changes (such as the evolution of a new species) occur as a result of many small changes. The fossil record, however, rarely reveals fossils that show this gradual transition. Instead, paleontologists most often find species that appear suddenly in the fossil record and then disappear from the record just as abruptly. (It should be remembered, however, that not all species have necessarily left fossils, and many fossils have not yet been discovered.)

The different rates of evolution and evidence in the fossil record that show periods of rapid change (for example, rapid speciation after mass extinctions) have led to another model to explain the rate of evolution: **punctuated equilibrium**. This model proposes that evolutionary history consists of long periods of equilibrium where there is little change, "punctuated" or interrupted by periods of speciation. According to the model of punctuated equilibrium, most species undergo most of their morphological changes when they first diverge from the parent species—for example, if a population colonizes a new area. After that, species change relatively little, even as they give rise to other species. Gradualism and punctuated equilibrium are modelled in Figure 4.20.

Questions about the pace of evolution have stimulated much

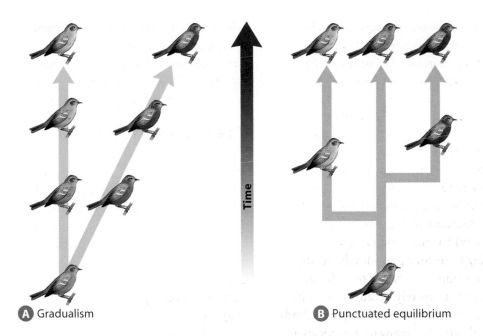

Figure 4.20 Two models have been proposed to explain the pace of evolution: **(A)** gradualism and **(B)** punctuated equilibrium.

A Gradualism

B Punctuated equilibrium

discussion and research, as do all good scientific hypotheses. Debate over the specific details of the mechanisms of evolution by natural selection will continue; details may be adjusted as new technologies and scientific techniques are developed. Nevertheless, the theory of evolution by natural selection forms the backbone of biology as a science, and provides a framework to understand the world in which we live. The theory of evolution explains observations seen in fossils, anatomy, animal behaviours, molecular biology, biogeography, genetics, and geology. It is summarized in the box below.

The theory of evolution by natural selection includes the following ideas:

1. Life forms have developed from ancestral species.

2. All living things are related to one another by varying degrees through common descent.

3. All living things on Earth have a common origin (share a common ancestor).

4. The mechanism by which one species evolves into another species involves random heritable genetic mutations. Some mutations result in a survival advantage for an individual; if so, the individual is more likely to survive and pass this mutation on to its offspring. Eventually, the successful mutation increases in the population and causes the population as a whole to start to change.

Section 4.3 Summary

- A species consists of a reproductively compatible population.
- A new species can form via one of two pathways: transformation or divergence. Both are the result of natural selection; only divergence increases biological diversity.
- Speciation (the formation of a new species) can occur when two populations are prevented from interbreeding. Barriers to reproduction can be geographical or biological. Speciation has occurred when populations become reproductively isolated (they cannot interbreed).
- Adaptive radiation is the diversification of a common ancestral species into a variety of species, all of which are differently adapted.
- Scientific debate about the pace of evolution continues. Two models are being proposed: gradualism, that is,

gradual change occurred in a steady, linear way over time; and punctuated equilibrium, whereby evolutionary history is said to consist of long periods of equilibrium, interrupted by periods of speciation.

Section 4.3 Review

1. Explain how geographical isolation leads to speciation.

2. Use word processing or other software to create a flow chart illustrating the two pathways that can lead to the formation of a new species. Identify the pathway that leads to an increase in biodiversity. **ICT**

3. Explain the difference between habitat isolation and a geographical barrier to reproduction.

4. In the Hawaiian Islands, there are thousands of species of plants and animals that are found nowhere else on Earth. How would you explain this phenomenon?

5. Suppose that you are asked to catalogue the species of birds living in a remote area that has never before been visited by biologists. List the criteria you would use to determine whether the individual birds you observe or collect are the same species or different species.

6. Use word processing or spreadsheet software to create a table or chart that compares and contrasts the ideas of gradualism and punctuated equilibrium. **ICT**

Use the following information to answer the next question.

Red Island and Blue Island are hypothetical islands 500 km off the coast of South America. Red Island is volcanic in origin and is only five million years old. Blue Island separated from South America more than 80 million years ago.

7. Predict the origins of the animals on both islands and explain how they may be similar to or different from the animals of South America.

Use the following information to answer the next question.

Adaptive Radiation

A team of researchers led by Washington University biology professor Jonathan Losos has spent the last several years studying lizards of the genus *Anolis* (commonly called "anoles") that live on large Caribbean islands. He has focussed on Puerto Rico, Cuba, Haiti, and Jamaica. All four islands are inhabited by a diverse array of anole lizards (there are 57 species on Cuba alone), and all four islands have quite similar habitats and vegetation.

Unlike rats and cockroaches, which are generalists and are much the same wherever you find them, anole lizards are specialists. In Puerto Rico, for example, one slender anole species with a long tail lives only in the grass. On narrow twigs at the base of trees you find a different species, also slender, but with stubby legs. On the higher branches of the tree a third species is found, of stocky build and long legs. High up in the leafy canopy of the tree lives a fourth giant green species.

The DNA data are clear-cut: specialist species on one island are not closely related to the same specialists elsewhere and are closely related to other anoles inhabiting the same island.

8. Explain how the situation described above would be an example of adaptive radiation.

Sexual reproduction, which combines the genetic information from two parents, results in variations in the characteristics of offspring. These variations may or may not give the organism a survival advantage. If it does, the variation is likely to be passed on to an increasing number of organisms in the population.

The main source of variations is mutations. Mutations occur when DNA is copied during cell division; mutations that occur in reproductive cells are the ones that can be passed on. When the characteristics of a population change because more individuals with certain inherited traits survived in the local environment and passed the traits on, it is called the process of natural selection. For this reason, the environment can be considered to be the driving force of population changes as time passes. If, however, an environmental change is so sudden or severe that no individuals of a population have characteristics that enable them to survive it, extinction is inevitable.

The theory of evolution was developed from the ideas and observations of a number of scientists. Darwin and Wallace developed similar theories to explain evolution by natural selection, and Darwin published his version in *On the Origin of Species* in 1859. Since publication, discoveries in fields such as paleontology, biogeography, anatomy, embryology, genetics, and molecular biology have produced supporting evidence for the theory.

Organisms that can interbreed and produce healthy offspring that can also reproduce are considered to be a biological species. New species form when populations become reproductively isolated, due to either geographical or biological barriers. Natural selection will occur differently within isolated populations, resulting in variations that could mean the isolated populations can no longer mate. Speciation may or may not result in increased biodiversity.

Chapter 4 Graphic Organizer

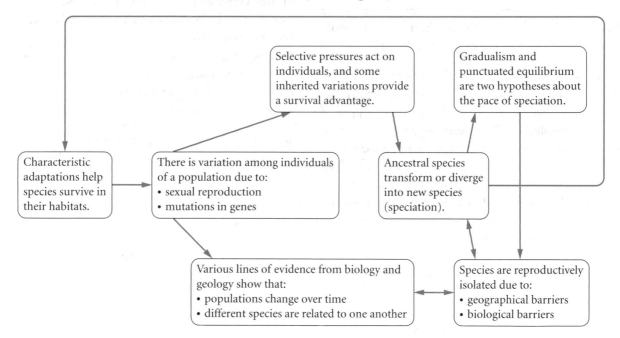

Understanding Concepts

1. Explain the term "selective pressure" as it relates to the study of evolution.

2. How might the colour of a field mouse affect its survival?

3. Describe the possible fates of a mutation and the effects that a mutation may have on a population.

4. Describe the relationships among variations, adaptations, and natural selection.

5. Darwin incorporated observations he made on the *Beagle* expedition into what would eventually become the theory of evolution by natural selection. Summarize some of these observations.

6. Explain why Darwin referred to "descent with modification" rather than "evolution" in *On the Origin of Species*.

Use the following information to answer the following question.

Ord's Kangaroo Rat

The Ord's kangaroo rat seems perfectly suited to its habitat, the sand dunes of southwestern Alberta. Using its long tail and long hind legs, this small mammal can jump 2 m in the air as it hops away from predators, such as snakes and owls.

7. Explain how (a) Lamarck and (b) Darwin would account for the origin of the long hind legs of the Ord's kangaroo rat.

Use the following information to answer the following question.

Homologous vs. Analogous Structures

The wing of a butterfly and the wing of a bird share a common function and are both called wings. The bird wing and insect wing did not arise from an original ancestral structure that became modified through evolution into bird wings and butterfly wings.

8. Are the bird wing and the bat wing homologous structures? Explain.

9. Describe how the anatomy of animals is used to explain evolution.

10. Baleen whales, such as grey and humpback whales, have teeth and body hair as embryos, but not as adults. What does this suggest to you about the evolutionary history of these animals?

11. Explain the role of the environment in the pace of speciation.

Applying Concepts

12. Describe a breeding program that would help a farmer develop a herd of dairy cows that produced more milk per cow than another herd of dairy cows.

Use the following information to answer the following question.

Fruit Flies

A researcher sets up an experiment involving two populations of fruit fly that are genetically very different from each other. The two populations are placed in two enclosed areas that are connected by a narrow tube through which the flies can fit.

13. Illustrate, using words or diagrams or both, how these populations could develop as separate species.

Use the following information to answer the next question.

Bean Seeds

A bean is an example of a dicotyledon (having two embryonic seed leaves). The cotyledons make up the majority of the bean seed. The cotyledons store food for the developing embryo in the form of starch.

Suppose that you measured variations in a population of bean seeds and found that 80% of the population you measure had seeds that were 13 to 17 mm long.

14. a) Describe an advantage a large seed size might have to a newly germinated bean seedling.
   b) Identify two environmental pressures that might favour a small seed over a larger seed.
   c) Briefly outline a breeding strategy that a gardener could use to produce beans with larger cotyledons.

Use the following information to answer the next question.

Proteins

Proteins are a class of organic compounds that are present in and vital to every living cell. Proteins are made of a long chain of amino acids. The primary structure of protein molecules is determined by the sequence of amino acids. The amino acid sequence of a protein determines the higher levels of structure of the molecule. A single change in the primary structure (the amino acid sequence) can have a profound biological change in the overall structure and function of the protein.

Scientists compare differences in amino acid sequences to determine evolutionary relationships among organisms. Some short amino acid sequences are given below.

Amino Acid Sequences in Four Primates

Baboon	Chimpanzee	Lemur	Human
ASN	SER	ALA	SER
THR	THR	THR	THR
THR	ALA	SER	ALA
GLY	GLY	GLY	GLY
ASP	ASP	GLU	ASP
GLU	GLU	LYS	GLU
VAL	VAL	VAL	VAL
ASP	GLU	GLU	GLU
ASP	ASP	ASP	ASP
SER	THR	SER	THR
PRO	PRO	PRO	PRO
GLY	GLY	GLY	GLY
GLY	GLY	SER	GLY
ASN	ALA	HIS	ALA
ASN	ASN	ASN	ASN

15. a) Count how many amino acids in a baboon differ from the amino acids in a human. Calculate the percentage difference by determining the number of different amino acids divided by the total number of amino acids studied, and multiply by 100. Do the same for the chimpanzee and for the lemur.

b) Identify the primate that appears to be most closely related to the human and identify the primate that appears to be least closely related to the human.

c) Would an evolutionary biologist draw a conclusion based solely on the evidence provided in this chart? Explain.

Use the following information to answer the next question.

Garter Snakes

The northwest garter snake (*Thamnophis ordinoides*) (**A**) and the common garter snake (*T. sirtalis*) (**B**) occupy different habitats in a similar geographic area. The northwest garter snake prefers open areas such as meadows and rarely enters water. The common garter snake is most commonly found near water.

16. Explain why these garter snakes are likely to remain separate species.

Making Connections

17. Choose a fossil, either one described in this chapter or one you have researched. Describe how this particular fossil helps provide scientists with information on how populations change over time.

18. Suppose that you are a family physician who often prescribes antibiotics. Make a list of criteria for your patients, to help them understand (in terms of developing antibiotic resistant bacteria), why they must take antibiotics only as prescribed.

Use the following information to answer the next question.

Hawaiian Plants

You are a biologist who is working with a student to collect plants in Hawaii. You notice that your assistant did not label a plant with the name of the island on which is was collected. When asked, he explains that he did not think this was necessary because he thought that the plant was found on all the Hawaiian Islands.

19. Write a memo to your assistant clearly outlining why it is necessary to label the exact island and location where the plant was found, as well as the time when the plant was found. Focus your memo on the concepts presented in this chapter.

Career Focus: **Ask a Paleontologist**

Since childhood, Dr. Darla Zelenitsky has been fascinated by dinosaurs. Today, she is a paleontologist and researcher at the University of Calgary. She works in conjunction with the Royal Tyrrell Museum in Drumheller, Alberta. Dr. Zelenitsky's research on dinosaur eggs is changing the way that scientists look at dinosaur evolution and may help to explain the success of many dinosaur species.

Q **Why are other scientists interested in your research findings?**

I've been looking at the interrelationships or relationships of dinosaurs based on their reproduction. This is an approach that's never been used before.

Q **What made you think of studying dinosaur reproduction?**

Generally, scientists have looked more at the demise of the dinosaurs and why they went extinct. However, I'm interested in why dinosaurs survived for so long [165 million years]. I think their long evolutionary success can be explained by studying their reproductive strategies.

Q **How do you study the reproductive strategies of dinosaurs?**

We examine evidence from dinosaur eggs and compare this to evidence from eggs of modern crocodiles and birds. We can look at the number of eggs in a clutch, the size and shape of the eggs, or the pores in the eggshells, which would have allowed the embryos inside the eggs to breathe. These features can tell us what kind of nesting environment dinosaurs most likely used: open, like bird nests, or buried, like crocodile nests.

Q **What else can you learn about dinosaur reproduction from dinosaur eggs?**

We can learn about their nesting behaviours. There are fossils of dinosaurs sitting on top of their eggs, much like modern birds do, from the Gobi Desert in Mongolia. Birds use their bodies to incubate or brood their eggs.

Q **Do you think dinosaurs are more related to birds than to reptiles?**

Actually, birds are a lineage of dinosaurs—and they represent an extremely successful group of living animals. With respect to reproduction, I suspect that dinosaurs shared strategies with crocodiles and birds, or just with birds, or they had reproductive strategies unique to themselves. Brooding is an example of a reproductive strategy that some dinosaurs share with modern birds, but do not share with alligators and crocodiles. On the other hand, crocodiles and birds only have one functional oviduct, whereas we suspect that dinosaurs had two functional oviducts and that they laid two eggs at a time. We see evidence of this in some dinosaur nests, where the eggs appear to be laid in pairs.

Q **Which dinosaurs' eggs do you work with?**

I've worked with eggs from various dinosaurs all over the world—some meat-eating, some plant-eating. I've looked at giant sauropod eggs from France, hadrosaur (duck-billed dinosaur) eggs from Alberta, prosauropod eggs from South Africa, and the eggs of bird-like dinosaurs, called oviraptorids, from Asia.

Q **Where are you currently doing most of your fieldwork?**

In southern Alberta at Devil's Coulee, a fossilized nesting site with preserved dinosaur eggs, embryos, and nests. Dinosaurs are a tremendous natural resource in Alberta, and we've got some of the most prolific dinosaur sites in the world.

Q **Does one have to be a research scientist to be involved in paleontology?**

No. There are a lot of amateurs involved in paleontology, looking for and studying fossils. The Royal Tyrrell Museum has volunteer programs in which people help to excavate and prepare fossils.

Other Careers Related to Paleontology

Paleoartist Trained artists, or researchers with a skill for drawing, rely on fossils and other evidence to create visual representations of what past life might have looked like. Paleoartists may illustrate books, research papers, and magazine articles, and may create paintings and other visuals for museums, films, and television.

Paleotechnician Technicians (also called fossil preparators), along with researchers and volunteers, search for and excavate fossils and prepare fossils for study. For example, paleotechnologists may carefully remove rock from fossilized bones and create models of dinosaurs. Paleotechnologists may also help researchers reconstruct dinosaur skeletons. An undergraduate degree in geology, paleontology, or zoology is good preparation for a career as a paleotechnician.

Professional Paleontologist Researchers with expertise in vertebrate or invertebrate paleontology, or other areas of paleontology, may work as curators at natural history museums. Some paleontologists are professors at universities; they teach, train graduate students, and conduct various kinds of paleontological research.

Paleoclimatologist Scientists examine evidence of Earth's ancient climates by studying tree rings, glaciers, and rocks. Paleoclimatologists, who may have graduate degrees in Earth sciences, sometimes work with paleoecologists, who study ancient environments and populations. Paleoclimatologists can help to develop computer models for predicting future climate change.

Stratigrapher Geoscientists study the formation of rock layers in order to learn about past environments. As well, they help governments and industries make decisions about resource development. To conduct fieldwork and analyses for government agencies, such as the Geological Survey of Canada, a doctorate degree in geology is required.

Micropaleontologist Microscopic fossils, such as diatoms, are the most abundant type of fossils, and their presence can indicate nearby oil or gas deposits. Micropaleontologists, who have undergraduate degrees in geology, work with petroleum companies to find sources of fossil fuels.

This model shows what a newly hatched dinosaur may have looked like in a nest.

Go Further...

1. List and research three methods, other than studying dinosaur eggs, that paleontologists could use to study the evolutionary relationships between dinosaurs and birds.

2. How might geneticists contribute to the study of past life forms?

3. Why is it important to understand the process of evolution in order to make informed decisions about human actions that could affect Earth's biodiversity?

Understanding Concepts

1. Define the term "population."

2. Describe the study of ecology.

3. Hypothesize what might happen if all the predators were eliminated from an ecosystem.

4. Explain why organisms are not evenly distributed across Earth.

5. Identify three abiotic factors that create different habitats within a pond, and illustrate their effects on the pond ecosystem.

6. Identify four factors that might limit the population size of animals (such as a raven) that live as scavengers.

7. Give an example of (a) biome, (b) an ecosystem within the biome, and (c) a community within this ecosystem.

8. Explain why two species classified in the same family must also be in the same order.

9. Give an example of how (a) an abiotic factor and (b) a biotic factor can limit population growth.

10. Identify the factors that might produce regular population cycles typical of small herbivore species, such as mice and squirrels.

11. The following metaphor can be used to describe the terms habitat and niche. "The habitat of a species can be compared to an address, while its ecological niche can be compared to a job." Write another metaphor to describe the range of an organism.

12. Pick an organism that lives in an environment you are familiar with. List the factors that might limit the growth of its population.

13. Give three examples of how a population of deer mice in a field might compete for the available resources.

14. Explain why diversity within a population is necessary for evolution.

15. Explain the differences among structural (physical), physiological, and behavioural adaptations. Give an example of each.

16. Are a bat wing and a butterfly wing homologous structures? Explain your answer.

17. Explain why it is correct to talk about the evolution of populations, but it is incorrect to talk about the evolution of individual organisms.

18. Distinguish between a fact and a theory. Give an example of each.

19. Explain why DNA is a useful tool for determining possible relationships among species of organisms. Give an example to support your answer.

20. Describe how the following items contributed to Darwin's theory of evolution:
    a) his experiences on the voyage of the *Beagle*
    b) Lyell's *Principles of Geology*
    c) Malthus's essay about populations

21. a) Describe the possible fates of a mutation and the effects that a mutation may have on a population.
    b) Explain what could happen in a population when a mutation provides a selective advantage.

22. a) Give an example of a geographical barrier and a biological barrier.
    b) Explain how each barrier keeps species separate.

23. Life is very diverse, but all species share many features, especially at the cellular and molecular level. How can evolution explain this seeming contradiction?

24. You are a paleontologist and find a fossilized skeleton of a whale-like aquatic animal with tiny legs. Is this a transitional fossil? Explain your answer.

Applying Concepts

Use the following information to answer the next question.

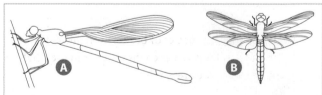

Dichotomous Key
1a. front and hind wings similar in size and shape, and folded parallel to the body when at rest… damsel fly

1b. hind wings wider than front wings near base, and extended on either side of the body when at rest… dragonfly

25. a) Use the dichotomous key provided to identify the organisms in the diagrams. Explain how you arrived at your decision.
    b) From the key and the diagrams, explain why you could infer that dragonflies and damsel flies evolved from a common ancestor.

Use the following information to answer the next question.

The following shows the levels of classification for a grey wolf. These levels are not in order according to the hierarchical classification system in use today.

order: Carnivora
class: Mammalia
kingdom: Animalia
phylum: Chordata
domain: Eukarya
species: lupus
family: Canidae
genus: Canis

26. a) Place the levels of classification in order from most general to most specific.
   b) Identify the scientific name of the grey wolf.

Use the following information to answer the next question.

Grizzly Bears
Female grizzly bears typically have only one offspring every three to five years. Black bears, however, have their offspring (often twins or even triplets) every two years. Female grizzlies do not begin breeding until they are five to seven years old, whereas female black bears begin breeding when they are from three to five years old. Grizzly bears and black bears are omnivores, but grizzly bears have a more restricted diet and are more particular about their dining sites. Grizzly bears are also larger than black bears.

27. a) Identify which species of bear is more likely to become endangered as changes occur in their habitat and explain your reasoning.

Use the following information to answer the next question.

Grizzly bears can mate with black bears, but the offspring are not fertile. On the other hand, grizzly bears can mate with polar bears, and the offspring are fertile.

   b) Infer the evolutionary relationship among grizzly bears, black bears, and polar bears.

Use the following information to answer the next question.

Stomata are openings on the surfaces of leaves that allow plants to release water. The following graph shows the number of stomata on the leaves of one tree species.

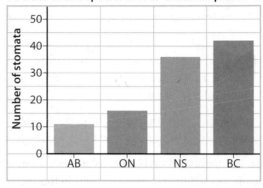

Average number of stomata in 10 leaves of 10 trees of one species in four Canadian provinces

28. a) Describe what these data might tell you about the precipitation in the areas where the data were collected.
   b) Based on these data, infer the relationship between precipitation and number of stomata on trees.

Use the following information to answer the next question.

Transect
In order to estimate the size of a population of oak tress, a forester runs several 100 m transects through a 100 ha (hectare) woodlot and counts the number of oaks within 5 m of the transect line. Five transects produced counts of: 15, 17, 25, 16, and 20 oak trees respectively.

29. a) Use this information to calculate the density of oak trees in this area.
   b) Estimate the size of the oak population in the woodlot.
   c) Identify another method the forester could have used to sample the population of trees in this woodlot.

30. Outline an experimental procedure that would demonstrate variation within a population of corn. Consider using the length of corn cob or the number of kernels of corn per cob in your experimental design. Include a suitable hypothesis.

31. Describe the relationships among mutations, variations, adaptation, and natural selection.

32. An evolutionary biologist said, "Evolution is like modifying a machine while it's still running." Interpret this statement.

33. a) Use graphics software and point-form notes to show the two pathways that can lead to the formation of a new species. **ICT**

b) Identify the evolutionary pathway that leads to an increase in biodiversity and explain why.

34. Explain how the following situations are reproductive barriers that keep species separate.

a) Species of fireflies use distinctive patterns of flashes.

b) Two species of grass flower at different times of year, yet live in the same environment.

c) The crossing of two species of fly produces a fertile hybrid offspring, whose offspring is weak and infertile.

35. Use word processing or graphics software to make a graphic organizer showing the relationship among climate, soil, plants, and animals in a biome. **ICT**

Use the following information to answer the next question.

Protecting our Forests

Governments restrict the movement of plants or animals across boundaries, including provincial borders. In Alberta, for example, people are not allowed to transport wood with bark on it into the province. These measures are designed to help prevent the spread of mountain pine beetles and Dutch elm disease that can harm Alberta's forests—one of the prime concerns during outbreaks of pine mountain beetle is the death of high-value pines in thousands of hectares of forest.

The fungus that accompanies the mountain pine beetle larvae reduces the aesthetic value of forests by staining the wood blue; the mountain pine beetle also reduces the timber volume, and the monetary gains of the high-value mature tree. During the last mountain pine beetle outbreak (1977 to 1987) in Alberta, an estimated 1 068 167 m³ of lodgepole pine were killed.

36. Explain, both in terms of the ecosystems in Alberta and the economic impact of these types of pest outbreaks, why it is important for all citizens to respect this type of restriction.

Use the following information to answer the next question.

Trout

The population of trout in a small lake has fluctuated around 2000 for the last 10 years. The owner of a fishing resort on the lake wants to increase the number of trout available for clients to catch. The owner plans to stock the lake with 1000 more individuals of the same species.

37. Predict the short term and long terms effects of adding the additional fish on the population of trout in this lake.

38. Compare the diversity of habitats and the biodiversity in a forest that has been logged and replanted with a single species of tree to a forest that has not been logged.

39. Explain how the examination of proteins in individual organisms can demonstrate relatedness among species.

40. Explain the conditions in which a seemingly neutral mutation that is present in a small portion of a population might become quickly perpetuated in, and advantageous to, the entire population.

Use the following information to answer the next question.

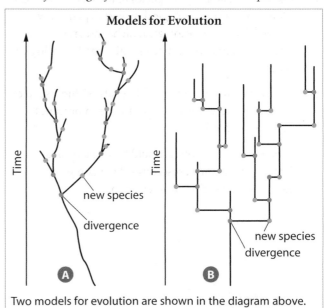

Models for Evolution

Two models for evolution are shown in the diagram above.

41. Identify each model, and explain how each is used to model evolution.

42. Use word processing or graphics software to produce a timeline outlining the major events and ideas that have led to the current theory of evolution. **ICT**

Making Connections

Use the following information to answer the next question.

Frog Populations
Imagine two frog populations in two different locations. The frogs differ only in the colour of their skin.

43. a) Suggest data that would help you decide if both populations belong to the same species of frog.

b) Assume that the two populations are different species. Suggest data that would help you decide how closely related these two species are to each other.

44. Should people be as concerned about some species of mosses becoming extinct as they are about whales becoming extinct? Explain.

45. All populations eventually face limits to their population because of abiotic and biotic factors. Compare a micro-organism (such as the bacteria *E. coli*), a plant species (such as a tree), and a mammal (such as a deer), with respect to the types of factors that might limit the growth of populations of these species.

46. Many of the endangered species in the world have very specific, or narrow, ecological niches. Explain why species with narrow ecological niches are more likely to become extinct than species with broader ecological niches.

47. Given your understanding of diversity within a species and natural selection, explain why it is important to maintain biodiversity.

48. Do you think antibiotics should be available in a pharmacy without a prescription? Explain your answer in terms of natural selection.

Use the following information to answer the next question.

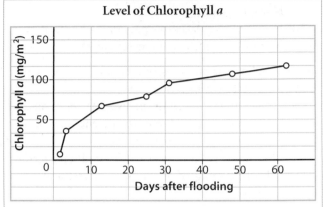

The graph above shows the level of chlorophyll *a* (a pigment needed for photosynthesis) in a stream, in the days following a flood that nearly scoured all life from the stream. The chlorophyll indicates the growth of algae in the stream.

49. a) Compare the amount of growth in the first 30 days with the amount of growth in the second 30 days.

b) Explain what might be enhancing or limiting the algae growth in this 60-day period.

c) The main animals in this stream are invertebrates that feed off the algae. Predict what might be happening to the populations of these herbivorous invertebrates during this 60-day time period.

Use the following information to answer the next question.

Pests
You are a gardening expert who runs a local greenhouse and nursery. A gardener calls you and explains that she had an insect infestation in her garden. When she applied an insecticide, 99 percent of the insects were killed. After a few weeks, she noticed that the insect problem was back so she applied more pesticide. This time, only 50 percent of the insects were killed by the pesticide.

50. Explain why the insecticide did not work as well the second time it was applied.

UNIT
3

Photosynthesis and Cellular Respiration

General Outcomes

In this unit, you will

- relate photosynthesis to the storage of energy in organic compounds
- explain the role of cellular respiration in releasing potential energy from organic compounds

Unit 3 Contents

Focussing Questions

1 How does light energy from the Sun enter living systems?

2 How is the energy from light used to synthesize organic matter?

3 How is the energy from organic matter released for use by living systems?

Unit PreQuiz ⑦
www.albertabiology.ca

This is a common view of the Great Plains—herds of animals grazing on a seemingly endless ocean of grasses. The interaction between producers and consumers is the way in which the Sun's energy enters, is transformed by, and exits living systems. At the same time, vital chemicals such as water, carbon, nitrogen, and sulfur cycle continuously, linking organisms with one another and with their environment.

Today, the Prairie landscape is punctuated by the products and practices of technology. The petroleum industry "taps into" long-buried stores of energy, in the form of crude oil and natural gas. These resources developed with the passage of time as natural chemical processes slowly changed the bodies of ancient producers and consumers into the compounds that fuel modern society and serve as building blocks for plastics and other synthetic materials.

In Unit 1, you explored the interactions between living and non-living systems at a macroscopic level. In this unit, you will consider the same interactions at a microscopic level. You will examine the cellular processes of photosynthesis and cellular respiration that provide the energy and matter all organisms need to survive.

Prerequisite Concepts

This unit builds on your knowledge of photosynthesis and cellular respiration, as well as the investigations you have conducted to explore them (Chapters 1 and 2).

Plant and Animal Cells

Plants and animals (as well as fungi and protists) are organisms that are made up of eurkaryotic cells. These are cells that have a nucleus.

Cells are the microscopic components that make up all organisms. Cells exhibit the characteristics of life, but they can also be specialized for specific tasks.

The cells that make up plants and the cells that make up animals have some structures that distinguish one type from the other. For example, plant cells are surrounded by a rigid structure called

a cell wall, while animal cells lack this feature.

Plant and animal cells also share several basic structural and functional similarities. For example, both types of cell contain organelles, which are structures that have a specific function in the cell. Many organelles are surrounded by a membrane. The various organelles work together as part of a cellular system that effectively carries out the essential life-related tasks of the cell. Figure P3.1 and P3.2 summarize and review the basic structures and functions of plant and animal cells.

Figure P3.1 In general, plant cells are larger than animal cells. The most distinctive features that distinguish plant cells from animal cells are their cell wall and chloroplasts.

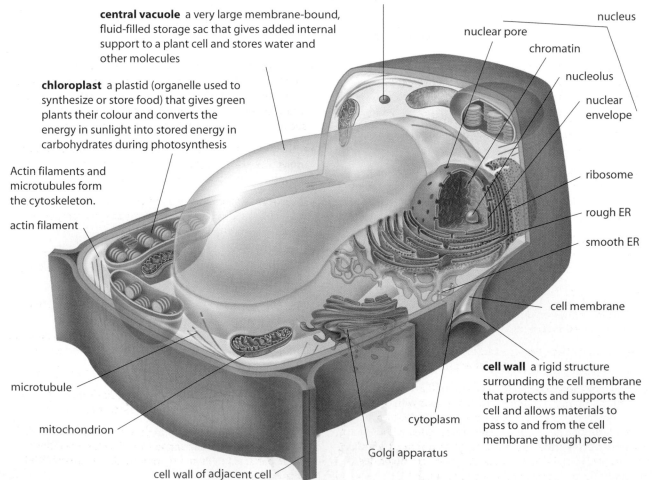

peroxisome a membrane-bound vesicle containing enzymes that convert fatty acids in seeds to sugars (providing a useable food source for a germinating plant) and help the cell use carbon dioxide during photosynthesis

central vacuole a very large membrane-bound, fluid-filled storage sac that gives added internal support to a plant cell and stores water and other molecules

chloroplast a plastid (organelle used to synthesize or store food) that gives green plants their colour and converts the energy in sunlight into stored energy in carbohydrates during photosynthesis

Actin filaments and microtubules form the cytoskeleton.

actin filament

microtubule

mitochondrion

cell wall of adjacent cell

Golgi apparatus

cytoplasm

cell wall a rigid structure surrounding the cell membrane that protects and supports the cell and allows materials to pass to and from the cell membrane through pores

cell membrane

smooth ER

rough ER

ribosome

nuclear envelope

nucleolus

chromatin

nucleus

nuclear pore

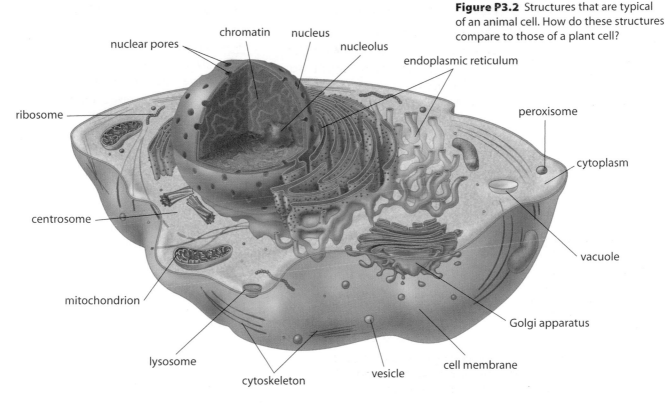

Figure P3.2 Structures that are typical of an animal cell. How do these structures compare to those of a plant cell?

Labels in figure: nuclear pores, chromatin, nucleus, nucleolus, endoplasmic reticulum, peroxisome, ribosome, cytoplasm, centrosome, vacuole, mitochondrion, Golgi apparatus, lysosome, cell membrane, cytoskeleton, vesicle

- **cell membrane** a structure that separates the cell interior from the outside world and controls the movement of materials into and out of the cell

- **cytoplasm** a gel-like material consisting mostly of water that contains dissolved materials and creates the chemical environment in which the other cell structures work

- **nucleus** the command centre of the cell that contains the DNA blueprints for making proteins and is surrounded by a double membrane to protect the DNA from potentially damaging byproducts of biochemical reactions

- **nuclear pores** pores in the nuclear membrane large enough to allow macromolecules to enter and ribosomes to leave the nucleus

- **chromatin** uncoiled chromosomes (DNA)

- **nucleolus** a specialized area of chromatin inside the nucleus responsible for producing ribosomes

- **ribosome** tiny two-part structures found throughout the cytoplasm that help put together proteins

- **endoplasmic reticulum (ER)** a system of flattened membrane-bound sacs and tubes continuous with the outer membrane of the nuclear envelope that has two types of membrane: rough ER, which is studded with ribosomes and synthesizes proteins, and smooth ER, which synthesizes phospholipids and packages macromolecules in vesicles for transport to other parts of the cell

- **Golgi apparatus** a stack of flattened membrane-bound sacs that receive vesicles from the ER, contain enzymes for modifying proteins and lipids, package finished products into vesicles for transport to the cell membrane (for secretion out of the cell) and within the cell as lysosomes

- **mitochondrion** the powerhouse of the cell where organic molecules, usually carbohydrates, are broken down inside a double membrane to release and transfer energy

- **lysosome** a membrane-bound vesicle filled with digestive enzymes that can break down worn-out cell components or materials brought into the cell

- **peroxisome** a membrane-bound vesicle containing enzymes that break down lipids and toxic waste products, such as alcohol

- **centrosome** an organelle located near the nucleus that organizes the cell's microtubules, contains a pair of centrioles (made up of microtubules), and helps to organize the even distribution of cell components when cells divide

- **vesicle** a small membrane-bound transport sac

- **vacuole** a large membrane-bound, fluid-filled sac for the temporary storage of food, water, or waste products

- **cytoskeleton** a network of three kinds of interconnected fibres that maintain cell shape and allow for movement of cell parts: actin filaments, intermediate filaments, and microtubules

The Cell Membrane

The cell membrane is a boundary that separates the internal environment of a cell from its external environment. Cell membranes are composed mainly of a double layer of phospholipid molecules, which are a type of lipid. (Lipids are organic compounds that do not dissolve in water, such as fats, oils, and steroids like cholesterol.) Each phospholipid molecule has a shape with a distinctive head region at one end and a tail region at the other. These two ends have different chemical compositions that cause them to interact differently with water. The head end dissolves easily in water, while the tail end is insoluble in water.

Because of these different responses to water, phospholipid molecules arrange themselves spontaneously in water into a two-layered, sandwich-like structure. In this structure, the head ends are on the outside layers, where they are exposed to the watery fluid outside and inside the cell. The tail ends face each other on the inside of the structure, away from water.

As shown in Figure P3.3, cell membranes are composed of these double-layer phospholipids as well as various proteins and other molecules that are embedded within them and that extend from them. Some of the embedded proteins create passageways through which water-soluble molecules and ions can pass. Other proteins help transport substances across the membrane.

Passive Transport: Diffusion and Osmosis

The cell membrane is *selectively permeable* (or semi-permeable), which means that it allows some molecules to pass through it while preventing others

Figure P3.3 A model of cell membrane structure. Note the two layers of phospholipids (called a phospholipids bilayer), with the distinctive head-and-tail shape of the phospholipid molecules. Inside the cell, parts of the cell's "skeleton" (called the cytoskeleton) support the membrane.

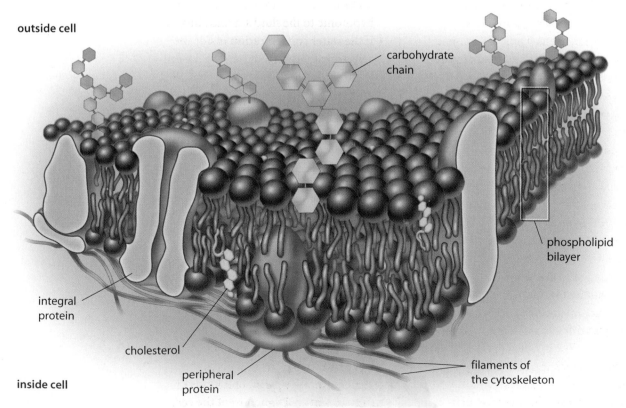

outside cell

carbohydrate chain

phospholipid bilayer

integral protein

cholesterol

peripheral protein

filaments of the cytoskeleton

inside cell

Figure P3.4 Diffusion is a spontaneous process in which molecules move down their concentration gradient—that is, from an area of higher concentration to an area of lower concentration. In this photograph, for example, the ink particles will become dispersed evenly as time passes due to diffusion.

from doing so. One method by which small molecules and ions move through the cell membrane is diffusion. *Diffusion* is the natural movement of molecules or ions from a region where they are more concentrated to one where they are less concentrated (Figure P3.4).

Many molecules—especially small, uncharged ones such as oxygen—can move easily through the cell membrane by diffusion. The cell membrane cannot prevent this movement of certain molecules and ions, because it is permeable to them. Thus, diffusion is a passive process that does not require energy from the cell.

The natural tendency of a substance to move from an area of high concentration to an area of lower concentration is often described as "moving down" or "following" its *concentration gradient*. A gradient is a general term that refers to a difference in some quality between two adjacent regions. Differences in concentration, in pressure, in electrical energy, and in pH all establish gradients.

Water inside the cell (intracellular fluid) and outside the cell (extracellular fluid) also diffuses freely through the cell membrane. The diffusion of a solvent (in this case, water) across a semi-permeable membrane that separates two solutions is called *osmosis*. The direction of osmosis depends on the relative concentration of water molecules on either side of the cell membrane.

- If the water concentration inside the cell equals the water concentration outside the cell, equal amounts of water move in and out of the cell at the same rate. (The cell is isotonic to the fluid surrounding it.)
- If the water concentration outside the cell is greater than that inside the cell, water moves into the cell. (The cell is hypotonic to the fluid surrounding it.)
- If the water concentration inside the cell is greater than that outside the cell, water moves out of the cell. (The cell is hypertonic to the fluid surrounding it.)

The cell membrane cannot prevent the movement of water, because it is permeable to water molecules. Thus, osmosis is a passive process that does not require energy from the cell.

Facilitated Diffusion

Substances such as water, oxygen, and carbon dioxide can pass through the cell membrane without assistance. However, other substances cannot do so without help. For example, a glucose molecule is too large to diffuse between the structural molecules of the cell membrane. Specialized transport proteins in the cell membrane help different kinds of substances move in and out of the cell.

The structure of these transport proteins makes them very selective. A particular transport protein will recognize and help to move only one type of dissolved molecule or ion based on its shape, size, and electrical charge.

A type of membrane protein called a carrier protein facilitates (helps) the movement of glucose molecules from where they are more concentrated to where they are less concentrated. A carrier protein will accept only a non-charged molecule with a specific shape (Figure 3.5A). However, carrier proteins allow molecules to move both in and out of the cell.

A different type of membrane protein called a channel protein transports charged particles across the membrane (Figure 3.5B). Channel proteins have a tunnel-like shape. To pass through, an ion in solution must be small enough to fit through the "tunnel." It must also have the right charge. In much the same way that like poles of two magnets repel each other, a positively charged channel protein repels positively charged ions, and a negatively charged channel protein repels negatively charged ions.

In diffusion, osmosis, and facilitated diffusion, any substances crossing the cell membrane follow their concentration gradient. No energy from the cell is required, regardless of whether the substance moves into or out of the cell.

Active Transport

Active transport uses energy to enable a cell to take in a substance that is more concentrated inside the cell than outside the cell. Energy for active transport often comes from a molecule called **a**denosine **tri**phosphate (ATP). (You will learn about this molecule and its importance to plants, animals, and other organisms in Chapter 5.)

When one of the three phosphates is split from ATP in a chemical reaction, energy is released that is harnessed to power a cellular function. Often, this function is to move a molecule through a membrane against its concentration gradient.

Endocytosis and Exocytosis

Some of the substances that a cell must take in or expel are too large to cross

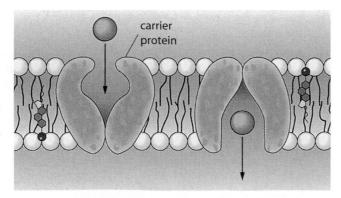

carrier protein

Figure P3.5A Carrier proteins change shape to allow certain molecules to cross the cell membrane.

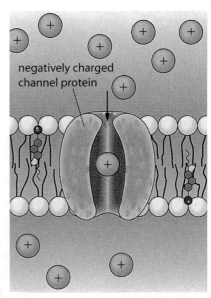

negatively charged channel protein

Figure P.3.5B Channel proteins provide water-filled passages through which small dissolved ions can diffuse.

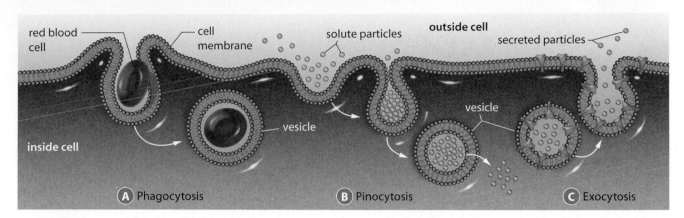

red blood cell

cell membrane

solute particles

outside cell

secreted particles

vesicle

vesicle

inside cell

A Phagocytosis

B Pinocytosis

C Exocytosis

Figure P3.6 Examples of endocytosis and exocytosis

the cell membrane. Cholesterol is one example. The cell uses a specialized method to move such substances. It can fold in on itself to create a membrane-enclosed, bubble-like sac called a vesicle. The cell uses vesicles to "swallow" or expel various substances (Figure P3.6).

When the cell membrane folds inward, trapping and enclosing a small amount of matter from outside the cell, the process is called endocytosis. There are three forms of this process: pinocytosis, phagocytosis, and receptor-assisted endocytosis.

Pinocytosis involves the intake of a small droplet of extracellular fluid along with any dissolved substances or tiny particles that it may contain. This process occurs in almost all cell types nearly all of the time.

Phagocytosis involves the intake of a large droplet of extracellular fluid, often including bacteria or bits of organic matter. This process occurs only in specialized cells such as certain white blood cells of our immune system.

Receptor-assisted endocytosis involves the intake of specific molecules that attach to special proteins in the cell membrane. These membrane receptor proteins possess a uniquely shaped projection or cavity that fits the shape of

only one specific molecule. Cholesterol is transported into cells using this process.

Exocytosis is the process for removing substances from the cell. In exocytosis, a vesicle from the inside the cell moves to the cell surface. There, the vesicle membrane fuses with the cell membrane. The contents of the outward-bound vesicle are secreted into the extracellular fluid. Exocytosis is important in cells that specialize in the secretion of cell products such as hormones.

Mechanisms for the Movement of Substances across the Cell Membrane

Membrane Transport Mechanism	Characteristics
diffusion	follows concentration gradient; no energy from the cell is required
osmosis	follows concentration gradient; no energy from the cell is required
facilitated diffusion	follows concentration gradient, assisted by channel proteins or carrier proteins; no energy from the cell is required
active transport	moves against concentration gradient, assisted by channel or carrier proteins and with the input of energy (usually from ATP molecules)
endocytosis (may be pinocytosis, phagocytosis, and receptor-assisted endocytosis)	membrane engulfs a substance and draws it into the cell in membrane-bounded vesicle
exocytosis	membrane-bounded vesicle fuses with cell membrane, releasing the cell's contents outside of the cell

CHAPTER 5

Photosynthesis and Cellular Respiration

Chapter Concepts

5.1 Matter and Energy Pathways in Living Systems

- Photosynthesis, the process in which certain organisms trap solar energy, occurs in chloroplasts.

- Cellular respiration, the process in which energy-rich compounds are broken down to generate ATP, occurs in mitochondria.

- ATP is the source of energy for many of the chemical reactions that occur in cells.

5.2 Photosynthesis Stores Energy in Organic Compounds

- In light-dependent reactions, chloroplasts trap solar energy and transform the energy to the reducing power of NADPH and the chemical energy of ATP.

- Chemiosmosis is the mechanism by which energy stored in a concentration gradient is used to generate ATP.

- In light-independent reactions, the energy of ATP and NADPH is used to reduce carbon dioxide to synthesize glucose.

5.3 Cellular Respiration Releases Energy from Organic Compounds

- Aerobic cellular respiration involves three metabolic pathways: glycolysis, the Krebs cycle, and an electron transport system.

- Aerobic cellular respiration is the complete oxidation of glucose to release energy.

- Fermentation is the incomplete oxidation of glucose to release energy.

More than half of all oxygen generated on Earth is produced by phytoplankton—photosynthetic producers—in the oceans. When conditions of water temperature and nutrients are just right, the phytoplankton grow rapidly, or "bloom," producing large amounts of chlorophyll, which are visible to orbiting satellites (light blue in this photograph). Scientists have discovered that these "blooms" might do more than provide oxygen. They might also serve as an early warning of earthquakes along coastal regions. Prior to an earthquake, the ocean floor begins to shift. This causes an upwelling of nutrient-rich water from the ocean bottom. As the nutrients near the surface, they contribute to conditions that stimulate a bloom. When unexpected blooms appear near regions where tectonic plates meet, they may indicate that an earthquake and possibly a tsunami are imminent.

Seeing Green

In a functioning green plant, light energy is trapped by light-absorbing molecules called pigments and used to synthesize carbohydrates from carbon dioxide and water. The main photosynthetic pigment is chlorophyll. What effect does light have on chlorophyll if it is removed from a living plant?

Materials

- beaker of prepared chlorophyll solution (provided by your teacher)
- strong light source (such as a slide projector)

Procedure

1. In a darkened room, shine a strong beam of light at a sample of chlorophyll solution.

2. Observe the colour of the chlorophyll by viewing the sample at a slight angle.

3. Observe the colour of the chlorophyll by viewing the sample at a right angle to the beam of light.

4. Describe the colour you see in steps 2 and 3.

Analysis

1. Recall, from previous studies, that visible light is a mixture of different colours (wavelengths). Which colours of light do you think chlorophyll absorbs? Explain your reasoning.

2. Chlorophyll has a property called fluorescence. When a pigment molecule absorbs a specific colour (wavelength) of light, its electrons become "excited"—that is, they move to a higher energy state. Almost immediately, the excited electrons return to their original, lower-energy state as they emit (give off) the energy they absorbed. The emitted energy is visible as light of a longer, lower-energy wavelength. In which step did you observe fluorescence? Suggest a possible explanation for what you observed.

Only plants, algae, and some species of bacteria can convert the Sun's light energy into chemical energy. Is the way that plants use energy different from the way that your body uses energy?

SECTION 5.1

Matter and Energy Pathways in Living Systems

Section Outcomes

In this section, you will
- **compare** and **summarize** the essential features of chloroplasts and mitochondria in relation to the role of photosynthesis in storing energy and the role of cellular respiration in releasing energy
- **summarize** and **explain** the role of ATP in cellular metabolism

Key Terms

photosynthesis
cellular respiration
chloroplast
thylakoids
mitochondria
metabolism
reducing power

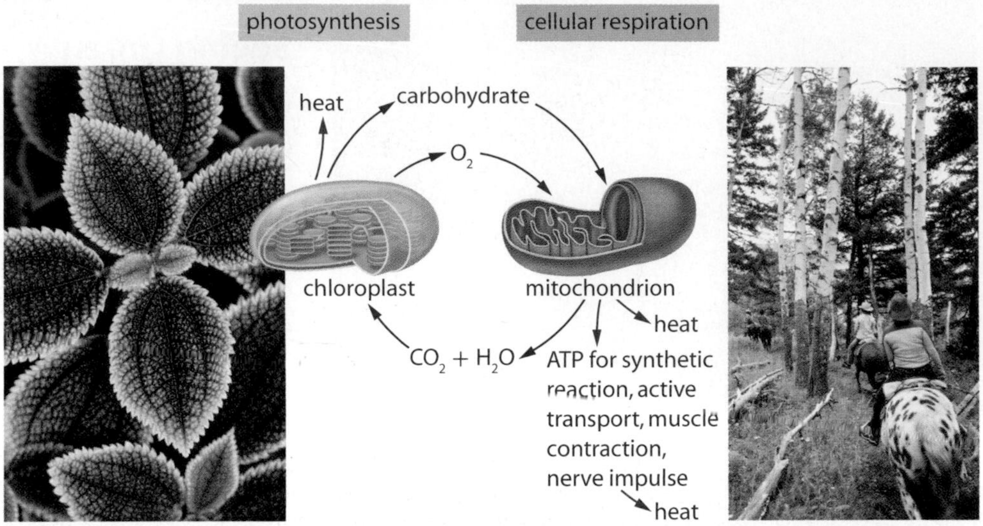

Figure 5.1 Chloroplasts trap the Sun's energy and use it to synthesize energy-rich compounds. Animals either eat the plants or other plant-eating animals. These consumers then use the stored, energy-rich compounds to generate ATP to fuel all life functions.

In Unit 1, you examined the processes of photosynthesis and cellular respiration as they relate to the connections between organisms and the biosphere. In this chapter you will look more closely at these energy-capturing and energy-releasing processes as they relate to the needs of individual organisms.

Photosynthesis: Capturing and Converting Light Energy from the Sun

Life on Earth is possible only because the Sun provides a constant input of energy in the form of light. Living organisms trap, store, and use energy to maintain and sustain cells. An overview of these general life processes is shown in Figure 5.1. All organisms need some form of energy to survive. Green plants and most other photosynthesizing organisms (autotrophs) have chloroplasts that contain the molecules that trap the Sun's energy and convert it to chemical energy. Non-photosynthesizing organisms (heterotrophs) must consume photosynthetic organisms or other heterotrophs to obtain the chemical energy they need.

In the process of **photosynthesis,** chloroplasts in autotrophs convert solar energy into chemical energy and store this in sugars and other carbohydrates. The by-products of photosynthesis are oxygen, molecules of ATP (which you will learn about shortly), and some heat. Some of the energy-rich compounds that result from photosynthesis are used immediately, and some are stored (as starch or converted to fat) for future use.

Cellular Respiration: Releasing Stored Energy

The chemical energy of compounds such as glucose is stored in their chemical bonds. All organisms must break down the energy-rich compounds—break down the chemical bonds—to release and use the energy.

In the process of **cellular respiration,** mitochondria in the cells of plants, animals, and other multicellular organisms break down carbohydrates (and other energy-rich products derived from them such as fats) to generate molecules of ATP. ATP is short for adenosine triphosphate, and it is the source of energy that all organisms use

BiologyFile

FYI

Some species of bacteria can perform photosynthesis. They do not have any membrane-bound organelles such as chloroplasts. However, the folds of membranes connected to their plasma membrane contain molecules that capture the Sun's energy for photosynthesis.

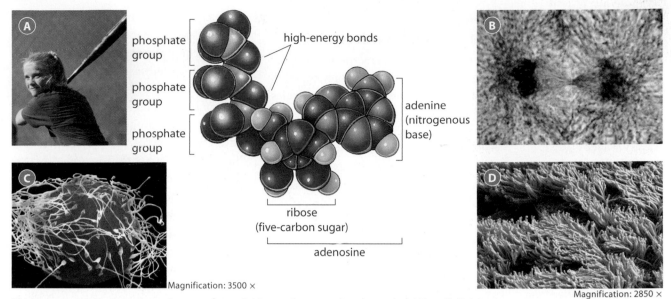

Figure 5.2 ATP is the source of energy for activities such as muscle contraction (**A**), cell division (**B**), flagella movement (**C**), and cilia movement (**D**). The adenosine part of ATP is composed of a molecule called adenine, which is bonded to a five-carbon sugar called ribose. Our bodies use about 40 kg of ATP daily. The amount of ATP available at any moment is enough to meet only immediate cellular needs. Thus, ATP must be synthesized constantly.

Magnification: 3500 ×

Magnification: 2850 ×

for nearly all cellular activities (Figure 5.2). This molecule is sometimes referred to as "the energy currency" of cells because when cells need energy they "spend" ATP.

ATP and Cellular Activity

ATP supplies the energy for cellular activities that include those listed below. Although ATP is always being used, sometimes quite rapidly, cells maintain an amazingly constant supply of ATP.

- active transport of ions and molecules across cell membranes
- moving chromosomes during cell division
- causing cilia and flagella to move
- causing muscles to contract
- synthesizing compounds such as carbohydrates, proteins, fats, and nucleic acids

How does ATP supply energy for cellular activity? As you can see in Figure 5.3, when the bond to the third phosphate group in ATP breaks, the energy from ATP is released. The reaction produces ADP or adenosine diphosphate—adenosine plus *two* phosphate groups—and a free phosphate group Ⓟ. ATP is then regenerated by the addition of a free phosphate group Ⓟ to ADP—a process that requires an input of energy. Molecules of ATP are broken down and regenerated thousands of times each day. The chemical energy that is released when the bond to the third phosphate group is broken enables most life-sustaining cellular activities to take place.

• • •

1. What is accomplished by the process of photosynthesis?

2. What is the function of cellular respiration?

3. What is ATP?

4. In terms of energy consumed and energy released, how is ATP related to ADP?

• • •

BiologyFile

Web Link
What if heart pacemakers, which are powered by batteries that require replacement every five to ten years, could be fueled by ATP? This is one of the questions guiding the investigation of ATP as a possible source of energy for implanted devices. What is the current state of this research?

www.albertabiology.ca
WWW

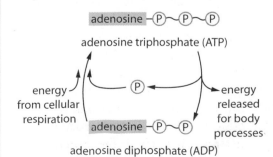

adenosine triphosphate (ATP)

energy from cellular respiration

energy released for body processes

adenosine diphosphate (ADP)

Figure 5.3 The release of a phosphate group from ATP and the subsequent regeneration of ATP from ADP creates a continuous cycle.

Chloroplasts: Site of Photosynthesis

Parts of plants and many species of algae are green in colour because they contain chlorophyll, the green-coloured molecules that trap solar energy. Chlorophyll is the pigment you used in the Launch Lab on page 161 and is contained within cell organelles called **chloroplasts**. Most photosynthetic cells contain anywhere from 40 to 200 chloroplasts. A typical leaf may have 500 000 chloroplasts per square millimeter!

Chloroplasts are about 4 μm– 6 μm in diameter and 1 μm–5 μm thick. They are bound by two membranes: an outer membrane and an inner one. The fluid in the inner space of a chloroplast, called the *stroma*, contains a concentrated mixture of proteins and other chemicals that are used in the synthesis (making) of carbohydrates. A third membrane system within the stroma is organized into interconnected flattened sacs called **thylakoids**. In some regions of the stroma, thylakoids are stacked up in structures called *grana*. Chlorophyll molecules are located in the thylakoid membranes of the chloroplast (Figure 5.4).

Mitochondria: Site of Cellular Respiration

The cells of eurkaryotic organisms (plants, animals, fungi, and protists)

contain **mitochondria**. These are the organelles that enable cells to efficiently extract energy from their food (Figure 5.5). Mitochondria are smaller than chloroplasts, ranging from 0.5 μm– 1.0 μm in diameter and 2 μm–5 μm in length. Like chloroplasts, mitochondria are bounded by two membranes. The fluid-filled space of the inner membrane is called the *matrix*. It contains proteins and other chemicals needed to break down carbohydrates and other high-energy molecules. The inner membrane has numerous folds, called *cristae*, which provide a large surface area for the production of ATP.

• • •

⑤ What is chlorophyll?

⑥ Where, in a typical plant cell, are the green parts located? Name the organelle, where it is often located in the cell, and the part of the organelle to which the green material is attached.

⑦ What is the function of mitochondria?

⑧ Name the life forms that contain mitochondria in their cells.

• • •

Figure 5.4 The flattened thylakoids in the chloroplasts of plant cells are stacked into columns called grana (singular: granum). Surrounding the thylakoids and filling the interior of the chloroplast is the fluid stroma, in which the chemical reactions that synthesize carbohydrates take place.

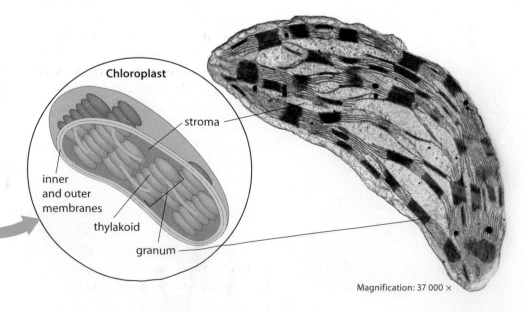

Chloroplast

stroma

inner and outer membranes

thylakoid

granum

Magnification: 37 000 ×

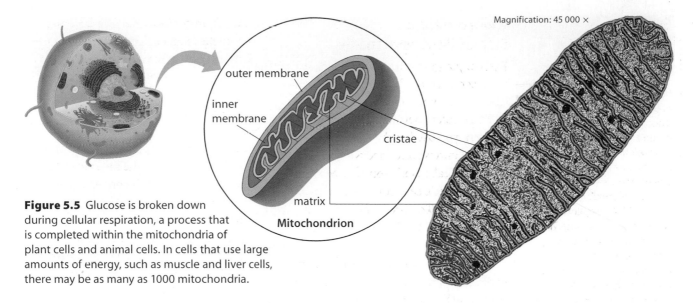

outer membrane

inner membrane

cristae

matrix

Mitochondrion

Figure 5.5 Glucose is broken down during cellular respiration, a process that is completed within the mitochondria of plant cells and animal cells. In cells that use large amounts of energy, such as muscle and liver cells, there may be as many as 1000 mitochondria.

Metabolic Pathways and Energy for Cellular Reactions

As you have seen in Unit 1, the chemical reaction for photosynthesis can be summarized as:

$$6CO_2(g) + 6H_2O(\ell) + energy \rightarrow C_6H_{12}O_6(s) + O_2(g)$$

The chemical reaction of cellular respiration can be summarized as:

$$C_6H_{12}O_6(s) + O_2(g) \rightarrow 6CO_2(g) + 6H_2O(\ell) + energy$$

Photosynthesis in chloroplasts and cellular respiration in mitochondria are intimately related. Photosynthesis uses the products of respiration as its starting reactants, and cellular respiration uses the products of photosynthesis as its starting reactants.

The reactions appear to be exact opposites of each other. However, these are *overall* reactions. They represent a *summary* of a series of reactions that, in combination, result in the reactions shown here. By analyzing the cellular respiration reaction, you will see why the summary equation represents a series of reactions.

The reaction that releases energy during cellular respiration is essentially the same as the combustion reaction that releases energy during the burning of wood, as shown in Figure 5.6. The cellulose in wood that burns in air is made of thousands of units of glucose ($C_6H_{12}O_6(s)$). A very high temperature is needed to start and maintain the burning of wood. The cells in living systems could not survive the high temperatures and large energy output of a combustion reaction. Instead, the reactions that occur in living cells take place in a very large number of controlled reactions. They occur in step-by-step sequences called *metabolic pathways*. In a metabolic pathway, the product of one reaction becomes the starting reactant for another.

Enzymes Catalyze Cellular Metabolism and Energy Production

The term **metabolism** refers to all the chemical reactions that occur within a cell to support and sustain its life functions. Two broad categories of reactions make up metabolism. *Anabolic* metabolic pathways synthesize larger molecules from smaller ones and require energy. *Catabolic* metabolic pathways break down larger molecules into smaller ones and release energy.

These chemical reactions do not occur unless they are activated in some way. Often, the energy for activating a reaction comes from heating the reactants. (Think of using a match to start those logs burning.) However, heating would destroy living cells, so another method is needed to activate metabolic reactions. All metabolic reactions are catalyzed by enzymes—specialized proteins that lower the energy needed to activate

Figure 5.6 An initial input of energy is necessary to start logs burning. The burning of each bit of wood almost immediately starts the combustion reaction in adjacent bits of wood. A very high temperature is necessary to keep the logs burning.

Target Skills

Collecting and **interpreting**
experimental data to identify the gases
released as a result of metabolic processes

Gases Released During Photosynthesis and Cellular Respiration

Photosynthesis and cellular respiration are chemical reactions that produce by-products in the form of gases. How can you detect and identify the gas that plants release? How can you determine what gases you are exhaling?

Question

How can you identify the gases released by plants and animals?

Safety Precautions

- NaOH(aq) is caustic and will burn skin. If contact occurs, inform your teacher immediately and wash your skin under cold running cold water for 10 min.

- When you blow into any solution, *do not inhale* at any time.

Materials

- 600 mL beaker
- NaHCO$_3$(s)
- *Cabomba* (or other aquatic plant)
- bright lamp (or grow light)
- test tube and stopper
- short stemmed funnel
- wooden splint
- matches
- 0.1 mol/L NaOH(aq) in dropping bottle
- 50 mL Erlenmeyer flask and stopper
- bromothymol blue
- straw

Procedure

Part 1: Gas Released by Plants

The first 5 steps must be completed the day before the remainder of the investigation is completed.

1. Fill a 600 mL beaker with aquarium water or tap water. Add 2 g of sodium hydrogen carbonate to the water.

2. Hold the small branches of *Cabomba* (or other aquatic plant) under water and clip off the ends of the stems so that air bubbles do not block the vessels.

3. Place a short-stemmed funnel over the branches.

4. Fill a test tube with water and cover the top while you invert it. Hold it under water and position it over the

stem of the funnel as shown. Be sure there is no air in the test tube.

5. Place the apparatus in bright light and leave it until the next class period.

6. After about 24 h, carefully remove the test tube, keeping it inverted, put your thumb over the mouth of the test tube, and stopper it. Follow the directions below to test for the type of gas in the tube. Record your results.

> ### Testing for Gases
>
> **Note: For safety purposes, your teacher may conduct some or all of these steps.**
>
> 1. Wear goggles.
>
> 2. Keep the stoppered test tube containing a collected gas inverted and clamp it to a ring stand.
>
> 3. Ensure that there are no flammable materials, other than those with which you are working, in the room.
>
> 4. Light the wooden splint. Let it burn briefly then blow out the flame. The splint should still be glowing.
>
> 5. Gradually insert the glowing splint up into the inverted test tube. Observe the reaction.
>
>   - If the gas is hydrogen, you will hear a loud pop when the splint reaches the gas.
>
>   - If the gas is carbon dioxide, the splint will go out.
>
>   - If the gas is oxygen, the splint will burn faster and you will see a flame.

Part 2: Gas Exhaled by Animals

1. Add about 35 mL of water to a 50 mL Erlenmeyer flask. Add a few drops of bromothymol blue to the water and swirl. (Place the flask on a piece of white paper to see the colour more clearly.)

2. Add sodium hydroxide one drop at a time and gently swirl the flask. Stop adding the sodium hydroxide when the water turns a deep greenish-blue colour.

3. Obtain a straw and blow gently into the flask. *Do not suck on the straw.* Continue to blow into the solution until you can no longer see any colour change.

4. Add a piece of *Cabomba* to the water and stopper the flask. Place it in a brightly lighted place. Leave it in place until you see a change. Record any changes over the next 24 h.

Analysis

1. What happened when you inserted the glowing splint into the test tube that had been collecting gas from the *Cabomba* plant? What is the identity of the gas?

2. Bromothymol blue is called a pH indicator because it changes colour with changes in pH (acidity) of a solution. It is a dark greenish-blue colour in a basic solution and a pale yellow colour in an acidic solution. What happened when you blew into the flask?

3. Read the following points then identify the gas in your exhaled breath.

   - Oxygen gas has very low solubility in water and does not react chemically with water.
   - Hydrogen gas is nearly insoluble in water and does not react with water.
   - Carbon dioxide is relatively soluble in water and reacts with water to produce carbonic acid.

Conclusion

4. Explain the source of the gas that you collected in the test tube over the *Cabomba* plant.

5. Explain the source of the gas that you exhaled.

6. Explain any changes in the appearance of the solution after Step 4 of Part 2.

---

biological reactions. Each of the thousands of reactions that occur in living cells has a specific enzyme that enables the reaction to proceed rapidly.

• • •

Q 9 Which releases energy: metabolic pathways that synthesize larger molecules from smaller ones or metabolic pathways that break down larger molecules into smaller ones?

• • •

Linking Reactions through Oxidation and Reduction

When an atom or molecule loses an electron, it is said to be oxidized, and the process by which this occurs is called *oxidation*. Conversely, when an atom or molecule gains an electron, it is said to be reduced, and the process is called *reduction*.

The electrons that are lost by one atom or molecule cannot exist on their own. They must combine with another atom or molecule. Thus, when one compound is oxidized (loses electrons),

another compound must be reduced (gain electrons). This link between oxidation and reduction reactions is shown in Figure 5.7.

All compounds or atoms contain more energy in their reduced form than they do in their oxidized form. Energy-rich compounds (such as glucose) are in their reduced form. Molecules that, in their reduced form, contain a large amount of available energy are said to have **reducing power**.

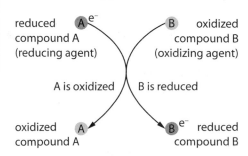

Figure 5.7 Oxidation and reduction reactions take place at the same time. If one compound is oxidized, another compound must be reduced. (That is, when one compound loses electrons, another compound gains those electrons.) Oxidation-reduction reactions are often called redox reactions for short.

BiologyFile

FYI

A simple way to help you remember what happens to electrons in an oxidation reaction and a reduction reaction is to remember the phrase, "LEO the lion says GER." LEO stands for "Loss of Electrons is Oxidation" and GER stands for "Gain of Electrons is Reduction." In Alberta, it might be more appropriate to use the acronym, OIL RIG. **O**xidation **I**s **L**oss. **R**eduction **I**s **G**ain.

• • •

10 What happens to the electrons that are lost by a compound that is undergoing an oxidation reaction?

11 Which contains more energy: a compound in its oxidized form or a compound in its reduced form?

• • •

Section 5.1 Summary

• Photosynthesis is the process by which plants and other photosynthetic organisms trap the Sun's energy and transform it into energy-rich chemical compounds.

• Cellular respiration is the process by which cells break down high-energy compounds and generate ATP.

• ATP is the direct source of energy for nearly all types of energy-requiring activities of living organisms.

• Chloroplasts have two outer membranes, an inner solution called the stroma, and a membrane system consisting of flattened sacs called thylakoids. Stacks of thylakoids are called grana.

• Chlorophyll molecules, the molecules that trap solar energy, are bound to the thylakoid membranes in chloroplasts.

• Chlorophyll gives plants their green colour.

• Mitochondria have outer and inner membranes that surround a fluid-filled region called the matrix. The inner membrane has many deep infoldings called cristae.

• The chemical reactions of photosynthesis and cellular respiration take place in a series of many step-by-step reactions called metabolic pathways.

• Enzymes are biological catalysts that reduce the amount of startup energy needed for the reactions in the metabolic pathways. In the absence of enzymes, the reactions could not occur at temperatures at which living organisms thrive.

• When a compound is oxidized in a chemical reaction, it loses electrons.

• When a compound is reduced in a chemical reaction, it gains electrons.

• Compounds contain more chemical energy in their reduced form than they do in their oxidized form.

Section 5.1 Review

1. Trace, in general terms, the path of energy from the sun to the contraction of a muscle in a predator such as a mountain lion (*Puma concolor*).

2. An autotroph is defined as an organism that makes its own food. Explain how this term describes photosynthetic organisms.

3. Use word processing or spreadsheet software to create a chart that compares and contrasts the process of photosynthesis and cellular respiration. **ICT**

4. Explain why it is appropriate to call ATP the "energy currency" of cells.

5. Use graphics software to draw a sketch or model of a molecule of ATP. Label the different groups that make up this molecule. **ICT**

6. Use graphics or word processing software to sketch the ATP energy cycle. Use the sketch to explain how this cycle enables life-sustaining cellular activities. **ICT**

7. Identify the regions of the chloroplast indicated on this diagram. Describe what happens in B and C.

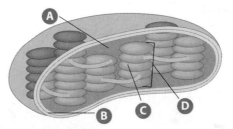

8. Identify the part of a mitochondrion that performs a function related to the processes that occur in the stroma of chloroplasts. Explain your reasoning.

9. Define the term "metabolism," and explain the meaning of the term "metabolic pathway."

10. Explain the meaning of the term "reducing power."

SECTION 5.2

Photosynthesis Stores Energy in Organic Compounds

Section Outcomes

In this section, you will

- **describe** how pigments absorb light energy and transfer it as reducing power in NADPH
- **explain** how absorbed light energy is transferred to the chemical potential energy of ATP by chemiosmosis
- **describe** where the energy transfer processes take place in chloroplasts
- **explain** how scientific knowledge may lead to the development of new technologies
- **collect** and **interpret** data and calculate R_f values from chromatography experiments
- **conduct** investigations in print and electronic resources on C_3 and C_4 photosynthetic mechanisms

Key Terms

light-dependent reactions
light-independent reactions
electron transport system
photosystems
chemiosmosis
carbon dioxide fixation
Calvin-Benson cycle

Photosynthesis transforms the energy of sunlight into the chemical energy of glucose. As you know from Chapter 1, only a small portion of the Sun's total energy output reaches Earth's surface. An even smaller portion of this is used for photosynthesis. Even so, photosynthesizing organisms use that tiny fraction of the Sun's energy to synthesize about 1.4×10^{15} kg of energy-storing glucose and other sugars each year. That's enough sugar to fill a chain of railway boxcars reaching to the Moon and back 50 times.

Much of the glucose produced by plants is converted to cellulose (fibre) and other structural tissues. Glucose may also be converted to other sugars as well as storage forms of carbohydrates such as starch. In addition, sugars produced by photosynthesis are involved in the synthesis of other essential cellular substances such as amino acids, which are needed to make proteins. In fact, the products of photosynthesis account for nearly 95 percent of the dry weight of green plants. Other organisms—including humans—depend on the molecules, tissues, and substances that plants synthesize for their own use (Figure 5.8).

The Process of Photosynthesis

$$6CO_2(g) + 6H_2O(\ell) + \text{energy} \rightarrow C_6H_{12}O_6(s) + O_2(g)$$

The summary equation for photosynthesis tells you that the starting reactants are carbon dioxide and water, and the end products are glucose and oxygen. There is, however, much that takes place between what appears on the left side of the equation and the result on the right side of the equation.

The arrow in the photosynthesis equation represents over 100 distinct

Figure 5.8 Plants produce structural and metabolic substances for their own use. Humans have developed numerous technologies to take advantage of the properties of these plant substances.

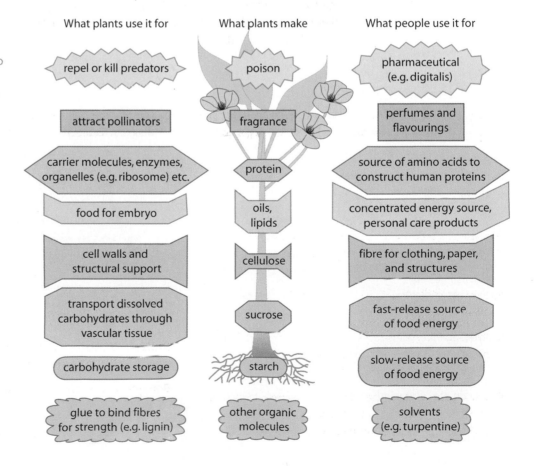

What plants use it for | What plants make | What people use it for

repel or kill predators — poison — pharmaceutical (e.g. digitalis)

attract pollinators — fragrance — perfumes and flavourings

carrier molecules, enzymes, organelles (e.g. ribosome) etc. — protein — source of amino acids to construct human proteins

food for embryo — oils, lipids — concentrated energy source, personal care products

cell walls and structural support — cellulose — fibre for clothing, paper, and structures

transport dissolved carbohydrates through vascular tissue — sucrose — fast-release source of food energy

carbohydrate storage — starch — slow-release source of food energy

glue to bind fibres for strength (e.g. lignin) — other organic molecules — solvents (e.g. turpentine)

chemical reactions that lead to the end products. The term photosynthesis suggests that the process involves two sets of reactions. *Photo*, meaning light, refers to the reactions that capture light energy; *synthesis* refers to the reactions that produce a carbohydrate. The two sets of reactions that make up photosynthesis are called the light-dependent reactions and the light-independent reactions.

In the **light-dependent reactions**, solar energy is trapped and used to generate two high-energy compounds: ATP and NADPH (reduced nicotinamide adenine dinucleotide phosphate), which has a large amount of reducing power. In the **light-independent reactions**, the energy of ATP and the reducing power of NADPH are used to reduce carbon dioxide to make glucose. Glucose can then be converted into starch for storage.

• • •

12 What are the two sets of reactions that are involved in photosynthesis?

• • •

The Light-Dependent Reactions of Photosynthesis

During the light-dependent reactions, the pigments within the thylakoid membranes absorb light energy. A *pigment* is a compound that absorbs certain wavelengths of visible light, while reflecting others that give the pigment its specific colour. A photosynthetic pigment is a compound that traps light energy and passes it on to other chemicals, which use the energy to synthesize high-energy compounds. Photosynthetic organisms have a variety of photosynthetic pigments, although chlorophyll, which is green, is the main type of photosynthetic pigments in plants.

Chlorophyll does not absorb green light. To understand why chlorophyll is green, examine Figure 5.9A.

When you shine white light through a prism, the prism separates the colours (wavelengths) of light into a spectrum.

As you can see in Figure 5.9A, a chlorophyll solution absorbs red and blue light while it transmits or reflects green light. Therefore, the light that reaches your eyes is green.

An *absorbance spectrum* is a graph that shows the relative amounts of light of different colours that a compound absorbs. Figure 5.9B shows the absorbance spectra of two chlorophylls—chlorophyll *a* and chlorophyll *b*. Figure 5.9B also includes the absorbance spectrum of another pigment called beta-carotene. Beta-carotene is a member of a very large class of pigments called carotenoids. The carotenoids absorb blue and green light, so they are yellow, orange, and red in colour (see Figure 5.9C). Beta-carotene is responsible for the orange colour of carrots. It can be converted into vitamin A, which can then be converted into retinal, which is the visual pigment in your eyes.

Each photosynthetic pigment absorbs light of different colours. Having a variety of pigments enables a plant to use a greater percentage of the Sun's light.

Figure 5.9D shows another type of spectrum, called an action spectrum. An action spectrum shows the relative effectiveness of different wavelengths of light for promoting photosynthesis. This is reflected by a response in the rate at which oxygen is released. Observe that the action spectrum parallels the absorbance spectra of the three pigments together. This observation links the production of oxygen in photosynthesis with selected wavelengths of light, as well as with the specific pigments that absorb these wavelengths.

• • •

13 What is a pigment?

14 In reference to the properties of light, what makes chlorophyll green?

15 What is the advantage to a plant of having more than one pigment?

• • •

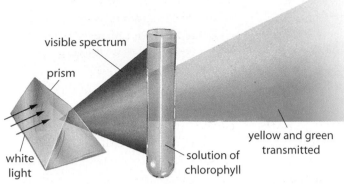

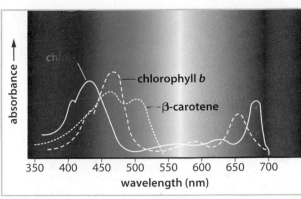

A When you look at an object, you see the colours that were *not* absorbed by the object. Leaves appear green because chlorophyll molecules in leaf cells reflect green and yellow wavelengths of light and absorb the other wavelengths (red and blue).

B This absorbance spectrum for three photosynthetic pigments shows that each pigment absorbs a different combination of colours of light.

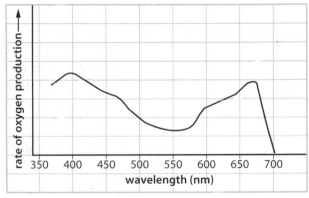

C During spring and summer months, chlorophyll masks the presence of carotenoids and other plant pigments in leaves. Cooler temperatures in autumn cause leaves to stop making chlorophyll. With the green pigment no longer present to reflect green light to our eyes, the colours reflected by carotenoids and other plant pigments become visible.

D This action spectrum for photosynthesis shows the rate at which oxygen is produced during photosynthesis. Notice that the shape of the graph line generally mirrors the shape of the graph lines in Figure 5.9B.

Figure 5.9 Light-reflecting and light absorbing characteristics of pigments.

The Path of Electrons in the Light-Dependent Reactions

In Section 5.1, you read that chlorophyll is bound to the membranes of the thylakoids inside the chloroplast. Chlorophyll and other pigments are arranged in the thylakoid membranes in clusters called **photosystems**. The chloroplasts of plants and algae have two photosystems, called photosystem I (abbreviated to PSI) and photosystem II (abbreviated to PSII). The photosystems are named for the order in which scientists discovered them, not for their sequence in the process of photosynthesis.

Each photosystem is made up of pigment molecules that include one dozen or more chlorophyll molecules, as well as a few carotenoid molecules. Also present in the photosystem is a molecule that accepts electrons. All the pigment molecules in each photosystem can absorb light energy of various wavelengths. However, they always pass the energy along to one specialized, electron-accepting chlorophyll *a* molecule called the *reaction centre*. (Some biologists refer to pigment molecules in a photosystem as antennas because they collect light energy just as radio and television antennas collect electromagnetic energy.)

• • •

Q **16** What is a photosystem?

Q **17** Identify the types of molecules that are present in a photosystem.

• • •

Biology File

FYI
When chlorophyll is free in a solution and it absorbs light, it fluoresces. When a molecule fluoresces, it re-emits the energy it absorbed in the form of light that has a longer wavelength than the absorbed light. You observed fluorescence when you performed the Launch Lab at the start of this chapter.

Using Chromatography to Separate Plant Pigments

Chromatography is a technique that is used to separate and analyze complex mixtures, such as plant pigments. You will use this technique to examine the pigments in a green leaf.

Question

Which pigments can you identify in a green leaf?

Prediction

Predict at least three pigments that you will observe.

Safety Precautions

The solvent is volatile. Ensure that there are no flames in the classroom, and avoid breathing the vapours from the solvent. The classroom must be well-ventilated.

Materials

- coleus or spinach leaves (or pigment mixture supplied by your teacher)
- isopropanol (solvent)
- chromatography paper
- paper clip
- retort stand
- test-tube clamp
- cork stopper
- watch glass
- large test tube

paper clip

chromatography paper

2 cm

pigment spot

pencil line

solvent

Procedure

1. Attach the large test tube to a retort stand.

2. Set up the cork stopper and the paper clip as shown.

3. Measure a piece of chromatography paper so that it is long enough to hang from the paper clip but not so long that it touches the bottom of the test tube. (Refer to the diagram.) Cut the paper to a point at one end.

4. Place a coleus or spinach leaf over the pointed end of the chromatography paper. Run the edge of a watch glass over the leaf, about 2 cm up from the tip of the

paper. Use the watch glass to squeeze out the pigment mixture. Repeat this at least 10 times in the same spot to ensure that enough pigment mixture has been deposited onto the paper.

5. Place 5 mL to 10 mL of solvent in the test tube.

6. Hang the chromatography paper from the stopper in the test tube so that the tip of the paper is in the solvent but the pigment mixture is not.

7. Wait until the solvent has travelled up to about 2 cm from the top of the paper.

8. Remove the paper from the test tube. Immediately, before the solvent evaporates, mark the location of the solvent front with a pencil. Also mark the edges of each pigment, as shown in this diagram.

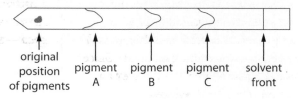

original position of pigments   pigment A   pigment B   pigment C   solvent front

9. Measure and record the distance that each pigment travelled, starting from where you applied the pigment mixture to where each pigment stopped moving up the paper strip.

10. Measure and record the distance that the solvent front travelled.

11. Prepare a data table with the following headings, and record your observations and measurements in the first three columns.

Observations and Data for Chromatography of Plant Pigments

Pigment colour	Distance travelled by pigment (cm)	Distance travelled by solvent (cm)	R_f (reference flow) value	Name of pigment

12. Calculate the R_f (reference flow) value of each pigment, using the following formula:

$$R_f \text{ value} = \frac{\text{distance travelled by pigment (solute)}}{\text{distance travelled by solvent}}$$

Analysis

1. Sketch your paper strip, using different colours to show the different pigments and their positions. Your sketch is called a chromatogram.

2. Which pigment is (a) most soluble and (b) least soluble in the solvent you used? Explain how you decided.

3. Compare your observations and R_f values with those of your classmates. Identify sources of error in this investigation that might account for any differences.

4. Use the following chart as a guide to help you complete the last column in your data table. (You may not have observed all the pigments in this chart, or you may have observed other pigments.)

Examples of Plant Pigments and Their Colours

Pigment or pigment group	Colour
chlorophyll *a*	bluish-green
chlorophyll *b*	yellowish-green
carotenoids	orange
pheophytin	olive-green
xanthophylls	yellow
phycocyanin	blue
phycoerythrin	red

Conclusion

5. **a)** Which pigments did you identify in your leaf?

   b) Do you think additional pigments could still be present? Hypothesize how you could find out.

When a reaction centre has received the energy passed on to it, an electron in the reaction centre is "excited." This means that the electron is raised to a higher energy level. The electron is then passed to an electron-accepting molecule. Since this electron-acceptor has received an electron, it becomes reduced so it is at a high energy level. Figure 5.10 outlines four steps that occur after the energized electron reaches the electron-acceptor.

Step 1 When the electron leaves the reaction centre in photosystem II and goes to the electron-acceptor, the reaction centre is missing an electron. This electron must be replaced before photosystem II can absorb more light energy to excite an electron. The source of the new electron is a water molecule. A water molecule is split in a series of reactions that release electrons, hydrogen ions, and oxygen atoms. The oxygen that is released by plants comes from these water-splitting reactions.

Step 2 From the electron-acceptor, the energized electron is transferred along a series of electron-carrying molecules. Together, these molecules are referred to as an **electron transport system**. With each transfer along the electron transport system, the electron releases a small amount of energy (Figure 5.11). This released energy is used to push hydrogen ions from the stroma, across the thylakoid membrane, and into the *thylakoid space*—the area inside the thylakoid.

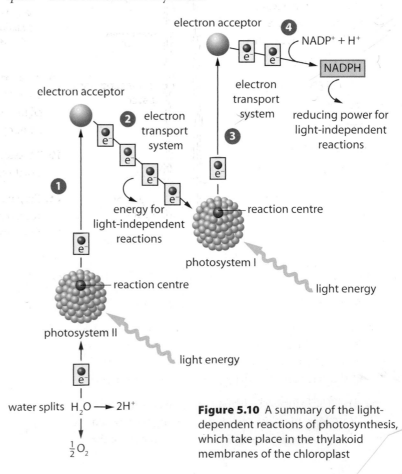

Figure 5.10 A summary of the light-dependent reactions of photosynthesis, which take place in the thylakoid membranes of the chloroplast

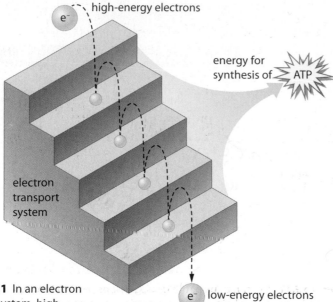

high-energy electrons

energy for
synthesis of → ATP

electron
transport
system

e⁻ low-energy electrons

Figure 5.11 In an electron transport system, high-energy electrons give off a small amount of energy with each step as they pass from one electron-carrying molecule to another. (These molecules, called cytochromes, are a class of proteins specialized for transferring electrons.) The energy given off from these energy transfers is used to synthesize ATP.

The energy that is released as an electron is passed through the electron transport system is stored temporarily in a hydrogen ion concentration gradient across the thylakoid membrane. There are many more hydrogen ions in the thylakoid space than there are in the stroma. You can compare this concentration gradient to water behind a dam. Energy is stored in the potential energy of the water. In a dam, the energy is used by allowing the water to flow down and turn turbines that will generate electric energy. In the hydrogen ion gradient, the energy will be used to generate ATP from ADP and free phosphate groups.

Step 3 When the events of steps 1 and 2 are taking place, light energy is absorbed by photosystem I. This energy is transferred to a reaction centre, where an electron becomes excited. Once again, the excited electron is passed to a high-energy electron-acceptor. In photosystem I, the lost electron is replaced by an electron that has reached the end of the electron transport system from photosystem II.

Step 4 The electron that was received by the electron-acceptor from photosystem I is used to reduce NADP⁺ to form NADPH. The reducing power of NADPH will be used in the light-independent reactions.

- - -

18 Describe or sketch what happens to electrons in the electron transport system.

19 How does NADP⁺ become converted to NADPH?

20 How are electrons replaced in photosystem I, and what is the source of the replacement electrons?

21 What is the effect of having a greater concentration of hydrogen ions in the thylakoid space than in the stroma?

- - -

Making ATP: Chemiosmosis

When the hydrogen ions are forced from the stroma to the thylakoid space, they cannot diffuse back across the membrane because the membrane is impermeable to these charged particles. A special structure called ATP synthase, embedded in the thylakoid membrane, provides the only pathway for the hydrogen ions to move down their concentration gradient (Figure 5.12). This pathway is linked to a mechanism that bonds a free phosphate group to an ADP molecule to form ATP. As the hydrogen ions move down their concentration gradient through the ATP synthase, the energy of the gradient is used to generate ATP molecules. This linking of the movement of hydrogen ions to the production of ATP is called **chemiosmosis**. You will encounter this process again in Section 5.3 when you consider the making of ATP in the mitochondria during cellular respiration.

- - -

22 Explain why hydrogen ions cannot diffuse out of the thylakoid space.

23 What is ATP synthase, and what is its significance?

24 What two events are linked in chemiosmosis?

- - -

Mimicking Nature

Scientists and engineers are fascinated by the ability of plants to use chlorophyll to trap solar energy and convert it into chemical energy. Engineers have been able to design and construct technology that traps solar energy and converts it into electrical energy (see Figure 5.13 on page 176). The technology is practical for the space station with its large solar receptors and small devices such as your calculator. However, the amount of electrical energy that can be produced by solar cells at Earth's surface is not enough to supply much of the energy that society needs. As a result, a large percentage of the energy that is used every day comes from the burning of fossil fuels, which add large amounts of carbon dioxide to the atmosphere. Since carbon dioxide is a greenhouse gas, it contributes to global warming.

In the search for an alternative source of energy, many scientists have been looking closely at hydrogen. Hydrogen is a totally clean fuel. When hydrogen burns in oxygen, the only

Chemiosmosis

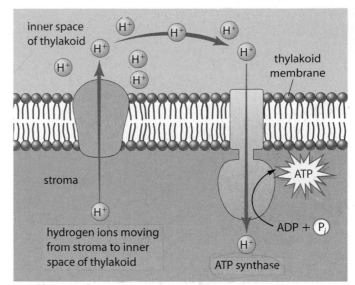

Figure 5.12 You can think of the hydrogen ions passing through the ATP synthase as being like water passing through a dam. The water turns a turbine that generates electrical energy. The movement of hydrogen ions through ATP synthase "turns a molecular turbine" that generates ATP.

product is pure, clean water. So why not use hydrogen as a fuel? There is very little hydrogen found free, as a gas, in nature. To split water into hydrogen and oxygen gases requires the input of more energy than can be produced when the hydrogen is burned. Obtaining hydrogen from

---

Thought Lab 5.1 — Modelling the Source of Oxygen in the Light-Dependent Reactions

In the 1930s, a graduate student at Stanford University in California, C.B. van Niel, demonstrated that the source of the oxygen given off during photosynthesis was water molecules, not carbon dioxide as was commonly hypothesized. When radioactive isotopes came into widespread use in biology laboratories in the early 1950s, it became possible to test and verify van Niel's findings. (Isotopes are atoms of an element that are chemically similar but differ in the number of neutrons in their nucleus.) A radioactive isotope of oxygen was used as a tracer. Tracers are used to follow a particular molecule through a chemical reaction.

Procedure

1. Examine the following general equation that resulted from the van Niel experiment:

$$CO_2(g) + 2H_2O^*(\ell) \rightarrow CH_2O(s) + H_2O(\ell) + O_2^*(g)$$

2. Radioactive water tagged with an isotope of oxygen as a tracer (shown by the *) was used. Note where the tagged oxygen ends up on the right side of the equation.

3. Assume that the experiment was repeated, but this time a radioactive tag was put on the oxygen in CO_2.

4. Using materials provided by your teacher, model what you predict the appearance of the results would be. Your model must include a "tag" to indicate the oxygen isotope on the left side of the arrow as well as where it ends up on the right side of the arrow.

5. Use labels or different colours in your model to indicate what happens to the carbon and hydrogen in this reaction.

Analysis

1. Explain how an isotope can be used as a tracer.

2. Using your model, predict what happens to:

   a) all oxygen molecules that originated from carbon dioxide

   b) all carbon molecules that originated from carbon dioxide

   c) all hydrogen molecules that originated from water

Figure 5.13 Like chloroplasts, solar collectors can absorb light energy from the Sun and convert this energy to other forms. In plants, solar energy is converted to chemical energy. In solar collectors, the solar energy is usually converted to heat or to electrical energy. The electrical energy may be stored for later use by using it to charge storage batteries. (A car battery is an example of a storage battery.)

BiologyFile

FYI
Certain types of partial blindness occur when cells in the retina lose the ability to trap light and send signals to the brain. Some research scientists are studying a protein from photosystem I as a potential replacement for these missing functions in the retina. The scientists are looking for a way to attach these proteins to the retina and replace cells that have stopped functioning. Much more research is needed before the system will be feasible.

other compounds usually results in the release of carbon dioxide.

As you know, photosystem II uses the energy of light to split water. Plants release oxygen gas but not hydrogen gas. The hydrogen from the water becomes part of the concentration gradient or is added to NADP$^+$ to reduce it to NADPH. Teams of scientists are now looking for a way to produce an artificial system similar to photosystem II that will use solar energy to split water but convert the released ions and electrons into hydrogen gas instead of using them for reducing power. Should the scientists succeed with their research, hydrogen, a completely clean fuel, will become available in the future.

• • •

25 State two reasons why hydrogen is not easily used as a fuel.

26 Explain why scientists are investigating ways to produce hydrogen using an artificial system similar to photosystem II.

• • •

The Light-Independent Reactions of Photosynthesis

When there is a sufficient amount of NADPH and ATP in the stroma of the chloroplasts, the energy of these molecules can be used to synthesize glucose in the presence or absence of light. The series of reactions by which carbohydrates are synthesized is called the **Calvin-Benson cycle** in honour of Melvin Calvin and Andrew Benson, the researchers most responsible for the discovery of the process. They used a radioactive isotope of carbon as a tracer to discover the reactions that make up the cycle. Although many chemical reactions are involved, the reactions of the Calvin-Benson cycle can be summarized as shown in Figure 5.14 and as described below.

1. *Fixing Carbon Dioxide*: The first stage in the synthesis of carbohydrates is **carbon dioxide fixation**, which means that the carbon atom in carbon dioxide is chemically bonded to a pre-existing molecule in the stroma. This molecule is a five-carbon compound called **ribulose bisp**hosphate, or RuBP for short. The resulting six-carbon compound is unstable and immediately breaks down into two identical three-carbon compounds. Because these three-carbon compounds are the first stable products of the process, plants that demonstrate this process are called C_3 plants. You could summarize the reaction that leads to these three-carbon compounds as:
   $$CO_2 + RuBP \rightarrow \text{unstable } C_6 \rightarrow 2\ C_3$$

2. *Reduction*: In this stage, the newly formed three-carbon compounds are in a low-energy state. To convert them into a higher energy state, they are first activated by ATP and then reduced by NADPH. The result of these reactions is two molecules of PGAL. (PGAL is short for glyceraldehyde-3-phosphate.) In their reduced (higher-energy) state, some of the PGAL molecules leave the cycle and may be used to make glucose. The remaining PGAL molecules move on to the third stage of the cycle.

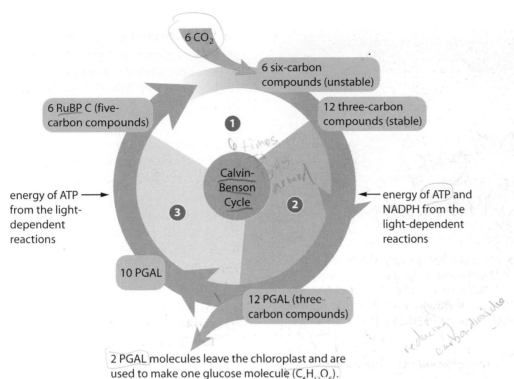

6 CO₂

6 six-carbon compounds (unstable)

6 RuBP C (five-carbon compounds)

12 three-carbon compounds (stable)

①

Calvin-Benson Cycle

energy of ATP from the light-dependent reactions

③

②

energy of ATP and NADPH from the light-dependent reactions

10 PGAL

12 PGAL (three-carbon compounds)

2 PGAL molecules leave the chloroplast and are used to make one glucose molecule ($C_6H_{12}O_6$).

Figure 5.14 For every 12 PGAL molecules that are synthesized in the Calvin-Benson cycle, two leave the chloroplasts and go into the cytoplasm. There, they are used to make glucose and other high-energy compounds.

3. *Replacing RuBP*: Most of the reduced PGAL molecules are used to make more RuBP. Energy, supplied by ATP, is required to break and reform the chemical bonds to make the five-carbon RuBP from PGAL. As described in Figure 5.14, the Calvin-Benson cycle must be completed six times in order to synthesize one molecule of glucose. Of the 12 PGAL molecules that are produced in six cycles, 10 are used to regenerate RuBP, and 2 are used to make glucose.

• • •

27 Briefly outline the function and significance of the Calvin-Benson cycle.

28 What does the term "carbon dioxide fixation" mean?

• • •

Section 5.2 Summary

• Photosynthesis consists of two separate sets of chemical reactions: light-dependent reactions and light-independent reactions.
• Chlorophylls *a* and *b* and the carotenoids are photosynthetic pigments that absorb light.

• Light energy trapped by a pigment molecule energizes (excites) electrons.
• When an electron in photosystem II is excited, it is transferred to and then passed along an electron transport system.
• Energy released during electron transport is used to force hydrogen ions across the thylakoid membrane and create a concentration gradient.
• Energy from the concentration gradient is used to generate ATP from ADP and phosphate by means of chemiosmosis. As hydrogen ions move down their concentration gradient, they drive the reaction that generates ATP.
• An electron from water replaces the electron that was lost from photosystem II. The oxygen from the water molecule is converted to molecular oxygen.
• When an electron from photosystem I is excited, it is eventually used to reduce NADP⁺ to NADPH.
• The series of reactions that synthesize carbohydrates is the Calvin-Benson cycle, which occurs in the stroma.
• In this cycle, carbon dioxide combines with RuBP to form a six-carbon

BiologyFile

FYI
The enzyme that catalyzes the reaction between carbon dioxide and RuBP at the start of the Calvin-Benson cycle is known as rubisco (**ribu**lose **bis**phosphate **c**arboxylase). All enzymes are proteins, and rubisco is probably the most abundant protein on Earth. Biologists estimate that photosynthetic organisms synthesize 1000 k of rubisco every second

Target Skills

Investigating and **integrating** information from print and electronic sources to learn about photosynthesis and possible applications of our knowledge

Working cooperatively to investigate, synthesize, and present information about photosynthesis and its possible technological applications

Rubisco is essential for the fixing of carbon, and yet it is also the reason for the inefficiency of photosynthesis. Biologists estimate that the maximum efficiency of photosynthesis—assuming that each photosystem absorbs the maximum possible amount of light—is 30 percent. Some laboratory-grown plants, raised under tightly controlled conditions, have yielded efficiencies of up to 25 percent. In "the field," however, photosynthetic efficiency is actually much lower, ranging from as little as 0.1 percent to 3 percent. Sugar cane, one of the most efficient photosynthesizers in nature, has an efficiency of about 7 percent.

The Calvin-Benson cycle takes place in all plants, but different species of plants are adapted to use it in different ways, largely due to temperature conditions in different environments. At the heart of these adaptations, and the photosynthetic efficiency of plants, is a process called photorespiration. Photorespiration works against photosynthesis because rubisco can catalyze reactions involving oxygen as easily as it does reactions involving carbon dioxide. Thus, rubisco can *remove* carbon from carbon-related reactions. This means that plants can fix carbon and release carbon dioxide at nearly equal rates, which basically counteracts the fixation process.

Procedure

1. Working in a small group, use print and electronic resources to investigate the following topics and their relationship to one another. Use the Analysis questions to help you focus your research.

   • photorespiration   • CAM photosynthesis

   • C_4 photosynthesis

2. Decide how group members can share the tasks of researching information and presenting your findings, ideas, and decisions.

Analysis

1. a) Identify at least three examples each of the following groups of plants: C_3, C_4, and CAM.

   b) Select one plant from each group. Explain the environmental limiting factors affecting the plant, and describe the adaptations that enable the plant to survive in its typical environment.

2. Illustrate, using pathway diagrams, the essential similarities and differences in the light-independent stage of C_3, C_4, and CAM photosynthesis.

3. In what ways can our understanding of photosynthesis enhance practices in the following areas:

   • growing desired crops

   • protecting desired crops from disease and disease-causing organisms

Extension

4. Biologists and plant technologists have long viewed photorespiration as a wasteful leftover from the evolutionary past of photosynthetic organisms. Thus, biotechnology research into improving efficiency of photosynthesis in crop plants has tended to work from the assumption that photorespiration must be engineered out of the genetic makeup of the plants. However, researchers at the University of California-Davis published a study, in 2004, that suggests the desire to minimize or remove photorespiration may be wrong-headed. Plants, they discovered, may need photorespiration to absorb and process inorganic nitrogen (as nitrate) from the soil. This discovery, if satisfactorily confirmed, has implications for global warming and our assumptions about how plants will, and won't, respond to elevated temperatures and rising concentrations of atmospheric carbon dioxide. Investigate the findings of the UC-Davis researchers as well as the implications of these findings for global warming scenarios. Write a paragraph outlining your opinion of the following statement: "Despite our good intentions, where biotechnology is concerned, our ignorance may lead to unhealthy, harmful consequences to the biosphere and, thus, to ourselves."

Wheat (**A**) is a C_3 plant. Sugar cane (**B**) is a C_4 plant. A pineapple (**C**) is a CAM plant. Why do these three types of plants have different adaptations for synthesizing sugars?

compound that immediately splits into two three-carbon compounds.
- ATP and NADPH from the light-dependent reactions provide energy and reducing power to form PGAL

from the newly formed three-carbon compounds.
- Six cycles produce 12 PGAL molecules, 10 of which regenerate RuBP and 2 of which are used to make glucose.

Section 5.2   Review

1. List four ways that a plant uses the glucose it produces.

2. Compare, in general terms, the light-dependent and light-independent reactions that make up photosynthesis.

3. Use graphics or spreadsheet software to sketch the absorbance spectrum for chlorophyll *a*, chlorophyll *b*, and beta-carotene. **ICT**

4. Compare the absorbance spectrum to the action spectrum in a green plant.

5. Predict why most green plants contain more than one photosynthetic pigment.

6. Describe or define the term "photosystem."

7. Summarize, in point form, the events that take place in the light-dependent reactions of photosynthesis.

8. Describe or define the term, electron transport system. Explain what happens to electrons in this system.

9. Is NADPH an oxidized or a reduced molecule? Explain.

10. Explain how the electrons "lost" from chlorophyll molecules when light is absorbed at the beginning of photosynthesis are replaced.

11. Explain, in general terms, the process of chemiosmosis.

12. Identify the source of ATP and NADPH required to synthesize glucose.

13. Use graphics or word processing software to summarize the main events in the Calvin-Benson cycle. **ICT**

Use the following information to answer the next question.

In 1882, a British biologist named T.W. Englemann used the rate of oxygen production to measure the rate of photosynthesis in a green alga. He chose aerobic bacteria as an indicator for oxygen production. To produce the view shown below, Englemann projected a visible spectrum onto a slide under a light microscope. Then he arranged a filament of algal cells parallel to the spectrum. The dark spots represent the bacteria.

14. **a)** Interpret the pattern of bacteria and the graph line in figure below.

b) Englemann's purpose in designing this experiment was to describe the action spectrum of photosynthesis. State a hypothesis he might have used for the experiment. Explain how the results he obtained supported or refuted this hypothesis.

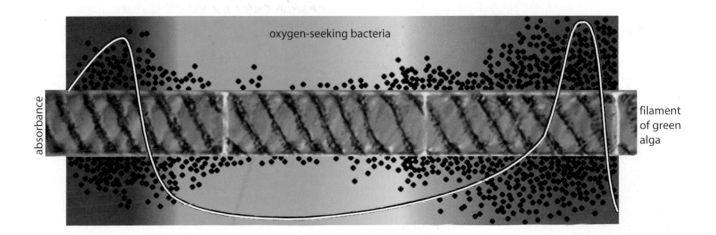

The Rate of Photosynthesis

Oxygen is one of the products of the light-dependent reactions of photosynthesis. The volume of oxygen that is produced by the plant can therefore be used to measure the rate of photosynthesis taking place. However, it is often difficult to accurately measure the volume of gas produced. In this activity, you will use small disks cut from the leaf of a plant to perform a basic floating leaf disk assay. (An assay is a procedure that is used to analyze or determine the amount of substance in a sample.) Once you have mastered this technique, you will use the floating leaf disk assay to design your own investigation of variables that affect the rate of photosynthesis. In preparation for the investigation, review the structure of leaves and the chambers through which gases move as shown in the diagram.

Question

What variables affect the rate of photosynthesis?

Part 1: Floating Leaf Disk Assay

Materials

- plant leaf
- single-hole punch
- 10 mL plastic syringe (without the needle)
- liquid dish soap
- 0.25% sodium bicarbonate
- medicine dropper
- 200 mL beaker
- lamp with a reflector and 150 W bulb
- timer

Procedure

1. Obtain 100 mL of the 0.25% sodium bicarbonate solution and place it in the beaker.

2. Use the medicine dropper to add 5 drops of liquid dish soap to the bicarbonate solution.

3. Use the single-hole punch to cut 10 uniform leaf disks. Avoid cutting through major leaf veins. Remove the plunger and place the leaf disks in the barrel of a plastic syringe. Tap the syringe gently until the leaf disks are near the bottom of the barrel.

4. Replace the plunger in the syringe. Push the plunger down until only a small volume of air remains in the barrel. Be careful, however, not to crush any of the leaf disks.

5. You are going to infiltrate the leaf disks with sodium bicarbonate solution by removing most of the air from the leaf tissue and replacing it with the sodium bicarbonate solution. To do this:

   - Use the plunger to draw 5 mL of solution into the barrel of the syringe.

   - Tap on the syringe to suspend the leaf disks in the solution.

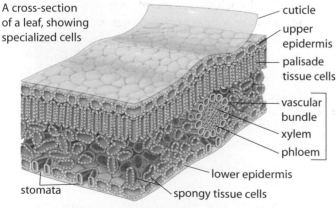

A cross-section of a leaf, showing specialized cells

- cuticle
- upper epidermis
- palisade tissue cells
- vascular bundle
- xylem
- phloem
- lower epidermis
- spongy tissue cells
- stomata

D Stomata: small openings in the outer (epidermal) layer that allow carbon dioxide into the leaf and oxygen out of the leaf. Water also diffuses out of the leaf through stomata.

A Palisade tissue cells: long, narrow cells packed with chloroplasts. These cells lie under the upper surface of the leaf and are the sites where most photosynthesis occurs in the leaf.

B Vascular tissue cells: cells that form bundled arrangements of tubes that transport fluids throughout the plant. Xylem tubes carry water and minerals from the roots to the leaves. Phloem tubes carry sugars to various parts of the plant.

C Spongy tissue cells: round and more loosely packed than palisade cells, with many air spaces between them. These cells have chloroplasts, so they perform some photosynthesis. Their structure helps the cells to exchange gases and water with the environment.

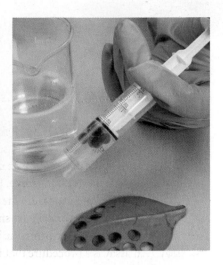

- Hold a finger over the open end of the syringe and draw back on the plunger. This creates a vacuum inside the syringe.

- Hold this vacuum for 10 to 15 seconds and then remove your finger from the open end of the syringe. The sodium bicarbonate solution will gradually infiltrate the air spaces inside the leaf disks.

- Hold the open end of the syringe over the beaker of solution and slowly push the plunger back down, again taking care not to crush the leaf disks.

- Repeat the infiltration procedure at least 5 times; otherwise your leaf disks may not sink to the bottom of the solution in the beaker.

6. Pour the disks and solution from the syringe back into the beaker of sodium bicarbonate and dish soap.

7. If your leaf disks are still floating, carefully add more dish soap—1 drop at a time. You may have to remove the leaf disks and repeat the infiltration procedure if you can't get the disks to sink to the bottom of the beaker.

8. Once all of the leaf disks are resting on the bottom, direct white light onto the beaker. Start the timer.

9. At the end of each minute, record the number of disks that have floated to the surface of the solution. Swirl the beaker gently if some disks get stuck to the side, but keep the beaker in the light.

10. Record your results in a suitable data table.

Analysis

1. Use a computer and spreadsheet software to construct a graph of your data. (ICT)

2. Using the graph, estimate the time at which 50 percent of the leaf disks were floating on the surface. The

point at which 50 percent of the leaf disks are floating will be your point of reference for future investigations.

3. Normally the extracellular spaces within the mesophyll layer of a plant leaf are filled with air for purposes of gas exchange. As a result, leaf disks float on the water. Explain how you removed most of the air from these extracellular spaces. What was the result of the removal of most of the air from the air spaces in the leaf disks?

Conclusions

4. What variable were you testing in this experiment?

5. Based on your current understanding of photosynthesis, explain why the leaf disks started to float after being exposed to white light.

Part 2: Design your Own Investigation

There are a number of variables that affect the rate of photosynthesis in a plant leaf. The variables include the amount of carbon dioxide in the water, different wavelengths of light, and the intensity of light, to name only a few. Your challenge is to design an investigation to test the effects of one of these variables on the rate of photosynthesis. Be sure to:

- state your own question

- make a hypothesis based on this question

- identify the materials that you will require

- write out the experimental procedure you will use

- conduct your investigation

- collect and graph your data

- determine if your results support or disprove your hypothesis

- communicate the results of your investigation in the form of a formal lab report.

Cellular Respiration Releases Energy from Organic Compounds

Section Outcomes

In this section, you will
- **distinguish**, in general terms, among aerobic respiration, anaerobic respiration, and fermentation
- **explain** how carbohydrates are oxidized by glycolysis and the Krebs cycle to produce reducing power in NADH and FADH$_2$ and chemical potential in ATP
- **explain** how chemiosmosis converts the reducing power of NADH and FADH$_2$ to the chemical potential of ATP
- **design** an experiment to demonstrate that oxygen is consumed during aerobic cellular respiration and that heat is produced
- **explain** that science and technology are developed to meet societal needs such as the production of foods and fuels
- **investigate** and **integrate**, from print and electronic sources, information on the action of metabolic toxins such as hydrogen sulfide and cyanide

Key Terms

aerobic cellular respiration
anaerobic cellular respiration
glycolysis
Krebs cycle
electron transport system
chemiosmosis
fermentation

Figure 5.15 Running and other forms of strenuous activity require large amounts of energy. Even when you are still and resting, however, the cells of your body still need energy to continue functioning.

The runner in Figure 5.15 is clearly exhausted. Have you ever been playing a sport or running so hard that you thought you could not take another step? Even after you stopped, you probably kept breathing deeply and felt the heat within your body. What caused your muscles to heat up so much? Why does your breathing rate stay high for a long time after you stop exerting yourself? The answers to these questions are related to the process that provides energy in individual cells: cellular respiration.

The Process of Cellular Respiration

You know that photosynthesis reduces carbon dioxide to glucose. That is, electrons (and hydrogen ions) are chemically added to carbon dioxide to produce high-energy glucose molecules. The summary equation for cellular respiration is shown below:

$$C_6H_{12}O_6(s) + O_2(g) \rightarrow$$
$$6CO_2(g) + 6H_2O(\ell) + energy\ (ATP)$$

Cellular respiration releases the energy of these molecules by oxidizing glucose to carbon dioxide. That is, electrons (and hydrogen ions) are removed from glucose, releasing energy and producing carbon dioxide and water. You can see the reduction-oxidation relationship in photosynthesis and cellular respiration more clearly in Figure 5.16.

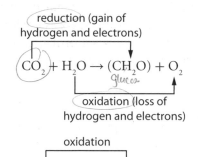

Figure 5.16 The summary equations for photosynthesis and cellular respiration are sometimes written as shown here. Notice that if you multiply all the chemical formulas on both sides of the equation by six, you get the summary equations for these processes.

Three Pathways for Energy Release

Different species of organisms are adapted to release energy from their food sources in different ways. Organisms that live in *oxic* (oxygen-containing) conditions carry out **aerobic cellular**

respiration. The term "aerobic" means that the process requires oxygen to produce ATP. Animals, plants, and many types of fungi, protists, and bacteria use aerobic cellular respiration for energy.

Organisms that live in *anoxic* (no-oxygen) conditions carry out **anaerobic cellular respiration**. The term "anaerobic" means that the process does not require oxygen to produce ATP. In fact, for some organisms, oxygen may be lethal.

Some types of bacteria carry out anaerobic cellular respiration, as do members of archaea. The deep-ocean producers (chemosynthetic organisms) that you read about on page 12 are examples of organisms that depend on anaerobic cellular respiration. Some nitrogen-fixing bacteria and some other types of soil bacteria (see page 49) are also examples of organisms that carry out anaerobic cellular respiration.

A third pathway for releasing energy from food sources is **fermentation**. Fermentation is an anaerobic process, but it is not technically classified as anaerobic cellular respiration. Yeasts and the bacteria that cause milk to sour (*Lactobacillus bulgaricus*) are examples of organisms that carry out fermentation. Fermentation also occurs in the muscle cells of mammals.

• • •

29 Explain the difference between oxic conditions and anoxic conditions.

30 Describe how aerobic cellular respiration is different from anaerobic respiration.

• • •

Examining Aerobic Cellular Respiration

Aerobic cellular respiration is an oxidation reaction in which a series of enzyme-catalyzed reactions transfer electrons from high-energy molecules—mainly glucose—to oxygen. This process is the main means for releasing energy, in the

form of ATP, in plants, animals, and most other eukaryotic cells.

Figure 5.17 on page 186 outlines the key events in cellular respiration. You will learn about each of these events in the pages that follow. Note that cellular respiration begins with **glycolysis**, which occurs in the cytoplasm of all cells. *Glycolysis is an anaerobic process*, which means that it can proceed without oxygen. Glycolysis generates a small amount of ATP. However, the product of glycolysis, a molecule called pyruvate, still contains a large amount of chemical energy. If oxygen is not available to eukaryotic cells, pyruvate proceeds to the process of fermentation.

When sufficient oxygen is present, pyruvate is transported from the cytoplasm into the mitochondrion. In the mitochondrion, pyruvate undergoes a reaction that prepares it for entry into the Krebs cycle. The major function of the **Krebs cycle** is to transform the energy of glucose into reducing power of molecules called NADH and $FADH_2$. These molecules supply high-energy electrons to an **electron transport system** that produces a large amount of ATP. Water is the final end-product of this process.

Outside the Mitochondria: Glycolysis

Glycolysis occurs in all living cells. For some types of cells, it is the only source of energy because it can proceed anaerobically. For example, yeast can live indefinitely without oxygen. However, yeast also can use oxygen when it is available. Your muscles can function anaerobically for awhile but must obtain oxygen eventually.

As shown in Figure 5.18, the role of glycolysis is to split glucose (a six-carbon molecule) into two molecules of pyruvate (a three-carbon molecule). You might be surprised to see that ATP molecules are *used* at the start of glycolysis. Although glucose is a high-energy molecule, more energy must be added to start the series of reactions. After energy has been added

Oxygen Consumption and Heat Production in Germinating Seeds*

When seeds germinate (begin to grow and develop), they cannot trap energy from the Sun because they have not yet developed any chlorophyll. As well, they often germinate under a layer of soil. Therefore, seeds must have enough stored energy to germinate—developing roots and shoots as well as the chloroplasts and chlorophyll they will need as they mature and are exposed to sunlight.

To germinate, seeds need suitable temperatures, water, and oxygen. Oxygen initiates cellular respiration. The amount of oxygen consumed by the seeds is approximately equal to the amount of carbon dioxide produced as the seeds respire. In Part 1 of this investigation, you will use an apparatus called a respirometer to measure the consumption of oxygen. The respirometer contains limewater and germinating seeds. As the seeds consume oxygen, they give off carbon dioxide. The carbon dioxide is then absorbed by the limewater, creating a slight vacuum in the respirometer. This vacuum will draw a drop of liquid detergent in the tubing inward. This movement will be measured using a ruler taped to the tubing. Note: If suitable probeware and interfaces are available, your teacher will explain how to modify the procedure for Part 1 with this equipment.

In Part 2, you will design your own investigation to demonstrate and measure the heat produced as germinating seeds respire.

Part 1: Oxygen Consumption in Cellular Respiration

Question

How can you demonstrate quantitatively that germinating seeds consume oxygen?

Prediction

Based on the experimental set-up, predict what will happen to indicate that oxygen is being consumed as the seeds respire.

Safety Precautions

If glass tubing is used instead of plastic tubing, handle the tubes very carefully to avoid breakage.

Materials

- large test tube
- ruler
- 1 g of seeds of any kind
- one-hole stopper
- limewater
- pipette
- wad of cotton
- marker
- liquid detergent
- balance
- paper towels
- spatula
- scotch tape
- support stand and clamp
- rigid plastic tubing, 20 cm long and bent at right angle

Procedure

1. Obtain some small plant seeds. If possible, have a different type of seeds from those used by your classmates. Germinate the seeds by spreading them on wet paper towel a day or two before the lab.

2. Start to make a respirometer by inserting the short end of the tube into the hole of the stopper. The long end of the tube should be sticking out at a right angle as shown in the photograph.

3. Draw a line 0.5 cm above the bottom of the test tube with the marker. Add limewater to the tube up to this mark.

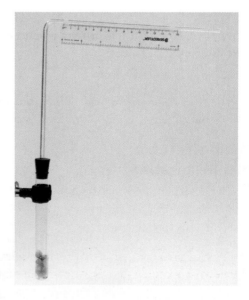

4. Moisten a small wad of cotton and place it on top of the limewater. Now place one gram of germinating seeds on top of the moistened cotton.

5. Tape the ruler to the tubing as shown in the photograph. Use a pipette to add a drop of detergent to the tubing near the end.

6. Carefully insert the stopper and tubing into the test tube to form an airtight seal. Use a support stand and clamps to keep the respirometer apparatus in an upright position.

7. Wait five minutes to allow for the absorption of any carbon dioxide that was in the respirometer when it was assembled. Take an initial reading wherever the drop of detergent is with respect to the ruler. Always take the measurement from the same part of the detergent drop. Record the initial reading in a suitable data table.

8. Take readings every minute for 15 minutes and record them in the data table. Graph your data.

Analysis

1. How did the rate of oxygen consumption in different types of plant seeds compare?

Conclusions

2. Describe what you observed that indicated cellular respiration was occurring in the germinating seeds.

3. Name at least two sources of error that could have affected your observations and data. Explain how significant these sources of error are to the outcome of your investigation.

Part 2: Heat Production in Cellular Respiration

Question

How can you demonstrate that heat is a product of germinating (respiring) seeds?

Hypothesis

State a hypothesis that enables you to obtain quantitative data about the heat given off by germinating seeds.

Prediction

Make a prediction about the outcome of your investigation.

Safety Precautions

The buildup of gases in an enclosed container such as a test tube or flask could cause the container to rupture or shatter. Provide a means for venting gases out of any system you use.

Materials

- germinating seeds (e.g., chickpeas)
- other materials your group decides are needed

Note: Consider using probeware or similar data-logging equipment if it is available.

Experimental Plan

1. With your group, develop a written plan that outlines the procedure you will follow to test your hypothesis. Be sure to consider the following in your procedure:
   - safety
   - controlled variables
   - data collection and recording

2. In the course of your planning, you may wish to consult other investigations you have performed earlier this year (for example, Investigation 2.B in Chapter 2) or in previous science courses. These investigations may provide ideas or procedures that you can adopt or modify.

3. Review your hypothesis and procedure with your teacher before you perform it.

Data and Observations

4. Decide how you will measure the heat given off by germinating seeds.

5. Decide how you will record and display your data to assist you in analyzing and drawing conclusions about your results.

Analysis

1. What variables did you manipulate and control?

2. Compare your results with those obtained by others in the class. Use the differences, if any, to identify possible sources of error in your procedure and/or data collection.

Conclusions

3. Explain why your results either supported or refuted your hypothesis.

4. Predict the results of your investigation if you let it run for a longer period of time, such as several days or a week. Justify your prediction by explaining your reasoning.

*Part 1 adapted from *Agri-science Resources for High School Sciences*, P.E.I. Agriculture Sector Council

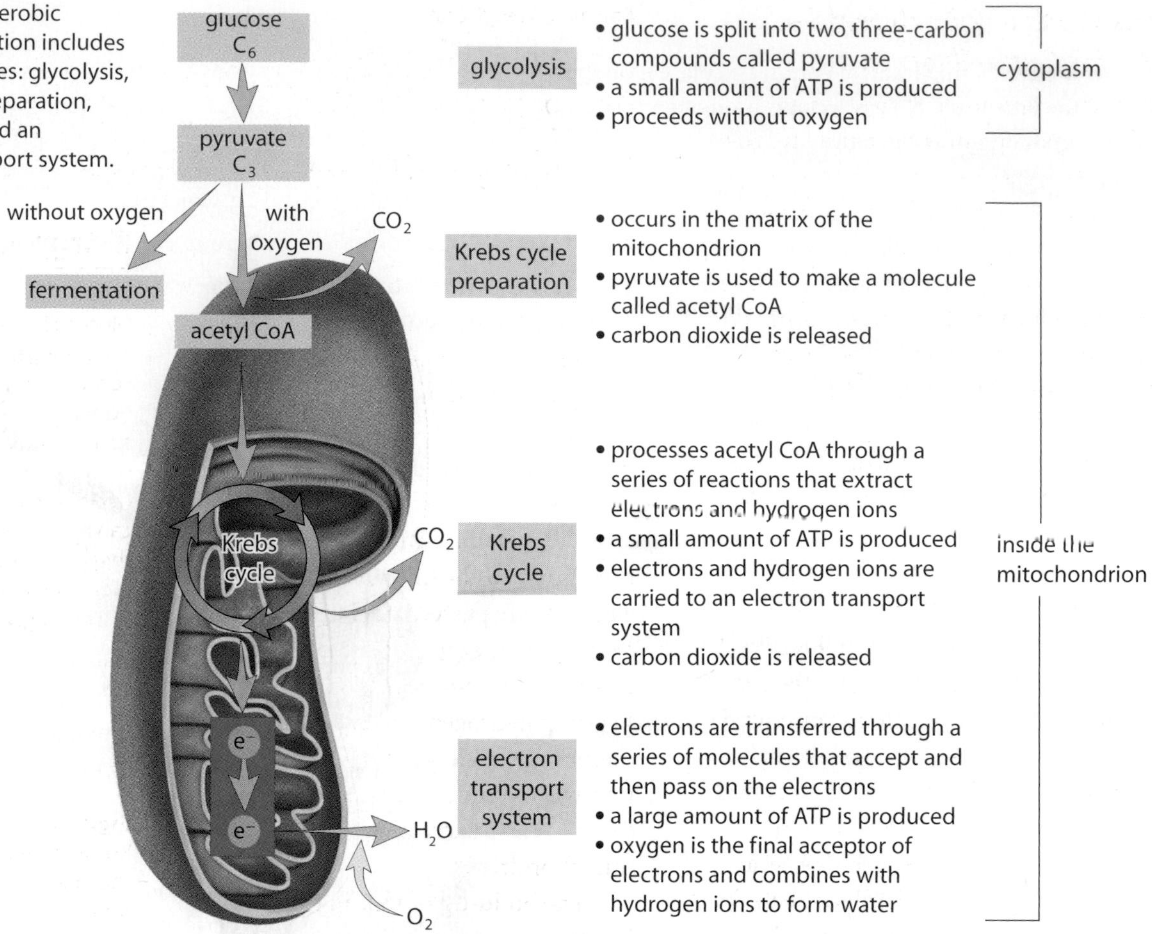

Figure 5.17 Aerobic cellular respiration includes four main stages: glycolysis, Krebs cycle preparation, Krebs cycle, and an electron transport system.

glucose
C_6

pyruvate
C_3

without oxygen

with oxygen

CO_2

fermentation

acetyl CoA

Krebs cycle

CO_2

e^-

e^-

H_2O

O_2

glycolysis
- glucose is split into two three-carbon compounds called pyruvate
- a small amount of ATP is produced
- proceeds without oxygen

cytoplasm

Krebs cycle preparation
- occurs in the matrix of the mitochondrion
- pyruvate is used to make a molecule called acetyl CoA
- carbon dioxide is released

Krebs cycle
- processes acetyl CoA through a series of reactions that extract electrons and hydrogen ions
- a small amount of ATP is produced
- electrons and hydrogen ions are carried to an electron transport system
- carbon dioxide is released

inside the mitochondrion

electron transport system
- electrons are transferred through a series of molecules that accept and then pass on the electrons
- a large amount of ATP is produced
- oxygen is the final acceptor of electrons and combines with hydrogen ions to form water

to glucose, it splits and two intermediate three-carbon molecules are formed. Several more reactions occur in which some ATP is synthesized and a molecule called NAD$^+$ (nicotinamide adenine dinucleotide) is reduced to NADH. The amount of ATP that is synthesized (4 molecules) is greater than the amount of ATP that was used to start the process

(2 molecules). Thus, there is a net gain of two molecules of ATP in the cell. When glycolysis is complete, there are two identical three-carbon molecules of pyruvate.

When oxygen is not available, or for species that cannot utilize oxygen, glycolysis is the *only* pathway by which the cell can extract energy from glucose. However, the products of glycolysis, pyruvate, must be processed further through fermentation, as you will see later. When sufficient oxygen is present in the cell, pyruvate is transported into the matrix of the mitochondria in preparation for the Krebs cycle.

Summary of Glycolysis

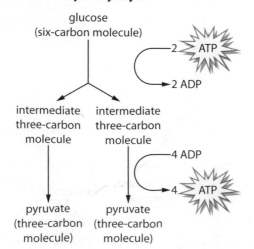

glucose
(six-carbon molecule)

2 ATP

2 ADP

intermediate three-carbon molecule

intermediate three-carbon molecule

4 ADP

4 ATP

pyruvate (three-carbon molecule)

pyruvate (three-carbon molecule)

Figure 5.18 Glycolysis breaks down glucose to form two molecules of pyruvate. This process also generates a small amount of ATP and NADH.

31 State where glycolysis occurs in a cell and whether or not oxygen is required.

32 Name three products that result from glycolysis.

Inside the Mitochondria: Krebs Cycle Preparation

Pyruvate must undergo one reaction before a portion of it can enter the Krebs cycle. As shown at right, pyruvate loses a carbon atom in the form of carbon dioxide, and the other two carbon atoms are bonded to a molecule called Coenzyme A (often shortened to CoA). During this reaction, another NAD$^+$ is reduced to NADH. You could think of CoA as being like a tow truck. It attaches to the two-carbon compound (called an acetyl group) and "tows" it to the Krebs cycle where the CoA releases the acetyl group.

The Krebs Cycle

The Krebs cycle is outlined in Figure 5.19. It is called a cycle because the last compound—a four-carbon compound that picks up a group of two carbons from acetyl-CoA—must be regenerated so it can pick up more two-carbon groups. During one complete cycle, a two-carbon group is added to the Krebs cycle and two carbon atoms are fully oxidized to carbon dioxide. (The carbon dioxide is a waste product—the gas that you exhale when you breathe.)

Most of the energy released when the carbon atoms are oxidized is transformed into reducing power in the form of reduced NADH and another molecule called FADH$_2$ (flavin adenine dinucleotide). FADH$_2$ is very similar to NADH and to NADPH. Also during the Krebs cycle, an ATP molecule is generated.

• • •

33 State where the reactions of the Krebs cycle occur in a cell.

34 What compound that is derived from glucose actually enters the Krebs cycle?

35 The carbon atoms that are derived from glucose are fully oxidized in the Krebs cycle. What becomes reduced during the Krebs cycle?

• • •

Forming Acetyl-CoA

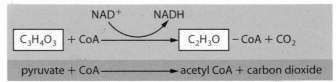

$$C_3H_4O_3 + CoA \longrightarrow C_2H_3O - CoA + CO_2$$

NAD$^+$ → NADH

pyruvate + CoA ⟶ acetyl CoA + carbon dioxide

Electron Transport

The vast majority of the ATP molecules in aerobic cellular respiration are produced during electron transport. The electron transport system in mitochondria is very similar to the electron transport system in chloroplasts. High-energy electrons are passed to a chain of electron-carrying molecules that are attached to the inner membrane of the mitochondrion. As electrons are passed from one carrier to another, energy is released in small, controlled amounts. The energy is used to pump hydrogen ions across the membrane from the matrix to the intermembrane space (the space between the inner and outer membranes of the mitochondrion).

The build-up of ions in the intermembrane space creates a hydrogen-

BiologyFile

FYI
Glucose in not the only simple sugar that you consume in your diet. Common table sugar is sucrose. Milk contains the sugar lactose. Many foods contain starch. Your body can break down any of these sugars and convert them into glucose so they can enter glycolysis.

Figure 5.19 The role of the Krebs cycle is to transfer the energy that was originally stored in glucose to the reducing power of NADH and FADH$_2$.

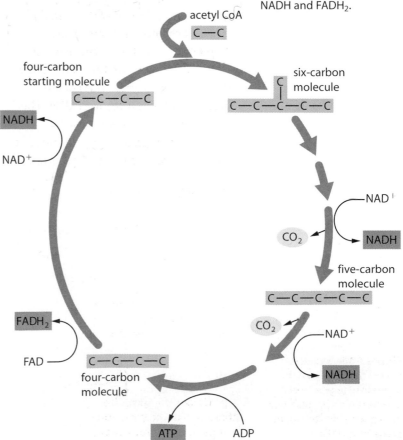

Some biologists and biochemists call the Krebs cycle the citric acid cycle because the cycle begins with citric acid (which contains the two carbon atoms from acetyl-CoA). Many biochemists call the Krebs cycle the TCA cycle because citric acid is a **tri**carboxylic **a**cid. If you encounter either of those terms when you are doing research, keep in mind that they are exactly the same as the Krebs cycle.

ion concentration gradient. The ions can diffuse back across the membrane but only through channels created by the enzyme ATP synthase. This enzyme uses the energy of the concentration gradient to bind a phosphate group to ADP, forming ATP. This process is chemiosmosis. As in the chloroplast, **chemiosmosis** in the mitochondrion couples the movement of hydrogen ions down their concentration gradient to the synthesis of ATP from ADP and phosphate.

Oxygen is the final electron-accepting molecule in the electron transport system. The oxygen accepts electrons and hydrogen ions. The resulting molecule is water.

The Role of Oxygen in Aerobic Cellular Respiration

You learned earlier that glycolysis does not require oxygen. Oxygen is not part of the Krebs cycle, either. In fact, oxygen does not play any role in aerobic cellular respiration until the very last set of reactions in electron transport. So why is this type of cellular respiration called *aerobic*?

The reason becomes clear if you trace the route of the reactions backwards from the end of the process. If oxygen were not present to receive electrons, the whole process would ultimately fail. The last electron carrier would not be able to

release its electron. This means that the previous carrier would not be able to pass *its* electron, and so on up the line of electron transport. Soon, all of the carriers would have electrons and the reduced NADH and FADH$_2$ would be unable to lose *their* electrons. All of the compounds would remain in their reduced, energized state. There would be no oxidized NAD$^+$ or FAD to pick up electrons from the Krebs cycle. All reactions would cease.

The only part of aerobic cellular respiration that would be able to proceed without oxygen is glycolysis. However, glycolysis does not produce enough energy to sustain the needs of most eukaryotic cells.

Compare the amount of ATP produced by glycolysis with the yield of ATP harvested from glucose during all the stages of aerobic cellular respiration in a typical cell (Figure 5.20). Notice that the majority of the ATP in aerobic cellular respiration is generated by chemiosmosis, using the energy of a hydrogen ion concentration gradient that is formed by the electron transport system. All the energy, in the form of ATP, that your body uses to carry out every task is produced by the chemical reactions summarized here.

Figure 5.20 In aerobic cellular respiration, only a small amount of ATP is generated by glycolysis, and only a small amount of ATP is generated by the Krebs cycle. The majority of the ATP is generated by chemiosmosis using energy generated via the electron transport system.

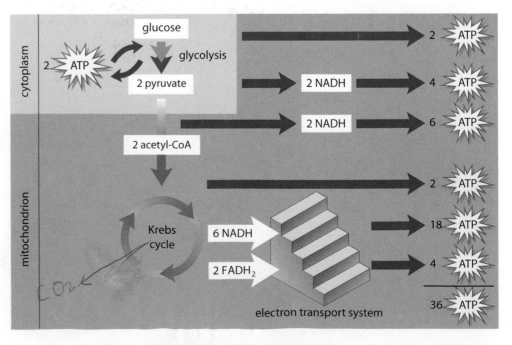

Anaerobic Cellular Respiration Uses a Different Final Electron-Acceptor

In anoxic (no oxygen) environments such as swampy sediments and your colon (large intestine), some organisms use anaerobic cellular respiration for their energy needs. These organisms are prokaryotes—that is, various species belonging to the domains Bacteria and Archaea.

As is the case with aerobic respiration, anaerobic cellular respiration usually includes an electron transport system and a concentration gradient to generate molecules of ATP. Anaerobic cellular respiration is not as efficient as aerobic respiration, however, providing less energy (fewer ATPs).

Since oxygen is not available as the final electron-accepting molecule, a different chemical must serve as the final electron acceptor. For most anaerobic

BiologyFile

Web Link
Pyruvate dehydrogenase complex deficiency is a rare genetic disorder in which the enzyme that converts pyruvate to acetyl-CoA is missing or functions poorly. What are the symptoms of this disorder, what treatments are available, and how successful are they?

www.albertabiology.ca
WWW

Thought Lab 5.3 — The Effects of Metabolic Toxins on Cellular Respiration

Target Skills

Investigating and **integrating**, from print and electronic sources, the action of metabolic toxins on cellular respiration

Evaluating the reliability, accuracy, and validity of information sources consulted

Working cooperatively to investigate metabolic toxins

In the 1930s, a chemical called dinitrophenol (DNP) was used in diet pills. DNP affects chemiosmosis by disrupting the hydrogen ion concentration gradient, thus interfering with the production of ATP. This leads to rapid oxidation of compounds in the Krebs cycle, and encourages the metabolizing of carbohydrates and fats. Since the production of ATP is severely impaired, energy production in the body is instead given off as significant amounts of heat. People lost a lot of weight quickly, but many people lost a lot more—their health and, in some cases, their lives. DNP was quickly banned from public consumption, but it is still used in industry to make products such as dyes, preservatives for wood, and pesticides. It is, unfortunately, also popular with bodybuilders who use it at great risk to their personal safety.

DNP is an example of a metabolic toxin—a chemical that impairs or disrupts metabolic pathways. In this activity, you will investigate and report on metabolic toxins that affect the function of mitochondria.

Procedure

1. Choose one of the following metabolic toxins to investigate:

   - antimycin
   - malonate
   - rotenone
   - cyanide
   - oligomycin
   - arsenic
   - hydrogen sulfide

2. Find four different sources of information about your chosen metabolic toxin. Include information from two print sources and two electronic sources. Search for and collect the following information:

   - What are its physical properties?
   - When and why was it first developed and used?
   - How does it work? (That is, what is its effect on metabolism?)
   - How dangerous is it?
   - What, if any, evidence is there to link it to human disorders?
   - What, if any, antidotes or treatments for exposure are there?

3. Create a "Metabolic Toxin Profile" for the toxin you investigate. Your profile should include an introductory paragraph that summarizes the results of your research findings. Use appropriate headings to organize the information in your profile. Also include the sources of information you have used to construct your profile.

4. Share your profile with your classmates. As a class, decide on a suitable format in which to collect and present profiles of all the metabolic toxins investigated. (For example, you could construct a comparison chart or an electronic database.)

Analysis

1. Classify the metabolic toxins you investigated on the basis of the metabolic pathway they affect.

2. Consider each of the information resources you used to construct your profile.

   a) How did you assess the accuracy of its information?

   b) How did you assess the validity (truth) of its information?

   c) Examine the profiles and information sources from other students who investigated the same metabolic toxin. Re-examine and assess the reliability of the information sources that you used to construct your profile.

   d) Which do you think provided information in which you have greater confidence: print sources or electronic sources? Give reasons to support your opinion.

   e) Are four sources of information sufficient for providing accurate and reliable information? Justify your answer.

cells, this is an inorganic chemical such as sulfate, nitrate, or carbon dioxide. Depending on the inorganic chemical, common by-products are elemental sulfur, nitrite, elemental nitrogen, or methane.

• • •

36. Where, in the mitochondria, are the electron carriers located?

37. What is the source of the high-energy electrons for electron transport in mitochondria?

38. Describe the function of oxygen in cellular respiration.

• • •

Fermentation

Anaerobic organisms do not use oxygen, and some cells in aerobic organisms are sometimes without oxygen. These cells and organisms use metabolic pathways that do not require oxygen or an electron transport system to produce ATP from energy sources. These pathways, called fermentation, typically occur in the cytoplasm of the cell. **Fermentation** is a metabolic pathway that includes glycolysis and one or two reactions in which NADH is oxidized to NAD^+ by reducing pyruvate to other compounds. Fermentation is much less efficient at supplying energy than aerobic cellular respiration, because fermentation only produces the amount of ATP that is generated in glycolysis.

Many single-celled organisms such as yeasts and some bacteria, carry out fermentation. Fermentation also occurs in parts of an organism that are in an anaerobic environment such as in a plant that is partly submerged in a pond or in cells that are deep within a multicellular organism without direct access to oxygen. There are many types of fermentation pathways. Two common types are *lactate fermentation* and *ethanol fermentation*.

Lactate Fermentation

Some single-celled organisms and some animal cells that are temporarily without oxygen carry out lactate fermentation.

They use NADH to convert pyruvate to a molecule called lactate (also called lactic acid) in a single step (Figure 5.21). The resulting NAD^+ is recycled to continue the process. This process occurs in your muscle cells when they are working strenuously. During such times, the demand for energy exceeds what can be produced aerobically. Glycolysis, then, is increased to a point where it exceeds the oxygen supply, creating a condition of "oxygen debt." In this condition, pyruvate starts to accumulate, since it cannot be broken down fast enough in the Krebs cycle and the electron transport system. To sustain glycolysis, the muscle must remove excess pyruvate by converting it to lactate, which is temporarily stored in the muscle cells. If enough lactate builds up, the muscle fatigues and cramps. When oxygen is present again (through heavy breathing after exercise), the lactate is converted back to pyruvate. The pyruvate may then be processed as usual through aerobic pathways.

Ethanol Fermentation

Some organisms are able to function aerobically as well as anaerobically. When they function anaerobically, they carry out ethanol fermentation. Yeasts and some kinds of bacteria convert pyruvate to ethanol and carbon dioxide through ethanol fermentation. The process involves two steps, as shown in Figure 5.22.

Fermentation by brewer's yeast (*Saccharomyces cerevisiae*) is used in industry to manufacture baked goods and alcoholic beverages (Figure 5.23). Depending on the substance being fermented, the variety of yeast used, and

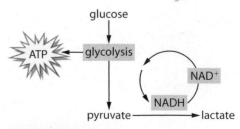

Figure 5.21 In lactate fermentation, pyruvate is converted to lactate in a single step that oxidizes NADH to NAD^+.

whether carbon dioxide is allowed to escape during the process, yeast fermentation may be used to produce wine or champagne from grapes, the syrupy drink called mead from honey, and cider from apples. Beer is brewed by fermenting sugars in grain such as barley, rice, or corn.

Depending on the organism, fermentation can yield other substances besides lactate and ethanol. Table 5.2 lists several examples. Two other examples, acetone and butanol, were essential during World War I. The British needed butanol to make artificial rubber for tires and machinery and acetone to make a smokeless gunpowder called cordite. Prior to the war, acetone was made by heating wood in the absence of oxygen (a technique called pyrolysis). Up to 100 tonnes of lumber were needed to produce 1 tonne of acetone. When war broke out in 1917, the demand for acetone was intense. A swift and efficient means for producing the chemical was needed. Two years earlier, Chaim Weizmann, a chemist working in Manchester, England, had developed a fermentation process using the anaerobic bacterium *Clostridium acetobutylicum*. Through this process, Weizmann converted 100 tonnes of molasses or grain into 12 tonnes of acetone and 24 tonnes of butanol. For the war effort, Weizmann modified the technique for large-scale production. (Today, both acetone and butanol are produced more economically from petrochemicals.)

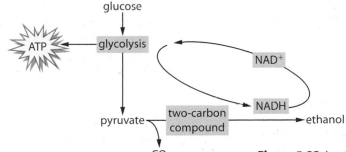

Figure 5.22 In ethanol fermentation, pyruvate is converted to a two-carbon molecule and then to ethanol. In the process, NADH oxidizes to NAD^+.

39 What does it mean to say that glycolysis is an anaerobic process?

40 Under what conditions does fermentation occur?

41 Describe how lactate fermentation is similar to and different from ethanol fermentation.

Ethanol Fermentation and Fuel Production

Glucose is the main fuel for many organisms. However, much of the chemical energy of glucose remains in the compounds that form after glycolysis

Table 5.2 Selected Fermentation Products and their Uses

Product of Fermentation	Possible Sources	Uses
acetic acid	Bacteria: *Leuconostoc* sp. *Acetobacter xylenam*	sours beer; produces vinegar
diacetyl	Bacteria: *Streptococcus diacetilactis*	provides fragrance and flavour to buttermilk
lactic acid (lactate)	Bacteria: *Lactobacillus bulgaricus*	aids in changing milk to yogurt
propionic acid + CO_2	Bacteria: *Proprionibacterium shermani*	produces the "eyes" (holes) and flavour of Swiss cheese

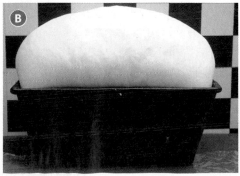

Figure 5.23 In **(A)**, bread dough with yeast is being left in a warm place so that yeast has time to ferment. After a few hours, the bread dough in **(B)** has doubled in size (risen) due to the carbon dioxide produced by fermentation. When the dough is baked, the carbon dioxide gas will be driven off, leaving small holes that help give the bread a light, chewy texture.

Energy from Manure

Alberta raises about 3.5 million pigs each year—about 15 percent of the Canadian total. Pork is a valuable resource. Canada exports over $2 billion worth of pork per year, making us one of the world's top exporters. But is what's good for the economy harming the environment? According to figures from Statistics Canada, pig manure is the largest source of greenhouse gas emissions from the hog-production system. Pig manure is also, however, a source of biogas (methane from animal wastes), which can be used as an alternative to traditional fuels. Around the world, especially in developing countries, biogas is used to heat homes, cook food, and power generators.

How Biogas Is Made

The process of anaerobic digestion is used to treat sewage, animal wastes, and municipal solid wastes. An anaerobic digester is an airtight tank with heating coils and sometimes a mechanical mixer. Oxygen is poisonous to anaerobic bacteria, so an oxygen-free environment is important.

Anaerobic digestion is a two-part process that works best at a temperature of 35 °C or higher. First, acid-forming bacteria break down the manure into simple organic compounds. Then a second group of anaerobic micro-organisms break down the acids into methane and carbon dioxide. Biogas consists of 60 to 80 percent methane gas, 20 to 40 percent carbon dioxide, and trace amounts of other compounds, such as hydrogen sulfide, ammonia, and water vapour. The set-up cost varies greatly, since there are different types and sizes of anaerobic digesters.

The Value of Biogas

Research and small-scale case studies indicate that about 1 kg of hog manure produces between 0.5 m³ and 1 m³ of biogas (with 60 to 65 percent methane). 1 m³ of biogas is enough to cook three meals daily for a family of four to six people, replacing approximately 11 kg (one tank) of propane. To produce 1 m³ of biogas, a family needs at least 5 L of pig manure per day, requiring about five mature pigs. Many variables, such as the pigs' diet, the type of digester used, and the digester temperature, influence these figures.

• • •

1. Manure digestion for the production of electricity is currently in use in Vegreville, Alberta, at Highmark Renewables. Find out more about this and other integrated manure utilization systems (IMUS).

2. Yuanhui Zhang, an agricultural engineering professor at the University of Illinois, has been able to convert small amounts of hog manure into crude oil. Subsequent experiments have yielded a refined product with the approximate heating value of diesel fuel. Investigate the current status of this ongoing work.

is complete. The process of fermentation does not remove much of this chemical energy. Therefore, the products of fermentation can still be used for fuel.

In organisms that carry out ethanol fermentation, the ethanol they produce is released as a waste product. In fact, the ethanol waste is toxic to yeast. As ethanol concentrations approach 12 percent, the yeast cells begin to die. However, humans learned long ago that this "waste" burns. Ethanol was a common lamp fuel during the 1800s, and it was used for early internal combustion engines and cars, also starting in the 1800s.

Historically, because gasoline costs less to produce than ethanol, its use was limited to small-scale, specialized applications. This situation changed in the late 1970s. At that time, rising oil prices, dwindling petroleum reserves, and environmental concerns caused some governments to invest in alternative energy resources such as ethanol fuels. Whenever gas prices rise, some of these alternative resources become commercially viable sources of fuel. In cars, the use of gasohol (a mixture of 10 percent ethanol and 90 percent gasoline) is becoming more common. Cars manufactured after 1980 can use gasohol without any engine modification. As well, auto companies are designing engines that can use fuels with ethanol percentages that are much higher than 10. Brazil is currently leading the world in the production of ethanol and its use as a fuel. Most cars designed and built is Brazil today can burn pure ethanol (Figure 5.24) or several combinations of gasoline and ethanol.

Ethanol Production

In Canada, the most common source of ethanol is the fermentation of corn and wheat. First the grain is ground into a meal. Then it is mixed with water to form a slurry called "mash." Enzymes added to the mash convert the starches into glucose. The mash is heated to destroy any bacteria, then cooled and placed in fermenters. In the fermenters, yeast is added to the mash. The yeast grows on the glucose under anaerobic conditions and releases the end products, ethanol, and carbon dioxide. When the fermentation is complete, the resulting product, called "beer," is approximately 10 percent ethanol and 90 percent water.

Distilling the beer to eliminate as much of the water as possible yields nearly pure ethanol. A small amount of gasoline is added to make the ethanol unfit for human consumption (called denaturing). The solid residues from the grain and yeast are dried to produce a vitamin- and protein-rich product called Distiller's Dried Grains and Solubles (DDGS). DDGS is used as feed for poultry and cattle.

The combustion of ethanol produces carbon dioxide, which is one of the greenhouse gases that contributes to global warming. However, unlike gasoline, the source of ethanol (grain) is a renewable resource. Ethanol is made by the fermentation of corn, grain, sugar cane, and many other crops that can be regrown quickly. In addition, these same crops also absorb carbon dioxide in order to produce more sugars and, through processing, more ethanol. Even so, the burning of ethanol is not "carbon-neutral." In other words, the production and burning of ethanol release more CO_2 into the atmosphere than is absorbed by growing plants. So why use it? As an additive to gasoline, ethanol increases the octane rating of the fuel; that is, it burns more slowly and prevents engine "ping." As well, ethanol-gasoline mixtures reduce the amount of carbon monoxide in the exhaust. Burning pure ethanol on its own also eliminates the release of partially burned hydrocarbons and volatile organic compounds (VOCs) that contribute to smog.

Section 5.3 Summary

- Three metabolic pathways make up aerobic cellular respiration.
- The first set of reactions in aerobic cellular respiration is called glycolysis.

BiologyFile

FYI
Red Deer, Alberta has one of only seven ethanol production plants in Canada. Seven more plants are in the planning stages.

Figure 5.24 Many modern Brazilian cars are called flex-cars because they can operate on gasoline or ethanol.

BiologyFile

Web Link

The First Nation Ethanol Development Corporation was established in 2004 with an initial focus on establishing an ethanol plant in southwestern Ontario. What other products are planned for this plant? And why is the use of corn, as the main fermentation feedstock, an appropriate choice for this venture?

www.albertabiology.ca
WWW

It is an anaerobic process that takes place in the cytoplasm of the cell.

- During glycolysis, a small amount of ATP is generated, and NAD^+ is reduced to NADH.
- The fate of pyruvate, the final product of glycolysis, depends on the availability of oxygen and on the type of organism.
- When oxygen is available, pyruvate enters the matrix of the mitochondrion. A series of reactions yield carbon dioxide and acetyl-CoA. NAD^+ is reduced to NADH.
- Acetyl-CoA enters the Krebs cycle by combining with a four-carbon compound.
- During the Krebs cycle, two carbon atoms are fully oxidized to carbon dioxide, NAD^+ and FAD are reduced to NADH and $FADH_2$, and a small amount of ATP is produced.
- The reduced NADH and $FADH_2$ that are formed during the Krebs cycle donate their electrons to the electron carriers in electron transport.

- As electrons are passed from one carrier to the next, the energy that is released is used to pump hydrogen ions across the mitochondrial inner membrane into the intermembrane space, creating a concentration gradient.
- The energy stored in the gradient is used to generate ATP by chemiosmosis.
- Organisms that carry out anaerobic cellular respiration use inorganic chemicals other than oxygen as the final electron-acceptor. This produces ATP for the cell, but not as much as in aerobic respiration.
- In muscle that is functioning anaerobically, pyruvate is converted to lactate and the reduced NADH is reoxidized so that glycolysis can continue.
- In yeast growing anaerobically, pyruvate is converted to carbon dioxide and ethanol.
- Fermentation is used on an industrial scale to produce ethanol.
- Ethanol is used as an additive to gasoline to reduce some environmental contaminants.

Section 5.3 Review

1. Summarize photosynthesis and cellular respiration in terms of reduction and oxidation of carbon-based molecules.

2. Compare, in general terms, aerobic cellular respiration, anaerobic cellular respiration, and fermentation.

3. Identify the three energy-releasing metabolic pathways associated with aerobic cellular respiration.

4. Use graphics or word processing software to summarize glycolysis, the first stage of aerobic cellular respiration. Include where this process takes place, whether or not oxygen is required for these reactions, the products that are formed as a result of glycolysis, and where these products go next. **ICT**

5. Use graphics or word processing software to summarize the Krebs cycle, the second stage of aerobic cellular respiration. Include where this process takes place, whether or not oxygen is required for these reactions, the products that are formed as a result of the Krebs cycle, and where these products go next. **ICT**

6. Use graphics or word processing software to summarize the electron transport system, the third stage of aerobic cellular respiration. Include where this process takes place, whether or not oxygen is required for these reactions, the products that are formed as a result of the electron transport system, and where these products go next. **ICT**

7. Explain the term "chemiosmosis."

8. Identify the final electron acceptor in aerobic cellular respiration, and explain what happens if this molecule is not present in the cell.

9. Explain why aerobic cellular respiration produces so much more ATP than does anaerobic cellular respiration.

10. Describe the term "fermentation," and explain why this process is considered to be anaerobic.

11. Compare lactate fermentation to ethanol fermentation in terms of starting and ending material and ATP production.

The summary equations for photosynthesis and cellular respiration represent dozens of different reactions. The central function of photosynthesis and cellular respiration is to produce energy-rich compounds and break them down to release their stored energy. The useful form of energy is ATP (adenosine triphosphate). The energy is contained in the bonds between the phosphate groups, leaving ADP (adenosine diphosphate) and a free phosphate group. When the bond to the last phosphate group is broken, the energy released is available to do cellular work. Energy stored in energy-rich compounds is used to add a phosphate group back to ADP to regenerate ATP.

In photosynthesis, the carbon dioxide and water are involved in two separate sets of reactions. Water is split into hydrogen ions, electrons, and oxygen in the light-dependent reactions; carbon dioxide is incorporated into carbohydrates in the light-independent reactions.

In the light-dependent reactions, which take place in the thylakoid membranes of the chloroplasts, pigments capture light energy and use it to excite electrons that are channelled away to produce ATP and NADPH. During the light-independent reactions in the stroma of the chloroplasts, the chemical potential energy of ATP and the reducing power of NADPH are used to reduce carbon dioxide and form glucose and other carbohydrates via the Calvin-Benson cycle.

The glucose synthesized by plants and other photosynthesizing organisms (autotrophs) is the source of energy for virtually all living organisms. The glucose is processed to extract the energy in a series of three major sets of chemical reactions: glycolysis, the Krebs cycle, and electron transport. Glycolysis is an anaerobic process that occurs in the cytoplasm and breaks down glucose to form pyruvate. In most organisms, the pyruvate passes into the mitochondria where it is broken down into carbon dioxide and acetyl CoA in preparation for the Krebs cycle, which occurs in the matrix. Energy released from the breakdown of compounds in the Krebs cycle is used to reduce NAD^+ and FAD to NADH and $FADH_2$. These reduced compounds contribute their electrons to electron carriers embedded in the inner mitochondrial membranes. As the electrons are passed from one carrier to the next in electron transport, the energy that is released in a stepwise manner is used to pump hydrogen ions across the inner mitochondrial membrane, forming a concentration gradient that generates ATP through chemiosmosis.

In some organisms, glycolysis is their only source of energy. In these organisms, the pyruvate is broken down into carbon dioxide and alcohol (ethanol fermentation) or lactate (lactate fermentation). Humans have long been using the fermentation process to obtain ethanol, which is becoming popular as a fuel for transportation.

Chapter 5 Graphic Organizer

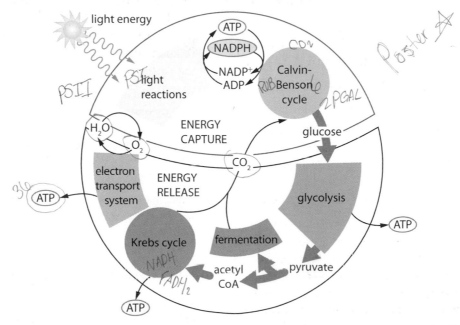

Career Focus: Ask a Research Scientist

Dr. Salim Abboud has always been interested in science as a way to solve problems. Today, he is a research scientist at the Alberta Research Council and an Adjunct Professor at the University of Alberta, where he applies scientific knowledge to solve some of the most urgent issues facing our society today. Dr. Abboud's current research focusses on improving waste management techniques and developing environmentally friendly and waste-free methods of composting organic materials and other wastes. This research is on the cutting edge of science, particularly as our society begins to move to a more sustainable way of life. Dr. Abboud's goal, like the goals of most research scientists, is to find ways of solving current problems and to develop technologies and solutions for issues that will be facing us in the future.

Q What are the main areas of your research?

I am working on finding the optimal conditions and technologies to maximize the process of composting and make it as clean and complete as possible. Using compost as a soil amendment gives us an alternative to using chemicals (such as fertilizers and pesticides) on land, thereby saving energy and natural resources. As well, I am interested in the biofiltration of gaseous emissions from municipal and industrial sites.

Q What is biofiltration?

If you take a material, such as a volatile organic compound (VOC), that causes air pollution, you may be able to oxidize it into non-harmful compounds, such as CO_2 and water. This also works on other noxious emissions, such as reduced sulfur compounds that have such a strong smell. They can be oxidized into SO_2 and water, which eliminates the negative effects of the sulfur compound.

Q Do you spend all your time in a laboratory, or do you get to go out and do field work?

I spend a significant amount of time out in the field. I set up pilot experiments and test new conditions in different locations, such as industrial sites. In addition, I am involved in work at the Edmonton Waste Management Centre of Excellence, which houses a leading edge composting facility.

Q What makes the Edmonton composter so special?

The Edmonton composter is the largest composter in North America, handling almost 1200 t of compost every day. All household solid waste in Edmonton goes to the composter, where it is treated. About 65 to 70 percent of the waste ends up as compost or recyclable commodities, and about 30 percent is a residual that is sent to the landfill.

Q So no household garbage in Edmonton goes directly to the landfill?

No, it doesn't. In fact, we are still working to reduce the 30 percent. We are aiming to keep about 95 percent of waste from landfills by gasification techniques (burning), which will extract energy that can be used to create electricity.

Q Why do you think these issues are so important?

At the moment, as a society, we produce an enormous amount of garbage and other pollutants. I believe that it is possible to use resources in environmentally and socially friendly ways. It is no longer appropriate to take a natural resource, use part of it, and then throw the rest away. My focus is industrial ecology, organizing industries in ways that are similar to nature. In nature, there is no waste—one process feeds into the next. My question is why throw out garbage? Compost it, and return it to where it came from. Close the loop, and eventually we won't have a pollution problem.

Q Can you give me an example of what you mean?

Sure. Let's talk about organic waste. It comes from food and fibre produced from plants. After we use plants, we can compost them and add the compost to the soil, which will produce more plants and complete the cycle.

Other Careers Related to Science

Conservation Biologist Researchers who focus on conservation biology have many opportunities to work on relevant and meaningful projects at local as well as global levels. Some areas of conservation biology include protecting endangered or threatened species and increasing their numbers, reclaiming polluted sites, developing barriers to protect ecosystems from the impact of nearby developments, and developing policies to ensure long-term protection of the natural environment.

Biophysicist As the name suggests, biophysicists combine knowledge and techniques from the disciplines of biology and physics in order to investigate the mechanisms by which organisms function at an environmental as well as a cellular level. Applications of biophysical research affect fields as diverse as biotechnology, agriculture, ecology, and medicine.

Agronomist Agronomists study food, food production, and the earth material, soil, that both anchors plants and supplies them with nutrients that are made available through biogeochemical cycles. Drawing upon their knowledge of chemistry as well as plant biology, agronomists investigate methods to enhance existing agricultural techniques as well as to supplement or replace them with alternative technologies. Some agronomists work with "high-tech" technologies such as genetic manipulation (for example, so that plants may be grown without pesticides or synthetic fertlizers). Other agronomists prefer to work from a more "natural" foundation by concentrating on organic farming techniques.

Environmental Microbiologist Researchers in this field combine interests in chemistry, ecology, molecular genetics, and the biology of microscopic life in order to examine the activity of cellular processes in soil, water, and the atmosphere. Practical applications of such research include wastewater treatment, bioremediation, environmental risk assessessment, and control techniques for water- and air-borne pathogens.

Go Further...

1. Research the methods of waste disposal that are used in your community. How much of your community waste goes to a landfill? How much is recycled or composted?

2. Why is waste disposal such an important issue? What can you do in your daily life to improve the situation?

3. Volatile organic compounds, or VOCs, are a significant pollution problem. Research and list some common sources of VOCs and what is being done to solve the problem.

Understanding Concepts

1. Describe, in general terms, the role of autotrophic organisms in an ecosystem.

2. Describe, in general terms, how both autotrophs and heterotrophs release the energy stored in glucose.

3. List four cellular activities that rely on ATP as a source of energy.

4. Explain how the release of a phosphate group from ATP and the subsequent regeneration of ATP from ADP creates a continuous cycle.

5. Describe the function of the chloroplast.

6. Use graphics software to draw a sketch of a chloroplast and label the following structures. **ICT**
   a) outer membrane
   b) inner membrane
   c) stroma
   d) thylakoids
   e) grana

7. Explain the relationship between thylakoids and grana in a chloroplast.

8. Explain the significance of NADPH in photosynthesis and NADH in aerobic cellular respiration.

9. Use graphics software to draw a sketch of a mitochondrion and label the following features. **ICT**
   a) cristae
   b) inner membrane
   c) outer membrane
   d) matrix

10. Identify simple tests that you can do in a lab to detect the presence of the following.
    a) oxygen gas
    b) carbon dioxide dissolved in water

11. Compare a metabolic pathway that synthesizes larger molecules from smaller ones to a metabolic pathway that breaks down larger molecules to smaller ones.

12. Explain why many of the chemical reactions that occur in living organisms are linked to oxidation and reduction reactions.

13. Describe how matter and energy are linked through the reactions that take place in the chloroplasts and in the mitochondria.

14. Describe the major function of photosynthetic pigments.

15. Explain what happens when you shine white light through a glass prism. Describe how you can use this phenomenon to study the properties of photosynthetic pigments.

16. Explain how an action spectrum differs from an absorbance spectrum.

17. Describe, in general terms, the function of the photosystems and identify where you would find these systems in a chloroplast.

18. When electrons travel down the electron transport system between photosystem II and photosystem I, a small amount of energy is released at each step. Describe how this energy is temporarily stored in the chloroplast.

19. When an electron is emitted from photosystem II, it does not return. The photosystem cannot trap any more light energy until the "hole" in the photosystem is filled with another electron. Identify the source of the electron that fills the "hole" in photosystem II.

20. Identify the source of oxygen that is released from the chloroplast during photosynthesis. Explain the main function of the reaction in which oxygen is released.

21. Identify the source of the electrons that reduce NADP$^+$ during the light-dependent reactions of photosynthesis.

22. NADPH is said to have reducing power. Explain the meaning of reducing power in this context.

23. The membranes of the thylakoids are impermeable to hydrogen ions (H^+), meaning that these ions cannot diffuse across the membranes from the inner space of the thylakoid to the stroma.
    a) Identify the only path by which the hydrogen ions can move down their concentration gradient across the membrane to the stroma.
    b) Identify the process that is associated with the movement of hydrogen ions through this pathway and identify the end product of this process.

24. Identify the location in the chloroplast where the reactions that form glucose take place.

25. Outline the Calvin-Benson cycle in terms of carbon dioxide fixation, reduction, and regeneration.

26. Identify where the reactions of glycolysis take place.

27. Identify the products of glycolysis that contain useful energy.

28. Explain the cause of the burning sensation in muscles when they have been working anaerobically for awhile.

29. Identify the products of fermentation in yeast.

30. Explain what happens to lactate (lactic acid) in muscle cells when oxygen becomes available while resting after a strenuous workout.

31. List the end products of the following.
   a) glycolysis
   b) Kreb's cycle
   c) electron transport

32. Identify the stage of aerobic cellular respiration during which the greatest number of ATP molecules is produced.

Applying Concepts

33. Outline, in the form of a paragraph, a drawing, or both, the meaning and significance of chemiosmosis in the mitochondrion. **ICT**

34. The function of the Calvin-Benson cycle is to use six carbon dioxide molecules to produce one glucose molecule. Describe why this set of reactions is called a cycle.

35. Explain what is meant by the following statement: "The reactions of glycolysis occur anaerobically."

36. Four molecules of ATP are formed when one glucose molecule goes through the reactions of glycolysis. Is it correct to say that glycolysis yields two molecules of ATP? Explain your answer.

37. Describe what happens to the pyruvate produced during glycolysis in muscle cells when there is very little oxygen available.

38. Explain how a lack of oxygen stops the process of electron transport and the reactions of the Kreb's cycle.

39. What is "oxygen debt," and how is it "repaid?"

40. Identify the structure in a chloroplast that is analagous (has a similar structure and performs a similar function) to each of the following structures in a mitochondrion. How do the functions of these structures differ?
   a) matrix
   b) outer membrane
   c) inner membrane
   d) cristae

Making Connections

41. Explain the following statement in terms of what green plants make.
"As the rainforest species disappear, so do many possible cures for life-threatening diseases."

42. An analogy is a type of comparison in which you compare two similar systems or ideas by using something that is familiar to help describe or explain something that is less familiar.
   a) Use the idea of a rechargeable battery as an analogy for the cycle that "recharges" ATP from ADP and a free phosphate group.
   b) Outline, in the form of a paragraph or a diagram, an analogy to compare the structure and function of chloroplasts with an active solar system. (An active solar system uses a mechanical, chemical, or electrical device to transfer light energy from the Sun to another part of the system for the purpose of doing useful work.)

43. Pyruvate is available as a dietary supplement. Its reported benefits are controversial but include enhanced weight loss and increased endurance levels during physical exercise. Infer how taking pyruvate could lead to these effects.

44. Research scientists are investigating methods for getting photosynthesis to proceed outside a chloroplast. Identify three practical uses and societal benefits that would come from the successful achievement of this goal.

45. Dinitrophenol (DNP) is a chemical that interferes with the production of ATP in both chloroplasts and mitochondria. In an attempt to identify the minimal concentration of DNP required to inhibit ATP production, DNP was applied to separate suspensions of both organelles. Data are shown in the table below.
   a) Which data represent the chloroplast?
   b) Which organelle would be considered the most active? Explain your answer.
   c) Which organelle is more at risk to changing concentrations of DNP? Explain.

DNP Concentration and ATP Production

Organelle	Concentration of DNP			
	5%	15%	25%	35%
volume of $CO_2(g)$ released (mL)	0.50	0.11	0.05	0.01
volume of $O_2(g)$ released (mL)	0.88	0.04	0.01	n/a

Human Systems

General Outcomes

In this unit, you will

- explain how the human digestive and respiratory systems exchange energy and matter with the environment

- explain the role of the circulatory and defense systems in maintaining homeostasis

- explain the role of the excretory system in maintaining homeostasis through the exchange of energy and matter with the environment

- explain the role of the motor (muscular) system in the function of other body systems

Unit Contents

Focussing Questions

1 What factors influence the healthy functioning of the body?

2 How can technology assist the healthy functioning of the body?

Unit PreQuiz ?
www.albertabiology.ca

Don't tell Sarah Reinertsen it can't be done, unless you want to be proven wrong. In the world of running, she has just about done it all: 100 m, 200 m, 400 m, 5 km, 10 km, marathon, and triathlon. Compared with an athlete with two legs, Sarah Reinertsen must use 40 percent more oxygen and twice as much energy to accomplish the same basic feats. All of her organ systems—circulatory, respiratory, digestive, and muscular systems, to name only a few—are finely tuned through training to work together in the most effective and efficient manner. In this regard, however, she is no different from you or anyone else. Everyone's organ systems have the same vital function of providing and using matter and energy for all life-sustaining activities of the body. In this unit, you will explore the means by which your body obtains necessary materials from the environment, rids itself of materials it does not need, and transforms matter into energy. These processes are closely unified and regulated in a way that even the finest medical technologies cannot replicate.

Prerequisite Concepts

This unit builds on your knowledge of the structure and function of animal cells (Unit 3 Preparation), the cell membrane (Unit 3 Preparation), and cellular respiration (Chapter 5).

Human Systems

Each of the cells of the human body is a living unit that performs a specific function. Cells of the same type interact both structurally and functionally to form specialized tissues, such as those that line your stomach. One or more tissues interact to form more complex structures known as organs, such as your stomach. Several organs—for example, your stomach, small and large intestines, liver, and pancreas—are linked either physically or functionally as organ systems, such as the digestive system.

Figure P4.1 Organ systems of the human body

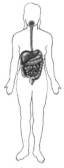

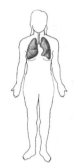

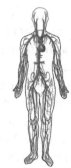

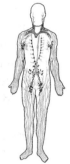

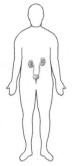

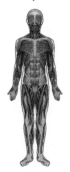

Digestive system
- breaks down food into chemical components that are small enough to enter circulation
- eliminates undigested food

Respiratory system
- delivers oxygen to blood
- removes carbon dioxide from cells
- helps to control blood pH

Circulatory system
- transports blood, nutrients, gases, and metabolic wastes
- defends body against disease
- helps to control temperature, fluid balance, and pH balance

Lymphatic and immune systems
- help to control fluid balance
- defend against disease
- absorb fats (lymphatic)

Excretory system
- removes metabolic wastes
- helps to control fluid balance
- helps to control pH balance

Muscular system
- maintains posture
- moves body and organs
- produces heat

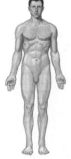

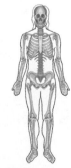

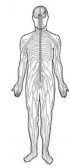

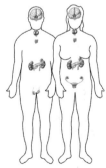

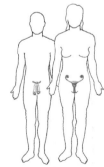

Integumentary system
- protects body from infection
- receives sensory input
- helps to control body temperature
- synthesizes vitamin D

Skeletal system
- provides framework for muscles to attach to, making movement possible
- produces blood cells
- stores minerals
- protects soft organs

Nervous system
- detects, interprets, and responds to stimuli from outside and within body
- with endocrine system, coordinates all organ-system functions

Endocrine system
- produces hormones
- helps to coordinate organ systems
- responds to stress
- helps to regulate fluid and pH balance
- helps to regulate metabolism

Reproductive system
- produces gametes (sperm or ova)
- transports gametes
- produces sex hormones
- nourishes, nurtures, and gives birth to offspring in females

The first six organ systems shown and summarized in Figure P4.1 are the subject of this unit. You will study other organ systems in your next biology course.

Homeostasis and Negative Feedback

Whether you are resting or working out, your body temperature will stay near a set point of 37 °C. The pH of your blood will stay near 7.4. Your blood glucose level will stay around 100 mg/mL. Regardless of external conditions, the internal environment of your body remains stable or relatively constant. The tendency of the body to maintain a relatively constant internal environment is known as *homeostasis*.

Body systems maintain homeostasis through a mechanism that has three components: a *sensor*, which detects a change in the internal environment; an *effector*, which brings internal conditions back into a normal range; and a *control centre*, which activates the effector based on information received from the sensor.

The main homeostatic mechanism that works in the body to keep a variable, such as body temperature, stable is *negative feedback*. Figure P4.2A compares negative feedback to the way a seesaw moves. A seesaw is level when the forces acting on it are balanced. If a change occurs to disrupt this balance, the seesaw can be made level again by applying a force to reverse the change.

In terms of negative feedback, a sensor detects a change that disrupts a balanced state and signals a control centre. The control centre then activates an effector, which reverses the change and restores the balanced state. Figure P4.2B shows how this idea applies to the control of body temperature.

Prerequisite Concepts

This unit provides opportunities to practice and further develop your skills in the use of the microscope and in the illustrating of scientific drawings.

Figure P4.2 Negative feedback in general **(A)** and in a biological example—maintenance of body temperature **(B)**.

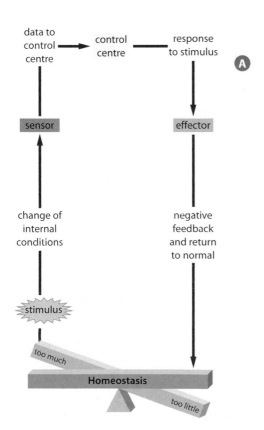

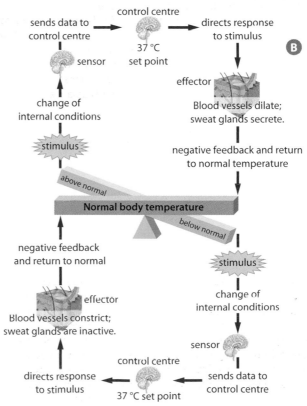

Digestion and Human Health

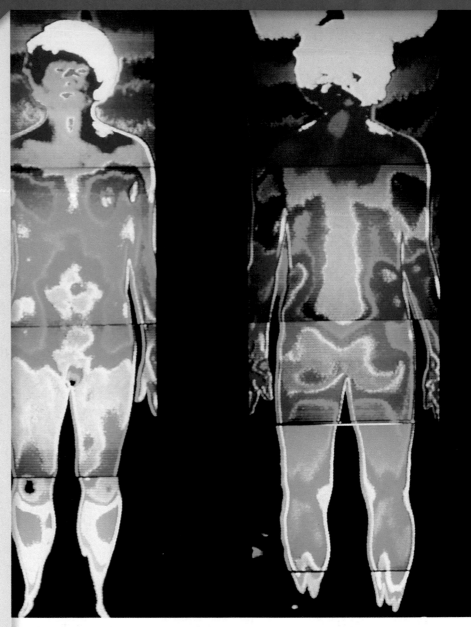

Chapter Concepts

6.1 The Molecules of Living Systems

- Macromolecules such as carbohydrates, lipids, proteins, and nucleic acids are made up of smaller subunits that are chemically separated through hydrolysis.

- Enzymes are biological catalysts.

6.2 The Human Digestive System

- The digestive tract is a tube extending from the mouth to the anus through which food is broken down, nutrient molecules absorbed, and undigested material eliminated.

- Food is processed mechanically and chemically to reduce macromolecules to a form in which they may be absorbed into the bloodstream.

6.3 Health and the Digestive System

- An excess or deficiency of nutrients can lead to disorders that can be diagnosed and treated but not necessarily cured.

Modern technology provides us with new insights into how the human body works. An infrared camera took the pictures above, called thermograms, mapping the heat given off by the human body. The colours correspond to a range of temperatures, from light blue (coolest) through pink, yellow, red, and white (warmest). This heat is generated by ATP, and fuelled by oxygen from the air and nutrient molecules from food. It is evidence of the constant transformation of food into matter and energy that takes place within the trillions of specialized cells that make up each of the body's diverse, interconnected organ systems. In this chapter, you will find out how food is transformed into the matter and energy that enable you to survive.

Launch Lab

Visualizing the Human Body

Thermograms permit a view of the body that otherwise would be beyond the range of our human senses. Capsule endoscopy and similar internal-camera technologies provide views of the body from the inside out, in a manner of speaking. These technologies are powerful aids for diagnosis as well as for developing new understandings of the body and how it works. One of the oldest and still most often-used technologies for peering inside and imaging the body is the X-ray machine.

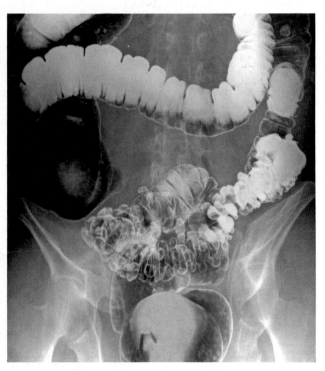

Procedure

1. Examine the coloured X-ray image. Sketch all the organs and body parts that you can see or recognize.

2. On your sketch, add any other organs and body parts that you know or recall.

Analysis

1. Compare your sketches with others in the class. Modify your sketch or labels as necessary.

2. Based on memory or personal knowledge, briefly describe the function of all the organs on your sketch. Write "unsure" for those you do not know or recall. Return to your sketch throughout the unit to assess and modify your sketch.

Capsule endoscopy is a technology that uses a camera-containing pill to capture video footage of the same path that food takes through the digestive system. This photo shows the pylorus—the opening from the stomach to the small intestine.

The Molecules of Living Systems

Section Outcomes

In this section, you will
- **describe** the chemical nature of carbohydrates, lipids, and proteins
- **explain**, in general terms, how carbohydrates, lipids, and proteins are synthesized and how they are broken down (hydrolyzed)
- **perform** standard tests to identify macromolecules

Key Terms

macromolecules
dehydration synthesis
hydrolysis
carbohydrates
lipids
proteins
peptide bond
nucleic acids
vitamins
minerals
catalyst
enzyme

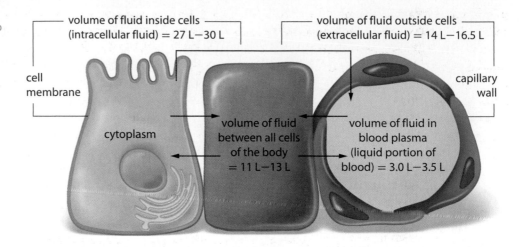

Figure 6.1 Distribution of body fluids in the adult human. These fluids are mostly water and move freely in both directions from inside to outside the cells.

In Figure 6.1, you see the three main fluid compartments of your body: the cytoplasm inside your cells, the fluid between your cells, and the fluid in your blood. The fluid in these compartments is mostly water, which makes up more than 60 percent of your body. These compartments also contain and are composed of thousands of different kinds of molecules and ions. Some of these molecules and ions—such as water, phosphates, hydrogen ions, and sodium ions—are small and simple. They are inorganic (non-living) matter. Other molecules, called organic molecules, contain carbon bonded to hydrogen,

as well as to other atoms, such as oxygen, sulfur, and nitrogen. Larger, more complex assemblies of organic molecules, called **macromolecules**, are often grouped into four major categories: carbohydrates, lipids (such as fats), proteins, and nucleic acids. Many macromolecules are polymers—long molecules formed by linking many small, similar chemical subunits, much like linking railroad cars to form a train. Table 6.1 outlines the four categories of macromolecules and their subunits. You will learn about these macromolecules in this section, as well as in Section 6.2.

Table 6.1 The Macromolecules of Life

Macromolecule	Example(s) of subunits	Main functions	Examples of macromolecules
carbohydrates	sugars (such as glucose) and polymers of glucose	energy storage	sugars, starches, and glycogen
lipids	glycerol and three fatty acids or glycerol and two fatty acids	energy storage and cell membranes	fats, oils, and phospholipids
proteins	polymers of amino acids	transport, blood clotting, support, immunity, catalysis, and muscle action	hemoglobin, fibrin, collagen, antibodies, enzymes, actin, and myosin
nucleic acids	polymers of nucleotides	transfer and expression of genetic information	DNA and RNA

Assembling Macromolecules

Although the four categories of macromolecules contain different kinds of subunits, they are all assembled in cells in the same basic way. To form a covalent bond between two subunit molecules, an −OH (hydroxyl) group is removed from one subunit and a hydrogen atom is removed from the other subunit (see Figure 6.2A). This chemical reaction is known as **dehydration synthesis**, because removing the −OH group and H atom during the synthesis of a new biological molecule essentially removes a molecule of water (H_2O). (Dehydration means "without water.") Dehydration synthesis, like many other reactions that occur in the body, requires the correct chemical bonds to be broken at the right time. The process of positioning and breaking the chemical bonds is carried out in cells by a special class of proteins called enzymes. You will learn more about enzymes later in this section.

Disassembling Macromolecules

Cells disassemble macromolecules into their component subunits by performing a chemical reaction that basically reverses dehydration. In this reaction, called **hydrolysis**, a molecule of water is added instead of removed. (*Hydrolysis* comes from two Greek words for "water" and "break.") During a hydrolysis reaction (see Figure 6.2B), a hydrogen atom from water is attached to one subunit and the hydroxyl group is bonded to another subunit, effectively breaking a covalent bond in a macromolecule. As in dehydration, hydrolysis involves enzymes.

• • •

1. Identify the four categories of macromolecules that make up living systems, such as your body.

2. Name and describe the process that builds macromolecules.

3. Name and describe the process that breaks down macromolecules.

• • •

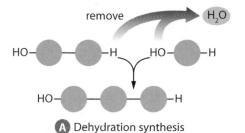

A Dehydration synthesis

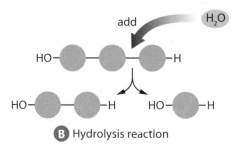

B Hydrolysis reaction

Figure 6.2 This simplified diagram shows how molecular subunits are put together (synthesized) to form macromolecules and broken apart through hydrolysis.

Carbohydrates

Carbohydrates are macromolecules that always contain carbon, hydrogen, and oxygen—and almost always in the same proportion: two atoms of hydrogen and one atom of oxygen for every atom of carbon. Carbohydrates provide short-term or long-term energy storage for organisms. There are two main types of carbohydrates: simple sugars and polysaccharides.

Simple Sugars

A carbohydrate molecule with three to seven carbon atoms (and the corresponding number of hydrogen and oxygen atoms) is called a monosaccharide, or a simple sugar (*mono* means one; *saccharide* comes from a Sanskrit word that means "sugar"). A disaccharide, or double sugar, is made up of two simple sugars (*di* means "two"). Figure 6.3 illustrates the synthesis and hydrolysis of maltose, which is a disaccharide.

Polysaccharides

A polysaccharide is a complex carbohydrate that consists of many linked simple sugars (*poly* means "many"). Figure 6.4 shows the structure of the polysaccharides starch, glycogen, and cellulose. Starch performs the important function of energy storage in plants. Glycogen performs the same function in

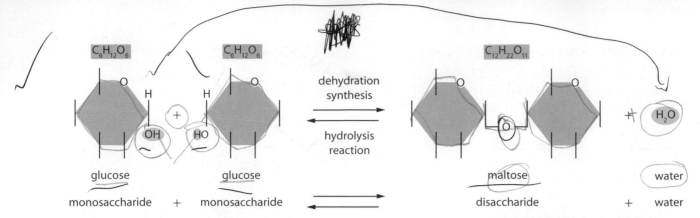

$C_6H_{12}O_6$ $C_6H_{12}O_6$ $C_{12}H_{22}O_{11}$

dehydration synthesis

hydrolysis reaction

glucose   glucose   maltose   water

monosaccharide + monosaccharide   disaccharide   +   water

Figure 6.3 During the synthesis of maltose, a chemical bond forms between two glucose molecules, and the components of one water molecule are removed. During the hydrolysis of maltose, the components of one water molecule are added and the bond is broken, yielding two glucose molecules. (The double arrow indicates that the chemical reaction, represented by the chemical equation, can proceed in both directions—from left to right and from right to left.)

animals. Compare the structure of the starch and glycogen molecules, and note the many "branches" on the glycogen molecule. The larger amount of branching on the glycogen molecule means that it packs more glucose units into a single cell than a starch molecule does.

> **Q 4** Identify two types of carbohydrates, and name the subunits that make up each type.

Lipids

Lipids are a diverse group of macromolecules that have one important property in common: they are insoluble in water. Lipids store 2.25 times more energy per gram than other biological molecules. Not surprisingly, therefore, some lipids function as energy-storage molecules. Other lipids, called phospholipids, form a membrane that separates a cell from its internal environment. Still others, called steroids, form the sex hormones estrogen and testosterone.

The lipids that you are probably most familiar with are those found in fats and oils. Fats, such as butter and lard, are usually of animal origin and are solid at room temperature. Oils, such as olive oil and safflower oil, are of plant origin and are liquid at room temperature.

Fats and oils form when one glycerol molecule reacts with three fatty acid molecules (see Figure 6.5). A fat is sometimes called a *triglyceride* because of its three-part structure. You might also hear the term "neutral fat," referring to the fact that a fat molecule is non-polar.

In a triglyceride, the glycerol always has the same composition, but the composition of the three fatty acids may differ. (You can see an example of this in Figure 6.5.) The three fatty acids may be identical or different, short or long, and saturated or unsaturated. A saturated fatty acid does not have double covalent bonds between its carbon atoms, so it contains all the hydrogen atoms it can bond with. An unsaturated fatty acid has double bonds between some of its carbon atoms, leaving room for additional

Figure 6.4 Compare the structural differences among starch, glycogen, and cellulose. Notice that all three polysaccharides consist of glucose subunits.

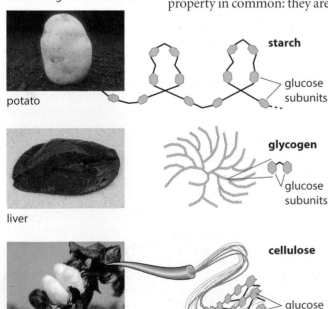

potato

starch

glucose subunits

glycogen

glucose subunits

liver

cellulose

glucose subunits

cotton

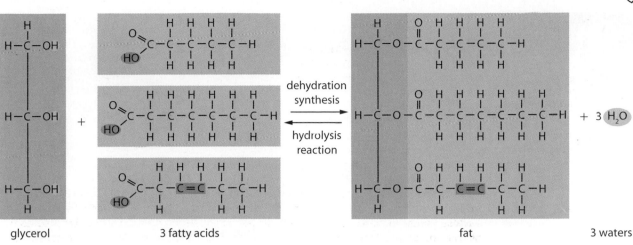

| glycerol | 3 fatty acids | | fat | 3 waters |

Figure 6.5 During the synthesis of a fat molecule, three fatty acid molecules bond with one glycerol molecule, and three water molecules are produced. What happens during the hydrolysis of a fat molecule?

hydrogen atoms. Unsaturated fatty acids cause the resulting fat to be liquid at room temperature. Saturated fatty acids usually cause the resulting fat to be solid at room temperature.

. . .

Q5 Identify the subunits that make up fats.

Q6 List the key differences between a saturated and an unsaturated fat.

. . .

Proteins

Most cellular structures are made of different types of **proteins**. Proteins serve many functions in cells and display greater structural complexity and functional diversity than either lipids or carbohydrates. Both your hair and fingernails are made of the same type of protein, keratin, but each has its own distinctive properties. The bones and muscles inside your hand and the ligaments and tendons that connect them contain very different proteins.

Like other macromolecules, proteins are assembled from smaller subunits. The subunits in proteins are amino acids. An amino acid has a central carbon atom bonded to a hydrogen atom and three other groups of atoms—amino group, acid group, and R group—as shown in Figure 6.6. The R group is a group of one or more atoms that determines identity and is what distinguishes the 20 types of

amino acids from one another. The body can synthesize 11 of these 20 amino acids. The other nine must come from the diet, so they are termed essential amino acids.

Amino acids bond together in strands to form proteins. Individual amino acids are connected by a type of bond called a **peptide bond**. Figure 6.7 on the next page shows how a peptide bond between two amino acids is formed and broken. Regardless of which R group is present, amino acids always bond to each other as shown in Figure 6.7. A chain of several amino acids bonded together is called a peptide. If amino acids are bonded, the chain is called a polypeptide.

A strand of amino acids must undergo additional changes before it becomes a protein. Different amino acids along the strand attract and repel each other, and this causes the strand to coil and twist as the amino acids are drawn toward or pushed away from one another. The end result is a complex three-dimensional structure, such as the one shown in Figure 6.8. The final shape of a protein's three-dimensional structure determines its properties and functions.

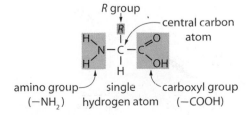

Figure 6.6 An amino acid is the subunit of proteins. An amino acid is composed of an amino group, an acid (carboxyl) group, and one of 20 R groups attached to a central carbon atom.

Thought Lab	6.1	How Do You Take Your Macromolecules?

Most foods, especially in raw form, spoil quickly. It has been a challenge to preserve foods for later consumption since the earliest times, and, almost since then, people in all cultures have been devising ways to alter raw food so it will last longer. In this part of the world, food can only be grown during certain months, and then it has to be stored for use through the winter and spring. In earlier generations food had to be carefully preserved and stored to ensure survival. Now it must be carefully preserved for handling and transportation to distant markets.

There are two main reasons why food spoils: the growth of microorganisms (mostly bacteria and fungi) and/or the breakdown of fats, which makes foods rancid. Bacteria, which can cause life-threatening illnesses, need water to grow in, and the earliest technologies involved drying and smoking the foods to remove the water and kill any potential bacteria or parasites.

A variety of techniques to preserve foods are used today; some are improvements on old technologies, some are best suited to particular types of foods, and a combination of techniques is often used. Most techniques simply prolong the "shelf life" of the food, and no technique is perfect. Some are better than others at preserving the nutrients in food. Salt, one of the earliest food preservatives, is still in use and is currently being targeted by physicians as a cause of high blood pressure. A more modern technology—the use of trans fats—was thought to solve the problem of food going rancid, but it is being re-evaluated amid charges that it causes heart disease.

Other techniques fall into broad categories of lowering the pH, raising the temperature, lowering the temperature, using preservative spices or chemicals as additives, and sealing the food from air. One of the newer and more controversial techniques is known as irradiation and involves treating the food with ionizing radiation.

Procedure

1. Choose one example each of a food that is mostly carbohydrate, fat, or protein that you have on hand at home.

2. Examine the items, their ingredient lists, and the packaging for clues to how each has been preserved for long-term storage.

Analysis

1. Create a chart and list each of the foods and the technologies used to preserve them.

2. Choose one of the foods and use library resources or the Internet to research the method behind the technology or combination of technologies used to preserve the food and why it works.

3. Describe the advantages of this technology.

4. Describe the disadvantages of this technology.

Extension

5. Identify any chemical preservatives and use the Internet to research the role of the preservatives and any possible side effects. **ICT**

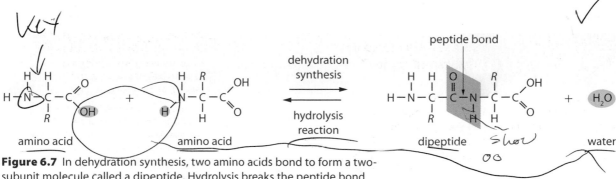

Figure 6.7 In dehydration synthesis, two amino acids bond to form a two-subunit molecule called a dipeptide. Hydrolysis breaks the peptide bond that links the amino acids. The *R* groups are shown here only as "*R*," because they do not take part in the reactions that make or break peptide bonds.

The *R* group also affects the structure of a protein. Some *R* groups are electrically charged, making them attracted to water. As a result, they end up on the outside of the final protein structure. Proteins with these *R* groups, such as enzymes and hemoglobin, are soluble in water. Other *R* groups are not electrically charged and are repelled by water. Thus, they appear on the inside of the protein structure, away from the water in the body's internal environment. Proteins with these *R* groups, such as the keratin in your fingernails, are not soluble in water.

• • •

7 Name the subunits that make up proteins.

8 Explain why proteins are more structurally and functionally diverse than carbohydrates and lipids.

• • •

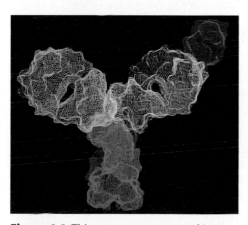

Figure 6.8 This computer-generated image of a protein molecule makes the protein's complex, three-dimensional structure easier to visualize.

Nucleic Acids

Nucleic acids direct the growth and development of all organisms using a chemical code. Nucleic acids determine how a cell functions and what characteristics it has. There are two types of nucleic acids: RNA (ribonucleic acid) and DNA (deoxyribonucleic acid). Recall that DNA contains genes, which hold the information needed to build the cell. When needed, a gene is first copied into RNA, which then is involved in making a protein.

Like proteins and carbohydrates, nucleic acids consist of long chains of linked subunits. These subunits are called nucleotides, as shown in Figure 6.9. Both DNA and RNA are made up of just four different nucleotides.

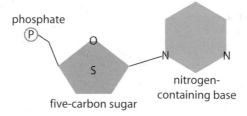

Figure 6.9 This model shows a generalized nucleotide. All nucleotides consist of a five-carbon simple sugar (ribose in RNA and deoxyribose in DNA), a nitrogen-containing base, and a phosphate group.

Vitamins and Minerals

Vitamins and **minerals** are not macromolecules, but they are essential to the structure and function of all cells. They are key components of many of the chemical reactions that yield energy, synthesize compounds, and break down compounds.

Testing for Macromolecules

Biochemists have developed standard tests to determine the presence of the most abundant macromolecules made by cells: carbohydrates (sugars, starches), lipids (fats), and proteins. In this investigation, your group will conduct one or more of the standard tests to identify the presence of sugars, starch, lipid, and protein in known samples. Some of these tests involve the use of an indicator—a chemical that changes colour when it reacts with a specific substance. You will share the results of your tests with the class.

Question

How can you recognize and identify the presence of macromolecules in various samples?

Safety Precautions

Be careful when handling iodine, Benedict's solution, and Biuret reagent because they are toxic and can stain skin and surfaces. To prevent test tubes from breaking, do not allow the hot-water bath to boil vigorously. Clean up all spills immediately, with plenty of water, and inform your teacher immediately if a spill occurs.

Materials

- distilled water
- Biuret reagent
- albumin solution
- pepsin solution
- starch suspension
- iodine solution in dropper bottle
- Benedict's solution
- glucose solution
- onion juice
- large beaker (500 mL or larger) for hot-water bath
- potato juice
- vegetable oil
- butter or margarine
- 11 test tubes
- 3 test-tube racks
- 3 small squares of brown paper
- millimetre ruler
- wax pencil
- hot plate
- tongs

Procedure

Part 1: Test for Proteins

Biuret reagent has a blue colour that changes to violet in the presence of proteins or to pink in the presence of peptides.

1. Use a millimetre ruler and a wax pencil to mark and label four clean test tubes at the 2 cm and 4 cm levels. Fill each test tube as follows:
   - Test tube 1: Fill to the 2 cm mark with distilled water, and then add Biuret reagent to the 4 cm mark.
   - Test tube 2: Fill to the 2 cm mark with albumin solution, and then add Biuret reagent to the 4 cm mark. (Albumin is a protein.)
   - Test tube 3: Fill to the 2 cm mark with pepsin solution, and then add Biuret reagent to the 4 cm mark. (Pepsin is an enzyme.)
   - Test tube 4: Fill to the 2 cm mark with starch suspension, and then add Biuret reagent to the 4 cm mark.

2. Record the final colour of the contents of all four test tubes in a table like the one below.

Biuret Test for Protein

Test tube	Contents	Colour change	Conclusions
1	distilled water		
2	albumin		
3	pepsin		
4	starch		

3. Dispose of the contents of the test tubes as directed by your teacher. Clean and dry the test tubes.

Part 2: Test for Starch

Iodine solution turns from a brownish colour to blue-black in the presence of starch.

1. Use a millimetre ruler and a wax pencil to mark and label two clean test tubes at the 1 cm level. Fill each test tube as follows:
   - Test tube 1: Fill to the 1 cm mark with starch suspension, and then add five drops of iodine solution. (Be sure to shake the starch suspension well before taking your sample.)
   - Test tube 2: Fill to the 1 cm mark with distilled water, and then add five drops of iodine solution.

2. Note the final colour change. Record your results in a table like the one below.

Iodine Test for Starch

Test tube	Contents	Colour change	Conclusions
1	starch		
2	distilled water		

3. Dispose of the contents of the test tubes as directed by your teacher. Clean and dry the test tubes.

Part 3: Test for Sugars

Sugars react with Benedict's solution after being heated in a boiling-water bath. Increasing concentrations of sugar give a continuum of colours, as shown in the table below.

Typical Reactions for Benedict's Solution

Chemical	Chemical category	Benedict's solution (after heating)
distilled water	inorganic	blue (no change)
glucose	monosaccharide (carbohydrate)	varies with concentration: • very low: green • low: yellow • moderate: yellow-orange • high: orange • very high: orange-red
maltose	disaccharide (carbohydrate)	varies with concentration (See results for glucose.)
starch	polysaccharide (carbohydrate)	blue (no change)

1. Use a millimetre ruler and a wax pencil to mark and label five clean test tubes at the 1 cm and 3 cm levels.

   • Test tube 1: Fill to the 1 cm mark with distilled water, and then add Benedict's solution to the 3 cm mark. Heat in a boiling-water bath for about 5 min.

   • Test tube 2: Fill to the 1 cm mark with glucose solution; add Benedict's solution to the 3 cm mark. Heat in a boiling-water bath for about 5 min.

   • Test tube 3: Put a few drops of onion juice in the test tube. Fill to the 1 cm mark with distilled water, and then add Benedict's solution to the 3 cm mark. Heat in a boiling-water bath for about 5 min.

   • Test tube 4: Put a few drops of potato juice in the test tube. Fill to the 1 cm mark with distilled water, and then add Benedict's solution to the 3 cm mark. Heat in a boiling-water bath for about 5 min.

   • Test tube 5: Fill to the 1 cm mark with starch suspension; add Benedict's solution to the 3 cm mark. Heat in a boiling-water bath for about 5 min.

2. Note the final colour change. Record your results in a table like the one below.

Benedict's Test for Sugars

Test tube	Contents	Colour (after heating)	Conclusions
1	distilled water		
2	glucose solution		
3	onion juice		
4	potato juice		
5	starch suspension		

3. Dispose of the contents of the test tubes as directed by your teacher. Clean and dry the test tubes.

Part 4: Test for Fats

Fats leave a translucent, oily spot on paper. Liquid fats penetrate paper, while solid fats rest predominantly on top.

1. Place a small drop of water on a square of brown paper. Describe the immediate effect.

2. Place a small drop of vegetable oil on a square of brown paper. Describe the immediate effect.

3. Place a small quantity of butter or margarine on a square of brown paper. Describe the immediate effect.

4. Wait about 5 min. Examine each piece of paper to determine which test material penetrates the paper. Record your results in a table like the one below.

Paper Test for Fats

Sample	Results
distilled water	
oil (liquid fat)	
butter or margarine (solid fat)	

Analysis

1. Identify the control sample in each test you conducted. Explain how you know that it is the control and why it is included.

2. If the results of any of your tests were not as you expected, offer a possible explanation.

Conclusions

3. Describe a positive test for

   a) protein

   b) starch

   c) sugars

   d) fats (lipids)

Vitamins are organic compounds. Only small amounts of vitamins are typically required by the body. Among other functions, vitamins serve as *coenzymes*—chemicals needed to make enzymes function. As well, they are involved in tissue development, tissue growth, and resistance to disease.

Minerals are inorganic compounds. Like vitamins, only small amounts of most minerals are required by the body. Minerals enable certain chemical reactions to occur and help to build bones and cartilage. Minerals are readily absorbed into the bloodstream. They are essential components of molecules such as hemoglobin, hormones, enzymes, and vitamins.

Enzymes

One of the chemical reactions that occurs in the red blood cells in your body is the reaction of carbon dioxide with water to form carbonic acid. If you performed this reaction in the laboratory, you would find that it proceeds quite slowly. Perhaps 200 molecules of carbonic acid would form in about one hour. Reactions this slow are of little use to a cell. One way to increase the rate of any chemical reaction is to increase the temperature of the reactants. In living things, however, this approach to speeding up reactions has a major drawback. The temperatures at which chemical reactions would normally occur to sustain life are so high that they would permanently *denature* body proteins. (They would lose their three-dimensional shape). This has very real implications for people when they have a fever. If the fever stays too high for too long, major disruptions to cellular biochemical reactions occur, and in some cases they can be fatal.

Another way to increase the rate of chemical reactions without increasing temperature is to use a catalyst. A **catalyst** is a chemical that speeds up a chemical reaction but is not used up in the reaction. It can be recovered unchanged when the reaction is complete. Catalysts function by lowering the amount of energy needed to initiate a reaction. Cells manufacture specific proteins that act as catalysts. A protein molecule that acts as a catalyst to increase the rate of a reaction is called an **enzyme**. In red blood cells, for example, an enzyme (called carbonic anhydrase) enables carbon dioxide and water to react to form about 600 000 molecules of carbonic acid each second!

How Enzymes Speed Chemical Reaction Rates

Each enzyme in the body has a precise three-dimensional shape that is specific to the kind of reactant molecule with which it can combine. The enzyme physically fits with a specific *substrate*—its reactant molecule. The enzyme is specific because it has a particular shape that can combine only with its substrate molecule. The part of the enzyme that binds to the substrate is called the active site. When the substrate binds to the active site, its bonds become less stable and, thus, more likely to be altered and to form new bonds.

You can think of an enzyme as a tool that makes a task easier and faster. For example, using an open-end crescent wrench can make the job of removing or attaching a nut and bolt go much faster than doing that same job with your fingers. To accomplish this task, the proper wrench must be used. Another type of tool (a screwdriver or a hammer, for example) won't work. Similarly, an enzyme must also physically attach itself to the substrate in a specific place and in a specific way (see Figure 6.10). Note that the fit between the wrench and nut is very specific, just like the fit between active site and substrate. Note also that a wrench and an enzyme are recovered unchanged after they have been used. Thus, they can be used over and over

• • •

Q 9 Explain what an enzyme is.

Q 10 Describe how an enzyme speeds up the rate of a chemical reaction.

• • •

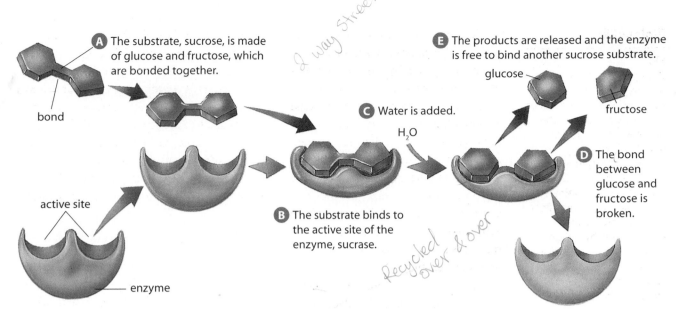

A The substrate, sucrose, is made of glucose and fructose, which are bonded together.

bond

active site

enzyme

2 way Street

B The substrate binds to the active site of the enzyme, sucrase.

C Water is added.

H_2O

Recycled over & over

E The products are released and the enzyme is free to bind another sucrose substrate.

glucose

fructose

D The bond between glucose and fructose is broken.

Figure 6.10 In this enzymatic reaction, the disaccharide sucrose is hydrolyzed to form its component simpler sugars, glucose and fructose.

again for the same task. Eventually, however, like wrenches, enzymes wear out, so cells must synthesize replacements.

Factors Affecting Enzyme Action

Temperature and pH can affect the action of enzymes. Enzyme activity is affected by any change in condition that alters the enzyme's three-dimensional shape. When the temperature becomes too low, the bonds that determine enzyme shape are not flexible enough to enable substrate molecules to fit properly. At higher temperatures, the bonds are too weak to maintain the enzyme's shape. It becomes denatured, meaning that its molecular shape and structure (and, thus, its properties) are changed. (Think of the changes that occur to egg white—a protein—when it is heated.) Therefore, enzymes function best within an optimal temperature range, as shown in Figure 6.11A. This range is fairly narrow for most human enzymes.

Enzymes also function within an optimal pH range (Figure 6.11B). Most human enzymes work best within the range of pH 6 to 8. Some enzymes, however, function best in very acidic environments, such as is found in the stomach.

Inhibitors can also affect enzyme activity. *Inhibitors* are molecules that attach to the enzyme and reduce its ability to bind substrate. There are two classes of inhibitors: competitive

11 Describe how temperature and pH can affect the action of enzymes.

inhibitors and non-competitive inhibitors. *Competitive inhibitors* attach to the enzyme in its active site. When both inhibitor and substrate are present, the two compete to occupy the active site. If the inhibitor is plentiful, it will occupy the active site, blocking the substrate from binding and stopping enzyme activity. In biological systems, the competitive inhibitor is often the end product of the enzymatic reaction. As more end product is created and binds to the active site, enzyme activity is inhibited. That's a negative feedback loop.

Figure 6.11 The activity of an enzyme is affected by **(A)** temperature and **(B)** pH. Most enzymes in humans, such as trypsin, which helps break down protein in the small intestine, work best at a temperature of about 40 °C and within a pH range of 6 to 8.

Enzyme reaction rate by temperature

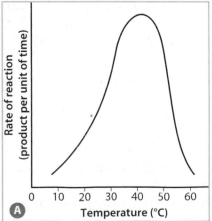

A

Enzyme reaction rate by pH

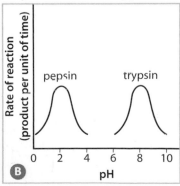

B

Non-competitive inhibitors attach elsewhere on the enzyme, not on the active site. Their attachment changes the three-dimensional shape of the enzyme, including the active site. Since the fit between active site and substrate is specific, the change in the shape of the active site makes the enzyme less able to bind substrate and carry out the reaction. Enzyme activity is inhibited.

Section 6.1 Summary

- Carbohydrates, lipids, proteins, and nucleic acids are macromolecules that are made up of smaller, chemically simpler subunits.
- The macromolecules are assembled by dehydration synthesis and disassembled by hydrolysis reaction, which are processes involving the removing or adding of a molecule of water.
- A monosaccharide, such as glucose, is a carbohydrate that consists of three to seven carbon atoms. A disaccharide, such as maltose, is made up of two monosaccharides. A polysaccharide, such as starch (cellulose), is made up of many monosaccharides linked together.
- Lipids, such as fats, do not dissolve in water. All fats have a three-branched structure made up of a glycerol and three fatty acid molecules. Fats are also called triglycerides.
- Proteins make up most cellular structures. They consist of amino acids joined by peptide bonds and then twisted into three-dimensional structures.
- The nucleic acids RNA and DNA direct an organism's growth and development by a chemical code. DNA carries genetic information, and RNA copies the genetic information so a cell can synthesize proteins.
- Vitamins are organic compounds; minerals are inorganic compounds. Neither are macromolecules, but they are key components of many of the chemical reactions that synthesize and break down compounds and yield energy in cells.
- Enzymes are proteins that increase the rate of biochemical reactions.

Section 6.1 Review

1. Explain how macromolecules, such as carbohydrates, differ from inorganic substances, such as water and sodium ions.

2. Use graphics software to sketch a representation of the dehydration synthesis and the hydrolysis of each macromolecule listed below. Design symbols to represent the molecules involved. Explain your reasoning for distinguishing each symbol as you did. **ICT**

   a) a disaccharide from two molecules of glucose

   b) a triglyceride from one molecule of glycerol and three fatty acid molecules

   c) a dipeptide from two amino acid molecules

3. Compare a fat with an oil, and explain why both are examples of lipids.

4. Use word processing or spreadsheet software to design a table that compares the structure and function of the following macromolecules: sugars, polysaccharides, lipids, proteins, and nucleic acids. **ICT**

5. A dessert topping for ice cream contains maltose, hydrogenated soybean oil, salt, and cellulose. Identify the macromolecules in this dessert topping.

6. Use word processing or spreadsheet software to design a table summarizing the standard tests for identifying the presence of starch, sugar, proteins, and fats in a food source. Include the colour change that indicates the presence of that macromolecule in each case. **ICT**

7. Explain the significance of this statement: An enzyme is a biological catalyst.

8. Explain how an enzyme can take part in a reaction involving sucrose, but not in a reaction involving maltose.

9. Relate the importance of shape to an enzyme's function.

10. Use spreadsheet software to sketch a graph that illustrates how the rate of an enzyme-controlled reaction is affected by temperature. Identify the optimum temperature for this enzyme-controlled reaction and explain why the rate of the reaction is slower when the temperature is colder and warmer than this point. **ICT**

The Digestive System

Section Outcomes

In this section, you will
- **identify** the main structures and functions of the digestive system
- **describe** the physical and chemical processing of food through the digestive system and into the bloodstream
- **explain** the action of enzymes in chemical digestion
- **identify** and **describe**, in general terms, how digested molecules enter the bloodstream

Key Terms

digestive system
mouth
amylase
esophagus
peristalsis
esophageal sphincter
stomach
pyloric sphincter
pepsin
small intestine
segmentation
duodenum
villi
microvilli
pancreas
liver
gall bladder
carbohydrases
lipases
proteases
nucleases
gastrin
secretin
CCK
GIP
large intestine

Every cell in your body needs nourishment in the form of water, carbohydrates, fats, proteins, vitamins, and minerals. Most cells, however, cannot leave their location in the body and move into the external environment to find food. Thus, food must be delivered to the cells, in a form they can use. This task belongs to the digestive system, with the assistance of the circulatory system. The **digestive system** is specialized to ingest food, move it through a tube approximately 8 m long (the digestive tract), and break it down into smaller components (digest it). Digestion involves both physical breakdown, through motions such as chewing, churning and segmenting, and chemical breakdown, through hydrolysis.

The resulting substances are absorbed into the bloodstream and delivered to all the body cells by the circulatory system. Solid wastes that cannot be broken down for use by the cells are eliminated to the external environment via the anus.

Figure 6.12 shows the organs associated with the human digestive system and their main functions. Figure 6.13 presents a modified view of the digestive system to emphasize the length of the continuous tube that makes up the digestive tract. (Note that the digestive tract is commonly referred to as the gastrointestinal or GI tract, as well. It is also referred to as the alimentary canal. The term *alimentary* comes from a Latin word that means "nourishment.")

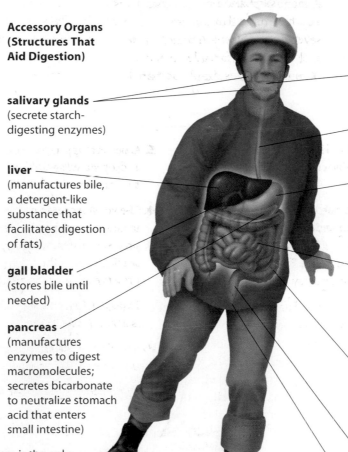

Accessory Organs (Structures That Aid Digestion)

salivary glands (secrete starch-digesting enzymes)

liver (manufactures bile, a detergent-like substance that facilitates digestion of fats)

gall bladder (stores bile until needed)

pancreas (manufactures enzymes to digest macromolecules; secretes bicarbonate to neutralize stomach acid that enters small intestine)

The Digestive Tract (Organs That Contain Food)

mouth (chews and mixes food with saliva)

esophagus (directs food from mouth to stomach)

stomach (adds acid, enzymes, and fluid; churns, mixes, and grinds food to a liquid mass)

small intestine (secretes enzymes that digest macromolecules; absorbs hydrolyzed molecules into bloodstream)

large intestine (absorbs water and salts; passes remaining undigested material and some water out of body)

rectum (stores waste prior to elimination)

anus (holds rectum closed; opens to allow elimination)

Figure 6.12 The digestive system is the only body system that provides two points of contact (the mouth and the anus) between the internal environment of the body and the external environment. Most of the other body systems are completely internal.

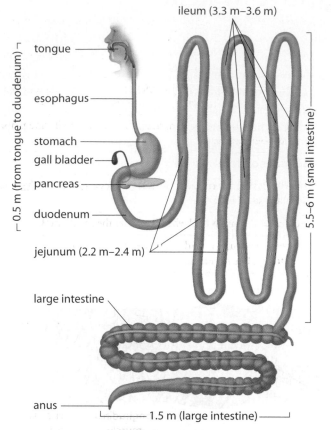

Figure 6.13 An average-sized digestive tract is approximately 8 m long in an adult human.

Labels on figure:
- ileum (3.3 m–3.6 m)
- tongue
- esophagus
- stomach
- gall bladder
- pancreas
- duodenum
- jejunum (2.2 m–2.4 m)
- large intestine
- anus
- 0.5 m (from tongue to duodenum)
- 5.5–6 m (small intestine)
- 1.5 m (large intestine)

---

⑫ Identify the organs that make up the human digestive tract.

⑬ Identify the accessory organs that assist the digestive system in performing its function.

Digestion Begins: The Mouth and the Esophagus

The idea, smell, or taste of food triggers three pairs of salivary glands near the **mouth** to secrete a watery fluid, called saliva. Saliva is one of many fluids and substances that are secreted by the digestive tract to aid digestion. Table 6.2 lists the major secretions of the digestive tract. Refer to this table as you continue your study of the digestive system.

Chemical digestion (hydrolysis) starts in the mouth, when an enzyme in saliva, called salivary **amylase**, begins to break down starch into simpler sugars (disaccharides). You can test this yourself at home. Slowly chew a polysaccharide-containing food, such as a cracker, a piece of boiled potato, or a piece of bread, until you notice the starchy food tastes sweet. The sweet taste results from the hydrolysis reaction of starch, catalyzed by salivary amylase.

The physical digestion of food also begins in the mouth as you use your teeth to chew your food. Water and mucus in saliva aid the teeth as they tear and grind food into smaller pieces, increasing the surface area available for the chemical digestion of any starch that has been ingested.

As you chew, your tongue rolls the food into a smooth lump-like mass, called a *bolus*, and pushes it to the back of your mouth for swallowing. The bolus enters the esophagus, passing the covered opening of the trachea (windpipe) on the way. If you place your fingers on your "Adam's apple" and swallow, as shown in Figure 6.14, you will notice that both it and your trachea move up. This movement closes the trachea against a flap of tissue (the epiglottis) and prevents food from passing through the trachea into your lungs.

Figure 6.14 The digestive and respiratory systems share a common pathway for bringing food and air into the body. Use this photo to help you find your Adam's apple, which is the front part of the voice box (larynx). When you swallow, food enters the esophagus, rather than the trachea, because the passage to the trachea becomes blocked. You do not breathe when you swallow.

Table 6.2 Important Secretions of the Digestive Tract

Secretion	Site of production	Function
saliva	mouth	contributes to starch digestion via salivary amylase; lubricates the inside of the mouth to assist in swallowing
mucus	mouth, stomach, small intestine, and large intestine	protects the cells lining the innermost portion of the digestive tract; lubricates food as it travels through the digestive tract
enzymes	mouth, stomach, small intestine, and pancreas	promote digestion of food masses into particles small enough for absorption into the bloodstream
acid	stomach	promotes digestion of protein
bile	liver (stored in gall bladder)	suspends fat in water, using bile salts, cholesterol, and lecithin to aid digestion of fats in small intestine
bicarbonate	pancreas and small intestine	neutralizes stomach acid when it reaches the small intestine
hormones	stomach, small intestine, and pancreas	stimulate production and/or release of acid, enzymes, bile, and bicarbonate; help to regulate peristalsis

The **esophagus** is a muscular portion of the digestive tract that directs food from the mouth to the stomach. The bolus moves through the esophagus partly by gravity, but mainly through a wavelike series of muscular contractions and relaxations called **peristalsis** (see Figure 6.15). As peristalsis continues, food is propelled through the esophagus toward the stomach, where the next stage of digestion occurs. Entry to the stomach is controlled by a ringlike muscular structure, called the **esophageal sphincter**. Relaxation of the esophageal sphincter allows the bolus to pass into the stomach. Contraction of this sphincter usually prevents the acidic contents of the stomach from backing up into the esophagus. (If the acidic contents of your stomach escape into your esophagus, you may feel a burning pain rising up your throat. This experience is commonly known as heartburn.)

• • •

Q14 Identify and describe the digestive processes that begin in the mouth.

Q15 Describe how food moves through the esophagus.

Q16 Name the structure that controls the movement of food from the esophagus into the stomach.

• • •

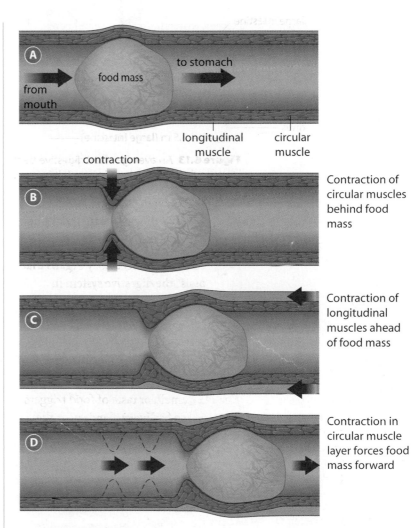

Contraction of circular muscles behind food mass

Contraction of longitudinal muscles ahead of food mass

Contraction in circular muscle layer forces food mass forward

Figure 6.15 Peristalsis moves food through the esophagus. Peristalsis involves two layers of muscles that line the digestive tract. One layer of longitudinal muscles runs parallel to the length of the tract. Beneath these muscles, and perpendicular to them, is a circular layer of muscles. To move food, the circular muscles over a bolus relax, while the longitudinal muscles in front of the bolus contract. The circular muscles behind the bolus then contract, while the longitudinal muscles over it relax. Repetition of these movements pushes the bolus along.

The word sphincter comes from a Greek word that means "bind tightly." The esophageal sphincter is not a true sphincter, because it does not completely seal the esophagus from the stomach. This is an advantage, since it allows for the regurgitation of food—vomiting—when you are sick or have ingested spoiled food. Some animals, such as mice, horses, and goats, have a true esophageal sphincter, so they are unable to vomit.

Storing, Digesting, and Pushing Food: The Stomach

The **stomach**, shown in Figure 6.16, is a J-shaped, muscular, sac-like organ with three important functions: storage, some digestion, and pushing food into the small intestine. When empty, the stomach is the size of a large sausage with a capacity of about 50 mL. It can, however, expand to hold 2 L to 4 L of food! Folds in the stomach's lining unfurl like the pleats of an accordion to accommodate a large meal. A true sphincter, called the **pyloric sphincter**, controls the exit of the stomach's contents into the small intestine. (The word *pyloric* comes from a Greek word that means "gatekeeper.")

Physical and chemical digestion occur in the stomach. Waves of peristalsis push food against the bottom of the stomach, churning it backward, breaking it into smaller pieces, and mixing it with gastric juice to produce a thick liquid called *chyme*. About 40 million cells that line the interior of the stomach secrete

2 L to 3 L of gastric juice each day. Gastric juice is responsible for chemical digestion in the stomach. It is made up of water, mucus, salts, hydrochloric acid, and enzymes. The strong hydrochloric acid has a pH of 1 to 3. It provides a highly acidic environment that begins to soften and break down proteins in the chyme. The low pH also serves to kill most bacteria that are ingested along with the food we eat. (Some disease-causing bacteria escape this fate, however, because they have an outer coating that resists stomach acid.)

The stomach usually does not digest the proteins that make up its own cells, because it has three methods of protection. First, the stomach secretes little gastric juice until food is present. Second, some stomach cells secrete mucus, which prevents gastric juice from harming the cells of the stomach lining. Third, the stomach produces its protein-digesting enzyme, **pepsin**, in a form that remains inactive until hydrochloric acid is present. Once active, pepsin hydrolyzes proteins to yield polypeptides—a first step in protein digestion in the digestive tract.

Absorption in the Stomach

Very few substances are absorbed from the chyme in the stomach because most substances in the chyme have not yet been broken down sufficiently. The stomach does absorb some water and salts, however, as well as certain anti-inflammatory medications such as Aspirin™, and alcohol. (This explains why Aspirin™ can irritate the lining of the stomach and why many people feel alcohol's intoxicating effects so quickly.)

• • •

17 Describe what happens to food, physically and chemically, to transform it into chyme.

18 What is the function of pepsin in the stomach?

19 Explain why few substances are absorbed in the stomach.

• • •

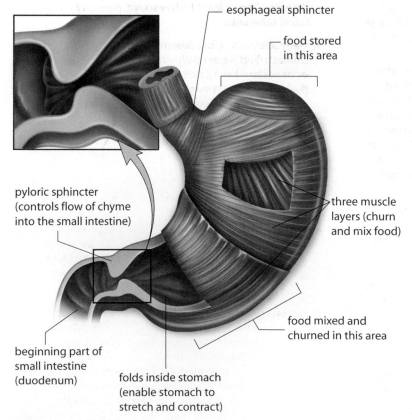

esophageal sphincter

food stored in this area

three muscle layers (churn and mix food)

pyloric sphincter (controls flow of chyme into the small intestine)

food mixed and churned in this area

beginning part of small intestine (duodenum)

folds inside stomach (enable stomach to stretch and contract)

Figure 6.16 The folds in the interior of the stomach are called *rugae*—a Latin word that means "creased" or "wrinkled."

On June 6, 1822, an army surgeon at Mackinac Island, on Lake Huron, recognized a unique opportunity to learn how the stomach works. A French-Canadian trapper, Alexis St. Martin, arrived with a shotgun wound to his stomach. The surgeon, William Beaumont, pushed back protruding parts of the lung and stomach, and cleaned the wound. Upon healing, the stomach lining had fused to the outer body wall, leaving an opening directly to the stomach. Beaumont found that he could look directly through this "window" and observe and perform tests on the stomach in action. Beaumont's discoveries marked the start of a new understanding of human digestion. In this Thought Lab, you will infer some of what Beaumont discovered based on excerpts from the journal he kept.

Procedure

During a period of several years, Beaumont gathered gastric juice, had its components identified, introduced food into the hole in Alexis St. Martin's stomach with a string attached so he could retrieve the food particles that were partially digested, and observed the effect of emotion on digestion. Much of what Beaumont discovered was new to science—and contrary to the accepted teachings of the time. He recounted many of his observations and experiments in his journal. The following are selections from that journal.

Note: You might be wondering how Alexis St. Martin felt about serving as a human guinea pig in these experiments. For awhile, he submitted to them. He was, after all, receiving free room and board. Boredom eventually took its toll, and St. Martin returned to Canada, where he married and resumed his former life as a trapper. He lived until the age of 83, having spent over 60 years of his life with a hole in his stomach.

Excerpt A: I consider myself but a humble inquirer after truths—a simple experimenter. And if I have been led to conclusions opposite to the opinions of many who have been considered luminaries of physiology, and in some instances, from all the professors of this science, I hope the claim of sincerity will be conceded to me, when I say that such difference of opinion has been forced upon me by the convictions of experiment, and the fair deductions of reasoning.

Excerpt B: But from the result of a great number of experiments and examinations, made with a view to asserting the truth of this opinion, in the empty and full state of the organ,…I am convinced that there is no alteration of temperature.

Excerpt C: I think I am warranted, from the result of all the experiments, in saying, that the gastric juice, so far from being "inert as water," as some authors assert, is the most general solvent in nature of alimentary [food-related] matter—even the hardest bone cannot withstand its action.

Excerpt D: The gastric juice does not accumulate in the cavity of the stomach until alimentary matter is received and excites its vessels to discharge their contents for the immediate purpose of digestion.

Excerpt E: At 2 o'clock P.M.— twenty minutes after having eaten an ordinary dinner of boiled, salted beef, bread, potatoes, and turnips, and drank a gill [about 142 mL] of water, I took from stomach, through the artificial opening, a gill of the contents… Digestion had evidently commenced, and was perceptually progressing, at the time.

Excerpt F: To ascertain whether the sense of hunger would be allayed without food being passed through the oesophagus, he fasted from breakfast time, til 4 o'clock, P.M., and became quite hungry. I then put in at the aperture, three and a half drachms [about 13 mL] of lean, boiled beef. The sense of hunger immediately subsided, and stopped the borborygmus, or croaking noise, caused by the motion of the air in the stomach and intestines, peculiar to him since the wound, and almost always observed when the stomach is empty.

Analysis

1. The prevailing view of Beaumont's time was that the stomach heated up when people ate. Beaumont discovered this was not the case. Identify the excerpt in which he makes this statement.

2. It was believed that once food had been ingested the stomach remained idle for an hour or more before digestion began. Identify the excerpt in which Beaumont found otherwise.

3. Many scientists before Beaumont's time asserted that stomach fluid is essentially water. Although some evidence had been produced to disprove this assertion, the belief proved strong enough to persist to the 1800s. What evidence did Beaumont cite in response to this belief?

4. In which excerpt did Beaumont suggest that gastric juice is not stored in the stomach, as was believed to be the case?

5. Summarize the significance of the discoveries Beaumont describes in Excerpt F.

6. Based on what you have learned about the stomach and its actions, how accurate do you think Beaumont's observations and conclusions were? Quote passages from this textbook or your own research to support your answer.

7. Beaumont was a surgeon by profession. In what ways was he also a research scientist? Justify your answer.

The sound of your "stomach growling" actually comes from your intestines and is the sound of gas and fluid moving through them. The scientific name for these sounds is *borborygmi* (bore-bore-IG-mee), which comes from a Greek word meaning "rumble." The scientific names for two other common digestive-system sounds are *eructation* (from a Latin word meaning "to belch") and *flatulence* (from a Latin word meaning "a blowing" or "a breaking wind").

Digesting and Absorbing Nutrients: The Small Intestine

The **small intestine** is small only in terms of its diameter, compared with that of the large intestine. In terms of length, the small intestine is poorly named, because it is more than four times the length of the large intestine. It is, in fact, the longest part of the digestive tract. Some physical digestion occurs in the small intestine as a result of a process called **segmentation**. During this process, the chyme sloshes back and forth between segments of the small intestine that form when bands of circular muscle briefly contract. Meanwhile, peristalsis pushes the food along the intestine.

The main function of the small intestine is to complete the digestion of macromolecules and to absorb their component subunits. Although both digestion and absorption occur simultaneously throughout the small intestine, these processes and the structures associated with them will be discussed separately to help you understand how and where macromolecules are hydrolyzed so they can be absorbed into the bloodstream.

Regions and Structures of the Small Intestine

The small intestine can be subdivided into three regions. The first 25 cm of the small intestine is called the **duodenum**. The duodenum is generally U-shaped and is the shortest and widest of the three regions. Ducts (channels) from the liver and pancreas join to form one duct that enters the duodenum. Thus, the duodenum is an important site for the chemical digestion of the chyme received from the stomach.

As you can see in Figure 6.17, the innermost surface of the duodenum, like the rest of the small intestine, is corrugated with circular ridges about 1.3 cm high. The surface of every "hill" and "valley" of these ridges has a velvety appearance due to additional folds—about 6 million tiny finger-like projections called **villi** (see Figure 6.18A). The surface of the villi bristle with thousands of microscopic extensions called **microvilli**. Because the microvilli give the villi a fuzzy, brush-like appearance in electron photomicrographs, they are often referred to as the "brush border" of the cells that line the intestinal wall.

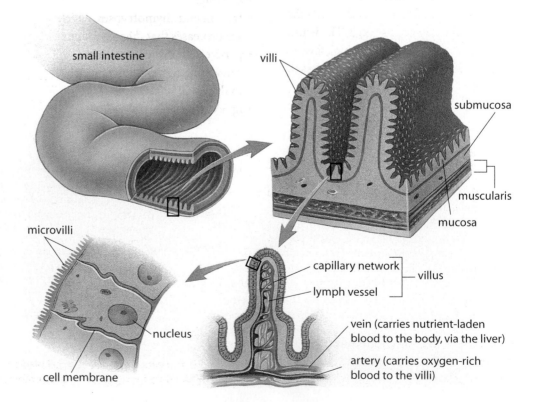

Figure 6.17 The ridges in the inner lining of the small intestine are covered in tiny projections called villi, which, in turn, are covered in microvilli. Together, the ridges, villi, and microvilli vastly increase the absorptive surface area of the small intestine.

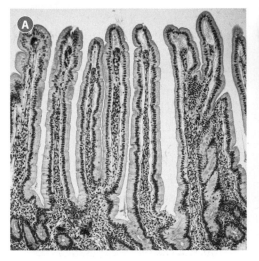

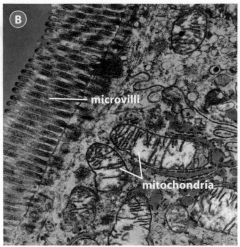

microvilli

mitochondria

Figure 6.18 Villi **(A)** and microvilli **(B)** in the small intestine: Note the number of mitochondria near the innermost surface of the small intestine, just below the microvilli. Infer the significance of their presence. Each villus is about 1 mm long and is covered by thousands of microvilli. Microvilli are measured in μm.

In Figure 6.17, you can see that each villus contains tiny structures called capillary networks and lymph vessels. These structures are part of the circulatory system. They conduct absorbed substances from the small intestine into the bloodstream and the lymphatic system. (You will learn more about capillaries and lymph vessels in Chapter 8.)

The other regions of the small intestine are the jejunum and the ileum, and they are quite similar to the duodenum. The jejunum, which is about 2.5 m long, contains more folds and secretory glands than the duodenum. It continues to break down food so that the end products can be absorbed. The ileum, which is about 3 m long, contains fewer and smaller villi. Its function is to absorb nutrients and to push the remaining undigested material into the large intestine.

• • •

20 Describe how the physical movements of the small intestine aid in the physical digestion of food. Include the name of this process.

21 Explain how surface area is maximized in the small intestine.

• • •

Accessory Organs

To digest the macromolecules that are still present in chyme, the small intestine has its own arsenal of enzymes that are

secreted from its microvilli. Digestive assistance is provided by substances that are secreted by three organs located near the stomach and small intestine: the pancreas, liver, and gall bladder. These organs, shown in Figure 6.19, are often referred to as *accessory organs* of the digestive system, because their role in the process of digestion is vital, but they are not physically part of the digestive tract.

Pancreas The **pancreas** delivers about 1 L of pancreatic fluid to the duodenum each day. Pancreatic fluid contains a multitude of enzymes, including the following:

- trypsin and chymotrypsin, which are proteases that digest proteins
- pancreatic amylase, which is a carbohydrase that digests starch in the small intestine
- lipase, which digests fat

BiologyFile

Try This
The ridges in the lining of the small intestine increase its surface area about three times. The villi increase its surface area another 30 times, and the microvilli increase its surface area another 600 times. Calculate the surface area of a small section of smooth tubing that is 280 cm long and 4 cm in diameter. How does this compare with the surface area of a section of the small intestine, with the same length and diameter, but including the ridges, villi, and microvilli?

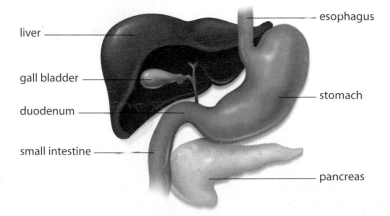

esophagus

liver

gall bladder

duodenum

small intestine

stomach

pancreas

Figure 6.19 The pancreas, liver, and gall bladder produce and/or store secretions necessary for digestion of macromolecules.

FYI
The colour of bile is responsible for the brown colour of feces and the pale yellow colour of blood plasma and urine. If the liver's removal of bile pigments becomes impaired, the bile pigments can accumulate in the blood and cause a yellow staining of skin. This condition is called jaundice.

These enzymes are released into the duodenum, mainly in an inactive form. They are then activated by enzymes secreted by the brush border of the duodenal lining. The pancreatic enzymes digest proteins into smaller polypeptides, polysaccharides into shorter chains of simpler sugars, and fats into free fatty acids and other products. Further digestion of these molecules is completed by the brush border enzymes.

Pancreatic fluid also contains bicarbonate, which neutralizes the hydrochloric acid from the stomach and gives the chyme in the duodenum a slightly alkaline pH of about 8.

Liver The **liver** is the largest internal organ of the human body. In an adult, it is the size of a football, with a mass of about 1.5 kg . The main digestion-related secretion of the liver is bile, a greenish-yellow fluid mixture that is made up of bile pigments and bile salts. Bile pigments do not take part in digestion. They are waste products from the liver's destruction of old red blood cells, and they are eventually eliminated with the feces.

Bile salts, on the other hand, play a crucial role in the digestion of fats. Because fats are insoluble in water, they enter the intestine as drops within the watery chyme. Lipases, however, are water soluble, so they can only act at the surface of a fat droplet where it is in contact with water. Bile salts assist lipases in accessing fats because they are partly soluble in water and partly soluble in fats. As shown in Figure 6.20, bile salts work like a detergent, dispersing large fat droplets into a fine suspension of smaller droplets in the chyme. This emulsification process produces a greater surface area of fats on which the lipases can act. As a result, the digestion of fats can occur more quickly.

Gall Bladder After bile is produced in the liver, it is sent to the **gall bladder**, which stores the bile between meals. The arrival of fat-containing chyme in the duodenum stimulates the gall bladder to contract. This causes bile to be transported through a duct (shared by both the gall bladder and the liver) and injected into the duodenum.

• • •

22 How do secretions of the pancreas, liver, and gallbladder aid digestion?

• • •

Digestion and Absorption in the Small Intestine

The digestive secretions from the brush border of the small intestine, the liver, and the pancreas contribute mucus, water, bile, and enzymes. Most of the chemical digestion in the small intestine occurs in the duodenum and acts on all four categories of macromolecules and their components. Enzymatic digestion

Figure 6.20 Emulsifiers, such as detergents, cause fats to mix with water. They contain molecules with a non-polar end and a polar end. These molecules position themselves around a fat droplet so that their non-polar ends project. The fat droplet disperses into a fine suspension of smaller fat droplets in the water.

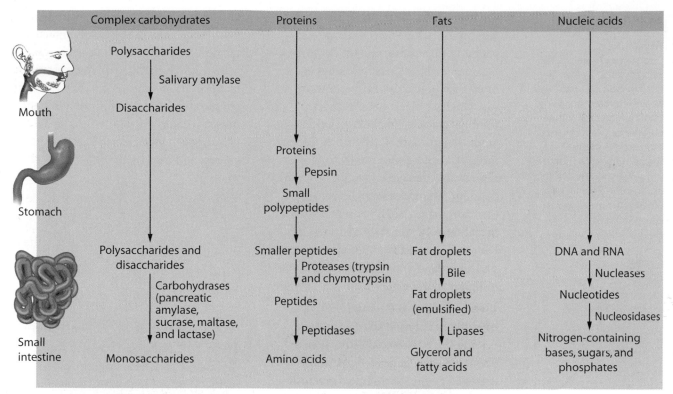

Figure 6.21 An overview of chemical digestion and absorption in the small intestine

of macromolecules is performed by **carbohydrases** (which digest carbohydrates), **lipases** (which digest fats), **proteases** (which digest larger polypeptides), and **nucleases** (which digest nucleic acids). Figure 6.21 provides an overview of the sites of digestion for the four categories of macromolecules and their stepwise "dismantling" by enzymes. Table 6.3 outlines some of the digestive enzymes and their activities. You may find it helpful to refer to Table 6.3 and Figure 6.21 as you read about the digestion and absorption of carbohydrates, proteins, lipids, and nucleic acids on the next few pages.

Table 6.3 Selected Enzymes of the Digestive System

Enzyme	Where enzyme acts/pH	Substrate (food) digested	Products of digestion	Origin of enzymes
salivary amylase	mouth/7	starch, glycogen	maltose (disaccharide)	salivary glands
pancreatic amylase	small intestine/8	starch, glycogen	maltose	pancreas
carbohydrases • sucrase • maltase • lactase	small intestine/8	sucrose maltose lactose	glucose + fructose glucose glucose + galactose	small intestine
pancreatic lipase	small intestine/8	lipids	fatty acids and glycerol	pancreas
proteases • pepsin • trypsin • chymotrypsin	stomach/1–2 small intestine/8 small intestine/8	protein peptides peptides	peptides smaller peptides smaller peptides	stomach pancreas pancreas
peptidases	small intestine/8	peptides	smaller peptides and amino acids	pancreas and small intestine
nucleases	small intestine/8	nucleic acids	nucleotides and components	pancreas
nucleosidases	small intestine/8	nucleotides	bases, sugars, and phosphates	small intestine

BiologyFile

Web Link

Deficiency of a particular carbohydrase can cause digestive distress when a person eats certain foods. For example, lack of the enzyme lactase prevents a large proportion of the human population from digesting the monosaccharide lactose, which is a common component of dairy products. What are the symptoms of lactose intolerance? Which segments of the population are most likely to experience it, and why?

www.albertabiology.ca
WWW

Carbohydrate Digestion and Absorption

The digestion of starch begins in the mouth with the action of salivary amylase. Since food stays in the mouth for only a short time, however, carbohydrate digestion is usually minimal there. When undigested starch enters the stomach, the hydrochloric acid interrupts its digestion. Salivary amylase is most active at a pH of about 7, but the pH in the stomach is about 2 because of the hydrochloric acid. Thus, the digestion of starch and other carbohydrates does not continue until the chyme enters the small intestine, where the pH is about 8. In the small intestine, pancreatic amylase completes the digestion of starch into disaccharides. Other carbohydrases hydrolyze the disaccharides into monosaccharides, such as glucose, galactose and fructose.

As shown in Figure 6.22, monosaccharides are absorbed by active transport into the cells of the intestinal villi. (Recall the mitochondria in Figure 6.18B. The active transport of glucose and other monosaccharides requires ATP, which is produced in the mitochondria of cells.) From the cells of the intestinal lining, the monosaccharides enter the bloodstream and are transported directly to the liver. Monosaccharides other than glucose are converted into glucose by the liver. Glucose is circulated from the liver by the bloodstream to all the body cells, where it is used as a source of energy. Excess glucose is converted by the liver into glycogen, which is temporarily stored in the liver and muscles. Later, when blood glucose levels fall, glycogen is converted back into glucose and used by the cells.

• • •

23 Outline in words, a sketch, or a flowchart the processes by which carbohydrates are digested in the small intestine and absorbed into the bloodstream.

• • •

Protein Digestion and Absorption

The polypeptides that are produced in the stomach by the action of pepsin are further digested in the small intestine by two proteases secreted by the pancreas. These proteases, trypsin and chymotrypsin, are secreted as inactive enzymes and then activated by a different enzyme secreted in the small intestine. Both trypsin and chymotrypsin hydrolyze the peptide bonds between specific but different amino acids, resulting in the formation of short peptide chains. The short peptide chains vary in length from 2 to 10 amino acids. During the hydrolysis of these peptide

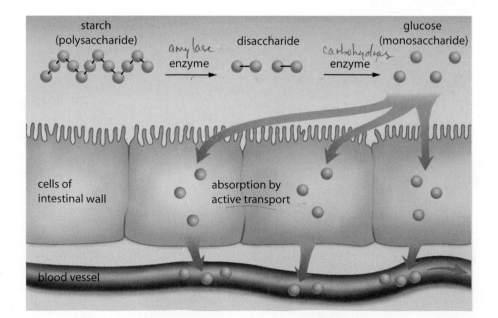

Figure 6.22 The monosaccharide glucose is actively transported into cells of the intestinal wall in order to move into the bloodstream.

chains, a few single amino acids are separated from their ends.

All that is left to complete the digestion of protein is for the short peptide segments to be split into single amino acids. This is done by different peptidase enzymes secreted by the pancreas and the small intestine. The amino acids are then absorbed by active transport into the villi in the small intestine (see Figure 6.23). From there, the amino acids diffuse into the blood capillaries and are carried, like the sugars, directly to the liver. In the liver, the amino acids may undergo a variety of reactions. Some have their amino group removed (a process called deamination) before they are used in energy-releasing reactions or converted into sugars. These amino groups combine with carbon dioxide in a series of reactions that lead to the formation of the nitrogenous waste urea, which is excreted in the urine. Other amino acids are released into the bloodstream from the liver, for distribution to the body cells. In the body cells, they are used to make proteins for a variety of functions, such as enzymes and cellular structures.

Fat Digestion and Absorption The salivary glands and stomach of an infant produce lipases, so fat digestion can begin quickly in the infant's digestive system. In adults, however, this

24 Outline in words, a sketch, or a flowchart the processes by which proteins are digested in the small intestine and absorbed into the bloodstream.

production is greatly reduced, and so very little fat digestion occurs early on.

The arrival of fats in the duodenum stimulates the secretion of bile, which emulsifies the fat droplets, as described earlier. Note that emulsification is a physical process, not a chemical process. The bonds that join the glycerol and fatty acids in fats are not hydrolyzed by emulsification. The breakdown of fats by hydrolysis is carried out by lipase secreted in the duodenum. The resulting glycerol and fatty acids are absorbed into the cells of the villi by simple diffusion (see Figure 6.24). Inside the cells of the intestinal lining, the fat subunits are reassembled into triglycerides and then coated with proteins to make them soluble before they enter the lymph vessels in the villi. The lymph vessels carry the coated triglycerides to the chest region, where they join the bloodstream. Once in the bloodstream, the protein coating is removed by lipase in the lining of the blood vessels. Lipase hydrolyzes the

BiologyFile

FYI
Protein molecules are normally too large to pass through the cell membranes of the cells that make up the intestinal lining. Occasionally, however, whole proteins are absorbed by these cells. When this happens, the undigested proteins are recognized as "foreign" by the body's immune system, leading to unpleasant allergic reactions. This is why some people must avoid certain protein-rich foods, such as eggs, fish, and nuts.

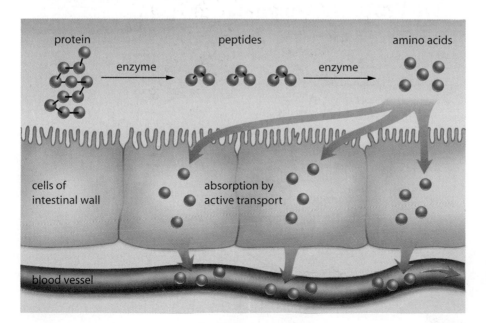

Figure 6.23 Amino acids are actively transported into the cells of the intestinal wall in order to move into the bloodstream.

Figure 6.24
Glycerol and fatty acid molecules diffuse into the cells of the intestinal wall where they are resynthesized into fats, coated with proteins, and move into lymph vessels for eventual transport into the bloodstream.

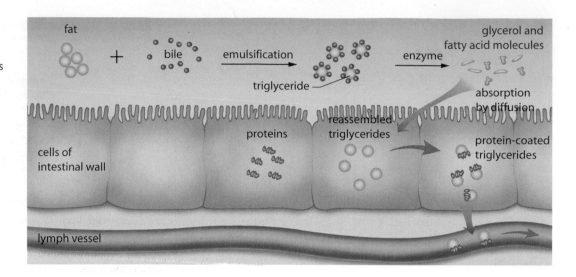

triglycerides, making free fatty acids and glycerol available for use by the body cells.

Nucleic Acid Digestion and Absorption Nucleic acids are not abundant enough to be considered a major nutrient that must be ingested in the diet. The food you eat contains sufficient quantities of these macromolecules for the body to use. In the small intestine, nucleic acids are digested by enzymes called nucleases to yield nucleotides. Nucleosidases hydrolyze the nucleotides to their constituent bases, sugars, and phosphates. These molecules are then absorbed, like glucose and amino acids, into the bloodstream by active transport.

• • •

25 Describe how fats are digested in the small intestine and absorbed into lymph vessels.

26 Describe how nucleic acids are digested and absorbed.

• • •

INVESTIGATION 6.B

Target Skills

Performing an experiment to investigate the influence of pH on the activity of pepsin and trypsin

Designing an experiment to investigate the influence of other variables on the activity of pepsin and trypsin

Assessing the validity of collected data and observations, as well as conclusions drawn from them

Optimum pH for Two Protease Enzymes

Two proteases, pepsin and trypsin, are secreted at different stages and at different sites during digestion. Each protease works best at an optimum pH. The stomach has a pH of about 2, while the small intestine has a pH of between 7 and 8. In this investigation, you will observe evidence to verify historically obtained results related to the optimum pH at which these two proteases work.

Question

How can you use pH to determine which protease, pepsin or trypsin, is secreted into the stomach and which protease is secreted into the small intestine?

Hypothesis

State a suitable hypothesis for this investigation.

Safety Precautions

• Hydrochloric acid is a strong acid, and sodium hydroxide is a strong base. Both are very corrosive and must not be mixed together.

• Other chemicals used in this investigation may be toxic. Take extra care to avoid getting them in your eyes, on your skin, or on your clothes. Flush spills immediately with plenty of cool water, and inform your teacher.

Materials

- 18 cubes of boiled egg white (protein samples)
- 10 mL distilled water
- 10 mL 2% pepsin solution
- 10 mL 5% trypsin solution
- 15 mL dilute hydrochloric acid (0.01 mol/L)
- 15 mL dilute sodium hydroxide (0.01 mol/L)
- wax pencil
- metric ruler
- 6 test tubes
- 10-mL graduated cylinder
- test-tube rack
- test-tube holder
- water bath or incubator at 37 °C

Procedure

1. Use a wax pencil to label the test tubes as follows: C-2, C-8, P-2, P-8, T-2, and T-8. The test tubes labelled C are your controls. The test tubes labelled P will contain pepsin, and the test tubes labelled T will contain trypsin. The numerals indicate the pH of the contents of the test tubes.

2. Put three cubes of boiled egg white into each test tube. Observe the size and appearance of the cubes in each test tube. Record your observations in a data table like the one below.

Size and Appearance of Egg White Before and After Digestion by Pepsin and Trypsin

Test tube	Before digestion		After digestion	
	Size of cubes	Appearance of cubes	Size of cubes	Appearance of cubes
C-2				
C-8				
P-2				
P-8				
T-2				
T-8				

3. Add 5 mL of distilled water to each test tube labelled C. Add 5 mL of pepsin solution to each test tube labelled P. Add 5 mL of trypsin solution to each test tube labelled T.

4. Add 5 mL of dilute hydrochloric acid to each test tube labelled 2. Add 5 mL of dilute sodium hydroxide solution to each test tube labelled 8.

5. Place the test tubes in a water bath or incubator at 37 °C, and leave them overnight. The temperature must be maintained between 35 °C and 39 °C during this time.

6. Observe the contents of the heated test tubes. Note any changes in the size and appearance of the cubes of egg white in each test tube. Record your observations in your data table.

7. Dispose of the contents of the test tubes as directed by your teacher, and clean up your work area.

Analysis

1. How did the contents of the test tubes with protease differ from the control test tubes?

2. a) At what pH did pepsin break down protein more completely?

   b) At what pH did trypsin break down protein more completely?

Conclusions

3. Based on your results, which protease would break down protein in the small intestine? Justify your answer.

4. Based on your results, which protease would break down protein in the stomach? Justify your answer.

Extensions

5. a) What is the significance of maintaining the temperature of the test tubes between 35 °C and 39 °C?

   b) Based on the experimental design, describe the degree of certainty you have in the conclusions you stated in questions 3 and 4. (**Hint:** Think carefully about all the conditions and variables you tested in this investigation. Identify any possible sources of error, both in the experimental design and the way you conducted it.)

6. What, if any, difference do you think there would be if you manipulated a different variable, rather than pH? Design a procedure to investigate the possible impact of manipulating a different variable. With your teacher's permission, and with careful attention to safety, carry out your procedure.

Table 6.4 Characteristics of hormones that regulate digestion

Hormone	Source	Stimulus	Target	Response
Gastrin	Stomach	Entry of food into stomach	Stomach	Increased acid production
Secretin	Duodenum	Entry of chyme into duodenum	Stomach	Decreased stomach motility
CCK	Duodenum	Entry of chyme into duodenum	Stomach	Decreased stomach motility

Regulation of Processes in the Small Intestine

The activities of the digestive tract are coordinated by the nervous system and the endocrine system. The nervous system, for example, stimulates salivary and gastric secretions in response to the sight, smell, and consumption of food. When food arrives in the stomach, proteins in the food stimulate the secretion of a stomach hormone called **gastrin**. Gastrin then stimulates the secretion of hydrochloric acid and the inactive precursor molecule of pepsin from glands in the stomach. The secreted hydrochloric acid lowers the pH of the gastric juice, which acts to inhibit further secretion of gastrin. Because the inhibition of gastrin secretion reduces the amount of hydrochloric acid that is released into the gastric juice, a negative feedback mechanism is completed. In this way, the secretion and concentration of gastric fluid is kept under tight control.

The passage of chyme from the stomach into the duodenum inhibits the contractions of the stomach, so that no additional chyme can enter the duodenum until the previous amount has been processed. This inhibition of stomach contractions is guided, in part, by hormones that are secreted into the bloodstream by the duodenum (see Table 6.4). These hormones include **secretin**, **CCK** (cholecystokinin), and **GIP** (gastric inhibitory peptide). Chyme with a high fat content is the strongest stimulus for the secretion of CCK and GIP. Chyme with a high acidity is the strongest stimulus for the release of secretin. All three hormones inhibit stomach movements and secretions, enabling fatty meals to remain in the stomach longer than non-fatty meals. Figure 6.25 summarizes the relationship among the enzyme-secreting activities in the accessory organs, the stomach, and the duodenum.

CCK and secretin also have other regulatory functions in digestion. CCK stimulates increased pancreatic secretions of digestive enzymes and gall bladder contractions. Gall bladder contractions inject more bile into the duodenum, which enhances the emulsifying and digestion of fats. Secretin also stimulates the pancreas to release more bicarbonate to neutralize acidic chyme.

• • •

27 Describe briefly how the actions of the accessory organs are orchestrated with the digestive functions of the stomach and gall bladder.

• • •

Completing Nutrient Absorption and Elimination: The Large Intestine

The material that remains in the small intestine after nutrients are absorbed

Figure 6.25 Gastrin, secretin, and CCK are hormones that must be transported by the bloodstream from their place of origin to the place where they act to stimulate the release of digestive secretions. Lymph vessels carry absorbed fats.

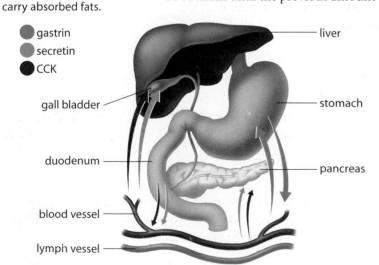

- gastrin
- secretin
- CCK

gall bladder

duodenum

blood vessel

lymph vessel

liver

stomach

pancreas

enters the final part of the digestive tract: the **large intestine**. The large intestine is much shorter than the small intestine, measuring only about 1.5 m long, but it has a larger diameter of about 2.5 cm.

Digestion does not occur in the large intestine. Its main function is to concentrate and eliminate waste materials. Each day, the large intestine receives about 500 mL of indigestible food residue, reduces it to about 150 mL of feces by absorbing water and salts, and eliminates the feces.

Undigested chyme that enters the large intestine passes up, along, and down the colon, which is the main portion of the large intestine. In the colon, water and salts are absorbed from any undigested food, while billions of anaerobic intestinal bacteria break it down further. As well, these bacteria produce vitamins B-12 and K, and some amino acids. At the end of this process, any remaining indigestible materials, along with the colon bacteria, form the feces. The feces pass into the rectum and anal canal, which comprise the last 20 cm of the large intestine. From there, the feces pass out of the body through the anus. The function of the rectum is to store the feces until they are eliminated. The rectum has three folds that enable it to retain the feces while passing gas.

The opening to the anus is usually controlled by two sets of sphincters. You are able to control contraction and relaxation of one of these sets of sphincters. The other set is under the control of the nervous system. When the rectum is full, receptor cells trigger a reflex that moves the feces out of the body by peristalsis.

Section 6.2 Summary

- Digestion begins in the mouth. By the time food leaves the small intestine digestion and absorption are nearly complete.
- The digestive tract is a tube that extends from the mouth to the anus. Food passes through the digestive tract and is broken down into its molecules through physical and chemical processing.
- The stomach secretes acidic gastric juices, which chemically break down food. The stomach physically breaks down food through muscular contractions.
- The small intestine is where most macromolecule digestion and absorption occur, and where nutrients pass out of the digestive tract and into the bloodstream.
- The accessory organs of digestion are the liver, the pancreas, and the gall bladder. The liver performs many functions, such as removing toxins and maintaining a constant level of glucose in the blood.
- The pancreas produces enzymes and hormones. The gall bladder stores bile that is produced in the liver.
- The large intestine absorbs most of the water and salts from chyme, leaving semi-solid feces that are eliminated from the body through the anus.

Section 6.2 | Review

1. Use word processing software to create a flow chart that lists, in order, the organs of the digestive tract through which food passes. **ICT**

2. Identify the accessory organs of the digestive system. Explain why these organs are considered to be accessories to the system.

3. Explain the impact on the digestive system if mechanical digestion did not take place.

4. Most of the digestive enzymes are secreted into the small intestine. Suggest two reasons why these enzymes are secreted into this organ, rather than into the stomach.

5. Explain how the secretions of the pancreas, liver, and gall bladder aid digestion.

6. Based on the structure of its internal lining, explain why you could infer that absorption of most nutrients occurs in the small intestine.

Sorting Out Nutritional Supplements

Many Canadians regularly take vitamin and mineral pills. Are such food supplements necessary for good health? Can they help increase your energy, strengthen your immune system, or reduce the risks of some illnesses? How do scientists assess these different claims? Why are there so many different opinions about the value of supplements?

The Case of Calcium

Consider the question, "How much calcium do I need each day?" Calcium is the most abundant mineral in your body. It forms your bones and teeth, and plays roles in several activities such as blood clotting and enzyme activation. The amount of calcium a person needs, however, depends on age, sex, level of activity, diet, and state of health. For example, women after the age of 30 lose bone mass each year and are at greater risk of developing osteoporosis—a disease in which bones become more porous, break more easily, and heal more slowly. For this reason, healthcare professionals often recommend calcium supplements to older women.

What is Bioavailability?

Calcium is found in milk and other dairy products, dark, leafy vegetables, and a variety of supplements. But your body may not use all the calcium you ingest. The source of the calcium is just as important as the quantity. *Bioavailability* refers to the amount of calcium that a person absorbs from a source, rather than the total amount of calcium actually in the source. For example, 1 g of calcium carbonate contains more elemental calcium than 1 g of calcium citrate, but it is not as readily available to the body. As a result, a smaller quantity of calcium citrate gives the body more calcium than a larger quantity of calcium carbonate.

Other nutrients that you eat with calcium also affect how efficiently the body is able to use the mineral. For example, magnesium and vitamin D increase calcium absorption.

Weight-bearing exercise is as important in the prevention of osteoporosis as adequate calcium intake—especially in women.

Designing Nutrition Tests

Suppose you are a researcher and want to compare the bioavailability of calcium present in: a) milk, b) calcium carbonate tablets, and c) calcium carbonate plus vitamin D.

• • •

1. List the variables in your test.

2. 50 people volunteer to take part in the test. They include men and women ranging in age from 28 to 59. Explain why this is not a good sample for testing and suggest a better sample.

3. The calcium uptake of volunteers can be measured by changes in the levels of calcium excreted in their urine. How will you set up a fair test of the variables you wish to study?

4. Follow up your study of supplements by an informal survey at your local pharmacy or health food store. Pick a supplement such as calcium, vitamin C, or glucosamine hydrochloride. How many different forms of the supplement are available? How does one form differ from another? Why do you think the cost of supplements varies?

Health and the Digestive System

Section Outcomes

In this section, you will
- **recognize** and **appreciate** the relationship between health and nutritional decisions
- **identify** conditions that adversely affect the health of the digestive system and the technologies that are available to treat them

Key Terms

ulcer
inflammatory bowel disease
hepatitis
cirrhosis
gallstones
anorexia nervosa
obesity

Figure 6.26 Good nutrition is essential for high-performance athletes.

Competitive athletes, like those shown in Figure 6.26, are careful about the food they eat because they know that their performance is related to nutrition. This link is not immediately obvious to non-athletes, however. The effects of poor dietary and lifestyle habits may take weeks, months, or even years to show up. Good nutrition is the only way to provide the energy our bodies need to carry out their many activities, such as nerve transmission, muscle contraction, and cell repair and replacement. As well, good nutrition provides the raw materials our bodies need as building blocks but are unable to manufacture themselves.

What we eat is influenced by our lifestyles and attitudes. For example, we live in a society that often promotes unrealistic body images as the desired norm. The societal pressure to be thin can lead to unhealthy personal decisions. So can the confusing array of dietary plans, some of which are endorsed by medical professionals and some of which are not. The truth is that all individuals are unique, and it is impossible for everyone to fit an "ideal" body image. Maintaining a healthy body mass and

feeling energized and healthy results from eating a well-balanced diet, getting regular rest and exercise, and adopting positive, self-enriching attitudes. Deficiencies in any of these areas can severely affect our ability to function.

Since the end result of digestion is the absorption of nutrients, salts, and water, most disorders of the digestive system affect either the nutritional state of the body or its salt and water content. Examples of digestive system disorders include ulcers, inflammatory bowel disease, hepatitis, cirrhosis, and gallstones.

• • •

28 What is the connection between healthy dietary practices and a healthy functioning body?

• • •

Ulcers

An **ulcer** forms when the thick layer of mucus that protects the lining of the stomach from the acids in the digestive juices is eroded. Research has shown that most ulcers are caused by acid-resistant bacteria, *Helicobacter pylori*, which attach to the stomach wall. The sites of attachment stop producing the protective mucus, and the stomach acid eats away at the stomach wall (see Figure 6.27). Other factors, such as smoking, caffeine and alcohol intake, and stress, can contribute to the formation of ulcers. Treatments for ulcers include medications that reduce the amount of acid in the stomach or strengthen the layer of mucus, antibiotics, and sometimes lifestyle adjustments. If these treatments do not work, surgery to block nerve signals or even to remove part of the stomach is possible.

Inflammatory Bowel Disease

Inflammatory bowel disease is the general name for diseases that cause inflammation in the intestines (bowels). Crohn's disease (also called ileitis or enteritis) is a serious inflammatory bowel disease that usually affects the ileum of the small intestine, but it can affect any part of the digestive tract from the mouth to the anus. The inflammation extends deep into the lining of the affected organ, causing the intestines to empty frequently. This results in diarrhea and sometimes rectal bleeding. Thus, Crohn's disease is very painful. Crohn's disease can be difficult to diagnose because its symptoms are similar to the symptoms of other intestinal disorders, such as irritable bowel syndrome and ulcerative colitis. Research into Crohn's disease shows that it may be an autoimmune disorder, in which the body recognizes part of its own digestive tract as a foreign substance. (You will explore the immune system and autoimmune disorders in more detail in Chapter 8.) Crohn's disease is chronic and may be inherited. There is no cure, so treatments focus on medications to reduce pain, suppress the inflammation, reduce the immune response, and allow time for the tissue to heal. If medications do not control the symptoms, surgery is sometimes performed to remove the diseased portions of the digestive tract.

Colitis is another inflammatory bowel disease. It is the inflammation and ulceration of the lining of the colon. While Crohn's disease affects the entire thickness of the colon, colitis is restricted to the innermost lining of the colon. The symptoms are similar to Crohn's disease and include loose and bloody stool, cramps, and abdominal pain. There may be skin lesions, joint pain, and (in children) a failure to grow properly. Treatments include medications that are similar to those given for Crohn's disease. Surgery is a final option. The entire bowel and rectum are removed, and an external opening is created for waste. Less drastic procedures are still being developed.

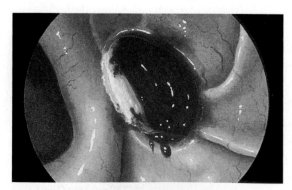

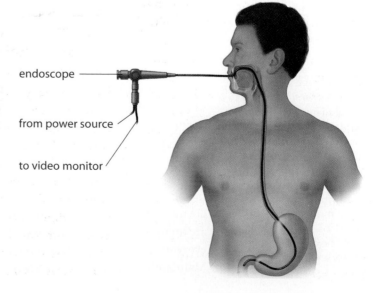

endoscope

from power source

to video monitor

Figure 6.27 This photo of a bleeding ulcer in the stomach was taken with an endoscope, a tube-shaped instrument with a tiny lens and light source that is inserted into the abdominal cavity. Capsule endoscopy—the technology you saw in the opening to this chapter—now enhances the range of diagnostic tools available to health professionals.

Disorders of the Accessory Organs

Two of the most serious disorders of the liver are hepatitis and cirrhosis, and both are life-threatening. **Hepatitis** is an inflammation of the liver. There are three types of hepatitis: A, B, and C. Hepatitis A is usually contracted from drinking contaminated water. Hepatitis B is spread by sexual contact and is more contagious than the AIDS virus, but a vaccine has been developed to protect against it. Hepatitis C is usually contracted by contact with infected blood. There is no vaccine for hepatitis C.

Figure 6.28 shows **cirrhosis**—a chronic disease of the liver that occurs when scar tissue replaces healthy liver tissue and prevents the liver from functioning properly. Chronic alcoholism and hepatitis C are the most common causes of cirrhosis of the liver. There are few symptoms in the early stages of the disease. Blood tests, however, can determine if the liver is becoming fatty—an early warning sign that cirrhosis is developing. The liver is amazing in its ability to heal itself, but, in many cases, there is not enough regeneration to avoid liver failure. A liver transplant is the primary treatment for liver failure. There is active research on a bioartifical liver, which uses pig cells to perform the functions that are normally carried out by the human liver. Experimental trials have been successful, but more research is necessary to develop this treatment fully.

Another common disorder of the digestive system is **gallstones**, which are small hard masses that form in the gall bladder. Remember that the gall bladder stores bile from the liver. Sometimes, cholesterol in the bile can precipitate out of the bile and form crystals. The crystals continue to grow in size and become gallstones. Three factors that are related to the formation of gallstones are obesity, alcohol intake, and heredity. Gallstones are usually treated with medications or with ultrasound shock waves to disintegrate the stones so that they

can be passed out in the urine. Since gallstones often reoccur, it is important to reduce the causal factors. Cholesterol in the gall bladder can be lowered by losing weight, increasing the intake of the omega-3 fatty acids that are present in fish, and decreasing the size of meals. If the gallstone problem is serious, the entire gall bladder may need to be surgically removed.

• • •

29 What is an ulcer?

30 Briefly describe inflammatory bowel disease.

31 Explain why disorders of the liver are so threatening to the health of the body.

• • •

Psychological, Social, and Cultural Dimensions of Digestion-Related Conditions

Current ideas of physical attractiveness have sent many people in search of a quick way to lose weight and keep it off. Some people may become obsessed with their weight and deprive their bodies of basic nutrients in order to become or stay thin. For example, **anorexia nervosa** is an eating disorder that is characterized by a morbid fear of gaining weight. People with this disorder starve themselves and typically have a body mass that is less than 85 percent of what

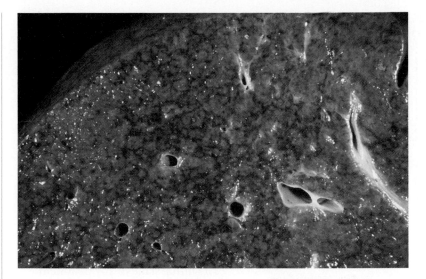

Figure 6.28 A liver affected by cirrhosis. The word cirrhosis comes from a Greek word that means tawny, referring to the brownish-orange colour of the diseased liver.

Biology File

Web Link
Inflammation of the pancreas is called pancreatitis. Being a disease of the digestive tract, perhaps it's not surprising that it is linked to many other aspects of digestion and metabolism. For example, which of its most common causes is a disease of another accessory organ? What enzyme you've just learned about is used in diagnosis of pancreatitis? And what role does nutrition play in managing the condition?

www.albertabiology.ca
WWW

BiologyFile

Web Link

Gastric bypass surgery is a procedure that alters the digestive tract and reduces the size of the stomach. Under what circumstances is this procedure usually performed? How successful is it, statistically?

www.albertabiology.ca
WWW

Figure 6.29 The Inuit of Canada's north are healthier when they eat the traditional diet of their ancestors, which includes foods such as the caribou shown here, as well as Arctic char, seal, and whale meat. What did your ancestors eat?

is considered to be their normal body mass. They have a distorted self-image, seeing themselves as fat even when they are dangerously thin. All of the symptoms of starvation are present in this serious disorder, including low blood pressure, irregular heartbeat, and constipation. As the disorder progresses, the body begins to shut down. Menstruation in females stops, internal organs have trouble functioning, and the skin dries out. As the digestive tract stops working, even fewer nutrients can be absorbed. At this point, death is imminent.

The initial stage of any treatment begins by stabilizing the life-threatening complications of starvation. Once the person is out of immediate physical danger, the distorted perceptions that have caused the eating disorder must be treated. Psychological therapy, including behavioural and family therapy, can be used to treat this disorder successfully.

While taking in too few nutrients is dangerous, eating too many can lead to **obesity**—a body mass that is 20 percent or more above what is considered to be an ideal body mass for a person's height. In Canada, more than half of Canadians are classified as overweight or obese. Obesity is most likely caused by a combination of hormonal, genetic, lifestyle, and social factors. Research scientists have shown that people who are obese have more fat cells than people who are not obese. When weight is lost, the fat cells simply get smaller; they do

not disappear. Social factors that influence obesity include the eating habits of other family members. Lifestyle choices, such as the consistent eating of fatty foods, sedentary activities, and inadequate aerobic exercise, also contribute to the development of excess body fat.

Surgery to remove body fat may be considered for people who are severely obese and at risk for associated conditions, such as high blood pressure and joint and bone impairment. When the cause is related more to lifestyle choices, the most successful approach is a commitment to more balanced and moderate dietary choices and to increase physical activity.

• • •

32 Are anorexia nervosa and obesity conditions related only to the digestive system? Explain why or why not.

• • •

Traditional vs. Modern Diets

Some peoples who have abandoned their traditional foods in favour of modern convenience foods are returning to the old ways (Figure 6.29). In 1985, a study involving native Hawaiians compared their modern dietary practices with those of their ancestors. As shown in Figure 6.30, the traditional diet included only 3 percent protein from animal

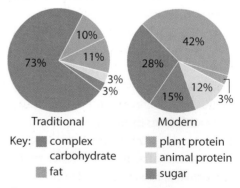

Key: complex carbohydrate / fat / plant protein / animal protein / sugar

Figure 6.30 The incidence of cardiovascular disease, cancers, and diabetes has dropped in native Hawaiians who have returned to their traditional diet. The switch to the traditional diet has been accompanied by a return to more traditional cultural and social values and practices.

HUNTING AND FISHING FOR A HEALTHY LIFESTYLE!

Getting out on the land is part of our way of life. It is a great way to be active. Hunting, fishing and eating traditional foods will help keep us healthy. Traditional foods give us the nutrients we need to be healthy.

FOR MORE INFORMATION CONTACT:

• Your local Health Centre
• Your Regional Nutritionist

or refer to the Nutrition Fact sheet Series on Nutrients found in the **Contaminants and Your Health: NWT Fact Sheets** binder.

HEALTHY EATING!

Boil fish heads in broth and add rice, onion, carrots and frozen peas for a tasty soup. Serve with bannock and a glass of milk or unsweetened juice. Enjoy a piece of fruit for dessert.

Produced by Baffin, Inuvik, Keewatin and Kitikmeot Health Boards, in conjunction with the Community Health Programs, Department of Health and Social Services, GNWT. Prototype developed by Dene Nation and Mackenzie Regional Health Services. Funded by Arctic Environmental Strategy. March 1996

Figure 6.31 The Health and Social Services department of the Northwest Territories publishes a comprehensive series of fact sheets (a portion of one page is shown here) to help Aboriginal peoples in northern provinces and territories in their food choices.

sources, compared with 12 percent in the modern diet. The differences in fat, sugar, and complex carbohydrate intake were even more dramatic. A statistical study showed that the rate of cardiovascular (heart and circulatory system-related) disease and cancer was higher than average among Hawaiians who followed the modern diet. Diabetes was also common in Hawaiians who followed the modern diet. Follow-up studies showed that their health greatly improved when they returned to the ancestral diet.

Some non-native Hawaiians have used this study to promote the recommendation that a diet emphasizing plant proteins and low to moderate fat intake should be adopted as a healthy diet for others. This would surprise many Aboriginal peoples, especially Inuit people who strive to follow a traditional diet and lifestyle. Aboriginal peoples of the Far North have traditional diets that are the lowest in carbohydrates and the highest in fats and protein of any other diets in the world. For millennia, with minimal and often no access to plant-based foods for months at a time, Inuit and other northern Aboriginal peoples obtained all the nutrients that are essential for healthy functioning. Today, with the increased encroachment of foods from non-Aboriginal society in the south and the erosion of traditional practices, northern Aboriginal peoples

are experiencing the same unhealthy conditions as those faced by modern native Hawaiians. In response to this situation, many Aboriginal peoples—not only in the Far North, but throughout North America—are returning to their dietary traditions, as well as to their cultural and social traditions (see Figure 6.31).

33 Describe the effect of returning to a traditional diet on the health of Aboriginal peoples.

Section 6.3 Summary

• Ulcers are caused when the walls of the digestive tract, usually in the stomach, are irritated by gastric secretions.
• Inflammatory bowel disease is the general name for a painful group of digestive disorders that can affect the digestive tract anywhere from the mouth to the anus.
• Hepatitis and cirrhosis are two major disorders of the associated digestive organs.
• Anorexia nervosa is a serious eating disorder, in which people starve themselves. Obesity which is also dangerous, results when people take in too much food and exceed a healthy weight.

BiologyFile

Web Link

Processed foods, a common feature of modern diets, often contain additives. These chemicals are put into food to preserve it, enhance its flavour, or improve its colour. The national government ensures the safety of these products. However, there is still much controversy over whether they can harm people.

www.albertabiology.ca
WWW

Thought Lab 6.3 Enzymes and Diet

Target Skills

Evaluating the role of technology to solve problems that involve dietary choices

Identifying and **evaluating** enzyme-related technologies and the problems they are developed to solve

In the 1960s, an American named Ann Wigmore spearheaded a dietary movement called "Living Foods." She based her ideas on her belief that cooked foods cause most mental and physical illnesses, because many proteins and enzymes are destroyed during the cooking process. The diet she recommended was a vegetarian, raw-food diet.

Wigmore's philosophy found an appreciative audience in North America. Bookstores carry many raw-food diet cookbooks, restaurateurs have set up cafes serving raw foods, and many alternative health-care practitioners recommend raw-food diets to help patients lose weight and prevent disease. The raw-food diet has also been extended to pets. Some veterinarians, noting the frequency of certain diseases in domestic animals—especially cats and dogs—suggest that ill health is the result of insufficient access to raw foods. As a result, some people have switched their pets to the BARF diet. (BARF stands for "Biologically Appropriate Raw Food" or "Bones and Raw Food," depending on who you consult.) The reasoning is that dogs and cats eat raw foods in the wild, and only raw foods produce the anti-bacterial enzymes in the gut and mouth that domestic animals need to be healthy.

Skeptics point out that people in many cultures have been eating cooked foods for centuries. They further suggest that although people do need enzymes to digest food, the cells make enzymes for this purpose. Some veterinarians also dismiss the need for pets to eat raw foods, saying that pets have become accustomed to a "domestic" diet and would not function well on a "wild" diet.

Procedure

1. Find out more about the Living Foods diet. Research Web archives and dietary journals. If possible, interview dietitians or health-care providers. Summarize the main concepts behind this diet. **ICT**

2. Investigate a specific food and the enzymes it contains to determine whether there would be any benefits and dangers associated with eating this food raw rather than cooked. Possible foods to investigate include pineapples, tomatoes, soybeans, broccoli, and raw meats and fish.

Analysis

1. Using your understanding of the properties and functions of enzymes and the process of digestion, review what you learned in your research. Prepare a report to answer these questions:
   - Is a diet of raw foods healthy?
   - Is such a diet healthy for all people?
   - Is such a diet healthy for dogs and cats?

Extension

2. Research enzymes that have medical and industrial applications. Choose one application that interests you, and research it further. Some examples include the treatment of Alzheimer's disease and Chronic Fatigue Syndrome with NADH, DNA fingerprinting, prodrugs, nutraceuticals, and synthetic oligosaccharides.

Section 6.3 Review

1. **a)** List at least two factors that can cause the formation of an ulcer.

   b) Describe what an ulcer is, and identify two technologies that may be used to treat it.

2. Compare and contrast Crohn's disease and colitis. Identify at least three treatments for these inflammatory bowel diseases.

3. Explain why diseases that affect the liver pose serious health risks.

4. Explain why anorexia nervosa and obesity are more than simple physiological conditions. Discuss the impact of this on options for treatment.

Use the following information to answer the next question.

Pancreatitis

Pancreatitis is an inflammation of the pancreas. The pancreas is a large gland behind the stomach and close to the duodenum. Normally, digestive enzymes produced in the pancreas do not become active until they reach the small intestine, where they begin digesting food. Pancreatitis develops when the digestive enzymes become active inside the pancreas. Chronic pancreatitis occurs when digestive enzymes attack and destroy the pancreas and nearby tissues, causing scarring and pain.

5. Explain why a person with pancreatitis would have difficulty digesting carbohydrates, lipids, and proteins.

The human body takes in matter from the environment in the form of food and water. The human digestive system processes the food and water in order to obtain the macromolecules it needs for survival.

Food passes through the digestive tract—the mouth, pharynx, esophagus, stomach, small intestine, and large intestine—during physical digestion. The accessory organs—the salivary glands, liver, gall bladder, and pancreas—supply chemicals that also contribute to the digestion of food as it passes through the digestive tract. The stomach supplies chemicals to aid digestion as well as generating physical contractions to physically break down food. The food is eventually liquefied into soluble units that can pass through cell membranes for transport via the circulatory system to all the cells in the body. The waste materials from the digestive process leave the body via the large intestine.

The nutrients that food supplies include carbohydrates, lipids (fats), protein, and nucleic acids. Carbohydrates and lipids are broken down to supply energy; lipids also supply material for the cell membranes. Proteins are more structurally and functionally diverse than carbohydrates and lipids. They assist in transport, immunity, and muscle action and are used to make up most cellular structures. Nucleic acids direct growth and development. Enzymes speed up chemical reactions, particularly for the production of energy. Vitamins and minerals are organic and inorganic substances that enable chemical reactions to occur and aid in tissue development and growth and immunity. All of these substances are needed by a healthy, functional human body.

Disorders of the digestive system and its accessory organs include ulcers, inflammatory bowel disease, hepatitis, cirrhosis, and gallstones. All disorders that affect digestion, including eating disorders, can seriously damage overall health by depriving the body cells of the nutrients they need to survive.

Chapter 6 Graphic Organizer

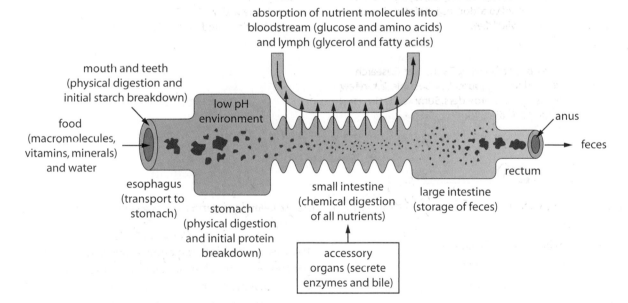

Understanding Concepts

1. Compare the dehydration synthesis of maltose to the hydrolysis reaction of this macromolecule.

2. What is a peptide bond? Use a diagram to illustrate the dehydration synthesis for the formation of a dipeptide.

3. Describe why some amino acids are classed as essential amino acids.

4. Use examples to distinguish a monosaccharide from a disaccharide and a polysaccharide.

5. Describe the function of proteins in the human body.

6. Explain the following statement. "The stomach is an organ in which both physical digestion and chemical digestion takes place."

7. Use a flow chart to summarize the chemical digestion of the following macromolecules. Include the enzymes (or group of enzymes) that would be involved in this process.
   a) starch
   b) protein
   c) fat

8. Explain the role of the liver in the physical digestion of fats and describe the importance of this process.

9. Identify the approximate pH of fluids in the stomach and explain the importance of having this pH level as far as chemical digestion is concerned.

10. Use a flow chart to illustrate the negative feedback mechanism that controls the secretion of the hormone gastrin.

11. Identify each organ shown in the diagram below and list the digestive process(es) (physical digestion, chemical digestion, or absorption) that takes place in each.

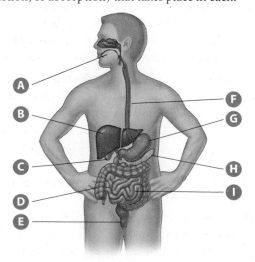

12. Summarize the following disorders of the digestive system.
   a) inflammatory bowel disease
   b) cirrhosis
   c) ulcer

Applying Concepts

13. After playing in the dirt, a child sticks her fingers in her mouth and ingests a significant number of bacteria but doesn't get sick. Explain how the digestive system protected this youngster from these potentially toxic bacteria.

14. Draw a concept map or other graphic organizer that summarizes the relationship between the organs of the digestive tract and the accessory organs.

Use the following diagram to answer the next two questions.

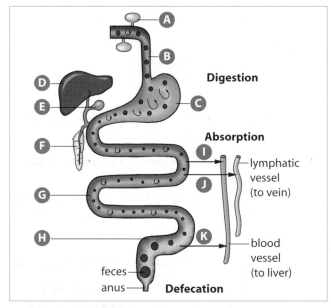

15. Copy the following chart into your notebook and fill in the blanks. The first one has been done for you.

Label	Structure	Secretion(s)	Function of each Secretion
A	salivary glands	• salivary amylase • saliva	• enzyme that contributes to the digestion of starch • lubricates the inside of the mouth to assist in swallowing
B			
C			
D			
F			
G			

16. Identify the substances on the diagram indicated by the arrows labelled (i), (j), and (k).

17. Sketch and label a line graph (including labels for the axes) that compares the optimal environmental pH for the digestive action of the enzymes pepsin and trypsin. Based on this information, infer the organs where each enzyme functions.

Use the following information to answer the next two questions.

Statistics Canada collected data on the obesity rates of Canadians in 1978 and again in 2004. The obesity rates were calculated using the body mass index (BMI), which is calculated by dividing mass in kilograms by height in metres squared. The table below shows representative data from these two studies.

Age Group	Obesity Rate 1978 (%)	Obesity Rate 2004 (%)
12–17	3	9
25–34	9	21
75+	11	24

18. Use spreadsheet software and a computer to create a bar graph of this data. **ICT**

19. a) Interpret what is happening to the obesity rate for each age group.
  b) Infer three possible reasons for the changing obesity rates for each age group in this sample.

Making Connections

Use the following information to answer the next two questions.

Alcoholism is a disease marked by, among other things, the inability to control drinking. Excessive consumption of alcoholic beverages can lead to other diseases such as cirrhosis of the liver. If the cirrhosis progresses too far, the only treatment is a costly liver transplant. Livers for transplant are in very short supply and may also be damaged if the recipients continue to drink alcohol. Many individuals believe that these potential recipients should not be eligible for a liver transplant.

20. List the ethical concerns of offering organ transplants to people who have an underlying medical condition that jeopardizes the chance of a successful outcome.

21. You have been asked to respond to the point of view provided in the textbox above. What are your recommendations?

Use the following information to answer the next two questions.

Acute cholecystitis is a sudden inflammation of the gallbladder that causes severe abdominal pain. In 90 percent of cases, acute cholecystitis is caused by gallstones, which obstruct the duct leading from the gallbladder to the common bile duct (which drains into the intestine). The trapped bile becomes concentrated and causes irritation and pressure buildup in the gallbladder. This can lead to bacterial infection and perforation. Gall bladder attacks may follow a large or fatty meal. The main symptom is abdominal pain—particularly after a fatty meal—that is located on the upper right side of the abdomen. Occasionally, nausea and vomiting or fever may occur. Although cholecystitis may clear up on its own, surgery to remove the gallbladder (cholecystectomy) is usually needed when inflammation persists or recurs.

22. Explain why gall bladder attacks usually follow a large or fatty meal.

23. How would having a cholecystectomy change your diet? Explain.

24. Meal X consists mainly of simple carbohydrates with some proteins. Meal Y consists mainly of complex carbohydrates with some proteins. Predict the blood glucose levels you would expect to find right after eating each meal. Explain your prediction.

Use the following information to answer the next question.

Gastric bypass surgery is the treatment of last resort for those who suffer from severe obesity. Gastrointestinal surgery is probably the best option for those who have been unable to lose weight by the traditional methods of dieting and exercise and can have great results. People who can be considered for surgery are those who are severely obese (i.e., with a body mass index of 40 or more) or people who are obese (with a BMI of between 35–40) who also have a significant disease (such as diabetes or high blood pressure) that could be improved if they lost weight.

There are two main types of digestive tract surgery: restrictive surgery (stomach stapling) in which the stomach walls are stapled together to create a small stomach pouch, and malabsorptive surgery, which involves shortening the overall length of the digestive tract.

25. Explain, in terms of specific digestive organs and processes, how:
  a) restrictive surgery (stomach stapling) would help an obese person lose weight
  b) malabsorptive surgery would help an obese person lose weight

The Respiratory System

Chapter Concepts

7.1 Structures of the Respiratory System

- The upper respiratory tract filters, warms, and moistens oxygen-containing air, and channels it into the lungs.

- The lower respiratory tract is made up of specialized structures that exchange oxygen for carbon dioxide in the bloodstream.

7.2 Breathing and Respiration

- Humans ventilate their lungs by the mechanism of breathing, which involves inspiration and expiration.

- The volume of air that is taken into the lungs can increase if the need for oxygen increases, such as during exercise.

- External respiration takes place in the lungs, between the air in the alveoli and the blood in the capillaries.

- Internal respiration takes place between the blood in the capillaries and tissue cells.

- Gas exchange occurs through the processes of simple diffusion and facilitated diffusion.

7.3 Respiratory Health

- Some disorders are specific to the respiratory system. Technologies are available to treat respiratory disorders, but they may not be able to restore the respiratory system to optimal health.

- Smoking causes respiratory diseases. Technologies can help some symptoms of smoking, but many symptoms are untreatable.

Mount Everest is the highest mountain on Earth. Each year, hundreds of people brave the extreme conditions of Mount Everest in an attempt to climb it. At 8850 m above sea level, the summit of Mount Everest poses a particular challenge to those who reach it— breathing! While oxygen and other gases are present in the same proportions as at lower elevations, the air pressure is much lower. As a result, gas particles are spread much farther apart and climbers cannot draw enough oxygen into their lungs when they breathe. By wearing oxygen masks, climbers can get enough oxygen to stay alive as they near the summit. Without this technology, climbers would become confused and soon lose consciousness. Oxygen is so important to life that even minutes without it can lead to brain damage and death.

Modelling Your Lungs

Your lungs work like a balloon. They expand and deflate with air, just like a balloon does. There is one difference, however, between how your lungs and a balloon work—a balloon fills with air when air is pushed in from the outside. If your lungs were like this, you would need an outside pump to push the air in. So, how do your lungs fill with air?

Procedure

1. Examine the model of human lungs shown in the diagram. With a partner or in a small group, share your ideas about how this model could work to cause the balloons to inflate.

2. If possible, obtain materials to build this model, or a similar model of human lungs, to test your ideas.

Analysis

1. Describe what happens to the balloons as the volume of air inside the container changes.

2. Would the model work (that is, would the balloons inflate) if the system were not airtight? Justify your answer.

3. Sketch a flowchart to show how air moves in and out of the balloons. Begin with the rubber membrane expanding.

- rubber stopper
- air-tight chamber
- glass tubing
- balloons
- bell jar
- rubber membrane
- handle to pull rubber membrane down

Magnification: 280 ×

The respiratory system delivers oxygen in the air you breathe to these delicate-looking tissues of the lungs. Why is oxygen essential to life?

Structures of the Respiratory System

Figure 7.1 When the warm air from your lungs meets the cold air outside your body, water droplets in your breath condense and form a visible cloud.

As you move about on Earth's surface, you wade through a colourless mixture of nitrogen, oxygen, carbon dioxide, and other gases. If you are like most people, you probably tend not to notice the air surrounding you because you cannot usually see any physical evidence that it exists. Figure 7.1 shows one situation in which you can see evidence of the invisible ocean of air that envelopes Earth.

The oxygen in air is vital to survival because it is needed to carry out cellular respiration, the process that produces the energy used to fuel all cell functions. Cellular respiration also produces carbon dioxide, and each cell must rid itself of this waste gas. The main function of the human **respiratory system**, therefore, is to ensure that oxygen is brought to each cell in the body and that carbon dioxide can leave each cell and be removed from the body. Respiration is the general term that is used to describe this overall process.

There are two main requirements for respiration. First, the surface area, or respiratory surface, must be large enough for the exchange of oxygen and carbon dioxide to occur at fast enough rates to meet the body's needs. Second, respiration must take place in a moist environment, so that the oxygen and carbon dioxide are dissolved in water. As summarized below, there are several stages in human respiration, and each stage has specialized structures to facilitate it. You will explore these stages in greater detail over the course of this chapter.

Stages in Respiration

- *Breathing* involves two basic processes: inspiration (breathing in, or inhaling) and expiration (breathing out, or exhaling). Inspiration moves air from the external environment to the lungs inside the body. Expiration moves air from the lungs back to the external environment.

- *External respiration* is the exchange of oxygen and carbon dioxide between the air and the blood.

- *Internal respiration* is the exchange of oxygen and carbon dioxide between the body's tissue cells and the blood.

- *Cellular respiration*, as you know from Chapter 5, is the series of energy-releasing chemical reactions that take place inside the cells. Cellular respiration is the final stage in respiration. It is the sole means of providing energy for all cellular activities, and it helps the body maintain homeostasis.

---

1. What is the main function of the human respiratory system?

2. How is external respiration different from internal respiration?

The Respiratory Tract

The lungs are the principal organs of respiration. The lungs are located deep within the body, where they are protected by the bone and muscular structure of the thoracic (chest) cavity. (The word "thoracic" comes from a Greek word meaning "chest plate," thus referring to the protective covering that warriors used in battle.) Because the lungs are located deep within the body, a suitable passageway is necessary for air to move from the external environment to the respiratory surface inside the body. This passageway is called the respiratory tract. As you can see in Figure 7.2, the respiratory tract consists of several structures and extends from the nose to the lungs. Air moves through the passageways of the upper and lower respiratory tract on its journey toward external respiration.

The Upper Respiratory Tract

Air begins its journey into the respiratory system by passing into the nose through the paired nostrils. Air can also enter through the mouth, especially if breathing is rapid, as it is during exercise. The **nasal passages** in the upper respiratory tract serve to warm, moisten, and clean the incoming air. They are lined with ciliated cells, like those shown in Figure 7.3. Other cells secrete mucus, which cleans the air by trapping foreign particles, such as dust and bacteria. The action of the ciliated cells moves the foreign particles back up into the nose and throat. The foreign particles can then be expelled by coughing or sneezing.

Very thin bones, called turbinate bones, project into the nasal cavity. These bones serve an important function by increasing the surface area of the nasal passages. They are covered in cilia, which

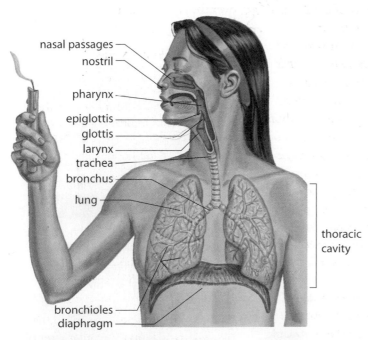

nasal passages
nostril
pharynx
epiglottis
glottis
larynx
trachea
bronchus
lung
bronchioles
diaphragm
thoracic cavity

Figure 7.2 The structures of the respiratory tract provide a passageway for air to move from the external environment to deep within the lungs, where external respiration (gas exchange) occurs.

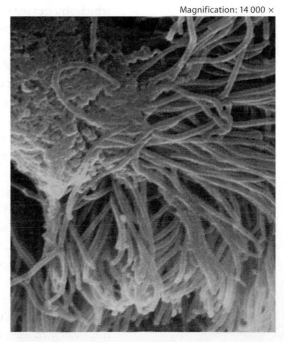

Magnification: 14 000 ×

Figure 7.3 Ciliated cells, like the ones shown here, line the interior of the nasal passages and upper respiratory tract.

The curved shape of the turbinate bones causes the air that enters the nasal passages to churn and circulate before it moves into the throat (pharynx). The name of these bones comes from the Latin word *turbinatus*, which means "like a spinning top." The English word "turbine" also comes from this Latin word.

Biology File

Web Link
Respiration is studied in biological science, but the mechanics of breathing are governed by the laws of physical science. What are these laws? What other phenomena do they describe in the natural world and in technology?

www.albertabiology.ca
WWW

catch and remove particles in the air. The turbinate bones, and the rest of the lining of the nasal passages, are covered with a thin membrane that secretes mucus and is well-supplied with blood vessels. The heat from the blood warms the air as it passes through, and the mucus moistens the air. Both the warming and the moistening of the air are necessary to protect the delicate structures that are found in the lower respiratory tract.

The **pharynx**, commonly known as the throat, is the passageway for air into the respiratory system, as well as the passageway for food and water into the digestive system. The **epiglottis** is a flap of cartilage that lies behind the tongue and in front of the larynx. The epiglottis closes over the opening to the trachea, the **glottis**, when a person swallows. This prevents food and drink from entering the trachea and passing into the bronchi of the lungs. When the epiglottis is at rest, it is upright and allows air to pass unobstructed into the lower respiratory tract.

The **larynx**, or voice box, is made from cartilage and contains the vocal cords. (Cartilage is a tough and firm connective tissue.) When you breathe normally, there is a large gap between the vocal cords. When you speak, however, the muscles around the larynx contract and the vocal cords are drawn together. Air passes through this narrower space, causing the vocal cords to vibrate and make a sound. The pitch (highness or lowness) of the sound changes, depending on how long the vocal cords are. Longer cords create a lower sound, and shorter cords create a higher sound. Because men generally have longer vocal cords than women, men tend to have lower-pitched voices and women tend to have higher-pitched voices. During puberty, the larynx and vocal cords grow very quickly in males. This can cause their voices to "break" (fluctuate in pitch) occasionally, until the cords finish growing.

After passing through the larynx, air moves down the flexible tube of the trachea, also known as the windpipe. The trachea is strengthened by semicircular, cartilaginous arches that prevent it from collapsing. The open part of the semicircle faces the esophagus and allows the esophagus to expand when food is being swallowed.

• • •

③ Identify the structures that make up the upper respiratory tract.

④ Describe the roles of mucus and cilia in the upper respiratory tract.

• • •

The Lower Respiratory Tract
The trachea branches into two smaller passageways, called **bronchi** (singular: bronchus), that enter the right and left lungs. Each bronchus subdivides many times to create a branching network of smaller and finer tubes, called **bronchioles**, within each lung. The bronchi contain C-shaped cartilaginous rings that surround and are part of the bronchus wall. They are stacked one on the next, running the length of the bronchus and providing support. Bronchioles do not have C rings. Both the bronchi and bronchioles are lined with cilia and mucus-producing cells, just as in the upper respiratory tract. The mucus captures foreign particles, such as microscopic pollutants and pathogens. The cilia move the foreign particles up into the upper respiratory tract. From there, the foreign particles can be ejected from the body by coughing or sneezing, or they can be swallowed.

Each lung is divided into distinct regions called lobes. The right lung has three lobes, and the left lung has only two, leaving space for the heart. Each lobe is made up of many lobules that extend from each bronchiole.

Each lung is surrounded by a thin, double-layered membrane called the **pleural membrane**. The outer layer of this membrane attaches to the inside of the chest wall. The inner layer of the membrane attaches to the lung. Fluid fills the space between these two membrane layers so that they adhere to each other in the same way that a film of water can cause two plates to stick together. The pleural membrane layers serve as a means for connecting the lungs to the thoracic cavity, enabling them to expand and contract with the movement of the chest.

Each bronchiole ends in a cluster of tiny sacs called **alveoli** (singular: alveolus). It is within these alveoli that the actual exchange of gases takes place during external respiration. Each alveolus is enclosed by a membrane called the alveolar wall. The alveolar wall is one cell thick and is surrounded by a network of tiny capillaries, as shown in Figure 7.4.

Capillaries are tiny blood vessels— their walls are also one-cell thick—that link the arteries with the veins. (Arteries carry oxygen-rich blood from the heart to the body tissues. Veins carry oxygen-poor blood from the body tissues back to the heart.) Where capillaries surround the alveoli, carbon dioxide dissolved in the blood is exchanged for oxygen. You

will learn more about this important relationship between the alveoli of the respiratory system and the capillaries of the blood circulation system in the next section.

The arrangement of the bronchioles and alveoli is kept in a relatively permanent position by elastic connective tissue that fills the space between them. As well, the alveoli are lined with a lubricating film that helps to keep them from collapsing and prevents their sides from sticking together and closing.

• • •

5 Some biologists refer to the system of bronchi and bronchioles as the "bronchial tree." Why is this a suitable metaphor?

• • •

Section 7.1 Summary

• The respiratory tract extends from the nose to the lungs. It is a passageway for air to move from the outside environment into the lungs, where gas exchange occurs. It is lined with mucus-producing cells and ciliated

BiologyFile

FYI
The branching network that leads into and makes up the lungs is quite staggering to imagine. The 2 bronchi branch into 4 bronchioles, and then into 8, 16, 32, and so on, up to 60 000 bronchioles. The bronchioles themselves branch off into about 500 000 even smaller branches. *These* branches lead to approximately 8 million clusters of alveoli, containing a total of about 300 million alveoli in one pair of lungs.

Figure 7.4 Each bronchiole ends in several clusters of alveoli. Surrounding each alveolus is a fine network of capillaries from the circulatory system. Gas exchange occurs between the blood in the capillaries and the air in the alveolus, so that blood leaving the lungs has a high oxygen content.

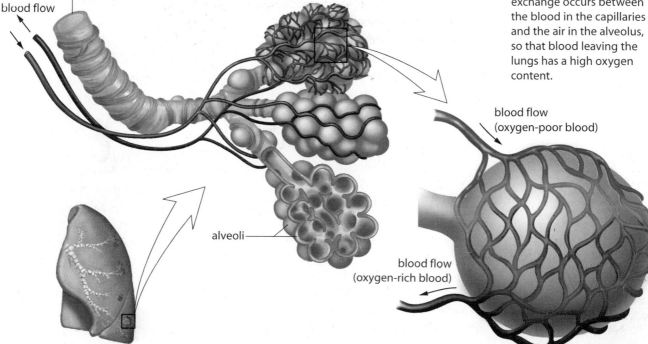

bronchiole

blood flow

alveoli

blood flow
(oxygen-poor blood)

blood flow
(oxygen-rich blood)

capillary network of one alveolus

cells that work together to capture foreign particles and move them out of the respiratory system.

- Respiration is the overall process that provides oxygen to tissue cells and removes carbon dioxide from the body. It is made up of four distinct stages: breathing, external respiration, internal respiration, and cellular respiration.

- The upper respiratory tract contains the nasal passages, pharynx, glottis, epiglottis, larynx, and trachea. It warms, moistens, and cleans the incoming air.
- The lower respiratory tract contains the bronchi, bronchioles, and alveoli that make up the lungs. The lungs are covered by a two-layer pleural membrane.

Section 7.1 | Review

1. Summarize the functions of the respiratory system.

2. Identify the two main requirements for respiration.

3. Define or describe the following stages in respiration:
   a) breathing
   b) external respiration
   c) internal respiration
   d) cellular respiration

4. Outline, in a chart or table, the different structures in the upper respiratory tract that alter the properties of air in preparation for gas exchange in the lungs. Explain how each structure modifies the air.

5. Explain the purpose of the epiglottis. Describe what would happen if the epiglottis did not function properly.

6. Some cough medicines work by inhibiting the production of mucus in the upper respiratory tract. Infer possible side effects of these medications.

7. Winter air can be very cold and dry. How would the air entering your lungs be different if you breathed through your mouth instead of your nose while walking on a cold winter day?

8. Illustrate, using a flowchart, the path that air would take from the nose to the alveoli.

9. In a medical emergency, a physician may insert a tube down a person's trachea to help the person breathe. Infer why the person would be unable to talk during this procedure.

10. Describe the pleural membranes and explain their function.

11. Explain why the trachea and bronchioles contain cartilaginous arches.

12. Sketch the following diagram into your notebook. Identify the structures indicated by the letters A to K on this diagram.

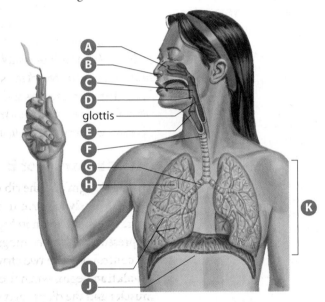

13. Sketch the following diagram into your notebook. Label the diagram and identify where gas exchange occurs.

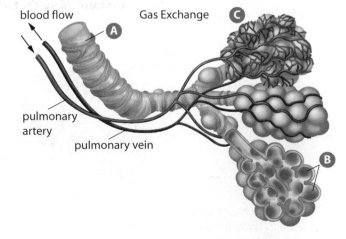

14. Identify two characteristics of the alveoli that facilitate gas exchange and infer their significance for this process.

Breathing and Respiration

Section Outcomes

In this section, you will
- **explain** the mechanics of breathing
- **explain** how gases are exchanged between the human respiratory system and the external environment
- **perform** an experiment to determine your respiratory volume
- **perform** an experiment to examine factors that affect the rate of respiration

Key Terms

diaphragm
rib muscles
inhalation
exhalation
spirograph
tidal volume
inspiratory reserve volume
expiratory reserve volume
vital capacity
residual volume
external respiration
internal respiration

The respiratory system is an elegant and specialized system that provides a passageway for air to move from the external environment to the interior of the body, where gas exchange occurs. Air does not just flow into and out of the lungs on its own, however. Two muscular structures—the diaphragm and the rib muscles—control the air pressure inside the lungs, causing air to move into and out of the lungs. The **diaphragm** is a dome-shaped layer of muscle that separates the region of the lungs (thoracic cavity) from the region of the stomach and liver (abdominal cavity). The **rib muscles**, or intercostal muscles, are found between the ribs and along the ventral (inside) surface of the ribs. The rib muscles extend down to the diaphragm.

The Mechanics of Breathing

The diaphragm and the rib muscles work simultaneously to move air into and out of the lungs, as shown in Figure 7.5. The air pressure within the lungs is under the control of these two structures. **Inhalation** begins when the external rib muscles and the diaphragm contract. This action expands the rib cage upward and outward, and the floor of the chest cavity downward. Since the thoracic

cavity is airtight, its volume increases. The increase in volume means that the same amount of air is contained in a larger space. When the molecules of a gas are farther apart, as they are when the volume of the thoracic cavity increases, they exert less outward pressure. As a result, the air pressure in the thoracic cavity decreases.

The lungs are suspended in the thoracic cavity and are sensitive to changes in the air pressure of the cavity. As the air pressure in the cavity decreases, the walls of the lungs are drawn outward into the thoracic cavity and the lungs expand. This expansion causes the air pressure in the lungs to be lower than the air pressure in the external environment. Since air moves from regions of higher pressure to regions of lower pressure, air rushes into the lungs from the external environment.

The opposite muscle movements expel air from the lungs. **Exhalation** begins when the diaphragm and the rib muscles relax, reducing the volume of the thoracic cavity. As a result, the volume of the lungs decreases, the air pressure inside the lungs increases, and air moves from the lungs to the lower-pressure environment outside the body.

Figure 7.5 The mechanics of breathing

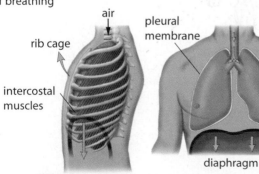

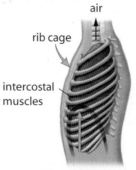

Rib cage moves up and out. Diaphragm contracts and moves down.

Pressure in lungs decreases, and air comes rushing in.

A **Inhalation** The intercostal muscles contract, lifting the rib cage up and out. At the same time, the diaphragm contracts and pulls downward. As the lungs expand, air moves in.

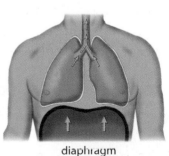

Rib cage moves down and in. Diaphragm relaxes and moves up.

Pressure in lungs increases, and air is pushed out.

B **Exhalation** The intercostal muscles relax, allowing the rib cage to return to its normal position. The diaphragm also moves upward, resuming its domed shape. As the lungs contract, air moves out.

BiologyFile

Try This
Normally, the pressure inside the lungs is greater than the pressure outside the lungs, or inside the pleura. This difference in pressure allows the lungs to inflate. If air collects between the two layers of the pleura because of an injury, the pressure outside the lung increases and causes the lung to "collapse." This condition is called a pneumothorax. Experiment with the lung model you made in the Launch Lab to see what happens if air enters the airtight apparatus that represents the thoracic cavity. Why would physicians insert a tube into the chest to "reinflate" the lung?

In other words, a change in air pressure causes air to move from an area of high pressure (the lungs) to an area of lower pressure (the external environment).

• • •

6 Outline briefly, in the form of a paragraph or diagram, the processes of inhalation and exhalation.

• • •

Respiratory Volume

Take a deep breath. How does this feel different from your normal breathing? Think about your breathing rate after you have physically exerted yourself in some way. It is probably faster that your normal breathing rate. Under normal circumstances, your regular breathing does not use the full capacity of your lungs. When your body needs more oxygen, however, the volume of air that is drawn into your lungs can increase. The graph in Figure 7.6, called a **spirograph**, represents the amount of air that moves into and out of the lungs with each breath. The terms that are used in a spirograph are described below.

• **Tidal volume** is the volume of air that is inhaled and exhaled in a normal breathing movement when the body is at rest.

• **Inspiratory reserve volume** is the additional volume of air that can be taken into the lungs, beyond a regular, or tidal, inhalation.

• **Expiratory reserve volume** is the additional volume of air that can be forced out of the lungs, beyond a regular, or tidal, inhalation.

• **Vital capacity**, or total lung volume capacity, is the total volume of gas that can be moved into or out of the lungs. It can be calculated as tidal volume + inspiratory reserve volume + expiratory reserve volume.

• **Residual volume** is the amount of gas that remains in the lungs and the passageways of the respiratory system even after a full exhalation. This gas never leaves the respiratory system; if it did, the lungs and respiratory passageways would collapse. The residual volume has little value for gas exchange because it is not exchanged with air from the external environment.

Gas Exchange and External Respiration

Respiration is a combination of two separate processes: external respiration and internal respiration. **External respiration** takes place in the lungs. During external respiration, gases are exchanged between the alveoli and the

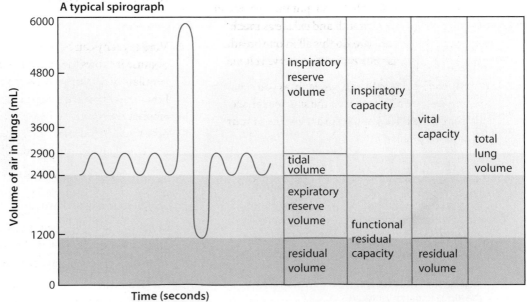

Figure 7.6 This graph shows typical values for human vital capacity: the maximum volume of air that can be moved into and out of the lungs during a single breath. The pattern of this graph is called a spirograph.

Measuring Respiratory Volumes

In this investigation, you will measure your respiratory volume using a device called a spirometer.

Question

How can you use a spirometer, which measures air as it is exhaled, to determine the volume of air you inhale in a normal breath and a deep breath?

Prediction

Predict what percentage of your vital capacity is represented by your tidal volume.

Safety Precautions

Do not inhale or exhale to the point of faintness.

Materials

- materials for recording data
- spirometer with disposable mouthpieces
- nose plug (optional)

Procedure

1. Set the spirometer gauge to zero, and insert a clean mouthpiece. If you are using a nose plug, put it on.

2. Begin by taking a few relaxed breaths. Then inhale normally, put the mouthpiece into your mouth, and exhale normally into the spirometer. Record the value as your *tidal volume*.

3. Reset the spirometer. Inhale and exhale normally. At the end of the normal exhalation, put the spirometer mouthpiece into your mouth and exhale as much as you can. Make sure you do this all in one breath. Record the value as your *expiratory reserve volume*.

4. Reset the spirometer. Inhale as deeply as you can, and then exhale normally into the spirometer. **Do not force the exhalation**. Record the value as your *inspiratory capacity*.

5. Calculate your *inspiratory reserve volume* by subtracting your tidal volume from your inspiratory capacity. Record your inspiratory reserve volume.

6. Calculate your *vital capacity* by adding your inspiratory reserve volume, expiratory reserve volume, and tidal volume. Record the value as your *calculated vital capacity*.

7. Reset the spirometer. Inhale as deeply as you can, and then exhale deeply into the spirometer, forcing out as much air as you can. Do this all in one breath. Record the value as your *recorded vital capacity*.

Analysis

1. Compare your calculated vital capacity with your recorded vital capacity. Explain any difference.

2. Compare your inspiratory reserve volume with your expiratory reserve volume. Explain any difference.

Conclusions

3. Can you use the spirometer to measure your total lung capacity? Explain.

4. How might an athlete use information about his or her vital capacity? Predict how respiratory volumes relate to athletic performance.

Extension

5. Compare your respiratory volumes with those of other students by creating a class data table. How much variation do you see? Are there patterns in this variation, such as differences between males and females, or differences based on height? What factors could contribute to differences in respiratory volumes? Design an experiment to test the effects of two of these factors.

Application

6. Vital capacity can be used to determine fitness, because it shows the extent to which individuals can ventilate their lung surface. Do research to determine how vital capacity is affected in two different respiratory disorders. Prepare a brief report about how these disorders affect the respiratory system and how they can be treated. **ICT**

7. A ventilator is a piece of medical equipment that maintains respiratory movements in a person who is unable to breathe. Consider a young, otherwise healthy person who is paralyzed as a result of a car crash. Would it be a good idea to adjust a ventilator to maximize the volume of air inhaled and exhaled? Explain.

blood in the capillaries. The walls of the alveoli and the capillaries are each one cell thick, which allows gases to diffuse through their cell membranes (see Figure 7.7). Recall that diffusion is the movement of molecules from a region of high concentration to a region of lower concentration. The air that enters the alveoli after inhalation has a higher concentration of oxygen than the blood in the capillaries next to the lungs. (The blood in the capillaries has had oxygen diffuse out of it into the tissue cells and has had carbon dioxide diffuse into it from the tissue cells.) As a result, oxygen diffuses out of the alveoli into the blood in the capillaries. Diffusion alone, however, is not always enough to transfer the necessary amount of oxygen to the blood. Approximately 30% of the oxygen transfer happens by facilitated diffusion. In facilitated diffusion, protein-based molecules in the wall of the alveoli facilitate diffusion by "carrying" oxygen across the cell membranes. This process does not require extra energy because the oxygen is still moving along the concentration gradient from an area of high concentration to an area of low concentration. Facilitated diffusion simply speeds up the gas exchange.

The blood in the capillaries has a higher concentration of carbon dioxide than the alveoli because it is returning from the body tissues. Thus, the carbon dioxide diffuses into the alveoli from the capillaries. The carbon dioxide is then, as you know, exhaled into the air.

Once oxygen and carbon dioxide have been exchanged between the capillaries and alveoli, the blood in the capillaries begins its journey back to the heart and then on to the tissue cells. There, it undergoes **internal respiration** and exchanges the oxygen for carbon dioxide once again.

In blood, oxygen and carbon dioxide are transported in different ways. Approximately 99 percent of the oxygen that reaches cells is carried by an oxygen-transporting molecule called hemoglobin, which is only in red blood cells. The rest is dissolved in the blood plasma.

Slightly less than one-quarter (23 percent) of carbon dioxide is carried in the blood by hemoglobin. Approximately 7 percent is carried in the plasma, and approximately 70 percent is dissolved and carried in the blood as bicarbonate ion (HCO_3^-). Carbonic acid (H_2CO_3) is formed in the blood when a carbon dioxide molecule (CO_2) reacts with a water molecule (H_2O). The carbonic acid quickly dissociates (breaks down) into a hydrogen ion (H^+) and a bicarbonate ion. This reaction occurs in the red blood cells. The H^+ then combines with hemoglobin, and the bicarbonate ions diffuse out of the red blood cells into the plasma, which is carried to the lungs. When the blood reaches the lungs, the whole process reverses to re-form carbon dioxide and water. The carbon dioxide then diffuses into the air in the alveoli and is exhaled.

• • •

7 What occurs during external respiration?

8 Briefly describe the process of gas exchange and the structures involved.

• • •

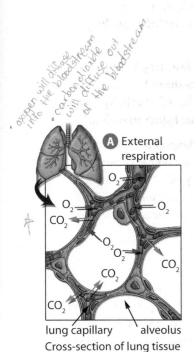

A External respiration

O_2
O_2 O_2
CO_2
$O_2 O_2$
CO_2
CO_2
CO_2

lung capillary   alveolus
Cross-section of lung tissue

B Internal respiration

O_2 CO_2
CO_2 CO_2
O_2
CO_2 O_2
O_2

muscle cell   tissue capillary
Cross-section of muscle tissue

Figure 7.7 External respiration (**A**) occurs between alveoli and the capillaries next to them. As blood moves away from the body tissues, it is oxygen-poor and carbon dioxide-rich. As it moves through the lung capillaries, oxygen from the air in the alveoli diffuses into the capillaries and carbon dioxide diffuses out of the blood. Internal respiration (**B**) occurs between the capillaries and the body tissues. Oxygen diffuses from the blood into the oxygen-poor tissues while carbon dioxide diffuses from the tissues into the blood.

Target Skills

Conducting investigations into relationships between and among observable variables with respect to the rate of respiration

Collecting, **communicating**, and **assessing** the validity of results, using appropriate terminology

Carbon Dioxide and the Rate of Respiration

When you exercise, the increase in your body activity triggers an increase in your rate of respiration. You might think your rate of respiration increases because your muscles are working hard and need more oxygen. Scientists have determined experimentally that the concentration of oxygen in the body is not the primary stimulus that affects the rate of respiration. Could the concentration of carbon dioxide, the other gas exchanged during respiration, be the primary stimulus? How could you test this idea?

Question

How can the level of carbon dioxide in the body be altered?

Prediction

Predict what will happen if the level of carbon dioxide in the body is increased.

Safety Precautions

- Students with respiratory and heart disorders should not be subjects in this experiment.

- Do not hold your breath or hyperventilate long enough to cause faintness. At the first sign of faintness or dizziness, stop the experiment and resume normal breathing.

- Do not substitute a plastic bag for the paper bag in this investigation. Do not breathe into a paper bag for any longer than 15 seconds, because carbon dioxide can build up very quickly in the bloodstream. At the first sign of distress, remove the paper bag immediately and take several calm, natural breaths.

Materials

- paper bag
- stopwatch
- materials for recording data

Procedure

1. Prepare a data table like the one shown below.

2. Work with a partner. Count the number of breaths your partner takes while resting in a sitting position for 3 min. Divide the number of breaths by 3 to calculate the number of breaths per minute. Record this value under "Resting" in your data table.

3. Have your partner hold her or his breath for about 45 s. Then count the number of breaths that she or he takes in the next 3 min. Divide the number of breaths by 3, and record this value under "After holding breath" in your data table.

4. Ask your partner to take 10 fast, deep breaths. Then count the number of breaths she or he takes in the next 3 min. Divide the number of breaths by 3, and record this value under "After hyperventilating."

5. Ask your partner to place a large paper bag over her or his mouth. Then count the number of breaths she or he takes in the next 15 s. Multiply the number of breaths by 4, and record this value under "While breathing into a paper bag" in your data table.

6. Switch roles, and repeat steps 2 to 5.

Analysis

1. What effect did each condition—holding your breath, hyperventilating, and breathing into a paper bag—have on the level of oxygen and carbon dioxide in your body? Explain your results, with reference to the concentration of respiratory gases.

Conclusion

2. Based on your observations, describe the role of carbon dioxide in breathing.

Extension

3. Compare your results with the results of other students. What similarities and differences can you identify? Provide a hypothesis to account for the differences. Write a procedure to test your hypothesis.

Condition	Resting	After holding breath	After hyperventilating	While breathing into paper bag
Rate of respiration (in breaths per minute)				

Section 7.2 Summary

- Two muscular structures, the diaphragm and the rib muscles, work together to move air into and out of the lungs.
- The volume of air in your lungs can change depending on how much oxygen you need and your level of activity.
- External respiration takes place in the lungs. Internal respiration occurs in the tissues. Oxygen and carbon dioxide are exchanged between the alveoli and the capillaries by the processes of passive and facilitated diffusion. Oxygen (O_2) diffuses into the blood from the alveoli, and carbon dioxide (CO_2) diffuses out of the blood into the alveoli.
- Oxygen is carried in the blood bound to hemoglobin in red blood cells. Most carbon dioxide is carried as bicarbonate dissolved in blood plasma.

Section 7.2 | Review

1. Explain how the two basic requirements for gas exchange identified in Section 7.1 are met by the structure of the lungs.

2. Describe the role of the diaphragm in inhalation and exhalation.

3. Use the following diagram to explain the mechanics of breathing.

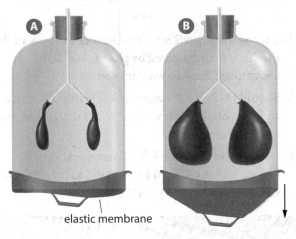

elastic membrane

4. a) Describe the purpose of a spirograph.

   b) Sketch an example of a spirograph. Include the following terms: tidal volume, inspiratory reserve volume, expiratory reserve volume, vital capacity, and residual volume.

   c) Describe or define all of the volumes of air that you represented on your sketch.

5. a) Identify the three "volumes" of air that make up an individual's vital capacity.

   b) Explain the purpose of the residual volume of air in the lungs.

6. Sketch two diagrams in your notebook that compare external respiration with internal respiration. Describe these two processes and discuss the role of diffusion and facilitated transport in gas exchange.

7. Describe the role of hemoglobin and bicarbonate ions in gas exchange.

8. In an automobile accident, the diaphragm of a passenger is punctured. How would this affect the person's ability to breathe?

Use the following information to answer the next two questions.

> **Pneumothorax**
>
> A pneumothorax is commonly known as a collapsed lung. Normally, the outer surface of the lung sits next to the inner surface of the chest wall. The lung and the chest wall are covered by thin membranes called pleura. A collapsed lung occurs when air escapes from the lungs or leaks through the chest wall and enters the space between the two membranes (pleural cavity). As air builds up, it causes the nearby lung to collapse. A collapsed lung can result from blunt force trauma, rib fractures, or a foreign object entering through the thoracic cavity and into the lung.

9. Explain how a pneumothorax would impair gas exchange in the collapsed lung.

Use the additional information to answer the next question.

> When this is the case in larger mammals, the lung will sometimes reinflate after the air is evacuated by inserting a needle or a chest tube into the thoracic cavity.

10. Why would removing the air from the thoracic cavity help the lung to reinflate?

11. You may have experienced a situation when a toddler gets upset and states emphatically that they are going to hold their breath until they get their way. Explain, in terms of the control of breathing, why most people can only hold their breath for less than a minute.

Traditional Healing in Modern Times

Humans have been treating ailments for millennia. Before universities and medical schools, a community's specialized knowledge about healing techniques and technologies was passed on orally and through apprenticeships with skilled healers. The teachings would include extensive knowledge about the most effective parts of local plants—leaves, flowers, or roots—and the best way to preserve materials and prepare and administer the treatments. Dried and ground roots or leaves, made into pastes and teas, are just two of the ways traditional medicines are prepared. Practitioners also need to know how to find and properly identify medicinal plants and, depending on the culture, offer appropriate prayers of thanks for them.

Examples of traditional remedies include:
- **white willow** (*salix species*) In use since Roman times, teas made from the bark of this tree contain salicin, which reduces fever. The synthetic form of salicin is called acetyl salicylic acid (brand name, Asprin™).
- **boswellia** (*Boswellia serrata*) The sap of this tree has been used as an anti-inflammatory since ancient times in India. The active ingredients are boswellic acids, which are considered to be effective herbal alternatives to nonsteroidal anti-inflammatory drugs (NSAIDs) for the treatment of arthritis.
- **Seneca snakeroot** (*Polygala senega*) Snakeroot contains a milky liquid that the Seneca First Nations used to treat snakebite, which is the source of its common name. Aboriginal people across North America have used the dried root for centuries as a decongestant and to loosen mucus in the lungs.
- **Pleurisy root** (*Asclepias tuberosa*) First Nations people used this powerful remedy to treat chest and upper respiratory problems, including colds, coughs, bronchitis, pneumonia, and pleurisy.

Dr. Malcolm King of the University of Alberta is a descendant of a long line of traditional native healers in the Six Nations confederacy and is a member of the Mississaugas of New Credit First Nation. He is also a research scientist and professor in the pulmonary division of the University of Alberta's department of medicine. He studies the flow of mucus in the lungs and other organs and the treatment of asthma, bronchitis, and cystic fibrosis. Dr. King's special area of interest is the use of traditional aboriginal remedies to treat illnesses related to the respiratory system.

Dr. King and his students have examined the use of rat root (*Acorus calamus*) to improve the excretion of mucus in the lungs and found it could be helpful in clearing lung infection. They have also tested extracts of licorice root (*Glycyrrhiza glabra*) in the lab, and Dr. King has used the extract to treat his own colds.

Dr. King's challenge is to find funding for his research. Natural products cannot be patented, and drug companies are therefore reluctant to invest in research. In addition, Dr. King feels that traditional native healers "would not be interested in sharing with drug companies."

• • •

1. Do you think traditional remedies are safer than the products manufactured by pharmaceutical companies? Explain your answer.

2. Should traditional remedies be scientifically tested and regulated the same way that manufactured drugs are? Why or why not?

3. Does anyone own traditional remedies? Do you think companies should be allowed to patent them? Give reasons to justify your opinion.

Cree elders boil the leaves of the Labrador tea plant (shown here) to make a drink loaded with vitamin C and helpful in the treatment of colds, sore throats, and insomnia. Too much of this remedy can be toxic, so the elder's knowledge of the correct dosage is vital to the health of the community.

Respiratory Health

BiologyFile

Like the digestive system, the respiratory system directly links the internal environment of the body with the external environment. The quality of both environments plays a key role in the health of the respiratory system. Changes in the external environment, as well as personal lifestyle choices, can have a significant impact on how well the respiratory system functions and, by extension, on how well the whole body functions.

Upper Respiratory Tract Infections

Infections of the upper respiratory tract are usually caused by viruses or bacteria. When the cause of an infection is bacterial, antibiotics are often used to treat it. How viral and bacterial infections develop, and how our bodies fight them, will be explored in the next chapter.

Tonsillitis

Tonsillitis is an infection of the tonsils, which are located in the pharynx. (Refer to Figure 7.2 for the location of the pharynx.) A viral infection, rather than a bacterial infection, is the more common cause of tonsillitis. The tonsils can be removed surgically if the infections are frequent and breathing is impaired. In the past, many children had their tonsils removed as a precaution, but this surgery is no longer as common. The tonsils help to prevent bacteria and other foreign pathogens from entering the body, so removing them can increase the number of infections later in life.

Laryngitis

Laryngitis is an inflammation of the larynx (see Figure 7.2). Recall that the larynx contains the vocal cords. The most common cause of laryngitis is a viral infection; allergies and over-straining of the voice can also lead to laryngitis. When the larynx is inflamed, the vocal cords are not able to vibrate as they normally do. This reduces the ability to speak in a normal voice or even to speak at all. Symptoms of laryngitis include a sore throat and hoarseness.

> **9** Which pathogens, bacteria or viruses, are most likely to cause a case of tonsillitis or laryngitis?

Lower Respiratory Tract Disorders

More than three million Canadians, of all ages, experience serious respiratory disorders in the lower respiratory tract. The primary causes of these respiratory disorders are infections, obstructive pulmonary disorders (OPD), and lung cancer. Figure 7.8 on the next page highlights some of the more common lower respiratory tract disorders.

Bronchitis

Bronchitis is a disorder that causes the bronchi to become inflamed and filled with mucus, which is expelled by coughing. Acute bronchitis is a short-term disorder that is caused by a bacterial infection and can be treated with antibiotics. Chronic bronchitis is a long-term disorder that is caused by regular exposure to irritants and foreign bodies. Because exposure to the irritants has been over a long period of time, the cilia are destroyed, so their cleansing action no longer occurs. This means that the bronchi become even more inflamed and infection is even more likely. The most common cause of chronic bronchitis is one that is preventable—cigarette smoking. There is no cure for chronic bronchitis. Treatment is aimed at reducing the symptoms and complications with medication and regular exercise. Along with the treatment, it is important to

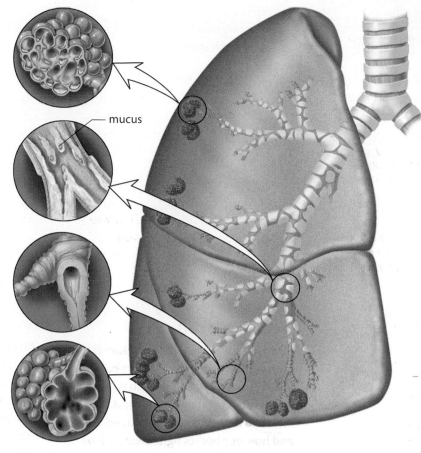

Pneumonia
Alveoli fill with thick fluid, making gas exchange difficult.

Bronchitis
Airways are inflamed due to infection (acute) or due to an irritant (chronic). Coughing brings up mucus.

mucus

Asthma
Airways are inflamed due to irritation, and bronchioles constrict due to muscle spasms.

Emphysema
Alveoli burst and fuse into enlarged air spaces. Surface area for gas exchange is reduced.

Figure 7.8 Several lower respiratory tract disorders are shown. Exposure to infectious pathogens and/or air pollutants, including cigarette and cigar smoke, often cause the disorders shown here.

avoid the causal irritant—which most often means quitting smoking.

Pneumonia

Pneumonia is a disease that occurs when the alveoli in the lungs become inflamed and fill with liquids. This interferes with gas exchange, and the body becomes starved for oxygen. There are two main types of pneumonia: lobular pneumonia and bronchial pneumonia. As shown in Figure 7.9, lobular pneumonia affects a lobe of the lung and bronchial pneumonia affects patches throughout both lungs.

There are several different causes of pneumonia. The main causes are bacterial infection and viral infection. Lobular pneumonia is caused by the bacterium *Streptococcus pneumoniae*. This bacterial infection can spread out of the lungs, via the bloodstream, and affect other tissues. There is a preventative vaccine, called the

pneumoncoccal vaccine, which provides long-term protection from the bacterium. You will learn more about vaccines and the immune system in Chapter 8.

Viral pneumonias are usually less severe than bacterial pneumonias, and they can be treated with anti-viral medications. Viral pneumonias may be followed, however, by a secondary bacterial infection, which must be treated separately with antibiotics or with preparations that have antibiotic properties. People who have AIDS often

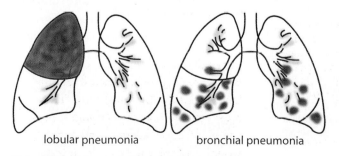

lobular pneumonia   bronchial pneumonia

Figure 7.9 The two main types of pneumonia

BiologyFile

Web Link

Asthma is the only major respiratory ailment that is increasing in the population. Approximately 20 years ago, 2.3 percent of Canadians over the age of 15 were diagnosed with asthma. Today, this figure has increased to more than 8 percent. The United States has seen more than a 60 percent increase in the diagnosis of asthma. What hypotheses do medical experts have to explain these dramatic increases?

www.albertabiology.ca
WWW

Figure 7.10A This device, called an inhaler, delivers medicine in aerosol form to provide relief for people who have emphysema. People who have asthma also use inhalers.

experience a rare type of bacterial pneumonia, which is hardly ever seen in people with strong immune systems.

Pleurisy

Pleurisy is a lung disorder that is caused by the swelling and irritation of the pleura, the membranes that surround the lungs. There are many different causes of pleurisy, including viral or bacterial infections, a blood clot in a lung, or cancer. The symptoms include a sharp stabbing pain in the chest, usually localized in one particular area. Treating pleurisy involves treating the cause of the swelling and irritation.

• • •

10 Why does bronchitis affect a person's ability to breathe properly?

11 Why does pneumonia affect a person's ability to breathe properly?

• • •

Emphysema

Emphysema is an obstructive respiratory disorder in which the walls of the alveoli break down and lose their elasticity. This reduces the surface area for gas exchange and causes oxygen shortages in the tissues. Exhaling becomes difficult because of the loss of elasticity, so breathing is laboured. Almost all cases of emphysema are caused by smoking. Emphysema is permanent and incurable, although medications that open up the bronchioles can help to improve breathing (Figure 7.10A). People who have emphysema often need to use a low-flow oxygen tank in order to breathe and acquire sufficient oxygen. A low-flow oxygen tank provides concentrations of oxygen that vary with the individual's rate of breathing. This type of supplemental oxygen system is called a variable performance system. A high-flow system, or fixed performance system, provides a constant concentration of oxygen that meets or exceeds the individual's needs.

Lung volume reduction surgery (LVRS) is an experimental surgery for the treatment of emphysema. Up to 30 percent of the most damaged tissue from each lung is removed. The goal is to have the healthy portions work more effectively once the damaged areas are removed, and thus become more efficient in their gas exchange. The effectiveness of LVRS is still uncertain.

Cystic Fibrosis

Cystic fibrosis is a serious genetic condition that affects the lungs. Cystic fibrosis is caused by an abnormal gene that disrupts the function of the cells lining the passageways of the lungs. When these cells do not function properly, the homeostatic balance of salt and water cannot be maintained, causing the thin mucus and liquid coating on the insides of the lungs to become very thick and sticky. The mucus in the lungs normally traps pathogens and then is expelled from the body by coughing. In people who have cystic fibrosis, the mucus is so thick that the pathogens are trapped but cannot be expelled. As a result, the lungs get repeated infections that reduce lung function, and the individual has trouble breathing.

Currently, cystic fibrosis is treated with medicines to thin the mucus and antibiotics to treat the lung infections. New treatments for cystic fibrosis are still being perfected. In one of these new treatments, gene therapy, an inhaler (Figure 7.10A) is used to spray healthy versions of the abnormal gene deep into the lungs. The healthy genes are able to correct the function of the cells lining the lungs and cause them to produce normal mucus.

Asthma

Asthma is a chronic obstructive lung disease that affects the bronchi and bronchioles, making breathing difficult or impossible because of reduced air flow. Asthma can develop at any age, and the effects vary from mild reactions to severe reactions that can cause death.

People with asthma have a constant inflammation in their airways and are extremely sensitive to some triggers, such as pollen, dust, cigarette smoke, and other air pollutants. These triggers can cause an asthma attack. During an asthma attack, the bronchi and bronchioles swell, the bronchial muscles tighten, and mucus production increases. These changes obstruct the airways and make breathing difficult or impossible.

Asthma can be managed but not cured. Most people with asthma use an inhaler, which is a hand-held device that delivers medication deep into the lungs. There are two main types of inhalers: metered dose inhalers and dry powder inhalers. Metered dose inhalers force the medicine out of the inhaler when the inhaler is compressed through the action of a chemical propellant. The person squeezes the inhaler canister to compress the inhaler and, at the same time, inhales the medicine deep into the lungs. Dry powder inhalers do not contain a chemical propellant, so the medicine does not come out as fast. Therefore, the person must inhale rapidly when the inhaler canister is compressed. Some people who have asthma, especially those who are very young or very ill, are unable to use an inhaler properly. Instead, they can use a nebulizer, which is a mask worn over the mouth and nose. The mask contains the medicine suspended in a mist.

Asthma medications work to reduce the inflammation in the airways and relax the bronchiole muscles, both of which open up the airways. Asthma attacks can be fatal, so some people with asthma use a device called a peak flow meter (see Figure 7.10B). The peak flow meter measures lung volume and can show when lung volume is decreasing compared with normal volumes. This is an early warning that an attack is coming and medication is needed.

Lung Cancer

Lung cancer is the uncontrolled and invasive growth of abnormal cells in the lungs. It is the leading cause of cancer deaths for men and women in Canada. Figure 7.11 shows the difference between healthy lung tissue and cancerous lung tissue.

The abnormal cells multiply and form malignant tumours, or **carcinomas**. The tumours reduce the surface available for gas exchange and may stop air from entering the bronchioles. Growing tumours may damage tissue or produce toxins that are harmful to the lung cells. Most cases of lung cancer are caused by smoking, which makes this type of cancer preventable. Many substances in tobacco smoke are known **carcinogens**, or cancer-causing agents. These carcinogens have been linked to lung cancer in smokers as well as non-smokers exposed to second-hand smoke. Another cause of lung cancer is exposure to radon, a heavy gaseous radioactive element that is colourless and odourless. It is found in small quantities in rocks and soil, and it can gather in buildings, entering through cracks in the foundation. Radon can be measured using specially designed kits. Finally, exposure to asbestos, a fibrous mineral resistant to heat and fire, increases the risk of lung cancer.

BiologyFile

Web Link
Cancer is a devastating disease, with more than 14 000 new cases diagnosed in Alberta each year. Due to cancer's impact, extensive research has been done to try to understand cancer, its causes, and how it progresses. Use the following terms to build a story of how cancer develops: oncogene, malignant, tumour, and metastasis.

www.albertabiology.ca
WWW

Figure 7.10B These different peak flow meters all work to measure lung volume. Changes in peak flow warn that an asthma attack might be coming.

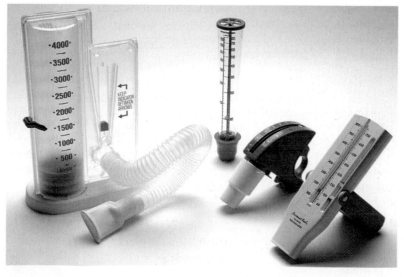

---

12 Use a Venn diagram to compare and contrast emphysema with asthma.

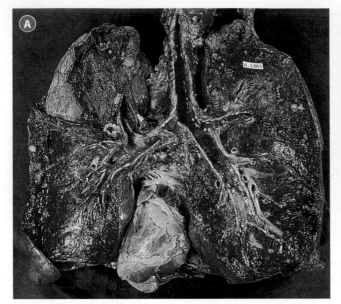

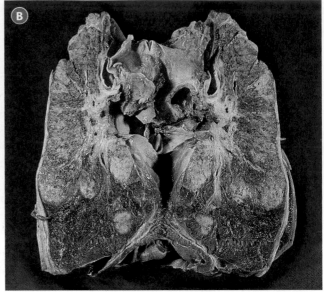

Figure 7.11 (A) These normal lungs have healthy red tissue. (The heart is visible near the lower centre.) **(B)** These diseased lungs have black tissue caused by heavy smoking. The white areas are tumours, or carcinomas.

Technologies for Detecting and Treating Lung Disorders

Successfully treating lung disorders is challenging because these disorders are usually difficult to diagnose before they have progressed to an untreatable stage. For example, lung cancer can be detected using a specialized X ray, called a CT scan, that locates abnormalities in the lungs. A new type of scan, called a helical low-dose CT scan, is able to detect lung cancer when the tumours are still very small. Unfortunately, even when a tumour is diagnosed with a helical low-dose scan, it has usually progressed past a stage where it can be treated and the cancer stopped. Figure 7.12 shows a lung tumour that has grown and started to spread. The spread of a tumour throughout the body is called metastasis,

---

Thought Lab 7.1 | **Smoking and the Respiratory System**

There are more than 4000 chemicals in tobacco smoke. At least 10 percent of these cause cancers of the mouth, lungs, and other body organs. In this activity, you will add to your understanding of body systems by conducting research to explore the effects of smoking on the respiratory and other body systems.

Note: For many Aboriginal peoples, tobacco is a sacred plant used as a key part of many traditional ceremonies. The focus of this activity is on the "common" use of tobacco in society, not its ceremonial use.

Procedure

Working alone or in small groups, plan a public-awareness product such as a poster, pamphlet, or multimedia presentation. Decide what audience your public-awareness product will address. Use your knowledge of the path of inhaled smoke through the respiratory system in your project. Make sure your research answers the following questions.

• By law, which chemicals in tobacco smoke must be listed on tobacco products? In what concentrations are they present, and what are their effects? (For example, ammonia is a chemical found in cigarette smoke in concentrations ranging from 50 to 130 μg/cigarette. Ammonia is a fatal poison in large-enough amounts in the body.)

• What other chemicals are found in tobacco smoke? List at least five, and give their concentrations and effects.

• How can tobacco chemicals appear in other body organs such as the bladder, heart, and reproductive organs?

• What are examples of long-term and short-term effects of smoking?

• In what ways is tobacco smoke particularly harmful for women who are pregnant?

• What technologies are available to assist people who choose to quit smoking?

Analysis

1. List three harmful effects of smoking on the respiratory system and three harmful effects on other body systems.

2. Because smoking has clearly identified health risks, why do you think people smoke? Give at least two reasons.

3. Identify at least two technologies developed to assist people who choose to quit smoking.

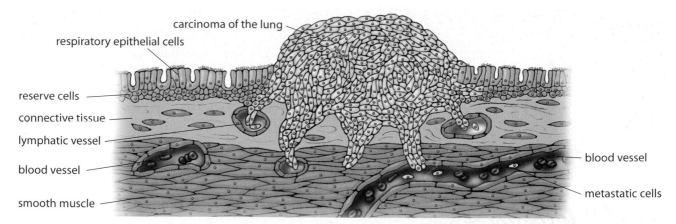

Figure 7.12 The large ball of cells in the centre of the image is a carcinoma that has developed from the interior surface cells of the human lung. The carcinoma continues to grow and invade surrounding tissues, including the lymphatic and blood vessels in the lung. The lymphatic and blood vessels circulate through the body and carry the cancerous cells, or metastatic cells, to new locations where they can grow and invade new tissues.

and the cancerous cells that spread are called metastatic cells.

Several new technologies are being developed to fight the development and spread of lung cancer. Researchers have recently developed a breakthrough technology that pinpoints the cells that are most likely to become cancerous. This technology uses DNA analysis to look for genetic changes that warn the cell may become cancerous. The focus of the research is to find a method to detect lung cancer before the tumours have grown too large to treat.

Another recent technology uses liposomes, which are artificial microscopic vesicles that consist of a liquid centre surrounded by phospholipid layers. They are manufactured in a lab, filled with cancer-fighting drugs, and released into the bloodstream. Their tiny size allows them to follow the spread of the cancerous cells and attack the cells before the cells start their uncontrolled growth at a new location.

Biology File

FYI
While often touted as being a safer alternative to cigarettes, smokeless tobacco or chewing tobacco contains nicotine and several cancer-causing chemicals. Chewing tobacco has been linked to an increase in oral cancer and the precancerous condition called leukoplakia. Chewing tobacco also damages the teeth and gums.

Thought Lab | 7.2 | You Diagnose It

Target Skills

Inferring and **drawing** conclusions from evidence

Working cooperatively to collect, assess, and communicate results

Imagine that you have been working on a team at a medical clinic that specializes in helping people with respiratory problems. It is the summer, and there is smog in the hot humid air. Your team has collected the following information about two people who recently visited your clinic complaining of having trouble breathing.

Person A: Male, age 15, is a non-smoker. He is complaining of wheezing and trouble breathing. He started having episodes in which he had difficulty breathing last summer, but the problem seemed to go away in the winter.

Person B: Female, age 35, smokes 10 to 15 cigarettes per day. She has started having trouble exhaling and gets tired very easily. She is also coughing a lot and bringing up mucus when she coughs.

Procedure

1. Review the symptoms for these two people.

2. Working together, make a list all of the possible respiratory disorders that could be causing their symptoms.

Analysis

1. Create a table that lists the symptoms of the most common respiratory disorders. Is it clear, from your table, which respiratory disorders the people are suffering from? Is there more that one possible disorder, given the symptoms? Explain your answer.

2. What else would you need to know to make a complete diagnosis? Explain how you would collect the information.

3. Create an information sheet for each person, listing what they should do to reduce their symptoms. What behaviours should they change? How would these changes improve their respiratory health?

Section 7.3 Summary

- The respiratory tract is one of the main connections between the internal environment of the body and the external environment. It is exposed to many different irritants that can cause infection and disease.
- Many upper respiratory tract infections begin with a virus and are followed by a secondary bacterial infection.
- Lower respiratory tract disorders are usually caused by infections, obstructive pulmonary disorders, and lung cancer.
- Smoking is a serious health risk. Smoking causes diseases in the respiratory tract, and it affects the cardiovascular system and other organs.
- Technologies can treat, but not cure, most respiratory tract disorders.

Section 7.3 | Review

1. Identify the structures indicated in the illustration below. Describe their function as well as an illness that is associated with these lymph nodes.

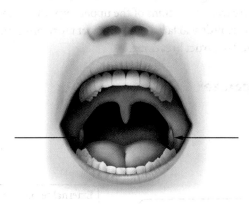

2. Describe the causes, symptoms, and breathing problems associated with bronchitis and pneumonia.

3. Describe emphysema and explain why a person with this disease is treated using a low-flow oxygen system.

4. Explain why a person with cystic fibrosis is prone to repeated respiratory system infections.

5. Describe the causes, symptoms, and breathing problems associated with asthma.

Use the following information to answer the next question.

Bronchial dilators

Bronchial dilators are the mainstay of asthma treatments. These can be given orally or by inhaled aerosol treatments. Usually, the inhaled route of administration is preferred because more of the medication gets to the lungs and there is less that gets to the rest of the body to cause side effects and unwanted problems.

6. Explain how bronchial dilators help reduce the symptoms associated with asthma.

7. Explain what lung cancer is. Describe how a carcinoma forms and how the cancer spreads throughout the body.

8. Identify two causes of lung cancer, and describe two ways that you can reduce your risks of getting this form of cancer.

9. Briefly describe how each of the following technologies could be used to detect or treat lung disorders.

   a) CT scan

   b) liposomes

Use the following information to answer the next question.

Asbestosis

Asbestosis (Pulmonary Fibrosis) is a serious, chronic, non-cancerous respiratory disease. Inhaled asbestos fibres aggravate lung tissue, which causes them to scar (fibrosis). Scarred lung tissue does not expand and contract normally and cannot perform gas exchange. The severity of the disease depends upon the duration of exposure to asbestos and the amount inhaled.

Asbestos fibres were commonly used in construction before 1975. Asbestos exposure occurs in asbestos mining and milling industries, construction, fireproofing, and other industries. In families of asbestos workers, exposure can also occur from particles brought home on the worker's clothing.

10. Predict four symptoms that an individual with asbestosis would display, and explain why this individual would have each symptom. Focus your answers on the respiratory system only.

11. You have discovered that a friend has started smoking. What reasons might your friend give you to explain why he or she started smoking? What information could you give your friend to convince your friend to stop smoking?

12. An individual with lung cancer might display the following symptoms: a chronic cough; hoarseness; coughing up blood; shortness of breath; and repeated bouts of bronchitis or pneumonia. Explain why lung cancer would be associated with each of these symptoms.

Respiration enables the body to take oxygen from the external environment and process it for delivery to the cells and, at the same time, rid itself of carbon dioxide.

Oxygen is delivered to the cells and carbon dioxide is removed from the cells and the body in a number of exchanges. Inspiration (breathing in, inhaling) and expiration (breathing out, exhaling) exchange air between the environment and the lungs. External respiration exchanges oxygen and carbon dioxide between the air in the lungs and the blood. Internal respiration exchanges oxygen and carbon dioxide between the blood and the body's tissue cells. Cellular respiration is the final step, when the oxygen delivered to the cells is used to provide the energy for all cellular activities; carbon dioxide is the waste product of cellular respiration.

The respiratory tract is the passageway for air to move from the external environment into the lungs. The upper respiratory tract begins at the nostrils and includes the nasal passages, pharynx, larynx, and trachea. These passageways all clean and warm the air as it passes through. The lower respiratory tract consists of two bronchi that each lead to a lung. Within the lungs are small, fine tubes called bronchioles, where the air continues to be cleaned and warmed. The exchange of gases takes place in a cluster of tiny sacs at the end of each bronchiole, called alveoli, where the oxygen diffuses through the membranes of the alveoli into the capillaries of the circulatory system.

A number of disorders of the respiratory tract can impair the delivery of oxygen to the cells, including bronchitis, pneumonia, pleurisy, emphysema, cystic fibrosis, asthma, and lung cancer. These are all disorders of the lower respiratory tract. Infections of the upper respiratory tract, such as tonsillitis and laryngitis are short term infections that do not obstruct breathing.

Chapter 7 Graphic Organizer

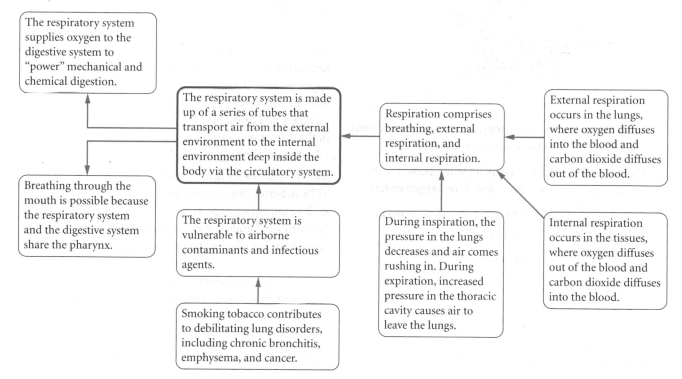

The respiratory system supplies oxygen to the digestive system to "power" mechanical and chemical digestion.

The respiratory system is made up of a series of tubes that transport air from the external environment to the internal environment deep inside the body via the circulatory system.

Respiration comprises breathing, external respiration, and internal respiration.

External respiration occurs in the lungs, where oxygen diffuses into the blood and carbon dioxide diffuses out of the blood.

Breathing through the mouth is possible because the respiratory system and the digestive system share the pharynx.

The respiratory system is vulnerable to airborne contaminants and infectious agents.

During inspiration, the pressure in the lungs decreases and air comes rushing in. During expiration, increased pressure in the thoracic cavity causes air to leave the lungs.

Internal respiration occurs in the tissues, where oxygen diffuses out of the blood and carbon dioxide diffuses into the blood.

Smoking tobacco contributes to debilitating lung disorders, including chronic bronchitis, emphysema, and cancer.

Understanding Concepts

1. Arrange the following structures in the order that they would be encountered by air entering the human respiratory system: glottis, pharynx, alveoli, bronchiole, nasal cavity, larynx.

2. Decide whether each of the following statements is true or false. If a statement is false, rewrite it to make it true.
   a) Respiration can be divided into two processes: inspiration and expiration.
   b) Carbon dioxide is one important factor in regulating the rate of respiration.
   c) Air enters the human lungs because the air pressure inside the lungs is greater than the air pressure in the external environment.
   d) The maximum volume of air that can be moved into and out of the lungs during a single breath is called the tidal volume.

3. Identify the four stages of respiration, and briefly describe each stage.

4. Identify the two basic requirements of a gas exchange system. Explain how these requirements are met in the human respiratory system.

5. Describe three lower-tract respiratory system disorders, and explain why they make breathing difficult.

6. Explain how lung cancer cells spread throughout the body.

7. Use word processing software to create two flow charts that compare inspiration to expiration. **ICT**

8. Identify two immediate benefits of quitting smoking. If someone has tried to quit smoking but has not been successful, what two aids might lead to success?

9. Explain how these two processes are involved in gas exchange.
   a) dissolving
   b) diffusion

Applying Concepts

10. The illustration shows the spirograph of a healthy, non-smoking, adult male. Use this illustration to answer the following questions.
    a) Estimate the tidal volume and the vital capacity for this individual. Record your answer in millilitres.
    b) Each vertical line on this graph represents a time interval of 12 seconds. Estimate the breathing rate of this individual. Record your answer in breaths/minute.

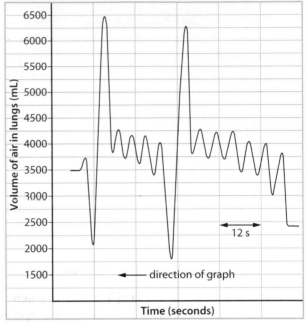

Spirograph of a healthy, non-smoking, adult male

c) Compare the total lung capacity of this individual with the total lung capacity of an adult male who has been smoking for several years.

11. Practitioners of some forms of exercise teach that special breathing techniques can help to relieve stress and improve physical (as well as emotional) well-being. One school of yoga, for example, recommends first inhaling normally and exhaling deeply, and then inhaling deeply and exhaling normally. Infer the effect on the body after a few minutes of this breathing exercise.

12. Explain how diffusion is involved in external respiration. Use graphics software to draw a diagram to support your answer. **ICT**

13. The Canadian Lung Association states, "Just because the air doesn't stink, doesn't mean the air doesn't stink." Explain what you think the CLA means by this statement. Use examples to support your answer.

14. Use word processing software to draw a flowchart that illustrates why you breathe faster during strenuous exercise. Write a caption for your flowchart, and include all the following terms in your caption: inspiratory reserve volume, waste product, oxygen concentration, rib muscles. **ICT**

15. Breathing is partially under voluntary control, which explains why you can hold your breath. When carbon dioxide levels in the blood reach too high a concentration, however, breathing is triggered involuntarily. Given this information, explain why some swimmers and divers breathe very quickly and hyperventilate before they dive.

Use the following information to answer the next question.

Heimlich Manoeuvre

You are having lunch at a restaurant when someone at the next table begins choking. A bystander rushes over, stands behind the person who is choking, and wraps her arms around him. Then, holding her hands together, just below the person's rib cage, she squeezes with a rapid, upward movement.

16. a) What is this technique intended to accomplish? Explain how it works, with references to the structures and processes involved in respiration.
   b) Another bystander suggests giving the choking person a glass of water. Would this be a good idea? Explain your answer.

Use this additional information to answer the next question.

The rescuer is successful in dislodging the obstruction that caused the choking. By this time, however, the person has stopped breathing. A medical team with resuscitation equipment arrives on the scene.

   c) Although carbon dioxide levels stimulate the breathing centre in the brain, why would this individual receive high levels of oxygen gas on his way to the hospital?

Use the following information to answer the next question.

Smoker's Cough

When you inhale tobacco smoke, the respiratory system tries to protect itself by producing mucus and stimulating coughing. Normally, the cilia that line the trachea and bronchi beat outward to sweep harmful substances out of the lungs. Chemicals in smoke paralyze the sweeping action of the cilia. As a result, some of the toxins remain in the lungs and mucus remains in the airways. When you sleep, some cilia recover and start functioning again. On waking, you cough because your lungs are trying to get rid of the toxins from the previous day's smoking. Eventually, after long-term exposure to tobacco smoke, the cilia stop functioning completely.

17. a) Explain why smokers usually wake up coughing in the morning.
   b) What substances do you expect to be coughed up?
   c) Identify a lower respiratory disease that could result from smoking, and explain how this disease is related to the long-term exposure to tobacco smoke.

Making Connections

18. Explain how the environment can influence the respiratory system. Identify three respiratory system disorders that are directly related to the environment. Describe the steps that you could take to reduce the effects of the external environment on these disorders.

Use the following information to answer the next question.

Toxic Smoke

You are walking through town when you come to a construction site where waste material is being burned. You want to minimize the amount of smoke you inhale as you pass the site, but the distance is too far for you to simply hold your breath.

19. Do you think the total amount of smoke you inhale will be greater if you take occasional deep breaths or more frequent shallow breaths? Will there be any difference? Explain your reasoning.

Use the following information to answer the next question.

Tracheostomy

Tracheotomy is a surgical procedure that is usually done in the operating room under general anesthesia. A *tracheotomy* is an incision into the trachea (windpipe) that forms a temporary or permanent opening, which is called a *tracheostomy*. Sometimes the terms "tracheotomy" and "tracheostomy" are used interchangeably. The opening, or hole, is called a *stoma*. The incision is usually vertical in children and runs from the second to the fourth tracheal ring.

20. a) Identify the functions that are affected by this alternation to the respiratory system.
   b) Describe some of the features that must be incorporated into the artificial tracheal cover in order to maintain the integrity of the respiratory system.

Use the following information to answer the next question.

Viral Pharyngitis

You have gone to see your doctor because you have a sore throat, runny nose, post-nasal drip, and a cough. Your doctor diagnoses your symptoms and tells you that you have a viral infection called pharyngitis.

21. a) Identify the parts of the upper respiratory tract that are affected by this disease.
   b) Explain the symptoms of the disease with respect to the protective mechanisms of the respiratory system.

Circulation and Immunity

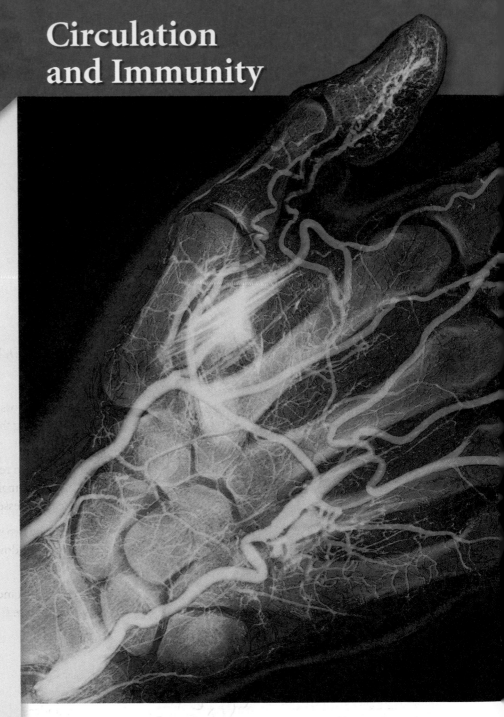

Chapter Concepts

8.1 Structures of the Circulatory System

- The heart and blood vessels are collectively called the cardiovascular system.

- The mammalian heart is a muscular organ that contains four chambers and acts as a double pump.

- There are three circulatory pathways through the body: the pulmonary pathway, the systemic pathway, and the coronary pathway.

8.2 Blood and Circulation

- Blood is a tissue made up of plasma, red blood cells, white blood cells, and platelets.

- Blood transports materials throughout the body and regulates temperature to maintain homeostasis.

8.3 The Lymphatic System and Immunity

- The lymphatic circulatory system is closely associated with the blood vessels of the cardiovascular circulatory system.

- The lymphatic system helps to maintain the balance of fluids within the body and is a key component of the immune system.

- The body's defence system is made up of non-specific defences and specific defences (immunity).

- The specific immune system contains a variety of cells that are specialized to recognize foreign substances and neutralize or destroy them.

Y ou breathe oxygen into your lungs, and it reaches the cells of your fingers. You swallow pain-relief medication, and it eases the swelling in a sprained ankle. Blood vessels provide a transportation network that links the different parts of your body and its trillions of cells.

Your hand contains well over a kilometre of blood vessels. Some of these blood vessels you can see through the skin on the back of your hand. Many more can be revealed using medical technologies. However, even a spectacular image, such as the one shown here, would not include all the blood vessels in your hand. The circulatory system extends through every part of your hand, right down to the microscopic level, so that no cell in your hand is more than a cell's breadth away from a blood vessel.

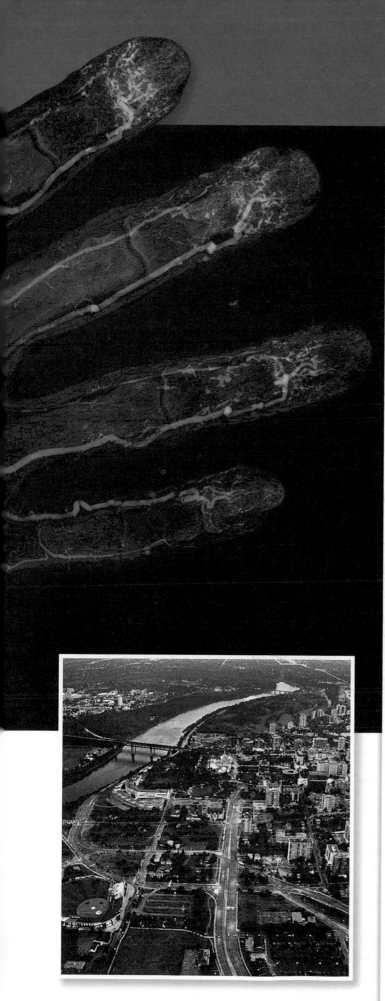

Watching Blood Flow

Your teacher will either show you a movie or direct you to the McGraw-Hill Ryerson web site, where you can observe a video clip showing the flow of blood through the tail of a goldfish.

Materials

- movie or video clip showing blood flow in a goldfish tail

Procedure

1. Observe the movie or video.
2. Discuss the following Analysis questions.

Analysis

1. What are possible functions of the blood that you saw flowing through the tiny vessels (tube-like structures)?

2. Suggest two reasons why the vessels in the goldfish's tail are so small. Why does the goldfish not have just one large vessel?

3. Describe two situations that could either speed up or slow down the movement of blood in the goldfish.

4. What substance or substances are in the vessels you observed?

5. What do you think is responsible for the movement of blood in the goldfish? Would this be responsible for the movement of blood in all animals? What about other organisms, such as plants? Explain your ideas.

6. Did the goldfish's blood appear to change direction, or did it flow in one direction? Write a hypothesis to explain what you observed.

In what ways is the transportation network of a city or town like the transportation network of your circulatory system?

Structures of the Circulatory System

In a single-celled organism such as *Amoeba*, nutrients and respiratory gases enter the cell either by diffusion or by being actively transported across the cell membrane. Once inside the cell, these substances are distributed to the cell's organelles by the movement of its cytoplasm—a process called cytoplasmic streaming. Active transport and cytoplasmic streaming require energy, which is supplied by the energy-carrier molecule, ATP. Waste materials leave the cell by diffusion or through active transport and are released into the environment. Thus, single-celled organisms exchange matter directly with their external environment.

In multicellular organisms, such as humans, the process of matter exchange is more complex. The trillions of specialized cells of a multicellular organism are organized into functional, structural units, such as tissues and organs. The individual cells that make up these structural units require nutrients and oxygen, and they must rid themselves of wastes, just as single-celled organisms do. Thus, an efficient system for transporting materials within the body is necessary. The **circulatory system** is this transportation system.

Main Functions of the Circulatory System

The circulatory system has the following three main functions:

1. The circulatory system transports gases (from the respiratory system), nutrient molecules (from the digestive system), and waste materials (from the excretory system). You have already studied two of these systems. In Chapter 9, you will study the excretory system.

2. The circulatory system regulates internal temperature and transports hormones. Much of the body's heat is generated by the motor system, which you will examine in Chapter 10. Hormones are reaction-triggering chemicals that are produced by the endocrine system. You have already seen hormones in action in Chapter 6. Gastrin, secretin, and CCK are involved in regulating digestion. You will study the endocrine system and its role in homeostasis in your next biology course. (If you are interested in reading ahead to learn about this system, turn to Chapter 13.)

3. The circulatory system protects against blood loss from injury and against disease-causing microbes or toxic substances introduced into the body. In Section 8.2, you will learn about the role of platelets in protecting against blood loss and the role of white blood cells in providing immune responses to foreign agents. In Section 8.3, you will learn about a companion to the circulatory system, the lymphatic system, which also has a protective role in the body.

Major Components of the Circulatory System

The circulatory system is made up of three major components: the heart, the blood vessels, and the blood. The heart is an organ that pushes blood through the body with its pumping action and generates blood flow. The blood vessels serve as the "roadways" through which the blood moves. Together, the heart and blood vessels comprise the cardiovascular system. ("Cardio-" comes from a Greek word meaning "heart," and "-vascular" comes from a Latin word meaning "vessel.") The blood carries nutrients, oxygen, carbon dioxide, water, wastes, and many other materials throughout the body.

In the remainder of this section, you will focus on the cardiovascular system—the heart and blood vessels. You will focus on the blood in Section 8.2.

- - -

Q1 What are three main functions of the human circulatory system?

Q2 Name the three components that make up the human circulatory system.

- - -

The Structure of the Heart

Make a fist with each of your hands, and then hold your fists together at the knuckles. This is the approximate size of an adult human heart, such as the one shown in Figure 8.1. Now imagine holding a tennis ball in one hand and squeezing it as strongly as you can. This is the approximate force that the heart uses for a single contraction to pump blood through the body. The amount of energy that the heart needs to generate the force for one contraction, multiplied by the number of contractions over 50 years of life, would be sufficient to raise a battleship (more than 1 million tonnes) out of the water!

Located slightly to the left of the middle of the chest, the heart has several important functions. These functions include pumping blood through the body, keeping oxygen-rich blood separate from oxygen-poor blood, and ensuring that blood flows only in one direction through the body. The walls of the heart are made up of a special type of muscle tissue, called cardiac muscle, that is found nowhere else in the body. The contractions of cardiac muscle tissue are rhythmical and involuntary—you cannot consciously affect your heartbeat. The muscle cells relax completely in the brief milliseconds between contractions, thus preventing the heart from becoming fatigued.

The human heart, like the hearts of all mammals and birds, has four chambers: one top chamber and one bottom chamber on both the right and left sides. The two top chambers are called the **atria** (singular: atrium), and they fill with blood returning either from the body or the lungs. The two bottom chambers are called the **ventricles**. They receive blood from the atria and pump it out to either the body or the lungs. The atria and the ventricles are separated from each other by the thick muscular wall called the **septum**. Figure 8.2 shows some of the external and internal structures of the human heart.

The right side of the heart receives blood coming back from the body and then pumps this blood out to the lungs. Two large vessels, called the **vena cavae** (singular: vena cava), open into the right atrium. The superior vena cava collects oxygen-poor blood coming from the tissues in the head, chest, and arms. The inferior vena cava collects oxygen-poor blood coming from the tissues elsewhere in the body. The oxygen-poor blood flows from the right atrium into the right

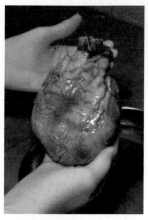

Figure 8.1 Cradled in the hands of a surgeon, this human heart is about to be transplanted into a person whose own heart no longer functions properly.

Figure 8.2 An external view (**A**) and a cross-sectional view (**B**) of the human heart

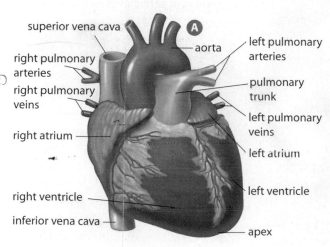

superior vena cava
right pulmonary arteries
right pulmonary veins
right atrium
right ventricle
inferior vena cava
aorta
left pulmonary arteries
pulmonary trunk
left pulmonary veins
left atrium
left ventricle
apex

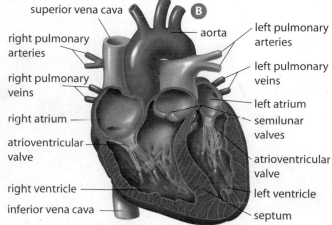

superior vena cava
right pulmonary arteries
right pulmonary veins
right atrium
atrioventricular valve
right ventricle
inferior vena cava
aorta
left pulmonary arteries
left pulmonary veins
left atrium
semilunar valves
atrioventricular valve
left ventricle
septum

BiologyFile

FYI
The bicuspid and tricuspid valves are held in place by long cord-like tendons called the chordae tendinae. These tendons attach the valves to small muscles on the inside wall of the ventricles. They ensure that during ventricular contraction the valves are not pushed back into the atria by the force of the flowing blood. Without them, blood would rush back into the atria, disrupting the direction of flow.

ventricle and then out into the pulmonary trunk before entering the left and right **pulmonary arteries**. From there, it continues to the left and right lungs for gas exchange. (These are the only arteries in the circulatory system that contain oxygen-poor blood.) The left side of the heart does the reverse. It receives oxygen-rich blood from the left and right lungs and pumps this blood out to the body. The oxygen-rich blood flows from the lungs through the **pulmonary veins** to the left atrium. (These are the only veins in the circulatory system that contain oxygenated blood.) The left atrium pumps blood into the left ventricle, where all the blood going to the body tissues leaves through a large vessel—the largest in the body—called the **aorta**. You will examine the route of blood flow in more detail later in this section.

As you can see in Figure 8.3, the heart has four valves inside it. These **valves** ensure that blood flows in the correct direction. The atria and ventricles are separated from each other by two valves called the atrioventricular valves. The atrioventricular valve on the right side is called the tricuspid valve because it is made up of three flaps. The atrioventricular valve on the left side is called the bicuspid valve because it has only two flaps. The other two valves are called semilunar valves because of their half-moon shape.

3. Name the four chambers of the mammalian heart.

4. What is the function of the valves in the heart? How many valves does the heart have?

The Structure of the Blood Vessels

There are three main types of blood vessels: arteries, veins, and capillaries. **Arteries** carry oxygen-rich blood away from the heart, and **veins** carry oxygen-poor blood toward the heart. Joining each artery and vein is a network of capillaries. Blood travels from an artery into the **capillaries**, where gases, nutrients, and other materials are transferred to tissue cells and wastes, including gases, move into the blood. The blood then moves from the capillaries into the veins and back to the heart. Compare the structure of arteries, veins, and capillaries in Figure 8.4.

An artery has highly elastic walls. This elasticity allows the artery to expand as a wave of blood surges through it during the contraction of the ventricles, and then to snap back again during the relaxation of the ventricles. The action of the artery keeps the blood flowing in the right direction and provides an additional

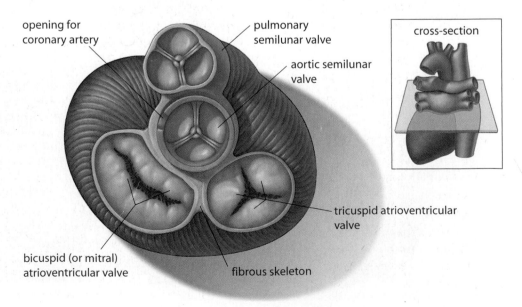

Figure 8.3 This cross-section of a mammalian heart shows the structure of the four valves. The bicuspid valve is also called the mitral valve because it is shaped like a mitre—the ceremonial headdress worn by high officials of the Roman Catholic church.

opening for coronary artery

pulmonary semilunar valve

aortic semilunar valve

cross-section

tricuspid atrioventricular valve

bicuspid (or mitral) atrioventricular valve

fibrous skeleton

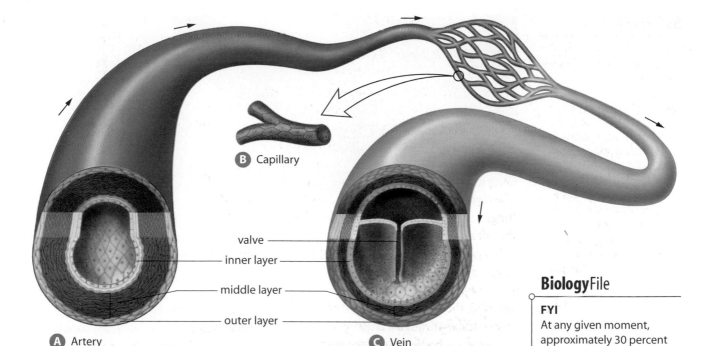

B Capillary

valve
inner layer
middle layer
outer layer

A Artery

C Vein

Figure 8.4 Arteries **(A)** and veins **(C)** have three layers. The outer layer is a covering of connective tissue mixed with elastic tissue. The middle layer consists of alternating, circular bands of elastic tissue and smooth muscle tissue. The inner layer is only one cell thick and consists of flat, smooth cells. The shape and texture of these cells serve to reduce friction as blood moves through them. Capillaries **(B)** consist of a single layer that is one cell thick.

pumping motion to help force the blood through the blood vessels. When you measure your pulse, what you feel is the rhythmic expansion and contraction of an artery as blood moves through it. Veins have thinner walls than arteries and a larger inner circumference. Veins are not as elastic, and they cannot contract to help move the blood back to the heart. Instead, the contraction of muscles keeps the blood flowing toward the heart (see Figure 8.5). Veins also have one-way valves that prevent the blood from flowing backward. These one-way valves are especially important in your legs because they ensure that the blood flows upward to your heart, against the downward pull of gravity.

Capillaries are the smallest blood vessels—so small that 10 capillaries bundled together would have the diameter of a single human hair. Capillaries are spread throughout the body in a fine network. The capillary wall is a single layer of cells, and the average diameter of a capillary is about 8 μm, which is just large enough for the largest blood cells to pass through in single file (see Figure 8.6). In the next section, you will learn more about the role of capillaries in the exchange of matter and energy.

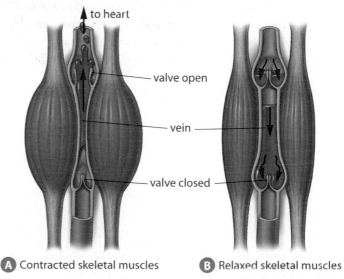

to heart

valve open

vein

valve closed

A Contracted skeletal muscles   **B** Relaxed skeletal muscles

Figure 8.5 Blood is moved through the veins by the contraction and relaxation of muscles. **(A)** The muscles contract and squeeze the vein, pushing blood past the one-way valve. **(B)** The muscles relax, and the blood in the vein begins to flow back briefly. The slight backward flow forces the valve closed and prevents further back flow.

BiologyFile

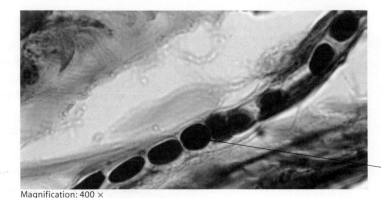

Figure 8.6 Networks of capillaries are present throughout your body. Their diameter is so small that red blood cells can pass through them only one cell at a time.

red blood cell

Magnification: 400 ×

• • •

5 Which blood vessels carry blood away from the heart?

6 Which blood vessels carry blood to the heart?

7 Which blood vessels link the blood vessels you named in questions 5 and 6?

8 Briefly compare the structures of the three types of blood vessels, and explain how the structure of each suits its function.

• • •

The Beating Heart

The stimulus that triggers a heartbeat is an electrical signal that originates from within the heart itself. (The rate and strength of a heartbeat is under the control of the nervous system.) A bundle of specialized muscle tissue, called the **sinoatrial (SA) node**, stimulates the muscle cells to contract and relax rhythmically. (The SA node is also referred to as the pacemaker, because it sets the pace for cardiac activity.)

The SA node is located in the wall of the right atrium. It generates an electrical

---

INVESTIGATION 8.A

Identifying Structures of the Circulatory System

In this investigation, you will perform a real or virtual dissection to examine the internal structures of the circulatory system. As necessary, refer to the table in Appendix F, Fetal Pig Dissection, to review the anatomical terms used to locate organs or incisions mentioned in the procedure.

Question

What features of a mammalian heart can you identify in a real or virtual heart? What route does blood take through the heart?

Target Skills

Observing and **identifying** external and internal features of a mammalian heart through either a real or virtual dissection

Tracing the direction of blood flow through a mammalian heart

Safety Precautions

• Be extremely careful when using dissecting instruments, particularly scalpels. Wherever possible, make cuts away from your body.

• The hearts are preserved in a chemical solution. Wear plastic gloves, safety glasses, and an apron at all times, and work in a well-ventilated area. If some of the chemical comes in contact with your skin, wash it off. At the end of the investigation or class, wash your hands thoroughly.

• Dispose of all materials as instructed by your teacher, and clean your work area.

Materials

- disposable plastic gloves
- apron
- safety glasses
- dissecting instruments
- large tongs
- dissecting tray
- preserved sheep heart (or another mammalian heart)
- plastic bag and tie (to store the heart if necessary)
- newspapers and/or paper towels

Procedure

1. Obtain a preserved sheep's heart, and observe its external features. Rinse the heart thoroughly with water. This will remove any excess preservatives. Observe the pericardium, which is the sac surrounding the heart. If it is still attached, remove it. Note the fatty tissue accumulated on the heart. This is usually found along the edges of the heart chambers and surrounding the coronary arteries. Remove as much of the fatty tissue as possible.

2. Identify the apex, or pointed bottom, of the heart.

3. Use the illustrations and Figure 8.2 to help you locate the following structures:
   a) the aorta
   b) the superior vena cava
   c) the pulmonary artery
   d) the pulmonary vein
   e) the inferior vena cava

4. Begin a frontal cut through the heart at the apex, and move toward the base. Open the heart, and identify the chambers on the lower left and right sides. These are the left and right ventricles. There is a thick muscular structure separating the two ventricles. This is the septum. Identify the right and left atria, located above the ventricles. Compare the structures of the different chambers of the heart. Make a labelled drawing, and describe the structures in your own words.

5. The ventricles are separated from the atria above them by the atrioventricular valves. Identify these valves. You should also be able to see strong fibrous strings, called the chordae tendineae. Identify the left atrioventricular valve, which has two flaps or cusps, and the right atrioventricular valve, which has three cusps.

6. Complete a labelled drawing of your specimen, showing the external and internal features of the heart.

Analysis

1. Explain how the appearance of the following structures relates to their function as part of the circulatory system. Give as much detail as possible, including size, texture, external structure, and internal structure.
   a) right atrium
   b) left atrium
   c) right ventricle
   d) arteries, including the aorta
   e) left ventricle
   f) veins
   g) heart valves

2. Using your own drawings and your current understanding of the route that blood takes through the body, trace the movement of blood from the tissues through the heart and back to the tissues. Start with the superior and inferior vena cavae.

Conclusions

3. Answer part **(a)** if you performed a real dissection. Answer part **(b)** if you performed a virtual dissection.
   a) In what ways was your understanding of the heart and circulation enhanced by your observation of a real heart?
   b) In what ways was your understanding of the heart and circulation enhanced by your observation of a virtual heart?

4. What experiences did you have that limited your observations or understanding? How could these limitations be overcome?

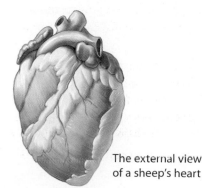
The external view of a sheep's heart

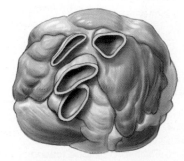
The large vessels of a sheep's heart

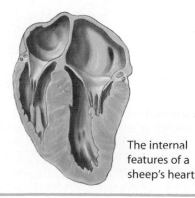
The internal features of a sheep's heart

FYI
During the past minute, your heart beat approximately 80 times, sending your blood through a complete circuit of your circulatory system three times—a journey of almost 15 km. During the next minute, the same sequence of events will occur, as it will in the minute after that, and in the minute after that. Imagine the power, precision, and sophisticated structure of an organ that is capable of carrying out this sequence of events every minute, 24 hours a day, seven days a week, during your lifetime!

signal that spreads over the two atria and makes them contract simultaneously. As the atria contract, the signal reaches another node called the **atrioventricular (AV) node**. The AV node transmits the electrical signal through a bundle of specialized fibres called the *bundle of His*. These fibres relay the signal through two bundle branches that divide into fast-conducting *Purkinje fibres*, which initiate the almost simultaneous contraction of all cells of the right and left ventricles (Figure 8.7).

The change in voltage produced by the electrical signal can be measured using an electrocardiogram (ECG). This device records the electrical activity of the heart as it contracts and relaxes (see Figure 8.8). In this normal ECG reading, the small voltage increase marked as P shows the electrical activity just before atrial contraction. The large spike at QRS shows the electrical activity just before ventricular contraction. The small spike at T shows the electrical activity as the ventricles recover from their contraction, before the next stimulation by the SA node. The recovery of the atria cannot be measured because it takes place at the same time as when the ventricles

contract. Changes in the spacing of these waves, or their total disappearance, can be used to diagnose different heart conditions.

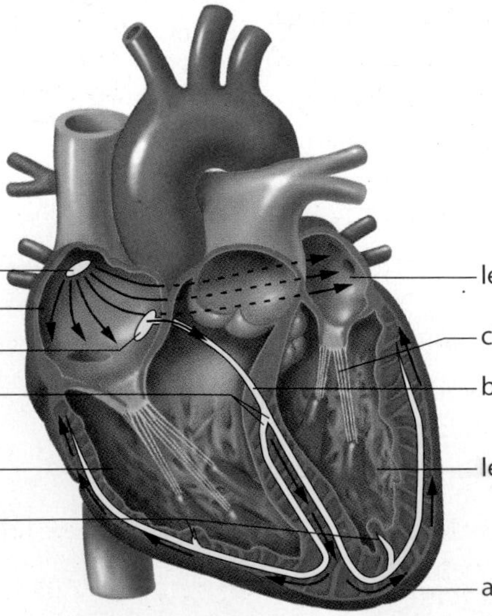

⦾ ⦾ ⦾

9 What are the SA and AV nodes, and how are they related to the beating of the heart?

10 Explain what an ECG tracing shows.

⦾ ⦾ ⦾

Blood Pressure

As blood passes through the vessels in the body, it exerts pressure against the vessel walls. This is called **blood pressure**. Changes in blood pressure correspond to the phases of the heartbeat. When the ventricles contract and force blood into the pulmonary arteries and the aorta, the pressure increases in these vessels. The maximum pressure during the ventricular contraction is called the **systolic pressure**. The ventricles then relax and the pressure in the pulmonary arteries and the aorta drops. The lowest pressure before the ventricles contract again is called the **diastolic pressure**.

Blood pressure is usually measured at an artery in the arm. It is recorded in millimetres of mercury, or mmHg (1 mmHg = 0.133 kPa) using a device called a sphygmomanometer (commonly known as a blood pressure cuff). The systolic pressure is presented over the diastolic pressure in the form of a fraction. The blood pressure of an average healthy young person is below 120 mmHg over 80 mmHg, or $\frac{120}{80}$. As the heart rate increases, such as during exercise, the ventricles must push a greater volume of blood per unit of time, so the pressure within the arterial system also increases. Although the diastolic blood pressure in a relaxed ventricle drops to almost 0 mmHg during each heartbeat, the blood pressure in the arteries never drops this low, so blood keeps flowing to the tissues. In Investigation 8.B, you will measure your own blood pressure.

SA node
right atrium
AV node
bundle branches
right ventricle
Purkinje fibres

left atrium
chordae tendinae
bundle of His
left ventricle
apex of heart

Figure 8.7 The SA node sends out an electrical stimulus that causes the atria to contract. When this stimulus reaches the AV node, it is passed through the bundle of His and the Purkinje fibres. The stimulus causes the ventricles to contract, starting from the apex and then upward, which forces blood toward the pulmonary artery and aorta. The chordae tendinae are strong, fibrous strings that prevent the valves in the heart from inverting when the heart contracts.

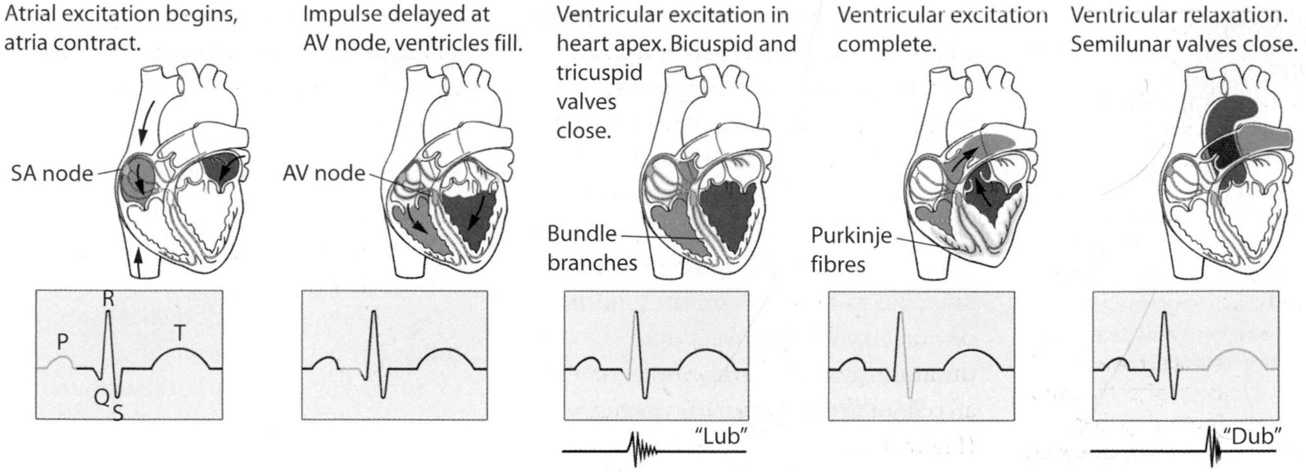

| Atrial excitation begins, atria contract. | Impulse delayed at AV node, ventricles fill. | Ventricular excitation in heart apex. Bicuspid and tricuspid valves close. | Ventricular excitation complete. | Ventricular relaxation. Semilunar valves close. |

Figure 8.8 An electrocardiogram records the electrical activity measured by an electrocardiograph. The voltage changes are very small, measuring only a few milliVolts. Note the places on the electrocardiogram where the "lub" and "dub" sounds of the heartbeat occur. The closing of the AV valves during ventricle contraction produce the "lub" sounds, and the closing of the semilunar valves during ventricular relaxation causes the "dub" sound.

Q 11 Explain what a blood pressure reading of $\frac{120}{80}$ means.

Cardiac Output and Stroke Volume

The amount of blood pumped by the heart is often referred to as cardiac output and is measured in mL/min. Cardiac output is an indicator of the level of oxygen delivered to the body and the amount of work the body's muscles can perform. Two factors affect cardiac output: heart rate and stroke volume. Heart rate is the number of heartbeats per minute. Stroke volume is the amount of blood forced out of the heart with each heartbeat. Cardiac output = heart rate × stroke volume.

Stroke volume depends on how easily the heart fills with blood and how readily the heart empties again. The former is related to the volume of blood returning to the heart from the veins and the distensibility, or stretchiness, of the ventricles. The latter is related to the strength of the ventricular contraction and the pressure exerted by the artery walls.

The average person has a stroke volume of about 70 mL and a resting heart rate of about 70 beats per minute, for a cardiac output of about 4900 mL/min.

Remember that the average person has about 5 L of blood in their body. This means that for the average person, the total volume of blood in the body circulates through the heart about once every minute.

Cardiovascular Fitness

Table 8.1 shows a hypothetical comparison of resting heart rate, stroke volume, and cardiac output for three individuals. For ease of comparison, cardiac output is assumed to be most often average. According to this table, individual C's heart is exceptionally fit, having a very high stroke volume. C can maintain the same level of cardiac output (and oxygen delivery) at a much lower heart rate than the less fit heart of B or the average heart of A. This means that C's heart is working more efficiently than A's and B's. A low resting heart rate is considered an indicator of cardiovascular fitness because it means that stroke volume is high.

Table 8.1 Relationship between stroke volume, heart rate, and cardiac output.

Individual	Resting heart rate (beats/min)	Stroke volume (mL/beat)	Cardiac output (mL/min)
A	70	70	4900
B	98	50	4900
C	35	140	4900

BiologyFile

Web Link
The artificial pacemaker generates electrical signals (also called impulses) to keep the heart beating. Two Canadian surgeons, Wilfred Bigelow and John Callaghan, and a Canadian electrical engineer, Jack Hopps, invented this life-saving device. How did the amputation of frostbitten fingers lead to the invention of the artificial pacemaker? What improvements to this device have been made to its original design?

www.albertabiology.ca
WWW

BiologyFile

Maximum heart rate is the highest heart rate attained during an all-out physical effort. This rate diminishes with age. Maximum heart rate does not appear to be related to cardiovascular fitness, however. The more important cardiovascular fitness indicator is the length of time it takes for the heart to return to its resting heart rate following physical activity. Recovery time diminishes as the heart becomes more fit.

Regular cardiovascular exercise will increase the resting stroke volume of the heart. Cardiovascular exercise enlarges the ventricular chambers, increases the distensibility of the ventricles, and strengthens the ventricle walls. As a result, the heart develops more power to push blood out with each contraction. (Strength training such as weight lifting, on the other hand, may simply increase the thickness of the walls. This may actually limit stroke volume by reducing the elasticity of the ventricles.) A good exercise program should include regular cardiovascular activity.

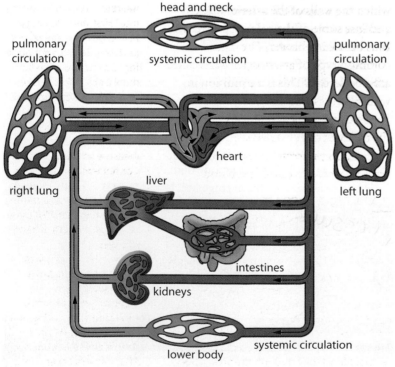

Figure 8.9 Trace the flow of blood through the pulmonary and systemic pathways. Arteries carry blood away from the heart; veins carry blood toward it. Note that in the systemic pathway, arteries carry oxygen-rich blood (red) and veins carry oxygen-poor blood (blue). The reverse is true in the pulmonary pathway: arteries carry oxygen-poor blood and veins carry oxygen-rich blood.

Pathways of the Circulatory System

The blood vessels are organized to carry blood along three different pathways: the pulmonary pathway, systemic pathway, and coronary pathway. As shown in Figure 8.9, the **pulmonary pathway** transports oxygen-poor blood to the lungs. When the blood reaches the lungs, oxygen and carbon dioxide are exchanged by diffusion between the blood in the capillaries and the air in the alveoli of the lungs through the actions of the respiratory system. Oxygen-rich blood returns to the left side of the heart by way of the pulmonary veins. The **systemic pathway** moves the oxygen-rich blood from the left ventricle of the heart to the body tissues. Oxygen and nutrients move into the tissue cells, and waste products move out of the tissue cells into the blood. The **coronary pathway** (see Figure 8.10) is dedicated to provide blood to the muscle tissue of the heart itself.

Tracing Blood Flow through the Pulmonary and Systemic Pathways

Blood flows through the different pathways in the body in a continuous cycle. To follow the route that blood takes, you can start at any point in the system. For example, begin by examining the oxygen-poor blood that is returning to the heart from the body. The oxygen-poor blood enters the pulmonary pathway by first flowing through the vena cavae into the right atrium. When the atria contract, the blood is pumped into the right ventricle. The ventricle contracts and pumps the blood out into the pulmonary trunk, which then divides into the left and right pulmonary arteries. The pulmonary arteries lead to capillaries in the left and right lungs, where the exchange of respiratory gases occurs. The blood simultaneously picks up oxygen from the alveoli in the lungs and gives up carbon dioxide.

The freshly oxygen-enriched blood continues through the capillaries of the lungs into the left and right pulmonary veins, which both enter the left atrium of the heart. The blood is now entering the systemic pathway. When the atria contract again, the left atrium pumps the blood into the left ventricle. All the blood going to the body tissues leaves the left ventricle through the aorta. The aorta divides into several large arteries that supply blood to the body tissues.

Tracing Blood Flow through the Coronary Pathway

The heart does not use the blood inside its chambers to get nutrients and remove wastes. The heart cannot use this blood because the oxygen in the blood cannot effectively diffuse through all the cell layers of the heart. An alternative pathway is needed to serve the functional needs of the heart cells.

The coronary pathway in Figure 8.10 provides matter and energy to the cardiac muscle cells by way of capillaries that are embedded directly in the heart wall. These capillaries receive blood from two coronary arteries that split off from the aorta just as it exits the ventricle, immediately after the semilunar valve. Each artery continues to branch into smaller and smaller vessels, so the entire surface of the heart is covered in a network of tiny blood vessels that encircle the heart like a crown. (The term "coronary" comes from the Latin word for crown, *corona*.) The oxygen-rich blood moves through these vessels into the capillary bed, where gas exchange occurs between the capillaries and the cells of the cardiac tissue. The oxygen-poor blood then flows out, into vessels that get progressively larger, finally forming the coronary veins. The coronary veins join together, and the oxygen-poor blood enters the right ventricle, ready to flow to the lungs to pick up more oxygen.

• • •

12 How is systemic circulation different from pulmonary circulation?

13 What is coronary circulation?

• • •

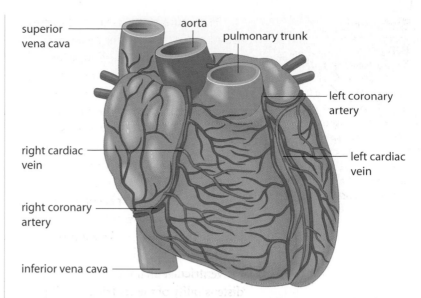

Figure 8.10 Only a few of the many blood vessels that "feed" the heart are shown in this view of the coronary pathway.

Cardiovascular Disorders and Treatments

Cardiovascular disease is the leading cause of death for Canadians. Many of the risk factors associated with cardiovascular disease, such as smoking, obesity, and insufficient exercise, can be reduced or eliminated by lifestyle changes.

Arteriosclerosis is a general term that is used to describe several conditions in which the walls of the arteries thicken and lose some of their elastic properties, thus becoming harder. The most common type of arteriosclerosis is called atherosclerosis. This is a condition in which there is a buildup of plaque (fatty deposits, calcium, and fibrous tissues) on the inside of artery walls (see Figure 8.11). As the artery narrows due to this buildup, blood flow is decreased and blood

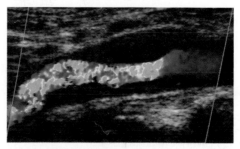

Figure 8.11 An accumulation of plaque can restrict blood flow through the artery. Such buildups are especially dangerous if they occur in arteries of the heart, neck, brain, legs, and kidneys. In this ultrasound scan of blood flow through a neck artery, blood flow is greatest when red and slowest when green.

Target Skills

Designing a procedure to investigate factors that affect heart rate and blood pressure

Measuring blood pressure

Determining a relationship between blood pressure and a factor selected for investigation from patterns and trends in data

Working cooperatively to measure and record blood pressure and another factor selected for investigation

Factors Affecting Heart Rate and Blood Pressure

In this investigation, you will design an experiment to determine how your heart rate and your blood pressure change after exposure to different factors, such as physical activity, different foods, and caffeinated beverages.

Question

How can you isolate factors that affect blood pressure and heart rate?

Hypothesis

Make and record a hypothesis about the effects of at least two different factors on heart rate and blood pressure.

Safety Precautions

Do not over-inflate the blood pressure cuff. Students with circulatory or blood pressure problems should not be test subjects.

Materials

- blood pressure cuff
- watch with a second hand or a digital display of seconds

Experimental Plan

1. Working in a group, prepare a list of ideas for testing your hypothesis, using the materials available in your classroom.

2. Decide on one idea you can use to design an experiment that can be conducted in your classroom.

3. What will be your manipulated variable? What will be your responding variable(s)? What will be your control variable(s)? How many trials will you run? Remember that you should test one variable at a time. Plan to collect quantitative data.

4. Outline, step-by-step, a procedure for your experiment. Assemble the materials you will require.

5. Design a table for collecting your data.

6. Obtain your teacher's approval before starting your experiment.

Data and Observations

7. Conduct your experiment, and record your results. Prepare a graph or chart to help you communicate your findings to other groups in the class.

Analysis

1. What was the resting blood pressure and heart rate for each test subject?

2. How did the blood pressure change as a result of the factor you were testing? How did the heart rate change as a result of the variable you were testing?

3. How long did each change last after termination of the testing factor?

Conclusions

4. Compare your results with the results of other groups in the class. Explain any differences.

5. What is the adaptive advantage of a temporary increase in blood pressure? What is the adaptive advantage of a temporary increase in heart rate?

Extension

6. High blood pressure is a common problem in North America. Fortunately, many different treatments are available. Some examples include treatments used in Western medicine, traditional Aboriginal medicine, traditional Chinese medicine, Ayurvedic medicine, naturopathy, homeopathy, massage therapy, and yoga. Research three different treatments for high blood pressure, and prepare a brief report to compare the main features of these treatments. If someone wanted to receive treatment for high blood pressure, which would you recommend? Justify your choice.

7. If possible, obtain two types of blood pressure cuffs. Newer cuffs give digital readings, while older cuffs require the use of a stethoscope to listen to the sounds of blood moving through the vessels. Use both types of blood pressure cuff to measure a partner's blood pressure. Compare the readings you got, and describe the differences in your experiences with the two cuffs.

pressure is increased. Depending on where the buildup of the plaque occurs in the body, atherosclerosis may lead to angina (chest pain), blood clots, shortness of breath, heart attack, or heart failure. Self-respectful lifestyle choices (such as exercise, not smoking, and eating a diet low in saturated fat and high in fruits and vegetables) contribute to reducing the risk of developing this condition.

Once arteriosclerosis sets in, several treatment options are available. Medicines such as Aspirin™ are able to prevent platelets from sticking together, thus reducing the formation of clots. Special "clot-busting" medicines such as urokinase and t-PA can be used to break down existing clots and improve blood flow. Surgical treatment is also possible. Angioplasty is a procedure in which a surgeon inserts a tube into a clogged artery, as shown in Figure 8.12. When the tube reaches the site where the artery is clogged, a tiny balloon is inflated to force the artery open. Sometimes, a small, permanent metal tube, called a vascular stent, is inserted into the blockage during the procedure. This stent holds the vessel open and reduces the chance of the blockage redeveloping.

Another increasingly common surgical procedure is called a coronary bypass operation. A segment of healthy artery or vein is taken from elsewhere in the body and used to create a new pathway around a blocked vessel near the heart. One end of the new segment is attached to the aorta, and the other end is attached to a point in the blood vessel beyond the blockage to bypass it, as shown in Figure 8.13. The words "double" and "triple" refer to the number of vessels with blockages that must be bypassed.

Some cardiovascular problems are congenital, meaning they are defects in the heart that have been present since birth. Some of the more common congenital heart defects include problems in the walls dividing the chambers of the heart, in the valves, or in the structure of the blood vessels near the heart. A heart

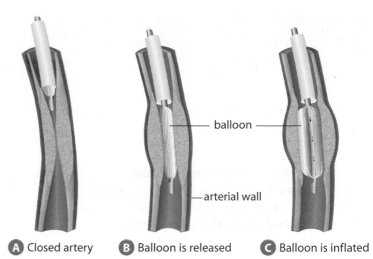

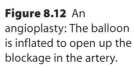

balloon

arterial wall

A Closed artery   **B** Balloon is released   **C** Balloon is inflated

Figure 8.12 An angioplasty: The balloon is inflated to open up the blockage in the artery.

murmur is a relatively common heart defect that describes any misflow of blood through the heart, such as one or more of the valves not opening or closing properly. Valve defects can be heard with a stethoscope as a whooshing or rasping sound, which is caused when blood leaks through the valve. Note that these defects may also arise later in life, in which case they are called acquired, not congenital.

The latest technology has been applied to help surgeons successfully repair or reduce the damage caused by congenital

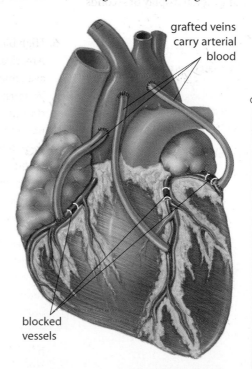

grafted veins carry arterial blood

blocked vessels

Figure 8.13 Coronary bypass operation: this heart shows a triple bypass, meaning that three new pathways were constructed to avoid blockages in three separate blood vessels.

BiologyFile

FYI
If blood is not kept flowing through the large deep veins of the legs, it can pool and begin to coagulate. The resulting blood clots are called thrombi (sing. thrombus) and result from a number of factors including lack of activity and use of oral contraceptives. Because airline passengers remain inactive on long flights, you may have heard the condition called "economy class syndrome," though its proper name is "deep vein thrombosis." This can be a fatal condition if the thrombus travels to the lungs and blocks the flow of blood there.

heart defects. Digitizing technology can take data from a CT (computed tomography) scan, CAT (computed axial tomography) scan, or MRI (magnetic resonance imaging) scan and create an exact plastic or wax model of a body part, such as a heart (see Figure 8.14). This model allows surgeons to plan and even practise the surgery before performing the surgery on the patient. The Internet allows surgeons from all over the world to input data and create models for their patients.

Thought Lab 8.1 — Cardiovascular Health, Technology, and Society

Target Skills

Exploring solutions to problems associated with the circulatory system

Consulting a wide variety of sources that reflect different viewpoints on existing and proposed solutions to problems associated with the circulatory system

Analyzing society's support of solutions to problems associated with the circulatory system

Evaluating the validity of the gathered viewpoints

The heart-lung machine is one of the most significant medical breakthroughs of the twentieth century. During open heart surgery, this machine, shown in the photograph, takes over a person's circulatory and respiratory functions, allowing surgeons to repair or replace valves, perform a heart bypass operation, or perform a heart transplant.

According to statistics compiled by the Canadian Heart and Stroke Foundation, cardiovascular disease is the leading cause of death in Canada, and (combined with stroke) the main cause for hospitalization. Cardiovascular disease is also the most costly disease in Canada, putting the greatest burden on our national health care system. For example, the total cost to the Canadian economy of cardiovascular disease in 1998 was estimated at 18.5 billion dollars. Nearly one-third of that cost was accounted for by hospital care. More startling, perhaps, is the fact that, for many people, cardiovascular disease is preventable.

Procedure

1. Use a variety of print and/or electronic resources to identify the factors that either individually or in combination lead to cardiovascular disease. Summarize how each factor contributes to cardiovascular disease.

2. Identify two technologies that are used or that are being developed to treat cardiovascular disease. What investment of time, people, and money was (or is) required to develop these technologies?

3. Describe how certain lifestyles can predispose an individual to cardiovascular disease.

Analysis

1. Healthcare costs represent a large investment on the part of society. The money to support these costs comes from taxpayers—members of society. Although some people feel that our healthcare dollars can be spent more wisely, many people agree that the development of technologies for treating disease is worth the financial cost. In your opinion, should more money be allocated toward preventing disease or toward treating disease? Justify your response.

2. Why are most heart and cardiovascular problems preventable?

3. What can every Canadian do to reduce the impact of cardiovascular disease on our health care system?

Extension

4. Write a newspaper-style editorial that addresses the question, "Should our health care system continue to pay for individuals who lead a lifestyle that predisposes them to cardiovascular disease?"

The heart-lung machine was invented during a period of approximately 20 years, starting in 1930, by surgeon John Gibbon and his wife Mary Gibbon, a laboratory technician. In 1953, Dr. Gibbon used the machine to perform the first successful open-heart surgery.

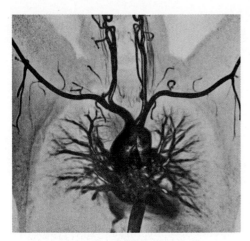

Figure 8.14 Magnetic resonance imaging scans are digitized to make three-dimensional models that help with corrective heart surgery.

Section 8.1 Summary

- The human circulatory system is made up of the heart, blood vessels, and blood.
- The blood delivers nutrients and oxygen to the tissues and removes waste materials from the tissues.
- The heart is a muscular pump with two atria that receive blood and two ventricles that propel blood through the body.

- There are three pathways for blood through the body: the pulmonary pathway, the systemic pathway, and the coronary pathway.
- Arteries, veins, and capillaries are the three main types of blood vessels. In the circulatory and coronary pathways, arteries carry oxygen-rich blood; veins carry oxygen-poor blood. (In the pulmonary pathway, arteries carry oxygen-poor blood and veins carry oxygen-rich blood.) The arteries and veins are joined by the capillaries, where gases, nutrients, and other materials are transferred to tissue cells, and wastes move into the blood.
- The pumping action of the heart is triggered by an electrical signal from the sinoatrial node (pacemaker) in the right atrium.
- Changes in blood pressure correspond to phases in the cardiac cycle.
- Many cardiovascular disorders can be treated with lifestyle changes, medications, and/or surgery.

BiologyFile

FYI
Because blood passes through the mammalian heart twice to complete a full circuit, mammals are said to have a double circulatory system with two pumps: one to send blood into the pulmonary pathway and one to send blood into the systemic pathway. Birds and some reptiles also have a double circulatory system, but fish, amphibians, and most reptiles have a single circulatory system. In a single circulatory system, blood goes through the heart only once to complete a circuit, so the heart has only one ventricle.

Section 8.1 | **Review**

1. Use graphics software to sketch a diagram that shows the four chambers of the mammalian heart. Label your diagram, and use arrows to show the route that blood takes through the heart. Use one colour of arrows (such as red) to indicate the flow of oxygen-rich blood and another colour of arrows (such as blue) to indicate the flow of oxygen-poor blood. **ICT**

2. Describe two structural differences between an artery and a vein.

3. Do all arteries carry oxygen-rich blood and all veins carry oxygen-poor blood? Explain your answer.

4. Arrange the following structures in the order that blood flowing through the coronary pathway encounters them: pulmonary artery, pulmonary vein, aorta, superior vena cava, right atrium, left atrium, right ventricle, left ventricle. Begin with the pulmonary artery.

5. Illustrate, using a flowchart or other graphic organizer, how the "lub" and "dub" sounds of the heart are created. Be sure to include proper labels if you are using a diagram to answer this question.

6. Copy the diagram into your notebook and then label the SA node, the AV node, branches of the atrioventricular bundle, and the Purkinje fibres.

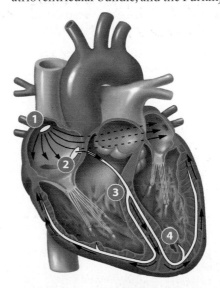

7. Identify two possible causes of high blood pressure. Describe a treatment you could use to lower your blood pressure if it were too high.

Blood and Circulation

Section Outcomes

In this section, you will
- **describe** the main components of blood
- **perform** a microscopic analysis of blood
- **explain** the role of blood in regulating body temperature
- **explain** the role of the circulatory system, at the capillary level, in the exchange of matter and energy
- **identify** certain blood disorders and the technologies used to treat them

Key Terms

plasma
formed portion
red blood cells
erythrocytes
hemoglobin
white blood cells
leucocytes
platelets
vasodilation
vasoconstriction
interstitial fluid
hemophilia
leukemia

Blood is sometimes called a connective tissue because it plays a role in linking all the cells and organs in the body. It is considered to be a tissue even though (unlike most of the body tissues) it appears to be a fluid. In fact, blood consists of two distinct elements: a fluid portion and a solid portion. The fluid portion is called **plasma**, and it consists of water plus dissolved gases, proteins, sugars, vitamins, minerals, hormones, and waste products. Plasma makes up about 55 percent of the blood volume. The solid portion of the blood is called the **formed portion**. It consists of red blood cells, white blood cells, and platelets. These cells and platelets are produced in the bone marrow, which is found inside the bones. The formed portion makes up the other 45 percent of the blood volume, as shown in Figure 8.15.

The Formed Portion of Blood

Table 8.2 compares the features of the main components in the formed portion of human blood. Note the differences in the form and function of these cells, even though they all belong to the same tissue.

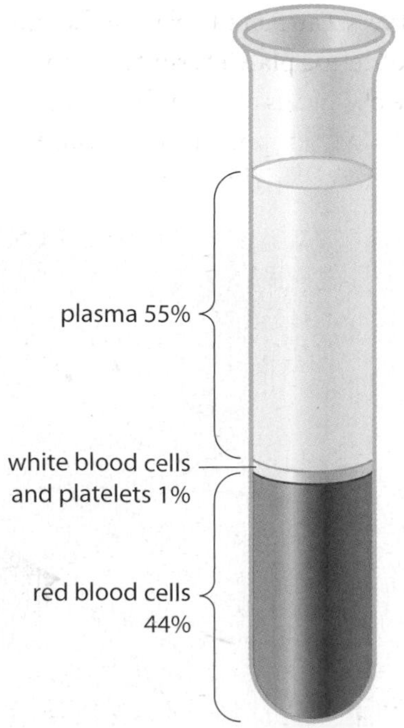

plasma 55%

white blood cells and platelets 1%

red blood cells 44%

Figure 8.15 The three main components of blood can be separated using a special medical device called a blood centrifuge. When the blood is separated, it briefly settles into layers, as shown here.

Red Blood Cells

Red blood cells, also called **erythrocytes**, make up approximately 44 percent of the total volume of blood. ("Erythroctye" comes from two Greek words that mean "red" and "cell.") Red blood cells are specialized for oxygen transport. The oxygen-carrying capacity of the blood is dependent on the number of erythrocytes that are present and the amount of hemoglobin that each red blood cell contains (see Figure 8.16).

A mature red mammalian blood cell has no nucleus. Instead, each disk-shaped red blood cell is packed with about 280 million iron-containing molecules of the respiratory pigment **hemoglobin**. Hemoglobin allows large quantities of oxygen to be transported in the blood because it has special properties that allow it to pick up, or chemically bind with, oxygen. Hemoglobin then releases the oxygen, by the process of diffusion, in the presence of cells that require it. Recall that hemoglobin also transports some of the carbon dioxide waste from cells. After carbon dioxide diffuses into the blood, it enters the red blood cells, where a small amount is taken up by hemoglobin.

A condition called anemia occurs if there are too few red blood cells or too little hemoglobin inside the red blood cells in the bloodstream. Either of these

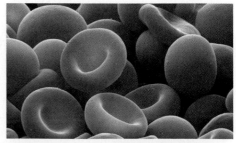

Figure 8.16 A mammalian red blood cell, also known as an erythrocyte, is a biconcave disk. Because the respiratory pigment hemoglobin reflects red wavelengths of light, oxygenated red blood cells appear to be a bright red colour. As oxygen is released, the colour that is reflected is a darker blue-red.

Table 8.2 The Cellular Components of Blood

Point of Comparison	Red blood cells	White blood cells — Granulocytes and monocytes	White blood cells — Lymphocytes	Platelets
Origin	red bone marrow	red bone marrow	thymus, red bone marrow	red bone marrow, lungs
Cells present per mm³ of blood (approximate)	5 500 000 (male) 4 500 000 (female)	6000	2000	250 000
Relative size	small (8 μm diameter)	largest (up to 25 μm)	large (10 μm)	smallest (2 μm)
Function	to carry oxygen and carbon dioxide to and from cells	to engulf foreign particles	to play a role in the formation of antibodies (defence function)	to play a role in the clotting of blood (defence function)
Life span	120 days	a few hours to a few days	unknown	2–8 days
Appearance				

deficiencies will reduce the amount of oxygen that is flowing through the body. A person who has anemia may appear pale and usually experiences fatigue. Anemia may be caused by a dietary deficiency of iron, a key component of hemoglobin.

White Blood Cells

White blood cells, also called **leucocytes**, are part of the body's response to infection. Leucocytes make up about one percent of your total blood volume but may increase to more than double normal levels when your body is fighting an infection. All white blood cells have nuclei and appear to be colourless.

Leucocytes can be divided into three groups: granulocytes, monocytes, and lymphocytes. Granulocytes consist of neutrophils, basophils, and eosinophils; monocytes can leave the bloodstream and become further specialized as macrophages, which destroy bacteria. Granulocytes and monocytes, typically found in circulating blood, engulf and destroy foreign bodies, as shown in Figure 8.17. Some lymphocytes produce proteins (called antibodies) that incapacitate pathogens and allow them to be easily detected and destroyed. The next investigation introduces the different types of white blood cells. The body's defence system is discussed in greater detail in Section 8.3.

Platelets

Platelets are the third major substance in the formed portion of the blood. **Platelets** are fragments of cells that form when larger cells in the bone marrow break apart. These fragments contain no nucleus and break down quickly in the blood.

Platelets play a key role in clotting blood, which prevents excessive blood loss after an injury. Many (but not yet all) of the stages of clotting have been determined.

- Injury to a blood vessel starts a cascade of cellular events.
- Substances released by the broken blood vessel attract platelets to the site.
- The collecting platelets rupture and release chemicals that combine with other blood components to produce an enzyme called thromboplastin.

Figure 8.17 A leucocyte, or white blood cell, attacking *Escherichia coli (E. coli)* bacteria. A single red blood cell is also visible.

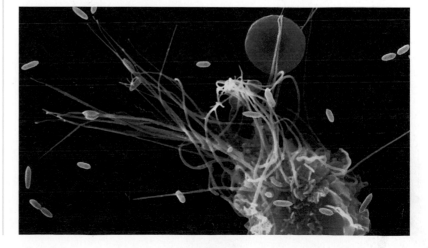

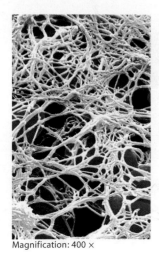

Magnification: 400 ×

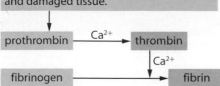

Cascade of enzyme-catalyzed reactions is triggered by platelets, blood components, and damaged tissue.

prothrombin → (Ca^{2+}) → thrombin

fibrinogen → (Ca^{2+}) → fibrin

Figure 8.18 Fibrin threads wind around the platelet plug in the damaged area of a blood vessel, providing the framework for a clot. Trapped red blood cells make the clot appear red.

- As long as there are calcium ions (Ca^{2+}) present, thromboplastin will react with prothrombin (a plasma protein produced by the liver) to produce thrombin.
- Thrombin is an enzyme that reacts with fibrinogen (another plasma protein) to produce fibrin.

Fibrin is an insoluble material that forms a mesh of strands around the injured area. This mesh traps escaping blood cells and forms the clot.

• • •

14 How could you demonstrate that blood is a mixture?

15 How does the structure and number of red blood cells compare with the structure and number of white blood cells?

16 What are platelets?

• • •

Plasma

Plasma, the fluid portion of the blood, is the medium in which the blood cells are suspended. In addition to carrying all the blood cells, plasma contains other substances, as shown in Table 8.3. Plasma also plays a role in the transport of carbon dioxide in the blood. Unlike oxygen, which is transported in the blood by the hemoglobin inside cells, carbon dioxide dissolves in the water portion of the blood and forms carbonic acid inside the cytoplasm of the red blood cells. It diffuses out of the red blood cells, into the plasma, as bicarbonate ions and is carried from tissues to the lungs for gas exchange.

The Functions of Blood

The functions of blood include serving as a medium for transporting materials in the body and regulating the concentration of substances and heat in the body.

Transport

One of the primary functions of blood is to transport materials throughout the body. As blood circulates around the body, it provides an ideal pathway for the distribution of materials and energy.

Blood is closely connected to the body systems that are responsible for digestion and for the action of hormones. For example, blood in capillaries in the walls of the small intestine absorb many of the nutrients that are end products of digestion. Blood also absorbs nutrients that are synthesized by cells in parts of the body other than the digestive tract. These nutrients, which include glucose and amino acids, are carried to the liver, where they are converted into storage products or prepared for transport to other parts of the body. As well, blood picks up chemicals and gases through the respiratory system and carries them throughout the body to where they are needed.

In another key transport role, blood transports and removes the waste products of cellular processes. Uric acid, the end products of protein metabolism, excess amounts of various mineral ions,

Table 8.3 The composition of plasma

Constituent	Percentage
Water	~ 92%

Blood proteins
  Fibrinogen
  Serum albumin
  Serum globulin
	~ 7%

Other organic substances
  Non-protein nitrogen (urea)
  Organic nutrients
	~ 0.1%

Inorganic ions:
  calcium, chlorine,
  magnesium, potassium,
  sodium, bicarbonates,
  carbonates, phosphates
	~ 0.9%

Target Skills

Determining, through microscopic inspection, the shape and abundance of the different cells in a prepared slide of human blood

Compiling and **displaying** information about the cells in human blood

Identifying Blood Cells

The different types of blood cells have different forms and functions. This investigation will enable you to examine these differences by looking at blood through a microscope.

Question

What characteristics of blood cells can you use to help you describe and compare them?

Safety Precautions

- Make sure that your hands are dry when you are handling electrical equipment.
- Handle microscope slides carefully, since they can break easily and cause cuts.

Materials

- light microscope
- prepared slides of human blood

Procedure

1. Place the slide of blood on the microscope stage, and focus using the low-power lens.

2. Scan the slide to find an area where you can observe individual blood cells.

3. Rotate the lens to medium power, and focus on the visible cells. Then rotate the lens to high power. Focus again on the visible cells. Note the differences between the red blood cells and the white blood cells.

4. Use the photographs to help you identify the cells you are observing.

5. Make a drawing of each type of cell. Label the cell membrane, the cytoplasm, and the nucleus (where applicable) of each cell, and estimate the size of the cell.

6. Repeat steps 1 to 5 until you have identified the types of blood cells shown in the photographs.

7. Summarize your observations using a table like the one below.

Formed element	Approximate number in one visual field	Approximate size (mm)	Appearance	Sketch

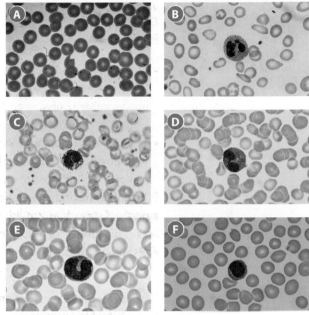

(A) Red blood cells **(B)** Neutrophil **(C)** Basophil **(D)** Eosinophil **(E)** Monocyte **(F)** Lymphocyte. Cells **(B)**–**(F)** are white blood cells among red blood cells. All images magnified 400 ×.

Analysis

1. The red blood cells of mammals do not have a nucleus, whereas the white blood cells do have a nucleus. Suggest one possible reason for this difference.

2. Were you able to observe any platelets? If yes, describe them and add the information to your table. If no, explain why you might not have seen any.

Conclusions

3. Which characteristics did you find most useful in helping you distinguish among the different blood cells?

4. **a)** Based on the blood samples you examined, how does the abundance of red blood cells compare with the abundance of the different white blood cells you observed?

   b) Compare your answer to part (a) with the data in Table 8.2 on page 283. What additional information or procedures would help you make more accurate estimates of the cells in human blood?

Web Link
Many serious athletes choose to train at high altitudes, where the air is thinner and the partial pressure of oxygen is lower. What benefit does this provide for athletes? There are several technological methods for achieving the same benefit. What are they, how do they affect the body, and why are they illegal?

www.albertabiology.ca
WWW

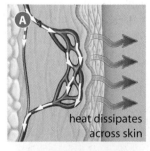

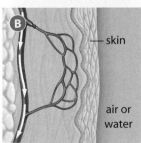

Figure 8.19 Vasodilation **(A)** and vasoconstriction **(B)**

and other waste products are carried by the blood to the kidneys for processing and excretion. Carbon dioxide is another waste product of cells that is carried by the blood to be released at the lungs.

In addition, blood serves as a medium for conveying chemical messengers, or hormones, from their origins in various glands to the organs on which they act. Hormones play a central role in regulating and coordinating the internal systems of the body. Without the bloodstream to serve as a pathway for hormones, the body would be unable to respond effectively to fluctuations in its external or internal environment, and the finely-balanced mechanisms that keep the many different components of the body functioning together would quickly break down.

Homeostatic Regulation

Another important function of blood is to maintain homeostasis within the body, especially in relation to temperature regulation. Temperature regulation involves balancing heat production with heat loss. Blood coming to the skin from the interior of the body is usually warmer than the skin. As more blood passes by the skin, more heat is lost from the body. Just as the rate of diffusion is affected by the concentration gradient, the rate of heat loss is affected by the heat gradient—the difference in temperature between the skin and the external environment. The greater the heat gradient is, the faster heat is lost through the body surface.

When the body's internal environment becomes too warm, the body must be able to rid itself of heat in order to maintain a constant internal temperature. Blood transports heat from where it is formed by cellular respiration and muscular activity to the blood vessels in the skin. Under the control of the nervous system, these vessels dilate to increase the amount of blood flowing and, therefore, to increase the amount of heat that can be lost from the skin. This

process is called **vasodilation** (see Figure 8.19A). There are several mechanisms for the release of heat, including the evaporation of water in sweat. Dehydration can be a serious problem if the body needs to rid itself of excessive heat through perspiring, for example, during a fever.

When the external environment is cold, body heat is conserved by **vasoconstriction**—the constriction of the blood vessels near the surface of the skin (see Figure 8.19B). This reduces the amount of heat that is dissipated from the skin. At the same time, waves of muscle contraction, called shivering, increase the production of heat by cellular metabolism. The heat that is produced is spread through the body by the blood.

Vasoconstriction and vasodilation are controlled by a number of factors. In some cases, they may be triggered by the brain in response to changes in blood pressure. If the blood pressure is too high, vasodilation will reduce it. If the blood pressure is too low, vasoconstriction will increase it. Vasodilation and vasoconstriction may also be triggered by increased metabolic activity. Exercise, for example, results in vasodilation to increase the blood flow to the tissues.

Some substances can interfere with the body's internal temperature regulation mechanisms by promoting either vasodilation or vasoconstriction. Alcohol and nicotine, for example, promote vasodilation and cause blood to rush to the surface of the skin.

Under normal conditions, a countercurrent heat exchange system helps to maintain a steady temperature in the core of the body. This system works because the deep arteries and veins entering and leaving the body's extremities lie adjacent to one another, so the warmer blood that flows from the body core to the extremities exchanges heat with the cooler blood returning from the extremities to the body core. Blood returning from the extremities can flow either through a surface vein

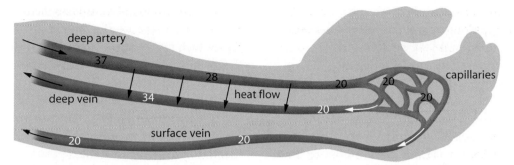

Figure 8.20 The countercurrent heat exchange mechanism between the blood vessels in the human arm: The deep vein and artery are adjacent to one another, so heat is exchanged from one to the other. As a result, arterial blood is cooled as it nears the hand, and venous blood is warmed as it leaves the hand and returns to the body core. When heat conservation is important, more blood returns to the heart through the deep vein. In higher-temperature conditions, when heat conservation is not a concern, more blood returns through the surface vein. Numerals indicate the temperature of the blood in degrees Celsius.

or through a deep vein. Figure 8.20 illustrates how the countercurrent exchange mechanism works to regulate the temperature in your arm. Keep in mind that the extremities and the skin are not kept at 37 °C. The temperature of these parts of the body may be significantly below the internal core temperature.

• • •

17 How does blood link the circulatory system with other body systems?

18 Name three factors that can trigger vasoconstriction or vasodilation.

• • •

Circulation and the Action of Capillaries

The proper functioning of all the body cells depends on capillaries because they are the only vessels that are thin enough for the exchange of matter by diffusion. Tissue cells need to be supplied with oxygen and nutrients, and they need to release the carbon dioxide and waste materials that have accumulated during cell processes. In fact, the prime function of the circulatory system is to deliver blood to the capillaries that lie close to the cells, thus supplying the cells with energy and nutrients and removing their metabolic waste products.

Capillaries are present in networks, or beds, throughout the body, and most of the cells in the body are located beside capillaries. There are about one billion capillaries in the human body, with a total surface area of approximately 6300 m^2. This is nearly the area of a football field!

Figure 8.21 shows the anatomy of a capillary bed. A capillary bed is formed by many capillary vessels lying between a branch of an artery and a branch of a vein. The blood flow through a capillary bed is not necessarily constant. If the cells beside a particular capillary bed do not need to be serviced, blood can be shunted directly from the artery to the vein, bypassing the capillaries through the action of sphincters that tighten and close the opening. Blood also bypasses

Figure 8.21 Anatomy of a capillary bed: The cells that make up living tissues are a distance of one to three cell-widths from a capillary. Why must cells lie so closely to capillaries?

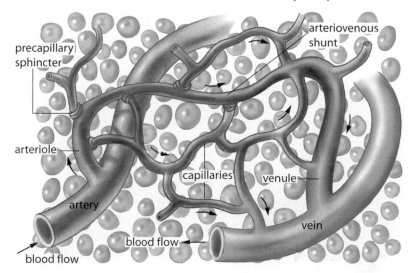

some capillary beds when it is needed in some other part of the body. After eating, for example, the capillaries of the digestive system are open, but the capillaries that supply blood to certain muscles are closed. This is one reason that exercising after eating is so difficult.

The cells of the body are constantly bathed in a liquid called **interstitial fluid**. (In some books, this fluid is called extracellular fluid or tissue fluid.) Any material exchanged between the capillaries and the cells must pass through the interstitial fluid.

Capillaries have an arterial end, a mid-section, and a venous end, as shown in Figure 8.22. When blood enters a capillary at the arterial end, it appears to be bright red because the hemoglobin in the red blood cells is rich in oxygen. The diffusion of materials, including the oxygen attached to the hemoglobin in red blood cells and the nutrients suspended in the blood's plasma, takes place along the mid-section of a capillary. The direction of diffusion is determined by a material's concentration gradient. For example, nutrients and oxygen are higher in concentration in the blood, so they diffuse into the interstitial fluid toward the cells. Carbon dioxide and other wastes are higher in concentration in the interstitial fluid, so they diffuse out of the cells through the interstitial fluid and into the capillaries.

The blood flow through the capillaries is slower than through any other part of the circulatory system, thus providing time for diffusion to occur.

The blood pressure in the capillary beds is lower than in the arteries but a little higher than in the veins, ensuring that the blood continues to flow in one direction from arteries to veins. The blood pressure decreases the farther away the blood is from the heart, which is why the blood pressure in the veins is lower that the blood pressure in the capillaries. Recall that muscle action and valves keep the slow-moving blood flowing in the correct direction in the veins.

• • •

(19) What is interstitial fluid?

(20) What role do capillaries play in maintaining homeostasis, in relation to gases, nutrients, and fluids?

• • •

Blood Disorders

There are several relatively common blood disorders. One of these disorders, an inherited, life-threatening disorder called **hemophilia**, is the result of insufficient clotting proteins in the blood. Severe hemophilia occurs when there is less than 1 percent of the clotting protein in the blood. Approximately 70 percent of people with hemophilia have this severe form, and they are in constant danger of bleeding to death if they injure themselves. People with hemophilia are treated with injections of a substance called Factor VIII, which is a protein involved in coagulation that is missing from their blood.

Figure 8.22 The exchange of materials between the blood in a capillary and the fluid surrounding the individual cells in the body takes place across the wall of the capillary.

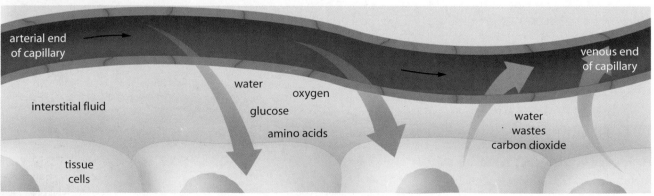

arterial end of capillary

venous end of capillary

interstitial fluid

water
oxygen
glucose
amino acids

water
wastes
carbon dioxide

tissue cells

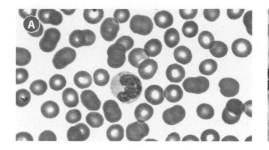

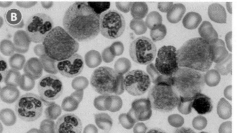

Figure 8.23 Normal blood cells **(A)** and blood cells from a person with myeloid leukemia **(B)**. Notice the relative numbers of white blood cells to red blood cells.

Leukemia is a cancer of the white blood cells. There are two main types of leukemia: myeloid and lymphoid. Myeloid leukemia is characterized by the presence of too many leucocytes. These leucocytes are immature and unable to fight infection. As well, they crowd out the red blood cells, which causes anemia and fatigue (see Figure 8.23). Lymphoid leukemia is a cancer of the lymphocytes, but the symptoms are very similar to those of myeloid leukemia. Both of these leukemias can occur in one of two states: acute or chronic. The symptoms of acute leukemia appear suddenly, and death follows quickly. Chronic leukemia may go undetected for months or years.

Thought Lab | 8.2 | Keeping the Blood Supply Safe

Target Skills

Identifying and **evaluating** possible solutions to blood shortages

Investigating the roles and responsibilities of governments, medical organizations, and members of society in making decisions regarding the application of scientific and technological developments

The earliest successful blood transfusions from person to person were done in the mid-1800s. Scientists discovered how to preserve and store blood in the 1910s, and blood banks became part of the medical scene, enabling physicians to save many more lives. While the technology to preserve and store blood ensured availability in times of need, other challenges in blood bank management have arisen. A key one is ensuring that the blood supply is not only plentiful but is also safe.

Canadian Blood Services has been managing Canada's blood supply since 1998, after Canada's tainted blood scandal of the 1980s. Prior to the creation of Canadian Blood Services, the Canadian Red Cross was in charge of Canada's blood supply. During the years of the scandal, blood donations were not screened for HIV and hepatitis C viruses despite officials' knowledge that these life-threatening viruses could be present in the blood supply system. Contaminated blood was used in transfusions, and hundreds of Canadians received it. Many developed AIDs, while others suffered liver damage from hepatitis C. A $150 million compensation package was eventually negotiated for 1200 victims of the tainted blood.

In this assignment, you will research blood transfusions. Based on your research, you will prepare a document or design a presentation describing society's interests and roles in the blood supply system and identify possible technological solutions to blood safety and blood shortages.

Procedure

1. Use print and/or electronic resources to research answers to the Analysis questions below. **ICT**

2. Summarize, in the form of a report or multimedia presentation, the results of your research. Include an explanation of the importance of blood transfusions and identify possible technological solutions to problems of blood supply and blood supply safety.

Analysis

1. Why is it considered important for members of society to donate blood on a regular basis? Do all members of society share this view? Explain.

2. Who can and who cannot donate blood?

3. What blood products are isolated from donated blood and how are each of these products used?

4. What are five common misconceptions that people have about donating blood?

5. Identify technologies that are being developed that one day might replace the need for people to donate blood.

Extension

6. Visit the web site for Canadian Blood Services and identify the procedures in place to safeguard Canada's blood supply. Do you think they are adequate for another blood-borne infection, such as West Nile? Justify your answer. **ICT**

7. Should the government and the public be involved in the management of Canada's blood supply or should its management be privatized? Choose a position and present your arguments in support of it.

The Tomorrow Project

Although research into the causes of cancer at the cellular level is continuing, scientists now know that at least 50 percent of human cancers can be attributed to environmental or behavioural factors. Launched in October 2000 by the Alberta Cancer Board, the Tomorrow Project is a long-term cancer study that aims to determine how individual lifestyle can affect a person's chances of developing the disease.

Strength in Numbers

The research team at the Tom Baker Cancer Centre in Calgary believes in big numbers—50 000 to be exact. That is the number of Albertans that the team intends to recruit to take part in the Tomorrow Project. The goal is to assemble a random sample of Albertans who are between the ages of 35 and 69 at the time of enrolment and who have never been diagnosed with cancer. Participants fill out surveys about their health and lifestyle, diet, and physical activity. Some participants are also asked to provide blood samples, allowing researchers to study genetic-environmental interactions. The project will continue to collect health and lifestyle information from participants every few years until age 85 or death.

In the surveys, participants answer a variety of questions about their family medical history, stress level, favourite foods, body measurements, and spirituality, as well as whether or not they smoke or are exposed to second-hand smoke. The researchers are looking at risk factors that are thought to influence the incidence of cancer. Different types of cancer can have different risk factors. For example, a high body mass index (BMI) is considered to be a specific risk factor that may increase a person's chance of developing endometrial, kidney, colon, or postmenopausal breast cancer.

The Day after Tomorrow

Cancer exacts a heavy toll on Canadian society. In April 2005, the Canadian Cancer Society estimated that 149 000 new cases of cancer and 69 500 deaths from cancer will occur in Canada in 2005. If the current trend continues, the Cancer Society estimates that during the next 30 years, 5.7 million Canadians will develop cancer and 2.7 million Canadians will die of the disease.

Why do some people remain healthy, while others develop cancer? The results of the Tomorrow Project will not be known for many years to come. By tracking the lifestyle choices of a large sample of people over a long period of time, however, researchers hope that they will eventually learn more about risk factors that could be modified to decrease the incidence of cancer.

· · ·

1. What is the current status of the Tomorrow Project? Elect one student to contact the Tomorrow Project headquarters in Calgary to find out information and then share it with the class. This person could also share information that is available on the project's web site. **ICT**

2. What type of cancer is the leading cause of premature death due to cancer for both men and women in Canada? What are the modifiable risk factors associated with this type of cancer?

Treatment of leukemia includes blood transfusions to increase the number of red blood cells and healthy white blood cells, and chemotherapy. Advances in chemotherapy have vastly improved survival rates, particularly for children. About 20 years ago, children diagnosed with leukemia had less than a 50 percent chance of survival. The survival rate is now greater than 85 percent. Another possible treatment is bone marrow transplants, which provide healthy marrow from which new, healthy white blood cells can grow. (Blood cells are formed in the bone marrow, which is the soft tissue of large bones in the body.) Bone marrow transplants are very invasive and painful, however, so they are usually considered as a last resort.

Section 8.2 Summary

- Blood is a tissue that is made up of a fluid portion (called plasma) and a formed (or cellular) portion.
- The fluid portion of the blood, plasma, is made up of water, blood proteins, other organic substances and inorganic ions. Water is the most significant component.
- The formed portion is made up of different types of cells, including red blood cells (erythrocytes), white blood cells (leucocytes), and platelets.
- Red blood cells transport oxygen, white blood cells are a key component of the body's defence system, and platelets are needed for clotting.
- Blood has various roles in the body, including transportation of materials and temperature regulation.
- Gases and other materials diffuse into and out of the blood through capillaries.
- There are various disorders of the blood. Advances in treatments and ongoing research in new areas, such as stem cell research, are improving the chances that people with blood disorders will have a full recovery.

BiologyFile

Web Link
Advances in the treatment of leukemia include the use of blood from umbilical cords and the transplanting of stem cells. Stem cells are cells from which specialized cells of the body develop. How do these two treatment options work? What are the controversies associated with them?

www.albertabiology.ca
WWW

Section 8.2 | **Review**

1. Use a word processor or spreadsheet software to create a chart similar to the one shown below. Use this chart to summarize the cellular components of blood. **ICT**

Point of Comparison	Red blood cells	White blood cells		Platelets
		Leucocytes	Lymphocytes	
Origin				
Cells present per mm^3 of blood				
Relative size				
Function				
Life span				
Appearance				

2. Identify seven substances normally found in blood plasma.

3. In your own words, explain the role the blood and circulatory system play in the following systems
   a) digestive system
   b) endocrine system
   c) respiratory system
   d) excretory system

4. Use graphics software to create a drawing that clearly illustrates which types of matter are exchanged between the capillaries and the cells. Label the forces that act and the direction of these forces. **ICT**

5. The hematocrit refers to the percentage of an individual's red blood cells. A small blood sample is placed in a special hematocrit tube. Blood can be separated into its components by putting it into a centrifuge and "spinning it down." When the centrifuge spins, the red blood cells are forced to the bottom of the tube because they are the heaviest element in the blood. A decreased hematocrit can be the result of a low number of red blood cells, decreased volume of red blood cells, or reduced hemoglobin concentration.

   a) Identify one blood disorder that may be indicative of a decreased hematocrit, and list the physical symptoms that are usually associated with this disorder.

   b) Use word processing software to create a flow chart summarizing the steps in the blood clotting mechanism. **ICT**

The Lymphatic System and Immunity

As you have seen, the circulatory system transports nutrients, respiratory gases (oxygen and carbon dioxide), and wastes. Hormones and other chemical messengers are also transported in the blood, enabling different organs and processes to communicate with each another. The cardiovascular circulatory system, however, is not the only vascular transport system in the body. As you can see in Figure 8.24, another system of vessels, called the lymphatic system, is closely associated with the capillaries and veins.

The **lymphatic circulatory system** is a network of vessels, with associated glands or nodes, that extends throughout the body (see Figure 8.25). The lymphatic vessels collect a fluid called **lymph**, which is made up of interstitial fluid. Lymph is either colourless or pale yellow and, in composition, is much like the plasma of blood. The lymphatic system helps to maintain the balance of fluids in the body.

As blood circulates through the body, some of the plasma escapes from the capillaries and becomes part of the interstitial fluid that constantly bathes all the cells of the body. Rather than re-entering the capillaries of the cardiovascular system, much of this

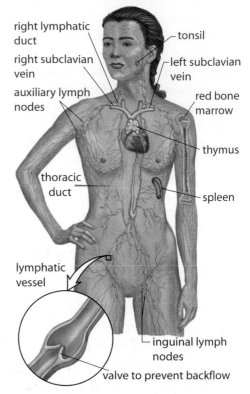

Figure 8.25 The human lymphatic system is spread throughout the body. Its largest vessels are in the region of the abdomen and thoracic cavity.

interstitial fluid is absorbed into the vessels of the lymphatic circulatory system. Eventually, it rejoins the main circulatory system through ducts that empty into the large veins near the heart. Unlike blood, which both arrives at and leaves the heart in a continuous circuit of cardiovascular vessels, lymph forms in closed-ended tubes in capillary beds. It is delivered to the heart to be mixed back into the general blood circulation. Figure 8.26 shows how the lymphatic system works to maintain the steady flow of water and other substances between the blood, the interstitial fluid, and the lymphatic system. Some specialized lymph capillaries are found in the intestinal villi. These capillaries carry some digested fats throughout the body.

The lymphatic system also works with the white blood cells to protect the body against infection. White blood

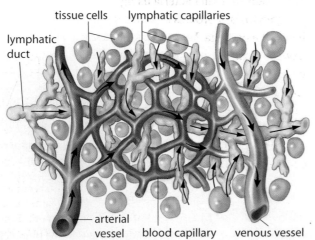

Figure 8.24 Lymph vessels are closely associated with the capillaries of the cardiovascular system. Fluid that escapes from the cardiovascular capillaries forms part of the interstitial fluid. Some of this fluid is collected in the lymphatic capillaries and eventually returned to the blood.

cells called lymphocytes mature in the lymph nodes, the glands that are found throughout the lymphatic system. The lymph nodes also contain macrophages, which trap and destroy bacteria that are circulating within the body. An infection may cause your immune system to increase in the number of macrophages and lymphocytes in the lymph nodes. When you become ill, you can sometimes feel the swelling in the lymph glands behind your jawbone or under your arms.

• • •

21 What is the lymphatic system, and how is it related to the circulatory system?

22 How does the lymphatic system help to protect the body from infection?

• • •

The Defence System

The air you breathe, the water you drink, and the food you eat are all inhabited by billions of microscopic organisms. The internal environment of the body, which is kept stable through homeostatic mechanisms, provides an ideal place for many types of microscopic organisms to live and reproduce. Many of these organisms cause little or no damage to us, but others, called pathogens, can be very dangerous. (The word "pathogen" comes from two Greek words that, together, literally mean "producer of suffering.")

The human body defends itself against the constant attack of pathogens by either preventing the entry of pathogens or destroying them if they do enter. These defences can be divided into three groups: barriers to keep pathogens out, general or non-specific defences against a wide variety of pathogens, and specific defences against particular pathogens.

The Skin: Preventing the Entry of Pathogens

The first lines of defence are all of the physical and chemical barriers of the body, such as eyelashes, the cilia of the respiratory tract, tears, and stomach acid. However, the largest barrier is the skin. Although thousands of bacteria, fungi, and other pathogens can be found on the skin, it is a hostile environment for the survival of many micro-organisms. The outer layer of the skin is dry and contains large amounts of tough, relatively indigestible keratin. The skin's oil contains bactericides, and perspiration forms an acidic layer that is inhospitable for microbial growth.

Non-Specific Defences (Cell-Mediated Immunity)

The second line of defence is the **non-specific defences**, which include three types of white blood cells—macrophages, neutrophils, and monocytes—and so is called **cell-mediated immunity**. Neutrophils and monocytes are white blood cells that kill bacteria using **phagocytosis**, a process in which they ingest the bacteria. **Macrophages**, which develop from monocytes, also use phagocytosis. They are found in the liver, spleen, brain, and lungs, and circulate in the blood and interstitial fluid. Non-specific defence also includes natural killer cells, which target body cells that have become cancerous or infected by viruses.

Specific Defences (Antibody-Mediated Immunity)

The third line of defence is **immunity**. Immunity is developed by the actions of the **specific defences**, using antibodies, and so is called **antibody-mediated immunity**. **Antibodies** are proteins that

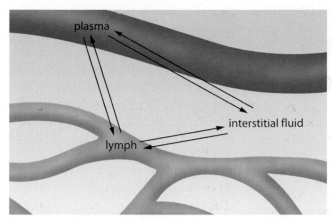

Figure 8.26 The lymphatic system plays an important role in maintaining the correct water balance in the interstitial fluid of the body. The arrows indicate a steady-state relationship between the lymphatic system, the circulatory system, and the interstitial fluid.

BiologyFile

FYI
Phagocytosis is a special form of ingestion used by cells of the immune system as well as other microbes such as bacteria. In phagocytosis, the cell extends its membrane to form a bag around the target. Eventually the edges of the bag meet, fuse together, and draw the target in. The result is a closed sac containing the target within the cell and an intact cell membrane.

recognize foreign substances and act to neutralize or destroy them. Because of exposure to foreign substances over time, as well as variations in genetic make-up, each person develops an immune system that is unique in its ability to deal with a wide variety of possible infections. We are not all exposed to the same diseases, and some diseases require a stronger response than others because they are more virulent than others.

The specific immune system is primarily a function of the lymphocytes in the circulatory system. The **lymphocytes** are divided into two specialized groups, depending on where they mature. B lymphocytes, or **B cells**, mature in the bone marrow. T lymphocytes, or **T cells**, mature in the thymus gland, which is located near the heart.

Before you were born, your body was already "cataloguing" the molecules that are present in your body. This cataloguing is critical, so that your body can recognize proteins and other molecules as part of the "self." If your body could not tell what molecules were supposed to be present, it would be unable to respond to invading pathogens. **Antigens** are molecules that are found on the surface of the cells and on pathogens. Antigens provide an identification system. Antigen receptors on T and B cells allow them to recognize foreign antigens and begin responding to the invasion. Antibodies have the same shape as the antigen receptor for a specific antigen, so they can bind with and neutralize the antigen. Figure 8.27 illustrates some of the roles played by

Figure 8.27 A simplified illustration of the body's immune response, triggered by the entry of pathogens at the site of an infection. Pathogens may include bacteria, viruses, fungi, protists, and other microscopic organisms.

A After the pathogens have breached the first line of defence, in this case the skin, they trigger the body's immune response. The second line of defence is the arrival of non-phagocytic leucocytes at the infection site. These cells release histamine, which causes blood vessels at the site to dilate and become more permeable to fluid and leucocytes. The increased blood flow and accumulation of fluid makes the area swollen and hot. The increase in temperature alone may be enough to destroy or neutralize some pathogens.

B Phagocytic macrophages engulf and destroy invading bacteria. The accumulation of dead macrophages and bacteria is visible as pus at the site of the infection.

C The third line of defence begins after a pathogen has been destroyed; the antigens from the pathogen protrude from the cell membrane of the macrophage.

D Receptor sites on the surface of helper T cells bind to the antigens on the surface of the macrophage. This union triggers the release of chemical messengers from both cells. These messengers cause T cells to multiply. Some of these T cells destroy infected tissue cells, breaking the reproductive cycle of the pathogen.

E The antibodies on B cells bind to the antigens, contributing to the destruction of the pathogens.

F T cells bind to the B cell antibody-antigen complex. This union of T and B cells activates the B cell, causing it to enlarge and divide, which produces plasma cells and memory cells.

G The plasma cells produce antibodies at a rate of 2000 per second, and release them into the blood stream. Antibodies and memory B cells remain in the blood, ready to fight a new infection by the same pathogen.

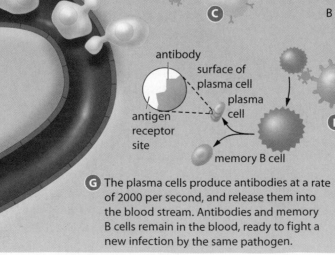

pathogen

pus

T cell

macrophage

B cell

antibody

surface of plasma cell

plasma cell

antigen receptor site

memory B cell

The immune response to antigen

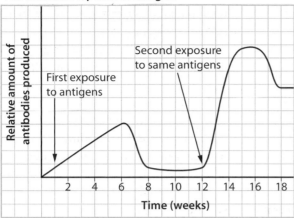

Figure 8.28 On the first exposure to an antigen, the immune response takes time to produce the antibodies necessary to fight the infection. If the same antigen is introduced again, the response is more rapid and generates much higher levels of antibodies.

BiologyFile

FYI

Helper T cells are also called T-4 cells. A T-4 cell count is a blood test that measures the number of helper T cells in the blood. T-4 cells signal other immune system cells to fight infections, and they are the prime target of the HIV virus. Too few T-4 cells indicates that your immune system is not capable of responding properly. A low T-4 cell count is a signal that HIV/AIDS patients should start taking medications to prevent AIDS-related infections.

both macrophages and lymphocytes as the second and third lines of defence.

Most antibodies are specific, so they can bind with only one type of antigen. Different B cells produce different antibodies, and this variation increases the possibility that the body will have an antibody that can recognize and bind to an invading pathogen. Once a B cell is activated, it enlarges and divides to produce memory B cells and plasma cells. The plasma cells produce enormous quantities of the same antibody carried by the B cell and release these antibodies into the bloodstream to fight the invading pathogens. After the infection has been fought off, memory B cells remain in the blood, ready to trigger another immune response when necessary (see Figure 8.28).

23 What are the three lines of defence that the body uses to protect itself from pathogens and other foreign invaders?

T Cells (Cellular Immunity)

Several different types of T cells work together to fight off invading pathogens, using a process called cellular immunity. When a pathogen is destroyed by phagocytosis, antigens from the pathogen move to the surface of the macrophage that destroyed it. When a specific type of T cell, called a **helper T cell**, recognizes

the antigen, it gives off chemical signals that stimulate the action of macrophages, B cells, and other T cells. **Killer T cells**, or cytotoxic T cells, bind with infected cells and destroy them by puncturing a hole in their cell membranes (see Figure 8.29). Killer T cells may be activated indirectly by the chemical signals from a helper T cell or directly by the presence of the invading pathogen and associated antigen. **Suppressor T cells** slow and suppress the process of cellular immunity to ensure that normal tissue does not get destroyed. Some T cells do not respond to the invading antigens the first time they are exposed to them. Instead, these **memory T cells** remain in the bloodstream and are able to act quickly if the antigen is encountered again.

24 Describe the importance of specific defenses to immunity.

25 What is the relationship between B cells and T cells?

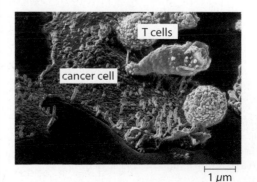

Figure 8.29 A scanning electron microscope shows killer T cells attacking and destroying an invading cancer cell.

Blood Types

A *blood transfusion* is the transfer of blood from one person into the blood of another. Many early blood transfusions resulted in the illness, and sometimes the death, of some recipients. Eventually, scientists discovered that only certain types of blood are compatible because red blood cell membranes carry specific substances that are antigens to blood recipients. Several groups of red blood cell antigens exist. The most significant of these is the group of antigens in the ABO system.

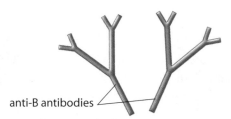

Type A blood: Red blood cells have type A surface antigens. Plasma has anti-B antibodies.

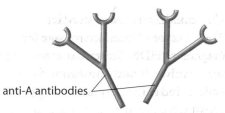

Type B blood: Red blood cells have type B surface antigens. Plasma has anti-A antibodies.

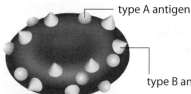

Type AB blood: Red blood cells have type A and type B surface antigens. Plasma has neither anti-A or anti-B antibodies.

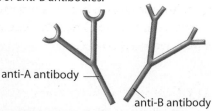

Type O blood: Red blood cells have neither type A nor type B surface antigens. Plasma has both anti-A and anti-B antibodies.

Figure 8.30 In the ABO system, blood type depends on the presence or absence of antigens A and B on the surface of red blood cells. In these diagrams, A and B antigens are represented by different shapes on the red blood cells. The possible anti-A and anti-B antibodies in the plasma are represented for each blood type.

The ABO System

In the **ABO system**, the presence or absence of type A and type B antigens on red blood cells determines a person's blood type. (Refer to Figure 8.30.) The presence or absence of these antigens is an inherited characteristic.

As shown in Table 8.4, a person who has type A antigen on the surface of the red blood cells has type A blood. A person with type B blood has type B antigen on the surface of the red blood cells. Notice that a person who has type AB blood has both antigens, and a person with type O blood has neither antigen on the surface of the red blood cells.

A person who has type A blood has anti-B antibodies in the plasma. A person with type B blood has anti-A antibodies, and a person with type O has both antibodies in the plasma. These antibodies appear within several months after birth. The presence of these antibodies can cause agglutination. *Agglutination* is a clumping of red blood cells that occurs when incompatible blood types are mixed. Agglutinated red blood cells can clog blood vessels, blocking circulation and causing severe damage to organs.

Table 8.4 The Human Blood Types

Blood Type	Antigen on Red Blood Cells	Antibody in Plasma
A	A	anti-B
B	B	anti-A
AB	A and B	none
O	none	anti-A and anti-B

The Rh System

Another group of antigens found in most red blood cells is the **Rh factor**. (Rh is an abbreviation for rhesus monkey—*Macaca mulatta*—in which these antigens were first discovered.) People with the Rh factor on their red blood cells are termed Rh positive (Rh⁺). People without it are Rh negative (Rh⁻). Individuals who are Rh⁻ usually do not

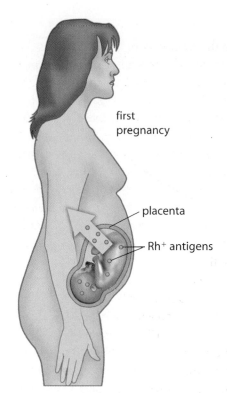

first pregnancy

placenta

Rh⁺ antigens

Mother is exposed to Rh antigens at the birth of her Rh⁺ child.

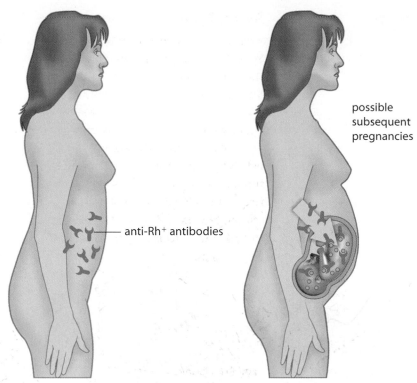

anti-Rh⁺ antibodies

possible subsequent pregnancies

Mother produces anti-Rh⁺ antibodies.

During the mother's next pregnancy, anti-Rh antibodies can cross the placenta and endanger the child.

Figure 8.31 If a baby inherits its Rh⁺ blood from the father and if the mother is Rh⁻, problems can develop if the blood cells of mother and baby mix prior to and during birth.

have antibodies to the Rh factor, but they may make them when they are exposed to the Rh factor during a blood transfusion or pregnancy.

As shown in Figure 8.31, during pregnancy, if a mother is Rh⁻ and the father is Rh⁺, a child may be Rh⁺. The Rh⁺ red blood cells of the child may leak across the placenta into the mother's bloodstream. The presence of these Rh⁺ antigens causes the mother's immune system to produce anti-Rh antibodies. Usually, in a subsequent pregnancy with another Rh⁺ baby, the anti-Rh antibodies may cross the placenta and destroy the child's red blood cells. This is called hemolytic disease of the newborn (HDN). (Hemolysis is the bursting of red blood cells.) This condition can lead to brain damage, deafness, and death.

In HDN, as the red blood cells break down, the liver produces a substance called bilirubin in such excess that bilirubin ends up in the blood and other tissues and fluids of the baby's blood. Bilirubin is a pigment that causes the baby's blood and tissue to turn yellow.

This condition is called jaundice. The presence of jaundice is a sign for diagnosing HDN. Treatment at this stage may involve a blood transfusion for the child or inducing early labour to prevent the situation from becoming worse.

The Rh problem is prevented by injecting Rh⁻ women with an antibody preparation against the Rh factor within 72 hours after the birth of an Rh⁺ child. The anti-Rh antibodies in the injection attack any of the baby's red blood cells in the mother's blood before these cells can stimulate her immune system to produce her own antibodies. This procedure will not help if the woman has already begun to produce antibodies. Thus, the timing of the injection is crucial.

• • •

26 Compare the four blood types in the ABO system.

27 What is the Rh factor, and what problems can the presence or absence of Rh antibodies cause during pregnancy?

• • •

BiologyFile

Web Link
Complications associated with hemolytic disease of the newborn include anemia, hyperbilirubemia, and hydrops fetalis. What are these conditions and how can they be treated before and after birth?

www.albertabiology.ca
WWW

While the immune system can trigger attacks on healthy tissues, as seen in autoimmune disorders, it can also be attacked by pathogens. The human immunodeficiency virus (HIV) infects the white blood cells, principally T cells. The result is a slow decline of the immune system, which renders the body vulnerable to infection by other pathogens. These opportunistic pathogens are ones that a healthy immune system would control with ease. In people with HIV, the resulting infections can be quite serious, even fatal.

Immune System Disorders

Recall that the body identifies "self" cells very early in development. When T cells or antibodies mistakenly attack the body's own cells (the "self" cells) as if they had foreign antigens, the condition is called an **autoimmune disorder**. The exact cause of autoimmune disorders is not known, but research is active. So far, researchers know that there is a tendency to inherit the condition and that the condition often begins after recovery from an infection.

Rheumatoid arthritis is a chronic autoimmune disorder that is characterized by inflammation of the lining of the joints (see Figure 8.32). It is most common in individuals between the ages of 25 and 50. It is caused by the body's own immune system attacking the joints, causing pain, stiffness, swelling, fever, fatigue, and decreased appetite. The immune response can continue attacking cartilage, bone, tendons, and ligaments. Rheumatoid arthritis can cause permanent disability.

Treatments include Aspirin™, non-steroidal anti-inflammatory drugs (NSAIDs), and steroids. These medications all act to reduce the pain and inflammation, but they do not address the cause of the disorder. Stronger

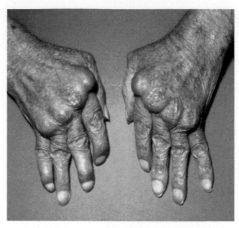

Figure 8.32 Rheumatoid arthritis can cause painful debilitating joint deformity.

medications, called disease-modifying antirheumatic drugs (DMARDs), work on the immune response and slow the progress of the disorder.

There have been some recent breakthroughs in drug treatments for autoimmune disorders, but they are still in the early stages of development. For example, researchers have been able to reverse Type 1 diabetes in mice by stopping the immune system from destroying its own insulin-producing cells in the pancreas. They "trained" immature white blood cells to properly distinguish "self" from "non-self" cells. These results are promising for the treatment of other autoimmune

---

Thought Lab 8.3 Barriers of Defence

Target Skills

Researching main components of the human immune system

Designing a model or simulation to demonstrate the functioning human immune system

In this assignment, you will research the human immune system. Based on your research, you will design a model or a simulation to represent the main components of the immune system.

Procedure

1. Conduct your research in a library or on the Internet. Identify the primary elements of the human immune system, including all three lines of defence. **ICT**

2. In a small group, decide how you would like to create your representation of the components of the immune system. Also decide what materials you will need.

3. Acquire the materials you need, and create your model or simulation. Ensure that all the parts are clearly labelled.

4. Display your model or simulation for the class to evaluate.

Analysis

1. Compare your model or simulation with those of other groups. Identify the differences.

2. Do you think that your model or simulation clearly shows the elements of the immune system? Explain why or why not.

3. If you could redo this activity, how would you improve what you did and the way you did it? What would you change?

disorders, although there is still considerable work to be done.

Allergies

An allergy is an exaggerated response by the immune system to a harmless material, such as pollen, mould, or animal dander. There are two major types of allergic reactions: immediate (or acute) and delayed. An immediate reaction is the most common type of allergic reaction. It occurs within seconds of exposure to the allergen and usually disappears within 30 minutes. In an immediate reaction, specialized antibodies trigger certain cells to release histamines, which are chemicals that increase the permeability of blood vessels, making the area red and swollen. The specialized antibodies can also trigger the release of cellular fluids, which can result in watery eyes and a runny nose.

Some forms of asthma, the most common chronic disease among North American children, are an immediate reaction to allergens that are inhaled. The inhaled allergens trigger a massive release of histamines, which sets off spasms of the bronchioles, the tiny air passageways in the lungs. In people who have asthma, these passageways are especially sensitive. Spasms can also be triggered by stimuli such as cold air and fatigue. The result can be coughing, wheezing, and sometimes fatal suffocation.

Asthma can be treated with anti-inflammatory drugs that can open the passageways of the bronchi, and thus ease the symptoms of an immediate reaction. Researchers are exploring new medications that may provide long-term relief from the inflammation that characterizes this disease.

Delayed allergic responses are set off by T cells that have been sensitized by previous contact with the allergens. In these cases, the reaction is slower and lasts for a longer time. Allergic reactions to certain types of cosmetics and jewellery are examples of this type of allergy.

Food allergies have become increasing common in Canada. Why have they become a health issue? Is it due to better diagnosis, the increased use of food additives, or unknown environmental factors? The answer is not yet clear, but researchers do know that people have become sensitized to foods that have been part of the human diet for thousands of years. Students and teachers in many schools now have EpiPens™ that contain single-dose injections of epinephrine (adrenaline), in case a person has an immediate, dangerous reaction—called anaphylaxis—to an allergen such as nuts or nut products.

Symptoms of food allergies can be immediate or delayed. Immediate reactions may include a runny nose, vomiting, severe diarrhea, or a life-threatening asthmatic attack. Delayed reactions may occur as skin problems, wheezing, or aches and pains. The following foods and food additives are associated with those reactions that occur most frequently or severely:

- peanuts, soybeans, nuts, seeds, and their oils or extracts
- corn products
- dairy products and/or lactose (a sugar common in dairy products)
- egg products
- fish and/or seafood
- monosodium glutamate
- sulfites (sulfur-based preservatives that are especially dangerous for people with asthma)
- tartrazine (also called Yellow Dye #5; used to colour foods and cosmetics)
- wheat and/or gluten

Section 8.3 Summary

- The lymphatic circulatory system is associated with the vessels of the cardiovascular circulatory system.
- The lymphatic system helps to maintain the balance of fluids in the body.
- The lymphatic system is an important part of the body's defence system.

Biology File

Web Link
Peanuts are not actually nuts, but the seeds of a member of the legume family. Peanuts are one of the most allergenic foods, and the reaction they cause can be fatal. When people who are highly sensitive to peanuts are exposed either directly or indirectly to them, they may experience anaphylaxis. What is anaphylaxis, and how is it treated? What advances have been made to improve our understanding and approaches to treating peanut allergies?

www.albertabiology.ca
www

Biology File

Web Link

The proliferation of spam in email inboxes around the world has spawned a host of technologies to combat this inconvenient and annoying practice. What does the development of anti-spam technology have to do with the battle against HIV and AIDS?

www.albertabiology.ca
WWW

- There are three lines of defence against invading pathogens: barriers, non-specific defences, and specific defences.
- Skin is the largest barrier against pathogens.
- Non-specific defences are made up of the actions of macrophages, neutrophils, and monocytes. All three kill pathogens by the process of phagocytosis.
- Specific, or immune, defences use a wide variety of cells, including B cells and T cells
- Antigens are molecules that are located on the surface of a cell and act as an identification badge.
- Antibodies recognize foreign substances and act to neutralize or destroy them. B cells are primarily responsible for antibody immunity.

- Helper T cells, suppressor T cells, killer T cells, and memory T cells work together to create cellular immunity.
- In the ABO system, blood is classed as type A, B, AB, or O. Membranes of red blood cells may contain type A and/or B antigens, or neither antigen.
- In the plasma, antibodies may be anti-A or anti-B. If the corresponding antigen and antibody mix, agglutination occurs.
- The Rh antigen is another type of antigen. During pregnancy, problems can occur if an Rh⁻ mother forms antibodies to the Rh antigen while carrying or during the birth of an Rh⁺ child. These antibodies can cross the placenta to destroy the red blood cells of any subsequent Rh⁺ child.

Section 8.3 Review

1. Explain how the lymphatic system is related to the cardiovascular system.

2. Describe the two main functions of the lymphatic system.

3. Use graphics software to make a sketch of a lymph vessel and a vein. Use the caption of this sketch to compare a lymph vessel with a vein. **ICT**

4. Describe the difference between an antibody and an antigen.

5. Use graphics software to draw sketches of a lymphocyte, a neutrophil, and a monocyte. (See Investigation 8.C: Identifying Blood Cells for help with your sketches.) Explain the function of these white blood cells. **ICT**

6. Use graphics software to draw a diagram that illustrates how harmful cells are destroyed by macrophages. **ICT**

7. Explain, in detail, what the letters represent in the ABO system.

8. Explain how a mother who is Rh⁻ and carrying an Rh⁺ baby could encounter no complications during her first pregnancy but could face blood compatibility problems during a second pregnancy with an Rh⁺ child.

9. Explain what is happening in region A and region B of this graph.

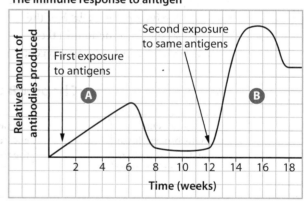

The immune response to antigen

10. Explain the general causes of an autoimmune disorder.

11. Use word processing or spreadsheet software to make a chart similar to the one below. Use the information in your textbook to complete the chart. **ICT**

Immune System Disorder	Causes	Symptoms	Treatments
rheumatoid arthritis			
food allergies			
asthma			

The cardiovascular system, made up of the heart and blood vessels of the circulatory system, delivers the nutrients and gases received and processed from the external environment to the body's trillions of cells. The blood circulates through this system, transporting the products of digestion and respiration along the circulatory pathways and moving waste materials from the excretory system. It regulates internal temperature by moving heat produced by the muscular system. It also transports hormones.

The heart is a four-chambered, double pump that moves the blood through the three circulatory pathways. The pulmonary pathway transports blood to the lungs. The systemic pathway moves blood from the lungs to the body tissues and back again. The coronary pathway circulates blood to the muscle tissue of the heart. In the systemic and coronary pathways, arteries carry oxygen-rich blood away from the heart, and veins carry oxygen-poor blood back to the heart, where it is pumped through the lungs to exchange carbon dioxide for oxygen. The tiny capillaries, which link the arteries and veins within the tissue cells, are where the exchange of gases, nutrients, and wastes actually takes place.

The blood itself is a tissue, made up of red blood cells, white blood cells, and platelets, contained in the formed portion, and plasma in the fluid portion. Each of the elements of the blood has specific functions in the circulatory system. Red blood cells transport oxygen; the white blood cells are part of the body's defence system; and platelets assist the circulatory system in healing itself.

The lymphatic circulatory system is a network of vessels, linked to glands or nodes, which circulates lymph to maintain the body's balance of fluids. The lymphatic system also works with the body's defense system to help defend the body against disease.

The body's defence system includes barriers (the skin, eyelashes, cilia, tears), non-specific defences found in the white blood cells (macrophages, neutropils, monocytes), and specific defences (antibodies). A person's blood type indicates the type of antigens found on the red blood cell surface. In the ABO system, a person may be type A (with only A antigens), type B (with only B antigens), type AB (with both A and B antigens), or type O (with neither A nor B antigens). Another group of antigens found in most red blood cells is the Rh factor. Within the plasma there are naturally occurring antibodies to the antigens that are *not* present on a person's red blood cells. Mixing blood types can result in agglutination.

Disorders of the cardiovascular system (such as arteriosclerosis, high blood pressure), the blood (such as hemophilia, leukemia), or the immune system (autoimmune diseases) all impair the transport of nutrients, gases, and wastes throughout the circulatory system.

Chapter 8 Graphic Organizer

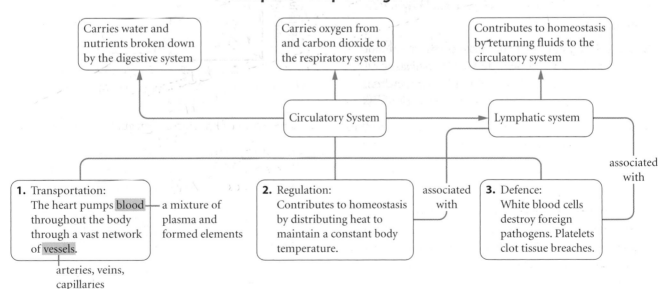

Understanding Concepts

1. List three factors that assist the flow of blood through the veins.

2. Which chamber of the heart is the largest and strongest chamber? Explain your reasoning.

3. Use word processing software to create a flow chart to trace the flow of blood through the heart. Start with the superior vena cava and end as blood enters the aorta. Include the names of all of the valves in the heart in your flow chart. **ICT**

4. Use word processing software to create a flow chart that explains the electrical activity in a mammalian heart. Relate the events that occur to specific regions of the heart muscle in your flow chart. **ICT**

5. What is the difference between a heart attack and a stroke?

6. List three functions of the blood, and identify the cells involved in each.

7. Describe the three primary pathways taken by the blood.

8. Identify the types of cells that are destroyed by the phagocytic activity of the macrophages.

9. How is lymph circulated in the body? How is this similar to how blood is circulated? How is it different?

10. Describe the role of T cells in the body's response to infectious agents.

11. The immune system helps the body resist pathogens. Identify three ways that pathogens can enter the body.

Applying Concepts

12. Design a simple test, based on just a few drops of a person's blood, that could determine whether or not the person is anemic. Provide detailed reasoning to support your design.

13. A person's blood pressure is measured before and after exercise. What effect would you expect the exercise to have on the systolic blood pressure and on the diastolic blood pressure? Explain.

14. You and your friends are sitting in a hot tub after a day of outdoor activity. What do you predict is happening to your circulatory system?

15. Design an experiment to test the effect of two separate factors on blood clotting. Provide detailed reasoning to support your design.

16. A pharmaceutical company develops an artificial blood cell that is very effective at transporting oxygen but is unable to transport carbon dioxide. Assuming that a blood transfusion has no effect on the level of plasma in the blood, explain what would take place if the artificial blood cell were used in a blood transfusion. How would this affect the patient?

17. Use graphics software to sketch cross sections of arteries, veins, capillaries, and lymph vessels. Use word processing or spreadsheet software to create a table to compare and contrast these blood vessels. **ICT**

18. Use graphics software to design a concept map or other graphics organizer that illustrates the relationships among different immune system cells. **ICT**

19. Some early transplant patients experienced life-threatening complications because their immune systems responded to "invading" cells that originated in another body. Which immune system cells increased? Draw a graph that would illustrate how the immune system is responding to this antigen organ.

20. Use word processing or spreadsheet software to make a chart that outlines the advantages and disadvantages of specific immunity and non-specific immunity. **ICT**

21. Imagine that you work in a hospital. You see on a patient's chart that she has type B blood, and she is about to receive blood from a donor blood container labelled type B. As an extra precaution, you mix a sample of the patient's blood with the donor blood on a glass slide. You observe that agglutination occurs. You need to discover whether it is the patient's chart or the blood container that is in error. You have access to samples of blood types A, AB, and O, but there is no more type B blood stored in the blood bank.
   a) Prepare a table illustrating the results that you would expect to see if you combine type B blood with each of the other blood types you have available.
   b) If it turns out that the label on the blood container is in error, what other blood type could be used instead of type B?

22. Describe how you would use a stethoscope to determine each of the following. Include details of what you would expect to find in each case.
   a) damage to the left atrioventricular valve
   b) damage to the aortic semilunar valve
   c) damage to the AV node

Use the following information to answer the next question.

Heart Failure

Heart failure is a progressive disorder in which damage to the heart weakens the circulatory system. Heart failure does not mean the heart has stopped working. Rather, it means that the heart's pumping power is weaker than normal. With heart failure, blood moves through the heart and body at a slower rate, and pressure in the heart increases.

23. Use computer software to create a graphic organizer illustrating how heart failure can affect
   a) the heart muscle itself
   b) blood pressure
   c) internal and external respiration
   d) temperature regulation **ICT**

Use the following graph to answer the next question.

Blood pressure and velocity at various points in the circulatory system

The illustration above compares blood pressure and the velocity of blood as it flows through the circulatory system.

24. a) Describe the change in blood pressure as blood flows from arteries through capillaries to veins.
   b) Describe the change in the speed of blood as it flows from arteries through capillaries to veins.
   c) Compare the pressure of the blood in the veins with the speed at which it flows in the veins, and use the total cross-sectional area of the blood vessels to suggest at least one reason for the pattern that you observe in the veins.

Use the information below to answer the next question.

Hemophilia

Hemophilia is a rare inherited bleeding disorder in which the blood does not clot normally. People with hemophilia may bleed for a longer time than others after an injury or accident. They also may bleed internally, especially in the joints (knees, ankles, and elbows). Babies born with hemophilia are missing or have a low level of a protein needed for normal blood clotting or blood coagulation. The protein is called a clotting factor.

25. a) Use word processing software to create a flow chart that summarizes the steps in the blood clotting process. Identify at least one step in this process that could be linked to hemophilia. **ICT**
   b) Explain why people with hemophilia would be prone to internal bleeding.

Making Connections

26. Explain why babies and young children might contract infectious diseases more frequently than adolescents do.

27. How do cells that provide cellular immunity sometimes trigger allergic reactions when they come in contact with environmental allergens?

28. What are some daily habits you could adopt to help reduce your chances of contracting a contagious disease (such as a cold or flu) from people you come into contact with on a regular basis?

29. Daphnia, a very small crustacean, has a heart rate that is much faster than a human heart rate. Why does such a small animal have such a fast heart rate? Would you expect the heart rates of large animals to be, on average, slower than the heart rates of small animals? Explain.

30. Explain how angioplasty can be used to open an obstructed coronary artery.

Excretion and the Interaction of Systems

Chapter Concepts

9.1 The Structures and Function of the Excretory System

- Each kidney receives blood that is processed to form urine, which drains through a ureter and into the urinary bladder for excretion.

- Each kidney contains over one million nephrons that process blood to form urine.

9.2 Urine Formation in the Nephron

- The functional unit of the kidney is the nephron.

- Each nephron filters blood, reabsorbs substances such as sodium and glucose for reuse in the body, and secretes excess or toxic substances such as urea to produce urine.

9.3 Excretory System Health

- Antidiuretic hormone (ADH) regulates the amount of water reabsorbed in the distal tubule.

- Aldosterone regulates the amount of salt that is reabsorbed or secreted.

- The acid-base balance of the blood is adjusted by the secretion of hydrogen ions and reabsorption of bicarbonate ions.

- Various technologies are used to solve problems involving dysfunctions and disorders of the excretory system.

Today, people commonly produce urine samples for chemical analysis to assess the health of the kidneys and organs of other body systems. This practice is far from modern, however. The first recorded evidence that people examined urine as a clue to the health of the body's internal environment appeared over two thousand years ago in Greece. It is likely, however, that keen observers from other cultures examined this liquid much earlier. This painting from the 1600s shows a physician examining a flask of urine from a woman who was experiencing swollen tissues. (This condition, known then as dropsy, is now referred to as edema.) The flask holding the urine, called a matula, was the symbol for the medical profession from the 1200s to the 1600s. This ancient practice of urine inspection has been replaced, improved, and quantified by the modern science of urology.

Physicians consulted wheels such as this, which related colour, odour, taste, and other characteristics of urine with different ailments.

Launch Lab

Dehydration and Urine Colour

Athletes whose sweat loss exceeds fluid intake may become dehydrated during activity. Even slight dehydration (a 1–2 percent loss in body weight) has a negative effect. A doctor of sports medicine, L.E. Armstrong, devised a standardized reference chart for urine colour. Athletes can use this chart to determine their hydration. People who are well-hydrated produce urine that is "very pale yellow", "pale yellow", or "straw coloured."

Urine Colour Chart

| 1 |
| 2 |
| 3 |
| 4 |
| 5 |
| 6 |
| 7 |
| 8 |

Validated in: Urinary Indices of Hydration Status, **Int. J. Sport Nutrition** 4: 265–279, 1994; Urinary Indices of Dehydration, Exercise and Rehydration, **Int. J. Sport Nutrition**, 8: 345–355, 1998; and Drinking behavior and perception of thirst in untrained women during heat Acclimation and outdoor training, **Int. J. Sport Nutr. & Exerc. Metab.** 13: 15–28, 2003. © Lawrence E. Armstrong, 2000; Human Kinetics Publishers

Materials

- 3 test tubes of simulated urine sample
- urine colour rating chart
- unlined white paper
- protective goggles and gloves

Procedure

1. Draw a data chart in your notebook similar to the one shown below.

Simulated Urine Sample	Match to Colour Chart	Interpretation
1		
2		
3		

2. Gather the materials listed.

3. Hold each sample in front of the unlined, white paper.

4. Match the sample to the Urine Colour Chart.

Analysis

1. Based on your observations, infer which sample(s) would indicate a person who is well-hydrated. Which sample indicates a person who is poorly hydrated? Which is the control?

2. Why would it be important for athletes to be able to assess their hydration during a game or practice?

Chapter 9 Excretion and the Interaction of Systems • MHR **305**

Overview of the Excretory System

Section Outcomes

In this section, you will
- **identify** the main structures and functions of the human excretory system
- **explain** the function of the nephron
- **dissect** a mammalian kidney and **observe** its structure

Key Terms

excretory system
excretion
kidneys
ureters
urinary bladder
urethra
nephrons
renal arteries
glomerulus
Bowman's capsule
filtrate
collecting duct
renal veins

Biology File

FYI
Bladder size varies with different people, but a typical bladder usually holds a maximum of 600 mL of urine. By the time the bladder is about half-full, sensory receptors in the walls of the bladder send impulses to the spinal cord, which signals muscles in the innermost sphincter of the bladder to contract. Most people can suppress the urge to urinate for a short time by contracting the other sphincter.

In the functioning human organism, cells are provided with nutrients and oxygen by the activities of the digestive and respiratory systems. The circulatory system ensures that each of the trillions of cells in the body receives the substances it needs for metabolic activities. These activities—energy release, maintenance, and repair—result in waste products that change the balance of volume of water and the concentration and composition of dissolved substances in the body's fluids. The basic function of the **excretory system** is to regulate the volume and composition of body fluids by removing wastes and returning needed substances to the body for reuse.

The Problem of Wastes

Imagine how your classroom would look if it were not cleaned each day and if the garbage can were left unemptied. Wastes—materials that are useless and unnecessary for normal functioning of your classroom—would build up over a period of time. Eventually, the environment of your classroom would become quite unhealthy.

The buildup of wastes in the human body has similar effects. In metabolic terms, a waste is any substance that is produced by the body and is present in excess of the body's needs. Examples of such wastes include carbon dioxide, water, ions such as those of sodium (Na^+), chloride (Cl^-), and hydrogen (H^+), and compounds that result from the breakdown of proteins and nucleic acids. Any waste can pose a threat to health if it is allowed to accumulate. Some wastes, however, pose a greater immediate threat than others. This is especially true of nitrogenous (nitrogen-containing) wastes such as ammonia, urea, and uric acid. Ammonia is highly toxic but is quickly converted to the less toxic compound, urea, in the liver. Urea makes up the majority of nitrogenous

waste in the body, and about half of it is eliminated in urine. Uric acid is present in much lower concentrations; it also passes out of the body in urine.

The Solution to Wastes: Excretion

Excretion is the process of separating wastes from the body fluids and eliminating them. Several body systems perform this function. The respiratory system excretes carbon dioxide and small amounts of other gases, including water vapour. The skin excretes water, salts, and some urea in perspiration. The digestive system excretes water, salts, lipids, and a variety of pigments and other cellular chemicals. (Note that the elimination of food residue—feces—is *not* considered to be a process of excretion.) Most metabolic wastes, however, are dissolved or suspended in solution and are excreted by the excretory (also called the urinary) system.

- - -

1 What is the basic function of the excretory system?

2 Identify four examples of metabolic wastes produced in the human body.

3 Why is it necessary for wastes to be removed from the body?

- - -

The Organs of the Excretory System

As shown in Figure 9.1, humans have two fist-sized **kidneys**, which are located in the area of the lower back on each side of the spine. If you stand up and put your hands on your hips with your thumbs meeting over your spine, your kidneys lie just above your thumbs. A large cushion of fat usually surrounds the kidneys. This fat layer, along with the lower portion of the ribcage, offers some protection for these vital organs. Although most people have two kidneys, humans are capable of functioning with only one. If one kidney ceases to work or if a single kidney is removed due to disease or because it is being donated to someone in need of a kidney, the single kidney increases in size to handle the increased workload.

The kidneys release urine into two muscular, 28-cm-long tubes called **ureters**. From the ureters, urine is moved by the peristaltic actions of smooth muscle tissue to the muscular **urinary bladder** where it is temporarily stored. Drainage from the bladder is controlled by two rings of muscles called sphincters. Both sphincters must relax before urine can drain from the bladder. The innermost sphincter is involuntarily controlled by the brain. During childhood we learn to voluntarily control relaxation of the other sphincter.

Urine exits the bladder and the body through a tube called the **urethra**. In males, the urethra is approximately 20 cm long and merges with the vas deferens of the reproductive tract to form a single passageway to the external environment. In females, the urethra is about 4 cm long and the reproductive and urinary tracts have separate openings.

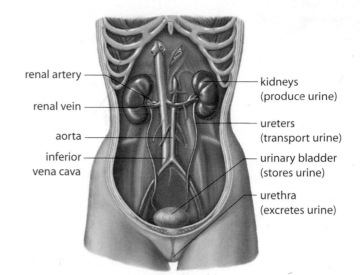

Q 4 List the structures of the human excretory system.

Q 5 Through which of these structures does urine leave the body?

The Kidneys: The Body's Blood-Cleansers

Within each kidney, the mouth of its ureter flares open to form a funnel-like structure called the renal pelvis. The renal pelvis has cup-like extensions that receive urine from the renal tissue. As shown in Figure 9.2, this tissue is divided

Figure 9.1 The organs of the excretory system are two kidneys, two ureters, the urinary bladder, and the urethra. Some vessels of the circulatory system also are shown in this illustration. (The word "renal", which appears in two of the labels, comes from the Latin word for kidney.) Although these vessels are not part of the excretory system, they are intimately connected with it. Why might that be?

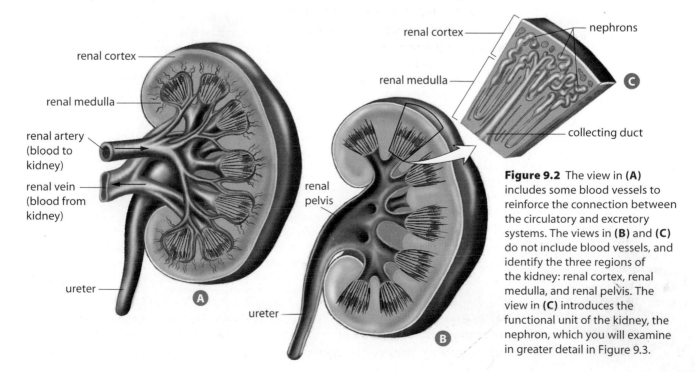

Figure 9.2 The view in (**A**) includes some blood vessels to reinforce the connection between the circulatory and excretory systems. The views in (**B**) and (**C**) do not include blood vessels, and identify the three regions of the kidney: renal cortex, renal medulla, and renal pelvis. The view in (**C**) introduces the functional unit of the kidney, the nephron, which you will examine in greater detail in Figure 9.3.

BiologyFile

FYI
An average nephron would measure approximately 0.5 cm if it were stretched lengthwise.

into two sections: an outer renal cortex and an inner renal medulla.

Embedded within the renal cortex and extending into the renal medulla are over one million microscopic structures called **nephrons**. Closely associated with these nephrons is a network of blood vessels. The nephrons are responsible for filtering various substances from blood, transforming it into urine. To perform this function, each nephron is organized into three main regions: a filter, a tube, and a duct. These are outlined in the box below and highlighted in Figure 9.3.

An Overview of the Nephron and its Three Functional Regions

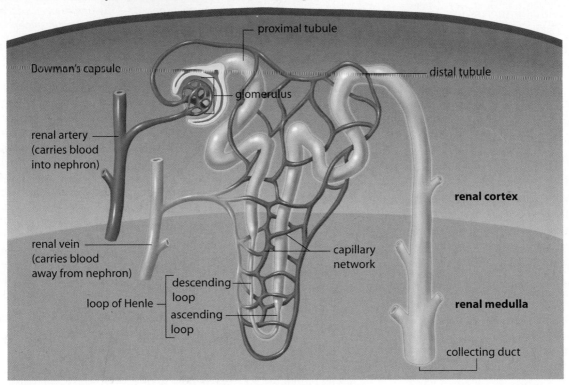

Figure 9.3 The structures of the nephron are labelled here to help outline the processes by which blood becomes urine in the nephron. The word "proximal" (in proximal tubule) means *nearby* and refers to the fact that this part of the tubule is located *near* the Bowman's capsule. The word "distal" (in distal tubule) means *distant* and refers to the fact that this part of the tubule is located more *distantly* from the Bowman's capsule.

1. A Filter: The filtration structure at the top of each nephron is a cap-like formation called the **Bowman's capsule**. Within each capsule, a **renal artery** enters and splits into a fine network of capillaries called a **glomerulus** (pronounced "glow-MEER-you-lus"; the term means "little ball" in Latin). The walls of the glomerulus act as a filtration device. They are impermeable to proteins, other large molecules, and red blood cells, so these remain within the blood. Water, small molecules, ions, and urea—the main waste products of metabolism—pass through the walls and proceed further into the nephron. The filtered fluid that proceeds from the glomerulus into the Bowman's capsule of the nephron is referred to as **filtrate**.

2. A Tubule: The Bowman's capsule is connected to a small, long, narrow tubule that is twisted back on itself to form a loop. This long, hairpin loop is a reabsorption device. The tubule has three sections: the proximal tubule, the loop of Henle, and the distal tubule. Like the small intestine, this tubule absorbs substances that are useful to the body, such as glucose and a variety of ions, from the filtrate passing through it. Unlike the small intestine, this tubule also secretes substances into the tissues surrounding it. (You will find out more about these twin processes of reabsorption and secretion in section 9.2.)

3. A Duct: The tubule empties into a larger pipe-like channel called a **collecting duct**. The collecting duct functions as a water-conservation device, reclaiming water from the filtrate passing through it so that very little precious water is lost from the body. The filtrate that remains in the collecting duct is a suspension of water and various solutes and particles. It is now called urine. Its composition is distinctly different from the fluid that entered the Bowman's capsule. The solutes and water reclaimed during reabsorption are returned to the body via the **renal veins**.

Identifying Structures of the Excretory System

In this investigation, you will perform a dissection of a sheep's kidney in order to identify the major parts of the organ. Note that your teacher may, instead, have you examine structures of the excretory system using a virtual dissection.

Question

What features of a mammalian kidney can you identify?

Safety Precautions

Extreme care must be taken when using dissecting instruments, particularly scalpels. To the extent possible, make cuts away from your body. The kidneys are preserved in a chemical solution. Wear plastic gloves, goggles, and an apron at all times, and work in a well-ventilated area. At the end of the lesson, wash your hands thoroughly. Dispose of all materials as instructed by your teacher, and clean your work area.

Materials

- preserved sheep kidney
- dissecting instruments
- disposable plastic gloves
- plastic bag and tie (to store your specimen if necessary)
- newspapers and/or paper towels
- large tongs
- dissecting tray
- apron

Procedure

1. Obtain a kidney and observe its external features. The renal capsule is a smooth semi-transparent membrane that is tightly bound to the outer surface of the kidney. You may notice fatty deposits clinging to the renal capsule. Identify and remove the renal capsule.

2. Under the renal capsule is the surface of the renal cortex. Locate the area where the renal blood vessels and the ureter are attached to the kidney.

3. Cut through the kidney lengthwise as shown in the photograph. Identify the renal cortex.

4. Locate the renal medulla. The renal medulla contains the collecting ducts. They are visible as a striped pattern throughout the medulla.

5. Locate the renal pelvis, which is continuous with the ureter.

Analysis

1. Based on your specimen, draw a labelled sketch of the kidney that includes the following structures.

   a) renal capsule   **d)** renal pelvis

   b) renal cortex   **e)** renal vein

   c) renal medulla   **f)** renal artery

2. Refer to Figures 9.2 and 9.3 and your sketch from question 1. Draw a new sketch of your specimen that shows the regions of the kidney in which you would expect to observe the following nephron structures: glomerulus, proximal tubule, loop of Henle, distal tubule, and collecting duct.

The renal capsule provides a thin layer of protection for the outer tissues of the kidney.

Remember to cut away from you as you open the kidney.

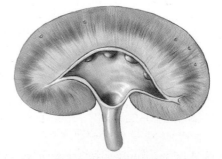

Internal features of the kidney

A more detailed account of the nephron's function in forming urine follows in Section 9.2.

• • •

6 Name the three regions of the kidney.

7 Trace, in general terms, either in words or with a sketch, the movement of blood through the nephron from the renal artery to the renal vein.

• • •

Section 9.1 Summary

- The human excretory system regulates the composition of the blood by removing wastes and excess substances from the blood plasma.
- The excretory system is responsible for removing liquid waste from the body.
- The kidneys are the primary excretory organs and are major organs of homeostasis.
- Kidney tissue is organized into three regions: cortex, medulla, and renal pelvis.
- The kidneys are composed of millions of functional units called nephrons that filter the waste from the blood and produce urine.
- Urine leaves the kidney through tubes called ureters. It passes into the bladder and exits the body through the urethra.

Section 9.1 | Review

1. Use word processing software to create a flow chart that traces the flow of urine through the various structures in the excretory system. **ICT**

2. Use word processing or spreadsheet software to create a table that lists the main structures of the human excretory system and identifies their functions. **ICT**

3. Describe the functions of the excretory system.

4. **a)** Use graphics software to sketch a cross-section of a mammalian kidney and label its three regions. **ICT**

   b) Identify the region(s) of the kidney where you would find the following structures: glomerulus, proximal tubule, loop of Henle, distal tubule, and the collecting duct.

5. Use graphics software to sketch the basic plan of the nephron. On your sketch indicate the part of the nephron where:

   a) blood enters

   b) filtrate is formed

   c) urine is excreted **ICT**

6. Use word processing or spreadsheet software to draw a chart or table that explains the following terms with respect to the nephron: a filter, a tubule, and a duct. **ICT**

7. Summarize the relationship among the human digestive, respiratory, circulatory, and excretory systems.

Urine Formation in the Nephron

Section Outcomes

In this section, you will
- **explain** the function of the nephron in maintaining the composition of blood plasma
- **describe** the function of the kidney in excreting metabolic wastes and expelling them into the environment

Key Terms

glomerular filtration
tubular reabsorption
tubular secretion
water reabsorption
proximal tubule
loop of Henle
distal tubule

Refer again to Figure 9.2. Note that the upper portions of each nephron are located in the renal cortex of the kidney, while the lower portions are located in the renal medulla of the kidney. Note also the presence of vessels of the circulatory system in association with the nephrons. These details indicate that nephrons are surrounded by the tissues of the medulla and cortex. Nephrons are also closely associated with a network of blood vessels that spreads throughout this surrounding tissue. Thus, any substances that are secreted from the nephrons enter the surrounding tissues of the kidney. Most of these substances return to the bloodstream through the network of blood vessels. The remainder leaves the body in the form of urine.

Four processes are crucial to the formation of urine. These processes are outlined below and summarized in Figure 9.4.

Glomerular filtration moves water and solutes, except proteins, from blood plasma into the nephron. (Recall that this filtered fluid is called filtrate.)

Tubular reabsorption removes useful substances such as sodium from the filtrate and returns them into the blood for reuse by body systems.

Tubular secretion moves additional wastes and excess substances from the blood into the filtrate.

Water reabsorption removes water from the filtrate and returns it to the blood for reuse by body systems.

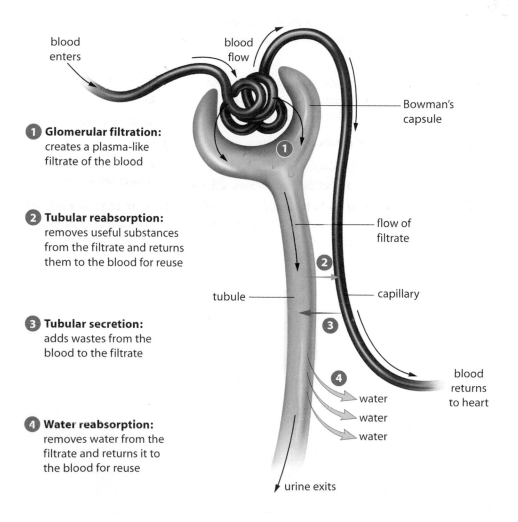

1 Glomerular filtration: creates a plasma-like filtrate of the blood

2 Tubular reabsorption: removes useful substances from the filtrate and returns them to the blood for reuse

3 Tubular secretion: adds wastes from the blood to the filtrate

4 Water reabsorption: removes water from the filtrate and returns it to the blood for reuse

blood enters
blood flow
Bowman's capsule
flow of filtrate
tubule
capillary
blood returns to heart
water
water
water
urine exits

Figure 9.4 This simplified depiction of the nephron outlines the four main steps in the process of forming urine. The tubule has been depicted in a straight line to help you focus on the processes, rather than on the parts.

Getting blood to and from the nephron involves a specialized series of arteries and veins. First, blood flowing to the kidneys comes directly from the aorta as it passes through the abdomen. The renal arteries enter the kidney through the renal medulla, or centre. As they travel to the cortex they branch into arterioles, which finally give rise to the fine capillaries of the glomerulus. Capillaries also enmesh the nephron; they feed into renal venules that join renal veins. Filtered blood returning to the circulation travels through the renal veins to join the vena cava and return directly to the heart.

Glomerular Filtration Filters Blood

The formation of urine starts with glomerular filtration. This process forces some of the water and dissolved substances in blood plasma from the glomerulus into the Bowman's capsule. (Keep in mind that this process is occurring in *millions* of nephrons, all at the same time. Here, you are focussing your attention only on a single nephron.) Two factors contribute to this filtration. One factor is the permeability of the capillaries of the glomerulus. Unlike capillaries in other parts of the body, capillaries of the glomerulus have many pores in their tissue walls. These pores are large enough to allow water and most dissolved substances in the blood plasma to pass easily through the capillaries and into the Bowman's capsule. On the other hand, the pores are small enough to prevent proteins and blood cells from entering. The other factor is blood pressure. Blood pressure within the glomerulus is about four times greater than it is in capillaries elsewhere in the body. The great rush of blood through the glomerulus provides the force for filtration.

Each day, 1600 L to 2000 L of blood passes through your kidneys, producing about 180 L of glomerular filtrate. This filtrate is chemically very similar to blood plasma, as you can see in Table 9.1.

Table 9.1 Concentration of Selected Chemicals in Plasma and Glomerular Filtrate

Chemicals	Blood Plasma (g/L)	Glomerular Filtrate (g/L)
Protein	44.4	0.0
Sodium (Na$^+$)	3.0	3.0
Chloride (Cl$^-$)	3.5	3.5
Glucose	1.0	1.0
Urea	0.3	0.3

Essentially, the filtrate is identical to blood plasma, minus proteins and blood cells. Further changes to this fluid lie ahead on its way to becoming urine.

8 Describe the two factors that contribute to glomerular filtration.

9 Compare the composition of the filtrate once it leaves the glomerulus with that of blood plasma.

Tubular Reabsorption: Recovery of Substances in the Proximal Tubule

About 65 percent of the filtrate that passes through the entire length of the **proximal tubule** (including the loop of Henle) is reabsorbed and returned to the body. Figure 9.5 shows that this process

- Nutrients (e.g., glucose, amino acids, Na$^+$, K$^+$) are actively reabsorbed.
- Negatively charged ions (e.g., Cl$^-$) are passively reabsorbed by electrical attraction.
- Water is reabsorbed by osmosis.

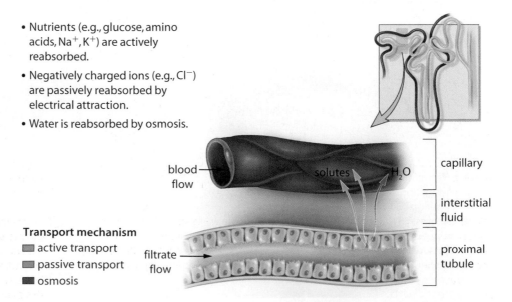

Transport mechanism
- ▨ active transport
- ▨ passive transport
- ■ osmosis

blood flow

filtrate flow

solutes   H$_2$O

capillary

interstitial fluid

proximal tubule

Figure 9.5 Reabsorption of substances and ions in the proximal tubule.

of reabsorption involves both active and passive transport mechanisms. The cells of the proximal tubule are richly endowed with mitochondria, which use the energy-releasing power of ATP to drive the active transport of sodium ions (Na^+), glucose, and other solutes back into the blood. Negatively charged ions tag along passively, attracted by the electrical charge on the transported ions. Water follows the ions by osmosis, so it, too, is reabsorbed into the blood flowing through the capillaries.

> **Q 10** What role does ATP play in the processes occurring in the proximal tubule?

Focussing on the Loop of Henle in the Proximal Tubule

The function of the **loop of Henle** is to reabsorb water and ions from the glomerular filtrate. As the descending limb of the loop of Henle plunges deeper into the medulla region, it encounters an increasingly salty environment. The cells of the descending limb are permeable to water and only slightly permeable to ions. As a result of the salty environment of the medulla and permeability of the descending limb, water diffuses from the filtrate to the capillaries by osmosis (see Figure 9.6A). As water moving through the descending limb leaves the filtrate, the concentration of sodium ion (Na^+) inside the tubule increases, reaching its maximum concentration at the bottom of the loop.

As the filtrate continues around the bend of the loop of Henle and into the ascending limb, the permeability of the nephron tubule changes. Near the bend, the thin portion of the ascending tubule is now impermeable to water and slightly permeable to solutes. Sodium ions diffuse from the filtrate along their concentration gradient and pass into nearby blood vessels (see Figure 9.6B).

Figure 9.6 Reabsorption in the loop of Henle.

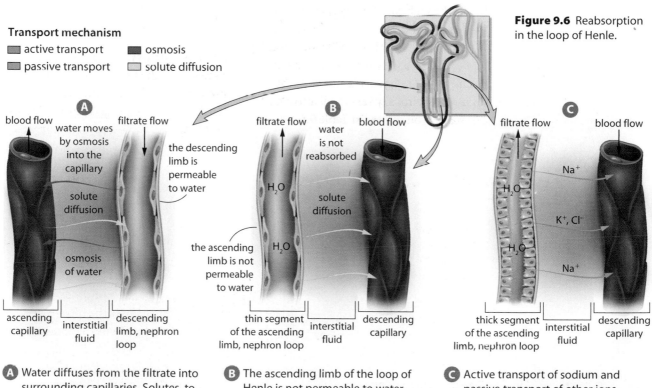

Transport mechanism
- active transport
- passive transport
- osmosis
- solute diffusion

A Water diffuses from the filtrate into surrounding capillaries. Solutes, to a much lesser extent, diffuse in the opposite direction.

B The ascending limb of the loop of Henle is not permeable to water. Solutes diffuse from the filtrate into the surrounding capillaries.

C Active transport of sodium and passive transport of other ions occurs in the thick segment of the ascending limb of the loop of Henle. There is no reabsorption of water in this part of the nephron.

At the thick-walled portion of the ascending limb of the loop of Henle, sodium ions are moved out of the filtrate by active transport (see Figure 9.6C). This transport of Na^+ out of the filtrate has two consequences. First, it helps replenish the salty environment of the medulla, which aids in the absorption of water from filtrate in the descending limb. Second, the removal of sodium ions from the filtrate in the thick-walled portion of the tubule makes the filtrate less concentrated than the tissues and blood in the surrounding cortex tissue. By now, about two thirds of the Na^+ and water from the filtrate has been reabsorbed.

• • •

11 Describe the composition of the filtrate as it moves up the ascending limb of the loop of Henle toward the distal tubule.

• • •

Tubular Reabsorption and Secretion in the Distal Tubule

The active reabsorption of sodium ions from the filtrate into the capillaries (see

Figure 9.7) depends on the needs of the body. Passive reabsorption of negative ions such as chloride occurs by electrical attraction. The reabsorption of ions decreases the concentration of the filtrate, which causes water to be reabsorbed by osmosis.

Potassium ions (K^+) are actively secreted into the **distal tubule** from the bloodstream in the capillaries. Hydrogen ions (H^+) are also actively secreted as necessary in order to maintain the pH of the blood. Other substances that are not normally part of the body, such as penicillin and other drugs, are secreted into the distal tubule. (Reabsorption and secretion in the distal tubule are under the control of hormones, as you will see in Section 9.3.)

Reabsorption from the Collecting Duct

The filtrate entering the collecting duct still contains a lot of water. Because the collecting duct extends deep into the medulla, the concentration of ions along its length increases. (This concentration of ions is the result of the active transport of ions from the ascending limb of the loop of Henle.) This causes the passive reabsorption of water from the filtrate in the collecting duct by osmosis. If blood plasma is too concentrated (for example, if a person is dehydrated), the permeability to water in the distal tubule and the collecting duct is increased. This causes more water to be reabsorbed into the surrounding capillaries in order to conserve water in the body. (In the collecting duct, as in the distal tubule, hormones control reabsorption and secretion.)

The reabsorption of water in the collecting duct causes the filtrate to become about four times as concentrated by the time it exits the duct. This filtrate—which is approximately 1 percent of the original filtrate volume—is now called **urine**. Table 9.2 summarizes the main functions of the nephron and where they occur.

Figure 9.7 Reabsorption in the distal tubule and collecting duct

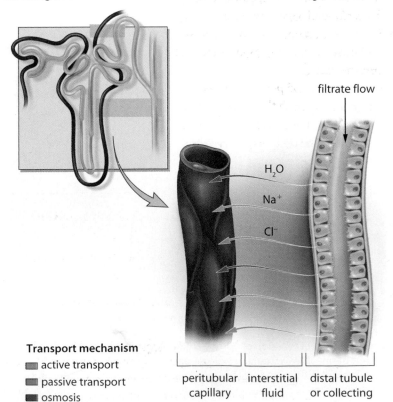

filtrate flow

H_2O

Na^+

Cl^-

Transport mechanism
- ▬ active transport
- ▬ passive transport
- ▬ osmosis

peritubular capillary | interstitial fluid | distal tubule or collecting duct

Table 9.2 A Summary of Nephron Functions

Part of the Nephron	Function
Glomerulus	**Filtration** • Glomerular blood pressure forces some of the water and dissolved substances from the blood plasma through the pores of the glomerular walls
Bowman's capsule	Receives filtrate from glomerulus
Proximal tubule	**Reabsorption** • Active reabsorption of all nutrients, including glucose and amino acids • Active reabsorption of positively charged ions such as sodium, potassium, calcium • Passive reabsorption of water by osmosis • Passive reabsorption of negatively charged ions such as chloride and bicarbonate by electrical attraction to positively charged ions **Secretion** • Active secretion of hydrogen ions
Descending loop of Henle	**Reabsorption** • Passive reabsorption of water by osmosis
Ascending loop of Henle	**Reabsorption** • Active reabsorption of sodium ions • Passive reabsorption of chloride and potassium ions
Distal tube	**Reabsorption** • Active reabsorption of sodium ions • Passive reabsorption of water by osmosis • Passive reabsorption of negatively charged ions such as chloride and bicarbonate **Secretion** • Active secretion of hydrogen ions • Passive secretion of potassium ions by electrical attraction to chloride ions
Collecting tube	**Reabsorption** • Passive reabsorption of water by osmosis

Section 9.2 Summary

• Filtrate moves through the nephron, and the processes of glomerular filtration, tubular reabsorption, tubular secretion, and water reabsorption modify the filtrate so that cleansed plasma and substances such as glucose, amino acids, and Na$^+$ return to the blood.

• In the glomerulus, filtration moves water and solutes (except for protein) from blood plasma into the nephron.

• Solutes are actively transported from the filtrate in the proximal tubule back into the blood.

• Approximately 65 percent of the filtrate that passes through the entire length of the proximal tubule is reabsorbed and returned to the body, while the urine becomes concentrated.

Section 9.2   Review

1. Use word processing or spreadsheet software to create a chart that identifies the major parts of the nephron and summarizes the function of each part. **ICT**

2. Use graphics software to draw a sketch of a simplified nephron. Include a series of captions on your diagram that identify the part(s) of the nephron responsible for each of the following:

  a) movement of sodium ions from the nephron to the surrounding capillaries

  b) movement of water from the nephron to the surrounding capillaries

  c) movement of glucose out of the nephron

  d) movement of penicillin and potassium ions into the nephron **ICT**

3. Compare and contrast blood entering the kidney to urine leaving the kidney.

4. Explain the difference between reabsorption and secretion in the nephron.

5. Based on what you have learned so far in this chapter, predict how perspiring heavily on a hot day would affect the composition and production of a person's urine. (Assume that the person has not yet consumed water to replenish body fluids.)

Maintaining the Excretory System

The amount of water reabsorbed from the filtrate influences two important characteristics of blood: its volume and the concentration of plasma solutes. The force generated as water moves by osmosis is called osmotic pressure. The greater the concentration gradient, the greater the osmotic pressure becomes. Osmotic pressure affects many cellular activities, especially the exchange of materials between cells and blood. Blood volume influences blood pressure and, thus, affects the health of the cardiovascular system.

The solute concentration of the blood remains constant despite variations in the amount of water people consume in food and liquids. If we drink too much, the kidneys allow more water to pass into the urine. If water is scarce, the kidneys conserve water by producing concentrated urine. How do the kidneys "know" when to conserve (reabsorb) water and when not to?

Regulating Reabsorption of Water

Osmoreceptors are cells that are sensitive to osmotic pressure. Most osmoreceptors are located in the hypothalamus, which is a part of the brain that regulates hunger, thirst, blood pressure, body temperature, fluid balance, and salt balance. In other words, the hypothalamus regulates mechanisms that enable the body to maintain homeostasis. When blood plasma becomes too concentrated (for example, if you are dehydrated), osmotic pressure increases. In response, osmoreceptors in the hypothalamus send impulses to the adjacent pituitary gland in the brain that causes the release of **antidiuretic hormone** (ADH). (Diuresis means "increased excretion of urine." Since the "anti-" prefix means "against" or "opposed to," antidiuresis means "decreased excretion of urine.") ADH

travels through the blood to the kidneys, where it increases the permeability of the distal tubule and the collecting duct, allowing more water to be reabsorbed into the blood. This dilutes the blood and lowers osmotic pressure to normal.

Conversely, if blood plasma is too dilute (that is, if the osmotic pressure is too low), osmoreceptors stop or prevent the release of ADH. As a result, the distal tubule and the collecting duct become less permeable to water. This allows more water to be excreted in the urine, concentrating the solutes in the blood. The osmotic pressure of the plasma and tissue fluids rises to normal. Figure 9.8 outlines the control mechanisms that lead to the release or inhibition of ADH.

In a condition called *diabetes insipidus*, ADH activity is insufficient, so a person urinates excessively—perhaps as much as 4 L to 8 L per day. Thirst is intense, but water is excreted more quickly than it is consumed, leading to severe dehydration and ion imbalances. People who have diabetes insipidus may take synthetic ADH to restore the balance of water reabsorption.

The ethanol in alcoholic beverages is a diuretic, so it increases the volume of urine. Alcohol stimulates urine production partly by decreasing ADH release, which decreases of the permeability of the tubules and collecting ducts. Because it increases water loss to urine, drinking an alcoholic beverage actually *intensifies* thirst and leads to dehydration. Caffeine, a common substance in coffee, black tea, and many carbonated drinks, is also a diuretic.

• • •

12 Describe the role of osmoreceptors in regulating water reabsorption.

13 What is the role of ADH in maintaining the volume of water in the body?

• • •

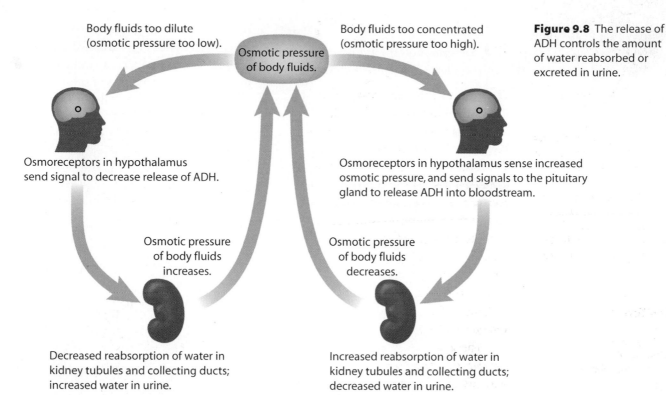

Body fluids too dilute (osmotic pressure too low).

Body fluids too concentrated (osmotic pressure too high).

Osmotic pressure of body fluids.

Figure 9.8 The release of ADH controls the amount of water reabsorbed or excreted in urine.

Osmoreceptors in hypothalamus send signal to decrease release of ADH.

Osmoreceptors in hypothalamus sense increased osmotic pressure, and send signals to the pituitary gland to release ADH into bloodstream.

Osmotic pressure of body fluids increases.

Osmotic pressure of body fluids decreases.

Decreased reabsorption of water in kidney tubules and collecting ducts; increased water in urine.

Increased reabsorption of water in kidney tubules and collecting ducts; decreased water in urine.

Reabsorption of Salts

The kidneys regulate salt balance in the blood by controlling the excretion and reabsorption of various ions. Sodium ion (Na^+) is the most abundant ion in blood plasma, but its concentration can fluctuate dramatically depending on diet and the consumption of beverages with diuretic effects. A drop in blood Na^+ concentration is normally compensated by the kidneys under the influence of the hormone **aldosterone**. This hormone stimulates the distal tubules and collecting ducts to reabsorb Na^+. Because the reabsorption of Na^+ is followed passively by chloride ions and water, aldosterone has the net effect of retaining both salt and water. Aldosterone also stimulates the secretion of potassium ions (K^+) into the distal tubes and collecting ducts if K^+ concentration in the blood is too high.

Maintaining Blood pH

The pH of body fluids stays at about 7.4 via three main mechanisms. The acid-base buffer system buffers the blood—prevents changes in pH by adding or removing hydrogen ions (H^+). One of the key buffering reactions in the blood involves carbonic acid (H_2CO_3) and bicarbonate ions (HCO_3^-); see the chemical equation below. An increase in H^+ pushes the reaction to the right. This reaction, and others, helps prevent major changes in blood pH. It is aided by a second mechanism that involves changes to breathing rate. An increased breathing (respiration) rate pulls the reaction to the right to generate CO_2 more quickly.

These mechanisms to control acid-base balance are aided by the more powerful actions of the kidneys. Think of the kidneys as excreting H^+ and reabsorbing HCO_3^- as needed to maintain normal blood pH. If the blood is too acidic, H^+ is excreted and HCO_3^- is reabsorbed. If the blood is too basic, H^+ is not excreted and HCO_3^- is not reabsorbed. Since urine is usually acidic, it follows that H^+ is usually excreted. The ability of the kidneys to control blood pH is crucial to maintaining an internal environment in which cell enzymes continue to function properly.

$$H^+ + HCO_3^- \rightleftharpoons H_2CO_3 \rightleftharpoons H_2O + CO_2$$
$$\text{pH increases} \leftarrow \quad \rightarrow \text{pH decreases}$$

BiologyFile

Try This
The release of aldosterone is stimulated directly by a rise or fall in Na^+ and K^+ concentrations in the blood. Aldosterone may also be stimulated indirectly through a drop in blood pressure. Do research to discover the main steps involved in the renin-angiotensin-aldosterone system of hormone control. Sketch a flowchart similar to Figure 9.8 to show how this system responds to a rise or fall in blood pressure and blood volume.

• • •

14 Describe how the kidneys regulate salt balance in the body.

15 How do the excretory and respiratory systems work together to regular blood pH?

• • •

Upsetting the Balance of the Excretory System

The composition of urine reflects the amounts of water and solutes that the kidneys must remove from or retain in the body to maintain homeostasis. Analyzing the physical and chemical composition of urine, therefore, enables physicians to make reasoned inferences and hypotheses about a person's health. Table 9.3 provides values for selected tests that are performed on urine. These values are consistent with those of urine from a healthy adult. Note, however, that urine composition varies greatly over the course of a day due to factors such as dietary intake, physical activity, emotional stress, and fatigue. In addition, unhealthy constituents of urine may not necessarily indicate illness or disease. For example, the presence of glucose in urine may result from a sugary meal. Proteins may appear in urine following vigorous exercise. Ketones—acids that result from the digestion of fats when the body lacks sufficient stores of carbohydrates—may

result from a short-term fast or a specially designed low-carbohydrate diet. Because so many factors can influence the presence and amounts of substances in urine, trained professionals must consider a wide variety of variables when evaluating a sample of urine. You will have a chance to examine a much narrower range of variables and substances in Investigation 9.B.

Disorders of the Excretory System

The excretory system is vital to maintaining homeostasis, so when it is affected by a disorder, the proper functioning of other body systems may be jeopardized. One of the most common disorders of the excretory system is a urinary tract infection. If the bladder has a bacterial or viral infection, the disorder is called cystitis; if only the urethra is involved, the condition is called urethritis. Urinary tract infections are more common in women than in men, primarily because of the differences in anatomy. In females, the urethral and anal openings are closer together, making it easier for bacteria from the bowels to enter the urinary tract and start an infection.

Symptoms of a urinary tract infection include a painful burning sensation during urination, a need to urinate frequently even if no urine is present, and bloody or brown urine. The upper abdomen or lower back may be tender, and chills, fever, nausea, and vomiting may be present. Urinary tract infections have the potential to become serious, and they can result in permanent damage to the kidneys and possible kidney failure. Treatment usually is with an antibiotic, but in serious cases of kidney infection, surgery may be needed. Preventative measures include maintaining hygienic personal behaviours, such as proper wiping from front to back after a bowel movement, and drinking lots of water.

Another fairly common disorder of the excretory system involves the

Table 9.3 Normal Values from Selected Common Urine Tests

Urine Test	Accepted Healthy Value*
Acetone and ketones	0
Albumin (protein)	0–trace
Bilirubin (a breakdown product of hemoglobin)	0
Calcium	< 150 mg/day
Colour and clarity	Pale yellow to light amber; transparent
Glucose	0
pH	4.5–8.0
Urea	25–35 g/day
Uric acid	0.5–1.0 g/day

*These values may vary with the type of equipment used for analysis.

development of crystalline formations called kidney stones (see Figure 9.9). Most kidney stones form due to excess calcium in the urine. In fact, about 85 percent of kidney stones are made up of calcium compounds. Recurrent urinary tract infections, insufficient water consumption, and low activity levels contribute to kidney-stone formation. Treatment varies depending on the size of the stones. Many stones pass through the urinary tract on their own. Depending on the cause of the stone formation, medications may help to break down the crystals. If the stones are less than 20 mm in diameter, ultrasound shock waves can be used to disintegrate the crystalline structure of the stones so that they can be passed naturally in the urine. For larger stones, surgery may be needed to remove them.

Problems with Kidney Function

Renal insufficiency is a general term used to describe the state in which the kidneys cannot maintain homeostasis due to damage to their nephrons. Some causes of nephron damage include:

- kidney infection
- high blood pressure
- diabetes mellitus
- trauma from a blow to the lower back or constant vibration from machinery
- poisoning (either from skin contact, inhalation of fumes, or ingestion of contaminated food) by heavy metals such as mercury and lead or solvents such as paint thinners
- atherosclerosis (which reduces blood flow to the kidneys)
- blockage of the tubules

Nephrons can regenerate and restore kidney function after short-term injuries. Even when some of the nephrons are irreversibly damaged, others can compensate for their lost function. In fact, a person can survive on as little as one-third of one kidney. If 75 percent or more of the nephrons are destroyed, however, urine output is inadequate to maintain homeostasis. Under these

circumstances, a person requires a means for replacing kidney function. This is achieved either with a kidney transplanted from a donor, if one is available, or with an artificial kidney that performs a blood-cleansing process called **dialysis**.

Hemodialysis and Peritoneal Dialysis

Dialysis is the diffusion of dissolved substances through a semipermeable membrane. These substances move across a membrane from the area of greater concentration to one of lower concentration. Substances more concentrated in blood diffuse into the dialysis solution, called the dialysate. Substances more concentrated in the dialysate diffuse into the blood. Other substances can be added to the blood following this same principle. For example, if the acid-base balance of the blood is off and the blood is too acidic, bicarbonate ions can be added to the dialysate where they will diffuse into the blood and reduce its acidity.

There are two main types of renal (kidney) dialysis: hemodialysis and peritoneal dialysis. **Hemodialysis** utilizes an artificial membrane in an external device—in essence, an artificial kidney—that is connected to an artery and a vein in a person's arm. **Peritoneal dialysis** utilizes the lining of the intestines, called the peritoneum, as the dialysis membrane. Dialysate is introduced to the abdominal

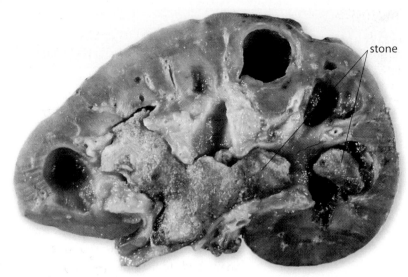

Figure 9.9 Kidney stones vary in size from a grain of sand to a golf ball. The larger ones, which cause extreme pain as they pass through the excretory system, can be broken into fragments with ultrasound technology in a procedure called lithotripsy.

Biology File

FYI
In 1946, Dr. Gordon Murray was the first Canadian scientist to develop and use kidney dialysis. To succeed, he solved the problem of getting the blood outside of the body and keeping it from clotting by pioneering the use of the anticoagulant drug heparin. (An anticoagulant hinders clotting.) Then he found a material porous enough to let wastes diffuse while retaining the larger particles and blood cells in the plasma—cellophane designed to wrap sausages

Urinalysis

Urinalysis is the physical, chemical, and sometimes microscopic examination of urine. Many diseases with no obvious symptoms can be revealed during urinalysis. Long before modern techniques such as chemical dipsticks and microscopic analysis were developed, medical practitioners used the appearance, odour, and even taste of urine to help them make inferences about a person's health. In this investigation, you will test samples of simulated urine to identify an imaginary criminal. In so doing, you will perform several of the tests that are performed when health professionals do a urinalysis.

Question

What physical and chemical tests can you use, and what data do they provide, in the analysis of urine?

Safety Precautions

- Do not taste the simulated urine.
- If observing odour, follow safe and proper methods.
- Be careful when handling the simulated urine. Clean up spills immediately, and notify your teacher if a spill occurs.

Materials

- 1 medicine dropper
- 1 test tube rack
- 10 mL graduated cylinder
- 5 test tubes
- 100 mL beaker
- hot water bath
- universal indicator paper with colour charts
- glucose test strips with colour charts
- simulated urine samples

Procedure

Consider this scenario. A theft was committed in the washroom of a community building. Forensic specialists collected a urine sample at the scene of the crime. The police have four suspects in custody. Your task is to find out who committed the crime.

Target Skills

Collecting and **interpreting** data in the analysis of simulated urine, and stating a generalization based on data analysis and interpretation

Identifying limitations of data collected

Comparing collected values to theoretical values

1. Copy the data table at the bottom of the page in your notebook.

2. You will start by doing a trial run of four tests to find out what information they provide. This will serve as the control for this investigation.

3. Perform the following tests on your simulated urine sample.

   Test 1—Colour, Odour, Clarity: Normal urine is a clear, straw-coloured liquid. Urine may be cloudy because it contains red or white blood cells, bacteria, or pus from a bladder or kidney infection. Normal urine has a slight odour. Foul-smelling urine is a common symptom of urinary tract infection. A fruity odour is associated with diabetes mellitus. Determine the colour, odour, and clarity of your simulated urine.

   a) Use the graduated cylinder to obtain 20 mL of the Control Urine Sample.

   b) Place the Control Sample into the beaker.

   c) Examine the urine carefully. Record the colour and the clarity (clear or cloudy) in your data chart.

   d) Using the proper technique, determine the odour of the urine. Record your observations in your data chart.

   Test 2—Protein: One sign of kidney damage is the presence of protein in urine. Find out if the sample contains protein by doing the following.

   a) Use the graduated cylinder to divide the sample equally between two test tubes (10 mL into each test tube).

   b) Put one tube into the hot water bath, and leave the other at room temperature.

Test	Control Tests	Crime Scene	Suspect 1	Suspect 2	Suspect 3	Suspect 4
1. Colour/odour/clarity						
2. Protein						
3. pH						
4. Glucose						

c) After a few minutes, remove the test tube from the hot water bath and compare the heated and unheated urine.

d) If the heated sample is cloudier, it contains protein. Record your observations.

e) Dispose of the heated sample as directed by your teacher. Use the unheated sample for the next test.

Test 3—pH: The wide range of pH values (pH 4.7 to 8.5) makes this is the least useful parameter for diagnosis of kidney disorders. Kidney stones are less likely to form and some antibiotics are more effective in alkaline urine. There may be times when acidic urine may help prevent some kinds of kidney stones. Bacterial infections also increase alkalinity, producing a urine pH in the higher 7–8 range.

a) Use a clean medicine dropper to place a drop of the urine on a small piece of universal indicator (pH) paper.

b) Leave the paper for about 30 seconds.

c) Determine the pH by comparing the new colour with the colour chart provided.

d) Record the pH of your urine sample in your data table.

Test 4—Glucose: One sign that a person has diabetes mellitus is the presence of glucose in urine. Find out if the sample contains glucose by doing the following.

a) Dip a glucose test strip into the test tube of unheated urine sample and immediately take it out.

b) Count to 10, then check the colour with the glucose colour chart.

c) Record whether the results are negative, light, medium, or dark. (The darker the colour, the greater the amount of glucose.)

4. Your group will be assigned to test one of the remaining samples of simulated urine. One sample was collected at the crime scene. The others have been provided by the four suspects in police custody. Run the four urinalysis tests and record your observations on a class data sheet provided by your teacher.

Analysis

1. Which suspect do you think committed the crime?

2. Explain how you arrived at this conclusion.

Conclusions

3. Based on your urinalysis, identify the disease that Suspect 4 might have. Explain.

4. List at least three other characteristics of urine that you would expect to observe (or not) in a healthy urine sample.

5. In what ways were the data that you collected in this urinalysis limited? What additional data would provide a more comprehensive picture of a urine sample?

Extension

6. Explain why you would not expect to find evidence of glucose or protein in a urine sample from someone whose kidneys are healthy. (Use details of nephron anatomy in your answer.)

7. The urine of athletes is routinely tested for evidence that they may have taken performance-enhancing drugs. Based on your understanding of urine formation, describe how molecules of a drug could appear in a person's urine.

---

cavity, where the large surface area and rich supply of capillaries of the peritoneum slowly filter the blood. Figure 9.10 on the next page illustrates these two methods of dialysis.

 16 What is renal insufficiency?

 17 Identify the two types of renal dialysis and briefly describe their similarities and differences.

Kidney Transplants

Dialysis enables people with kidney disease to live their lives in a relatively unchanged way. However, dialysis is not a cure, and it is not intended to be a long-term solution to the problem of kidney disease. Individuals with 10 percent or less kidney function will eventually have to replace their kidneys. The need for kidneys is much greater than the available supply. In Canada, the overall rate of organ donation is low compared to other developed countries, with about 14 donors

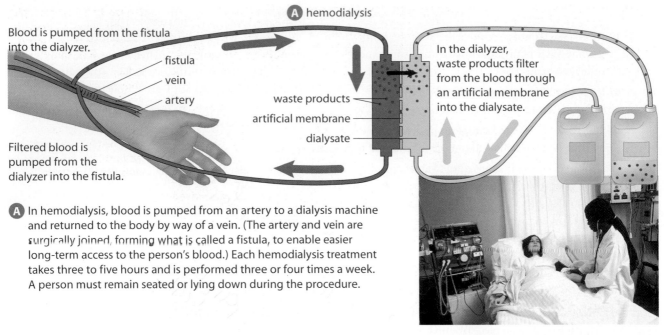

A hemodialysis

Blood is pumped from the fistula into the dialyzer.

fistula
vein
artery

Filtered blood is pumped from the dialyzer into the fistula.

waste products
artificial membrane
dialysate

In the dialyzer, waste products filter from the blood through an artificial membrane into the dialysate.

A In hemodialysis, blood is pumped from an artery to a dialysis machine and returned to the body by way of a vein. (The artery and vein are surgically joined, forming what is called a fistula, to enable easier long-term access to the person's blood.) Each hemodialysis treatment takes three to five hours and is performed three or four times a week. A person must remain seated or lying down during the procedure.

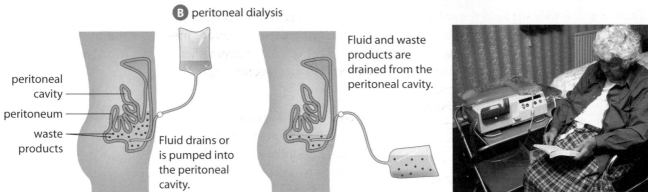

B peritoneal dialysis

peritoneal cavity
peritoneum
waste products

Fluid drains or is pumped into the peritoneal cavity.

Fluid and waste products are drained from the peritoneal cavity.

B In peritoneal dialysis, a catheter (flexible tube) is surgically inserted into the abdominal cavity and dialysate may be delivered, removed, and replaced. Because dialysate is always present, the blood is continuously filtered. The full name for this type of dialysis is continual peritoneal dialysis, or CPD. There are several types of CPD. In continuous

ambulatory peritoneal dialysis (CAPD), the procedure can be done at home, work, or school—any place that is clean and convenient. Usually, three to five exchanges of fresh dialysate for used dialysate are needed each day. In automated peritoneal dialysis (APD), a machine performs the exchange, which often is done at night for a period of up to 12 hours.

Figure 9.10
Hemodialysis **(A)** and peritoneal dialysis **(B)**

per million people. There are thousands of people in Canada waiting for organs, and the vast majority of them—over 75 percent—are waiting for kidneys.

Transplant organs can come from one of two sources. The first source is cadaveric donors. These are people who have died suddenly and who had previously discussed their desire to donate their organs with their families. The second source is live donors—individuals who wish to donate their organs while they are still alive. Organs suitable for live donations include the kidney, part of a

liver, or part of a lung, and the genetic makeup of the donor must be similar to the person who will be receiving the organ. A minimally invasive surgical technique used to remove a kidney from a living donor is called laparoscopy (see Figure 9.11). Instruments are used to locate, dissect, and remove the kidney from the donor through three small incisions in the abdomen.

The success rate of organ transplantation, particularly of kidneys, is fairly high. Generally, the success rate for kidney transplants from living

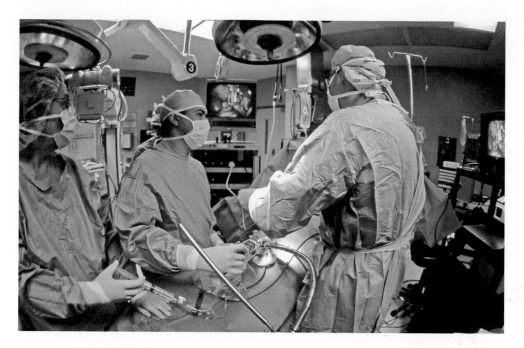

Figure 9.11 Laparoscopic surgery allows a kidney to be removed from a living donor. The location of the kidney, behind the abdominal organs, made it difficult to access using traditional laparoscopic instruments. Specially designed hand-assisted laparoscopes are being used with great success.

donors is higher than the success rate for transplants from cadaveric donors. A kidney from a living donor is usually a better genetic match, so rejection of the organ is less likely to occur. The success rate for living-donor transplants is about 98 percent, compared with up to 95 percent success with cadaveric-donor transplants.

In the future, these results likely will improve. Surgical techniques are constantly being improved, and new medicines to prevent rejection of the new organ are constantly being developed and improved. Recall from Chapter 8 that the immune system will react to destroy any cells that are considered foreign to the body. Some of the most common anti-rejection drugs cannot be used for kidney transplant recipients because these drugs, while revolutionizing the field of transplant surgery, cause kidney damage. For example, most heart transplant recipients have reduced kidney function as a result of their immune-suppression drugs, and a small percentage experience kidney failure, requiring dialysis and ultimately a kidney transplant.

Several medications have been developed for anti-rejection, but the treatment is given before the transplant takes place. Certain antibodies cause a temporary depletion of T cells (recall the function of T cells from Chapter 8). When these antibodies are used as a pre-treatment, the body may accept rather than reject the incoming new organ.

• • •

18 Why is a kidney transplant considered a cure for a serious kidney disorder, while renal dialysis is not?

19 What factors could affect the short-term and long-term success of a kidney transplant?

• • •

The Kidney-Coronary Connection

High blood pressure is one of the main reasons that kidneys begin to fail. Recall from Chapter 8 how blood flows through your body. When blood pressure is high for a prolonged period of time, the heart must pump a greater volume of blood, and blood vessels can be damaged. The blood vessels in the kidneys are very sensitive to changes in blood pressure, and if they become damaged by high blood pressure, the amount of waste and extra fluid that can be filtered from blood will be reduced. As the extra fluid accumulates in the body, it will increase the blood volume even more and cause

BiologyFile

Try This
Have you thought about organ donation? Would you want your organs given to someone else if you were to die unexpectedly? You may feel strongly for or against donating your organs, and there is no correct way to feel. If you are uncertain about what you feel, do some research on the process of organ donation. It is important that you make a decision about what you would like to happen, and that you let your family and close friends know your wishes.

Metabonomics

What happens inside your body after you swallow an Aspirin®? Although you may take this drug only to relieve a headache, the chemical ingredients in the Aspirin® can affect almost every part of your metabolism, producing a range of by-products called metabolites. Levels of these molecules rise or fall in response to the drug, and they are eventually excreted from your body in the urine. If you could obtain a measure of all these changes, you would have a "metabolic profile" that gives you a big picture of your body's overall health. That metabolic profile is one goal of a new approach to medical research called metabonomics.

What is a Metabolic Profile?

Just as genomics is the study of an organism's entire genetic makeup, metabonomics is the study of the complete metabolic response of an organism to various environmental or genetic stimuli. Almost everything that happens in your body produces metabolites. Changes in the levels of metabolites can be measured in body fluids such as blood or urine, and these changes give clues that can help diagnose diseases, identify genetic mutations, or measure the body's reaction to pharmaceutical drugs or other chemicals.

One technology used by researchers to analyze body fluids is nuclear magnetic resonance (NMR) spectroscopy. This technique measures chemical changes due to nuclear interactions and produces patterns that show many different biochemicals simultaneously.

Applying Metabonomics

Pharmaceutical companies develop and test thousands of new drugs every year at a cost of many billions of dollars. Many of these experimental drugs turn out to be ineffective or even toxic during testing. A major advantage of metabonomics is that it allows researchers to measure multiple effects of a drug in test animals simply by analyzing samples of their blood or urine. This is much quicker and cheaper than traditional methods, which often involve taking samples of tissues and cells from many animals for microscopic examination.

Rather than focus only on the metabolism of a drug compound itself, metabonomics research measures patterns of change in hundreds of different compounds. This holistic approach is made possible only by new technologies. For example, mass spectrometry combined with sophisticated data analysis and pattern recognition programs allow the German state of Bavaria to screen newborn infants for 30 metabolic disorders simultaneously, for a relatively low cost.

• • •

1. Why is urine such a valuable source of information about the body's metabolism?

2. How could metabonomics help a physician diagnose a metabolic disease before a person shows any symptoms?

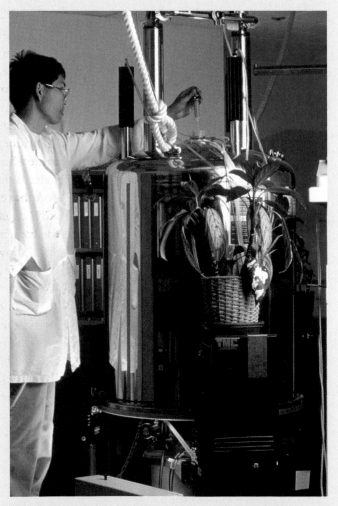

A pharmaceutical technician, working to develop drugs obtained from plants used in traditional healing, places a plant sample into an NMR spectrometer to identify the molecules in the plant extract.

the blood pressure to rise further. This cycle can continue until the kidney function is so reduced that symptoms become obvious. Unfortunately, both high blood pressure and kidney impairment do not have obvious symptoms until the damage is well underway.

Maintaining a healthy lifestyle supports the overall health of all of your body's systems. Remember that none of these systems functions in isolation, so any activity that affects one of your systems will affect other systems as well. Ensuring that you have adequate physical exercise, for example, can help to make your heart and circulatory system stronger and healthier (see Figure 9.12). One reason that exercise is effective at lowering blood pressure is that it stimulates the release of a substance called nitric oxide that is produced by cells on the inside of our blood vessels. Reduction in the amount of nitric oxide in the blood is one of the first signs that plaque is building up inside the blood vessels. High blood pressure has such an impact on kidney function that exercise to reduce blood pressure ultimately reduces the likelihood of kidney damage.

Section 9.3 Summary

- The kidneys maintain the water-salt balance in the body.
- The kidneys maintain blood pH within narrow limits by excreting excess hydrogen ions and reabsorbing bicarbonate ions.
- The kidneys excrete more concentrated urine when the body needs to conserve water and more dilute urine when the body has excess water.
- ADH regulates the amount of water in the body by reabsorbing water in the distal convoluted tubule and the collecting duct.
- Aldosterone regulates the amount of salt in the body by reabsorbing sodium ions in the distal convoluted tubule.
- Dialysis is a treatment for kidney failure where the blood is filtered using principles of diffusion. It can be internal (peritoneal dialysis) or external (hemodialysis).
- Kidney transplants are the only way to cure chronic kidney failure.
- The health of the excretory system affects the health of other body systems. Maintaining healthy blood pressure is a key way to protect both the kidneys and the excretory system.

Figure 9.12 People do not have to be athletes or play sports to experience the benefits of physical exercise. Activities such as walking, bicycle riding, and canoeing are simple ways to promote personal health.

BiologyFile

FYI
Nitric oxide is a gas that controls many functions in the body, including regulating the activity of many organs. Before 1987, nitric oxide was known only as a toxic environmental pollutant because it is a primary component of smog. However, scientists have discovered that cells on the inside of the blood vessels make nitric oxide in response to the pressure of the blood flowing through the vessels. The journal *Science* named nitric oxide its "Molecule of the Year" in 1992 because of its importance to the body's health.

1. Identify how the amount of water reabsorbed from the filtrate influences two characteristics of blood.

Use the following illustration to answer the next questions.

This diagram illustrates how the release of antidiuretic hormone (ADH) controls the amount of water reabsorbed or excreted in the urine.

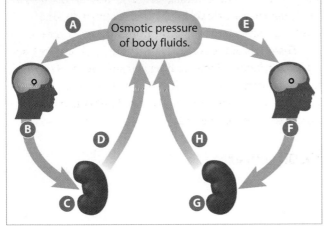

2. a) Complete captions for the areas on this diagram labelled A to H.

  b) Use this diagram to explain why drinking alcoholic beverages stimulates urine production.

3. Explain why an individual with diabetes insipidus urinates as much as 4 L to 8 L per day. Why would this individual have "intense thirst?"

4. a) Illustrate, using words or a sketch, the locations of the nephron that are involved in water absorption.

  b) Explain how the excretory system would respond if you drank very little water on a hot day. Modify your answer in part (a) to include this information.

5. Explain what would happen if the body were unable to release the hormone aldosterone.

6. Based on the data in the table below, identify the substances that are secreted and those that are reabsorbed. (You do not need to know what these substances are to answer this question.) Justify your answer.

Substance	Plasma (g/L)	Filtrate (g/L)	Urine (g/L)
Creatine	0.01	0.01	1.9
Uric acid	0.05	0.05	1.0
Bicarbonate ion	1.7	1.7	0.4

7. Describe briefly how the acid-base balance of the blood is maintained.

8. Predict the effect of very low blood pressure on kidney function.

9. Imagine that you are adrift at sea and your supply of fresh water has run out. You are surrounded by water. Explain why you will become dehydrated if you drink the sea water.

Use the following information to answer the following questions.

Urinalysis

The colour and appearance of the urine specimen is recorded. Usual colours are colourless, straw, yellow, amber; less commonly pink, red, brown. Usual appearances (opacity) are clear or hazy; less commonly turbid, cloudy and opaque, unless the specimen has remained at room or refrigerated temperatures.

The common chemical testing of urine utilizes commercial disposable test strips. Some strips can test for 10 substances: glucose, bilirubin, ketone, specific gravity, blood, pH, protein, urobilinogen, nitrite, and leukocyte esterase. The result of this testing is regarded as semi-quantitative.

10. The urine of different individuals is analyzed. Explain a possible disease or disorder that may be associated with each of the following observations:

  a) Individual 1: protein found in their urine

  b) Individual 2: blood found in their urine

  c) Individual 3: glucose found in their urine

  d) Individual 4: white blood cells (leucocytes) found in their urine

11. Use word processing or spreadsheet software to design a chart that summarizes the causes, symptoms, and treatments for the following disorders of the excretory system:

  a) kidney stones

  b) renal insufficiency

  c) urinary tract infections **ICT**

The metabolic activities of cells, including energy release, maintenance, and repair, produce substances that change the balance of the volume of water and the concentration and composition of dissolved substances in the body's fluids. The excretory system removes these materials to maintain the optimal volume of water and composition of body fluids, dispose of wastes, and recycle the non-waste substances. The substances in question include carbon dioxide; water; ions of sodium (Na^+), chloride (Cl^-), and hydrogen (H^+); and other compounds resulting from the breakdown of proteins and nucleic acids. The excretory system also plays a key role in maintaining the acid-base balance (pH) in the blood.

The organs of the excretory system are the kidneys, the ureters, the urinary bladder, and the urethra. The kidneys contain millions of tiny nephrons that each contain a filter, a tube, and a duct. The nephrons filter out waste and reabsorb substances such as sodium and water for reuse by the body's systems. The resulting filtrate, known as urine, is sent through the ureters to the urinary bladder for temporary storage until it is eliminated from the body through the urethra.

Disorders of the excretory system include urinary tract infections, kidney stones, and renal insufficiency. Renal insufficiency may require dialysis or a kidney transplant in order to ensure that wastes are secreted rather than building up to toxic levels in the body.

Chapter 9 Graphic Organizer

Using the nephrons of the kidneys, the excretory system removes metabolic wastes from the body, maintains water and pH balance through filtration and secretion, and returns required solutes by reabsorption.

1. Filtration (blue arrow) results in the movement of fluid from glomerulus into the nephron.

2. Solutes are reabsorbed (purple arrow) across the wall of the nephron into the interstitial fluid by active transport and diffusion. Solutes are transported back to the body for reuse.

3. Solutes are secreted (orange arrow) across the wall of the nephron into the filtrate for removal by excretion.

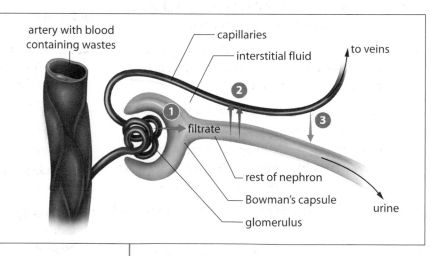

artery with blood containing wastes

capillaries

interstitial fluid

to veins

filtrate

rest of nephron

Bowman's capsule

glomerulus

urine

Excretory system utilizes these processes to help maintain homeostasis by regulating water-salt concentrations and pH of blood.

Healthful lifestyle practices support the excretory system. Disorders of the system may be addressed through technologies such as renal dialysis and kidney transplant operations.

Understanding Concepts

Use the following diagram to answer the next question.

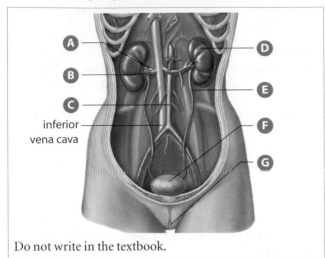

inferior
vena cava

Do not write in the textbook.

1. Identify the structures labelled A to G in the diagram above, and describe their function in terms of the excretory system

2. Explain how the process of active transport within the kidney helps control the volume of urine produced during the day.

3. Explain how increased secretion of ADH affects urine concentration and urine volume. Identify a possible situation in which the hypothalamus may be stimulated to release ADH.

4. Explain why proteins and blood are not normally found in urine.

5. Identify the parts of the nephron that are most involved in regulating the pH level of the blood.

6. Identify four differences between the blood entering the kidney in the renal artery and the blood leaving the kidney in the renal vein.

7. Identify four types of dissolved substances found in the filtrate that forms in the Bowman's capsule of the nephron.

8. Describe the causes and symptoms of a urinary tract infection. Identify two ways these disorders can be prevented.

9. Use word processing software to draw a flowchart or other graphic organizer to show the response of the body after drinking several cups of water on a cool evening. **ICT**

10. Distinguish between the processes of filtration, tubular secretion, reabsorption, and osmosis as they relate to the process of urine formation.

11. How would each of the following processes in the kidney change in response to serious dehydration in the body caused by excessive sweating on a hot day?
    a) glomerular filtration   c) ADH secretion
    b) tubular reabsorption

Use the following diagram to answer the next question.

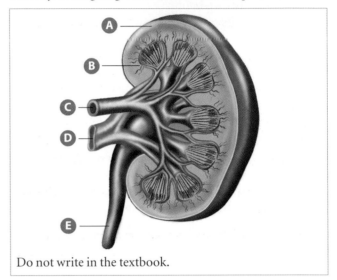

Do not write in the textbook.

12. a) Identify the structures labelled A to E on this diagram.
    b) Describe the primary functions of each of the following sections of the human kidney.
       i) cortex   iii) collecting duct
       ii) medulla   iv) renal pelvis

Use the following information to answer the next question.

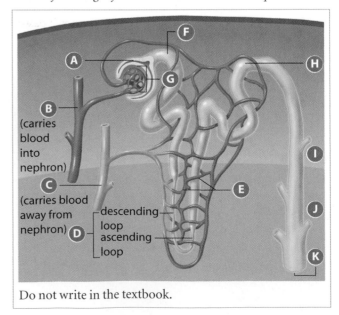

B
(carries blood into nephron)

C
(carries blood away from nephron) D

descending loop
ascending loop

Do not write in the textbook.

13. a) Identify each of the structures labelled A to K.

b) Describe the functions of the following structures
   i) glomerulus
   ii) Bowman's capsule
   iii) proximal tubule
   iv) descending loop of Henle
   v) ascending loop of Henle
   vi) distal tubule
   vii) collecting duct

Applying Concepts

Use the following information to answer the next question.

Diuretics
Alcohol, like caffeine, acts as a diuretic. A diuretic is a substance that removes water from the body by promoting urine formation and the loss of salt (sodium). Diuretics may be used as part of treatment for conditions that cause swelling from water retention (edema), such as heart failure, hypertension, or liver or kidney disease.

14. Explain how alcohol affects the concentration of urine produced.

Use the following information to answer the next question.

Substance	Glomerular filtrate (per day)	Urine (per day)	Reabsorption (%)
water, L	180	1.8	99.0
sodium, g	630	3.2	99.5
glucose, g	180	0.0	100.0
urea, g	54	30.0	44.0

Reabsorption from nephrons. L = litres, g = grams

15. Explain what is happening to each substance as it passes through the different regions of the nephron.
   a) water
   c) glucose
   b) sodium (salts)
   d) urea

16. Explain why doctors usually prefer to use kidneys provided by living donors rather than those from deceased donors in kidney tranplant cases.

17. The process of dialysis filters blood in people with reduced kidney function or kidney failure. Use word processing or spreadsheet software to create a chart or table comparing how the process is carrried out by dialysis machines and the human kidney. **ICT**

18. Use word processing software to create a flowchart that illustrates how the filtrate is modified by the processes of active and passive transport as it flows through a single nephon in the human kidney. **ICT**

Making Connections

Use the following information to answer the next question.

Glomerulonephritis
In diseases and conditions classified as glomerulonephritis (also called nephritis or nephritic syndrome), the glomerulus becomes inflamed and scarred. Most often, it is caused by an *autoimmune disease*, but it can also result from infection.

19. a) Explain how nephritis might affect urinary output and the removal of nitrogenous wastes from the blood.

b) Provide a possible explanation why the urine of a person with nephritis is usually brown instead of yellow in colour.

20. If you were to perform a urinalysis on the filtrate removed from a peritoneal dialysis machine, what would you expect to find in a chemical analysis? Assume the person is healthy other than suffering kidney failure.

Use the following information to answer the next question.

Dialysis vs. Kidney Transplants
Consider the following cost comparison of dialysis versus kidney transplants. Dialysis cost approximately $50 000 per year in 2006. A kidney transplant operation at this time cost approximately $20 000 and required $6000 per year in followup treatments. Kidney transplants have a 98 percent success rate using kidneys from a living donor and a 95 percent success rate using kidneys from a deceased donor.

21. a) In your opinion, to what extent should cost be considered as an important variable when people make decesions about whether to choose a transplant or dialysis?

b) What additional information would you like to have to help you write an informed, reasoned answer to this question?

The Muscular System and Homeostasis

CHAPTER

10

Chapter Concepts

10.1 Movement and Muscle Tissue

- There are three types of muscle tissue: skeletal muscle, smooth muscle, and cardiac muscle.

- Skeletal muscle produces body movement, maintains body temperature, and provides support for the body.

- Muscle fibres are filled with myofibrils that house thin (actin) and thick (myosin) contractile protein myofilaments.

- Actin and myosin slide past each other during a muscle contraction.

- Creatine phosphate, fermentation, and aerobic cellular respiration provide energy for muscle contractions.

10.2 Muscles, Health, and Homeostasis

- Three types of skeletal muscle—slow-twitch, fast-twitch, and an intermediate type—are found in different parts of the body.

- Muscles atrophy with inadequate stimulation and can hypertrophy with appropriate repeated stimulation.

- The muscular system works with other body systems to maintain homeostasis.

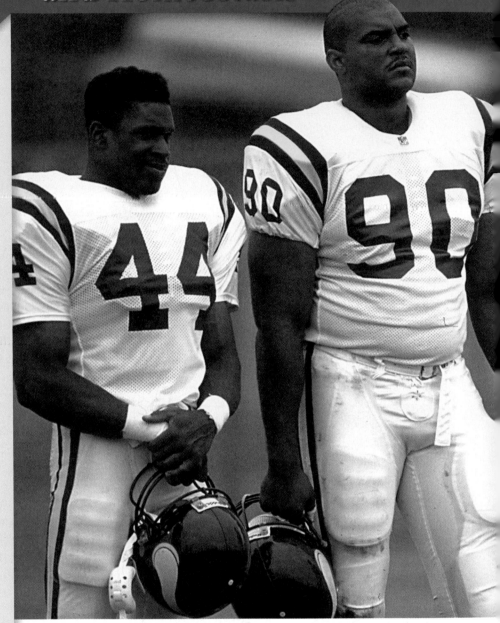

Much of the heat that maintains the core body temperature of 37 °C is generated by muscle activity. The muscles of high-performance athletes, such as the members of the Minnesota Vikings shown here, generate an enormous amount of heat—so much so that a hard workout on a hot day can take a player's core body temperature into the danger zone. In 2001, the Vikings lost a teammate to heat stroke after a tough July workout.

In this chapter you will find out how muscles work to move you, heat your body, and support other body systems. You will also look at the benefits of maintaining healthy muscle structure and function throughout your life.

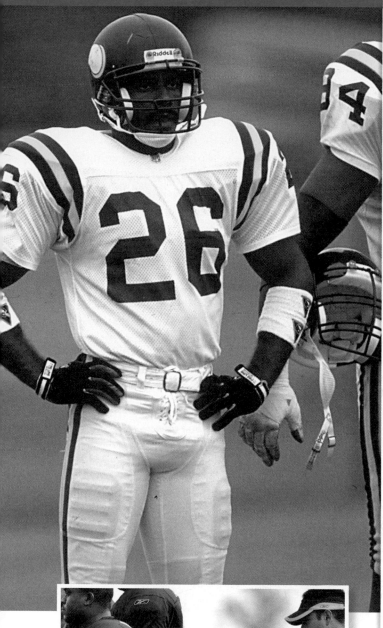

Working in Pairs

The muscles that enable you to move your body are attached to the bones of the skeleton. The contractions of these muscles cause the movements of the bones at a joint (a place where two or more bones meet). Because muscles shorten when they contract, they can only pull; they cannot push. Therefore, muscles work in pairs. One muscle of the pair causes a bone to move in one direction, and the contraction of the other muscle of the pair causes the same bone to move in the opposite direction. In this activity, you will flex your muscles in the name of science!

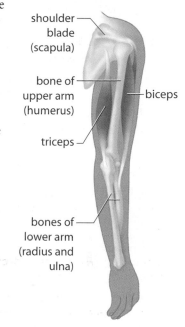

shoulder blade (scapula)

bone of upper arm (humerus)

biceps

triceps

bones of lower arm (radius and ulna)

Procedure

1. With a partner, try out different states of relaxation and contraction of the biceps and triceps—two paired muscles in your arm. While one of you does the flexing, the other should observe by sight and by touch how these two muscles change.

2. Switch roles with your partner.

Analysis

1. Sketch and label the arm to show the relationship between the biceps and triceps when the arm is relaxed (hanging down at your side).

2. Sketch and label the arm to show the two muscles when the arm is flexed.

3. Were you able to observe, through touch, any temperature increase in the biceps or triceps? If so, can you be sure that the heat you felt was the result of the activity of these muscles, rather than heat radiating from blood vessels in the skin? What would you need to do to help you decide?

Today, many coaches are using technology developed by NASA—an ingestible temperature-measuring device and a hand-held sensor—to safeguard the core body temperature of their players.

Movement and Muscle Tissue

Section Outcomes

In this section, you will

- **observe** and **compare** the three types of muscle tissue
- **describe**, in general, the action of actin and myosin in muscle contraction and heat production
- **identify** the sources of energy for muscle contraction

Key Terms

smooth muscle
cardiac muscle
skeletal muscle
muscle fibres
myofibrils
myofilaments
actin myofilament
myosin myofilament
sliding filament model

Muscle tissue is highly specialized to convert chemical energy into kinetic energy—the energy of movement. The intricate, precise movements of a dancer, a basketball player, and an artist occur through the coordinated contracting and relaxing of many muscles. All muscles, regardless of their type, can contract (shorten). When muscles contract, some part of the body, or the entire body, moves.

There are three types of muscle cells, as illustrated in Figure 10.1. Food moves through the intestines because of the contractions of smooth muscle. The heart accomplishes its unceasing movement because of cardiac muscle. The body is able to move because skeletal muscle pulls on the bones of the skeleton.

The cells of **smooth muscle** tissue are long and tapered at each end and

have one nucleus. They are usually arranged in parallel lines, forming sheets. You can find smooth muscle in many parts of the body. In the walls of certain blood vessels, for example, smooth muscle contracts, helping to regulate blood pressure and direct blood flow. In the iris of the eye, smooth muscle controls the size of the eye's opening to light. As well, smooth muscle is located in the walls of hollow internal organs, and it causes these walls to contract. Contraction of smooth muscle is involuntary—it occurs without conscious control. Although smooth muscle is slower to contract than skeletal muscle, it can sustain prolonged contractions and does not fatigue easily.

Cardiac muscle is unique to the heart and forms the wall of the heart.

Figure 10.1 Comparing and contrasting skeletal, smooth, and cardiac muscle cells.

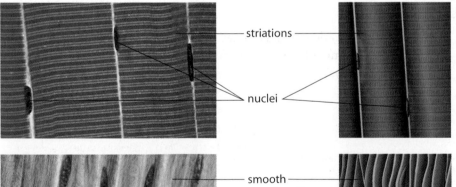
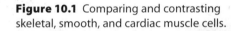

striations
nuclei

Skeletal muscle cells
- are striated and tubular
- have many nuclei
- contract voluntarily
- are usually attached to bones of the skeleton

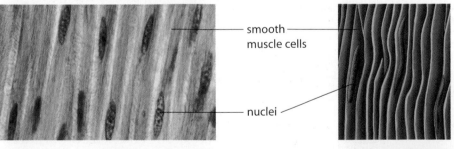

smooth muscle cells
nuclei

Smooth muscle cells
- are non-striated
- have one nucleus
- contract involuntarily
- are found in the walls of internal organs

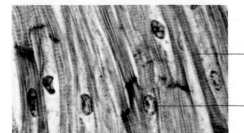
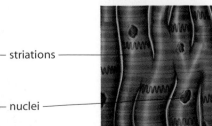

striations
nuclei

Cardiac muscle cells
- are striated, tubular, and branched
- have one nucleus
- contract involuntarily
- are found in the walls of the heart

The cells are tubular and striated (have bands of light and dark) and have one nucleus. Cardiac muscle cells are branched, creating a netlike structure. Like smooth muscle, cardiac muscle contraction is involuntary.

Skeletal muscle cells, like cardiac muscle cells, are tubular and striated. The "meat" (flesh) of animal bodies is skeletal muscle. Skeletal muscle contraction is voluntary, because its contraction is consciously controlled by the nervous system. The great range and types of movement in the human body are due to over 600 skeletal muscles. These muscles have numerous functions, as outlined in the box below.

Unlike smooth and cardiac muscle cells, skeletal muscle cells are very long and have many nuclei. Because of the length of a skeletal muscle cell, its needs for energy and materials are too much to be coordinated by a single nucleus. Multiple nuclei maintain the normal functions of these cells. Because of their structural organization and the presence of many nuclei, skeletal muscle cells are usually referred to as *fibres*, rather than cells.

The Functions of Skeletal Muscle

- *Skeletal muscle supports the body.* The contraction of skeletal muscle opposes the force of gravity and enables us to stand and remain upright.
- *Skeletal muscle makes the bones move.* Muscle contraction accounts not only for the movements of the arms and legs but also for the movements of the eyes and for facial expressions and breathing.
- *Skeletal muscle helps to maintain a constant body temperature.* Skeletal muscle contraction causes ATP to break down, releasing a considerable amount of heat, which is distributed throughout the body.
- *Skeletal muscle helps to protect the internal organs and stabilize the joints.* Skeletal muscle pads the bones that protect the organs. As well, it has tendons that help to hold the bones together at the joints.

> **Q 1** Briefly describe the main differences among smooth, cardiac, and skeletal muscle.

The Cooperation of Skeletal Muscles

When muscles contract, they shorten. This means that muscles can only pull; they *cannot* push. The work of any muscle is done during its contraction. Relaxation is the passive state of the muscle. There must always be a force available to stretch a muscle after it has stopped contracting and relaxes. Therefore, the muscles that permit movements of the skeleton are present in pairs (see Figure 10.2). For the action of each muscle, there is another muscle that has the opposite action. For example, the biceps muscle causes the arm to flex (bend) as the muscle shortens. The contraction of its "opposite," the triceps muscle, causes the arm to extend (straighten) and, at the same time, stretches the relaxed biceps muscle.

> **Q 2** Why do muscles that cause bones to move function as opposing pairs?

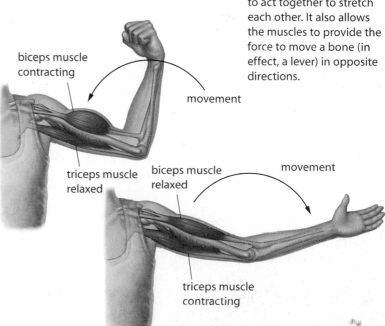

biceps muscle contracting

movement

triceps muscle relaxed

biceps muscle relaxed

movement

triceps muscle contracting

BiologyFile

FYI
The movement of the jaw to chew food requires the action of four pairs of skeletal muscles. Moving a foot involves eight pairs.

Figure 10.2 To lengthen, a muscle must relax so that an opposing force can pull the muscle back to its full length. The arrangement of opposing pairs of muscles around a joint (in effect, a fulcrum) allows the muscles to act together to stretch each other. It also allows the muscles to provide the force to move a bone (in effect, a lever) in opposite directions.

Observing Muscle Tissue

The three types of muscle tissue—skeletal, smooth, and cardiac—have characteristics that distinguish them from each other. In this investigation, you will observe the three types of muscle tissue and compare them to each other.

Questions

How do the three types of muscle tissue differ under microscopic examination? What conditions are necessary for a muscle fibre to contract?

Safety Precautions

Make sure that your hands are dry when handling electrical equipment. Handle microscope slides carefully, since they can break easily and cause cuts.

Materials

- petri dish with glycerol and skeletal muscle tissue
- light microscope
- small forceps or tweezers
- teasing needle
- prepared slides of different muscle tissues
- dropper pipette
- 2 microscope slides
- 2 cover slips

Procedure

Part 1

1. Design a data table, like the one shown here, to record your observations.

Data Table for Part 1

Type of muscle	Organization of fibres	Description of fibres	Description of nuclei
skeletal			
smooth			
cardiac			

2. Place the slide of the skeletal muscle tissue on the microscope stage, and focus using the low-power lens.

3. Scan the slide to find an area where you can observe individual muscle fibres.

4. Observe the fibres, using Figure 10.1 for reference. In your table, record your observations of the fibres, including their organization, the presence or absence of striations, and the presence (and number) or absence of nuclei in each fibre.

5. Make your own drawing of skeletal muscle tissue. Label your drawing as completely as you can, and estimate the size of the cells.

6. Repeat steps 2 to 5 until you have observed all three types of muscle tissue.

7. Answer Analysis questions 1 to 3 and Conclusion question 5.

Part 2

1. Make a copy of the data table for Part 2.

Data Table for Part 2

Solution	Length (mm)	
	Slide 1	Slide 2
glycerol alone		
potassium-magnesium salt solution alone		
ATP alone		
both salt solution and ATP		

2. Label two slides 1 and 2. On each slide, mount a strand of glycerinated muscle fibres in a drop of glycerol. Place each slide on a ruler, and measure the length of the strand. Record the length of each strand in the first row of your data table.

3. If there is more than a small drop of glycerol on each slide, soak up the excess with a piece of lens paper held at the edge of the glycerol, farthest from the fibre strand.

4. To slide 1, add a few drops of the salt solution that contains potassium ions and magnesium ions. Measure any change in the length of the strand, and record your results.

5. To slide 2, add a few drops of ATP solution. Measure and record any change in the length of the strand.

6. Now add ATP solution to slide 1. Measure and record any change in the length of the strand.

7. To slide 2, add a few drops of the potassium-magnesium solution. Measure and record any change in the length of the strand.

8. Answer Analysis question 4 and Conclusion questions 6 and 7.

Analysis

1. Describe each type of muscle tissue.

2. Explain the difference between voluntary and involuntary muscle. Is it possible to tell from your observations whether muscle tissue is voluntary or involuntary? Explain.

3. Cardiac muscle is only found in the heart. Suggest a reason why the heart needs a unique type of muscle.

4. Summarize your observations of the strand of muscle fibres in Part 2, noting which variables were controlled and which were manipulated.

Conclusions

5. Make a statement that correlates the observed structure of each type of muscle fibre to its function in the body.

6. Based on your observations, identify the factors required for a muscle fibre to contract.

7. Based on your observations, and given that a whole muscle is comprised of numerous muscle fibres, suggest a plausible mechanism for the contraction of skeletal muscle in the body.

Skeletal Muscle Consists of Bundles of Fibres

Figure 10.3 shows the levels of organization of skeletal muscle. Each muscle in the body lies along the length of a bone. A tough, heavy band of tissue, called a tendon, attaches each end of a muscle to a different bone. The long skeletal muscle fibres can be up to 20 cm in length. **Muscle fibres** are organized into many larger bundles. A muscle, then, consists of clusters of such bundles of muscle fibres. A layer of connective tissue wraps around each fibre. Another layer wraps around each bundle of fibres, and another around the whole muscle itself.

Blood vessels and nerves run between the bundles of muscle fibres. The rich blood supply provides muscle fibres with nutrients and oxygen to power contractions, and it removes cellular wastes. The nerves trigger and control muscle contractions.

Figure 10.3 A muscle is composed of many muscle fibres. The muscle fibres are made up of myofibrils, which are composed of two kinds of myofilaments.

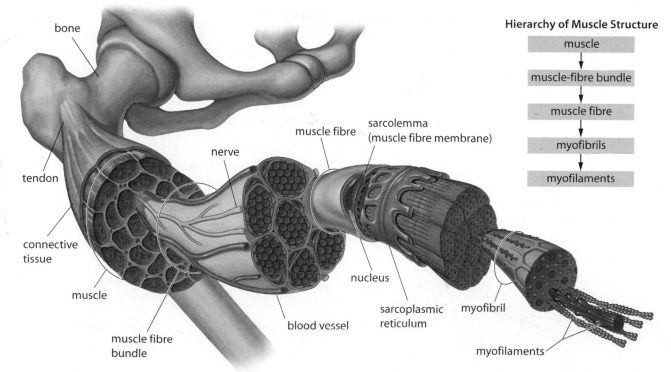

Hierarchy of Muscle Structure

muscle → muscle-fibre bundle → muscle fibre → myofibrils → myofilaments

Labels: bone, nerve, muscle fibre, sarcolemma (muscle fibre membrane), tendon, connective tissue, muscle, muscle fibre bundle, blood vessel, nucleus, sarcoplasmic reticulum, myofibril, myofilaments

Unlike the hollow organs of the body, which are made up of smooth muscle tissue, the diaphragm of the respiratory system is made up of skeletal muscle tissue. What do you know about the function of the diaphragm that would enable you to infer that the diaphragm is composed of skeletal, rather than smooth, muscle tissue?

Most of the volume of a muscle fibre consists of hundreds of thousands of cylindrical subunits called **myofibrils**. Each myofibril is made of even finer **myofilaments**, which contain protein structures that are responsible for muscle contractions. The rest of the volume of a muscle fibre consists of numerous mitochondria (about 300 per muscle fibre) and other organelles common to most cells. Table 10.1 outlines some of the main components of a muscle fibre. Note that some of the names of the components are different from the names used for these components in other types of cells. For example, the cell membrane of a muscle fibre is called the sarcolemma (from two Greek words that mean "flesh husk"), and the cytoplasm is called the sarcoplasm.

Q 3 Describe how skeletal muscle fibres are organized.

The Mechanism of Muscle Fibre Contractions

Muscle contractions involve the coordinated action of the two types of myofilaments: actin and myosin. A thin **actin myofilament** consists of two strands of protein (actin) molecules that are wrapped around each other, somewhat like two strands of beads loosely wound together. A thick **myosin myofilament** also consists of two strands of protein molecules wound around each other, but it is about 10 times longer than an actin filament and has a different shape. One end of a myosin myofilament consists of a long rod, while the other end consists of a double-headed globular region, often called the "head." Figure 10.4 compares the structures of actin and myosin.

Q 4 How is myosin different from actin?

How Myofilaments Contract

Examine the diagram of myosin and actin (Figure 10.5), and focus on the myosin heads. When a myofilament contracts, the heads of the myosin move first. Like flexing your hand at the wrist, the heads bend backward and inward. This moves them closer to their rod-like "backbone" and a few nanometers in the

Table 10.1 Some Components of Skeletal Muscle Fibres

Component	Description	Function
Muscle fibre	single muscle cell	is responsible for muscle contractions
myoglobin	oxygen-binding pigment (similar to hemoglobin) in a skeletal muscle fibre	stores oxygen for use during muscle contractions
sarcolemma	membrane of a muscle fibre	surrounds the muscle fibre and regulates the entry and exit of materials
sarcoplasm	cytoplasm of a muscle fibre	is the site of metabolic processes for normal cell activities; contains myoglobin and glycogen (which stores energy for muscle contractions)
sarcoplasmic reticulum	smooth endoplasmic reticulum in a muscle fibre (refer to Unit 3 Preparation to review the structure and function of cell organelles)	stores calcium ions needed for muscle contractions
Myofibrils	organized bundles of myofilaments; cylindrical structures, as long as the muscle fibre itself	contain myofilaments that are responsible for muscle contractions
thick filament	fine myofilament composed of bundles of protein called myosin (about 11 nm in diameter)	binds to actin and causes muscle contractions
thin filament	fine myofilament composed of strands of protein called actin (about 5 nm in diameter)	binds to myosin and causes muscle contractions

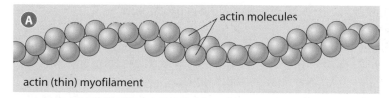

A Actin myofilaments are composed of globular actin proteins. Other proteins (discussed on the next page) are also associated with strands of actin.

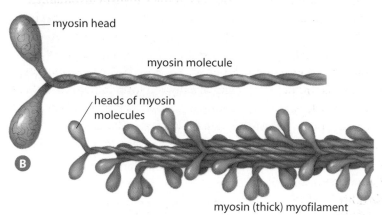

B Myosin myofilaments are composed of myosin molecules. Each myosin molecule consists of two polypeptide chains wrapped around each other. The end of each chain has a distinctive globular region, known as the head. Since the thick myofilaments are composed of bundles of myosin molecules, the heads protrude at regular intervals.

Figure 10.4 The structures of actin and myosin.

direction of the flex. Because the heads are attached (chemically bound) at this time to an actin myofilament, the actin is pulled along with the myosin heads as they flex. As a result, the actin myofilament slides past the myosin myofilament in the direction of the flex. As one after another myosin head flexes, the myosin, in effect, walks step by step along the actin. Each step requires a molecule of ATP to provide the energy that repositions the myosin head before each flex.

The sliding of actin past myosin is part of the **sliding filament model** of muscle contraction. As shown in Figure 10.6 on the next page, the actin is anchored at one end of each myofilament, at a position in striated muscle tissue called the Z line. Because the actin is anchored like this, its movement pulls its "anchor"

Figure 10.5 The movement of actin and myosin.

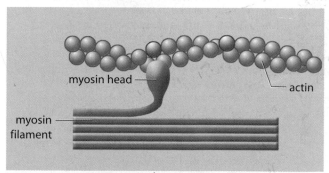

A The myosin head is attached to actin.

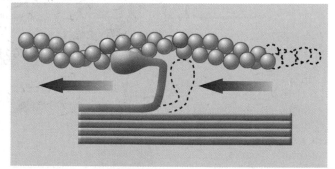

B The myosin head flexes, advancing the actin filament.

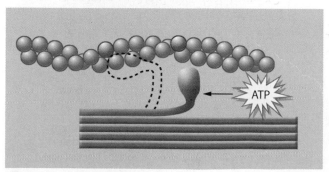

C The myosin head releases and unflexes, powered by ATP.

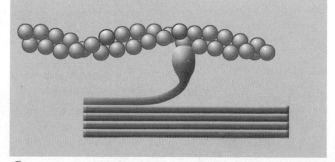

D The myosin reattaches to actin farther along the fibre.

BiologyFile

FYI

The year 1996 brought a surprising announcement from two American dentists, Gary Hack and Gwendolyn Dunn, at the University of Maryland. To study the muscles involved in chewing, they were performing a dissection from an atypical angle—entering from the front of the head, rather than from the side as is usual. To their astonishment, the scientists discovered muscle that had never been identified and described before. They named it the sphenomandibularis.

(the Z line) along with it. As actin moves past myosin, it drags the Z line toward the myosin. The mechanism of muscle contraction depends on the structural arrangement of myosin myofilaments in relation to pairs of actin myofilaments. With one actin myofilament being pulled inward in one direction and the other actin myofilament being pulled inward in the opposite direction, the two pairs of actin molecules drag the Z lines toward each other as they slide past the myosin core. As the Z lines are pulled closer together, the plasma membranes to which they are attached move toward one another, causing the entire muscle fibre to contract.

• • •

5 Explain how muscle fibres contract.

6 What is the sliding filament model?

• • •

The Role of Calcium Ions in Contraction

When a muscle is relaxed, its myosin heads are raised and ready, through the splitting of ATP. They are, however, unable to bind to actin. This is because the attachment sites for the myosin heads on the actin are physically blocked by another protein called tropomyosin. Therefore the myosin heads cannot bind to actin in the relaxed muscle, and the filaments cannot slide.

For a muscle to contract, the tropomyosin must be moved out of the way. This requires another protein called troponin, which binds to the tropomyosin. The troponin and tropomyosin form a complex that is regulated by the calcium ion (Ca^{++}) concentration of the sarcoplasm (muscle fibre cytoplasm).

When the calcium ion concentration in the sarcoplasm is low, tropomyosin inhibits myosin binding, and the muscle is relaxed (see Figure 10.7A). When the

A The heads on the two ends of the myosin filament are oriented in opposite directions. When the heads attach to the actin, they bend toward the centre of the myosin.

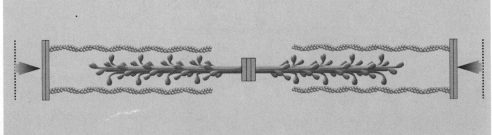

B As one end of the myosin filament draws the actin filament and its attached Z line toward the centre, the other end of the myosin filament does the same.

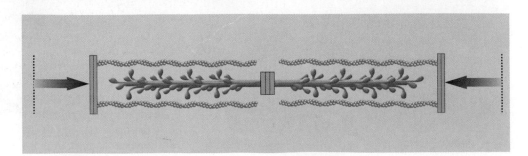

C Both Z lines move toward the centre, and contraction occurs.

Figure 10.6 The sliding filament model of muscle contraction

Thought Lab 10.1 Designing a Muscle Fibre Model

In this Thought Lab, you will design a working model of a skeletal muscle fibre. If time permits, your teacher may have you construct and test your model.

Procedure

1. In a group, review your understanding of the mechanics of muscle fibre contraction. Brainstorm ideas for designing a model to demonstrate how a skeletal muscle fibre works.

2. Choose one design, and sketch and label its components. Identify all the materials you would need to construct the model.

3. Prepare a summary sheet to outline how you expect your model to work.

4. With your teacher's permission, construct your model.

Analysis

1. Compare your model with the models of other groups. How does your model differ from the others? How is it the same?

2. How would the muscle fibre you modelled fit together with other muscle fibres to form muscle tissue?

---

calcium ion concentration is raised, Ca^{++} binds to troponin (see Figure 10.7B). This causes the troponin-tropomyosin complex to be shifted away from the attachment sites for the myosin heads on the actin. When the repositioning has occurred, the myosin heads attach to actin and, using ATP energy, move the actin filament to shorten the myofibril.

The source of calcium ions for this process is the sarcoplasmic reticulum. When a muscle fibre is stimulated to contract, Ca^{++} is released from the sarcoplasmic reticulum and diffuses into the myofibrils. When the nerve impulses that initiate muscle contractions stop and the contractions stop, the calcium ions are returned to the sarcoplasmic reticulum through active transport.

• • •

7 Can muscles in the body contract without calcium? Explain why or why not.

• • •

Energy for Muscle Contraction

The ATP that is produced before strenuous exercise lasts only a few seconds. The muscles then acquire new ATP in three different ways, depending on the availability of oxygen: the breakdown of a molecule called creatine phosphate, aerobic cellular respiration, and

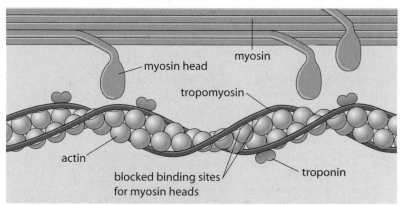

A The muscle is at rest. A long filament, composed of the protein molecule tropomyosin, blocks the myosin binding sites of the actin molecule. Without actin's ability to bind with myosin at these sites, muscle contraction cannot occur.

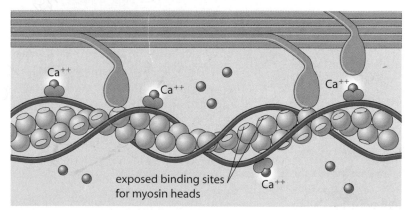

B Calcium ions have bonded to another protein molecule, troponin, which is part of the actin myofilament. The resulting complex repositions the tropomyosin, exposing the myosin binding sites of actin. The myosin heads can bind to the actin, and contraction occurs.

Figure 10.7 How calcium controls muscle contractions

Figure 10.8 Creatine phosphate builds up and is stored in a resting muscle (purple background). For the muscle to contract (green background), it needs to acquire ATP. **(A)** When the muscle starts contracting, it breaks down stored creatine phosphate. This generates some ATP that is used immediately. **(B)** To continue contracting, the muscle carries out aerobic cellular respiration as long as oxygen is available. When the oxygen has been used up, the muscle can carry out fermentation for a limited period of time. As you know from Chapter 5, fermentation results in only a small amount of ATP, compared with the amount produced by aerobic cellular respiration, and lactate builds up. Once the muscle resumes resting (purple background), creatine phosphate builds up again.

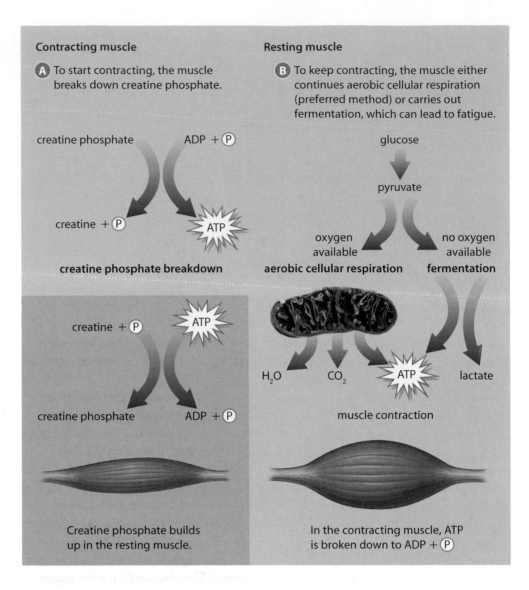

Contracting muscle

A To start contracting, the muscle breaks down creatine phosphate.

creatine phosphate   ADP + (P)

creatine + (P)   ATP

creatine phosphate breakdown

creatine + (P)   ATP

creatine phosphate   ADP + (P)

Creatine phosphate builds up in the resting muscle.

Resting muscle

B To keep contracting, the muscle either continues aerobic cellular respiration (preferred method) or carries out fermentation, which can lead to fatigue.

glucose

pyruvate

oxygen available   no oxygen available

aerobic cellular respiration   **fermentation**

H_2O CO_2 ATP   lactate

muscle contraction

In the contracting muscle, ATP is broken down to ADP + (P)

Biology File

Try This
When an animal dies, its cells can no longer produce ATP, so the linkages between the myosin heads and actin cannot be broken. This is what causes the death-related muscle rigidity called *rigor mortis* (Latin for "stiffness of death"). *Rigor mortis* is not permanent. After about 36 h, the body loses its stiffness. Infer a reason for this. Also infer factors that could affect the rate at which *rigor mortis* sets in when death occurs.

fermentation (see Figure 10.8). Creatine phosphate breakdown and fermentation are anaerobic, so they do not require oxygen. Creatine phosphate breakdown is used first. It is a way to acquire ATP before oxygen starts to enter the mitochondria. Aerobic cellular respiration can only occur if oxygen is available. If exercise is so vigorous that oxygen cannot be delivered fast enough to the working muscles, then fermentation occurs. Fermentation causes an oxygen deficit (or oxygen debt, as it is also called).

Creatine Phosphate Breakdown

Creatine phosphate is a high-energy compound that builds up when a muscle is resting. This compound cannot participate directly in muscle contraction.

Instead, it regenerates ATP by the following reaction:

ADP   ATP

creatine phosphate ⟶ creatine

This reaction occurs in the midst of sliding filaments. Therefore, it is the speediest way to make ATP available to muscles. Creatine phosphate provides enough energy for only about eight seconds of intense activity, and then it is spent. It is rebuilt when a muscle is resting, through the transfer of a phosphate group from ATP to creatine.

Aerobic Cellular Respiration

Aerobic cellular respiration, which takes place in the mitochondria, usually provides most of a muscle's ATP.

Glycogen and fat are stored in muscle cells. Therefore, a muscle fibre can use glucose from glycogen and fatty acids from fats as fuel to produce ATP when oxygen is available:

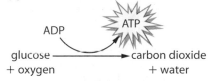

glucose + oxygen → carbon dioxide + water

Myoglobin—an oxygen-carrying molecule that is similar to hemoglobin—is synthesized in muscle cells. Its presence accounts for the reddish-brown colour of skeletal muscle fibres. Myoglobin has a higher affinity for oxygen than hemoglobin does. Therefore, it can temporarily store oxygen and make it available to the mitochondria when cellular respiration begins. The resulting carbon dioxide leaves the body at the lungs, and the water simply diffuses into the extracellular space. The third byproduct of this reaction, heat, helps to warm the entire body. Roughly two thirds to three quarters of the heat that maintains a constant body temperature comes from the aerobic cellular respiration of skeletal muscle throughout the body.

Fermentation

Fermentation, like creatine phosphate breakdown, supplies ATP without consuming oxygen. As you may recall from Chapter 5, glucose is broken down during fermentation to produce lactate:

glucose → lactate

The accumulation of lactate in a muscle fibre makes the sarcoplasm more acidic and, eventually, enzymes cease to function well. If fermentation continues longer than two or three minutes, cramping and fatigue set in. Biologists hypothesize that cramping results (in part, at least) from the lack of ATP needed to pump calcium ions back into the sarcoplasmic reticulum and to break the linkages between actin and myosin so that the muscle fibres can relax.

• • •

8 Describe the role of creatine phosphate in muscle contraction.

9 What is the benefit of fermentation in muscle contraction?

10 Identify the source of energy that usually provides most of a muscle's ATP.

• • •

Oxygen Deficit

When a muscle uses fermentation to supply its energy needs, it incurs an oxygen deficit (see Figure 10.9). The ability to run up an oxygen deficit is one of muscle tissue's greatest assets. Brain tissue, by contrast, cannot function nearly as long without oxygen as muscle tissue can.

In athletes and other people who train, the number of mitochondria in muscle tissue increases. Thus, fermentation is not needed to produce ATP. The mitochondria can start consuming oxygen as soon as the ADP concentration starts to rise during muscle contraction. Because the mitochondria can break down fatty acid instead of glucose, blood glucose is spared for the activities of the brain. (The brain, unlike other organs, can only use glucose to produce ATP.) Because less lactate is produced in people who train, the pH of the blood remains more steady, and there is less of an oxygen deficit.

Figure 10.9 Oxygen deficit is obvious when a person continues to breathe heavily after exercising.

Replenishing an oxygen deficit requires replenishing creatine phosphate supplies and disposing of lactate. Lactate can be changed back to pyruvate and metabolized completely in the mitochondria. As well, it can be sent to the liver to synthesize glycogen. The exhaustion of a marathon runner at the end of a race is often not due to an oxygen deficit. Instead, the runner has used up all the muscles' (and perhaps the liver's) supply of glycogen. The body takes about two days, on a high-carbohydrate diet, to replace its glycogen stores.

• • •

11 Explain why an oxygen deficit occurs and how it is overcome.

• • •

Section 10.1 Summary

• There are three types of muscle tissue: smooth, cardiac, and skeletal. Skeletal muscle contractions are voluntary, while smooth and cardiac muscle contractions are involuntary. Skeletal muscle has several functions, such as providing movement, producing heat, and maintaining posture.

• A skeletal muscle contains bundles of muscle fibres, which contain myofibrils. The myofibrils contain actin and myosin myofilaments.

• When calcium ions are released into muscle fibres, actin myofilaments slide past myosin myofilaments, resulting in contraction of the muscle fibres.

• Calcium ions bind to troponin, causing the tropomyosin threads that wind around actin to shift their position. This reveals sites that myosin can bind to.

• ATP energy enables myosin to detach from actin, ready to link to another binding site farther along the actin.

• A muscle fibre has three ways to acquire ATP for muscle contraction: (1) Creatine phosphate, built up when a muscle is resting, can rebuild ADP, quickly forming ATP. (2) Fermentation also forms ATP quickly, but it results in an oxygen deficit because oxygen is needed to complete the metabolism of the lactate that is produced and accumulates. (3) Aerobic cellular respiration takes longer because oxygen must be transported to the mitochondria in the muscle fibres.

Section 10.1 | Review

1. Use a word processor or spreadsheet program to make a table that lists the three types of muscle fibres (cells) and compares them based on the following criteria: shape, number of nuclei per fibre, presence of striations, voluntary or involuntary contractions, examples of locations in the body, and function in the body. **ICT**

2. Explain why muscles can pull but cannot push.

3. Outline, using a labelled sketch, the structural organization of skeletal muscle.

4. Explain why you expect to find a rich supply of blood vessels and mitochondria in skeletal muscle tissue.

5. Distinguish, both in sentence form and pictorially, actin from myosin filaments.

6. Use a word processor or spreadsheet program to make a table that describes the structure and function of the following components of skeletal muscle fibres: muscle fibre, myoglobin, sarcolemma, sarcoplasm, sarcoplasmic reticulum, myofibrils, actin myofilament, myosin myofilament. **ICT**

7. Use graphics software to sketch a diagram or series of diagrams illustrating the movement of actin and myosin filaments in the sliding filament model of a skeletal muscle contraction. Include a caption with each diagram that describes the events in this model. **ICT**

8. Justify the following statement: "Muscle contraction in the body cannot occur without calcium."

9. Identify three sources of energy for muscle contraction. Briefly describe the contribution of each source.

10. Explain why lactate forms in skeletal muscle tissue and explain how it is removed.

How Much Does It Cost To Be the Best?

Dr. Vivienne Nathanson, Head of Ethics at the British Medical Association, made this statement in a BBC Radio Broadcast in January 2004: "There are some very frightening bits of research which show that if you talk to people aspiring to be elite athletes and you say to them 'If we could give you a drug which would guarantee that you'd win a gold medal at the Olympics but you might be dead within five years, would you do it?', the majority would say yes."

Winners or Losers?

How would you respond to this question? How would your peers respond? In a recent study of more than 10 000 adolescents living throughout the United States, researchers found that 8 percent of females and 12 percent of males aged 12 to 18 reported using products to improve appearance, muscle mass, or strength. Approximately 4.7 percent of the males and 1.6 percent of the females used supplements such as protein powder or shakes, creatine, growth hormone, or anabolic/injectable steroids at least weekly to improve appearance or strength.

Where does the idea of success at any cost come from? The researchers found that adolescents involved in sports, particularly weight lifting and football, are more inclined to use substances that may be performance-enhancing. As the ongoing progress of sport through record breaking and higher achievement puts increasing demands on athletes, they are taking advantage of the scientific advances and technologies that are now available. Should their bodies be included in the equipment required to produce new records?

The researchers also found that males who read fashion, health/fitness, or men's magazines, and females who were trying to look like women in the media, were significantly more likely than their peers to use products to improve appearance or strength. What role do the media play in creating and perpetuating certain kinds of body types and images? What responsibilities do the media have in their portrayal of society?

What Now?

Long-term studies of teenagers' use of nutritional supplements have not been done, and for ethical reasons they probably never will be. No one can state with reasonable confidence, however, that prolonged use of supplements is safe until more data is compiled. But is the safety of supplements the issue we should be investigating?

• • •

1. Survey students at your school using the question in the first paragraph of this feature. Ask for reasons for their responses. Compile and discuss the statistical and anecdotal responses.

2. Debate the following statement: "Scientists already help athletes win through specially manufactured equipment. Performance-enhancing substances have been used for centuries and should not be viewed any differently."

Muscles, Health, and Homeostasis

Section Outcomes

In this section, you will
- **explain** how the skeletal muscles of the motor system support other body systems to maintain homeostasis
- **identify** conditions that impair the healthy functioning of muscles and technologies that are used to treat or prevent these conditions
- **describe** the benefits of exercise for maintaining the healthy structure and functioning of muscles

Key Terms

atrophy
hypertrophy
muscle twitch
slow-twitch fibres
fast-twitch fibres

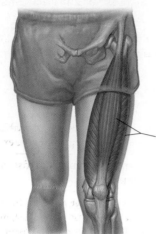
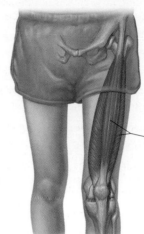

healthy rectus femoris and quadraceps femoris muscles

atrophied rectus femoris and quadraceps femoris muscles

Figure 10.10 Muscle atrophy is a concern for people not only on Earth, but also in the microgravity environment of space. During the early 1970s, experiments with the astronauts onboard the NASA *Skylab* missions led to modifications in diet and exercise programs that were able to compensate for some atrophy due to microgravity. Active research in this area continues today.

During active use, some muscle fibres are contracting and others are relaxing. Therefore, muscles rarely fatigue completely. Even when muscles appear to be at rest, some of their fibres are always contracting. This continuous, "low-level" activity of the muscles results in what is referred to as tone. Muscle tone is important for maintaining posture. If all the fibres within the muscles of the neck, torso, and lower limbs were to relax completely, the body would collapse.

Complications of the Muscular System

In general, the skeletal muscles of the motor system are subject to fewer disorders than other organ systems are. Muscles, however, are especially vulnerable to injuries that result from sudden and intense stress placed on them and on tendons. Table 10.2 lists some of the more common disorders of the muscular system.

Muscles also may be impaired simply from lack of use. This condition is referred to as atrophy (from two Greek words that mean "without nourishment"). **Atrophy** is a reduction in the size, tone,

and power of a muscle. If a skeletal muscle experiences reduced stimulation, its fibres decrease in size and become weaker. Even a temporary reduction in muscle use can lead to muscular atrophy. People who experience damage to the nervous system, or who become paralyzed by a spinal cord injury, gradually lose muscle tone and size in the areas that are affected. Initially, the atrophy is reversible, but dead or dying muscle fibres are not replaced. If extreme atrophy occurs, the loss of muscle function is permanent. This is why physical therapy is so important for people who have a temporary loss of mobility as a result of an injury or surgery (see Figure 10.10, as well as the Career Focus at the end of this unit).

• • •

 Explain how muscle atrophy can occur.

• • •

Exercise and Muscle Contraction

Regular, moderate exercise strengthens the muscular system and enables the

BiologyFile

FYI
In people who are bedridden or have a leg immobilized by a cast for two to three weeks, researchers have observed declines in the size and strength of calf and leg muscles that are comparable to those observed during space missions. In fact, immobilization of a leg in a cast results in more rapid declines in muscle size and performance than those observed for similar periods of time in bed rest or microgravity.

Table 10.2 Some Common Disorders and Ailments of the Skeletal Muscles

Condition	Description
muscular dystrophy	a collective term for several hereditary conditions in which the skeletal muscles degenerate, lose strength, and are gradually replaced by fatty and fibrous tissue that impedes blood circulation; this, in turn, accelerates muscle degeneration in a fatal spiral of positive feedback
botulism	a potentially fatal muscular paralysis caused by a toxin produced by the bacterium *Clostridium botulinum*; the toxin prevents the release of a muscle-stimulating compound (acetylcholine) released by muscle-related cells of the nervous system, thus leading to paralysis
cramps	painful muscle spasms triggered by strenuous exercise, extreme cold, dehydration, salt (electrolyte) imbalance, low blood glucose, or reduced blood flow
contracture	abnormal muscle shortening not caused by nerve stimulation; can result from inability to remove calcium ions from the sarcoplasm or from the contraction of scar tissue (as in people who have experienced severe burns)
fibromyalgia	chronic muscular pain and tenderness often associated with fatigue and sleep disturbances; can be caused by infectious diseases, physical or emotional trauma, or medications
crush syndrome	a shock-like state following massive crushing of the muscles (as in, for example, the aftermath of an earthquake, the collapse of a building following an explosion, or a traffic accident); associated with high fever, heart irregularities caused by potassium ions released from the muscles, and kidney failure caused by blockage of the renal tubules with myoglobin released by the traumatized muscles
delayed onset muscle soreness	pain, stiffness, and tenderness felt from several hours to a day after strenuous exercise; associated with trauma to the muscles, disruptions in the myofibrils and sarcolemma, and increased levels of myoglobin and muscle-fibre enzymes in the blood
myositis	muscle inflammation and weakness resulting from infection or an autoimmune disease

muscles to use energy more efficiently. During the first few months after a person (for example, a runner) starts training, gradually increasing distance, the leg muscles noticeably enlarge. This exercise-induced increase in muscle mass is called **hypertrophy**. It is due to an increase in the size of individual skeletal muscle fibres, not an increase in their number.

Becoming physically fit through exercise causes other changes to muscles as well. The enzymes within a trained runner's muscle fibres are more active

---

Thought Lab 10.2 Injuries Related to Athletics

Target Skills

Analyzing the effects of exercise on skeletal muscle and muscle fibre

Evaluating assumptions and behaviour related to athletics and physical conditioning

Consulting a wide variety of sources, and **assessing** the authority, reliability, and validity of the information gathered

Each year, tens of thousands of athletes—professionals, amateurs, and high-school students—sustain some kind of injury to their muscles, as do increasing numbers of people who have taken up running and other forms of physical exercise. Improper or inadequate warming up and conditioning are often the cause of these injuries.

Procedure

1. Select one of the athletics-related injuries listed below.

   - baseball finger
   - blocker's arm
   - charley horse
   - compactment syndrome
   - pitcher's arm
   - pulled groin
   - pulled hamstrings
   - rider's bones
   - rotator cuff injury
   - shin splints
   - tennis elbow
   - tennis leg

2. Research the injury you selected, as well as ways that this injury and most other common muscle injuries can be prevented. (Start with index and search-engine keywords related to exercise, warming up, and conditioning.)

Analysis

1. Using a suitable medium and format, outline the nature, cause, treatment, and prevention of the injury you selected. **ICT**

2. The phrase "no pain, no gain" is sometimes used in fitness and bodybuilding classes. Evaluate the use of the phrase and the potential effects on the health of the people who follow this advice.

and numerous, and the mitochondria are more abundant, than they are in the skeletal muscles of a person who engages in little or no exercise. Thus, a runner's muscles can withstand far more exertion than the muscles of an untrained person before fermentation begins. A runner's muscles also receive more blood (through the development of additional blood vessels) and store more glycogen than those of an untrained person.

• • •

 Explain how hypertrophy is different from atrophy.

• • •

Muscle Twitch

Isolated skeletal muscles have been studied by stimulating them artificially with electrodes. By attaching a muscle to a movable lever and stimulating it, the contraction can be recorded as a visual pattern, such as the one shown in Figure 10.11(A).

At first, the stimulus may be too weak to cause a contraction. As soon as the strength of the stimulus reaches a certain threshold, however, the muscle contracts and then relaxes. This action—a single contraction that lasts a mere fraction of a second—is called a **muscle twitch**. Figure 10.11A shows that a twitch can be divided into three periods: a latent period (the period of time between stimulation and initiation of contraction), a contraction period (when the muscle shortens), and a relaxation period (when the muscle returns to its former length).

Stimulation of an individual muscle fibre within a muscle usually results in a maximal, all-or-none contraction. The contraction of a whole muscle, however, can vary in strength depending on the number of muscle fibres contracting.

If a muscle is given a rapid series of threshold stimuli, it can respond to the next stimulus without relaxing completely. In this way, successive twitches partially "ride piggyback" on each other in a cumulative response called summation, as shown in Figure 10.11B. Eventually maximal sustained contraction, called tetanus, is achieved. (Do not confuse this term with the disorder that shares the same name, which is accompanied by a painful state of muscle contracture.) As you can see in Figure 10.11B, once tetanus occurs, the graph no longer shows individual twitches. The twitches are, instead, fused and blended completely into a straight line. Tetanus continues until the muscle fatigues due to depletion of energy reserves. Fatigue is apparent when a muscle relaxes even though stimulation continues.

• • •

 Why does a muscle eventually fatigue?

• • •

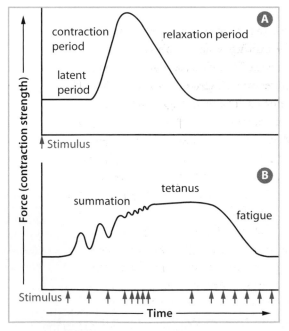

Figure 10.11 These graphs of the force of muscle contraction with time are called myograms. **(A)** A simple muscle twitch has three periods: latent, contraction, and relaxation. **(B)** When a muscle is not allowed to relax completely between stimuli, the contraction gradually increases in intensity until it reaches a maximum, which is sustained until the muscle fatigues.

Slow-Twitch and Fast-Twitch Fibres

You have seen that all muscle fibres metabolize both aerobically and anaerobically. Some muscle fibres, however, use one method more than the other to provide myofibrils with ATP. Slow-twitch fibres (also called Type I fibres) tend to be aerobic, and fast-twitch fibres (also called Type II fibres) tend to be anaerobic.

Slow-twitch fibres contract slowly but resist fatigue (that is, they have more endurance). These muscle fibres are most helpful in activities such as biking, jogging, swimming, and long-distance running. Because they produce most of their energy aerobically, they tire only when their fuel supply is gone. Slow-twitch fibres have many mitochondria. They are dark in colour because they contain myoglobin, the respiratory pigment found in muscles. They are surrounded by dense capillary beds and draw more blood and oxygen than fast-twitch fibres. Because slow-twitch fibres have a substantial reserve of glycogen and fat, their abundant mitochondria can maintain a steady, prolonged production of ATP when oxygen is available.

Fast-twitch fibres are adapted for the rapid generation of power. They are most helpful in activities such as sprinting, weight lifting, and swinging a hockey stick or tennis racket. These fibres are rich in glycogen. They are light in colour because they have little or no myoglobin. They also have fewer mitochondria and fewer blood vessels than slow-twitch fibres do. The dependence of fast-twitch fibres on anaerobically produced energy, however, leaves them vulnerable to an accumulation of lactate that causes them to fatigue quickly.

Human muscles have a third, intermediate form of fibres. These fibres are fast-twitch, but they also have a high oxidative capacity. Thus, they are more resistant to fatigue. Endurance training increases the proportion of these fibres in muscles. Note, however, that heredity also plays a role in the proportion of fast-twitch and slow-twitch fibres in the bodies of individuals. Figure 10.12 compares the twitch of three muscles of the body.

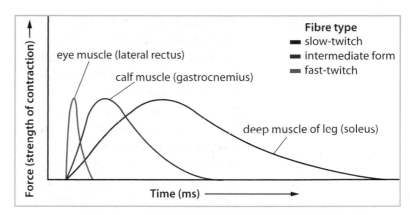

Figure 10.12 Skeletal muscles have different proportions of fast-twitch and slow-twitch fibres. Thus, the force and response times of their contractions differ.

• • •

15 The muscles that move the eyes reach maximal contraction (tetanus) in about 7 ms (milliseconds). The soleus muscle (in the lower leg) reaches tetanus in about 100 ms. Which muscle is composed of fast-twitch fibres, and which is composed of slow-twitch fibres?

• • •

The Value of Exercise

The depletion of muscle glycogen and the buildup of lactate place a limit on exercise. Therefore, any adaptation that spares muscle glycogen and/or efficiently removes lactate improves physical endurance. Because the aerobic capacity of endurance-trained athletes is higher than that of untrained people, athletes can perform more exercise before lactate production and glycogen depletion cause muscle fatigue.

Endurance training does *not*, however, increase the size of muscles. Muscle enlargement is produced only by frequent periods of high-intensity exercise in which the muscles work against high resistance, as in weight lifting. As a result of resistance training, fast-twitch muscle fibres become thicker, so the muscle grows by hypertrophy—an increase in the size of the muscle fibres. This happens because the myofibrils within a muscle fibre thicken due to the synthesis of actin and myosin, and the addition of new material to the fibre. Then, after a myofibril has attained a certain thickness, it may split into two myofibrils, each of which may also become thicker. Thus, muscle hypertrophy is caused by an increase in the size of the myofibrils and then an increase in the number of myofibrils within the muscle fibres.

The decline in the physical strength of people as they age is associated with reduced muscle mass, which is due to a loss of muscle fibres and a decrease in the size of fast-twitch muscle fibres. Aging is also associated with a reduced density of the blood capillaries that surround the muscle fibres, leading to a decrease in oxidative capacity. Resistance training can cause the surviving muscle fibres to hypertrophy and become stronger, thus partly compensating for the decreased number of muscle fibres in older people. As well, endurance training can increase the density of the blood capillaries in the muscles, improving the ability of the blood to deliver oxygen to the muscles. The muscle glycogen of seniors also can be increased by endurance training, but not to the levels present earlier in life.

• • •

16 Why is the aerobic capacity of endurance athletes higher than the aerobic capacity of untrained people?

17 Describe how a muscle can increase in size.

• • •

Homeostasis, Muscles, and Other Body Systems

Movement, which involves the muscular system in conjunction with the skeletal system, is essential for maintaining health and homeostasis throughout the life cycle (see Figure 10.13). This is evident in a simple way, when you move to respond to certain types of changes in the environment. For instance, if you are sitting in the Sun and start to feel too hot

after a period of time, you can move to a shady location or indoors. If you were unable to move to a cooler location, you would run the risk of developing heat stroke—an inability of the body to cope with elevated body temperature due to very high air temperature.

At a more physiological level, many body systems, including the muscular system, help to maintain a constant body temperature. When you are cold, smooth muscle in the blood vessels that supply the skin constrict, reducing the amount of blood that is close to the surface of the body. This helps to conserve heat in the body's core, where the vital organs lie. If you are cold enough, you might start to experience involuntary skeletal muscle contractions, commonly known as shivering. This action is initiated by temperature-sensitive cells in the hypothalamus of the brain. As you know, skeletal muscle contraction requires ATP, and using ATP generates much of the body's heat.

If you think about the body systems you have investigated in this unit, you can appreciate other ways in which the muscular system is involved in homeostasis, too. Contraction of the skeletal muscles associated with the jaw and tongue allow you to grind food with your teeth. The rhythmic smooth-muscle contractions of peristalsis move ingested materials through the digestive tract. These processes are necessary for supplying the body cells with nutrients. Skeletal muscles attached to the bones of the rib cage, along with the action of the diaphragm (which is comprised of skeletal muscles), permit the mechanics of breathing, which brings oxygen to the body cells and rids them of carbon dioxide waste. The ceaseless beating of the heart, which propels blood into the arteries, is the contraction of cardiac muscle. Contractions of skeletal muscles in the body, especially the skeletal muscles associated with breathing and leg movements, help to return venous blood to the heart by pushing the blood

Figure 10.13 The benefits of physical activity start early in life, and they extend throughout one's entire lifecycle. These benefits include the development and maintenance of flexibility, endurance, and strength of all the muscle tissues—smooth and cardiac, as well as skeletal—in the body. What roles do play, recreational physical activity, or formal exercise training occupy in your life? What are their whole-body benefits now and in the future?

back toward the heart. (This is why people are cautioned not to lock their knees when standing for long periods of time. The reduction in venous blood return causes a drop in blood pressure that can lead to fainting.) The pressure exerted by skeletal muscle contractions also helps to squeeze tissue fluid (lymph) into the lymphatic vessels. Finally, the smooth muscle tissue of the urinary bladder permits the storage and, through its sphincters, release of the nitrogenous waste materials that would otherwise poison the human body and its essential systems.

Section 10.2 Summary

- Muscle contractions can be described in terms of muscle twitch. Muscle twitch can be used to classify muscle fibres according to the speed at which they contract.

- Slow-twitch fibres are smaller than fast-twitch fibres, contract fairly slowly, and are more resistant to fatigue than fast-twitch fibres.
- Fast-twitch fibres are large in diameter compared with slow-twitch fibres, use a lot of ATP, and fatigue easily.
- Intermediate fibres are similar to fast-twitch fibres but are more resistant to fatigue.
- Muscles atrophy if stimulation is inadequate.
- Muscle hypertrophy is an increase in the size of muscle fibres. Repetitive stimulation causes more myofibrils to develop.
- The muscular system interacts with all the other systems of the human body in ways that promote and maintain homeostasis.

1. a) Describe the general cause of muscle atrophy.

b) Describe what happens to a muscle as it atrophies, and explain why extreme atrophy would lead to permanent loss of muscle function.

2. Explain how hypertrophy is different from atrophy.

3. Describe the term "muscle twitch."

4. Use a graphics software program to sketch a labelled myogram for a single skeletal muscle twitch. Describe the terms latent period, contraction period, and relaxation period. **ICT**

5. Use a graphics software program to sketch a labelled myogram for a skeletal muscle that is not allowed to completely relax between stimuli. Describe the terms summation, tetanus, and fatigue. **ICT**

6. Identify three beneficial changes to skeletal muscles that result from regular exercise.

7. Use word processing or spreadsheet software to design a table that compares fast-twitch muscle fibres to slow-twitch muscle fibres. **ICT**

Use the following information to answer the next question.

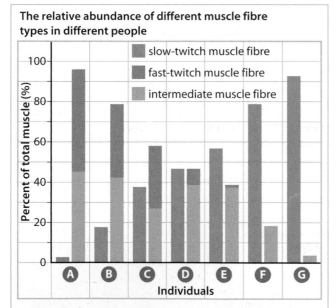

The bar graph above compares the relative abundance of different muscle fibre types in different people. These people are:
- a world-class sprinter
- an extreme endurance racer
- a world-class marathon runner
- a person with a spinal injury
- a sedentary person ("couch potato")
- a middle distance runner
- an average active person

8. Infer which individuals are represented by A through G, and explain your reasoning.

9. How does resistance training, such as weight lifting, cause muscle fibres to change?

Use the following information to answer the next two questions.

Hypothermia and Shivering
Shivering is one of the symptoms used to diagnose hypothermia. If the person is able to stop shivering voluntarily, then the hypothermia is only mild. But if it can't be stopped voluntarily, the person has moderate to severe hypothermia.

10. Define shivering and explain why an individual going into hyperthermia starts to shiver.

11. Explain why a person going into hyperthermia can only shiver for a few hours?

12. Muscles support the functions of other body systems in many ways to maintain homeostasis. Give one example of this for each of the following systems:

a) the circulatory system

b) the respiratory system

c) the digestive system

d) the excretory system

Use the following information to answer the next question.

Muscle Strain Injuries
Muscle strains are overuse injuries that result when the muscle is stretched without being properly warmed up. It's like pulling a rubber band too long. Eventually, the rubber band will either lose its shape or tear apart. The same options apply to muscles. Should you suffer a strain or other muscle or joint injury, treat it with the RICE method—**R**est, **I**ce, **C**ompression, and **E**levation. RICE can relieve pain, limit swelling, and protect the injured tissue, all of which help to speed healing. After an injury occurs, the damaged area will bleed (externally or internally) and become inflamed. Healing occurs as the damaged tissue is replaced by collagen, perhaps better known as scar tissue. Ideally, the scar tissue needs complete repair before a full return to sport is recommended.

13. Explain why the RICE method is used to treat most muscle strain injuries.

All muscles do their work by contracting (shortening). Relaxation is the passive state of a muscle. There are three types of muscle cells: skeletal, smooth, and cardiac. Skeletal muscle cells are attached to the bones of the skeleton, have many nuclei, are striated and tubular, and contract voluntarily. Smooth muscle cells are found in the walls of internal organs, have one nucleus, are not striated, and contract involuntarily. Cardiac muscle cells form the walls of the heart; have one nucleus, are striated, tubular, and branched; and contract involuntarily.

The fact that skeletal muscles can only either contract or relax means they can pull but not push. Therefore, they must work in pairs in order to move any part of the body—a relaxed muscle is only lengthened when the opposing muscle contracts to stretch it. Skeletal muscle contractions are explained by the sliding filament model.

Skeletal muscle produces heat as well as movement and also supports and pads the body. Each muscle is made up of clusters of bundles of muscle fibres, which enclose bundles of myofibrils containing thin myofilaments of actin and thick myofilaments of myosin. Blood vessels supply nutrients and oxygen to the fibre bundles and remove wastes. The oxygen fuels the cellular respiration that supplies most of the energy muscles use.

Nerves trigger and control muscle contractions, which last for only a fraction of second in each muscle fibre. It is the wave of successive contractions, or twitches, that result in a muscle contraction. Skeletal muscles have both slow- and fast-twitch fibres that are good for either endurance (slow-twitch) or intense (fast-twitch) activities. Using the skeletal muscles is the only way to maintain and build their function.

Chapter 10 Graphic Organizer

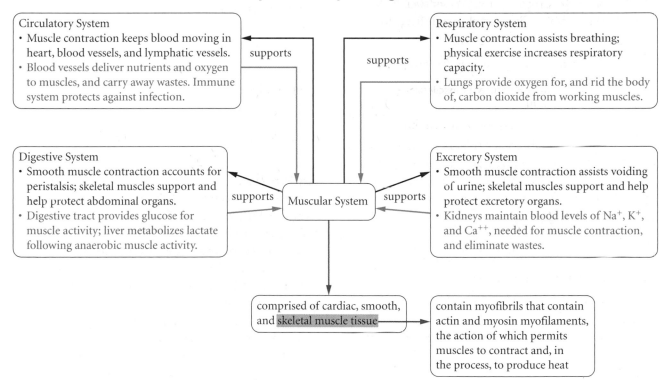

Circulatory System
- Muscle contraction keeps blood moving in heart, blood vessels, and lymphatic vessels.
- Blood vessels deliver nutrients and oxygen to muscles, and carry away wastes. Immune system protects against infection.

Respiratory System
- Muscle contraction assists breathing; physical exercise increases respiratory capacity.
- Lungs provide oxygen for, and rid the body of, carbon dioxide from working muscles.

Digestive System
- Smooth muscle contraction accounts for peristalsis; skeletal muscles support and help protect abdominal organs.
- Digestive tract provides glucose for muscle activity; liver metabolizes lactate following anaerobic muscle activity.

Excretory System
- Smooth muscle contraction assists voiding of urine; skeletal muscles support and help protect excretory organs.
- Kidneys maintain blood levels of Na^+, K^+, and Ca^{++}, needed for muscle contraction, and eliminate wastes.

supports

supports

Muscular System

supports

supports

comprised of cardiac, smooth, and skeletal muscle tissue

contain myofibrils that contain actin and myosin myofilaments, the action of which permits muscles to contract and, in the process, to produce heat

Understanding Concepts

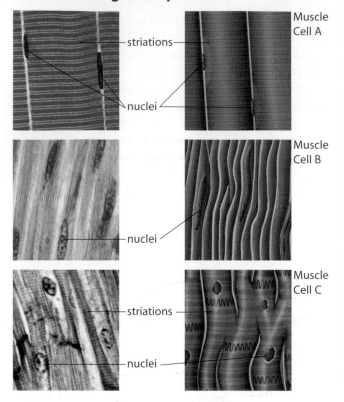

Muscle Cell A — striations, nuclei

Muscle Cell B — nuclei

Muscle Cell C — striations, nuclei

1. Identify and describe the three types of muscle tissue shown in the diagram above.

2. List three functions of skeletal muscle.

3. Use graphics software to draw a sketch explaining how myofilaments, muscle fibre, and myofibrils are related. **ICT**

4. Describe the major events that occur when a muscle fibre contracts.

5. Explain how ATP and creatine phosphate function in muscle contraction.

6. Describe how oxygen is supplied to muscle tissue.

7. Describe how an oxygen deficit may develop.

8. Explain how muscle fibres can become fatigued and how a person's physical condition can affect tolerance to fatigue.

9. Explain how the actions of skeletal muscles affect the maintenance of body temperature.

10. Give three examples of how the muscular system helps to maintain homeostasis.

11. Describe the role that myoglobin plays in muscle tissue.

12. Describe the three ways that energy is supplied for skeletal muscle contraction during strenuous exercise.

Use the following information to answer the next two questions.

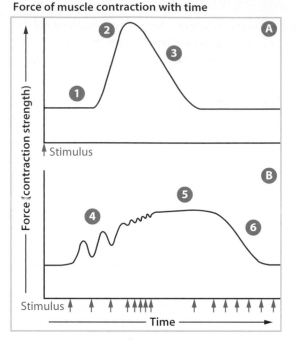

Force of muscle contraction with time

These graphs showing the force of muscle contraction with time are called myograms.

13. Identify the regions shown on Graph A, and describe what is happening to the muscle fibre at each region.

14. Identify the region shown on Graph B, and describe what is happening to the muscle fibre at each region.

Applying Concepts

15. In terms of contraction speed, infer the type of muscle fibre that comprises muscle tissue in the esophagus and in the heart. Justify your answer.

16. A muscle contracts and shortens because its myofibrils contract and shorten. When this happens, however, the myofilaments inside the myofibrils do not shorten. Explain why.

17. The events that occur in the sliding filament model follow a cyclical pathway.
    a) Use graphics software to sketch this pathway, and use this sketch to explain the cyclical nature of this pathway. **ICT**
    b) Identify two factors that can modify the activity of this cycle.

18. People who engage in physical activity generally perform better if they warm up by exercising lightly first. Suggest one possible reason for this.

19. As lactate and other substances accumulate in an active muscle, they stimulate pain-sensing nerves, and the

muscle may feel sore. How might the application of heat help to relieve such soreness?

20. A skeletal muscle can often maintain a moderate level of active tension for long periods of time, even though many of its fibres become fatigued. Explain how this occurs.

21. Compare hypertrophy of muscles to atrophy. Include potential causes of both and the impact that each has on the overall health of the individual.

Making Connections

Use the following information to answer the next question.

In the following bar graphs, the relative concentrations of blood glucose, blood free fatty acids, muscle triglyceride, and muscle glycogen are plotted against the energy consumption of exercising muscles. Data for heavy exercise performed at 90 to 120 min were not collected.

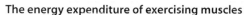

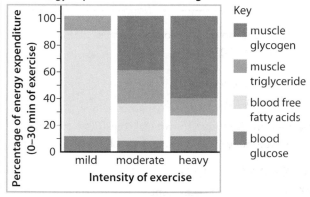

The energy expenditure of exercising muscles

Key
- muscle glycogen
- muscle triglyceride
- blood free fatty acids
- blood glucose

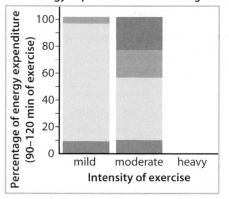

22. Use graphics or spreadsheet software to sketch a bar graph that you predict would reflect the data for heavy exercise performed at 90 to 120 minutes. Explain your reasoning. **ICT**

Use the following information to answer the next question.

A researcher is investigating the composition of muscle tissue in the calf muscles of several athletes. Samples of muscle tissue from each athlete are taken and examined. In this procedure, a needle is inserted into the muscle. A small "plug" of tissue remains in the needle when it is removed from the muscle.

23. Describe the main differences that this researcher would see when comparing the muscle tissues of athletes who perform in the following events:
   a) 100-m dash   **c)** 10 000-m run
   b) weight lifting

Use the following information to answer the next question.

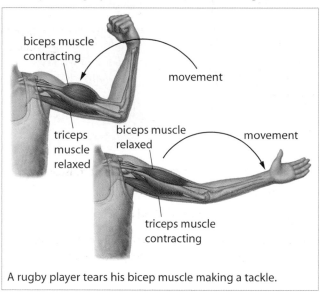

A rugby player tears his bicep muscle making a tackle.

24. Explain, in terms of skeletal muscle action, how this injury would affect his ability to flex his arm properly.

Use the following information to answer the next question.

Myosin, actin, tropomyosin, and troponin make up over three quarters of the protein in muscle fibres. Approximately two dozen other proteins make up the rest. These proteins serve such functions as attaching and organizing the filaments and connecting the filaments to the plasma membrane and the extracellular matrix.

Mutations in the genes encoding these proteins may produce defective proteins and resulting defects in the muscles. The muscular dystrophies (MD) are a group of more than 30 genetic diseases characterized by progressive weakness and degeneration of the skeletal muscles.

25. Based on your knowledge of skeletal muscles, explain why some individuals with MD would require the assistance of a respirator to breathe.

Career Focus: Ask an Athletic Therapist

Robyn Bagley has been a Certified Athletic Therapist for 6 years. She has a Bachelor of Kinesiology from the University of Calgary and a Diploma in Physical Education—Athletic Therapy from Mount Royal College. In addition to work with private clients, Robyn works as Assistant Athletic Therapist at the University of Calgary. She is also a registered massage therapist.

Q Athletes train to challenge the limits of the human body. What are the most common kinds of injuries you see?

Injuries vary with the sports, but generally injuries to the joints—ankles, knees, shoulders—are quite common because the joints are a point of weakness. Joints are where two bones come together, held by ligaments, and acted upon by muscles and tendons. They are susceptible to both acute and chronic, repetitive injuries.

Q What do you do in a typical session with a client?

An assessment would be completed first to determine the injury, and then, depending on the injury, rehabilitation could include heat, ultrasound, laser, manual therapy, electrical modalities, strengthening exercises, stretching, and cold.

Q Have advances in technology and equipment changed the stresses on the body? How?

Definitely. Advances in technology and equipment will always add new dimensions, both positive and negative, to a sport. In some aspects, advances have improved a sport so we see fewer injuries than we once did; for example, visors in hockey reduce the incidence of eye injuries. Unforeseen aspects that advances bring include athletes' ability to hit each other harder, which increases the severity of injury and the occurrence of spinal and head injuries; newfound ability to push themselves farther in training, which increases the risk of repetitive injuries; the ability to perform tasks they could not do without the new equipment; the creation of a longer season, which also increases the risk of repetitive injuries; and the creation of new sports, to name just a few.

Q Research into the human body is ongoing. How do you keep up with the new findings?

I belong to a professional association—the Canadian Athletic Therapists Association. Every member receives publications updating them on current research and is able to download information from the Internet. It is also helpful that many of our members are involved in new medical research and able to pass their findings on to the rest of the membership. As a part of our continued certification, all members of the association must continue to educate themselves regarding new techniques, research, and information.

Q How does the work of an athletic therapist differ from that of a physiotherapist?

Athletic therapists share a similar skill set with physiotherapists, however, athletic therapists specialize in musculoskeletal conditions. We traditionally follow the cyclical nature of sport from the field of play, to the clinic, and back to the field of play. Physiotherapists also work with patients with neurological, cardio, and respiratory conditions and traditionally work primarily in a clinical setting.

Q Do serious athletes inevitably suffer injuries? What do you advise them to do to protect themselves?

Balance in training and life is always important to help the body keep up with the demands we place on it. For high level athletes it is all the more important. Rest and recovery, along with proper training, including core strengthening and sport-specific drills, proper nutrition and hydration, all provide a strong base for all athletic pursuits. Core training—the strengthening of the postural and support muscles located primarily in the trunk of the body—is important for all people, regardless of their level of activity. The abdominal muscles, scapular muscles, and deep neck flexor muscles, for a start, provide the body with a good foundation to perform daily activities, let alone a high level of sport.

Other Careers Related to Athletic Therapy

Physiotherapist Physiotherapists help their clients manage physical damage and injury through a variety of physical methods. Musculoskeletal physiotherapy helps the body heal from soft-tissue injuries. Neurological physiotherapy helps the body regain functions lost due to stroke, brain injury, or neurological disease. Cardiorespirological physiotherapy helps the body improve breathing.

Occupational Therapist Occupational therapists help people with disabilities, long-term injuries and illnesses, or other conditions find ways to perform daily activities. Occupational therapists work in their clients' homes and workplaces, and in hospitals, schools, and universities.

Massage Therapist Massage therapists specialize in soft tissue manipulation, relaxation, and stretching techniques. They are often part of a team of physiotherapists, doctors, and other health-care professionals.

Kinesiologist Kinesiologists study factors that affect physical movement and look for ways to improve the efficiency of the body. They look at the psychological, physiological, biomechanical, historical, and social aspects of human movement. Kinesiologists design exercise equipment, do research, manage recreational facilities, coach, and teach physical education.

Go Further...

1. Is possible for the average athlete to achieve excellence without understanding the physiological function of the human body? Why or why not?

2. How can an understanding of how the human systems function and interact improve the life of the average person? Does the average person have a responsibility to society to use this knowledge to keep him- or herself healthy? Why or why not?

3. Research the latest technology related to one of the following and explain how recent design improvements draw on our knowledge of how the body works:

    a. Helmets

    b. Running shoes

    c. Rehydration drinks

Understanding Concepts

1. The digestive tract is one long tube that is classified into five segments or organs based on structure and function. Name these five segments and outline, in writing or in the form of a table, their main structural and functional characteristics.

2. Identify the accessory organs of the digestive system, and explain how they contribute to the digestion and absorption of ingested food.

3. Describe the function of the pleural membranes.

4. Use graphics software to sketch the organs and microscopic structures through which air passes during the inhalation and exhalation of one breath. **ICT**

5. Use graphics software to sketch a cross-section of the human heart and label the following structures on your sketch: atria, ventricles, septa, atrioventricular valves, semilunar valves, aorta, vena cavae, pulmonary arteries, and pulmonary veins. Make a second sketch of the human heart that identifies the sinoatrial node, the AV node, branches of the atrioventricular bundle, and the Purkinje fibres. **ICT**

6. Use word processing software to draw a flow chart that outlines the path of urine through the organs of the excretory system to the external environment. (Limit your answer to an organ-level response only; do not trace the flow of blood or urine through the nephrons.) **ICT**

7. Identify two organs of the excretory system you would expect to be made up of smooth muscle tissue. Explain why you think these organs are made up of smooth muscle tissue.

8. Explain how the ability to move, via the muscular (or motor) system, helps the body maintain homeostasis. Use two other body systems in your answer.

9. **a)** Identify the three main nutrient substances people must ingest, and list three similarities they share.
   b) Identify the types of enzymes that act on each of the nutrient substances you named in (a), and describe the means by which these enzymes make nutrient substances available for absorption in the small intestine.

10. Briefly explain why the three main types of nutrient substances are necessary components of the diet.

11. Describe the means by which an inhalation and an exhalation occur.

12. Outline the events that occur during the exchange of oxygen and carbon dioxide between the lungs and the blood.

13. The human heart is sometimes described as a double pump because of its left and right sides, rather than because of its upper and lower chambers. Explain why.

14. **a)** Use word processing software to draw a flow chart tracing the path of blood through the coronary circulation. Start your flow chart with the inferior vena cava and include all of the chambers of the heart as well as the valves that the blood would pass through on this pathway. **ICT**
   b) Explain how this circulatory pathway differs from the other two circulatory pathways.

15. Coronary circulation is facilitated by many small arteries that interconnect. Describe the significance of the interconnections.

16. Use word processing or spreadsheet software to draw a chart that compares and contrasts arteries and veins according to the following criteria: structure, function, oxygen composition of the blood carried, movement of blood through them, and pressure difference. **ICT**

17. Explain how capillaries differ from arteries and veins. State three differences.

18. Explain how blood pressure, the speed at which blood moves, and the diameter of blood vessels are related.

19. After standing for several hours, a whole blood sample separates into three distinct layers: two large layers separated by a narrow layer. Identify and describe the blood components that you would observe in each layer.

20. Identify the structures through which a molecule of water would travel as it moves from the renal artery (the artery that delivers blood to a kidney) to the renal pelvis (the region of the kidney that leads to the ureters).

21. Clearly distinguish the following three processes involved in the formation of urine: filtration, reabsorption, and secretion.

22. The filtrate substances that just enter the proximal tubule may be divided into two components: those that are reabsorbed from the tubule into blood and those that are not reabsorbed.
   a) Use word processing software to compare, in the form of a table, the substances that are reabsorbed and not reabsorbed as they enter the proximal tubule. **ICT**

b) Explain what happens to the components that are not reabsorbed at the start of the proximal tubule.

23. Explain how the nephron maintains normal body fluid with respect to each of the following:
    a) water   **b)** ions   **c)** pH

24. Describe, in terms of the sliding filament model, the events that occur as myosin interacts with actin to produce muscle contraction.

25. Why don't enzymes digest themselves?

26. **a)** The graph below shows enzyme-catalyzed reactions for two different species. Predict the curve that likely represents reactions that occur in humans, and explain your reasoning.

Enzyme Catalyzed Reactions for Two Different Species

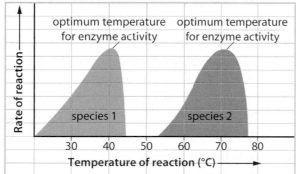

b) Identify two other factors, besides temperature, that influence the action of enzymes.

27. **a)** Describe, in terms of the acquisition of ATP, the events that occur to produce muscle contraction.
    b) How are these ways of acquiring ATP interrelated?

28. Identify one function of blood in relation to each of the following body systems:
    a) digestive   **c)** excretory   **e)** immune
    b) respiratory   **d)** muscular

29. Compare plasma, glomerular filtrate, and urine in terms of their composition of glucose, protein, sodium ions, and nitrogenous wastes.

30. Describe the significance of the concentration gradient in the interstitial fluid surrounding the nephron.

31. Explain what prevents the interstitial fluid from becoming diluted when water from the collecting duct is reabsorbed.

32. Blood plays a role in absorbing heat and dissipating it at the body's surface. Explain the significance of this function of blood. Also explain how it differs from

the role of blood in the exchange of matter such as respiratory gases and nutrient molecules. (Hint: What types of blood vessels are involved in these activities?)

33. Explain why fast-twitch muscle fibres are better-suited for quick, short bursts of speed than slow-twitch muscle fibres.

34. The stomach is capable of producing vigorous, churning action. Describe the function of this action in the stomach.

35. **a)** Identify the organs in which physical processing of food mainly occurs and in which the chemical processing of food mainly occurs.
    b) Explain why both physical and chemical processing of food are necessary for the digestive system to perform its functions.

36. Describe how carbohydrates and proteins are absorbed into the bloodstream, and explain how the absorption of fats differs.

37. List the major parts of a skeletal muscle fibre, and briefly describe the function of each part.

38. Outline the key features of the lymphatic system, and identify three ways in which it is similar to and/or different from the blood-related circulatory system.

39. Describe how lymph is formed.

40. Explain how the blood-related and lymphatic circulatory systems work together.

41. Distinguish between the following:
    a) lymph capillaries and blood capillaries
    b) lymph vessels and veins
    c) lymph and interstitial fluid

42. Trace, in general terms, the pathway of lymph from your right foot to the bloodstream.

43. Identify the different T cells and describe their specific functions in the immune response.

44. Explain the role of memory in B cell lymphocytes and T cell lymphocytes in defending the body against infection.

45. Immunity involves specific defences and non-specific defences. Trace the activities associated with the immune response to an accidental puncture by a sharp object.

Applying Concepts

46. a) Explain how it is possible for the small intestine to have such a large internal surface area.

b) Describe the significance of the small intestine having such a large surface area.

Use the following information to answer the next question.

Potassium Ion Concentration

A person's blood potassium concentration is determined to be 4 mmol/L (millimoles per litre) when she is eating food containing 150 mmol/L of potassium per day. One day she doubles her potassium intake and continues to eat that amount indefinitely. Potassium is regulated homeostatically in the body.

47. If her blood is analyzed, do you think her blood potassium concentration is likely to be 8 mmol/L or about 4 mmol/L? Explain. (Note: The answer to this question does not require any knowledge about potassium or the unit mmol/L.)

48. Substance X is found to be present in a urine sample. Is it reasonable to infer, therefore, that Substance X should have been (but was not) filtered at the glomerulus? Justify your answer.

Use the following information to answer the next question.

Antony van Leeuwenhoek

Antony van Leeuwenhoek, a Dutch amateur scientist and perhaps the greatest microscope inventor and observer in the late seventeenth and early eighteenth century, described the previously discovered blood capillaries of the intestine in 1683. In his description, he also noted a different kind of capillary in which he observed "a white fluid, like milk."

49. Infer the structure that van Leeuwenhoek observed, as well as its contents.

50. If the salivary glands were unable to secrete amylase, predict the effect this would have on the digestion of starch.

51. Predict the effect of the absence of bile salts on fat digestion.

52. Explain why myosin is not bound to actin when a muscle is relaxed.

Making Connections

Use the following information to answer the next question.

Digestion Times

The flowchart illustrates the approximate length of time that food spends in each part of the human digestive system.

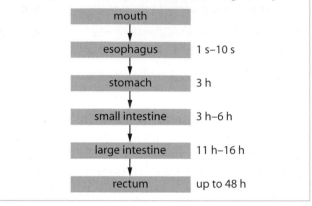

53. Infer the significance of these lengths of time in relation to the processes that occur in each part.

54. Explain how skeletal muscle function affects the maintenance of body temperature.

55. Explain why the breast meat of a bird is typically made up of fast-twitch fibres.

Use the following information to answer the next question.

Respiration Rate

In a supervised laboratory experiment, the rate and depth of respiration for a resting student were determined. In experiment A, the student ran in place for 30 s and then immediately sat down and relaxed, and respiration rate and depth were again determined. Experiment B was the same as Experiment A, except that the student held his breath while running in place.

56. Predict the differences in respiration you would observe in these two experiments, and explain the basis for your predictions.

57. a) Predict and explain the response if the ATP concentration in a muscle that was exhibiting rigor mortis could be instantly increased. Assume the endoplasmic reticulum is fully intact.

b) How does your answer to part (a) change if the endoplasmic reticulum is not fully intact?

58. Outline the internal changes that occur in three systems of the body as the intensity of exercise is increased.

59. A person who is brought to a hospital after a period of prolonged vomiting has an elevated heart rate and decreased blood pressure. Explain these symptoms in terms of the consequences of excessive vomiting.

60. A person had a head injury. He appears to have recovered but is thirsty all the time. Suggest a possible cause.

Use the following information to answer the next question.

Colorectal Cancer

Colorectal cancer—cancer of the large intestine and rectum—is the third most common type of cancer affecting Canadians, next to lung and breast cancer. According to a study published by the American Medical Association, a significant reduction in the risk of colorectal cancer in an average-risk population was associated with long-term, regular use of Aspirin™ (more than two standard tablets per week). Researchers observed the greatest reduction in risk when doses exceeded 14 standard Aspirin™ tablets per week for a period more than 10 years. The researchers hypothesize, based on their results and those of other studies, that Aspirin™ may have a greater influence on preventing cancerous tumours from forming than on reducing the progression of established colorectal cancers.

---

61. Given that the use of Aspirin™, especially in large doses, can cause gastrointestinal bleeding, assess the risks and benefits of using Aspirin™ as a means for preventing colorectal cancer for those with established risk factors (diets high in fat but low in fibre; advancing age; family history of colorectal cancer; history, in women, of breast, ovarian, or uterine cancer).

62. Through the use of technology, many body-system disorders and their symptoms may be modified and sometimes cured. Select two body systems, and identify one disorder that affects each. Explain how a particular technology is used to address the disorder, noting how successful the technology is in solving the problem it is intended to solve.

Use the following information to answer the next questions.

Kidney Failure

Kidney failure (or end-stage renal disease, ESRD) is rare, occurring in about one of every 2000 people. Some of the problems associated with kidney failure include reduced production of red blood cells, as well as the inability to remove nitrogenous and other wastes, regulate the volume of water, balance chemicals, control blood pressure, and produce the active form of vitamin D.

There are two types of renal dialysis commonly used today: hemodialysis and peritoneal dialysis. Both are equally effective at maintaining homeostasis.

Hemodialysis is the most common type of renal dialysis used to treat people suffering from ESRD. The patient's blood is circulated through the dialysis machine, which contains a *dialyzer* (also called an artificial kidney). The patient's blood is connected to the dialysis machine using a surgically constructed path called a *vascular access*. The vascular access creates a way for blood to be removed from the body, circulate through the dialyzer, and then be returned to the body.

The dialyzer has two spaces, separated by a thin, semipermeable cellulose membrane. During hemodialysis, a small quantity of blood passes on one side of the membrane, while a dialysis solution is on the other side of the membrane. The dialysis solution consists only of glucose, amino acids, and mineral ions. The concentrations of these substances are either similar to those of normal plasma, or slightly higher.

The difference in osmotic pressure between the blood and the dialysis solution allows water from the blood to diffuse across the membrane (by osmosis) to dilute the dialysis solution. The semipermeable membrane allows small molecules to pass out of the blood into the dialysis solution, as well. However, large molecules, such as proteins and blood cells, stay in the blood. The dialysis fluid is then discarded, along with the wastes and excess water. The cleansed blood is returned to the cardiovascular system.

---

63. a) Describe how nitrogenous wastes are removed from the blood of a person on dialysis.

 b) In a healthy kidney, nutrients are actively removed from the filtrate and returned to the cardiovascular system. Identify where this process occurs in the healthy kidney, and explain how these nutrients are replaced during dialysis.

The Nervous and Endocrine Systems

General Outcomes

In this unit, you will

- explore how the nervous system regulates physiological processes in the body
- explain how the endocrine system contributes to homeostasis in the body

Unit Contents

Focussing Questions

1 How does the human body react to changes in its internal and external environment? How does the nervous system regulate these reactions to change?

2 How do the senses enable us to detect sensory information and perceive our environment?

3 What are the roles of hormones in the human body? How do environmental factors and technologies affect hormone regulation? What societal issues are related to these effects?

magine that you are a wildland firefighter, battling a blaze like the 2003 fire at Lost Creek, which burned 21 000 ha of land in the Crowsnest Pass area of Alberta. You are sweating and breathing hard. The swiftly moving flames are over 50 m high and as hot as 1000 °C. A series of 16 h shifts of digging and hauling heavy equipment have taken their toll, and you are hungry, thirsty, and near exhaustion. Then the team leader radios your crew to warn you that the firestorm—the heart of the fire—is almost on top of you. You look up and see flames leaping through the treetops. You feel a rush of adrenaline. Your heart pumps faster, and you find the energy to run.

Even in an extreme situation like this, physiological processes regulate the body systems in order to maintain homeostasis—the narrow parameters of internal conditions that the body requires to survive. In Unit 5, you will learn how the nervous system and the endocrine system (a system of chemical messengers) work together to maintain homeostasis.

Prerequisite Concepts

This unit draws and builds upon your understanding of human systems, homeostasis, and the flow of matter in living systems from your Biology 20 studies.

Organization of Systems in the Human Body

The trillions of cells that make up your body can be organized into about one hundred different types. Similarly specialized cells that perform a common function make up a tissue. Tissues of different types are organized as organs, which themselves are organized structurally and functionally as systems that work together to perform functions necessary to sustain and maintain the human organism. These functions may be divided into groups with a common purpose.

Transport

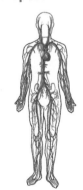 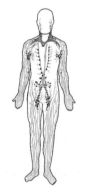

Circulatory system   Lymphatic and immune systems

The circulatory system consists of the heart and the blood vessels, which pump and carry blood through the body. Blood transports nutrients and oxygen to cells and removes waste molecules excreted by cells. While blood is moving throughout the body, it distributes heat produced by the muscles.

The lymphatic system consists of lymphatic vessels, lymph, and lymph nodes. Lymphatic vessels absorb fat from the digestive system and collect excess tissue fluid, which is returned to the blood and, thus, the circulatory system.

The circulatory system and the lymphatic system are also involved in protecting the body against disease and substances that are foreign to the body. Certain blood cells—white blood cells (leukocytes and lymphocytes) and platelets—are part of the body's immune system.

Maintenance of the Body

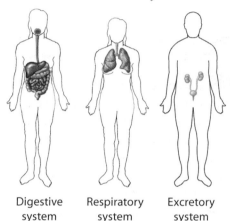

Digestive system   Respiratory system   Excretory system

Three systems—the digestive, respiratory, and excretory systems—add and/or remove substances from the blood.

The digestive system consists of the digestive tract and various organs that directly or indirectly process food into nutrient molecules that enter the blood.

The respiratory system consists of the lungs and tubes that take air to and from the lungs. This system brings oxygen into the body and removes carbon dioxide from the body. It also exchanges gases with the blood.

The excretory (urinary) system includes the kidneys and the urinary bladder, along with tubes that process and transport urine. This system rids the body of wastes and helps regulate the fluid level and chemical content of the blood.

Sensory Input and Motor Output

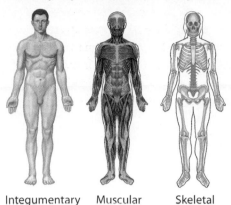

Integumentary system

Muscular system

Skeletal system

The integumentary system consists of the skin and its accessory structures. The sensory receptors in the skin, and in organs such as the eyes and ears, are sensitve to certain external stimuli and communicate with the brain and spinal cord via nerve fibres.

The muscular and the skeletal systems include the muscles and the bones to which they are attached. This system enables the body and its parts to move. The motor system, along with the integumentary system, also protects and supports the internal environment of the body.

Control

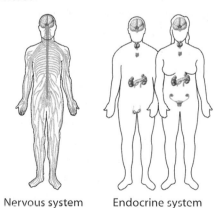

Nervous system

Endocrine system

The nervous system consists of the brain, spinal cord, and associated nerves that conduct nerve impulses from receptors to the brain the spinal cord. Nerves also conduct impulses from the brain and spinal cord to the muscles and glands, allowing the body to respond to both external and internal stimuli.

The endocrine system consists of the hormonal glands that secrete chemicals that serve as messengers between body cells. Both the nervous and the endocrine systems coordinate and regulate the functions of the body's other systems.

You will be studying these two systems in greater detail in Unit 5.

Reproduction

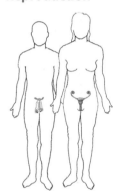

Reproductive system

The reproductive system involves different organs in the male and the female. The male system consists of the testes and other glands, as well as ducts, that conduct semen to and through the penis. The testes produce sex cells called sperm. The female system consists of the ovaries, oviducts, uterus, vagina, and external genitals. The ovaries produce sex cells called eggs or ova. When a sperm fertilizes an egg, an offspring begins development.

You will be studying the male and female reproductive systems in greater detail in Unit 6.

The Nervous System

Chapter Concepts

11.1 Structures and Processes of the Nervous System

- Homeostasis is maintained in the human body by the various parts of the nervous system.

- Neural transmission occurs along axons, due to an action potential that causes depolarization of the neuron.

- Electrochemical communication occurs between cells at the synapse.

11.2 The Central Nervous System

- The central nervous system is the body's control centre. It consists of the brain and spinal cord.

- The brain includes centres that control involuntary responses and voluntary responses.

- The cerebrum is the largest part of the brain. It contains four pairs of lobes, each of which is associated with particular functions.

11.3 The Peripheral Nervous System

- The peripheral nervous system is comprised of the somatic (voluntary) system and the autonomic (involuntary) system.

- The autonomic system is divided into the sympathetic and parasympathetic nervous systems.

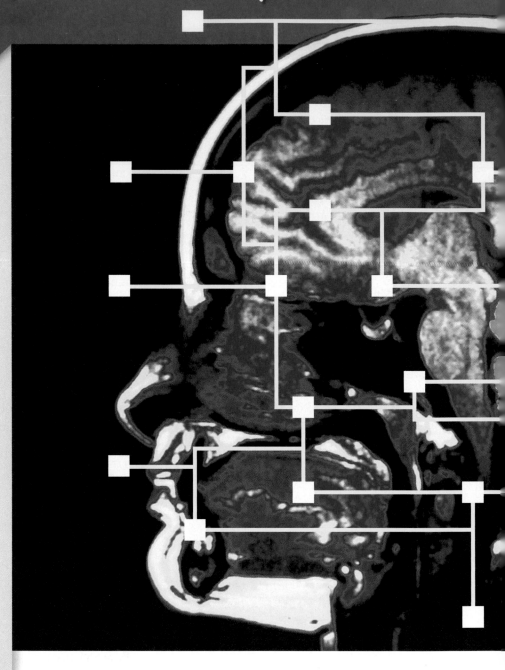

For thousands of years, humans have aspired to create intelligent machines that can interact with their surroundings. More recently, engineers have created sophisticated robots by mimicking aspects of the human nervous system. Modern robots can collect sensory information, use complex signalling networks, and respond to various situations. Even the most advanced robot, however, is about as complex as an insect and processes information at a rate of only 500 million instructions per second. Superimposed on the image of the human brain, shown above, the robotic neural network looks relatively simple. The human nervous system allows us not only to interpret sensory information, but also to learn, reason, imagine, and experience emotions. In addition, the nervous system enables the body to maintain homeostasis.

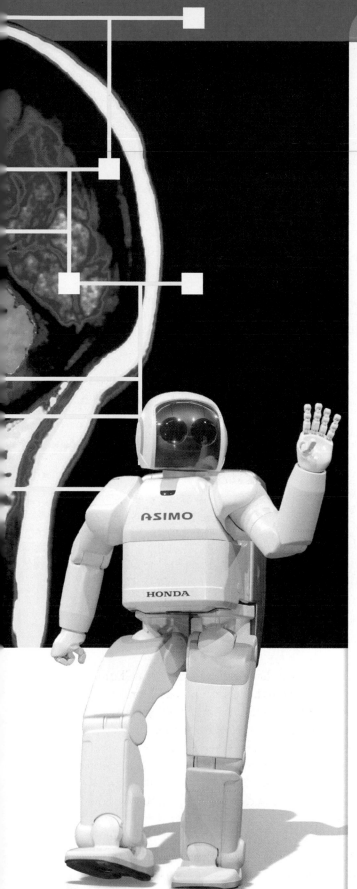

You, Robot?

Modern robots are designed to mimic basic human nervous system processing, which includes sensory input, integration (sorting and putting together information), and motor output. However, modern robots cannot match the capabilities of the human nervous system. This activity is designed to reduce your neural capabilities to those of a fairly advanced robot. How will this affect your ability to perform simple motor output tasks?

Materials

- new ear plugs or cotton batting
- 2 pairs of pliers
- tongue depressor
- blindfold
- masking tape
- shoes with laces
- heavy gloves
- stopwatch

Procedure

1. Make a data table in your notebook to record the trial times.

2. Work with a partner. With untied shoes, Partner A should sit on a chair in front of Partner B.

3. Time how long Partner B takes to tie Partner A's shoelaces.

4. Repeat step 3 with Partner B wearing a blindfold and earplugs.

5. Now repeat step 3 with Partner B wearing heavy gloves.

6. Now repeat step 3 with tongue depressors taped to Partner B's forefingers and thumbs.

7. Have Partner B hold a pair of pliers in each hand. Repeat step 3 with Partner B using the pliers to untie the shoelaces. Then repeat the task using only one hand.

8. Switch places and repeat steps 3 to 7.

Analysis

1. Describe how each sense impairment affected the ability to integrate (sort, interpret, and determine responses to) and process sensory information.

2. For each trial, how did impairing the senses affect the ability to perform a simple motor output task?

3. Describe your impressions of the human nervous system's role, based on the results of this activity.

The Asimo project began in 1986. The first fully independent walking humanoid prototype was finished in 1997.

Structures and Processes of the Nervous System

Figure 11.1 This child is wearing the same kind of clothing that her people, the Inuit, have traditionally made and worn to protect them against the extremes of their Arctic environment. How is her nervous system adapted to enable her body to maintain homeostasis while living in a harsh climate?

The human nervous system is equipped to sense and respond to continuous change within the body and in its external environment. As you may recall from your previous studies of human systems, **homeostasis** is a state of relative stability within the body. Homeostasis is critical for survival, because the body can only survive within a narrow range of conditions. The nervous system regulates body structures and processes to maintain homeostasis despite fluctuations in the internal and external environment.

For example, the child in Figure 11.1 lives in what many people consider to be an inhospitable environment, with winter temperatures often falling to −50 °C and lower. For the Arctic Inuit, maintaining a constant internal temperature, while keeping blood and heat flowing to the extremities, is crucial. Researchers have discovered that the nervous systems of people living in warmer climates act to constrict blood flow to an extremity (and thus conserve body heat) when the extremity is cooled. In Inuit people who have lived for generations in the far North, however, the nervous system fluctuates the constriction and dilation of blood vessels to cooled extremities. This has the effect of conserving body heat, but it also allows for continued blood flow to prevent frostbite. In this way, homeostasis is maintained.

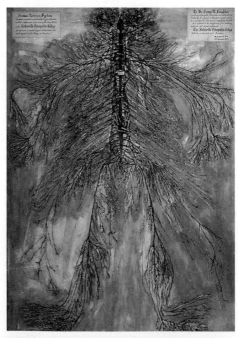

Figure 11.2 Dissections allow researchers to learn about the human body. This dissection of the human nervous system was donated to the Smithsonian Institution in 1935 from the Kirksville College of Osteopathic Medicine.

To maintain homeostasis, the human body must react to differences in temperature as well as respond to various internal and external stimuli, and it must regulate these responses. The human nervous system can regulate tens of thousands of activities simultaneously. In ways that scientists do not fully understand, it is intimately connected with human consciousness, intelligence, and creativity. The nervous system monitors and controls most body processes, from automatic functions (such as breathing) to activities that involve fine motor coordination, learning, and thought (such as playing a musical instrument). The brain and spinal cord, and the nerves that emerge from them and connect them to the rest of the body, make up the human **nervous system** (Figure 11.2).

• • •

Q1 Define homeostasis.

Q2 Explain why the nervous system is critical for maintaining homeostasis.

• • •

Organization of the Nervous System

The human nervous system is perhaps the most complex system of any organism. The human brain alone contains over 100 billion nerve cells, and each nerve cell can have up to 10 000 connections to other nerve cells. This means that a nerve impulse—an electrochemical signal—to or from the brain could travel along 10^{15} possible routes.

The nervous system has two major divisions: the central nervous system (CNS) and the peripheral nervous system (PNS). Early researchers made this distinction based on where nervous tissue was located in the body—centrally or away from the centre (peripherally). Together, the central nervous system and the peripheral nervous system control sensory input, integration, and motor output.

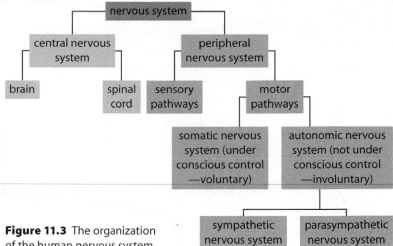

Figure 11.3 The organization of the human nervous system.

The **central nervous system**, which consists of the brain and spinal cord, integrates and processes information sent by nerves.

The **peripheral nervous system** includes nerves that carry sensory messages to the central nervous system and nerves that send information from the CNS to the muscles and glands.

The peripheral nervous system is further divided into the somatic system and the autonomic system.

The *somatic system* consists of sensory receptors in the head and extremities, nerves that carry sensory information to the central nervous system, and nerves that carry instructions from the central nervous system to the skeletal muscles.

The *autonomic system* controls glandular secretions and the functioning of the smooth and cardiac muscles.

The *sympathetic* and *parasympathetic* divisions of the autonomic system often work in opposition to each other to regulate the involuntary processes of the body. Involuntary processes, such as heartbeat and peristalsis, are those that do not require or involve conscious control.

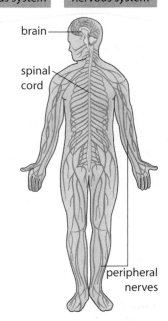

• • •

Q3 Create a table to identify the different systems in the nervous system and explain the structure and function of each.

• • •

Cells of the Nervous System

The nervous system is composed of only two main types of cells: neurons and cells that support the neurons, which are called glial cells. **Neurons** are the basic structural and functional units of the nervous system. They are specialized to respond to physical and chemical stimuli, to conduct electrochemical signals, and to release chemicals that regulate various body processes.

The activity of neurons is supported by another type of cells called glial cells. (The word glial comes from a Greek word that means "glue.") **Glial cells** outnumber neurons by about 10 to 1, and they account for about half of the volume of the nervous system. Collectively, glial cells nourish the neurons, remove their wastes, and defend against infection. Glial cells also provide a supporting framework for all the nervous-system tissue. Figure 11.4 shows a small sample of this tissue.

Individual neurons are organized into tissues called **nerves**. Figure 11.5 shows how hundreds of individual neurons are grouped into nerve bundles and surrounded by protective connective tissue. Like optical fibre cables, which carry many individual wires from one part of a network to another, the nerves extend the neurons throughout the peripheral nervous system. Some nerves consist of neurons that carry information from sensory receptors. Other nerves consist of neurons that carry information to the muscles or glands.

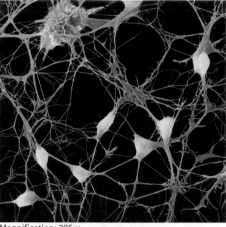

Magnification: 295 ×

Figure 11.4 This electron micrograph shows interconnecting neurons with their cell bodies (yellow) and a supporting glial cell (purple).

Neurons vary considerably in size and appearance, depending on their position and function in the body. Three main types of neurons, however, form the basic impulse-transmission pathway of the entire nervous system (Figure 11.6). This pathway, summarized in Table 11.1, depends on three overlapping functions: sensory input, integration, and motor output.

1. **Sensory input:** Sensory neurons gather information from the sensory receptors (senses) and transmit these impulses to the central nervous system (brain and spinal cord).

2. **Integration:** Interneurons are found entirely within the central nervous system. They act as a link between the sensory and motor neurons. They process and integrate incoming sensory information, and relay outgoing motor information.

Figure 11.5 Neurons are bundled together into nerves in the peripheral nervous system and into tracts in the central nervous system. Nerves are macroscopic structures. Neurons, however, are microscopic structures. Even a neuron that is over 1 m long cannot be seen with the unaided eye.

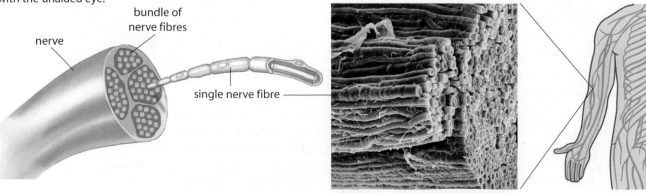

nerve

bundle of nerve fibres

single nerve fibre

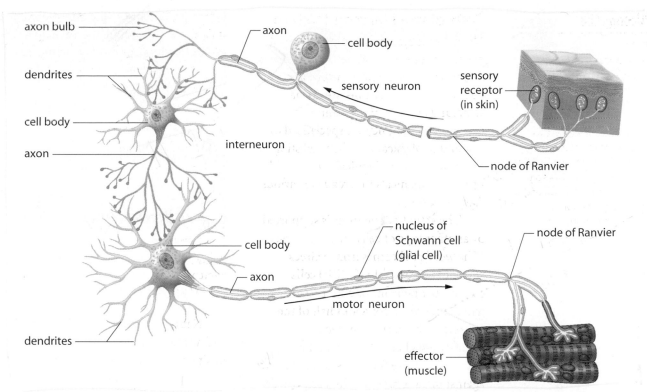

axon bulb

dendrites

cell body

axon

interneuron

axon

cell body

sensory neuron

sensory receptor (in skin)

node of Ranvier

cell body

nucleus of Schwann cell (glial cell)

node of Ranvier

axon

motor neuron

effector (muscle)

dendrites

Figure 11.6 This diagram shows how a sensory neuron, an interneuron, and a motor neuron are arranged in the nervous system. (The breaks indicate that the axons are longer than shown).

Table 11.1 Structures of the General Neural Impulse Transmission Pathway

Structure	Function
sensory receptors	receive stimuli and form a nerve impulse
sensory neurons	transmit impulses from the sensory receptors to the interneurons
interneurons	are found in the brain and spinal cord; act as an integration centre
motor neurons	conduct impulses from the interneurons to the effectors
effectors	muscles, glands, and other organs that respond to impulses from the motor neurons

3. Motor output: Motor neurons transmit information from the central nervous system to the muscles, glands, and other organs (effectors).

Figure 11.7 on page 370 provides an example of a basic neural transmission pathway. Suppose that you are driving a car, and a cat darts onto the road in front of you. Your eyes collect sensory information (the sight of the cat on the road), and sensory neurons transmit this information by conducting electrochemical signals to the brain and spinal cord. Here the information is integrated by interneurons. Motor neurons then carry motor output signals to the muscles (effectors), causing you to extend your foot and press the brake.

The Reflex Arc

Some neurons are organized to enable your body to react rapidly in times of danger, even before you are consciously aware of the threat. These sudden, unlearned, involuntary responses to certain stimuli are called reflexes. Examples of reflexes are jerking your hand away from a hot or sharp object, blinking when an object moves toward your eye, or vomiting in response to food that irritates your stomach. **Reflex arcs** are simple connections of neurons that explain reflexive behaviours. They can be used to model the basic organization of the nervous system.

Reflex arcs use very few neurons to transmit messages. As a result, reflexes can be very rapid, occurring in about 50 ms (milliseconds). Withdrawal reflexes, for example, depend on only

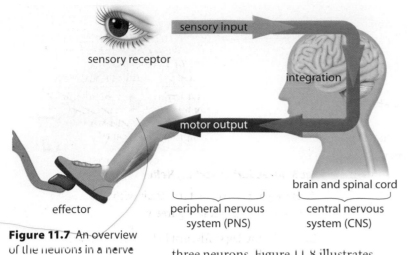

sensory receptor

sensory input

integration

motor output

effector

brain and spinal cord

peripheral nervous system (PNS)

central nervous system (CNS)

Figure 11.7 An overview of the neurons in a nerve impulse pathway

three neurons. Figure 11.8 illustrates a typical neural circuit, as well as a withdrawal reflex from a potentially dangerous situation. Receptors in the skin sense the pressure of the cactus needle and initiate an impulse in a sensory neuron. The impulse carried by the sensory neuron then activates the interneuron in the spinal cord. The interneuron signals the motor neuron to instruct the muscle to contract and withdraw the hand.

A reflex arc moves directly to and from the brain or spinal cord, before the brain centres involved with voluntary control have time to process the sensory

information. This is why, after stepping on a stone, you would not feel pain or cry out until *after* your foot was withdrawn, once the brain has had time to process the information. You can test your reflexes in Investigation 11.A.

4 Compare the basic function of neurons and glial cells.

5 List the three types of neurons, and identify their primary functions.

6 Identify the basic neural pathway that is involved as you dodge a wayward tennis ball. Compare this pathway with a withdrawal reflex.

The Structure of a Neuron

Neurons have many of the same features as other body cells. In addition, neurons have specialized cell structures that enable them to transmit nerve impulses. Different types of neurons are different shapes and sizes. In general, however, they share four common features: dendrites, a cell body (soma), an axon, and branching ends (Figure 11.9).

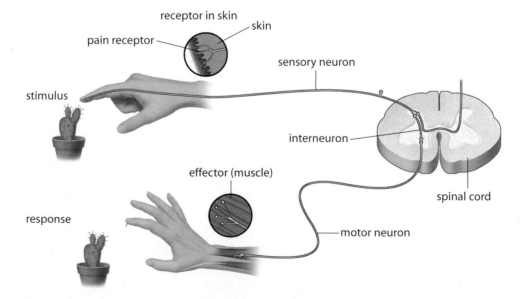

receptor in skin

skin

pain receptor

sensory neuron

stimulus

interneuron

effector (muscle)

spinal cord

response

motor neuron

Figure 11.8 A withdrawal reflex. Receptors in the skin perceive the stimulus. Sensory information is conducted from the senses into the spinal cord. Motor information is then conducted away from the spinal cord to the muscles and glands.

Move Fast! Reflex Responses

Target Skills

Performing an experiment to investigate the physiology of reflex arcs

Identifying a reflex arc not discussed in the textbook, and **designing an experiment** to investigate the physiology of this reflex arc

Reflexes are rapid, involuntary neural pathways that help to protect the body. The knee-jerk (patellar) reflex is an example of the numerous stretch adjustments your body makes every second to unconsciously maintain your balance and coordination. (Your teacher may add others.) Try to initiate the following three common reflexes. Then design an experiment to test a fourth reflex.

Question

How does a reflex arc help to protect the body from harm?

Safety Precautions

Do *not* use excessive force when testing the knee-jerk reflex.

Materials

- cotton balls
- 20 cm by 20 cm clear plastic sheet
- room light
- chair

Procedure

Part 1: Pupillary Reflex

1. Work with a partner. Dim the lights in the room for a few minutes. Look at the pupils in your partner's eyes.

2. Turn on the lights. Check the size of the pupils.

Part 2: Blink Reflex

1. Have your partner hold a piece of clear plastic in front of the face.

2. Without warning, quickly throw a cotton ball at your partner's eyes. Your partner should blink, demonstrating the blink reflex.

Part 3: Knee Jerk (Patellar) Reflex

1. Have your partner sit in a chair with legs crossed, so the top leg can swing freely.

2. Hit the top leg softly, just below the knee, with the side of your hand. The leg should kick out immediately, demonstrating the patellar reflex.

Analysis

1. Copy the diagram below into your notebook. Use it as a model to represent and summarize each of the reflex responses that you tested and observed in this investigation.

2. Explain why reflexes are important for the body.

Conclusion

3. Describe how the three reflexes tested in this investigation might protect the body.

Applications

4. A student puts her hand on hot glassware, but withdraws her hand *before* she feels the pain. Explain how and why her awareness of the pain is delayed.

5. Design a procedure to test one of the other reflexes of the body. Hypothesize what the reflex arc might look like for the reflex you are testing, and suggest a way in which this reflex would help to protect the body. Obtain your teacher's approval before carrying out your procedure.

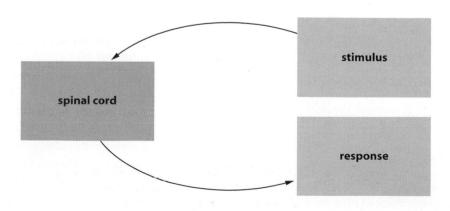

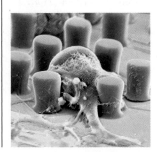
Dendrites are short, branching terminals that receive nerve impulses from other neurons or sensory receptors, and relay the impulse to the cell body. The dendrites are numerous and highly branched, which increases the surface area available to receive information. The **cell body** contains the nucleus and is the site of the cell's metabolic reactions. The cell body also processes input from the dendrites. If the input received is large enough, the cell body relays it to the axon, where an impulse is initiated.

A neuron typically has one **axon**, which conducts impulses away from the cell body. Axons range in length from 1 mm to 1 m, depending on the neuron's location in the body. For example, the sciatic nerve in the leg contains neuronal axons that extend from the spinal cord all the way to the muscles in the foot, a distance of over 1 m. The terminal end of an axon branches into many fibres. To communicate with adjacent neurons, glands, or muscles, the axon terminal releases chemical signals into the space between it and the receptors or dendrites of neighbouring cells.

The axons of some neurons are enclosed in a fatty, insulating layer called the **myelin sheath**, which gives the axons a glistening white appearance. These axons are said to be myelinated. Axons without a myelin sheath are said to be unmyelinated (Figure 11.9).

The myelin sheath protects myelinated neurons and speeds the rate of nerve impulse transmission. **Schwann cells**, a type of glial cell, form myelin by wrapping themselves around the axon. In the central nervous system, myelinated neurons form what is known as *white matter*, and unmyelinated neurons form the *grey matter*. Most neurons in the peripheral nervous system are myelinated.

• • •

(7) Draw a neuron, label its basic structures, and identify their functions.

(8) Describe the structure of a myelinated neuron.

• • •

Unmyelinated Nerve Impulse

A taser is a non-lethal weapon that some police officers use to immobilize threatening people. A taser sends 25 000 to 150 000 V (volts) of electricity through the human nervous system. This overloads the motor neurons of the somatic system, momentarily incapacitating the body. The electrical jolt interferes with the nervous system because neuron function depends on the cells' ability to conduct electrochemical impulses.

Neurons are able to establish a voltage difference between the inside and outside of the cell membrane. They use this voltage difference to generate a neural impulse. In the remainder of this section, you will focus on how these impulses are generated in neurons and how these electrical signals are transmitted along the length of a neuron.

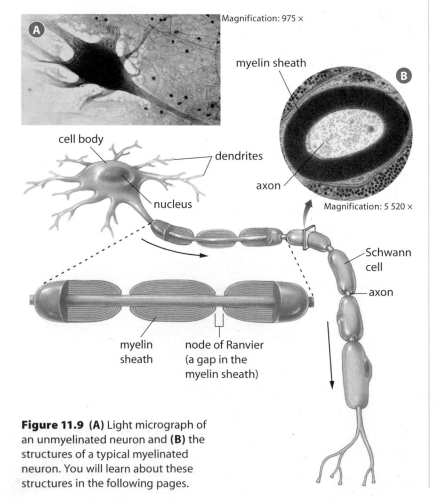

Magnification: 975 ×

Magnification: 5 520 ×

Figure 11.9 (A) Light micrograph of an unmyelinated neuron and **(B)** the structures of a typical myelinated neuron. You will learn about these structures in the following pages.

The Electrical Nature of Nerves

Luigi Galvani (1737–1798), an Italian physician and anatomist, discovered the electrical nature of nerve tissue in a simple experiment. Using two metal rods and some wire, he was able to activate a nerve within a frog's leg and cause the leg to twitch. No detailed information about the mechanisms by which nervous tissue transmitted electrical information was obtained until 1952. At that time, A.L. Hodgkin and A.F. Huxley performed experiments on the giant axon of the squid of the genus *Loligo*, shown in Figure 11.10. This squid has giant neurons used for rapid tail movements, with axons that reach from the head of the squid into its tail. A squid giant axon is up to 10 cm long and about 1 mm in diameter, or 100 to 1000 times the diameter of a human axon. The size of the axon allows scientists to measure the potential difference across the cell membrane quite easily, by inserting tiny electrodes into the axon and then reading the potential difference from a specialized voltmeter. This technique has provided extensive information about how a voltage is established across the axon membrane and how a neural impulse is generated.

Although neurons can conduct neural impulses from one area of the body to another, this process differs from electrical conduction along a wire. Nerve conduction is more complex and considerably slower. Unlike the movement of electrons along an electrical wire, nerve conduction depends on the movement of ions across the cell membrane of the axon.

Resting Membrane Potential

When microelectrodes are inserted in an inactive, or resting, neuron, measurements from a voltmeter indicate an electrical potential difference (voltage) across the neural membrane (Figure 11.11). The electrical potential difference across the membrane can be likened to the electric potential of a flashlight battery or car

Figure 11.10 *Loligo opalescens*, one of the species of *Loligo* studied by neurobiologists. What unique feature of this squid genus has helped scientists learn about the human nervous system?

battery. The chemical reactions maintain a separation of charges between the positive and negative poles. Similarly, in a resting neuron, the cytoplasmic side of the membrane is negative, relative to the extracellular side. The charge separation across the membrane is a form of potential energy, or **membrane potential**.

The potential difference across the membrane in a resting neuron is called the **resting membrane potential**. The resting membrane potential of most unstimulated neurons is −70 mV (millivolts), and it is negative on the inside, relative to the outside. The resting membrane potential provides energy for the generation of a nerve impulse in response to an appropriate stimulus.

The process of generating a resting membrane potential of −70 mV is called **polarization**. Neurons become polarized as a result of several mechanisms at work at the same time. Large protein molecules that are negatively charged are present in the intracellular fluid but not outside of the cell. These proteins are so large that they cannot pass through the cell

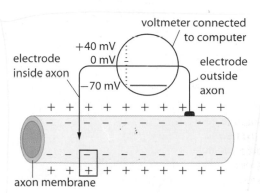

Figure 11.11 A diagram of a specialized voltmeter and a neuron with a resting membrane potential of −70 mV.

membrane. As well, the membrane is nearly impermeable to some smaller negatively charged ions such as chloride ions. Their presence in the intracellular fluid further contributes to the negative charge inside the cell.

The most important contributor to the separation of charge and the resulting electrical potential difference across the membrane is the **sodium-potassium exchange pump** (Figure 11.12). This system uses the energy of ATP to transport sodium ions out of the cell and potassium ions into the cell.

The sodium-potassium exchange pump exchanges three sodium ions for two potassium ions. As a result, an excess of positive charge accumulates outside of the cell. The cell membrane is not totally impermeable to sodium and potassium ions, so they leak slowly by diffusion across the membrane in the direction of their concentration gradient. However, potassium ions are able to diffuse out of the cell more easily than sodium ions can diffuse into the cell. The overall result of the active transport of sodium and potassium ions across the membrane, and their subsequent diffusion back across the membrane, is a constant transmembrane potential of −70 mV.

You might wonder why the −70 mV potential difference across the neuronal membrane is called the *resting* membrane potential when the sodium-potassium pump is constantly using energy to transport these ions. The term resting means that no nerve impulses are being transmitted along the axon. The resting potential maintains the axon membrane in a condition of readiness for an impulse to occur. The energy for any eventual impulses is stored in the electrochemical gradient across the membrane.

9. Explain what the resting membrane potential is, and why it is significant to the functioning of neurons.

10. Identify and explain the three factors that contribute to the resting membrane potential.

Action Potential

A nerve impulse consists of a series of action potentials. To understand an impulse, you first need to focus on an individual action potential taking place on one tiny segment of the axon membrane. In myelinated neurons, action potentials occur only at **nodes of Ranvier** (see Figure 11.9) because the myelin sheath insulates the axonal membrane that it encircles.

Figure 11.12 The sodium-potassium exchange pump actively transports three sodium ions (Na⁺) outside of the cell for every two potassium ions (K⁺) moved inside the cell. Small amounts of Na⁺ and K⁺ also diffuse ("leak") slowly across the cell membrane, following their concentration gradient.

Outside   Inside

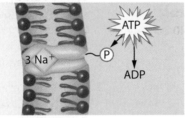

A. The carrier protein has a shape that allows it to take up three sodium ions (Na⁺).

- K⁺ diffusion
- 3 Na⁺
- carrier
- Na⁺ diffusion

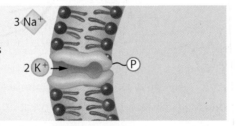

B. ATP is split, and a phosphate group is transferred to the carrier protein.

- 3 Na⁺
- ATP
- P
- ADP

C. A change in shape of the carrier protein causes the release of three sodium ions (Na⁺) outside the cell. The altered shape permits the uptake of two potassium ions (K⁺).

- 3 Na⁺
- 2 K⁺
- P

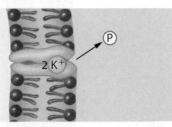

D. The phosphate group is released from the carrier protein.

- P
- 2 K⁺

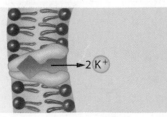

E. A change in shape of the carrier protein causes the protein to release the potassium ions (K⁺) in the cell. The carrier protein is once again able to take up three sodium ions (Na⁺).

- 2 K⁺

Target Skills

Gathering and analyzing data from a model of a neuron

Working as a team to carry out experimental procedures and assess results

Modelling Resting Membrane Potential

In this investigation, you will build a simple model of the neural membrane to demonstrate how the resting membrane potential is established.

Question

How does the resting neural membrane generate an electric potential?

Safety Precautions

Wash your hands after completing this investigation, or immediately if your skin is exposed to the solutions used. Wear goggles to protect your eyes against accidental splashes. The solutions used are irritating to the eyes.

Materials

- 3 mol/L sodium chloride solution
- 3 mol/L potassium chloride solution
- 22 cm of moistened dialysis tubing
- 2 strips of uninsulated copper wire, each 40 cm long
- string
- DC millivolt meter
- elastic band
- 400 mL beaker
- pen

Procedure

1. Create a table to record the data collected.

2. With your group, take the two 40-cm strips of copper wire and tightly wind one end of each around a pen in order to form a coil of about 8 cm.

3. Attach the uncoiled ends to the millivolt meter, as shown below. Each wire will serve as an electrode.

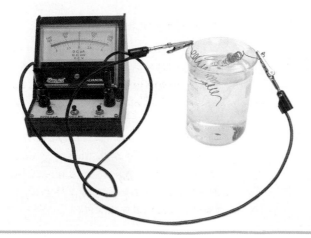

4. Pour about 300 mL of the sodium chloride solution into the 400 mL beaker. Take the copper electrode attached to the positive terminal of the meter, and immerse the free end in the solution.

5. Tie off one end of moistened dialysis tubing. Fill two thirds of the tubing with potassium chloride solution. Place the free end of the other copper electrode in the solution in the tubing. Secure the end of the tubing around the wire with an elastic band.

6. While another group member observes the needle on the millivolt meter, place the dialysis tubing in the beaker that contains the solution of sodium chloride. (If sensor probes are available, these can be used to measure and monitor the electric potential.)

7. Leave the dialysis tubing in the beaker, and continue to monitor the electric potential every 5 min, until a trend is established. Record each value in your data table.

Analysis

1. Graph the data from your data table.

2. Explain what the dialysis tubing, potassium chloride solution, and sodium chloride represent in this model of a resting neuron.

3. Compare the electric potential created in this model with a resting membrane potential in a neuron.

4. Compare your results with the results of other groups in your class. Provide a reason for any differences.

5. Hypothesize how you might be able to increase the electric potential across the dialysis tubing.

Conclusions

6. **a)** Describe what happened to the magnitude of the electric potential over time, and explain why this happened.

   b) If this occurred in a neuron, what would happen?

7. **a)** How did your model illustrate the mechanism of ion channel diffusion?

   b) Summarize all the factors that establish resting membrane potential in a neuron, including the mechanism of ion channel diffusion illustrated by your model.

Figure 11.13 Summary of the events in an action potential.

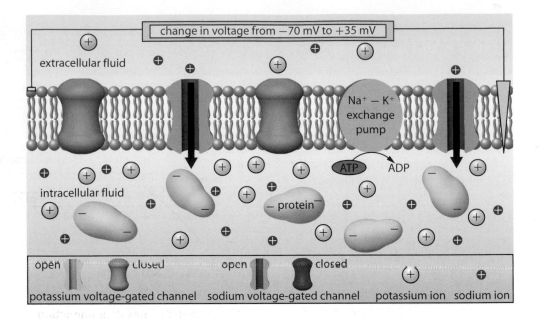

A neuronal membrane is said to be **depolarized** if the transmembrane potential is reduced to less than the resting potential of −70 mV. If, for any reason, the membrane at a node of Ranvier becomes depolarized to −55 mV, a dramatic change occurs in the membrane. This change is called an **action potential**. (As you will see later, this depolarization is usually caused by an action potential that has just occurred at an adjacent node of Ranvier.) An action potential is called an "all-or-none" event because a depolarization to between −70 mV and −55 mV has no effect. Any depolarization

to −55 mV, or any other amount up to 0, will produce identical action potentials. The potential difference of −55 mV is therefore called the **threshold potential**. Threshold potentials can vary slightly, depending on the type of neuron, but they are usually close to −55 mV.

When the transmembrane potential at a node of Ranvier reaches threshold, special structures in the membrane called voltage-gated sodium channels open and make the membrane very permeable to sodium ions. The sodium ions on the outside of the axon suddenly rush into the axon, driven by their

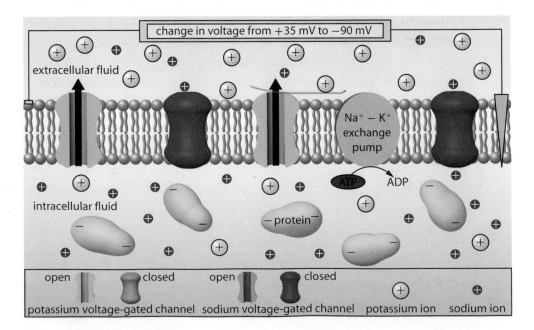

Figure 11.14 The repolarization of a neuron. Why must the neuron be repolarized before it can be stimulated again?

concentration gradient and the potential difference across the membrane as shown in Figure 11.13. Within a millisecond or less, enough positively charged sodium ions have crossed the membrane to make the potential difference across the membrane in that tiny region of the axon +35 mV.

As a result of the change in membrane potential, the sodium channels close and voltage-gated potassium channels open. As shown in Figure 11.14, the potassium ions now move down their concentration gradient (toward the outside of the axon), carrying positive charge out of the neuron. As a result, the membrane is **repolarized**—that is, returned to its previous polarization. In fact, the membrane potential overshoots to nearly −90 mV. At that point, the potassium channels close. The sodium-potassium exchange pump and the small amount of naturally occurring diffusion quickly bring the membrane back to its normal resting potential of −70 mV. For the next few milliseconds after an action potential, the membrane cannot be stimulated to undergo another action potential. This brief period of time is called the **refractory period** of the membrane.

Figure 11.15 summarizes the changes in the transmembrane potential that occur during an action potential. Notice that all of these events occur within a period of a few milliseconds. As well, they occur in one small region of the axon membrane.

• • •

11 Explain the difference between depolarization of a neuron and an action potential.

12 Describe the "all-or-none" response.

13 Describe the process of repolarization in the neuron, and explain its importance in the transmission of a neural impulse.

• • •

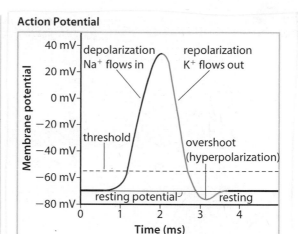

Action Potential

Figure 11.15 The changes in the transmembrane potential of the axon are a result of sodium ions flowing into the axon and potassium ions flowing out. An action potential lasts only a few milliseconds.

Myelinated Nerve Impulse

A nerve impulse consists of a series of action potentials. How does one action potential stimulate another? Examine Figure 11.16 on page 378. As you know, when an action potential occurs at a node of Ranvier, sodium ions flow into the axon. After the sodium channels close, there is still a relatively high concentration of sodium inside the axon at that node. Since particles such as ions always diffuse from an area of higher concentration to an area of lower concentration, the sodium ions inside the axon cannot diffuse out. Instead, they diffuse in both directions along the axon.

When the sodium ions reach neighboring nodes of Ranvier, the positive charges reduce the net negative charge inside the axonal membrane. The presence of the positively charged sodium ions causes the membrane at the nodes of Ranvier to become depolarized to threshold. Since an action potential just occurred at the node to the left (in the figure), that membrane is refractory, which means that it cannot be stimulated to undergo another action potential yet. This mechanism prevents impulses from going backwards. The membrane of the node of Ranvier to the right is not refractory so the depolarization initiates an action potential at this node.

The same process occurs at each node until it reaches the end of the neuron. This process of one action potential stimulating the production

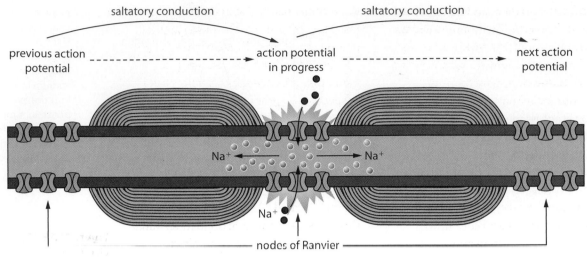

saltatory conduction — saltatory conduction

previous action potential — action potential in progress — next action potential

Na⁺ ← → Na⁺

Na⁺

nodes of Ranvier

Figure 11.16 Sodium ions that accumulate inside an axon during an action potential diffuse in both directions along the inside of the axon.

of another one at the next node constitutes the nerve impulse.

Because action potentials are forced to "jump" from one node of Ranvier to the next due to the myelin sheath, the conduction of an impulse along a myelinated neuron is called *saltatory conduction*. (The word "saltatory" comes from a Latin word that means to jump or leap.) A similar process occurs in unmyelinated neurons. In these neurons, however, action potentials can occur at all locations along a membrane. Therefore, they occur beside one another. As a result of so many action potentials occurring all along the axon, the transmission of an impulse along an unmyelinated axon is much slower than the saltatory conduction along a myelinated axon (about 0.5 m/s, compared with as much as 120 m/s in a myelinated axon).

The nervous system disorder called multiple sclerosis is caused by the breakdown of the myelin sheath surrounding the axons in the central nervous system (Figure 11.17). The neurons can no longer efficiently carry electrochemical signals between the brain and the body. Multiple sclerosis is thought to be an autoimmune disease, in which the body's own immune system breaks down the myelin. The symptoms of multiple sclerosis can include blurred vision, loss of balance, muscle weakness, fatigue, and slurred speech. Most people

with multiple sclerosis experience periods of remission and periods of progression of the disease.

In Investigation 11.C, you will examine myelinated and unmyelinated neural tissue.

Signal Transmission across a Synapse

The simplest neural pathways have at least two neurons and one connection between the neurons. Other neural pathways can involve thousands of neurons and their connections as an impulse travels from the origin of the stimulus, through the sensory neurons to the brain, and back through motor neurons to the muscles or glands. The connection between two neurons, or a neuron and an effector, is called a **synapse**. A **neuromuscular junction** is a synapse between a motor neuron and a muscle cell.

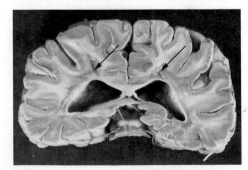

Figure 11.17 In this person, who has multiple sclerosis, the myelin sheath in the white matter of the brain has been destroyed, leaving lesions. Arrows show the affected areas of the brain.

BiologyFile

Web Link
View an on-line animation of neural impulse propagation. In what way is a neural impulse like a wave?

www.albertabiology.ca
WWW

An impulse travels the length of the axon until it reaches the far end, called the synaptic terminal. Most neurons are not directly connected, but have a gap between them called the synaptic cleft. These neurons are not close enough for the impulse to jump from one to the other. How, then, does the impulse proceed from the presynaptic neuron, which sends out information, to the postsynaptic neuron, which receives the information?

Chemical messengers called **neurotransmitters** carry the neural signal from one neuron to another. Neurotransmitters can also carry the neural signal from a neuron to an effector, such as a gland or muscle fibre. Figure 11.18 summarizes the events in the movement of an impulse across a synapse. When an action potential arrives at the end of a presynaptic neuron, the impulse causes sacs that contain neurotransmitters to fuse with the membrane of the axon. These sacs, called synaptic vesicles, release their contents into the synaptic cleft by exocytosis. The neurotransmitters then diffuse across the synapse, taking about 0.5 to 1 ms to reach the dendrites of the postsynaptic neuron, or cell membrane of the effector.

Upon reaching the postsynaptic membrane, the neurotransmitters bind to specific receptor proteins in this membrane. As Figure 11.18 illustrates, the receptor proteins trigger ion-specific channels to open. This depolarizes the postsynaptic membrane and, if the threshold potential is reached, initiates an action potential. The impulse will travel along the postsynaptic axon to its terminal and to the next neuron or an effector.

Neurotransmitters have either excitatory or inhibitory effects on the postsynaptic membrane. If the effect is excitatory, the receptor proteins will trigger ion channels that open to allow positive ions, such as sodium, to flow into the postsynaptic neuron. As a result, the membrane becomes slightly depolarized. The membrane of the neuron cannot experience an action potential but the slight depolarization spreads throughout the nerve cell, lowering its threshold level.

Figure 11.18 **(A)** An electron micrograph of a neural synapse. Note in green the synaptic vesicles in the axon terminal of the presynaptic neuron. **(B)** Neurotransmitters bind to receptor proteins. **(C)** Synaptic transmission.

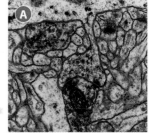

Magnification: 15 288 ×

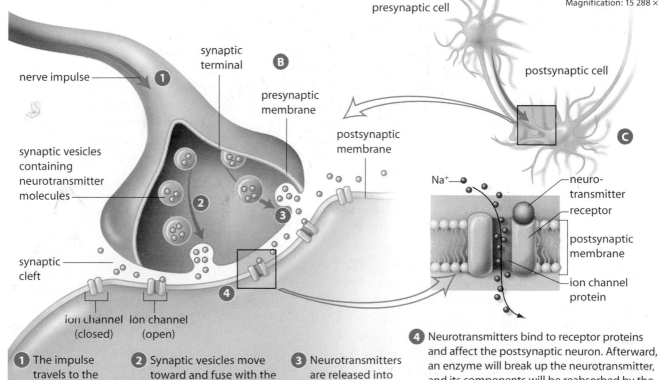

presynaptic cell

postsynaptic cell

nerve impulse

synaptic terminal

B

presynaptic membrane

postsynaptic membrane

synaptic vesicles containing neurotransmitter molecules

C

Na⁺

neuro-transmitter receptor

postsynaptic membrane

ion channel protein

synaptic cleft

ion channel (closed)   ion channel (open)

1 The impulse travels to the synaptic terminal.

2 Synaptic vesicles move toward and fuse with the presynaptic membrane.

3 Neurotransmitters are released into the synaptic cleft.

4 Neurotransmitters bind to receptor proteins and affect the postsynaptic neuron. Afterward, an enzyme will break up the neurotransmitter, and its components will be reabsorbed by the presynaptic neuron. The pink arrows show the direction of nerve impulse transmission.

BiologyFile

Web Link
View an on-line animation of neurotransmitters in action. Describe the role of the cell membrane in neurotransmitter release.

www.albertabiology.ca
WWW

If the neurotransmitter is inhibitory, the receptor will trigger potassium channels to open, allowing potassium ions to flow out. This results in a more negative transmembrane potential, resulting in hyperpolarization. A single cell body may be receiving signals from many presynaptic neurons at the same time. Some can be excitatory and others can be inhibitory. One of the functions of the cell body is to integrate all of the incoming signals. The combined effect of all of the stimuli spreads across the cell body. If the excitatory stimuli are strong enough, the depolarization will reach the point at which the axon is connected to the cell body and an impulse will be generated. The postsynaptic neuron will then return to resting potential.

After the neurotransmitter has had its effect, enzymes break it down and inactivate it so that its components can be reabsorbed by the presynaptic cell.

14 Summarize the events that occur as an impulse is propagated along the length of the neuron.

15 Summarize the events involved in impulse transmission from the presynaptic neuron to the postsynaptic neuron.

16 Identify the function of neurotransmitters in the nervous system.

Neurotransmitters in Action

Acetylcholine is a neurotransmitter that crosses a neuromuscular junction (Figure 11.19). Acetylcholine excites the muscle cell membrane, causing depolarization and contraction of the muscle fibre. Consider what would happen if acetylcholine remained in

Figure 11.19 (A) An electron micrograph and **(B)** a diagram showing a neuromuscular junction. Notice the axon of the motor neuron connecting (across a synapse) with muscle fibres in red.

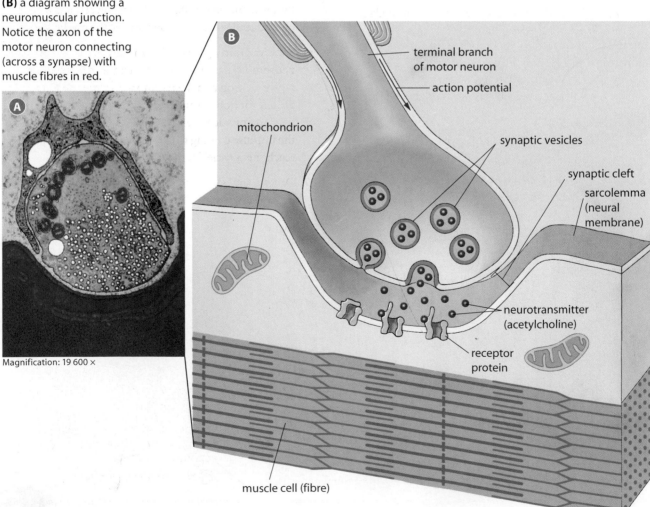

Magnification: 19 600 ×

terminal branch of motor neuron
action potential
mitochondrion
synaptic vesicles
synaptic cleft
sarcolemma (neural membrane)
neurotransmitter (acetylcholine)
receptor protein
muscle cell (fibre)

Target Skills

Observing neurons and neuromuscular junctions with a microscope

Identifying the principal structures in different types of neurons, and **relating** these structures to their functions

Examining Neural Tissue

In this investigation, you will examine microscope slides of neural tissue, along with some corresponding photographs. As you observe the tissues and make diagrams, identify the specialized structures that allow neurons to carry out their functions.

Question

How does the structure of different neurons relate to their functions?

Safety Precautions

Handle the microscope slides with care, so they do not break and cut you.

Materials

- microscope
- prepared neural slides similar to, but not limited to, the ones shown below

Procedure

Observe each slide provided by your teacher, as well as the micrographs below, and identify any key neural structures.

Analysis

1. Slide and micrograph 1 show a cross-section of the brain. Sketch your observations, and label the white and grey matter. Describe the structural differences between the two types of neural tissue.

2. Slide and micrograph 2 show a cross-section of a nerve. Sketch your observations, and label the nerve bundles and neurons. Explain the basic function of a neuron.

3. Slide and micrograph 3 show a cross-section of the spinal cord. Sketch your observations, and label a sensory neuron, a motor neuron, and an interneuron. (**Hint:** See Figure 11.6.) Explain the function of each neuron, and trace the neural pathway.

4. Slide and photograph 4 show several unmyelinated neurons. Sketch one neuron that you can see, and label the basic structures. Indicate the direction of impulse transmission down the neuron.

5. Slide and micrograph 5 show a longitudinal view of a myelinated axon. Sketch your observations, and label the axon, the myelin sheath, a Schwann cell, and a node of Ranvier. Describe the functions of the myelin sheath.

6. Slide and micrograph 6 show a view of the neuromuscular junction between the dendrites of a motor neuron and the receptors on a muscle fibre. Sketch your observations, and label the motor neuron, muscle fibre, and synapse. Hypothesize how the impulse coming from the motor neuron might reach the muscle fibre (effector).

7. Observe and sketch any additional slides provided by your teacher.

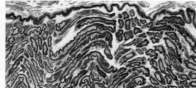
Magnification: 7 ×
1 White and grey matter

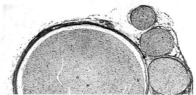
Magnification: 6.125 ×
2 Cross-section of nerve

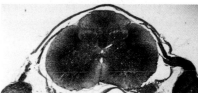
Magnification: 0.5 ×
3 Cross-section of spinal cord

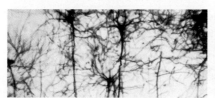
Magnification: 39 ×
4 Unmyelinated neurons

Magnification: 228 ×
5 Myelinated axons

Magnification: 28 ×
6 Neuromuscular junction

FYI
Acupuncture is a traditional Chinese medical practice in which needles are inserted at specific points on the body. Based on Western scientific thinking, it is hypothesized that the resulting stimulation of these points triggers the brain to release endorphins, neurotransmitters that ease the sensation of pain. Traditional Eastern scientific thinking explains acupuncture in terms of rebalancing the body's *chi*—its life-force energy.

the synapse. The muscle fibre cell could not repolarize and would remain in a state of excitation (contraction).

Normally, an enzyme called **cholinesterase** is released into a synapse, where it breaks down acetylcholine. Cholinesterase is one of the fastest acting enzymes. It breaks down acetylcholine so that it can be removed from the protein receptors, thus allowing the ion channels to close and the membrane to repolarize in a fraction of a second. A nerve gas called sarin destroys this function by blocking the release of cholinesterase into the neuromuscular junction. With the buildup of acetylcholine, critical muscles, such as the heart and diaphragm, enter a state of constant contraction or paralysis. Some insecticides affect insects in the same way and kill them.

There are more than 50 substances in the human body that can act as neurotransmitters. Table 11.2 lists some common neurotransmitters and their functions. The functions vary depending on where in the body the neurotransmitter acts. Several neurological disorders have been linked to neurotransmitter deficiencies or excessive production. In addition, certain drugs can alter the proper action of neurotransmitters, as described in Thought Lab 11.1.

17 Compare the excitatory and inhibitory effects of neurotransmitters on the postsynaptic membrane.

18 Compare and relate the functions of acetylcholine and cholinesterase.

Section 11.1 Summary

- The human nervous system is a complex system composed of many subsystems that all work together to maintain homeostasis in the body.
- The nervous system gathers and processes information from the external and internal environments and then relays a response to the necessary areas of the body.
- The neuron is the functional unit of the nervous system.
- There are three kinds of neurons: sensory neurons, interneurons, and motor neurons.
- Neurons allow the nervous system to relay sensory information to the brain and spinal cord for integration, and to produce a response, as needed, by the effectors.
- All cells have a membrane potential, but the neuron is unique in that it can change the potential of its membrane to generate an impulse. An impulse is

Table 11.2 Selected Neurotransmitters and Their Functions

Neurotransmitter	Function	Effects of abnormal production
dopamine	affects the brain synapses in the control of body movements; is linked to sensations of pleasure, such as eating	excessive production linked to schizophrenia, a disorder in which the individual's perception of reality is greatly distorted; inadequate production linked to Parkinson's disease, a progressive disorder that destroys neurons, causing tremors, slurred speech, and other coordination problems
serotonin	regulates temperature and sensory perception; is involved in mood control	inadequate amounts in the brain synapses linked to depression
endorphins	act as natural painkillers in synapses in the brain; also affects emotional areas of the brain	deficiency linked to an increased risk of alcoholism
norepinephrine	is used by the brain and some autonomic neurons; complements the actions of the hormone epinephrine, which readies the body to respond to danger or other stressful situations	overproduction linked to high blood pressure, anxiety, and insomnia; deficiency linked to hunger cravings and exhaustion

The Effect of Drugs on Neurons and Synapses

A drug is a non-food substance that changes the way the body functions. Most drugs, legal or illegal, affect the neurons and synapses by either promoting or decreasing the action of a neurotransmitter. Research has shown that many addictive drugs stimulate the brain's natural reward and pleasure centres, often by artificially elevating the levels of neurotransmitters, such as dopamine or endorphins. The table briefly describes the major effects of some commonly abused addictive drugs.

Procedure

1. Working with a partner, use the information in the table to create a drug information pamphlet about one of the drugs presented. If possible, research the drug further using Internet or library resources. Your information pamphlet should include

   - a detailed explanation of how the drug affects the nervous system and other body functions

   - hazards to the nervous system and the entire body from short-term and long-term use of the drug

2. Present your pamphlet to another group or to the rest of the class.

Analysis

1. Hypothesize what might make the drug you investigated addictive. Suggest a possible mechanism, based on how the drug affects the nervous system, that explains why the body could become addicted to the drug.

Extension

2. Debate the effects of drug use on society as a whole.

Effects of Selected Drugs on Human Systems

Drug	Effects on nervous system and body
nicotine	• is derived from the tobacco plant • is one of the main addictive ingredients in cigarettes and chewing tobacco, which cause cancer, respiratory problems, and other problems after long-term use • rapidly stimulates the reward centre of the brain to release dopamine, which promotes feelings of euphoria • stimulates certain areas of the body by mimicking the actions of acetylcholine, causing increased heart rate and blood pressure
marijuana	• is harvested from the flowers and leaves of certain types of *Cannabis* plant • when smoked, active ingredient (THC) interferes with synapses in the brain, including the reward centres • produces feelings of euphoria, and reduces concentration and muscle coordination
ecstasy (MDMA)	• affects neurons in the brain, causing overproduction of serotonin • in the short term, produces feelings of pleasure • can cause cardiac arrest, dangerously elevated body temperature, and rapid and permanent brain damage
cocaine	• is naturally found in leaves of *Erythroxylon coca*, a species of coca plant • targets neurons in the reward centre of the brain and prevents the re-uptake of dopamine • increases energy levels and produces feelings of euphoria • is highly addictive and can cause strokes and heart attacks
methamphetamine (meth, crystal meth)	• enters the neuron by passing directly through neuron membranes • causes excessive release of dopamine and blocks the dopamine transporter from pumping dopamine back into the transmitting neuron • increases energy levels and produces feelings of euphoria • often leads to extreme aggressiveness, delusions, and psychosis (greatly distorted perception of reality)

transmitted from one neuron to the
next through a synapse.
• Many substances, such as drugs,
painkillers, chemicals, and neurotoxins,
can interfere with the functions of
synapses and neurotransmitters.

Section 11.1 Review

1. Copy the letters A through H into your notebook.
Identify the division of the nervous system that is
represented by each letter.

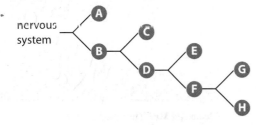

2. Analyze the following statement: "The neuron conducts
impulses in the same way as electricity moves through a
wire." Is a nerve impulse like electricity? Prepare a table
that compares a nerve impulse to the movement of an
electric current along a wire.

3. Compare the structure and functions of myelinated
neurons and unmyelinated neurons.

4. Using a diagram, explain how a neuron establishes the
resting membrane potential. What is the value of this
in mV?

5. Examine the graph below, and answer the questions
that follow.

Action Potential

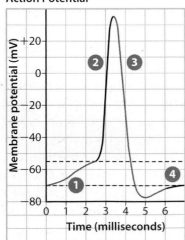

a) In your notebook, indicate the specific events that
are occurring at 1, 2, 3, and 4.

b) At which area of the graph are sodium ions rapidly
entering the neuron?

c) At which area of the graph are potassium ions
rapidly leaving the neuron?

d) At which area of the graph is the sodium ion
concentration higher outside than inside the neuron?

6. Hypothesize how overproduction of cholinesterase
might affect the body. Explain your answer.

7. Use word processing or spreadsheet software to
construct a table to compare an excitatory response
with an inhibitory response. Give an example of where
these responses are complementary in the body. **ICT**

8. Cocaine affects a synapse by blocking the re-uptake
of the neurotransmitter dopamine by the presynaptic
neurons. Therefore, the levels of dopamine continue to
build in the synapse, causing certain effects on the body.

a) Use word processing software to make a flowchart
summarizing the usual events in the transmission
of an impulse between the presynaptic and
postsynaptic neurons. **ICT**

b) Explain how cocaine interferes with neural
transmission across the synapse.

c) Describe the natural role of dopamine in the brain.

d) Formulate a hypothesis about how cocaine could be
addictive after only one use.

The Central Nervous System

Section Outcomes

In this section, you will
- **identify** the principal structures of the central nervous system
- **explain** the functions of the spinal cord and various regions of the brain
- **observe** the principal features of the mammalian brain
- **explain** how technological advances in neuroscience can provide solutions to practical problems

Key Terms

grey matter
white matter
meninges
cerebellum
medulla oblongata
pons
midbrain
thalamus
hypothalamus
cerebrum
blood-brain barrier
cerebrospinal fluid
cerebral cortex
corpus callosum
occipital lobes
temporal lobes
parietal lobes
frontal lobes
Broca's area
Wernicke's area

The central nervous system (Figure 11.20) is the structural and functional centre for the entire nervous system. The site of neural integration and processing, the central nervous system receives information from the senses, evaluates this information, and initiates outgoing responses to the body. Damage to the central nervous system can therefore affect temperament, motor control, and homeostasis. For example, the beef steer in Figure 11.21 has bovine spongiform encephalopathy (BSE), a disease that produces sponge-like holes in the brain. Also called "mad cow disease," BSE initially causes nervousness and over-sensitivity to touch. Affected animals then develop an unsteady gait and lose the ability to walk, and eventually die.

As you learned in Section 11.1, the central nervous system is composed of two types of nervous tissue: grey matter and white matter. **Grey matter** is grey because it contains mostly cell bodies, dendrites, and short, unmyelinated

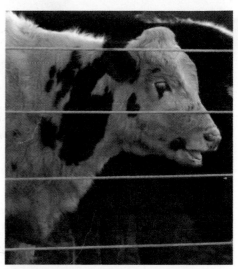

Figure 11.21 This cow has BSE, a progressive neurological disorder in cattle. Like chronic wasting disease in elk and some forms of sheep scrapie, BSE is caused by an infectious protein.

axons (nerve fibres). Grey matter is found around the outside areas of the brain and forms the H-shaped core of the spinal cord. **White matter** is white because it contains myelinated axons that run together in tracts. White matter forms the inner region of some areas of the brain, and the outer area of the spinal cord.

The Spinal Cord

The spinal cord is a column of nerve tissue that extends out of the skull from the brain, and downward through a canal within the backbone (see Figures 11.20 and 11.23 on page 386). The spinal cord is a vital communication link between the brain and the peripheral nervous system. Within the spinal cord, sensory nerves carry messages from the body to the brain for interpretation, and motor nerves relay messages from the brain to the effectors. The spinal cord is also the primary reflex centre, coordinating rapidly incoming and outgoing neural information.

A cross section of the spinal cord reveals both white matter and grey matter (Figure 11.22 on page 386). The outer

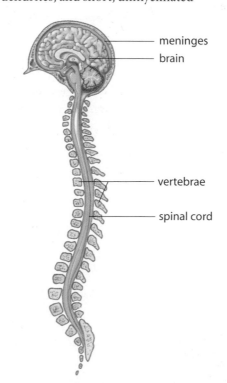

meninges
brain

vertebrae

spinal cord

Figure 11.20 The central nervous system

Figure 11.22 **(A)** Cross section of human brain showing right and left side. **(B)** Cross section through human spinal cord. The central nervous system is composed of both white matter (W) and grey matter (G).

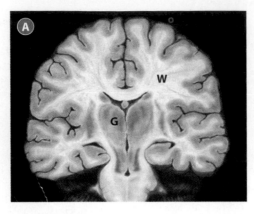

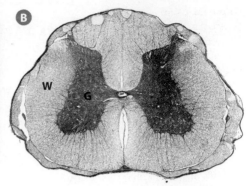

white matter consists of myelinated nerve fibres. The butterfly-shaped core is made up of grey matter, which contains unmyelinated neurons as well as the cell bodies and dendrites of many spinal neurons.

The delicate tissues of the spinal cord are protected by cerebrospinal fluid, soft tissue layers, and the spinal column, a series of backbones (vertebrae). Injury to the spinal column can also damage the spinal cord, resulting in paralysis.

The Brain

The ancient Egyptians were among the first neuroscientists, and were the first known civilization with a written word for "brain." The Greek philosopher

Figure 11.23 The spinal cord is protected by the meninges and the bony vertebrae.

spinal cord

spinal nerve

vertebra

intervertebral disk

A

dorsal horn
ventral horn
dorsal-root ganglion

Dorsal

white matter
grey matter
central canal

spinal nerve

dorsal root
ventral root

B

Ventral

meninges

Aristotle (384–322 B.C.E.) knew that directly touching the brain did not cause any sensation to the owner. Like many other anatomists through the centuries, Aristotle concluded that the heart must therefore be in control of human intelligence, sensations, and body functions.

It has only been in the last two centuries that researchers have begun to unravel the intricate workings of the human brain. Scientists have discovered the brain's central role in maintaining homeostasis and have identified the brain as the centre for intelligence, consciousness, and emotion. Yet, in many ways, researchers are just beginning to understand the relationship between the brain's structures and functions. Despite its relatively small size, scientists estimate that there are more neurons in the human brain than stars in the Milky Way Galaxy.

As shown in Figure 11.24, the brain can be subdivided into three general regions: the hindbrain, the midbrain, and the forebrain.

Despite its central importance, the brain is fragile and has a gelatin-like consistency. The skull, however, forms a protective bony armour around the brain. In addition, the **meninges**, three layers of tough, elastic tissue within the skull and spinal column, directly enclose the brain and spinal cord (Figure 11.25 on page 388). One way to visualize the brain, meninges, and skull is to think of a peanut, wrapped in its red skin, and inside its shell.

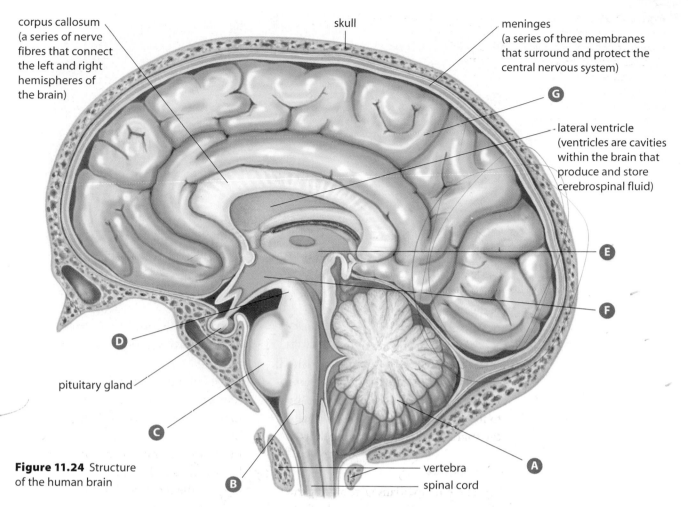

corpus callosum
(a series of nerve fibres that connect the left and right hemispheres of the brain)

skull

meninges
(a series of three membranes that surround and protect the central nervous system)

G

lateral ventricle
(ventricles are cavities within the brain that produce and store cerebrospinal fluid)

E

F

pituitary gland

D

C

B

vertebra

spinal cord

A

Figure 11.24 Structure of the human brain

HINDBRAIN

A The **cerebellum** is a walnut-shaped structure located below (inferior to) and largely behind (posterior to) the cerebrum, described below. The word *cerebellum* comes from the Latin word for "little brain." This part of the brain is involved in the unconscious coordination of posture, reflexes, and body movements, as well as fine, voluntary motor skills, such as those used to hit a tennis ball, ride a bicycle, or write. The cerebellum receives information from specialized sensors, called proprioceptors, located within skeletal muscles and joints.

B The **medulla oblongata** sits at the base of the brainstem, where it connects the brain with the spinal cord. The medulla oblongata contains centres that control automatic, involuntary responses, such as heart rate, constriction or dilation of blood vessels to control blood pressure, and the rate and depth of breathing, swallowing, and coughing.

C The **pons** is found above (superior to) and in front of (anterior to) the medulla oblongata in the brainstem. The pons serves as a relay centre between the neurons of the right and left halves of the cerebrum, the cerebellum, and the rest of the brain.

D The **MIDBRAIN** is found above the pons in the brainstem. It relays visual and auditory information between areas of the hindbrain and forebrain. As well, it plays an important role in eye movement and control of skeletal muscles.

FOREBRAIN

E The **thalamus** sits at the base of the forebrain. It consists of neurons that provide connections between various parts of the brain. These connections are mainly between the forebrain and hindbrain, and between areas of the sensory system (except for the sense of smell) and cerebellum. The thalamus is often referred to as "the great relay station of the brain."

F The **hypothalamus**, which lies just below the thalamus, helps to regulate the body's internal environment, as well as certain aspects of behaviour. The hypothalamus contains neurons that control blood pressure, heart rate, body temperature, and basic drives (such as thirst and hunger) and emotions (such as fear, rage, and pleasure). Brain damage or a tumour that affects the hypothalamus can cause a person to display unusual, even violent behaviour. The hypothalamus is also a major link between the nervous and endocrine (hormone) systems (which you will study in Chapter 13). The hypothalamus coordinates the actions of the pituitary gland, by producing and regulating the release of certain hormones.

G The **cerebrum** is the largest part of the brain and accounts for more than four fifths of the total weight of the brain. The cerebrum is divided into right and left cerebral hemispheres, which contain the centres for intellect, memory, consciousness, and language; it interprets and controls the response to sensory information.

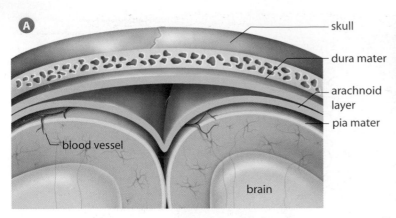

A

skull
dura mater
arachnoid layer
pia mater
blood vessel
brain

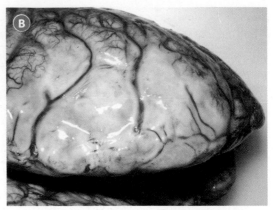

B

Figure 11.25 (A) Three layers of tissue, called the meninges, surround and protect the brain and spinal cord. **(B)** The dark brown-yellow patches on the meninges reveal a meningitis infection. Meningitis, or inflammation of the meninges, is caused by a bacterial or viral infection that can spread to underlying brain tissue. Meningitis can be life threatening and is diagnosed by examining a sample of the fluid surrounding the brain and spinal cord.

The meninges protect the central nervous system by preventing the direct circulation of blood through the cells of the brain and spinal cord. This separation of the blood and central nervous system is called the **blood-brain barrier** (Figure 11.26). Scientists discovered this barrier when they injected blue dye into the bloodstream of an animal and all the body tissues turned blue except for the brain and spinal cord. The brain, however, requires a constant supply of nutrients and oxygen. In fact, the brain, which comprises only 2 percent of the body's total weight, uses at least 20 percent of the body's oxygen and energy supplies. If the oxygen supply to the brain is disrupted for even a few minutes, massive damage can occur in the brain. For example, a stroke occurs when arteries that supply the brain with blood are blocked.

The blood-brain barrier both protects the brain and supplies the brain with nutrients and oxygen. The blood capillaries that lead to the brain are made up of tightly fused epithelial cells. Thus, the capillary walls form a barrier that blocks many toxins and infectious agents. Some substances, such as glucose and oxygen, can still pass through the barrier by special transport mechanisms. Other, lipid-soluble substances, are able to pass directly through the lipid bilayer of the cell membrane. This is why caffeine, nicotine, alcohol, heroin, and other lipid-soluble substances have such rapid effects on brain function. Why might researchers have difficulty treating neurological disorders with drugs that are not lipid soluble?

Circulating throughout the spaces, or ventricles, within the brain and spinal cord is the **cerebrospinal fluid**. The total volume of cerebrospinal fluid in an adult human is about 150 mL at any one time. The fluid is replaced about four times each day, and the total amount of fluid

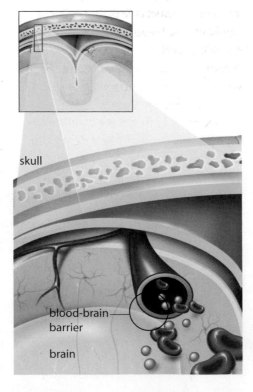

skull
blood-brain barrier
brain

Figure 11.26 The blood-brain barrier. Only certain substances can pass through the tight seal formed by the blood-brain barrier.

produced each day is about 500 mL. The cerebrospinal fluid transports hormones, white blood cells, and nutrients across the blood-brain barrier for cells of the brain and spinal cord. It also circulates between two layers of the meninges, the arachnoid and pia mater, and therefore acts as a shock absorber to cushion the brain.

19 Identify the main structures of the central nervous system, and describe its general functions.

20 Explain how the blood-brain barrier and the cerebrospinal fluid protect the brain and spinal cord.

21 Identify five homeostatic functions of the brain.

22 Identify the major structures in the hindbrain, midbrain, and forebrain, and the functions of these structures.

The Structure and Function of the Cerebrum

Each half of the cerebrum consists of an internal mass of white matter and a thin, outer covering of grey matter, called the **cerebral cortex**. Compared to a falcon with its keen eyesight or a dog with its sense of smell, humans lack many sensory capabilities. Due to the evolution of the cerebral cortex, however, humans are considered to have the most sophisticated intellect and behaviour of all animals. The cerebral cortex is responsible for language, memory, personality, vision, conscious thought, and other activities that are associated with thinking and feeling. The cerebral cortex is about 5 mm thick and, as shown in Figure 11.27, is highly convoluted. This allows it to fit a high concentration of grey matter within the confines of the skull. Relative to a smooth surface, the convolutions and fissures greatly increase the surface area, so that the cerebral cortex covers about 0.5 m², or about the area of an open newspaper.

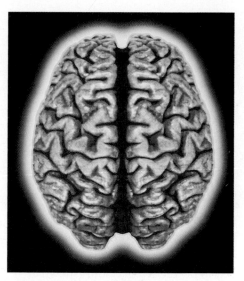

Figure 11.27 The human cerebrum. What are the functions of the right and left sides? Why are there so many folds along the surface of the cerebrum?

The right and left halves of the cerebrum are called the cerebral hemispheres. They are linked by a bundle of white matter called the **corpus callosum**. The corpus callosum sends messages from one cerebral hemisphere to the other, telling each half of the brain what the other half is doing. Surgical isolation of the hemispheres is sometimes used to treat epilepsy, a condition that causes uncontrollable seizures. Scientists think that epilepsy can be caused by an overload of neurological electrical activities, so the corpus callosum is cut to prevent the spread of the epileptic seizures from one hemisphere to the other.

Research indicates that, while every cognitive function contains right-brain and left-brain components, some functions seem to have a dominant hemisphere. In general, the right-brain, or right cerebral hemisphere, is associated with holistic and intuitive thinking, visual-spatial skills, and artistic abilities. The left-brain, or left cerebral hemisphere, is linked to segmental, sequential, and logical ways of thinking, and to linguistic and mathematical skills. This is why people who are right-brain dominant process and learn information differently from people who are left-

BiologyFile

Try This
Take two eggs and two plastic containers that are just large enough to contain the eggs. Fill one of the containers with water, and place one egg inside. Put the other egg in the other container, without water. Tightly close the lid of each container, and shake the containers. Which egg broke? How does this model demonstrate the function of the cerebrospinal fluid?

BiologyFile

FYI
In the 1800s, several scientists promoted the common misconception that humans use only 10 percent of their brains. Researchers now know that the destruction of even small areas of the brain can have devastating effects on behaviour and physiology. On the other hand, sometimes a different part of the brain is able to compensate for, or take over, the functions of the injured part. This can occur when someone has a stroke that damages the parts of the brain that are predominantly involved in speech. Other, usually less active parts may take over the speech functions.

YELLOW	BLUE	ORANGE
BLACK	RED	GREEN
PURPLE	YELLOW	RED
ORANGE	GREEN	BLACK
BLUE	RED	PURPLE
GREEN	BLUE	ORANGE

Figure 11.28 The Stroop effect. The right brain identifies the colour, while the left brain insists on reading the word.

brain dominant. One way to illustrate the difference between right-brain and left-brain processing is the Stroop effect. Try to say the actual colours shown in Figure 11.28, rather than the words themselves. This is difficult because, as one theory suggests, one side of the brain may dominate in word recognition, while the other side may dominate in colour recognition. In other words, this leads to a right-left brain conflict!

The Cerebral Cortex Consists of Four Pairs of Functional Lobes

Figure 11.29 The cerebral cortex is divided into four pairs of lobes: frontal, temporal, parietal, and occipital.

Figure 11.29 shows the division of each hemisphere of the cerebral cortex into four pairs of lobes. Each pair of lobes is associated with a different function.

The **occipital lobes** receive and analyze visual information. If the occipital lobes are stimulated by surgery or trauma, the individual will see light. The occipital lobes are also needed for recognition of what is being seen. Damage to the occipital lobes can result in a person being able to see objects, but not able to recognize them.

The **temporal lobes** share in the processing of visual information, although their main function is auditory reception. These lobes are also linked to understanding speech and retrieving visual and verbal memories.

The **parietal lobes** receive and process sensory information from the skin. The primary sensory areas extend in a band from the right to left side of the cerebrum. The proportion of a parietal lobe devoted to a particular part of the body is related to the importance of sensory information for this part of the body. The highest concentrations of sensory receptors occur in the face, hands, and genitals, making these areas of the body highly sensitive. The parietal lobes also help to process information about the body's position and orientation.

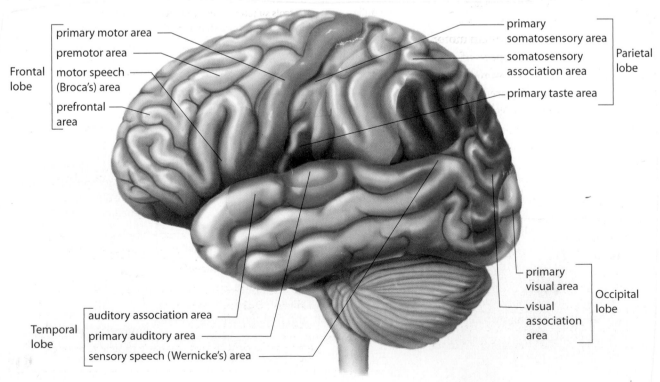

Frontal lobe
- primary motor area
- premotor area
- motor speech (Broca's) area
- prefrontal area

Parietal lobe
- primary somatosensory area
- somatosensory association area
- primary taste area

Temporal lobe
- auditory association area
- primary auditory area
- sensory speech (Wernicke's) area

Occipital lobe
- primary visual area
- visual association area

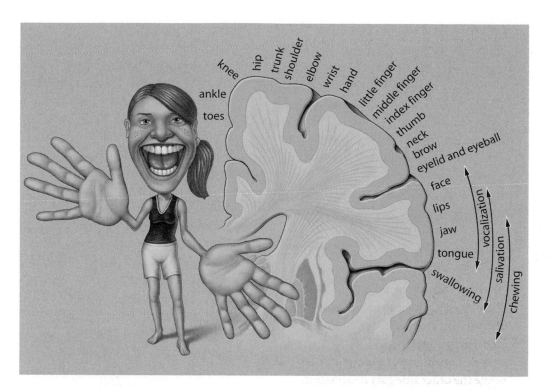

Figure 11.30 Based on this map of the motor cortex, which areas of the body have the greatest muscle control?

The **frontal lobes** are named for their location at the front of the cerebrum. This is the part of the head that some people may hit in jest with the palm of their hand when they finally remember something! The frontal lobes integrate information from other parts of the brain and control reasoning, critical thinking, memory, and personality. The Broca's area of the frontal lobes is associated with language use.

The frontal lobes also contain motor areas that control various aspects of precise, voluntary motor movement, such as playing a piano. Figure 11.29 identified the primary motor area in the frontal lobes of the cerebrum. Similar to the sensory areas in the parietal lobes, the proportion of motor area in the frontal lobes devoted to a particular part of the body correlates with the degree of complexity of movement that body structure can make. The stylized illustration in Figure 11.30 shows the disproportionate size of certain areas of the body in relation to the amount of motor area devoted to them. The nerves leading from the right and left frontal lobes cross over in the brainstem, so that each side of the brain controls muscles on the opposite side of the body.

Table 11.3 summarizes the functions of the principal structures in the brain.

Table 11.3 Major Structures and Functions of the Human Brain

Structure	Major functions
Hindbrain	
cerebellum	controls muscle coordination and balance
medulla oblongata	controls subconscious activities, such as heart rate, blood pressure, breathing, swallowing, and vomiting
pons	relays information between the cerebellum and cerebral cortex
Midbrain	receives specific sensory input; connects the hindbrain to the forebrain
Forebrain	
thalamus	connects various parts of the brain; relays information from the senses
hypothalamus	regulates the pituitary gland, heart rate, blood pressure, and temperature; controls drives such as hunger, thirst, and sexual desire
Cerebrum	
frontal lobes	associated with conscious thought, intelligence, memory, and personality; control voluntary muscle movements
temporal lobes	involved in auditory reception
parietal lobes	receive sensory information from the skin, and process information about body position
occipital lobes	process visual information
corpus callosum	connects the right and left cerebral hemispheres through nerve tracts

Biology File

Try This
While sitting at your desk, lift your right foot off the floor and make clockwise circles. While doing this, draw the number 6 in the air with your right hand. Your foot should change direction! Why does this happen?

Broca's Area and Wernicke's Area

The process of speech involves several areas of the cerebrum. Two important areas are on the left side of the cerebral cortex: **Broca's area** and **Wernicke's area** (see Figure 11.29). Broca's area coordinates the muscles for speaking and translates thought into speech. Damage to this area results in an inability to speak. It does not, however, affect the understanding of language. Wernicke's area stores the information involved in language comprehension. The ability to utter words is not affected if this area is damaged, but the words make little sense.

23. Identify the four lobes of the cerebrum, and describe the function of each.
24. Describe the primary areas of the brain that are responsible for the fine motor control of the muscles, as well as the area that processes sensory information from the skin.
25. Compare the locations and functions of Broca's area and Wernicke's area in the brain.

Mapping Brain Functions

Scientists first learned about brain functions by studying the brains of people with brain injuries or diseases. For example, injured soldiers would sometimes have damage to certain areas of the brain, but still survive. Researchers could then link the injured area of the brain to loss of functions in other areas of the body. In 1848, an accidental explosion at a railway site drove a metal bar through the frontal lobes of railway worker, Phineas Gage (Figure 11.31). Although he survived the accident, he experienced a type of personality change that scientists have now come to associate with frontal lobe injuries. Once considered reasonable and conscientious, Phineas Gage was described after the accident as "thoughtless, irresponsible, and fitful."

Because the brain itself does not contain any pain receptors, neurosurgeons are able to probe areas of the brain while people are conscious. This provides useful feedback about the functions of different areas of the brain. Canadian Nobel prize recipient Wilder Penfield (1891–1976) contributed greatly to our knowledge of the sensory and motor areas of the brain. Penfield, who operated on people with epilepsy, applied electric currents to the surface of their brains in order to find the problem areas. Since the people were awake during the operations, they could tell Penfield what they were experiencing. Probing different areas triggered different sensations and body movements. From this information, Penfield was able to map the sensory and motor areas of the cerebral cortex. As well, Penfield probed certain areas of the cerebral cortex that triggered whole memory sequences. For one person, Penfield triggered a familiar song that sounded so clear the person thought it was being played in the operating room. When Penfield stopped stimulating this area of the brain, the music ceased immediately.

Imaging Techniques Used to Study the Brain

Modern imaging techniques provide non-invasive ways for researchers to

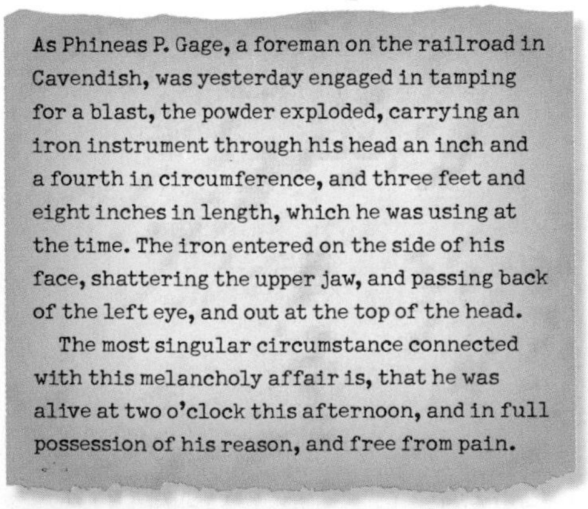
As Phineas P. Gage, a foreman on the railroad in Cavendish, was yesterday engaged in tamping for a blast, the powder exploded, carrying an iron instrument through his head an inch and a fourth in circumference, and three feet and eight inches in length, which he was using at the time. The iron entered on the side of his face, shattering the upper jaw, and passing back of the left eye, and out at the top of the head.

The most singular circumstance connected with this melancholy affair is, that he was alive at two o'clock this afternoon, and in full possession of his reason, and free from pain.

Figure 11.31 The news report of Phineas Gage's accident first appeared in the *Free Soil Union* (Ludlow, Vermont) on September 14, 1848.

Biology File

Web Link
Anatomy students often use computer simulations to complete animal dissections. You can try out a virtual sheep brain dissection online. What are some benefits and drawbacks to using virtual dissections for learning?

www.albertabiology.ca
WWW

The Brain

The proportions of the areas of the brain differ in different mammals, but the basic locations of the functional areas are similar. In this investigation, you will use models, photographs, and a mammalian brain to learn about the principal structural areas of the brain and their functions. As an alternative to doing the dissection, the photographs in this investigation, or a video or web dissection, could be used.

Question

What are the principal structures of the brain, and what are their functions?

Safety Precautions

- Use caution when handling sharp instruments.
- Wash your hands well when finished the dissection.
- Disinfect the equipment and area when finished.

Materials

- preserved sheep brain
- paper towel
- 10 percent bleach solution (to clean the dissecting tray)
- dissecting tray
- dissecting kit

Part 1: Lateral View—Whole Brain

Procedure

1. Obtain a sheep brain from your teacher. Follow your teacher's instructions for rinsing the brain. Then place the brain in the dissecting tray.

2. Examine photograph A, showing a lateral view of the sheep brain. Identify the frontal, parietal, temporal, and occipital lobes of the cerebrum.

3. If possible, examine the outer surface (dura mater) of the brain. Notice the convolutions and fissures on the outer surface. Also notice that the cerebrum is divided into a right side and a left side.

4. Sketch and label the outer surface of the brain.

Analysis

1. Make a table to record the functions of the structures you labelled in your diagram.

2. In humans, the left and right cerebral hemispheres of the brain are associated with different dominant functions. Describe these differences.

Part 2: Lateral View—Cross-Section

Procedure

1. Examine photograph B, showing a cross-section of the sheep brain.

2. Make a gentle incision through the corpus callosum of the sheep brain to separate the right and left hemispheres. Then separate the rest of the brain by cutting through the centre of the mid and hind parts.

3. Using photograph B as a guide, identify, sketch, and label the following structures: spinal cord, cerebellum, medulla oblongata, pons, midbrain, thalamus, hypothalamus, pituitary gland, corpus callosum, and cerebrum. Try to identify the small olfactory bulbs (connected to smell receptors) on the underside of the frontal lobes, as well.

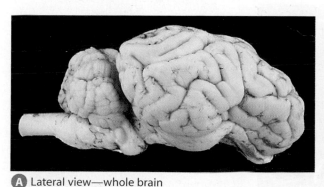

A Lateral view—whole brain

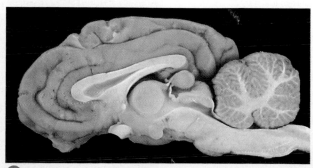

B Lateral view—cross-section

continued on next page

4. Follow your teacher's instructions to dispose of the sheep brain and wash the dissecting tray.

Analysis

1. Examine your diagram of the cross-section of the dissected brain. Make a table to record the functions of the structures you labelled in your diagram.

Conclusion

2. Compare the sheep brain with the human brain shown in Figure 11.29. What similarities and differences can you identify?

Extension

3. With a partner, build a model of the human brain and present it to the class. Include all the key structures and functions on your model.

---

see inside an active, human brain. Fundamental discoveries in physics have led to the development of positron-emission tomography (PET) and magnetic resonance imaging (MRI). These two techniques allow researchers to study the brain and help physicians diagnose brain diseases.

PET is based on the fact that more active areas of the brain have higher energy demands. A person receives an injection of radioactively-labelled glucose, and a scanner monitors glucose consumption in the person's brain. Different colours represent different activity levels in the brain (Figure 11.32). A PET scan can be used to diagnose conditions such as a stroke or Alzheimer's disease, in which the deterioration of the brain leads to memory loss and confusion, and eventual lack of conscious movement.

MRI can produce very clear and detailed images of brain structure (Figure 11.33). A giant magnet surrounds the person's head, and changes in the direction of the magnetic field induce hydrogen atoms in the brain to emit radio signals. These signals can then be detected, translated, and displayed as a structural or functional image. MRI can also be used to identify various brain disorders, such as brain tumours. Figure 11.33 also shows an MRI image of a human brain affected by Creutzfeldt-Jakob disease. This disease, like BSE, destroys the brain tissue, making it sponge-like.

• • •

26 Describe how early researchers studied brain structure and function.

27 Compare the technologies of MRI and PET for studying the brain.

• • •

Section 11.2 Summary

- The regulation centre for the nervous system is the central nervous system, which consists of the brain and spinal cord.
- The brain and spinal cord are protected by the cerebrospinal fluid, the meninges, and the skull and spinal column (vertebrae).
- The brain and spinal cord themselves are composed of myelinated neurons (white matter) and unmyelinated neurons (grey matter).
- The hindbrain is composed of the cerebellum (involved in controlling body movements), medulla oblongata (controls many involuntary responses), and pons (relay station between different parts of brain).
- The midbrain is a part of the brain stem.

Figure 11.32 This PET scan shows a cross section of the cerebrum, revealing the activity levels in different areas when the brain is performing certain tasks. Red, orange, and yellow indicate areas of high, medium, and low activity, respectively. What lobes of the cerebral cortex are active in the brain shown here?

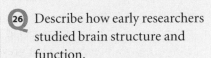
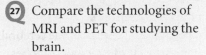

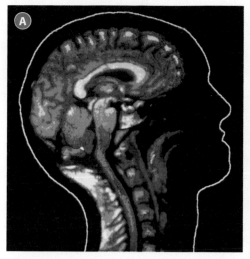

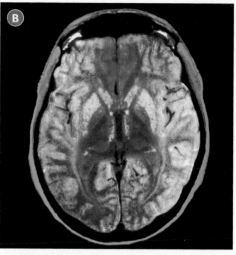

Figure 11.33 **(A)** A detailed magnetic resonance imaging (MRI) of a healthy brain **(B)** An MRI image of the brain of a person with Creutzfeldt-Jakob's disease. The affected areas are shown at the centre in red. People with Creutzfeldt-Jakob's disease experience memory loss, emotional instability (including inappropriate outbursts), and unsteadiness. These symptoms progress to marked weakness, dementia, and death, often within a year of the onset of the symptoms.

- The forebrain includes the thalamus and hypothalamus, involved in sensing the external and internal environment, as well as the cerebrum.
- The outer layer of the cerebrum, called the cerebral cortex, is composed of grey matter, and is thought to be the source of human intellect.
- The right and left halves of the cerebral cortex are made of four pairs of lobes, each of which is associated with particular functions: frontal lobes (conscious thought and movements, speech), parietal lobes (touch, taste), temporal lobes (hearing and speech), and occipital lobes (vision).
- MRI and PET scans are non-invasive tools that can be used to map human brain function and screen for diseases.

Section 11.2 Review

1. Explain why the brain has elevated requirements for nutrients and oxygen.

2. Describe the three main tissues that support and protect the central nervous system.

3. Explain why a physician takes a sample of cerebrospinal fluid to determine if a person has meningitis.

4. The letters on the diagram indicate possible areas of brain damage. In table format, list the possible areas of brain damage (A to G), and describe the functional problems that might result from damage in each area.

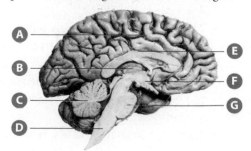

5. Use graphics software to sketch the cerebral cortex. Use it to identify the lobe that would be stimulated in each situation, and explain why. **ICT**

  a) Seeing this question.

  b) Thinking about this question.

  c) Hearing this question read to you by someone else.

  d) Reading this question to someone else.

  e) Reading this question using Braille.

6. A stroke has caused damage to certain areas of a person's brain. Upon examination, a doctor notices that the person has difficulty understanding speech and the left side of the body is paralyzed. Identify the specific areas of the brain that are damaged, and explain how this damage might cause the symptoms.

7. Explain how MRI and PET scans can be used to improve our understanding of human brain function.

The Peripheral Nervous System

Section Outcomes

In this section, you will
- **identify** the principal components of the peripheral nervous system
- **explain** the role of the peripheral nervous system in regulating the somatic (voluntary) and autonomic (involuntary) systems
- **compare** the functions of the sympathetic division and the parasympathetic division of the autonomic nervous system

Key Terms

somatic system
autonomic system
sympathetic nervous system
norepinephrine
parasympathetic nervous system

Figure 11.34 The peripheral nervous system is essential for various activities, such as catching a football. What types of motor neurons might be activated in the football player shown here?

As the football player in Figure 11.34 lunges for the ball, sensory nerves enable him to see the ball, feel its texture, hear the roar of the crowd, and gather information about the positions of his muscles and joints. Motor nerves enable the player to maneuver the ball and break free from the defender, and they increase his heart and breathing rates. The peripheral nervous system consists of nerves that link the brain and spinal cord to the rest of the body, including the senses, muscles, glands, and internal organs. Sensory neurons carry information from all parts of the body to the central nervous system, and motor neurons carry information from the central nervous system to the effectors.

The two main divisions of the peripheral nervous systems are the somatic system and the autonomic system.

The Somatic System

The **somatic system** is largely under voluntary control, and its neurons service the head, trunk, and limbs. Its sensory neurons carry information about the external environment inward, from the receptors in the skin, tendons, and skeletal muscles. Its motor neurons carry information to the skeletal muscles. Your decision to turn this page in order to continue reading exemplifies the action of the somatic motor nerves.

The somatic system includes 12 pairs of cranial nerves and 31 pairs of spinal nerves, all of which are myelinated. The cranial nerves are largely associated with functions in the head, neck, and face. An exception is the vagus nerve, which connects to many internal organs, including the heart, lung, bronchi, digestive tract, liver, and pancreas.

Figure 11.35 shows the basic divisions of the spinal nerves that emerge from each side of the spinal cord. Each spinal nerve contains both sensory and motor neurons, which service the area of the body where they are found. For example, thoracic nerves control the muscles of the rib cage.

28 What are the major structures involved in the somatic system?

29 What role does the somatic system play in the functioning of the body?

The Autonomic System

Imagine yourself in a stressful situation. Which systems of your body might be heightened? Which systems might be suppressed? How would these systems return to their initial states? Your internal reactions to the situation would be controlled by a division of the peripheral nervous system, called the **autonomic system**. In contrast to the somatic system, the autonomic system is under automatic, or *in*voluntary control. Its nerves either stimulate or inhibit the glands or the cardiac or smooth muscle. The autonomic system maintains homeostasis by adjusting the body to variations in the external and internal environments.

The hypothalamus and medulla oblongata control the autonomic system, which has neurons that are bundled together with somatic system neurons in the cranial and spinal nerves. The sympathetic and parasympathetic divisions of the autonomic system carry information to the effectors. In general, these two divisions have opposing functions (Figure 11.36 on page 398).

The **sympathetic nervous system** is typically activated in stressful situations and is often referred to as the *fight-or-flight* response. The sympathetic neurons release a neurotransmitter called **norepinephrine**, which has an excitatory effect on its target muscles. As well, the sympathetic nerves trigger the adrenal glands to release epinephrine and norepinephrine, both of which also function as hormones that activate the stress response. At the same time, the sympathetic nervous system inhibits some areas of the body. For example, in order to run from danger, the skeletal muscles need a boost of energy. Therefore, blood pressure increases and the heart beats faster, while digestion slows down and the sphincter controlling the bladder constricts. Some of these physiological changes in response to stress are detectable by lie detectors, or polygraphs. Polygraphs monitor changes in heart rate, blood pressure, breathing rate, and

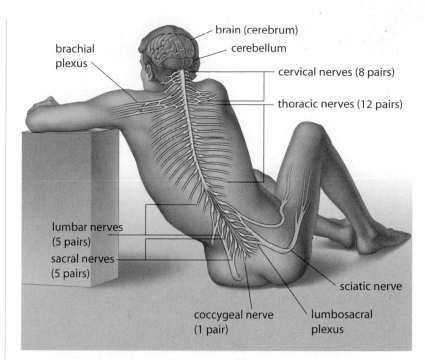

the sweatiness of palms, all of which tend to increase if someone is telling a lie (Figure 11.37 on page 399).

The **parasympathetic nervous system** is activated when the body is calm and at rest. It acts to restore and conserve energy. Sometimes referred to as the *rest-and-digest* response, the parasympathetic nervous system slows the heart rate, reduces the blood pressure, promotes the digestion of food, and stimulates the reproductive organs by dilating blood vessels to the genitals. The parasympathetic system uses a neurotransmitter called acetylcholine to control organ responses.

The two branches of the autonomic system are much like the gas pedal and brake pedal of a car. At a given instant, high levels of sympathetic stimulation might cause the heart to beat faster, while parasympathetic signals would counter this effect and bring the heart rate back down. Depending on the situation and organs involved, the sympathetic and parasympathetic systems work in opposition to each other in order to maintain homeostasis.

Certain drugs can act as either stimulants or depressants by directly affecting the sympathetic and parasympathetic nervous systems.

Figure 11.35 The spinal nerves are named for the region of the body where they are located: cervical, thoracic, lumbar, and sacral.

Figure labels: brachial plexus; brain (cerebrum); cerebellum; cervical nerves (8 pairs); thoracic nerves (12 pairs); lumbar nerves (5 pairs); sacral nerves (5 pairs); sciatic nerve; coccygeal nerve (1 pair); lumbosacral plexus

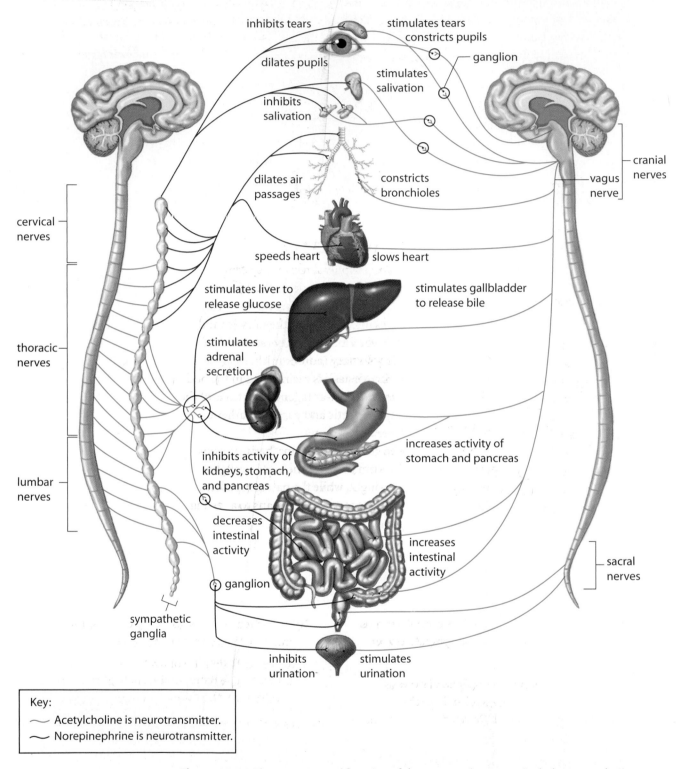

Sympathetic division

Parasympathetic division

inhibits tears

stimulates tears
constricts pupils

dilates pupils

ganglion

stimulates
salivation

inhibits
salivation

cranial
nerves

dilates air
passages

constricts
bronchioles

vagus
nerve

cervical
nerves

speeds heart

slows heart

stimulates liver to
release glucose

stimulates gallbladder
to release bile

thoracic
nerves

stimulates
adrenal
secretion

inhibits activity of
kidneys, stomach,
and pancreas

increases activity of
stomach and pancreas

lumbar
nerves

decreases
intestinal
activity

increases
intestinal
activity

ganglion

sacral
nerves

sympathetic
ganglia

inhibits
urination

stimulates
urination

Key:

⁓ Acetylcholine is neurotransmitter.

⁓ Norepinephrine is neurotransmitter.

Figure 11.36 The structure and function of the autonomic system: Both the sympathetic and parasympathetic nervous systems regulate the same organs, but with opposing effects.

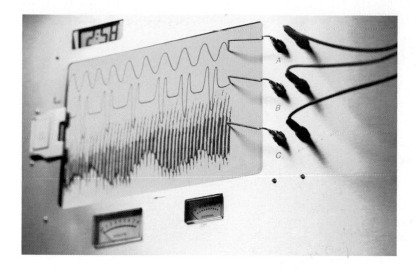

Figure 11.37 A polygraph. It can detect some of the physiological changes caused by the sympathetic nervous system when placed in a stressful situation. A racing heart and sweaty palms can be caused by many different factors, however, which is why polygraphs are not totally reliable.

Caffeine, for example, is a commonly used stimulant that causes the sympathetic nervous system to increase the heart rate and blood pressure.

• • •

30 What type of motor neurons are involved in the autonomic nervous system?

31 What generally triggers the sympathetic nervous system, and what are its effects on the body?

32 What generally triggers the parasympathetic nervous system, and what are its effects on the body?

• • •

Section 11.3 Summary

- The peripheral nervous system contains components that gather sensory information and then relay this information to the muscles and glands for a voluntary (somatic) or involuntary (autonomic) response.
- Homeostasis is maintained in the body by the often-antagonistic actions of the sympathetic and parasympathetic nervous systems.
- In general, the sympathetic nervous system prepares the body for fight-or-flight, while the parasympathetic system returns the organs to a resting state.

Section 11.3 | **Review**

1. Compare the general functions of the central nervous system with the functions of the peripheral nervous system.

2. Identify which division of the peripheral nervous system is under voluntary control and which division is under involuntary control. Compare the functions of these two divisions.

3. Imagine that you are hiking in the mountains one afternoon with friends. As you turn a corner, you come across a mother bear and her cubs standing in the middle of the trail.

   a) Identify the specific division of the nervous system that is responsible for the body's response to this situation.

   b) Describe at least six physiological responses you might have upon seeing the bears.

   c) Indicate the division of the nervous system that is responsible for returning the body back to equilibrium after the event is over.

4. Use word processing software to construct a three-column table. Use the following headings: Body structures, Sympathetic stimulation effect, and Parasympathetic stimulation effect. In the first column, list these structures: eyes, salivary glands, bronchioles, heart, liver, adrenal glands, kidneys, stomach, pancreas, intestines, and bladder. Then complete the rest of the table. **ICT**

5. Compare how stimulants and depressants affect the nervous system. Name a common stimulant.

Neurological Disorders

Humans are not the only members of the animal kingdom that can become victims of neurological and neuromuscular disorders. Symptoms may include seizures, limb weakness or paralysis, balance disorders, vision problems, head, neck or back pain, and swallowing difficulties. Increasing numbers of veterinary practices are dedicated solely to the diagnosis and treatment of neurological disorders. Our love and respect for pets and working and farm animals has spawned a growing industry devoted to implementing unique solutions for specific species and breeds.

Unique Solutions

Custom wheelchairs for pets were first manufactured about thirty years ago. They were crude and unwieldy, unlike today's streamlined designs that use aluminium tubing, lightweight plastic, neoprene supports, and light pneumatic wheels. 'Doggon' Wheels' has made wheelchairs for pets who are less than a kg to over 100 kg, including cats, rabbits, goats, gerbils, rats, ferrets, pot-bellied pigs, lemurs, and opossums. The majority of pets readily accept the freedom a wheelchair provides. It usually takes only a few days for them to adjust. In addition to wheelchairs, many other devices help those disabled by neurological and neuromuscular disorders.

Harnesses, which fit under an animal and have handles on each end for owners to grasp, provide support for either its front, back end, or middle. Slings and life jackets are used as flotation devices for aqua therapy rehabilitation and for building leg strength. Ramps greatly assist disabled animals in going up or down stairs, getting onto furniture, or into vehicles.

Some potential causes of limb weakness/paralysis include:
- spinal cord diseases (e.g. herniated intervertebral disks, tumours);
- peripheral nerve diseases (e.g. inflammation, degeneration); and
- neuromuscular diseases (e.g. muscle inflammation, metabolic or endocrine disorders).

Pain in the limbs may also be attributed to nerve root or peripheral nerve inflammation or tumours. Back and neck pain may be caused by:
- herniated disks,
- vertebral infections or tumours,
- fractured vertebra,
- arthritis, and/or
- neuritis (nerve root inflammation).

Neuromuscular Diseases in Horses

Whether horses are used for work, racing performance, riding pleasure, or are simply running wild, effective movement defines their existence. At the Neuromuscular Disease Laboratory at the University of California-Davis Center for Equine Health, veterinarians study, define, and diagnose equine neuromuscular diseases, which have been poorly understood and in many cases not yet identified. The two most commonly diagnosed to date are cervical vertebral malformation and equine protozoal myeloencephalitis. The new Equine Performance Laboratory at UC Davis houses two motorized equine treadmills for evaluating performance problems and implementing new therapeutic approaches for treating them. These treadmills are among the most sophisticated in the world, allowing horses to run uphill, downhill, or on the level and reach racing speeds of over 60 km/h. Because therapeutic options cannot be considered until an accurate definition and diagnosis is made, this research is critical.

• • •

1. Hold a debate on the following topic: It is a waste of time and money to provide adaptive devices for pets, and working and farm animals when people around the world are in need of help.

2. How could research on neuromuscular diseases in horses provide insight into human health?

3. Neurological disorders can also lead to blindness and deafness. Research to find out what adaptive devices and strategies can be used to help blind or deaf pets.

4. Imagine your pet is unable to use its back legs because of a neurological disorder. Find out the cost of the various adaptive devices required for it to have a continued happy life.

The nervous system plays a key role in maintaining homeostasis in the body. The functional unit of the nervous system is the neuron. This cell is specialized to transmit neural information throughout the nervous system. Bundles of neurons are called nerves.

A neuron can generate a resting membrane potential, which establishes a positive ion charge outside and a negative charge inside the resting neuron. The potential is due to a difference in charge across the membrane. If a stimulus causes sufficient depolarization to reach the threshold potential of the membrane, then an action potential will be sent along the length of the axon in an all-or-none response. The neuron must repolarize before another impulse can be sent.

Myelinated neurons make up the white matter of the human nervous system. Their axons are covered with a myelin sheath. The myelination allows for faster impulse conduction and protects nerve cells. The presynaptic neuron can communicate with the postsynaptic neuron or effector by releasing chemicals called neurotransmitters.

There are two main divisions that make up the human nervous system: the central nervous system (CNS) and the peripheral nervous system (PNS).

The central nervous system contains the brain and spinal cord, which function to integrate neural information. The cerebrum is the largest part of the brain. It includes two cerebral hemispheres, or four pairs of lobes. The top layer of the cerebrum is the cerebral cortex. The principal structures of the brain have been mapped to specific functions.

The peripheral nervous system contains sensory neurons that transmit information into the central nervous system and motor neurons that relay neural impulses to the muscles and glands. The peripheral nervous system is further subdivided into the somatic (largely voluntary) and the autonomic (largely involuntary) systems. The reflex arc is structured to carry out rapid responses that do not involve conscious control. The sympathetic and parasympathetic divisions of the autonomic system often act in opposition to each other. The sympathetic system prepares the body for stress, while the parasympathetic system returns the body to a resting state and operates when the body is resting.

Chapter 11 Graphic Organizer

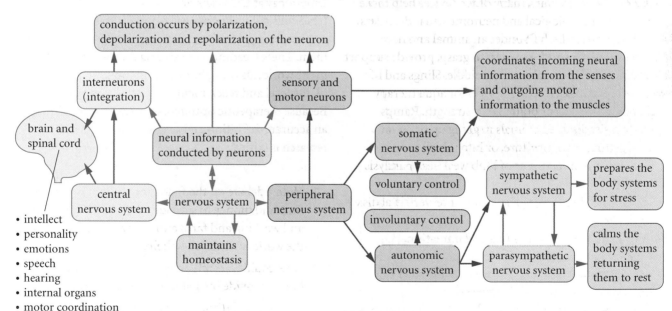

Understanding Concepts

1. Use word processing software to create a flow diagram showing the main divisions of the nervous system. Describe the key features of each division. **ICT**

2. If the motor area of the right cerebral cortex was damaged in an automobile accident, which side of the body would be affected? Why?

3. If the blood supply to an area of the brain is interrupted, as in a stroke, this part of the brain can be damaged, resulting in a loss of function. In the diagram below, the letters A to D indicate specific lobes of the cerebral cortex that have been damaged due to a stroke. Name the structures that correspond to each letter and describe which brain function would be affected in each case.

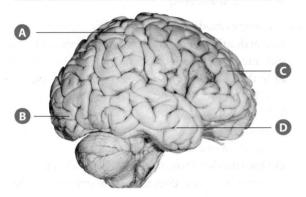

4. Compare the functions of the sympathetic and parasympathetic divisions of the autonomic system. Give specific examples of their physiological effects in the body.

5. A person with epilepsy can have severe epileptic seizures. Explain why severing the corpus callosum is used to treat some cases of epilepsy.

6. Explain the functions of acetylcholine and cholinesterase in the transmission of an impulse and the functioning of the synapse.

7. A person complains of a noticeable decrease in muscle coordination after an injury to the brain. Which area of the brain is most likely affected? Explain.

8. While nailing boards onto a fence, you accidentally hit your hand with a hammer. Use word processing or graphics software to trace the path of neural transmission from the original stimulus to your response as you drop the hammer. Include the types of neurons and their functions. **ICT**

9. In a snowmobile accident, a person receives a severe spinal cord injury. Explain why the person loses all sensation below the injured area.

10. Examine the diagram below, and use word processing software to create a table to record
    - the structures and types of neurons indicated by the letters in the diagram
    - the functions of these structures and neurons
    Under your table, indicate the direction of neuron transmission. **ICT**

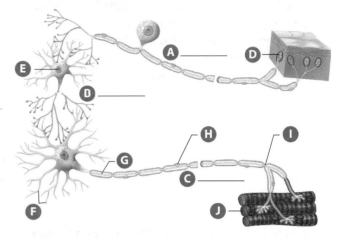

11. Compare white matter with grey matter. Identify the location of each, and describe its function.

12. Multiple sclerosis causes the myelin sheath to degenerate over time. Indicate the specific losses of myelinated nerve function caused by this condition.

13. The diagram below indicates different ion concentrations from the inside to the outside of a neuron while the neuron is at rest. Draw this diagram in your notebook, and indicate the sodium ions, potassium ions, sodium ion channels, and potassium ion channels. Also indicate the charge inside and outside the neuron. Explain how the different ion concentrations are established.

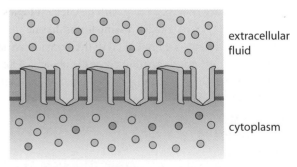

14. Using a diagram, explain depolarization, action potential, and repolarization of the neuron. What factors might stimulate an action potential?

15. Explain why saltatory conduction occurs in myelinated neurons but not in unmyelinated neurons.

16. Explain how one neuron can inhibit the actions of another neuron.

Applying Concepts

17. In a classic experiment, the strength of a neural stimulus and the resulting muscle contraction are compared. A single motor neuron that synapses with a muscle fibre is suspended. The other end of the muscle fibre is attached to a mass. If an electrical stimulus is sufficient to cause an impulse in the neuron, the muscle will contract and lift the mass. The following data were obtained from the experiment. Analyze the data, and answer the following questions.

Strength of stimulus (mV)	Mass lifted by muscle contraction (g)
1	0
2	10
3	?
4	?

a) Define "threshold potential." What is the minimum size of the stimulus required to reach the threshold potential for this motor neuron?

b) Explain the all-or-none response. Then predict the mass that could be lifted at 3 mV of stimuli and at 4 mV of stimuli.

c) Choose a specific example of a sensory neuron, and explain neural stimulation and impulses in terms of the threshold potential and the all-or-none response.

18. One of the tragic consequences of Alzheimer's disease is progressive memory loss. The memory pathways in the brain are complex and involve several different areas. Name the lobe of the cerebral cortex that is most related to memory, and state three other functions of this lobe.

19. Researchers are experimenting with new technologies that could help people with missing limbs. In one experiment, electrodes implanted in the nervous tissue of a monkey were connected to an artificial hand. The monkey's nervous system was able to direct the artificial hand to move. This photograph shows the monkey raising a piece of zucchini to its mouth using the thought-controlled robotic arm.

a) What area of the brain directs the movement of the robotic arm? (Assume that the structure of a monkey brain is similar to the structure of a human brain.)

b) Using a flowchart, illustrate the basic neural pathway from the sensory stimulus to the motor output.

c) Compare this artificial pathway with the actual neural pathway to a biologically functional limb.

d) What are some other potential applications for this technology?

e) Do the benefits to human life justify this form of animal research?

20. Describe a safeguard that prevents a neuron from carrying an impulse in the wrong direction. What would be the effect of an impulse travelling in both directions in a neuron?

21. One way to model the action potential is to line up several dominoes and initiate a cascade event, in which each successive domino knocks down the next domino.

a) In this model, the hand provides the initial energy. What provides the initial energy in a neural impulse?

b) The finger has to contact the first domino just hard enough to get it to fall. Which response does this represent in a real neuron?

c) Once the dominoes start to fall, they all fall in succession. What does this action represent in the real neuron?

d) The dominoes always fall in one direction. Contrast this with the direction of impulse transmission in a real neuron.

e) No matter how many times the dominoes fall, they always move at the same speed and intensity. What principle does this represent in the real neuron?

Making Connections

22. Meningitis is an infection of the meninges, which cover the brain and spinal cord. It is diagnosed by a spinal tap, which involves analyzing a sample of the cerebrospinal fluid. Explain why the same information could not be determined from a regular blood sample.

23. Based on what you know about threshold potential, explain why some people seem to be more tolerant of pain than others.

24. If food is not preserved properly, *Clostridium botulinum* bacteria can start to reproduce and release a neurotoxin called botulinum toxin. Botulinum toxin inhibits the action of acetylcholine, causing botulism. What symptoms would you expect to observe in someone suffering from botulism? Provide an explanation.

Sensory Reception

Chapter Concepts

12.1 Sensory Receptors and Sensation

- Sensory reception occurs at the senses. Sensation and perception occur in the brain.

- Various sensory receptors detect information in the internal and external environments.

12.2 Photoreception

- The human eye is similar to a camera. It contains a lens that focusses light, a pupil that lets in light, and a dark interior that contains light receptors.

- The retina contains rods and cones. Rods function in dim light and produce black and white images. Cones function in bright light and produce colour images.

12.3 Mechanoreception and Chemoreception

- The outer ear and middle ear transmit the energy of sound waves to the inner ear.

- The inner ear contains mechanoreceptors for hearing and balance.

- Tastes are detected by chemoreceptors in the taste buds of the tongue. Smells are detected by chemoreceptors in the nose.

- The skin contains receptors for light touch, pressure, pain, heat, and cold.

The woman meditating is trying to ignore all sights, sounds, and other sensory input from the outside world. It is a difficult task. Some people prefer the experience of relaxing inside a sensory deprivation tank for an hour or so. Many people find this experience relaxing for a short period of time—usually about an hour or so. If the brain is deprived of sensory information for an extended period of time, however, extreme anxiety, hallucinations, depression, memory loss, and antisocial behaviour can result. People who are in solitary confinement sometimes experience these effects, as do people who are confined to bed in hospital isolation wards. Why does sensory deprivation confuse the brain and upset homeostasis in the body? As you will discover in this chapter, the senses function together to allow the human body to detect and adjust to changes in the body and in the external environment.

Sense It

When one or more of the senses are inhibited, the brain's perception of the environment can change. Identifying even familiar objects can become difficult. In this activity, you will try to identify familiar objects while one or more of your senses is inhibited.

Safety Precautions

- Do not bring food meant for consumption into the laboratory.
- Do not taste any sample (you will use only the senses of touch and smell in this exercise).
- Before the exercise begins, alert your teacher to any allergies you have.

Materials

- new earplugs
- blindfold
- samples of unidentified but familiar objects supplied by your teacher

Procedure

1. Work with a partner. One partner will be the tester, and the other partner will be the subject.
2. The subject will use earplugs and a blindfold to block the senses of hearing and sight.
3. The tester will acquire samples of the unknowns provided by the teacher.
4. Now, with the subject gently pinching his or her nose shut to block the sense of smell, the tester will provide the first sample for the subject to hold.
5. The subject should use the sense of touch to identify the unknown sample, and then the subject should use the sense of smell if the sample remains unknown. The tester should record how and if the subject is able to identify the sample.
6. Repeat steps 4 and 5 using the other samples. Then switch roles, and repeat the activity with another set of samples.

Analysis

1. Which samples were the most difficult to identify? Which samples were the easiest to identify?
2. Which senses would you normally use to identify the samples?
3. You probably found it easier to identify the samples using a number of senses, rather than only one. Which senses would you use to
   a) check if milk is sour
   b) remove stones from a bag of dry lentils
   c) stand on one leg without falling over
4. Explain why integration is important for interpreting sensory information.

Sensory Receptors and Sensation

In this section, you will
- **explain** the difference between sensory reception, sensation, and perception
- **describe** the process of sensory adaptation
- **distinguish** among the major sensory receptors in the human body

Key Terms

sensory receptors
sensation
perception
sensory adaptation
photoreceptors
chemoreceptors
mechanoreceptors
thermoreceptors

Figure 12.1 What information would your senses detect if you were standing in this scene? How would this information help your body maintain homeostasis?

Imagine yourself in the fairgrounds shown in Figure 12.1. What sensory information would your nervous system be gathering? What would you see, hear, and smell? What foods would you taste? How would a light breeze feel on your skin? Your senses of sight, hearing, taste, smell, and touch keep you informed about the world around you, and allow your body to respond to your external environment. Internal sensors, such as those that regulate blood pH, blood pressure, and blood volume, also help your body maintain homeostasis.

The senses transmit sensory information, in the form of electrochemical impulses, to the brain. Different forms of energy stimulate the **sensory receptors**—the nerve endings and cells that detect sensory information. The sensory receptors then initiate neural impulses. **Sensation** occurs when the neural impulses arrive at the cerebral cortex. For example, your face may detect the warmth of a beam of sunlight. When the brain receives and processes this information, you will feel, or experience, the sensation of warmth on your cheek. The resulting sensation depends on the

area of the brain that has interpreted this information.

Neural impulses that begin in the optic nerve are sent to the visual areas of the cerebral cortex, and we see objects (Figure 12.2). Neural impulses that begin in the auditory nerve of the ear are sent to the area of the brain that perceives sound, and we hear sounds. Each person's unique **perception** results from how the cerebral cortex interprets the meaning of the sensory information.

- - -

Q1 Compare sensory reception and sensation. Provide an example of each.

Q2 Each type of sensory receptor functions by initiating neural impulses. How is the brain able to convert sensory information into perception?

- - -

Sensory Adaptation

A massive amount of sensory information, coming from many neural pathways, bombards the brain every second. Sometimes, the brain can filter out

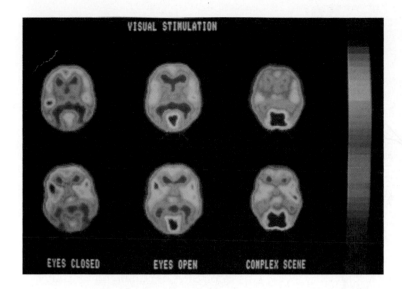

VISUAL STIMULATION

EYES CLOSED   EYES OPEN   COMPLEX SCENE

Figure 12.2 A PET scan of the human brain showing brain activity in a volunteer at different stages of stimulation. The orange-red colour indicates that the brain is active and perception is taking place. In the last two columns, the visual area at the back of the brain is activated and the perception of sight is occurring. In the first column, the subject's eyes are closed. Thus neural information is not getting from the senses to the brain, and there is no perception of sight.

redundant, insignificant information. This process is called **sensory adaptation**. For example, sensory adaptation has occurred when you no longer notice the ticking of a clock or feel the clothes on your skin. When the senses detect a significant change in external or internal conditions, the body readjusts (Figure 12.3).

In order to process sensory information quickly, the brain *parallels* or splits up this input to various areas of the brain—a form of neural multi-tasking. Sometimes the sensory information does not get reintegrated precisely, and what we sense is not necessarily what we perceive. This effect can be demonstrated with optical illusions, which scientists use to try to understand how the brain perceives sensory information. Use the illusions in Figure 12.4 on page 408 to determine the difference between the sensory information received and what your brain actually perceives.

• • •

(3) Describe an example of sensory adaptation, and explain why it occurs.

(4) What happens during integration that causes people to perceive optical illusions?

• • •

Sensory Receptors

Sensory receptors are specialized cells or neuron endings that detect specific stimuli. Human sensory receptors can

BiologyFile

FYI

Can an octopus experience pain and suffering? Most likely, say neuroscientists, which is why these common research animals need to be treated humanely and given behavioural enrichment. Support for this idea has come from experiments conducted by octopus expert Jennifer Mather, professor of psychology at the University of Lethbridge, and Roland Andersen of the Seattle Aquarium. The researchers gave empty plastic pill bottles to eight octopuses, who played with the pill bottles. This was the first time play had been observed in invertebrates.

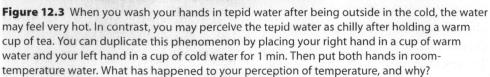

Figure 12.3 When you wash your hands in tepid water after being outside in the cold, the water may feel very hot. In contrast, you may perceive the tepid water as chilly after holding a warm cup of tea. You can duplicate this phenomenon by placing your right hand in a cup of warm water and your left hand in a cup of cold water for 1 min. Then put both hands in room-temperature water. What has happened to your perception of temperature, and why?

A Herman's Grid. When you look at the centre of the large square, the dots in the middle should look white, and the dots you see out of the corners of your eye should look black.

Figure 12.4 These diagrams produce various optical illusions.

B The Impossible Terrace, by D. MacDonald. Is down up, or is up down?

C Kitaoka's Rotating Snakes. Look at these circles from off centre. Do you think they are actually spinning?

D Fraser's Spiral. Try to follow the spiral into the centre.

BiologyFile

Web Link
Retinitis pigmentosa includes several inherited diseases that cause the photoreceptor cells (rods and cones) in the retina to degenerate and die. Dr. Paul Schnetkamp at the University of Calgary is one of the scientists studying this disorder, which affects an estimated 50 000 Canadians. What is the current state of understanding and treatment of retinitis pigmentosa?

www.albertabiology.ca
WWW

be classified into four categories: photoreceptors, chemoreceptors, mechanoreceptors, and thermoreceptors (Table 12.1). Each type of receptor is able to transduce, or convert, one form of energy from a specific stimulus into electrochemical energy, which can be processed by the nervous system.

Light energy stimulates **photoreceptors**. Our eyes contain photoreceptors, called rods and cones, that absorb light and allow us to sense different levels of light and shades of colour. **Chemoreceptors** are stimulated by certain chemicals. The tongue contains taste buds that detect various particles in the food we eat. The nose has olfactory cells that detect odours in the air. Other chemoreceptors detect changes in the internal environment. For example, chemoreceptors in the carotid arteries and aorta detect blood pH. **Mechanoreceptors** respond to mechanical forces from some form of pressure. For example, hair cells in the inner ear (hearing sensors) are activated when sound waves cause parts of the inner ear to vibrate. Other hair cells in the inner ear (sensors for balance) are stimulated when they bend, thus providing information about body and head position. Proprioceptors in and near the muscles also provide information about body position, as well as movement. There are various mechanoreceptors in the skin, which allow the body to detect light touch, pressure, and even pain. **Thermoreceptors** in the skin detect heat and cold.

Damage to particular sensory receptors such as photoreceptors can result in loss of the associated sense, even if the rest of the sense organ and nervous system are fully functional. Hundreds of thousands of Canadians have lost their sight due to eye injuries or degenerative eye disorders, such as retinitis pigmentosa and age-related degeneration of the photoreceptors. A newly developed artificial eye, however, offers hope to these people. The artificial eye includes a digital video camera that is mounted on glasses. The camera captures images and sends them to a small computer on a belt worn by a person who is visually impaired. The images are processed and sent to several electrodes that are implanted in the visual cortex, thus bypassing the damaged light receptors in the eye. The electrodes directly stimulate the brain, producing a pattern of bright

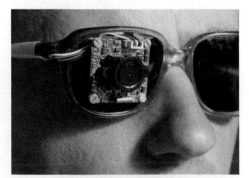

Figure 12.5 The artificial eye sends electrical impulses that directly stimulate the visual cortex of the brain. This man became blind in an accident over 20 years ago. He can now distinguish large letters and several objects, and he has even driven a car around a parking lot.

Table 12.1 Major Sensory Receptors in the Human Body

Category and type of receptor	Examples of receptor	Stimulus
Photoreceptors		
vision	rods and cones in the eye	visible light
Chemoreceptors		
taste	taste buds on the tongue	food particles in saliva
smell	olfactory receptors in the nose	odour molecules
internal senses	osmoreceptors in the hypothalamus	low blood volume
	receptors in the carotid artery and aorta	blood pH
Mechanoreceptors		
touch/pressure/pain	receptors in the skin	mechanical pressure
hearing	hair cells in the inner ear	sound waves
balance	hair cells in the inner ear	fluid movement
body position	proprioceptors in the muscles and tendons, and at the joints	muscle contraction, stretching, and movement
Thermoreceptors		
temperature	heat and cold receptors in the skin	change in radiant energy

BiologyFile

Web Link
What would happen if your optic and auditory nerves were switched? How would you perceive a flash of lightening or crash of thunder? Researchers at the University of Waterloo in Ontario, Canada, are studying what happens when senses blend, a condition called synesthesia. Visit the Web Links page to find out what some people with synesthesia experience.

www.albertabiology.ca
WWW

spots that the visual cortex perceives as a crude image. Currently, the resolution of this device is poor—about five pixels per square centimetre—but it allows users to distinguish objects with high contrast. Researchers predict that future developments will improve the device enough to restore vision completely, or perhaps to enhance vision beyond natural human capabilities.

Section 12.1 Summary

- The senses are the human brain's connection to the outside world.
- Sensation is initiated in the senses through sensory reception, but sensation and perception take place in the brain.
- Everyone's perception of the world is unique.
- Sensory receptors convert different forms of energy into electrochemical energy, which the nervous system can interpret.

• • •

Q 5 Identify five major senses and their corresponding sensory receptors.

Q 6 List three types of internal sensory receptors and their functions.

• • •

Section 12.1 **Review**

1. State the form of energy that stimulates
   a) thermoreceptors   **b)** photoreceptors

2. What types of sensory receptors are stimulated in someone who is performing a complicated yoga pose?

3. Crime-scene investigators are often frustrated by different eyewitness accounts of the same crime. With your knowledge of sensation and perception, explain how different people's perceptions of the same sensory information can be different.

4. When you put on your new winter boots one morning, you cannot help noticing how different they feel from your summer shoes. By the time you reach school, however, you have forgotten about your boots. Why does your perception of the way your boots feel change?

5. Describe, in general terms, what happens in the nervous system when someone receives a large amount of significant sensory information, such as when viewing an optical illusion.

Photoreception

Figure 12.6 The human sense of sight can tell us more about the world than any other sense can. How does the human eye detect the colour, contrast, depth, and three-dimensional shapes of this landscape?

Scientists estimate that, in sighted people (people who can see), vision supplies 80 to 90 percent of the important sensory information reaching the brain. The incredible variety of colours and shapes and the range of distance depicted in the landscape shown in Figure 12.6 would be difficult to conceive of without the sense of sight. How does the human eye carry out its varied functions?

The human eye is essentially a fluid-filled hollow ball, about 2.5 cm in diameter. It focusses incoming light energy on the photoreceptors of the retina. As shown in Figure 12.7, the eye has three layers: external, intermediate, and internal. The external layer of the eye is a white, tough, and fibrous protective layer called the **sclera**. Light enters the eye through the **cornea**, the transparent part of the sclera at the front of the eye.

The intermediate layer of the eye is called the **choroid**. The choroid absorbs stray light rays that are not detected by the photoreceptors. As well, the choroid contains blood vessels that nourish the eye. Toward the front, the choroid forms the doughnut-shaped, coloured **iris**, which contains a central dark **pupil**. Like

fingerprints, the pattern of colour in the iris is unique to each person. Thus, an iris scan could potentially be used for personal identification.

The iris allows light to enter the inner eye through the pupil. As shown in Figure 12.8, the iris adjusts the size of the pupil based on the light conditions— a process called **adaptation**. You can observe adaptation in your own eyes by turning off the lights for 1 min and holding a mirror in front of your face. When you turn the lights back on, you can see your pupils shrink, which allows less light to enter your eyes.

Behind the iris, the choroid thickens and forms the ciliary muscle. The ciliary muscle attaches to the lens, which focusses images on the retina. The **retina** is the internal layer of the eye. It is a thin layer of tissue that contains the photoreceptors— the rods and cones. The **rods** are sensitive to light intensity (level of brightness), and the **cones** are sensitive to different colours. The cones are packed most densely at the back of the eye in an area called the fovea centralis. The rods and cones send sensory impulses to the brain via the **optic nerve**.

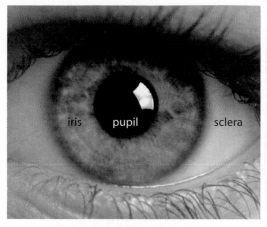

iris   pupil   sclera

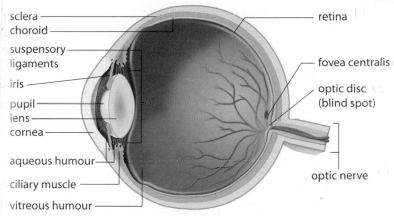

sclera
choroid
suspensory ligaments
iris
pupil
lens
cornea
aqueous humour
ciliary muscle
vitreous humour

retina
fovea centralis
optic disc (blind spot)
optic nerve

Figure 12.7 The anatomy of the human eye

If there were no fluid inside the eyeball, it would lose its shape, like an empty water balloon. The lens, which is attached to the ciliary muscles by suspensory ligaments, divides the eye into two chambers. The anterior chamber is in front of the lens, and the posterior chamber is behind the lens. In the anterior chamber, a clear, watery fluid called the **aqueous humour** maintains the shape of the cornea and provides oxygen and nutrients for the surrounding cells, including those of the lens and cornea. A small amount of aqueous humour is produced every day and drained by small ducts. If these ducts become plugged, pressure can build up in the eye, causing the delicate blood vessels in the eye to rupture. The cells of the eye then deteriorate, due to a lack of oxygen and nutrients. This results in **glaucoma**, which leads to blindness if untreated.

The posterior chamber, which is surrounded by the retina, contains a clear, jelly-like fluid called the **vitreous humour**. The vitreous humour also helps to maintain the shape of the eyeball, and it supports the surrounding cells.

The structures of the human eye, and their functions, are summarized in Table 12.2.

Table 12.2 The Principal Structures of the Human Eye and Their Functions

Structure	Function
External layer (Sclera)	
sides and back of sclera	protects and supports the eyeball
cornea	bends light rays into the eye
Intermediate layer (Choroid)	
sides and back of choroid	absorbs scattered light and contains blood vessels
iris	regulates the amount of light that enters the eye
pupil	is the opening for light to enter the inner eye
ciliary muscles	changes the shape of the lens in order to focus
Internal layer (Retina)	
rods	photoreceptors that are sensitive to dim light
cones	photoreceptors that are sensitive to different wavelengths of light (colour vision)
fovea centralis	contains a high density of cones, and provides acute vision
Other	
lens	focusses light rays onto the fovea centralis
humours	support the eyeball, with the pressure of the fluids they contain
optic nerve	transmits sensory information to the brain

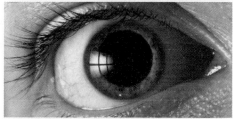

Figure 12.8 Light adaptation in the eye. In bright light, the iris constricts, which shrinks the pupil to let in less light. In dim light, the iris dilates, which widens the pupil and lets in more light.

Focussing

How do eyeglasses and contact lenses help people see? How do the lenses in cameras and microscopes work? If you could closely examine any artificial lens, you would find that light rays bend as they pass through the lens. In other words, the lens focusses the light in a particular direction. The lens of the eye focusses incoming light in a similar way. Eyeglasses and contact lenses make up for imperfections in the eyes that prevent them from focussing clearly.

Figure 12.9 shows what happens when the eye brings an image into focus. Light rays are bent as they pass through the rigid cornea, flexible lens, and fluid humours. Notice that, compared with the object being viewed, the image fixed on the fovea centralis of the retina is smaller, upside down, and reversed from left to right.

Because the **lens** is flexible, it can change shape. This allows for finer focus when viewing objects, whether they are nearby or far away. As shown in Figure 12.10, if an object is far away, the ciliary muscles relax and the suspensory ligaments become taut, causing the lens to flatten. If an object is nearby, the ciliary muscles contract and the suspensory ligaments relax, causing the lens to become more rounded. Similarly, a nondigital camera focusses by changing the distance between the lens and the film. The ability of the lens to change shape in order to focus images clearly on the retina is a reflex called **accommodation**. If you read your textbook up close for an extended period of time, the ongoing contraction of your ciliary muscles will likely cause muscle fatigue, which you will experience as eyestrain.

Figure 12.9 What happens to light rays as they pass through the cornea and lens?

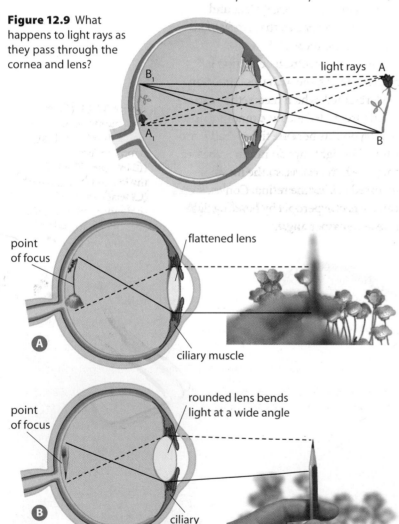

A   point of focus
flattened lens
ciliary muscle

B   point of focus
rounded lens bends light at a wide angle
ciliary muscle

Figure 12.10 Accommodation. **(A)** What happens to the shape of the lens when the eye is focussed on a distant object? **(B)** What happens when the eye is focussed on a nearby object? Note that the ability of the lens to bend light is exaggerated in this diagram. In reality, the cornea also bends light.

Conditions Affecting the Cornea and Lens

As the lens ages, its protein structure can start to degenerate, making it opaque and preventing light from passing through it. This condition can cause grey-white spots, called **cataracts**, on the lens. To prevent cataracts from impairing vision, the lens can sometimes be surgically replaced.

Inherited conditions that affect the eye's ability to focus light directly

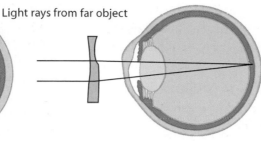
Light rays from far object

A The off-centre bending of light rays by an uneven cornea

B Unevenly ground glasses or contact lenses can correct for astigmatism

C A test for astigmatism. If any of the dark lines in the diagram seem darker than the others, you could have an asymmetrical cornea

Figure 12.11 Astigmatism and how it can be corrected

on the fovea centralis are common. **Astigmatism**, for example, is due to an uneven curvature of part of the cornea. Because the cornea is asymmetrical, it cannot bend light rays so that they meet at the correct focal point (Figure 12.11). As a result, vision is blurred.

When young, most people can clearly see a size 20 letter on an eye chart from a distance of 20 feet (about 6.1 m). This is referred to as 20/20 vision. People who have no difficulty seeing close objects but cannot see a size 20 letter from 20 feet are nearsighted. They have a condition called **myopia**. As shown in Figure 12.12, the eyeball of people with myopia is elongated, so the focussed light falls *in front* of the retina instead of on the photoreceptors. To see distant objects,

nearsighted people can wear concave lenses, which diverge incoming light rays so that the image falls directly on the retina. An alternative to wearing corrective lenses is corrective laser surgery. In this procedure, an ophthalmologist (eye doctor) uses a laser to cut and reshape the cornea so that it will focus light onto the retina.

Another common condition is **hyperopia**. People with this condition are farsighted, which means they can see clearly from 20 feet, but cannot focus on nearby objects because the eyeball is too short. The light rays do not meet before they reach the retina, so the image is focussed *behind* the retina. Convex lenses can correct hyperopia by bending light rays at a sharper angle.

Figure 12.12 **(A)** Image seen by someone who is nearsighted. Which object is most in focus? **(B)** Myopia. Where does the image fall in the eye? **(C)** Image seen by someone who is farsighted. **(D)** Hyperopia. Where does the image fall?

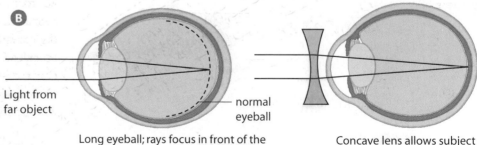

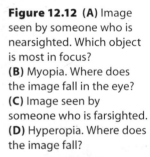

Light from far object

Long eyeball; rays focus in front of the retina when viewing distant objects

normal eyeball

Concave lens allows subject to see distant objects

Light from near object

Short eyeball; rays focus behind the retina when viewing close objects

normal eyeball

Convex lens allows subject to see close objects

There are about 150 000 cones per square millimetre in the fovea centralis of the human retina. In some predatory birds, however, the fovea centralis has over 1 000 000 cones per square millimeter. Thus, a falcon can see a mouse that is 10 cm long from 1.5 km away. The image stays sharp even when the bird dives at over 160 km/h.

10 Describe the functions of the cornea and lens of the eye.

11 What causes astigmatism, myopia, and hyperopia?

12 Compare adaptation with accommodation. Give an example of each.

The Photoreceptors: The Rods and Cones

Vision begins as light is focussed on the light-receiving cells, or photoreceptors. The human retina contains about 125 million rods and 6 million cones, which account for at least 70 percent of all sensory receptors in the human body.

The rods are extremely sensitive to light. In fact, a rod can be stimulated by a single photon of light. The rods do not enable us to distinguish colours, however, just degrees of black and white. This is why it is difficult to detect any colours in a dark room, although you may be able to see the shapes of the furniture. Rods also detect motion and are responsible for peripheral vision. In the human eye, the rods are spread throughout the retina, but are more concentrated in the outside edges.

The cones are the colour-detecting sensors of the eye. They are packed most densely at the **fovea centralis** (see Figure

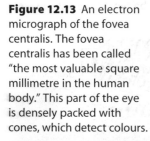

Figure 12.13 An electron micrograph of the fovea centralis. The fovea centralis has been called "the most valuable square millimetre in the human body." This part of the eye is densely packed with cones, which detect colours.

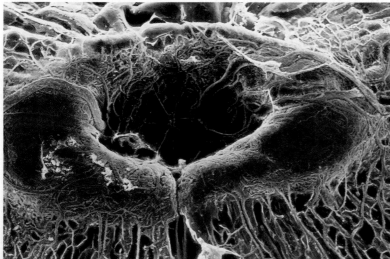

Magnification: 26.4 ×

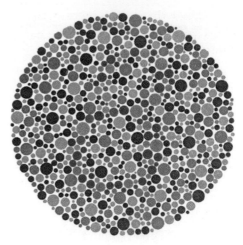

Figure 12.14 Check your colour vision by studying this colour blindness chart. Can you see the number 8?

12.13) at the back and centre of the retina. You may have noticed that your peripheral vision lacks colour. This is due to the central location of the fovea centralis. The cones require relatively intense light to stimulate them. Thus, the structures of the eye must focus light onto the fovea centralis in order to produce a sharp image. In daylight, you can see best (your eyes produce the sharpest image) if you look at an object straight on. In addition to allowing us to see "in colour," the cones allow us to perform high-acuity tasks, such as reading.

There are three types of cones, and each type absorbs a different wavelength of light. The combination of cones that can detect red, blue, and green wavelengths of light allows us to see a range of colours. **Colour blindness** is an inherited condition that occurs more frequently in males than in females. (You will discover why in Unit 7.) Colour blindness is actually colour *deficiency*, because it is caused by a lack or deficiency in particular cones, usually red and green cones. Thus, a red-green colour-blind person may find it difficult or impossible to distinguish between these colours. If you have a full range of colour vision, you should be able to see a number 8 in Figure 12.14. If you have red-green colour blindness, due to a lack of red cones, you will see a number 3.

How do the photoreceptors relay visual information to the brain? Figure 12.15 shows the structure of the rods and cones. The rods contain a light-absorbing pigment called rhodopsin, which is composed of retinal (a vitamin A derivative) and the protein opsin. In the dark, the rods release an inhibitory neurotransmitter that inhibits nearby nerve cells. When the rods absorb light, however, the rhodopsin splits into retinal and opsin. This triggers a chain reaction that *stops* the release of the inhibitory neurotransmitter, thus *allowing* transmission of a neural impulse to the optic nerve. A similar process occurs in the cones except the pigment is photopsin, which reacts only to certain wavelengths of light.

Figure 12.16 shows the three main layers of neurons in the retina. The layer that is closest to the choroid contains the rods and cones, which synapse with the bipolar cells in the middle layer. When light stimulates the rods and cones, they stop releasing an inhibitory neurotransmitter into the synapse. The bipolar cells then transfer a neural impulse to the ganglion cells, which

are in the layer closest to the vitreous humour. The axons of the ganglion cells form the optic nerve. Optic nerve fibres that emerge from the back of the eye transmit visual images to the occipetal lobe of the brain.

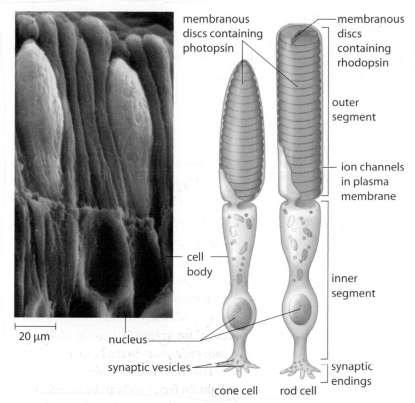

Figure 12.15 The rods and cones of the retina. When light strikes the cells, molecules in the membranous discs change shape. This triggers a cascade of reactions, which allow a nerve impulse to be sent to the optic nerve.

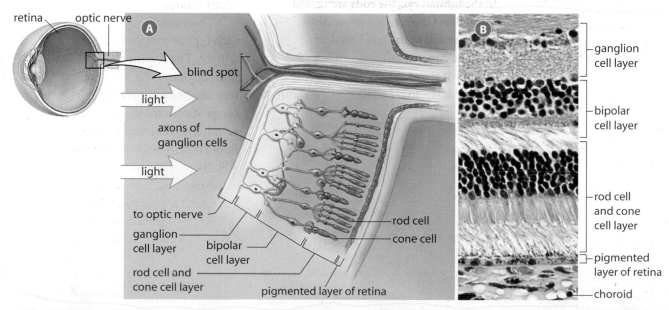

Figure 12.16 (A) The organization of the principal cells of the retina. Once stimulated, the rods and cones permit a neural impulse to pass through the bipolar cells to the ganglion cells, which form the optic nerve. **(B)** A light micrograph of the layers of the retina. The outer layer of the retina, called the pigmented layer, does not contain rods or cones. The pigmented layer stores vitamin A and prevents light from scattering in the eye.

Figure 12.17 Can you detect your blind spot? Hold the textbook about 30 cm from your eyes. Close your right eye and look at the black cross with your left eye. Slowly move your left eye toward this figure. The dot on the left will disappear when its image falls on the blind spot in your left eye.

• • •

13 Compare the locations and functions of the two photoreceptors found in the eye.

14 What is the direct cause of red-green colour blindness?

15 How does visual information get from the retina to the brain? List the main steps in this process.

• • •

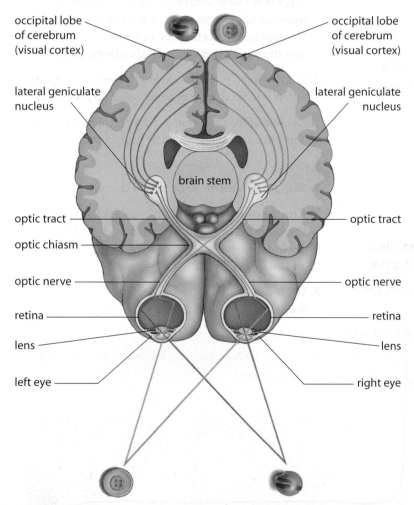

occipital lobe of cerebrum (visual cortex)

occipital lobe of cerebrum (visual cortex)

lateral geniculate nucleus

lateral geniculate nucleus

brain stem

optic tract

optic tract

optic chiasm

optic nerve

optic nerve

retina

retina

lens

lens

left eye

right eye

Figure 12.18 The neural pathway of the optic nerve from the retina to the occipital lobe. Data from the right half of each retina go to the right side of the occipital lobe, and data from the left half of each retina go to the left side of the occipital lobe. Integration of the image occurs in the brain.

Visual Interpretation

Figure 12.16 on the previous page shows where the ganglion cells merge to form the optic nerve. This area, called the **blind spot**, does not contain photoreceptors and is therefore incapable of detecting light. Use the illustration in Figure 12.17 to find the blind spot in each of your eyes. Usually you do not notice your blind spots because each eye compensates for the visual information that the other eye misses.

Before the brain can integrate visual information from both eyes, however, the retina must send information to the optic nerve. From there, the information travels to the thalamus and then to the occipital lobe of the cerebral cortex for interpretation (Figure 12.18). The image is split in the occipital lobe because the left optic tract carries information about the right portion of the visual field, and the right optic tract carries information about the left visual field. The eyes look at an object from different positions, so each neuron carries a slightly different view of the information to the brain. In the cerebrum, the various pieces of visual information are processed and integrated, and the image is perceived right-side up. Because humans (and other primates) have forward-facing eyes, we have what is called *binocular vision*. This means we use both eyes to look at and collect visual information about an object. This enables the brain to perceive depth and three-dimensional images.

The various aspects of sight, such as movement, colour, depth, and shape, appear to be handled simultaneously by different areas of the occipital lobe. This speeds up processing, which is important because the brain must constantly receive visual information in order to see.

• • •

16 What is the blind spot in the eye?

17 What aspects of vision are integrated in the human brain so that we can see?

• • •

Dissection of an Eye

The human eye and cow eye are very similar in structure and function. In this investigation, you will examine diagrams of a dissected cow eye and dissect a real cow eye to gain a better understanding of how the structures of the eye relate to their functions. As an alternative to doing the dissection, you can use only the diagrams or examine an online dissection of a mammalian eye.

Question

How do the structures of a cow eye relate to their functions?

Safety Precautions

- Handle sharp instruments with care.
- Wash your hands well when you are finished.
- Disinfect the dissection equipment and area with 10 percent bleach solution when you have finished.

Materials

- preserved cow eye
- paper towel
- safety goggles
- 10 percent bleach solution
- apron
- dissecting tray
- dissecting kit

Procedure

1. Put on safety goggles, gloves, and an apron. Rinse off the cow eye, and place it on the dissecting tray.

2. Examine and locate the fat, muscles, and optic nerve on the back of the eye.

3. Remove as much of the outer fat as possible. Then use the scalpel to cut the eye in half. Cut in a circle, about halfway between the cornea and the optic nerve, as shown in the diagram. Do not put too much pressure

on the eye; apply light slicing cuts until you penetrate the eye.

4. Use the diagrams and Figures 12.7 and 12.16, to help you identify the structures of the eye. Examine the posterior (rear) chamber of the eye. Notice the clear, jelly-like vitreous humour, which fills this chamber. Identify the tough, white sclera (external layer), the black choroid (intermediate layer), and the thin retina (internal layer). Follow the converging blood vessels to locate the area where the retina is attached to the back of the eyeball at the blind spot. Identify the fovea centralis in the middle of the retina.

5. Examine the anterior (front) chamber of the eye. Identify the large, central lens, as well as the ciliary muscle and suspensory ligaments attached to it. The aqueous humour is the fluid in the anterior chamber. Identify the iris and the pupil. Identify the cornea.

6. If the lens is not too cloudy, hold it over some typed letters on a scrap piece of paper. What do you observe?

7. Dispose of the cow eye and clean your dissecting tray and work area as instructed by your teacher.

Analysis

1. Sketch and label the structures of the eye.

2. Create a two-column table in your notebook. Use the following headings: Eye structure, Eye function. Record the structures you labelled in your diagram and their functions.

3. On your diagram, indicate where you would find the rods and cones. What is the function of each structure?

Conclusion

4. Summarize how the structures of the eye direct light onto the fovea centralis.

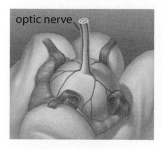

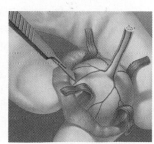

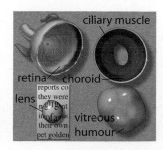

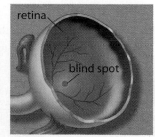

Preventing Vision Loss

You have already read about two of the most frequent causes of vision loss: glaucoma and cataracts. The leading cause of vision loss involves disorders of the retina. There are different kinds of retinal disorders. In diabetic retinopathy, for example, capillaries to the retina burst, spilling blood into the vitreous fluid between the lens and the retina. Careful regulation of blood glucose levels can help guard against this disorder.

Changes in the consistency of the vitreous fluid may also cause retinal detachment—a condition in which the retina becomes separated from the choroid vessels that supply it with nutrients and oxygen. These changes may be brought on by an inflammatory disorder, advanced diabetes, or an injury or trauma to the eye. Retinal detachment is a medical emergency, because it can cause permanent vision loss. If detected early, the condition may be corrected surgically.

Macular degeneration occurs when the cones are destroyed due to thickened choroid vessels that no longer function as they should. The result is a blurring of, or the development of, a blind spot in central vision. A principal factor in developing macular degeneration is age. The condition is the main cause of severe loss of vision in people of age 60 or older.

Cigarette smoking, obesity, and exposure to sunlight are other factors implicated in the condition. There is no cure. However, behaviours that reduce the risk of developing the condition and preventing further vision loss include exercise, not smoking, and a diet rich in green leafy vegetables and fish.

Section 12.2 Summary

- The cornea, lens, and humours focus light on the retina.
- The lens is flexible. Its ability to change shape in order to focus on near or far objects is called accommodation.
- The ability to focus is impaired if the cornea is uneven (causes astigmatism), or if the eyeball is too long (myopia) or too short (hyperopia).
- Each eye has a blind spot, where the optic nerve connects to the eyeball, but each eye compensates for what the other cannot see. Binocular vision also allows us to see in three dimensions.
- The retina contains the photoreceptor cells. The rods function in dim light and produce black and white images. The cones function in bright light and produce colour images.
- Once stimulated, the rods and cones send a neural message to the occipital lobe of the brain, which processes and integrates the information, and then perceives it as an image.

Section 12.2 Review

1. The sclera, choroid, and retina are the three main layers of the eye. Identify the structures associated with each.

2. Suppose that someone you think you recognize is walking toward you. Explain what happens to the lenses of your eyes as this person approaches. What is this reflex called?

3. How do the structures of the eye focus light on the retina? What happens if the light is focussed behind or in front of the retina?

4. Can a person who has a functioning optic nerve still be blind? Explain your answer.

5. As people age, the lenses become less elastic. How would this affect the accommodation reflex? Why might older people often need bifocals (a combination of convex and concave lenses) to correct their vision?

6. Use word processing software to make a three-column table. List the following eye conditions in the first column: glaucoma, cataract, astigmatism, nearsightedness (myopia), farsightedness (hyperopia), macular degeneration. In the other two columns, describe the specific problem that causes each condition and the method of treatment. ICT

7. A significant portion of the human brain is devoted to processing visual information. What does this suggest about how humans are adapted to perceive their surroundings?

Mechanoreception and Chemoreception

Figure 12.19 These blind Paralympic athletes are playing goalball, a sport developed in the 1940s specifically for people who are blind or vision-impaired.

Many animals exhibit senses that are beyond human capabilities. Elephants can hear sounds that are too low for us to detect, penguins can see into the ultraviolet range, and many snakes have sensors for infrared energy. Birds, whales, and insects migrate thousands of kilometres using a sense of navigation that humans have yet to understand. Nevertheless, human senses go well beyond vision (Figure 12.19). They include the senses of hearing, taste, touch, and smell, as well as internal senses, such as the sense of balance. This section explores the structures and functions of these vital senses.

Hearing and Balance

Humans spend considerable time talking and listening, and so, when we communicate, hearing is often our most important sense. Our hearing can also warn us of danger. When listening to a favourite tune, it can trigger a strong emotional response. In addition, sense receptors in the muscles and ears provide constant information about the body's orientation in space. This sensory input gives us our sixth sense—our sense of

balance, which allows us to move, sit, and stand without falling. The specialized sensory receptor cells for both hearing and balance are mechanoreceptors.

Capturing Sound

Sound causes particles around the source to vibrate and move. The auditory system (sense of hearing) detects these movements as small fluctuations in air pressure, called **sound waves**. You can visualize sound waves as ripples, like the ripples of water that move out from a stone when it is thrown into a pond. At room temperature in air, sound travels at about 1217 km/h. Mechanoreceptors in the inner ear convert the energy of sound waves into the electrochemical energy that the brain perceives as sound.

Three major divisions of the ear—the outer ear, middle ear, and inner ear—collect and direct auditory information to the hearing receptors (Figure 12.20 on page 420). The **outer ear** consists of the pinna and auditory canal. The **pinna** is the outside flap of the ear. It is made of skin and cartilage, shaped in a way that enhances sound vibrations and focusses them into the ear. The **auditory canal** is a tube, 2.5 cm long, that leads to the eardrum in the middle ear. The auditory canal amplifies sound waves, effectively making sounds louder. Hairs, as well as earwax secreted by glands in the auditory canal, prevent dust, insects, bacteria, and other foreign materials from proceeding deeper into the ear. This is one reason why physicians suggest that people do not use swabs to clean out earwax. As well, there is a risk that an object inserted into the ear could damage the auditory canal and eardrum.

The **middle ear** is an air-filled space that is bordered on one side by the **tympanum** (also called the eardrum or tympanic membrane). The tympanum is a round, elastic structure that vibrates in response to sound waves. (The word *tympanum* comes from the Greek word for "drum.") When sound waves push the tympanum, its vibrations are passed on and amplified by the neighbouring **ossicles**: three tiny, interconnected bones in the middle ear. The ossicles are the smallest three bones in the body (Figures 12.20 and 12.21). Each bone acts as a lever for the next, so that a small movement in one results in a larger movement in the next. As a result, the

strength of the vibrations is amplified as they pass from the malleus (hammer), to the incus (anvil), and finally to the stapes (stirrup). The stapes concentrates vibrations into the membrane-covered opening in the wall of the inner ear, called the **oval window**. The middle ear can significantly amplify and concentrate vibrations because the tympanum is 15 to 30 times larger than the oval window.

The middle ear is connected to the throat by the thin **Eustachian tube**. This tube allows air pressure to equalize when there is a difference in air pressure within and outside the otherwise contained middle ear. You may have noticed, while driving on a mountain road or travelling in an airplane, that when the external air pressure drops, the higher pressure within the middle ear can feel uncomfortable. Chewing gum or yawning allows air in the Eustachian tube to connect with air in the throat, thus equalizing the pressure and making the ears "pop."

The **inner ear** consists of three interconnecting structures: the semicircular canals, the vestibule, and the cochlea. The semicircular canals and vestibule contain sensors for balance, while the coiled **cochlea** (Latin for "snail") is used for hearing. It is within the structures of the cochlea that the mechanical energy of sound is converted into the electrochemical impulses that are transmitted to the brain. Because the inner ear is fluid-filled, vibrations in the oval window must be converted to pressure waves in the fluid.

Figure 12.21 also shows a cross section of a cochlea. The middle chamber contains the **organ of Corti**, which is the organ of hearing. Along the base of the organ of Corti is the **basilar membrane**, to which sensory mechanoreceptors known as **hair cells** are attached. The hair cells have thin projections called stereocilia, which stick out at the top of the cells (Figure 12.22). The far ends of the stereocilia are embedded within the **tectorial membrane**. When the stapes strikes the oval window, this vibrates the

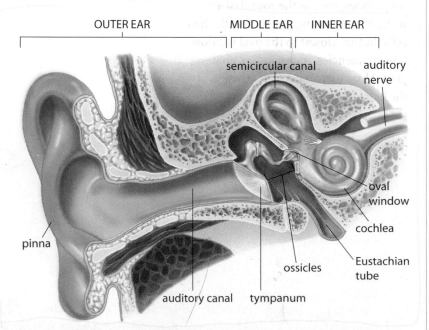

OUTER EAR   MIDDLE EAR   INNER EAR

semicircular canal

auditory nerve

oval window

cochlea

Eustachian tube

pinna

ossicles

auditory canal   tympanum

Figure 12.20 The anatomy of the human ear. How are sound waves that arrive at the outer ear amplified as their energy travels to the inner ear?

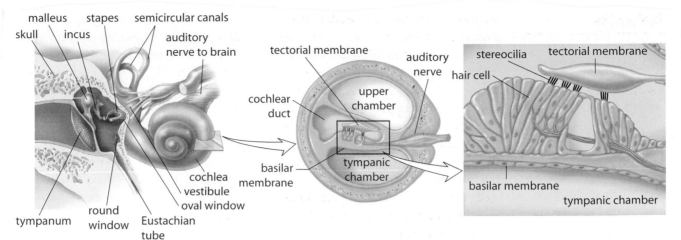

Inner ear

labels: malleus, skull, incus, stapes, semicircular canals, auditory nerve to brain, tympanum, round window, cochlea, vestibule, oval window, Eustachian tube

Cochlea, cross-section

labels: tectorial membrane, auditory nerve, cochlear duct, upper chamber, basilar membrane, tympanic chamber

Organ of Corti

labels: stereocilia, tectorial membrane, hair cell, basilar membrane, tympanic chamber

Figure 12.21 The structure of the cochlea. Notice how membranes separate its three fluid-filled chambers, the upper chamber, cochlear duct, and tympanic chamber. Since fluids cannot be compressed, the round window bulges out as pressure waves move through the inside of the cochlea.

window and creates pressure waves in the fluid of the cochlea. The pressure waves make the basilar membrane move up and down, which causes the stereocilia of the hair cells to bend against the tectorial membrane. The hair cells, which synapse with the nerve fibres of the auditory nerve, sense the bending of the stereocilia and relay this message to the nerves. The nerves then send an impulse to the brain.

• • •

18 List, in order, the structures of the ear that a sound wave encounters, starting with the outer ear.

19 What happens to the energy of sound waves, which travel through air, after it reaches the tympanum?

20 What is the role of the Eustachian tube?

• • •

Frequencies of Sound

The hair cells of the organ of Corti are able to distinguish both the frequency (pitch) and amplitude (intensity) of sound waves. Frequency is the number of waves that pass through a specific point every second. It is measured in hertz (Hz). The frequency of speech usually ranges from 100 to 4000 Hz, although humans can hear sounds that are between 20 and 20 000 Hz. If you could hear below 20 Hz, you would hear the blood moving through your ears! Different areas of the organ of Corti are sensitive to different frequencies. High frequencies, such as the sound of a whistle, most strongly stimulate the hair cells that are closest to the oval window. Low frequencies, such as a low note played by a tuba, most strongly stimulate the hair cells that are farthest from the oval window. In the next investigation, you will test your ability to detect sounds of different frequencies.

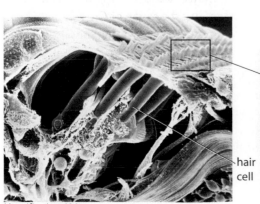

hair cell

Magnification: 836 ×

stereocilia

Magnification: 2196 ×

Figure 12.22 Electron micrographs of hair cells and stereocilia from the organ of Corti. What causes the stereocilia to move?

Target Skills

Performing experiments to measure the ability to discriminate objects visually and to hear a range of sounds

Gathering and **recording** data

Compiling and **displaying** data in an appropriate form

Distinguishing Sights and Sounds

The sensory receptors of the eyes and ears allow the brain to perceive a wide range of sights and sounds. In this investigation, you will determine your ability to discriminate different shades of colour, and you will examine the property of sound known as frequency or pitch.

Question

What range of sights and sounds can you distinguish?

Part 1: Distinguishing Shades of Colour

Hypothesis

Write a hypothesis about which factors might affect your ability to distinguish different shades of a colour.

Materials

- liquid food colouring
- water
- 5 beakers (100 mL) or 5 clear containers of equal size

Procedure

1. Read the procedure, and create a table to record your data.

2. Put an equal amount of water (about 50 mL) into the five beakers (or clear containers).

3. Label the beakers 1 through 5, so that the labels can be concealed. Put 1 drop of food colouring in the first beaker, 2 drops in the second, 3 drops in the third, 4 drops in the fourth, and 5 drops in the fifth. Jiggle the beakers gently to mix the samples.

4. Have someone else change the order of the beakers. Then try to arrange the beakers from darkest to lightest colour. Check your success, and record any mistakes.

5. Repeat step 4 with the five beakers in different lightings: dark room, moderate lighting, and, if possible, bright sunlight. Look straight at the beakers when you observe them.

6. Repeat step 5, but this time look at the beakers from out of the corners of your eyes.

7. Repeat step 4 with the five beakers at several different distances: for example, 1 m, 5 m, 10 m, and 20 m.

Analysis

1. What factors allowed you to discriminate the different shades most easily? Did your observations support or refute your hypothesis? Explain.

2. Compare your results with the results of other students.

Conclusions

3. Name the structures in the eye that are responsible for vision and colour discrimination. Which receptors did you rely on the most in step 5? Which receptors did you rely on the most in steps 6 and 7? Justify your answers by explaining how the different receptors work.

Part 2: Distinguishing Sound Frequencies **ICT**

Prediction

Predict the range of frequencies that you will be able to hear.

Materials

- device that produces a wide range of sound frequencies, such as a set of tuning forks, a frequency signal generator, a Vernier or Pasco computer program that aids in analyzing different sound frequencies, or an Internet site that provides different tone frequencies

- frequency sensor (optional)

Procedure

1. Make a three-column table in your notebook to record your data for steps 2 and 3. In the first column, list the frequencies that you will generate with your device. In the next column, *predict* whether or not you will be able to detect each frequency. You will use the third column in steps 2 and 3 to record whether or not you can hear each frequency and, if so, to describe what you hear.

2. Set up your test in a quiet location. If you are using a frequency generator, turn it on. If a frequency sensor is available, turn this on too, so you can use it to record the exact frequencies generated.

3. Starting with the lowest frequency, check your ability to hear the sound generated. Then switch to higher frequencies in 1000 Hz increments, until you reach the highest frequency that can be generated. At each increment, fill in your data table.

4. Close your eyes, and have a partner gencrate a 4000 Hz sound at different locations around your head. Indicate to your partner where the sound is coming from. After the test, check with your partner to see if you were correct. Note the locations that you identified correctly.

Analysis

1. Name the specific structures of the inner ear that allow us to discriminate different frequencies. How did these structures function to allow you to hear sounds of different frequencies?

2. What range of frequencies were you able to hear? Was your prediction correct?

3. Compare your results with other students' results or with data supplied by your teacher. Are there people who can hear frequencies that you cannot, or vice versa? Suggest a reason for this.

Conclusions

4. If you cannot hear certain frequencies within the range of 20 to 20 000 Hz, suggest a reason why. Explain specifically what damage might have occurred in your ears.

5. In step 5, why was it easier to locate the source of a sound when the sound was directly in front of you or behind you, and more difficult to locate the source when the sound came from either side of you?

Extension

6. Research different causes of hearing loss. Contact an audiologist (hearing specialist), and arrange for a visit to learn how hearing tests are performed.

Hearing Loss

Hearing loss generally results from nerve damage (damage to the hair cells, called nerve deafness) or damage to the sound-conduction system of the outer or middle ear (called conduction deafness). Birth defects, ear infections, noise, and aging are common causes of hearing loss.

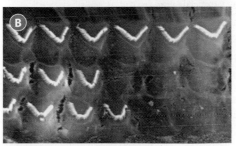

Figure 12.23 Scanning electron micrographs of stereocilia from a mouse ear. **(A)** Healthy stereocilia. **(B)** Stereocilia damaged by brief exposure to a 115 dB noise.

The amplitude of a sound wave is experienced as the intensity or volume of a sound. The louder the noise is, the more pressure that the fluid in the cochlea puts on the hair cells of the basilar membrane. The stereocilia of the hair cells are very delicate, however. Repeated or sustained exposure to loud noise destroys the stereocilia, and the resulting damage is permanent (Figure 12.23). Noise is measured in decibels (dB), and any noise over 80 dB can damage the hair cells. In today's society, people are commonly exposed to a variety of loud and potentially damaging noises (Table 12.3).

Table 12.3 Noises That Affect Hearing

Type of noise	Sound level (dB)	Effect
jet engine or rock concert	over 125	Noise is beyond the threshold of pain. There is a high potential for hearing loss.
boom box, chain saw, or snowmobile	100–125	Regular exposure for short periods of time may cause permanent hearing loss.
farm tractor, lawn mower, or motorcycle	90–100	15 min of exposure may cause hearing loss.
food blender or average city traffic	80–90	Continuous daily exposure for longer than 8 h can cause damage.

Source: United States National Institute of Deafness and Other Communication Disorders, September 2005.

While hearing aids to amplify sounds can often help people with conduction deafness, nerve deafness is more difficult to treat. In some cases, a device can be implanted in the ear to pick up sounds and directly relay signals to the auditory nerve. As well, researchers are exploring techniques to regenerate damaged or lost hair cells. One technique is to use a virus to insert a gene into the inner ear cells. The gene causes these cells to "sprout" new hair cells. So far, the technique has worked in guinea pigs, but scientists are not yet sure if it will work as a treatment for people with nerve deafness.

• • •

21 State the parts of the ear that have been damaged in someone with

a) nerve deafness

b) conduction deafness

• • •

The Perception of Sound

Sensory neurons in the ear send information through the auditory nerve to the brain stem, thalamus, and ultimately the temporal lobes of the cerebrum for processing. Depending on which sensory neurons are stimulated, the brain can perceive the frequency and amplitude of the sound. Recent research suggests that the source of the sound determines the specific neurons that are stimulated in the temporal lobes. Therefore, the brain can also perceive the location where the sound came from. Next time you hear a sound in front or behind you, imagine a cluster of neurons being stimulated in the corresponding area of your temporal lobes!

• • •

22 How is the brain able to perceive sounds of higher or lower frequencies and higher or lower amplitudes?

• • •

Balance and Coordination

Three major structures in the inner ear—the semicircular canals, utricle, and saccule—help us stand upright and move without losing our balance (Figure 12.24(A)). Thus, these structures function in our sense of equilibrium. The **semicircular canals** contain mechanoreceptors that detect head and body rotation (**rotational equilibrium**). The semicircular canals are three fluid-filled loops, arranged in three different planes—one for each dimension of space. The base of each semicircular canal ends in a bulge. Inside each bulge, the stereocilia of the hair cells stick into a jelly-like covering called a cupula. When the head rotates, the fluid inside the semicircular canals moves and bends the stereocilia, causing the hair cells to send rotational information to the brain (Figure 12.24(B)). On a fast-spinning midway ride, for example, the rapid circular motion causes the fluid within the semicircular canals to rotate and send information confirming this to the brain. When the ride stops, however, the fluid is still moving. Why might the moving fluid make someone feel dizzy or nauseous?

The balance required while moving the head forward and backward is called **gravitational equilibrium**. Gravitational equilibrium depends on the **utricle** and the **saccule**, which together make up the fluid-filled vestibule of the inner ear (Figure 12.24(A)). Both of these structures contain calcium carbonate granules, called **otoliths**. The otoliths lie in a cupula over a layer of hair cells. When the head dips forward or back, gravity pulls on the otoliths. This puts pressure on some of the hair cells, causing them to send a neural impulse to the brain, indicating the position of the head (Figure 12.24(C)).

Proprioceptors are another type of mechanoreceptor involved in coordination. Proprioceptors are found in muscles, tendons, and joints throughout the body, and they send information about body position to the brain. For

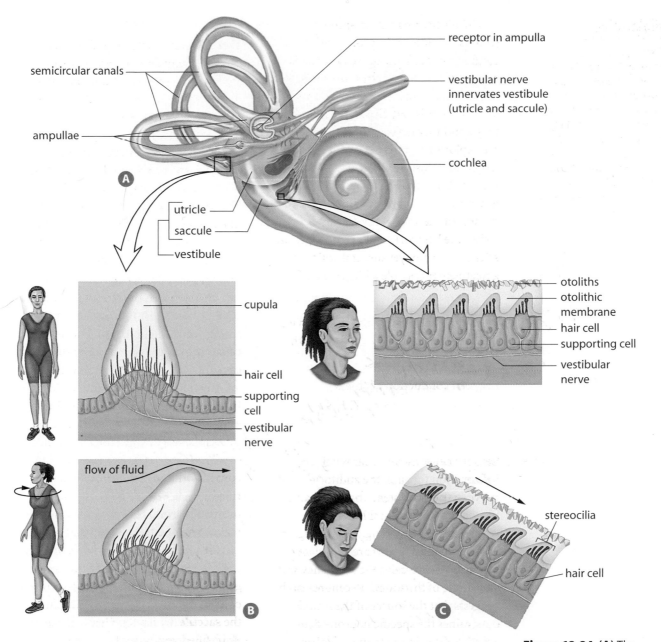

Figure 12.24 **(A)** The organs of balance: the semicircular canals, utricle, and saccule. Each semicircular canal ends in a bulge called an *ampulla*. **(B)** Rotational equilibrium. Rotating fluid bends the stereocilia in the cupula, and the hair cells send a message through the vestibular nerve to the brain. **(C)** Gravitational equilibrium. The hair cells of the utricle and saccule bend in response to head position.

example, proprioceptors give the brain enough information for you to get dressed in the dark—although they do not ensure that you will put on matching socks!

Q 23 Explain how the structures of the inner ear allow for rotational equilibrium.

Q 24 Explain how the structures of the inner ear allow for gravitational equilibrium.

Q 25 How does the brain perceive that the body is lying down?

Taste

The tongue contains chemoreceptors that allow us to taste substances entering the mouth. The ability to distinguish different tastes probably developed as an adaptation. Animals that avoided harmful substances and instead ate foods that were good for the body survived and reproduced. Poisonous plants, for example, often contain bitter-tasting molecules made of alkaloid compounds.

Most scientists recognize four basic tastes: sour, sweet, salty, and bitter. When we eat, saliva dissolves some of our food. Specific molecules dissolved in the saliva

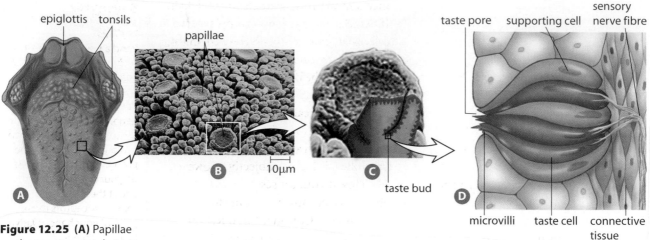

epiglottis   tonsils

papillae

10μm

taste bud

taste pore   supporting cell   sensory nerve fibre

microvilli   taste cell   connective tissue

Figure 12.25 (A) Papillae on the tongue contain taste buds that are sensitive to salty, sweet, sour, and bitter molecules. **(B)** Electron micrograph of many papillae. **(C)** Electron micrograph of one papilla. **(D)** Taste cells within the taste buds. The taste buds depolarize in response to particular tastes and generate an action potential that sends a neural impulse to the brain.

are detected by the **taste buds**: the sensory receptors in the bumps (papillae) on the tongue (Figure 12.25). Specific taste cells within the taste buds detect molecules from one of the four basic tastes.

Impulses from the taste buds travel to areas of the brain stem, to the thalamus, and then to the gustatory centre of the parietal lobe, which is responsible for the perception of taste. The combination of taste information sent from different areas of the tongue, as well as from sensory neurons in the nose, allows us to perceive flavours. The salivary glands are connected to the brain stem, which is why they are stimulated whenever we taste, smell, or think about something delicious.

 26 Describe how taste buds detect taste.

Smell

Scientists estimate that the human sense of smell can distinguish over 10 000 different odours. They think that each of these odours is produced from particles that fit, much like a lock and key, into specific chemoreceptors, called **olfactory cells**, lining the upper nasal cavity (Figure 12.26). When the particles bind to the olfactory cells, ion channels in the cell membrane open. This generates an action potential in the olfactory cells, which are directly linked to the **olfactory bulb** of the brain. From there, the impulse is sent to the emotional centres of the brain (the limbic system) and the frontal lobe, where the perception of odour occurs. Have you noticed that particular odours can instantly conjure up scenes and emotions from the past? Perfume experts create fragrances to evoke certain memories and emotions.

The sense of smell is closely linked to the sense of taste. In fact, someone who is born without a functional olfactory system has no concept of taste, despite having functional taste buds. As much as 80 to 90 percent of what we perceive as taste is actually due to the sense of smell. This is why everything tastes so bland when you have a cold. Molecules from food travel through the nose and the passages in the throat. There, they trigger the chemoreceptors which, in turn, trigger the olfactory sensory neurons. The sense of smell is what lets you experience the complex flavours that you associate with your favourite foods.

Many animals, including humans, release substances, called pheromones, that aid in the recognition and attraction of a mate, sometimes over long distances. These hormone-like chemicals are detected in the nose by a structure called the vomeronasal organ. Recently, scientists determined that the human nose also contains a vomeronasal organ, although people cannot consciously smell pheromones.

BiologyFile

FYI
There is evidence for a fifth basic taste, called *umami*. Umami is described as a savoury taste, characteristic of monosodium glutamate (MSG), and detectable in some meats and cheeses.

• • •

Q27 How do the olfactory cells detect odours?

Q28 Why might a particular scent evoke a strong emotional response in a person?

• • •

Touch

Unlike the mechanoreceptors associated with balance, hearing, taste, and smell, the mechanoreceptors associated with the sense of touch are located all over the body. The skin contains more than four million sensory receptors, but, as you learned in Chapter 11, they are not evenly distributed. Many of them are concentrated in the genitals, fingers, tongue, and lips.

Different receptors in the skin are sensitive to different stimuli, such as light touch, pressure, pain, and high and low temperatures. These receptors gather information and transmit it back through sensory neurons to the brain and spinal cord for processing and a possible reaction (Figure 12.27 on page 429).

Pain is a complicated sense that occurs when specialized sensors or nerve endings in the skin are activated by mechanical pressure or chemical signals. If tissue is damaged, for example, nerve cells called nociceptors release chemicals that trigger pain receptors to send impulses to the brain. Painkillers, such as ibuprofen and Aspirin™, block the release of these chemicals. Everyone is familiar with the sensation of pain. How we experience pain and the effects of different painkillers is highly subjective, however.

How do our senses, such as the ability to feel pain, contribute to homeostasis? Consider this question as you complete Investigation 12.C.

• • •

Q29 List the different types of stimuli that sensory receptors in skin can detect.

Q30 Where are the greatest concentrations of touch receptors in the body?

• • •

Sensation and Homeostasis

The senses allow us to navigate and experience the world around us. The senses relay information to the nervous system that allows the body to maintain homeostasis. Seeing the bright morning

BiologyFile

Try This
Bend a paper clip into a U-shape with the two ends about 2 mm apart. Close your eyes, and gently push down on the palm of your hand. Then try this on your shoulder. In which location could you distinguish the prongs as separate? What do your results suggest about the number of sensory receptors in the palm of your hand, relative to your shoulder?

Figure 12.26 (A) The human olfactory system. Trace how the smell of this rose is detected and then perceived in **(B)**. The cilia of each olfactory cell can bind to only one type of odour molecule (represented here with colour).

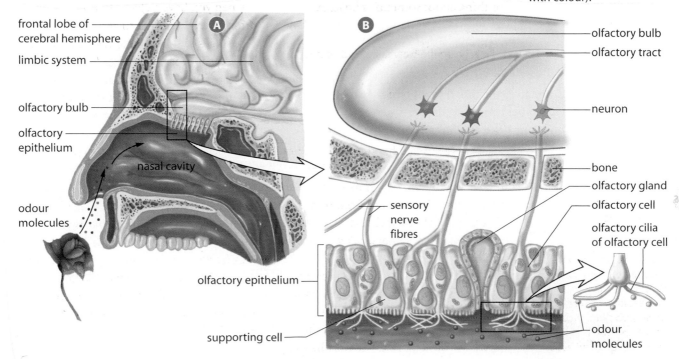

frontal lobe of cerebral hemisphere
limbic system
olfactory bulb
olfactory epithelium
nasal cavity
odour molecules

olfactory bulb
olfactory tract
neuron
bone
olfactory gland
olfactory cell
olfactory cilia of olfactory cell
odour molecules
sensory nerve fibres
olfactory epithelium
supporting cell

Feel, Taste, or Smell: Design Your Own Investigation

How can you determine the range and types of information that each of your senses can detect? Your group will explore one of the topics described below by designing, planning, and conducting an investigation. You will need to show clearly how a specific sense (touch, taste, or smell) can distinguish numerous sensations.

Question

How can you design an investigation to show how a particular sense, or a combination of senses, can distinguish various sensations?

Safety Precautions

- Do not bring food meant for consumption into the laboratory.
- Do not eat or drink anything in the laboratory.

Topic 1: Feel Those Sensations

Design an investigation to distinguish the different sensory receptors found in the skin, including the receptors for touch, pressure, pain, heat, and cold.

Suggested Materials

- 500 mL beaker of hot water (60 °C)
- 500 mL beaker of ice water (0–2 °C)
- non-permanent pen for marking gridlines on the body
- alcohol thermometer
- finishing nails

Topic 2: Tantalize Those Taste Buds

Design an investigation to distinguish the four basic tastes (sweet, salty, sour, and bitter) using the tongue. Also investigate the relationship between smell and taste. **Note:** You must conduct this investigation at home or in the school cafeteria, *not* in the laboratory.

Suggested Materials

- salty water
- sugary water or candy
- onion juice or tonic water
- clean toothpicks or cotton swabs
- lemon juice
- garbage bin
- blindfold

Topic 3: Expose Your Nose

Design an investigation to determine the ability of the olfactory receptors to distinguish various smells.

Suggested Materials

- ginger
- lemon
- menthol
- peppermint
- pine needles
- vanilla
- vinegar
- perfume
- blindfold

Experimental Plan

1. As a group, record the question(s) that you plan to investigate.

2. Write a hypothesis related to your experimental question(s).

3. Using the suggested materials as a starting point, develop a procedure to investigate your topic. List the manipulated, responding, and controlled variables. Note what you can use as a control test or trial (point of reference for your experimental trials).

4. Decide how your group will make the appropriate measurements, how many samples you will use, and whether you will pool your data with other groups' data. Design a table to record your data.

5. After obtaining approval from your teacher for your experimental design, conduct your investigation.

Data and Observations

Record your data. When you have completed your investigation, present your experimental design and results to the rest of the class. Include a diagram that shows the neural pathway from the sensory receptors to the area of the brain where perception occurs.

Analysis

1. Describe any unexpected results. Hypothesize if and how your results would have been different if you had tested a combination of senses.

2. How could you improve your experimental design?

Conclusion

3. How are the sensory receptors organized so that we can distinguish different strengths and types of touch, taste, and smell?

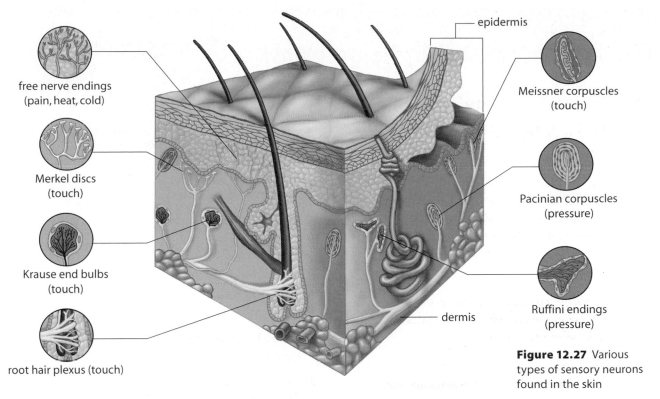

free nerve endings (pain, heat, cold)

Merkel discs (touch)

Krause end bulbs (touch)

root hair plexus (touch)

epidermis

Meissner corpuscles (touch)

Pacinian corpuscles (pressure)

Ruffini endings (pressure)

dermis

Figure 12.27 Various types of sensory neurons found in the skin

sunlight, for example, tells the body that it is time to wake up. Internal sensors help to prevent you from slipping in the shower. In Chapter 13, you will explore how hormones—chemical messengers in the body—trigger responses to sensations, as well as changes in the body that we do not consciously feel.

Section 12.3 Summary

- The mechanoreceptors for hearing and balance are located in the inner ear.
- The cochlea, semicircular canals, utricle, and saccule all contain hair cells that react to movement.

- The hair cells synapse with nerve fibres, which transmit the sensory information to the nerves. The nerves then send an impulse to the brain.
- Proprioceptors in the muscles, joints, and tendons also inform the brain about the position of body parts.
- Sensory receptors in the tongue (taste buds), nose (olfactory cells), and skin (temperature, pressure, and pain receptors) provide additional information to the brain.

Section 12.3	Review

1. Explain how the structures of the ear amplify sounds.

2. How do the inner ear and brain distinguish the high shriek of a sea gull from the low sound made by a drum? What area of the brain perceives these sounds?

3. Based on your understanding of the inner ear, explain why someone might feel unwell after riding in a fast elevator in a tall building.

4. Suppose that you have been swimming along the bottom of the deep end of a pool. When you surface, you experience discomfort in your ears. Explain why plugging your nose while gently exhaling may help to alleviate the discomfort.

5. Suppose that your aunt works long hours at a newspaper printing press, where she is constantly exposed to sounds over 97 dB. What precautions, if any, would you recommend to her? Explain your answer in terms of the cellular structures of the inner ear.

Pain Relievers or Deadly Neurotoxins?

Pain receptors called *nociceptors* are free nerve endings found throughout the skin and internal organs. When tissue injury or chemical messengers stimulate the nociceptors, they transmit information to the brain and we feel pain. Pain may be unpleasant, but it usually serves as a warning to the brain to take action to prevent further injury. However, for millions of Canadians who suffer from the chronic pain of headaches, back pain, muscular-skeletal disorders, fibromyalgia, cancer, or AIDS, pain can be debilitating. To help those with chronic pain, researchers are looking to natural—but deadly—neurotoxins for targeted pain relief.

Phyllobates terribilis

Poisonous Frogs and Pain

The golden poison arrow frog (*Phyllobates terribilis*) secretes a powerful neurotoxin called batrachotoxin. For centuries, aboriginal peoples of the Columbian rainforests have used batrachotoxin in traditional spiritual rituals and in healing and hunting practices. Before a hunt, arrows are dipped in a blend made from the frog's secretions. When the arrow penetrates the prey's skin, the animal dies swiftly. Batrachotoxin affects the victim's neurons by preventing sodium gates in the neural membrane from closing. The resulting constant stimulation leads to a depletion of neurotransmitters and irreversible depolarization of nerves and muscle cells. Muscles throughout the body, most significantly the heart and diaphragm, remain contracted, which causes rapid paralysis and death.

Researchers are now studying the neurotoxin for its use as a targeted pain medication. Severe pain is commonly treated with morphine, which suppresses the whole central nervous system as it blocks the transmission of pain signals to the brain from the receptors. Morphine also interferes with other parts of the nervous system, causing nausea, sedation, and confusion. In addition, patients can build up a tolerance for the drug that makes progressively higher doses necessary in order for it to work. Very small doses of neurotoxins such as batrachotoxin could, on the other hand, be used to stop impulse transmission in the cell membranes of the pain receptors, without the side effects associated with morphine. Scientists are searching the world's jungles and oceans to find organisms, including plants, snails, fish, bacteria, and amphibians, which contain similar neurotoxins.

Takifugu

Biodiversity: A Medicine Chest

Substances with medicinal potential come from some unlikely sources. For example, coral reefs are home to over 500 species of cone snail (*Conus*), each of which produces a version of the deadly venom called conotoxin, which the snails use to immobilize prey. Conotoxin contains a component that causes muscle paralysis, plus a pain-reducing component, which blocks the acetylcholine receptors on pain transmission neurons. It could potentially be used to control nerve pain caused by surgery, diabetes, cancer, or AIDS.

Puffer fish, or fugu (*Takifugu*), is a popular delicacy in Japan, despite containing the deadly neurotoxin tetrodotoxin. Ingesting even a milligram of tetrodotoxin can be fatal. The toxin appears to work by blocking sodium ion channels in the neurons, which can lead to respiratory paralysis. A Vancouver, British Columbia company produces a purified form of tetrodotoxin called Tectin™, which has shown promise as a pain reliever for some people undergoing cancer treatment. Tetrodotoxin is 3000 times stronger than morphine but in low doses appears to safely inhibit the pain neurons.

• • •

1. Why might some organisms have evolved to contain or secrete potent neurotoxins?

2. The bacterium *Clostridium botulinum* produces botulinum toxin, which can cause fatal food poisoning. Botulinum toxin inhibits the release of acetylcholine, resulting in paralysis. (A by-product, Botox®, is used to paralyze facial muscles and temporarily smooth wrinkles.) Knowing that one of the causes of migraine headaches is the constriction of arteries that bring blood to the brain, why might low doses of botulinum toxin be effective for controlling migraines?

3. What are the advantages of targeted painkillers over those with more general effects?

Sensory reception occurs at the senses. Sensation and perception occur in the brain. Various sensory receptors detect information in the internal and external environments. Photoreceptors detect light. Chemoreceptors detect tastes, odours, and internal conditions, such as blood pH and volume. Thermoreceptors detect temperature. Mechanoreceptors function in hearing, balance, and coordination.

The cornea, lens, and humours of the eye direct light on the photoreceptor cells in the retina. Rods function in dim light and produce black and white images. Cones function in bright light and produce colour images. The optic nerve transmits signals from the rods and cones to the occipetal lobe of the cerebral cortex, where images are perceived. The lens can accommodate to focus nearby or distant objects on the retina.

The outer ear transmits sound waves to the middle ear, which makes the tympanum vibrate. This, in turn, makes the bones of the middle ear vibrate. These bones amplify and transmit the vibrations to the oval window in the inner ear. The vibrations in the oval window produce pressure waves in the fluid of the cochlea in the inner ear. The pressure waves are detected by hair cells, which relay electrochemical messages to the brain via the auditory nerve.

Hearing aids that amplify sound can sometimes be used to treat conduction deafness caused by damage to the outer or middle ear. Noise-induced hearing loss, caused by destruction of the hair cells, is more difficult to treat. It results in a loss of ability to hear sounds of specific frequencies.

Hair cells in the semicircular canals of the inner ear allow for rotational equilibrium (balance). Hair cells in the utricle and saccule of the inner ear allow for gravitational equilibrium (balance). Proprioceptors are another type of mechanoreceptor involved in coordination.

Tastes are detected by chemoreceptors in the taste buds of the tongue. Smells are detected by chemoreceptors in the nose.

The skin contains receptors for light touch, pressure, pain, heat, and cold. Sensors in the nose, tongue, and skin all help the nervous system maintain homeostasis.

Chapter 12 Graphic Organizer

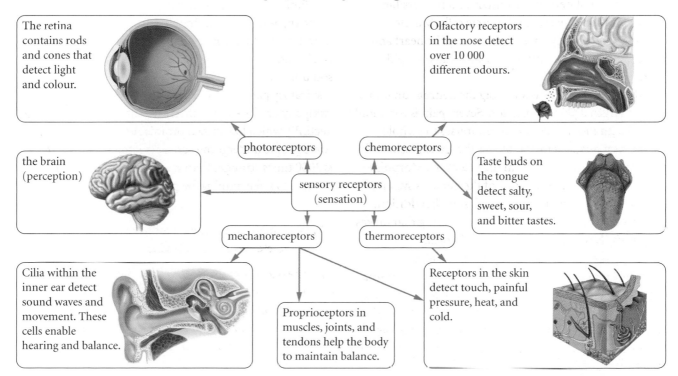

The retina contains rods and cones that detect light and colour.

Olfactory receptors in the nose detect over 10 000 different odours.

photoreceptors

chemoreceptors

the brain (perception)

sensory receptors (sensation)

Taste buds on the tongue detect salty, sweet, sour, and bitter tastes.

mechanoreceptors

thermoreceptors

Cilia within the inner ear detect sound waves and movement. These cells enable hearing and balance.

Proprioceptors in muscles, joints, and tendons help the body to maintain balance.

Receptors in the skin detect touch, painful pressure, heat, and cold.

Understanding Concepts

1. List the major structures in the pathway of neural conduction from the organ of smell to the appropriate area of the brain.

2. Draw a table in your notebook with the following headings: Photoreceptors, Mechanoreceptors, Chemoreceptors, Thermoreceptors. For each type of receptor, list what it detects and provide an example of a human sense organ that contains this receptor.

3. Copy the diagram of the eye into your notebook. Label the visible structures, and indicate their functions. Also indicate the locations and functions of the rods and cones.

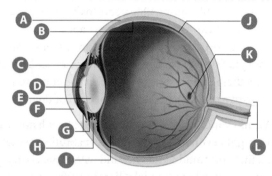

4. Describe how the touch receptors transduce energy into a form that the nervous system can use.

5. People who have lost a limb in a war or accident often report feeling sensations and even extreme pain in the limb that is no longer there. The cause of this phenomenon, called phantom limb syndrome, is unclear. Why is it possible for someone to perceive a sensation despite missing the associated sense receptors?

6. Explain how the inner ear and brain distinguish sounds of different frequencies and different volumes.

7. Once sensory neurons for a specific odour are stimulated, insensitivity to that odour rapidly occurs both in the sensory neurons of the nose and in the brain. What is this phenomenon called? Why would it be an adaptive advantage in certain circumstances?

8. Explain what happens to the pupils of your eyes if you walk into a dark movie theater after a stroll outside on a sunny day. What is this reflex called?

9. Which kind of photoreceptor would you expect to be most numerous in the retinas of an animal that hunts at night? Explain your reasoning.

10. When you close one eye, you may notice a blind spot in your field of vision. What is the blind spot? Why do you not see it all the time?

11. Use word processing or graphics software to make a flowchart mapping the events that occur from the time the light of a full Moon reaches your retina to the time your brain perceives it. **ICT**

12. Studies show that some people who play action video games can process visual information faster and pick out more objects in a scene compared to people with little or no experience playing video games. Which area(s) of the brain must have been affected in the video game players?

13. Which receptors does your body rely on when you are standing still for a photo? Explain where these receptors are located, how they are stimulated, and how they send information to the brain.

14. What happens in your eyes when you focus on the words on this page? What is the process called? Use graphics software to sketch what happens to the lens of the eye when you focus on the words, and then when you look out the window at a bird in a tree. **ICT**

15. Using an example, compare rotational equilibrium with gravitational equilibrium. Identify the specific structures involved.

16. The early stages of glaucoma tend to affect the peripheral vision. Why might someone with early stage glaucoma want to avoid driving at night?

17. Which senses might be affected by an injury to one of the temporal lobes of the brain?

18. Use word processing software to make a flowchart tracing the pathway of a sound wave as it travels through the outer, middle, and inner ear. Indicate where the auditory information is sent to the brain. Also indicate the principal structures involved and their functions, and the specific area of the brain where the perception of sound occurs. **ICT**

19. A heavy machinery operator is tested for hearing loss. It turns out that the operator has trouble hearing some frequencies of sound, but not others. Explain why.

Applying Concepts

20. List some possible effects of sensory deprivation on homeostasis. Suggest a hypothesis to explain why these effects occur.

21. A severe blow to a particular area of the head can cause blindness. Describe how you would design a safety helmet to protect a cyclist from damage to the visual centres of the brain.

22. How could you design a technology to treat red-blue colour blindness?

23. Scientists have devised both retinal and cochlear implants to compensate for non-functional sense receptors. Explain what such devices could offer people who have vision or hearing problems, compared with technologies such as eyeglasses and hearing aids.

24. Most parts of the body continue to grow new cells and discard old cells. The lens of the eye, however, is unique because it continues to get larger over time, and old, dead cells cannot escape. The lens of an 8-year-old has a mass of about 130 mg, while the lens of an 80-year-old has a mass of about 225 mg. Given this information, why do you think older people often need eyeglasses?

25. A dog's sense of smell is so keen that a dog can detect illegal drugs, and even evidence of bladder cancer in human urine. Suggest possible structural adaptations that a dog might have that would enable it to have such a superb sense of smell.

26. Stare at the green bird in the diagram for at least 1 min. Then look in the cage. Do you see the bird in the cage? Now stare at the red bird for 1 min. Then look in the cage. What do you see? The resulting effect in each case is called an afterimage. How would you explain the cause of an afterimage, given that the cone cells of the retina lose their sensitivity when they become fatigued?

27. Dogs have two types of cones in the retina: one type detects blue-violet light and the other type detects yellow light. Based on this information, which colours do you think dogs are most likely to see? Which colours would dogs likely have trouble distinguishing?

Making Connections

28. Using what you know about threshold potential (Chapter 11) and sensory receptors on the skin (Chapter 12), explain why some individuals seem to be more tolerant of pain than others.

29. Researchers have discovered that premature babies with apnea, a condition that causes them to stop breathing during sleep, can be somewhat helped by having them smell the scent of vanilla. Provide a possible explanation for this effect.

30. Deadly neurotoxins produced by some organisms, such as the rattlesnake and black widow spider, could have medical implications. One neurotoxin from rattlesnake venom blocks receptors on postsynaptic neurons. Venom from the female black widow spider stimulates exocytosis of synaptic vesicles from neurons. Speculate how these neurotoxins might affect the body, and suggest a possible medical use for each of them.

31. Would you use a technological device to enhance your eyesight beyond natural human capabilities, perhaps so that you could see farther and with more clarity, or sense infrared or ultraviolet light? Justify your response.

32. Throughout the world, many natural habitats are quickly disappearing as a result of human activities. Explain how this situation might affect the discovery of new medications.

33. The ancient Greeks, Egyptians, Sumerians, and Native Americans used an extract of willow bark known as salicin to treat aches and fever. The extract was later patented in a product known as Aspirin™. Some neurotoxins that Western scientists are now researching for use as painkillers have also been used in the traditional practices of Aboriginal peoples for centuries. Should traditional knowledge of medications continue to be patented and sold? If so, who should be paid for the patents on such "discoveries"?

Hormonal Regulation of Homeostasis

Chapter Concepts

13.1 The Glands and Hormones of the Endocrine System

- The endocrine system functions with the nervous system to regulate other body systems and maintain homeostasis.

- The endocrine glands secrete hormones directly into the bloodstream.

- Hormone secretion is regulated by the nervous system, other hormones, or negative feedback mechanisms.

13.2 Hormonal Regulation of Growth, Development, and Metabolism

- The hypothalamus regulates the pituitary gland, which secretes tropic hormones that affect various endocrine glands.

- Human growth hormone mainly affects bone and muscle growth. The thyroid hormones stimulate metabolism.

13.3 Hormonal Regulation of the Stress Response

- The hormones of the adrenal glands regulate the short-term and long-term stress responses.

13.4 Hormonal Regulation of Blood Sugar

- The hormones of the pancreas act antagonistically to maintain blood glucose levels within a narrow range. Diabetes results from improper regulation of blood glucose.

The bear moves cautiously toward the stream. For his body to maintain homeostasis, he must drink. But before he does, he is surprised by a growl from behind him. Terror pulses through his body and he whirls to face his attacker. It is another Kodiak bear (*Ursus arctos middendorffi*), the giant Alaskan grizzly. This could be the final challenge of his life. In this instant between survival and death, his body's endocrine system will ready him to fight or run away to safety. In humans and other animals, the endocrine system produces chemical messengers called hormones that regulate various systems of the body, including the response to perceived danger. When you are facing a threat, what physiological processes occur in your body? Which of these processes do hormones control? Chapter 13 explores the role of hormones in responding to danger and in regulating human systems.

Modern Stress!

Exams, deadlines, and bills can all trigger a person's stress response. These stressors are not life threatening. Nevertheless, the body often responds as if they were, and produces the same physiological changes that would occur in a truly dangerous situation. In this activity, you will monitor one of the changes that occur in the body in response to a stressful, although not life-threatening, situation.

Safety

Do not take the role of the subject in this activity if you have an underlying medical condition, such as high or low blood pressure, that is made worse by stress.

Materials

- test questions
- stopwatch

Procedure

1. Work with a partner. One person will be the subject, and the other partner will be the tester.

2. The tester will obtain a stopwatch from your teacher. The subject will sit at a desk for 1 min with eyes closed and taking deep, relaxing breaths.

3. At the end of the relaxation period, the tester will take and record the subject's pulse over 1 min.

4. The tester will obtain a test from your teacher. The tester will give the test to the subject, who will have 2 min to complete the test.

5. Start the stopwatch when the subject starts the test.

6. At the end of the 2 min, shout "time's up!" and immediately take and record the subject's pulse over 1 min.

Analysis

1. Calculate the subject's pulse rate (beats per min) before and after writing the test.

2. List the main physiological changes that occurred in the subject while writing the test. (**Hint:** See Chapter 11, page 397.)

3. How would the physiological changes that you listed in question 2 be useful responses to a life-threatening situation?

4. List ten or more stressful situations that people in modern societies may experience. Which of these are truly dangerous? Which, if any, might be considered positive?

The Glands and Hormones of the Endocrine System

Figure 13.1 This synchronized swimmer relies on various body systems in order to perform her routine. The organs of her body's systems are composed of trillions of cells, some of which help to carry oxygen, remove wastes, move muscles, and hear sounds. Some cells communicate critical information from one area of the body to another.

The synchronized swimmer in Figure 13.1 relies on complex internal systems in order to hold her breath and swim in time to the music, while continuing to maintain homeostasis. Her respiratory, metabolic, and muscular-skeletal systems, for example, are regulated and co-ordinated. This means that the functioning of the over 100 trillion diverse cells making up the tissues and organs of her body must also be regulated and co-ordinated, and, therefore, the cells must be able to communicate with one another. The body systems that facilitate cellular communication and control are the nervous and endocrine systems (Figure 13.2).

Nervous system messages tend to be transmitted rapidly to precise locations in the body, such as the reflex arc that causes you to withdraw your hand from a hot stove. In addition to cellular communication through neurons, the body secretes chemical messengers from glands. **Endocrine glands** secrete chemical messengers called **hormones** directly into the bloodstream, which transports the hormones throughout the body. The original Greek meaning of the word *hormone* is "to excite" or "set in motion." As shown in Figure 13.3, when hormones reach their target cells, their interaction with these cells sets in motion specific regulatory responses. The action of the pancreas is an example

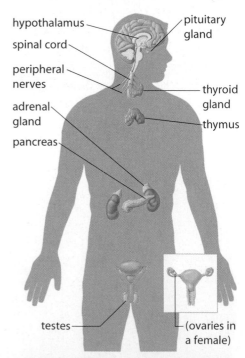

Figure 13.2 Some of the key glands of the endocrine system superimposed on the nervous system. How do the two systems work together to regulate homeostasis?

hypothalamus
spinal cord
peripheral nerves
adrenal gland
pancreas
pituitary gland
thyroid gland
thymus
testes
(ovaries in a female)

of this. Figure 13.4 shows the pancreas, an endocrine gland that secretes the hormone insulin into the bloodstream. Insulin affects its target cells by making them more permeable to glucose.

The endocrine glands and the hormones that they secrete make up the **endocrine system**. Compared to the rapid actions of the nervous system, the endocrine system typically has slower and longer acting effects, and affects a broader range of cell types.

Homeostasis depends on the close relationship between the nervous system and the endocrine system. Note, however, that the distinction between these two systems is often arbitrary. For example:

- Some nervous system tissues secrete hormones, such as cells in the hypothalamus, pituitary gland, and adrenal glands.
- Several chemicals function as both neurotransmitters and hormones, depending on their location in the body. An example is epinephrine, which acts as a neurotransmitter between certain neurons in the nervous system, and as a hormone released by the adrenal glands in the fight-or-flight response.
- The endocrine and nervous systems both include responses that are regulated by negative feedback loops.
- The regulation of several physiological processes involves both the nervous and endocrine systems acting in conjunction

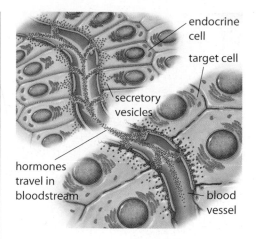

Figure 13.3 Endocrine gland secretion of hormones. How are the actions of the endocrine system different from the actions of the nervous system?

with each other. For example, when a mother breast-feeds her baby, the baby's suckling initiates a sensory message in the mother's neurons that travel to the hypothalamus, which in turn triggers the pituitary to release a hormone called oxytocin. Oxytocin travels in the bloodstream to the mammary glands of the breast, causing the secretion of milk.

• • •

1. Why do nervous system responses tend to be more rapid than endocrine system responses?

2. Define the term *hormone* using a specific example.

3. Provide four reasons why the distinction between the nervous and endocrine systems is sometimes blurred.

• • •

Figure 13.4 **(A)** A false-colour scanning electron micrograph and **(B)** a drawing of pancreas tissue. The hormone-producing cells are surrounded by blood vessels.

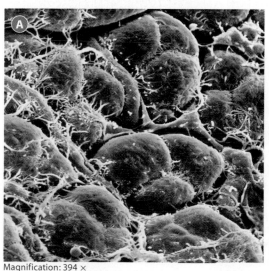

Magnification: 394 ×

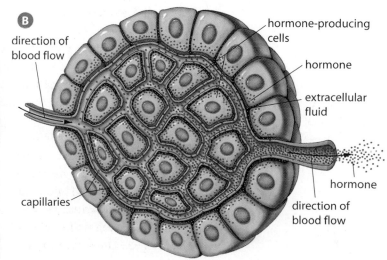

Figure 13.5 (A) An intact male rooster and **(B)** a castrated rooster (called a capon). What differences can you note between the capon and the other rooster?

From Hypothesis to Evidence

The first experiment to establish the link between hormones and the activity of their target organs is credited to Arnold Adolph Berthold of Göttingen University, in Germany. In 1849, Berthold experimented with roosters by removing their testes and observing the effects on the birds, now called *capons*. Unlike the intact roosters, the capons did not crow, fight with other roosters, or try to mate. The capons did not grow very large or develop the typical male rooster plumage (Figure 13.5). When Berthold replaced the testes into the capons, they began to look and behave like typical male roosters. Since the replaced organs were not connected to any nerves, Berthold concluded that the testes were releasing

something into the bloodstream that caused the developmental changes in the male birds. Scientists later identified this substance as the hormone testosterone.

Researchers went on to study the function of other endocrine glands by removing them from test animals and observing the effects. These early techniques did not always provide useful results, however, because different hormones often work together, and in fact, another gland or hormone can compensate for one that is missing. Also, some glands produce more than one hormone. For example, the parathyroid glands are embedded in the thyroid tissue. Both tissues produce different hormones, however, which have different effects on the body.

Another complication is that the concentration of most hormones in the bloodstream is extremely low (10^{-8} to 10^{-12} mol/L). This is comparable to one drop of water in a swimming pool. Furthermore, they are not released continuously. Their release can be triggered by environmental factors, or may follow a pattern that repeats over hours, weeks, or every year.

More recently, nuclear scanning devices (such as PET) and high-powered microscopes have allowed scientists to visualize glands, hormones, and target cell

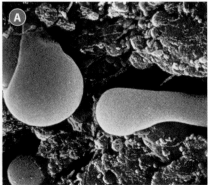

Magnification: 3720 ×

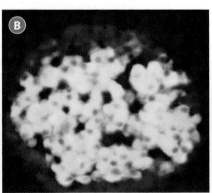

Magnification: 304.5 ×

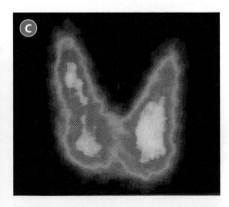

Figure 13.6 (A) A scanning electron micrograph of thyroid tissue. The image has been coloured using a computer so that the hormone (in yellow) can be seen being secreted from chambers in the thyroid (in pink), which are nourished by blood capillaries (in grey). **(B)** Stained hormone-secreting cells of the pancreas as seen using a fluorescence microscope. The different hormones of the pancreas are stained with different colours, which are attached to hormone-specific antibodies. **(C)** Nuclear scan of a thyroid gland. Radioactive iodide makes the thyroid highly visible. The orange and red areas indicate the most active areas of the tissue.

membranes in great detail. Figure 13.6A shows a portion of the thyroid gland and the capillary network that nourishes it. At a magnification of 3720 ×, this image also shows a hormone that is being secreted by the thyroid. In another technique, fluorescent stains are used to colour the different hormones in a tissue sample. To view endocrine glands in the living body, doctors can have patients ingest capsules containing a small amount of radioactive material—effectively the same amount of radiation someone would receive from a standard X ray. The radioactive material, or tracer, accumulates in specific glands, which makes them easy to distinguish in PET scans or by other nuclear scanning techniques.

• • •

4 How did Adolph Berthold's experiment with roosters demonstrate the function of an endocrine gland?

5 What are some of the challenges for researchers studying the endocrine system?

6 Briefly describe two technologies used to study hormones and endocrine glands.

• • •

Hormone Action on Target Cells

Scientists have identified over 200 hormones or hormone-like chemicals in the human body. Some regulate growth and development, others speed up or slow down the body's metabolism, while others regulate blood pressure or the immune response. Figure 13.7 shows the location in the body of the major and best studied endocrine glands: the hypothalamus, and pituitary, pineal, thyroid, parathyroid, and adrenal glands, as well as the pancreas, the testes, and the ovaries. Table 13.1 on page 440 provides an overview of some of these glands, the hormones they release, and their effects on target tissues and organs.

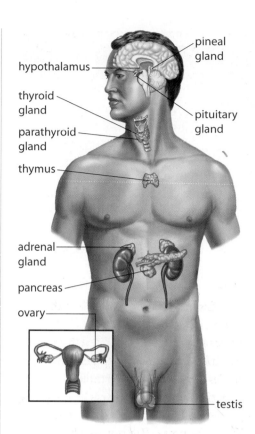

Figure 13.7 The anatomical location of the major endocrine glands of the body. The role of the thymus gland in the immune system is noted in Chapter 8.

When hormones encounter their target cells, how do they affect them? Each target cell contains *receptor proteins*. Circulating hormones bind to their specific receptor proteins, much like a key fits into a lock. For example, human growth hormone (hGH) circulates in the bloodstream and interacts with liver, muscle, and bone cells. Each of these cell types contains receptor proteins specifically shaped to bind with hGH (Figure 13.8). When the hormone binds to its receptor, this triggers other reactions in the target cell. In other words, the target cell receives and responds to the chemical message sent by the hormone.

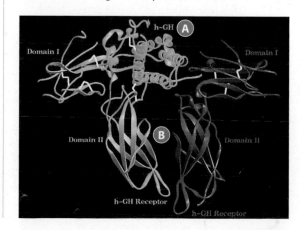

Figure 13.8 A model of **(A)** hGH (in green) bound to **(B)** its protein receptor (in blue and purple). Each hormone of the endocrine system has a unique molecular shape, which fits into a specific receptor protein on its target cells.

Table 13.1 The Principal Endocrine Glands and Some of their Hormones

Endocrine Gland	Hormone Secreted	Effects of Hormone on Target Tissues/Organs
hypothalamus	hypothalamic releasing- and inhibiting-hormones	regulates anterior pituitary hormones
anterior pituitary	human growth hormone (hGH)	stimulates cell division, bone and muscle growth, and metabolic functions
	thyroid-stimulating hormone (TSH)	stimulates the thyroid gland
	adrenocorticotropic hormone (ACTH)	stimulates the adrenal cortex to secrete glucocorticoids
	follicle-stimulating hormone (FSH)	stimulates production of ova and sperm from the ovaries and testes
	luteinizing hormone (LH)	stimulates sex hormone production from the ovaries and testes
	prolactin (PRL)	stimulates milk production from the mammary glands
posterior pituitary	antidiuretic hormone (ADH)	promotes the retention of water by the kidneys
	oxytocin (OCT)	stimulates uterine muscle contractions and release of milk by the mammary glands
thyroid	thyroxine (T_4)	affects all tissues increases metabolic rate and regulates growth and development
	calcitonin	targets bones and kidneys to lower blood calcium by inhibiting release of calcium from bone and reabsorption of calcium by kidneys
parathyroid	parathyroid hormone (PTH)	raises blood calcium levels by stimulating the bone cells to release calcium, the intestine to absorb calcium from food, and the kidneys to reabsorb calcium
adrenal cortex	glucocorticoids (e.g., cortisol)	stimulate tissues to raise blood glucose and break down protein
	mineralocorticoids (e.g., aldosterone)	promote reabsorption of sodium and water by the kidneys
	gonadocorticoids	promote secondary sexual characteristics
adrenal medulla	epinephrine and norepinephrine	fight-or-flight hormones raise blood glucose levels
pancreas	insulin	lowers blood glucose levels and promotes the formation of glycogen in the liver
	glucagon	raises blood glucose levels by converting glycogen to glucose
ovaries	estrogen	stimulates uterine lining growth and promotes development of the female secondary sexual characteristics
	progesterone	promotes growth of the uterine lining and prevents uterine muscle contractions
testes	testosterone	promotes sperm formation and development of the male secondary sexual characteristics

Lipid-Soluble and Water-Soluble Hormones

Hormones are composed of either lipids or amino acids. Steroid hormones, such as testosterone, estrogen, and cortisol, are lipid-based. Therefore, these hormones can easily diffuse through the lipid bilayer of cell membranes. Inside the target cell, steroid hormones bind to their receptor proteins. This interaction activates specific genes, causing changes in the cell. For example, estrogen can trigger cell growth.

Epinephrine, human growth hormone, thyroxine, and insulin are water-soluble hormones. Water-soluble hormones, such as amino-acid based hormones, cannot diffuse across the cell membrane. Typically, a water-soluble hormone will bind to a receptor protein on the surface of the target cell. This starts a cascade of reactions inside the target cell. Much like a phone fan-out in which everyone on a list phones several other people, each reaction that occurs in the target cell triggers many other reactions. As a result of this process, the impact of the hormone is greatly amplified. This is why a single molecule of epinephrine in the liver can trigger the conversion of available glycogen into about one million molecules of glucose. Once a hormone's message has been delivered, enzymes inactivate the hormone, since any lingering effect could potentially be very disruptive.

• • •

7 What are the two major groups of hormones? How do they interact with their target cells?

8 How does a hormone stimulate a response in a target cell?

9 Identify which glands secrete the following hormones: thyroxine, human growth hormone, cortisol, insulin, and glucagon.

• • •

Regulating the Regulators

Many hormones are regulated by **negative feedback mechanisms**, or loops. When a certain blood concentration of hormone is reached, or when target cells have responded to a specific hormone, the endocrine gland releasing the hormone is inhibited. Thus, the release of the hormone slows.

In Chapter 9, you learned how **antidiuretic hormone (ADH)** and aldosterone regulate water reabsorption by the kidneys (Figure 13.9). When the blood plasma becomes too concentrated, receptors in the hypothalamus detect this and send a neural signal to the posterior pituitary gland to release ADH. ADH targets the nephrons of the kidneys, causing the tubules to become more permeable to water. As a result, more water is reabsorbed, the body excretes less (but more concentrated) urine, and blood pressure increases. The hypothalamus detects this and sends a signal to the posterior pituitary to stop secreting ADH.

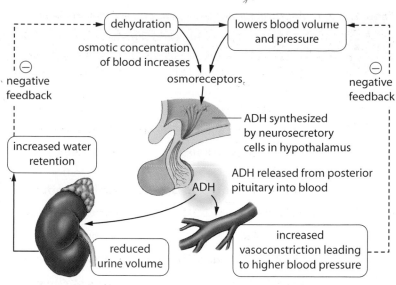

ADH causes water to be retained

Figure 13.9 A negative feedback mechanism controls the secretion of ADH from the hypothalamus.

The inability to produce ADH causes diabetes insipidus—a condition in which a person produces large volumes of urine with a resulting loss of ions from the blood. The condition can be corrected by administering ADH.

Many of the hormones released from the anterior pituitary and the hypothalamus are called **tropic hormones**, which means that their targets are other endocrine glands. Tropic hormones stimulate endocrine glands to release other hormones. Figure 13.10 shows the general mechanism of action of tropic hormones. Typically the hypothalamus secretes a releasing hormone into the anterior pituitary. This causes the anterior pituitary to release a tropic hormone into the bloodstream. The tropic hormone then stimulates the

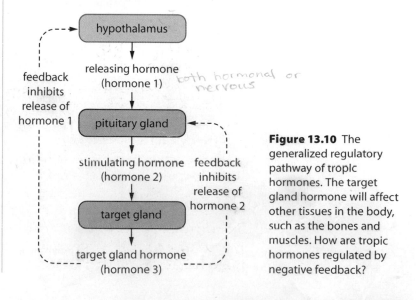

both hormonal or nervous

Figure 13.10 The generalized regulatory pathway of tropic hormones. The target gland hormone will affect other tissues in the body, such as the bones and muscles. How are tropic hormones regulated by negative feedback?

BiologyFile

FYI

Bedwetting is not always a matter of weak self-control. Some children wet their beds because their bodies do not produce enough ADH. In this case, an ADH nasal spray can be used to address the situation.

target gland to release a third hormone into the blood. This hormone travels to another target tissue and produces an effect. This system is also controlled by a negative feedback loop in which the third hormone prevents further release of the first two hormones in the pathway.

• • •

10 Describe how the secretion of ADH is regulated by negative feedback.

11 What is a tropic hormone?

12 How is the secretion of tropic hormones from the pituitary gland regulated?

• • •

Section 13.1 Summary

- The nervous and endocrine systems are self-regulating, and help regulate other body systems, thereby maintaining homeostasis.

- The nervous system rapidly affects specific tissues, to which it is directly connected by neurons. The endocrine system relies on chemical messengers called hormones, which circulate in the blood, and have broad, long-lasting effects.
- The endocrine glands have no ducts, and secrete hormones directly into the bloodstream.
- Hormones trigger changes in their target cells when they bind to receptor proteins on or within the cells.
- Tropic hormones stimulate endocrine glands to produce other hormones.
- Many hormones are regulated by negative feedback mechanisms. For example, ADH is released when the blood plasma concentration is high (and blood pressure is low). ADH stimulates the kidneys to absorb more water, which dilutes the blood plasma (and increases blood pressure).

Section 13.1 | Review

1. Define homeostasis and explain how the endocrine system helps to maintain homeostasis in the body.

2. Use an example to explain how the nervous and endocrine systems work together to regulate a response in the body.

3. Use the following diagrams to answer this question. For each diagram (1 and 2), in your notebook, list the hormones that are released by the pituitary and indicated by letters (A) through (I). List a major effect that each hormone has on its target organ.

4. Draw and describe a negative feedback mechanism for a thermostat. How is this feedback mechanism similar to how some hormones are regulated in the body? **ICT**

5. Suppose a scientist has discovered a new hormone. It is not clear what gland produces the hormone, but people who produce above average amounts of this hormone also produce very high levels of insulin. Based on your knowledge of how tropic hormones function, provide a possible explanation for the observation.

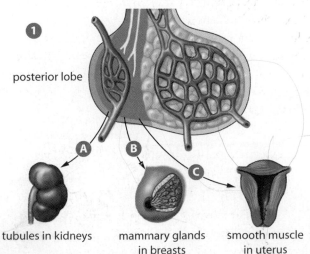

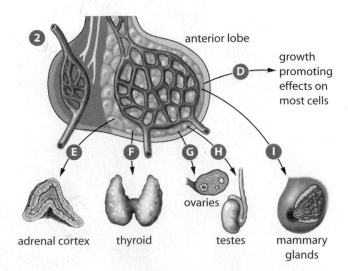

1 — posterior lobe — A: tubules in kidneys — B: mammary glands in breasts — C: smooth muscle in uterus

2 — anterior lobe — D: growth promoting effects on most cells — E: adrenal cortex — F: thyroid — G: ovaries — H: testes — I: mammary glands

Light up Your Life!

During our northern winters, daylight hours are few. One out of every four people living in North America has difficulty adjusting to this shortage of sunlight and may experience symptoms of Seasonal Affective Disorder (SAD). SAD can cause fatigue, poor concentration, irritability, carbohydrate cravings, weight gain, social withdrawal, and a low sex drive. These problems generally disappear in the spring when the days start becoming longer.

Melatonin: The SAD Hormone

Melatonin is a naturally produced hormone that lets the body know when it is time to sleep and when to wake up. Darkness stimulates the secretion of melatonin and light inhibits its secretion. It is made at night by the pineal gland, a pea-sized endocrine gland located in the middle of the brain. When light hits the retina, the eye sends a message to the hypothalamus. The hypothalamus then signals the pineal gland to stop producing melatonin. When people are not exposed to enough light to turn off melatonin secretion, they may experience the symptoms of SAD.

Consider how you feel on a bright summer day compared to a cloudy winter day. Since light plays a key role in melatonin secretion, some doctors use light therapy to treat people with SAD. The person is exposed to a bright light source for 15–60 min every day. The light source is usually a light board that produces a colour of light optimal for melatonin suppression. Light therapy also stimulates the body's production of serotonin, a hormone and neurotransmitter that makes people feel energized. The treatment provides benefit to about 80 percent of people who are experiencing SAD.

The Circadian Rhythm

Recently, light therapy has been used to help people overcome the fatigue associated with loss of sleep, shift work, and jet leg. Larry Pederson of Medicine Hat, Alberta, has been a long time user of light therapy for SAD. Along with a team of industrial design students from the University of Calgary, Pederson has developed the Litebook®, a small, portable light board. Standard light boards are fairly large, and people cannot travel with them. The Litebook®, however, makes it much easier for people to receive light therapy. Some libraries and airports now have Litebook® stations, and many gyms have installed the light board on exercise equipment.

Light therapy could even help you and other teens. Have you ever wondered why you just cannot stay awake in class, no matter how hard you try? Each day, your internal clock tells your body when to be sleepy and awake. This is called your *circadian rhythm*. Starting at puberty, in most people the circadian rhythm slows down by several hours. This can make you feel wide-awake at night, but sleepy in the morning. This shift in the circadian rhythm often lasts into the early twenties, which makes it difficult for many teens to be in learning mode before noon.

But there may be a way to help teenagers wake up in the morning. Clinical research confirms that light therapy administered to teens for 30–40 min in the morning reduces melatonin production. This helps teens to feel more alert in the morning, and allows them to fall asleep sooner at night. Maybe someday your desk at school will be equipped with a Litebook®, but unfortunately you will no longer have an excuse for dozing in class!

• • •

1. Explain why people living in Canada may be more susceptible to Seasonal Affective Disorder (SAD) compared to people who live farther south.

2. How do innovative technologies such as the Litebook® contribute to society?

Hormonal Regulation of Growth, Development, and Metabolism

Section Outcomes

In this section, you will
- **describe** the structure of the anterior and posterior pituitary and **explain** how they are regulated
- **explain** how human growth hormone (hGH) contributes to healthy growth and development
- **evaluate** the use of hormone therapy
- **describe** the structure and regulation of the thyroid gland, and its role in homeostasis
- **describe** the physiological effects of hormonal imbalances
- **formulate** a hypothesis about an environmental factor to which the endocrine system responds

Key Terms

pituitary gland
posterior pituitary
anterior pituitary
human growth hormone (hGH)
thyroid gland
thyroxine (T_4)
hypothyroidism
hyperthyroidism
thyroid-stimulating hormone (TSH)
goitre

BiologyFile

FYI
The hormones of the pituitary are released in such small quantities that when researchers were originally searching for them, four tonnes of hypothalamic tissue from animal subjects were needed to extract 1 mg of hormone.

The **pituitary gland** is an endocrine gland that has two lobes and is about one centimetre in diameter—about the size of a pea. It sits in a bony cavity attached by a thin stalk to the hypothalamus at the base of the brain (Figure 13.11). If you point a finger right between your eyes, and point another finger towards your auditory canal, you will be pointing at your pituitary gland, which is located at the spot where the imaginary lines cross. Despite its small size, this gland releases at least eight hormones involved in the body's metabolism, growth, development, reproduction, and other critical life functions. In fact, it has been called "the master gland" because it releases several tropic hormones. The pituitary gland is controlled by the hypothalamus via releasing hormones and neurons that run through the connecting stalk. Together, the hypothalamus and pituitary gland control many physiological processes that maintain homeostasis.

The anterior pituitary and posterior pituitary make up the two lobes of the pituitary gland. Each lobe is really a separate gland, and they release different hormones. The **posterior pituitary** is considered part of the nervous system. The posterior pituitary does not produce any hormones; instead, it stores and releases the hormones, ADH and oxytocin, which are produced in the hypothalamus and transferred to the posterior pituitary by neuronal axons (Figure 13.12).

The **anterior pituitary** is a true hormone-synthesizing gland. Its cells produce and release six major hormones: human growth hormone (hGH), prolactin (PRL), thyroid-stimulating hormone (TSH), adrenocorticotropic hormone (ACTH), follicle-stimulating hormone (FSH), and leutinizing hormone (LH). A series of blood vessels called a portal system carries releasing hormones from the hypothalamus to the anterior pituitary, and these hormones either stimulate or inhibit the release of hormones from this gland.

The hormones of the pituitary will be studied in detail in the remainder of this chapter and in the next unit on human reproduction.

Human Growth Hormone

The anterior pituitary regulates growth, development, and metabolism through the production and secretion of **human growth hormone (hGH)**. This hormone ultimately affects almost every body tissue. It can affect some tissues by direct stimulation, but the majority of the effects are tropic. Figure 13.11 shows how hGH stimulates the liver to secrete hormones called growth factors. Together, hGH and the growth factors influence many physiological processes. For example, they increase:
- protein synthesis
- cell division and growth, especially the growth of cartilage, bone, and muscle
- metabolic breakdown and release of fats stored in adipose (fat) tissue

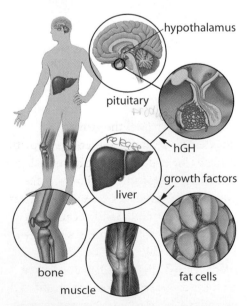

Figure 13.11 The targets of hGH in the body. Why is hGH considered a tropic hormone?

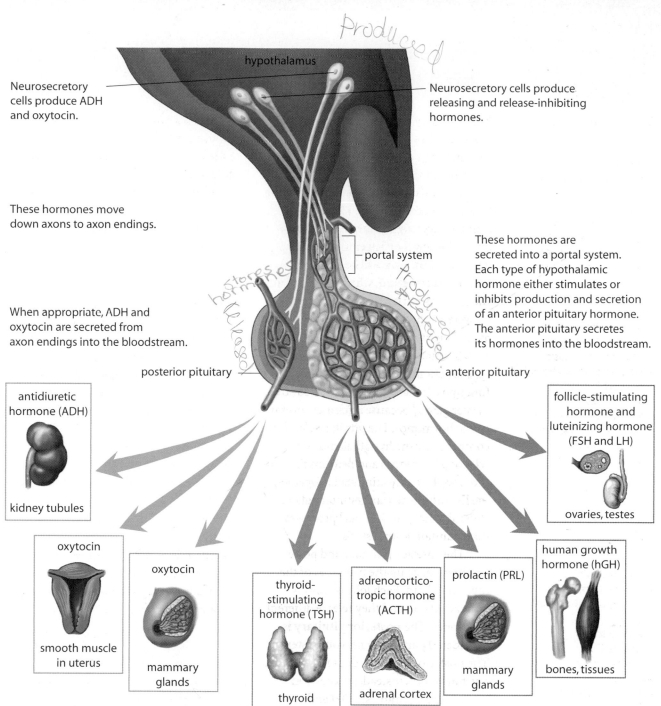

Produced

hypothalamus

Neurosecretory cells produce ADH and oxytocin.

Neurosecretory cells produce releasing and release-inhibiting hormones.

These hormones move down axons to axon endings.

portal system

These hormones are secreted into a portal system. Each type of hypothalamic hormone either stimulates or inhibits production and secretion of an anterior pituitary hormone. The anterior pituitary secretes its hormones into the bloodstream.

When appropriate, ADH and oxytocin are secreted from axon endings into the bloodstream.

stores hormones
released

Produced
released

posterior pituitary

anterior pituitary

antidiuretic hormone (ADH)

kidney tubules

follicle-stimulating hormone and luteinizing hormone (FSH and LH)

ovaries, testes

oxytocin

smooth muscle in uterus

oxytocin

mammary glands

thyroid-stimulating hormone (TSH)

thyroid

adrenocortico-tropic hormone (ACTH)

adrenal cortex

prolactin (PRL)

mammary glands

human growth hormone (hGH)

bones, tissues

Figure 13.12 The hormones of the pituitary gland. The hypothalamus regulates the release of hormones from the anterior pituitary and posterior pituitary.

hGH stimulates the growth of muscles, connective tissue, and the growth plates at the end of the long bones, which causes elongation of these bones. If the pituitary gland secretes excessive amounts of hGH during childhood, it can result in a condition called gigantism (Figure 13.13 on page 446). Insufficient hGH production during childhood results in pituitary dwarfism. In this case, an affected person will be of extremely small stature as an adult but will have typical body proportions (Figure 13.14 on page 446).

When someone reaches adulthood and skeletal growth is completed, overproduction of hGH can lead to a condition called acromegaly. The excess hGH can no longer cause an increase in height, and so the bones and soft tissues of the body widen. Thus, over time, the face widens, the ribs thicken, and the feet and hands enlarge. The condition not only affects a person's appearance. As Figure 13.15 shows, some of the effects of untreated acromegaly include cardiovascular diseases, sugar intolerance

Figure 13.13 Robert Wadlow, the tallest human being ever known, had an anterior pituitary tumour, which caused the over-production of hGH and his resulting growth. He stood 2.7 m tall and was growing taller when he died at 22 years. This photograph shows him with his brother and father.

Figure 13.14 Pituitary dwarfism results in short stature, but does not otherwise affect physical growth, or mental or sexual development.

leading to diabetes, breathing problems, muscle weakness, and colon cancer.

Scientists first began to understand the function of hGH by studying and treating children with insufficient hGH production, leading to dwarfism. Researchers found that by injecting the children with material from pituitary gland tissue from human cadavers, the children often grew taller. Sadly, some of the children who received hGH treatment were infected by a form of Creutzfeldt-Jakob disease and died. In addition to the risk of infection with this procedure, it is difficult to obtain sufficient quantities of hGH from organ donations. Since 1985, however, genetic engineering has been used to produce synthetic hGH. The gene that codes for hGH is inserted into bacteria. The altered and rapidly producing bacteria are biological factories that make hGH. You will explore the issues surrounding the use of synthetic hGH in the next investigation.

• • •

13 Compare the anterior and posterior pituitary.

14 List three effects of hGH on the body.

• • •

The Thyroid Gland: A Metabolic Thermostat

Do you know someone who can eat anything, without ever gaining weight? You might have heard that this person has a high metabolism (burns stored energy very quickly). Is it biologically possible to have a high or low metabolism? How do the thyroid hormones influence the metabolic rate? What happens when there is an imbalance of thyroid hormones or a nutrient deficiency?

As shown in Figure 13.16 on page 448, the **thyroid gland** lies directly below the larynx (voice box). It has two lobes, one on either side of the trachea (windpipe), which are joined by a narrow band of

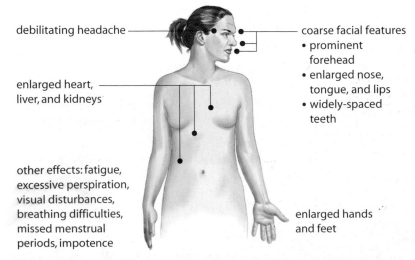

debilitating headache

enlarged heart, liver, and kidneys

other effects: fatigue, excessive perspiration, visual disturbances, breathing difficulties, missed menstrual periods, impotence

coarse facial features
• prominent forehead
• enlarged nose, tongue, and lips
• widely-spaced teeth

enlarged hands and feet

Figure 13.15 Acromegaly results from excessive production of hGH during adulthood. It may be difficult to diagnose the condition in the early stages before a person's appearance noticeably changes.

tissue. Millions of cells within the thyroid secrete immature thyroid hormones into the chambers between the cells. Here, one of these hormones, **thyroxine (T_4)**, will become functional and be released into the bloodstream. The primary effect of thyroxine is to increase the rate at which the body metabolizes fats, proteins, and carbohydrates for energy. Thyroxine does not have one specific target organ, but especially stimulates the cells of the heart, skeletal muscles, liver, and kidney to

INVESTIGATION 13.A

Target Skills

Evaluating the use of synthetic hGH treatment of humans

Working with a team in addressing an issue and **communicating** findings

Evaluating Potential Uses for Human Growth Hormone

Issue

Since the approval of the restricted use of synthetic hGH, concerns have arisen about its use and potential abuse. Health Canada has approved extremely limited use of the hormone, which is very expensive ($25 000 or more per year) and is associated with several negative health effects. Should Health Canada approve the widespread use of synthetic hGH for Canadians?

Gathering Data and Information

1. Suppose Health Canada is re-evaluating its regulations for the use of synthetic hGH and is asking for input on the matter. Your group will address one of the issues described in the table. Read the description of the issue. You may wish to research it further using library or Internet resources. As a group, you will write a list of questions that you think should be addressed before Health Canada takes action on this issue. Your questions should address ethical and safety concerns, and possibly specific guidelines for any new regulations.

Issue 1

Until recently, the use of synthetic hGH was approved only for those children who had malfunctioning pituitary glands and could not produce adequate amounts of the hormone themselves. Recently, the use of synthetic hGH has been approved for children who are genetically of short stature. Should people have the option to take synthetic hGH just to increase their genetically predetermined height?

Issue 2

In adults, the production of natural hGH declines with age. This makes it increasingly difficult to reduce one's body fat as one ages. Given that obesity has reached epidemic levels in the North American population, and one of the functions of hGH in the body is to reduce cellular fat, should synthetic hGH be approved as a diet treatment for obesity?

Issue 3

Because one of the functions of hGH in the body is to build lean muscle mass, its use has become widespread among various athletes. In fact, many athletes at the 1996 summer Olympic games in Atlanta, Georgia, referred to the event as the "hGH Games." Despite its expense, many athletes from baseball players to weightlifters are acquiring synthetic hGH because it is difficult for drug testers to detect. Should competitive athletes be allowed legal access to synthetic hGH?

Organizing Findings

2. Suppose you are attending a forum on hGH use held by Health Canada. Your group has 5 min to present your list of questions to the delegates (your class). You may use visual aids such as computer generated slides, overheads, or a poster. You will have another 5 min to respond to questions from the audience.

Opinions and Recommendations

3. Listen to the other presentations, and then answer the following questions:

   a) What are the main questions that Health Canada should investigate before changing its regulations on the use of synthetic hGH?

   b) Why might parents want synthetic hGH for their children? What should parents be aware of before deciding to obtain hGH for their children?

   c) Should athletes be allowed to use synthetic hGH? Why or why not?

   d) Should health insurance cover the use of synthetic hGH, and if so, in which circumstances?

4. Create a table in your notebook to record the major societal risks and benefits of approving the use of synthetic hGH in the three situations discussed in the forum. As a class, discuss the arguments for both sides of the issues.

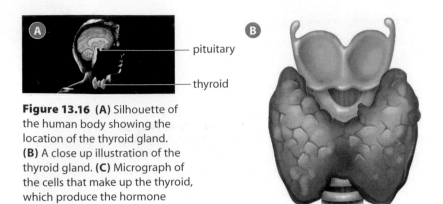

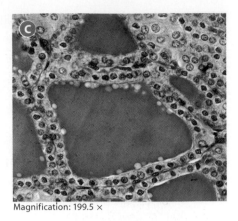

Figure 13.16 (A) Silhouette of the human body showing the location of the thyroid gland. (B) A close up illustration of the thyroid gland. (C) Micrograph of the cells that make up the thyroid, which produce the hormone thyroxine, also called T$_4$.

Magnification: 199.5 ×

BiologyFile

FYI

Hypothyroidism can be treated with daily doses of thyroxine. Traditionally, pills were made from desiccated cow, sheep, or pig thyroid. Ground-up extracts could contain varying levels of hormone. Current treatments usually use a pure synthetic form of thyroxine produced in a laboratory.

Hyperthyroidism can be treated with drugs that interfere with the efficiency of the thyroid gland in producing hormones. Radioactive iodine can also be used to selectively damage or kill thyroid cells.

increase the rate of cellular respiration. Thyroxine also plays an important role in the growth and development of children by influencing the organization of various cells into tissues and organs.

If the thyroid fails to develop properly during childhood, a condition called cretinism can result. In this case, the thyroid produces extremely low quantities of thyroxine, and the person is said to have severe **hypothyroidism**. Individuals with *cretinism* are stocky and shorter than average, and without hormonal injections early on in life, they will have mental developmental delays.

Adults with hypothyroidism tend to feel tired much of the time, have a slow pulse rate and puffy skin, and experience hair loss and weight gain. This explains

why someone with a slow metabolism due to an underactive thyroid may eat very little, but still gain weight. Hypothyroidism is rare, however. For most people, diet and activity are the main factors in weight gain.

Overproduction of thyroxine is called **hyperthyroidism**. Since thyroxine stimulates metabolism, which releases stored energy as ATP, the symptoms of hyperthyroidism include anxiety, insomnia, heat intolerance, an irregular heartbeat, and weight loss. *Graves' disease* is a severe state of hyperthyroidism that results when the body's immune system attacks the thyroid. In addition to the other symptoms of hyperthyroidism, Graves' disease produces swelling of the muscles around the eyes, which causes them to protrude and interferes with vision. Hyperthyroidism can be treated by medications, or removal or irradiation of part of the thyroid.

Thyroxine secretion is controlled by negative feedback. The anterior pituitary releases a hormone called **thyroid-stimulating hormone** (**TSH**), which causes the thyroid gland to secrete thyroxine. As thyroxine levels rise in the blood, thyroxine itself feeds back to the hypothalamus and anterior pituitary, which suppresses the secretion of TSH and, therefore, thyroxine (Figure 13.17). When the body is healthy, the amount of thyroxine in the bloodstream remains relatively constant.

The thyroid requires iodine in order to make the thyroid hormones. (The short form for thyroxine, T$_4$, refers to the

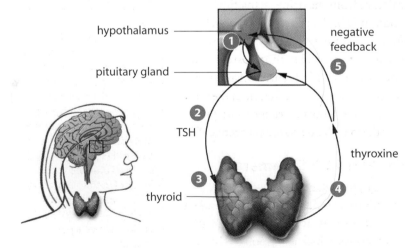

Figure 13.17 The regulation of the thyroid gland by negative feedback. (1) The hypothalamus secretes a releasing hormone that stimulates the anterior pituitary gland. (2) The anterior pituitary releases TSH into the bloodstream. (3) TSH targets the thyroid gland, (4) causing it to secrete thyroxine into the bloodstream. Thyroxine stimulates increased cellular respiration in target cells throughout the body. (5) High levels of thyroxine cause negative feedback on the pituitary and hypothalamus, shutting down production of TSH.

four iodine molecules in the hormone.) If there is insufficient iodine in the diet, thyroxine cannot be made, and there will be no signal to stop the secretion of TSH by the anterior pituitary. The relentless stimulation of the thyroid gland by TSH causes a **goitre** (an enlargement of the thyroid gland). In some places, such as the Great Lakes region in Canada, iodine is lacking in the soil and, therefore, in the drinking water. In Canada it is uncommon for people to have goitres, however, because salt refiners add iodine to salt, making it iodized.

• • •

15 Explain how the thyroid gland is like a metabolic thermostat.

16 Explain the role of thyroxine.

17 Why does hypothyroidism cause a goitre to develop?

• • •

The Thyroid Gland and Calcitonin

Calcium (Ca^{2+}) is essential for healthy teeth and skeletal development. This mineral also plays a crucial role in blood clotting, nerve conduction, and muscle contraction. Calcium levels in the blood are regulated, in part, by a hormone called *calcitonin*. When the concentration of calcium in the blood rises too high, calcitonin stimulates the uptake of calcium into bones, which lowers its concentration in the blood.

The role of calcitonin in regulating blood calcium levels is significant in some vertebrates such as fish and rodents. In humans, on the other hand, calcitonin appears to play a minor regulatory role. A different hormone, secreted by the parathyroid glands, plays a much more significant role in calcium homeostasis.

The Parathyroid Glands and Calcium Homeostasis

The parathyroid glands are four small glands attached to the thyroid. The parathyroid glands produce a hormone called *parathyroid hormone (PTH)*. The

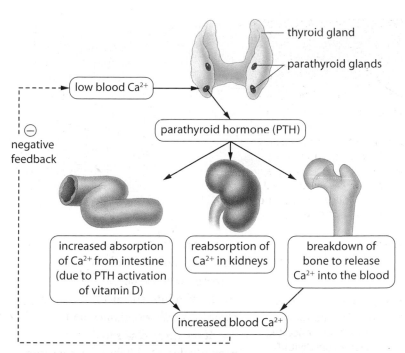

Figure 13.18 Negative feedback mechanisms regulate the concentration of calcium in the blood by parathyroid hormone (PTH). When blood concentration of calcium (Ca^{2+}) is low, PTH is released by the parathyroid glands. PTH directly stimulates the breakdown of bone and the reabsorption of Ca^{2+} by the kidneys. It indirectly promotes the absorption of Ca^{2+} in the intestine by stimulating the production of vitamin D.

body synthesizes and releases PTH in response to falling concentrations of calcium in the blood. PTH stimulates bone cells to break down bone material (calcium phosphate) and reabsorb calcium into the blood. PTH also stimulates the kidneys to reabsorb calcium from the urine, activating vitamin D in the process. Vitamin D, in turn, stimulates the absorption of calcium from food in the intestine. These effects, outlined in Figure 13.18, bring the concentration of calcium in the blood back within a normal range so that the parathyroid glands no longer secrete PTH.

Section 13.2 Summary

- The hypothalamus controls the pituitary gland. The pituitary gland has two lobes that store and release tropic hormones, which are regulated by negative feedback mechanisms.
- The anterior pituitary gland releases human growth hormone (hGH), which stimulates fat metabolism, and targets the liver to release hormones that

Biology File

FYI

Yoda, the world's oldest known mouse, lived for over four years—or about the equivalent of 136 human years! Richard Miller, a scientist at the University of Michigan Geriatrics Center in the United States found that Yoda's pituitary gland secreted unusually low levels of growth hormone. Miller hypothesizes that having low levels of hGH could increase a person's lifespan.

stimulate protein synthesis, and muscle and bone growth.

- The thyroid gland secretes hormones that regulate cell metabolism, growth, and development.
- Thyroxine (T_4) is required for healthy mental and physical development during childhood, and an active metabolism throughout life. Thyroxine contains iodine, and thus people require iodine in the diet.
- Thyroxine secretion is regulated by the release of thyroid-stimulating hormone (TSH) from the anterior pituitary. TSH is regulated by negative feedback by thyroxine on the hypothalamus and pituitary.
- The thyroid gland also produces calcitonin, which helps lower blood calcium levels.
- The parathyroid glands secrete parathyroid hormone (PTH), which raises blood calcium levels.

Section 13.2 | Review

1. In what way could hGH be considered a tropic hormone?

2. Construct a table or Venn diagram to compare and contrast hyperthyroidism with hypothyroidism. **ICT**

3. What causes the different effects seen in gigantism and acromegaly?

4. The diagram on the right shows feedback mechanisms associated with the thyroid gland. In your notebook, identify what is occurring at the labels (A) through (F), and name the hormones involved at each point.

5. Why might having an overactive thyroid make someone feel jittery and hungry?

6. A young child with cretinism is not growing and her parents would like her to take synthetic hGH. Will this treatment help the child? Explain your answer.

7. There has been research on the use of hGH to counteract the effects of aging. Some scientists claim that use of hGH has effects such as an increase in muscle mass, a decrease in body fat, and an increase in energy levels. Some of the known side-effects include heart problems, organ failure, and overgrowth of muscle and bone. Based on what you learned in Investigation 13.A, evaluate the advantages and disadvantages of using hGH for this purpose.

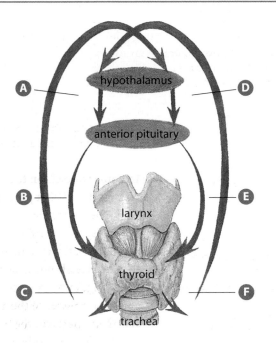

Hormonal Regulation of the Stress Response

Section Outcomes

In this section, you will
- **explain** how the nervous and endocrine systems act together to regulate the stress responses
- **identify** and **describe** the actions of epinephrine and norepinephrine in the human body
- **describe** the effects of cortisol and aldosterone on the human body during the long-term stress response
- **describe** the physiological effects of chronic stress or an imbalance in the stress hormones

Key Terms

adrenal glands
adrenal medulla
epinephrine
norepinephrine
short-term stress response
fight-or-flight response
adrenal cortex
long-term stress response
cortisol
adrenocorticotropic
    hormone (ACTH)
aldosterone

Figure 13.18 What happens to your body when you experience stress? How does the endocrine system help you cope with stressful situations?

Imagine yourself on the roller coaster in Figure 13.18. What physiological changes would be occurring in your body? The stress response involves many interacting hormone pathways, including those that regulate metabolism, heart rate, and breathing. In this section you will focus on the hormones of the adrenal glands and their effects on the body.

The human body has two **adrenal glands**, which are located on top of the kidneys (Figure 13.19). The adrenal glands are named for a Latin word that means "upon the kidney." Each gland is composed of an inner layer (the adrenal medulla) and an outer layer (the adrenal cortex). The adrenal cortex produces hormones that are different in structure and function from the hormones produced by the adrenal medulla.

adrenal medulla
adrenal cortex

left adrenal gland

Figure 13.19 (A) The location of the adrenal glands in the human body. **(B)** A close up view of the kidneys and adrenal glands.

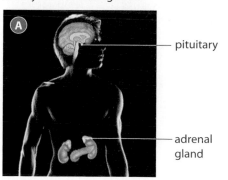

pituitary

adrenal gland

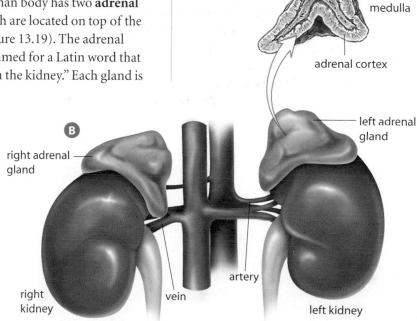

right adrenal gland

right kidney

vein

artery

left kidney

The Adrenal Medulla: Regulating the Short-Term Stress Response

The **adrenal medulla** produces two closely related hormones: **epinephrine** and **norepinephrine**. (These hormones are also called adrenaline and noradrenaline, respectively.) These hormones regulate a **short-term stress response** that is commonly referred to as the **fight-or-flight response**. The effects of these hormones on the body are similar to those caused by stimulation of the sympathetic nervous system. In fact, in the developing embryo, sympathetic neurons and adrenal medulla cells are both formed from nervous system tissue, which is why the adrenal medulla is considered a neuroendocrine structure.

Like the sympathetic nervous system, the hormones of the adrenal medulla prepare the body for fight-or-flight by increasing metabolism. In response to a stressor, neurons of the sympathetic nervous system carry a signal from the hypothalamus directly to the adrenal medulla. These neurons (rather than

hormones) stimulate the adrenal medulla to secrete epinephrine and a small amount of norepinephrine. These hormones trigger an increase in breathing rate, heart rate, blood pressure, blood flow to the heart and muscles, and the conversion of glycogen to glucose in the liver. At the same time, the pupils of the eyes dilate, and blood flow to the extremities decreases. Epinephrine acts quickly. This is why epinephrine injections can be used to treat different life-threatening conditions. For example, it can be used to stimulate the heart to start beating in someone with cardiac arrest. In cases of anaphylactic shock caused by severe allergies, injected epinephrine will open up the air passages and restore breathing (Figure 13.20).

The release of epinephrine and norepinephrine is rapid because it is under nervous system control. Although the hormonal effects are similar to those of the sympathetic nervous system, their influence on the body lasts about 10 times longer. Figure 13.21 shows some of the interactions between the sympathetic

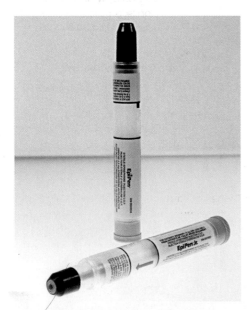

Figure 13.20 Some people are extremely allergic to nuts, bee sting venom, or certain medications, and exposure to these substances will cause the air passages to constrict. Epinephrine injections can be used to restore breathing. An EpiPen®, for example, is an automatic epinephrine injector that is easy to use in an emergency.

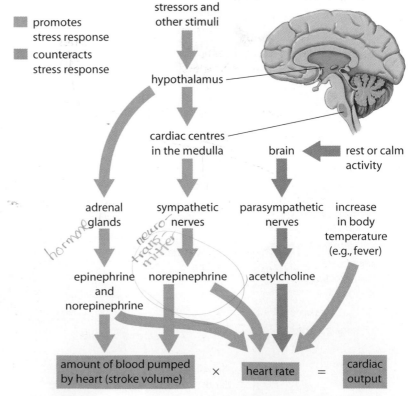

Figure 13.21 Hormonal and nervous system interaction in the stress response.

nervous system and endocrine system in the short-term stress response.

18 Describe what is meant by the fight-or-flight response.

19 How is the hypothalamus involved in the release of epinephrine and norepinephrine in the stress response?

The Adrenal Cortex: Regulating the Long-Term Stress Response

The stress hormones produced by the **adrenal cortex** trigger the sustained physiological responses that make up the **long-term stress response**. The glucocorticoids increase blood sugar, and the mineralocorticoids increase blood pressure (Figure 13.22). The adrenal cortex also secretes a small amount of female and male sex hormones, called gonadocorticoids, which supplement the hormones produced by the gonads (testes and ovaries). The different hormone-secreting cells of the adrenal cortex are shown in Figure 13.23.

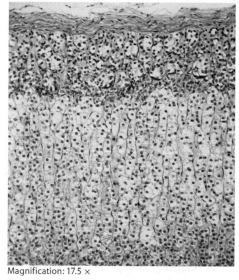

Magnification: 17.5 ×

Figure 13.23 A micrograph of the cells of the adrenal cortex. Notice the bands of cells. The cells in the lower and central bands produce glucocorticoids and gonadocorticoids. The cells in the upper band, underneath the capsule, secrete mineralocorticoids.

20 Compare and contrast the major physiological changes that occur in the short-term and long-term stress responses.

Figure 13.22 The adrenal medulla and adrenal cortex are under the control of the hypothalamus. The adrenal medulla provides a rapid and short-lived stress response, while the adrenal cortex provides a sustained stress response.

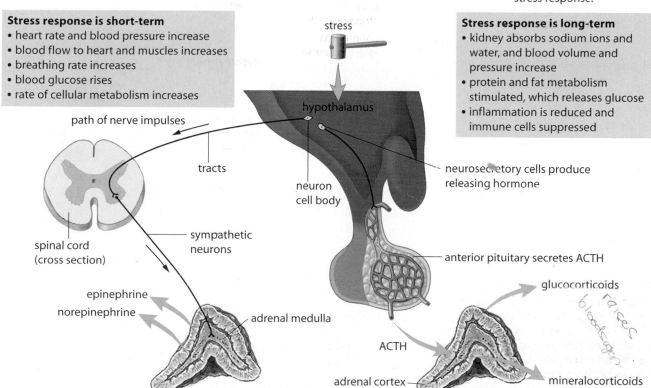

Stress response is short-term
- heart rate and blood pressure increase
- blood flow to heart and muscles increases
- breathing rate increases
- blood glucose rises
- rate of cellular metabolism increases

Stress response is long-term
- kidney absorbs sodium ions and water, and blood volume and pressure increase
- protein and fat metabolism stimulated, which releases glucose
- inflammation is reduced and immune cells suppressed

stress

hypothalamus

path of nerve impulses

tracts

neuron cell body

neurosecretory cells produce releasing hormone

spinal cord (cross section)

sympathetic neurons

anterior pituitary secretes ACTH

epinephrine
norepinephrine

adrenal medulla

ACTH

adrenal cortex

glucocorticoids

mineralocorticoids

raises blood sugar

BiologyFile

Web Link

Dr. Hans Selye was the first person to describe the stress response in terms of the General Adaptation Syndrome (GAS). Selye, who was a scientist at the University of Montréal in Québec, from 1932 to 1976, theorized that the GAS included three phases: alarm, resistance (during which the body adjusts to stress), and exhaustion. What causes the exhaustion phase? How have recent findings built on Selye's understanding of the stress response?

www.albertabiology.ca
WWW

BiologyFile

FYI

Cortisol (medically referred to as hydrocortisone) can be admistered to people with allergies, asthma, arthritis, and skin diseases because of its anti-inflammatory and anti-allergic properties. In people with Addison's disease (the adrenal glands fail to produce cortisol), hydrocortisone injections can reduce many symptoms. For people who produce too much corstisol, as in Cushing's disease, the options include surgery, radiation, and cortisol inhibitor medication.

Cortisol

Cortisol is the most abundant glucocorticoid. Like the other hormones produced by the adrenal cortex, cortisol is a steroid hormone synthesized from cholesterol. When the brain detects danger, it directs the hypothalamus to secrete a releasing hormone. The releasing hormone stimulates the anterior pituitary gland to secrete **adrenocorticotropic hormone** (**ACTH**). ACTH targets the adrenal cortex, which causes the release of the stress hormone cortisol. Cortisol works often in conjunction with epinephrine, but is longer lasting. The main function of cortisol in the body is raise the blood glucose levels. Cortisol does this by promoting the breakdown of muscle protein into amino acids. The amino acids are taken out of the blood by the liver, where they are used to make glucose, which is then released back into the blood. Cortisol also prompts the breakdown of fat cells, which also releases glucose. Increased cortisol levels in the blood cause negative feedback on the hypothalamus and anterior pituitary, which suppresses ACTH production, and stops the release of cortisol.

When faced with immediate danger, or playing a vigorous sport, epinephrine and cortisol are just what the body needs. In the long term, however, the sustained high levels of cortisol in chronic stress can impair thinking, damage the heart, cause high blood pressure, lead to diabetes, increase susceptibility to infection, and even cause early death. In Japan, where long work hours and high-stress jobs are common, so many business people have died from heart attacks and strokes that the phenomenon has been named, *karoshi*, which means "death from overwork."

One of the ways the body fights disease is by inflammation, in which cells of the immune system attack foreign material, such as invading bacteria.

Cortisol is a natural anti-inflammatory in the body, which is probably why sustained high levels of cortisol make people more susceptible to infections. Synthesized cortisol is commonly used as a medication to reduce the undesirable inflammation associated with asthma, arthritis, or joint injuries. Unfortunately, cortisol inhibits the regeneration of connective tissue, and should therefore be used only when necessary.

 21 How does cortisol make more glucose available to cells?

22 How does cortisol affect the immune system?

Aldosterone

The principal mineralocorticoid is a hormone called **aldosterone**. As you learned in Chapter 9, aldosterone stimulates the distal and collecting tubules of the kidneys to increase the absorption of sodium into the bloodstream. This increases the solute concentration of the blood, which then draws in more water from the nephrons, raising blood pressure.

If the adrenal cortex is damaged, Addison's disease can result. In this case, the body secretes inadequate amounts of mineralocorticoids and glucocorticoids. The symptoms of *Addison's disease* include hypoglycemia (low blood sugar), sodium and potassium imbalances, rapid weight loss, and general weakness. Low aldosterone results in a loss of sodium and water from the blood due to increased urine output. As a result, blood pressure drops. A person with this condition needs to be treated within days, or the severe electrolyte imbalance will be fatal (Figure 13.26). Former United States President John F. Kennedy had this condition. Doctors controlled his symptoms with injections of glucocorticoids and mineralocorticoids.

23 Describe how aldosterone increases blood pressure.

24 Describe how Addison's disease affects the body.

Section 13.3 Summary

- The adrenal glands release several hormones involved in the body's response to stress.
- Each adrenal gland is composed of an outer layer called the adrenal cortex, and an inner part called the adrenal medulla. The adrenal medulla is stimulated by neurons from the hypothalamus.
- In the short-term stress response, also called the fight-or-flight response, the adrenal medulla is stimulated to release epinephrine and norepinephrine. These hormones increase the body's metabolism, breathing rate, and heart rate. This provides more energy for the body to respond to danger.
- When the body is under stress, the hypothalamus secretes a releasing hormone. The releasing hormone stimulates the anterior pituitary to release adrenocorticotropic hormone (ACTH). ACTH in turn stimulates the adrenal cortex to release cortisol, a steroid hormone.
- Cortisol triggers the metabolism of proteins and fats to produce glucose. Cortisol also suppresses the immune system, which is probably one reason that chronic stress is unhealthy.
- Cortisol secretion is suppressed by negative feedback to the hypothalamus and anterior pituitary.
- The adrenal cortex also secretes aldosterone, which stimulates the kidneys to absorb sodium and thus water. This increases the blood pressure. When homeostasis is reached, negative feedback shuts off the secretion of aldosterone.
- Low aldosterone causes low blood pressure, an imbalance of electrolytes (sodium and potassium ions) in the blood, and unhealthy weight loss, which are symptoms of Addison's disease.

Section 13.3 | Review

1. Create two columns in your notebook. Label one column "short-term stress response" and the second column "long-term stress response." **ICT**

   a) Indicate which part of the adrenal gland is involved in each response.

   b) Note which system (nervous or endocrine) stimulates the adrenal glands in each response. What hormones are involved in either pathway?

   c) List the substances secreted by the adrenal gland. Briefly compare their effects on the body.

2. If you found yourself in each of the following situations, would the fight-or-flight response be useful or unhelpful?

   a) while playing soccer

   b) during a final exam

   c) when late for your bus

   d) just before heading on stage to act in the school play

3. Name or briefly describe a common but stressful situation that could occur over many weeks or months. Why is it that the body's response in this situation could result in ill health?

4. Suppose a family member has a stressful day. Why might this person crave something sweet to eat at the end of the day?

5. How can synthetic cortisol be used to help athletes suffering from joint injuries? How could its overuse make an injury worse?

6. Is norepinephrine a neurotransmitter or a hormone? Explain your answer.

7. Some skiers and snowboarders report feeling an "adrenaline rush" when they perform their sport. What is an "adrenaline rush" and how does it affect the body?

Hormonal Regulation of Blood Sugar

Section Outcomes

In this section, you will
- **describe** the structure of the pancreas and its role in homeostasis
- **explain** how insulin and glucagon regulate levels of blood glucose
- **describe** the physiological effects of diabetes and how the condition occurs
- **analyze** data and **infer** the role of various hormones based on observations
- **explain** how science and technology are developed to meet societal needs and expand human capability

Key Terms

pancreas
islets of Langerhans
beta cells
alpha cells
insulin
glucagon
diabetes mellitus
hyperglycemia
type 1 diabetes
type 2 diabetes

It had been a difficult afternoon. Josh didn't have time to eat lunch, because he had been studying for his biology exam. In gym class, the run was long and he should have paid attention to his body's warning signs that all was not well. At first he felt tired, then his pulse quickened and he started to perspire. By the time he recognised that his blood glucose was plummeting, his thinking and judgment were impaired. He collapsed, and paramedics had to be called to restore his blood glucose levels.

The above scenario describes some of the challenges faced by someone with diabetes. In diabetes, the physiological processes that maintain blood glucose levels in a narrow range do not function properly. In this section, you will learn why it is critical that blood glucose levels are kept in check, and how the pancreatic hormones regulate blood glucose to maintain homeostasis.

The Hormones of the Pancreas

The **pancreas** is located behind the stomach and is connected to the small intestine by the pancreatic duct (Figure 13.24). Much of the pancreatic tissue secretes digestive enzymes into the small intestine. For this reason, the pancreas is considered an *exocrine gland*, which

secretes its products through ducts. The pancreas also functions as an endocrine gland. Scattered throughout it are over 2000 groups of endocrine cells, which secrete their hormones directly into the bloodstream. These clusters of cells, called the **islets of Langerhans**, are named after their discoverer, the German anatomist and pathologist, Paul Langerhans.

The islets of Langerhans secrete two hormones, insulin and glucagon, which have opposite effects (they are antagonistic). The **beta cells** of the pancreas secrete insulin, which decreases the level of blood glucose. Glucagon, secreted by the **alpha cells**, increases the level of blood glucose.

Both insulin and glucagon are regulated by negative feedback mechanisms (Figure 13.25). When you eat a meal, your digestive system breaks down the food and releases a substantial amount of glucose into your bloodstream. When the blood glucose levels rise, the pancreatic beta cells secrete appropriate amounts of insulin. **Insulin** circulates throughout the body and acts on specific receptors to make the target cells more permeable to glucose. It especially affects muscle cells, which use large amounts of glucose in cellular respiration, and liver cells, where glucose is converted into

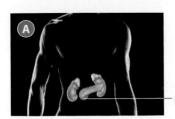

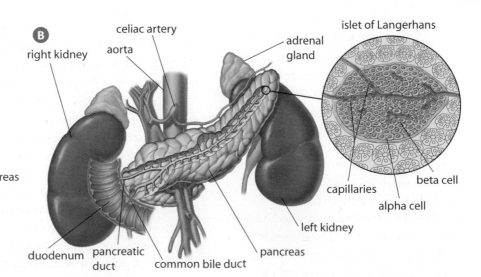

Figure 13.24 **(A)** The location of the pancreas in the human body. **(B)** A close up view of the pancreas and one of the many islets of Langerhans on the pancreas's surface.

A: pancreas

B: right kidney, celiac artery, aorta, adrenal gland, islet of Langerhans, beta cell, alpha cell, capillaries, left kidney, pancreas, duodenum, pancreatic duct, common bile duct

glycogen for temporary storage. Other cells of the body also take in and use glucose for energy. As the glucose levels in the blood return to homeostasis, insulin secretion slows.

Rigorous exercise or fasting (skipped meals) can cause blood glucose levels to drop. Low blood sugar stimulates the alpha cells of the islets of Langerhans to release glucagon. **Glucagon** stimulates the liver to convert glycogen back into glucose, which is released into the blood. Other hormones, such as hGH, cortisol, and epinephrine also contribute to increasing the level of blood glucose.

• • •

25 Identify two cell types of the islets of Langerhans and explain their functions.

26 Describe the roles of insulin and glucagon in maintaining homeostasis.

• • •

The Effects of Glucose Imbalance

Diabetes mellitus is a serious chronic condition with no known cure. It affects over 150 million people worldwide (as of 2004), including over two million Canadians. Diabetes results when the body does not produce enough insulin, or does not respond properly to insulin. As a result, levels of blood glucose tend to rise sharply after meals, and remain at significantly elevated levels. This condition is called **hyperglycemia**, or high blood sugar, from the Greek word parts *hyper* (too much), *glyco* (sugar), and *emia* (condition of the blood).

Hyperglycemia has various short-term and long-term effects on the body. Without insulin, cells remain relatively impermeable to glucose and cannot obtain enough from the blood. The individual experiences fatigue as the cells become starved for glucose. The body compensates to some degree by switching to protein and fat metabolism for energy. Fats and proteins are less

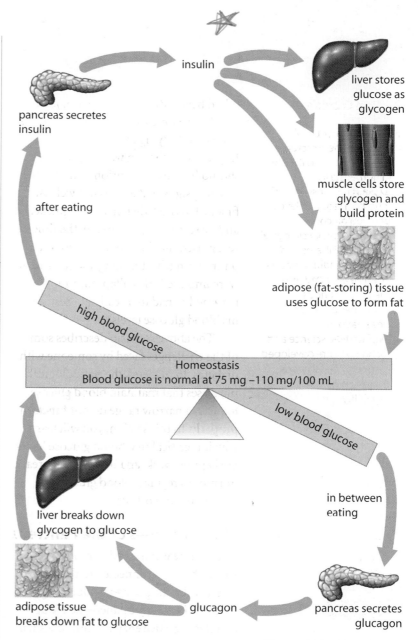

Figure 13.25 Negative feedback regulates blood glucose levels within a very narrow range. How are insulin and glucagon able to help maintain homeostasis in the body?

accessible, however, and more difficult than glucose to break down. Fat metabolism also releases ketones, such as acetone, as a toxic by-product, which can be smelled on the breath.

The kidneys are incapable of reabsorbing all of the glucose that is filtered through them from the blood, and so glucose is excreted in the urine. This changes the osmotic gradient across the nephrons of the kidneys. Large volumes of water therefore follow the glucose by osmosis into the kidneys, and get excreted. People with untreated diabetes experience low energy and great thirst, and produce large volumes of glucose-rich urine. In the long-term,

Biology File

FYI
Early physicians could diagnose diabetes by tasting the urine for sweetness—*mellitus* is Latin for "honey."

continued high levels of blood glucose can lead to blindness, kidney failure, nerve damage, and gangrene (a severe infection) in the limbs. Also, in many diabetics, the alpha cells that produce glucagon degenerate. Diabetes is one of the leading causes of death in North America.

• • •

27 What are the symptoms of diabetes mellitus?

28 What is hyperglycemia?

29 What are the effects of untreated diabetes mellitus on the body?

• • •

Causes of Diabetes

There are two major types of diabetes mellitus: **type 1 diabetes** (also called juvenile diabetes and insulin-dependent diabetes) and **type 2 diabetes** (also called adult-onset diabetes and non-insulin-dependent diabetes). In type 1 diabetes, the immune system produces antibodies that attack and destroy the beta cells of the pancreas. As a result, the beta cells degenerate and are unable to produce insulin (Figure 13.26). The condition is usually diagnosed in childhood, and people with it must have daily insulin injections in order to live.

Thought Lab 13.1 — Blood Glucose Regulation and Homeostasis

Target Skills

Analyzing and **interpreting** collected data on blood glucose levels

Identifying healthy patterns of changing blood glucose levels

Inferring the effects of diabetes mellitus on blood glucose levels

How do levels of blood glucose fluctuate throughout the day in someone with diabetes compared to someone without diabetes?

Procedure

Compare the following blood glucose concentration data provided for Maria and Tamika. One of these young women has diabetes. Blood glucose concentrations were monitored over 15 h for both. Both women ate identical meals at the same times, and got equal amounts of exercise at the same times. Neither is presently taking insulin.

Maria's and Tamika's Blood Glucose Levels over 15 h

Event/Time	Blood Glucose Concentration (mmol/L)	
	Maria	Tamika
Wake up: 8:00 A.M.	4.0	10.0
1 h after breakfast: 9:00 A.M.	7.0	14.0
Pre-lunch: 12:00 noon	4.5	10.0
2 h after lunch: 2:00 P.M.	6.0	15.0
Mid-afternoon: 3:00 P.M.	4.5	10.0
1 h after vigorous exercise: 4:00 P.M.	4.0	4.0
Pre-supper: 6:00 P.M.	4.5	9.0
1 h after supper: 7:00 P.M.	6.5	18.0
Bedtime: 11:00 P.M.	4.5	12.0

Source: Data provided by Dr. Edmund A. Ryan, Professor of Medicine, University of Alberta, Medical Director of the Clinical Islet Cell Transplant Program.

Analysis

1. Plot both sets of data on the same graph and draw a line of best fit for each. Label your graph appropriately.

2. A healthy range for blood glucose is between 4.5–5.0 mmol/L. In general, a person with moderate diabetes would take an insulin shot if the blood glucose level went above 13–15 mmol/L. On your graph, indicate which woman is diabetic and which is not. Write a paragraph to explain your answer.

3. Indicate the times and activities during which the pancreas of the healthy person would release insulin. How did insulin affect her body at these times?

4. Indicate the times and activities during which the pancreas of the healthy person would release glucagon. How did glucagon affect her body at these times?

5. Suggest a medication that the woman with diabetes could take to help her blood glucose levels return to healthy levels after a meal. Explain how this treatment would work.

6. During exercise, Tamika's blood glucose drops dramatically. What could she do to help raise her blood glucose to a healthy range?

To check blood glucose levels, a test strip with a drop of blood is inserted into the blood glucose monitor.

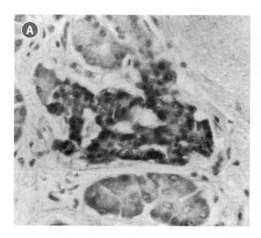

(A)

(B)

Figure 13.26 (A) A light micrograph of pancreatic beta cells from someone with type 1 diabetes. Many of the beta cells have been destroyed, leaving behind only non-beta cells (stained brown), and so the islet is malformed. **(B)** Oscar winner Halle Berry has had type 1 diabetes since childhood. She also actively promotes diabetes awareness and is shown here at a charity gala to benefit children with diabetes.

Type 2 diabetes tends to develop gradually, often because the insulin receptors on the body's cells stop responding to insulin. In other cases, the beta cells of the pancreas produce less and less insulin over time. People who are overweight have a greater chance of developing type 2 diabetes. It is usually diagnosed in adulthood and often can be controlled with diet, exercise, and oral medications. Most people with diabetes— about 90 percent—have type 2. Without proper care, type 2 diabetes can develop into type 1, which is insulin-dependent.

Type 2 diabetes is increasing worldwide at an alarming rate, especially among certain ethno-cultural groups. Among the Aboriginal peoples of Canada, for example, the incidence of type 2 diabetes is rising at three times the national rate. Health scientists describe the increase as an epidemic. One explanation for it could be that people of Aboriginal ancestry have inherited the ability to store food energy very efficiently, since their ancestors traditionally lived through cycles of "feast or famine." In the past, it would have been advantageous to gain weight when there was lots of food, and when food was scarce, go through a starvation period. Today, not only is food available year round, many people are now eating modern Western diets, which are high in refined carbohydrates. Type 2 diabetes is linked closely to unhealthy diet and weight gain, factors that are influencing the rate of diabetes in many populations.

---

30 What interferes with the secretion of insulin in type 1 diabetes?

31 What risk factors are associated with developing type 2 diabetes?

Towards a Cure for Diabetes

It was not until 1889, when physician Oscar Minkowski removed the pancreas from a healthy dog, and it developed the symptoms of diabetes, that the relationship between the pancreas and diabetes was established. For the next two decades, researchers attempted to isolate a substance from the pancreas that could be used to treat diabetes, but were unsuccessful.

In 1921, a research team from the University of Toronto, Ontario, led by Frederick Banting and his assistant Charles Best made a breakthrough (Figure 13.27). By tying off a dog's pancreatic duct with some string, they were able to remove some islets of Langerhans from the dog's pancreas, and then isolate insulin from the islets.

Banting and his research team soon found a way to isolate insulin from the pancreases of embryonic calves, which were a by-product of the beef industry. Working with a biochemist from the University of Alberta, J.B. Collip, they further purified the extracted insulin and used it to successfully treat a boy with diabetes.

Figure 13.27 Best (on the left) and Banting (on the right) and their diabetic dog, around 1922. Banting and J.R.R. Macleod, the head of the university laboratory where Banting and Best worked, were awarded the Nobel Prize in 1923. Best's contribution was not recognized, so Banting shared half his prize money with him.

INVESTIGATION 13.B

Analyzing Endocrine Disorders

Suppose you are a medical student working in the emergency room of a busy city hospital. The supervising medical resident calls you into the ward. She mentions that today would be a great day to review some endocrine disorders, as a number of patients in the ward have them. She informs you that the nurses have taken blood and urine samples from various patients. She also provides you with a chart of symptoms (shown below). You and your classmates must use your knowledge of the endocrine system to determine which of your five patients (referred to as patients A, B, C, D, and E) has:

- pituitary gland deficiency (limited hGH, epinephrine, and cortisol)
- no hormonal imbalance (is healthy)
- diabetes insipidus
- diabetes mellitus
- Addison's disease

Note: Diabetes insipidus is a rare condition that results from insufficient activity of antidiuretic hormone (ADH); refer to page 316. Diabetes insipidus is unrelated to diabetes mellitus.

Question

Using the information chart provided and some simulated blood and urine samples, how can you diagnose hormonal imbalances?

Safety Precautions

- Do not drink any of the solutions used in the laboratory.
- Wash up any spills and your hands after each trial.
- Benedict's solution is toxic and an irritant. If you get it on your skin or in your eyes, immediately inform your teacher and flush your skin or eyes with clean water.
- Be extremely careful around open flames.

Materials

- simulated samples of blood (5)
- simulated samples of urine (5)
- digital blood glucose monitor (if available)
- blood and urine test strips (if using a monitor)
- cotton swabs
- Benedict's solution (if not using a monitor)
- medicine dropper
- 400 mL beaker
- 10 mL test tubes (10)
- hot plate
- test-tube rack
- test-tube clamp
- 10 mL graduated cylinder
- beaker tongs
- Bunsen burner or small propane torch

Symptoms of Various Endocrine Imbalances

Patient's condition	Substances identified	Blood concentrations (mmol/L)	Present or absent in the urine	Additional information
healthy	glucose	5.0	absent	person experiences no additional symptoms
	sodium	140	absent	
diabetes mellitus	glucose	25	present	person reports being thirsty and must urinate frequently
	sodium	138	absent	
diabetes insipidus	glucose	4.5	absent	person is producing large volumes of dilute, pale urine
	sodium	150	absent	
Addison's disease	glucose	4.0	absent	person is under stress; urine output is high; there is sodium in the urine
	sodium	130	present	
pituitary gland and adrenal gland disorder (reduced cortisol, epinephrine, and hGH)	glucose	3.5	absent	this is an older person whose glucagon-producing cells have deteriorated
	sodium	142	absent	

Source: Data provided by Dr. Edmond A. Ryan, Professor of Medicine, University of Alberta, Medical Director of the Clinical Islet Cell Transplant Program

Procedure

Make a table in your notebook like the one below to record your data.

Patient (A, B, C, D, or E)	Blood glucose concentration	Glucose present or absent in the urine	Sodium present or absent in the urine	Name of the disorder

Part A: Testing for Glucose Concentrations in the Blood and Urine

1. If your school has a glucose monitor, place a drop of the first sample of simulated blood or urine on a clean test strip. Plug the strip into the monitor and take a glucose reading. Record the value that you obtain in your data table. Repeat the procedure for the other samples.

2. If a glucose monitor is not available, you can use the Benedict's test to determine the concentration of glucose in each of the blood samples, and to detect the presence or absence of glucose in the urine. Benedict's solution identifies simple sugars, such as glucose, by causing a colour change. As the concentration of glucose changes, so will the colour of the sample mixed with Benedict's solution, according to the following table.

Benedict's Test Colour Equivalence Table

Colour of Solution	Glucose concentration (percent)	Glucose concentration (mmol/L)
blue	0.0	0
light green	0.1–0.5	5.56–27.8
olive green	0.5–1.0	27.8–55.6
yellow	1.0–1.5	55.6–83.3
orange	1.5–2.0	83.3–111
red-brown	2.0+	111+

a) Test the 5 blood samples first. Label 5 test tubes A through E. Use the 10 mL graduated cylinder to measure 5 mL of Benedict's solution into each test tube.

b) With a medicine dropper, add 5 drops of simulated blood from each of the patient's samples to the appropriately labelled test tube. Rinse out the medicine dropper with clean water between samples.

c) Fill a 400 mL beaker about two-thirds full with water. Place the beaker on a hot plate and turn it on. When the water has had time to warm up, use the test-tube clamps to place the test tubes with the samples and Benedict's solution into the beaker. Leave the test tubes in the beaker until there is a colour change , or a maximum of 5 min.

d) Use the test-tube clamps to remove the test tubes from the water bath. Record the results in your data table.

e) Next, test the 5 urine samples. Use the procedural steps (a) through (d).

Part B: Testing for Sodium in the Urine (Teacher Demonstration)

3. Have your teacher ignite a Bunsen burner or propane torch. Your teacher will dip a cotton swab in one of the urine samples, then immediately place the wet end of the swab in the flame. If sodium is present in the urine, the flame should flare bright orange. If not, the flame should stay blue. Record your observations in your data table. Your teacher will repeat this step for the remaining urine samples, using a new cotton swab for each sample.

Analysis

1. Which patient in this investigation acted as a control?

2. Why were simulated blood and urine samples used in this investigation, instead of real samples?

Conclusions

3. Use the table listing the symptoms of different endocrine imbalances to diagnose the condition of each of the patients (A through E).

Application

4. List the hormones that are imbalanced in each of the patients. For each hormone, describe its effect on blood glucose regulation.

5. For the patient with the pituitary disorder, how would you account for the lack of hGH, epinephrine, and cortisol in the patient's blood? Could another hormone have compensated for these three? If so, how does this other hormone typically affect the body?

6. For each of the hormonal imbalances identified in the investigation, suggest a possible treatment.

Figure 13.28
A continuous blood glucose monitor and insulin pump. The pump releases small amounts of insulin throughout the day, which minimizes the need for insulin injections.

BiologyFile

Web Link
To learn more about the Edmonton Protocol, clinical trials, and transplantation, read the Career Focus at the end of this unit and check out the web site.

www.albertabiology.ca
WWW

Today, synthetic insulin is produced by genetically engineered bacteria and other organisms. Furthermore, the Edmonton Protocol, led by James Shapiro at the University of Alberta, has pioneered the first successful islet cell transplants to restore functioning beta cells to the pancreas.

The technology of blood glucose monitoring devices is also improving. Many people with diabetes use digital blood glucose monitors. Advances in insulin injection technology have led to the development of the insulin pump, which mimics the pattern of release of insulin from a healthy pancreas (Figure 13.28).

Although we all have in common the same types of body systems and the requirement for homeostasis, our particular perceptions, and conscious and autonomic responses, are unique. It is likely that, in the future, pain medication, drugs to correct hormonal imbalances, and other pharmaceuticals will be tailor-made for individuals, taking into account our genes. As imaging techniques continue to improve, scientists will have more tools to solve medical problems, and to piece together the many facets of homeostasis.

32 What was Banting and Best's contribution to the treatment of diabetes?

33 How can people with diabetes monitor their blood glucose levels?

Section 13.4 Summary

- Blood glucose levels must stay within a narrow range for the body to maintain homeostasis.
- The islets of Langerhans in the pancreas contain beta cells, which secrete insulin in response to high levels of blood glucose.
- Insulin stimulates the cells of the liver to take up and store glucose.
- Other cells respond to insulin by taking up more glucose for cellular respiration.
- The islets of Langerhans also contain alpha cells, which secrete glucagon in response to low levels of blood glucose.
- Glucagon stimulates the liver cells to break down glycogen, which releases glucose.
- If the beta cells are destroyed, type 1 diabetes results. Type 2 diabetes develops when the insulin receptors on the cells do not respond properly to insulin.

Section 13.4 | Review

1. Draw a negative feedback mechanism to show how a healthy pancreas regulates blood glucose levels after a meal high in carbohydrates.

2. Suppose you wake up late and skip breakfast in order to get to school on time. How would your pancreas enable you to have enough energy to get through the morning until you have a chance to eat lunch?

3. Why might insulin injections not be an effective treatment for type 2 diabetes? What other treatment options are available?

4. Insulin can be produced synthetically using genetically engineered bacteria. List an advantage and a drawback or risk of using synthetic insulin.

5. The graph shows a person's insulin and glucagon levels during a four hour hike with no break for food. Answer the following questions based on the graph.

a) When does the level of insulin drop? What is the effect on the body?

b) When does the level of glucagon rise? What is the effect on the body?

c) How would having a large meal at the 4 h time point affect the person's levels of insulin and glucagon?

d) Hypothesize what this graph would look like if this person had untreated type 1 diabetes mellitus.

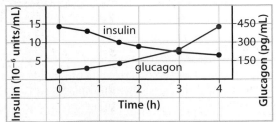

The nervous and endocrine systems work together to maintain homeostasis. The hormones and endocrine glands comprise the endocrine system. The endocrine glands release hormones directly into the blood stream. Hormones travel throughout the body and affect specific target cells. Tropic hormones, such as TSH, affect endocrine glands.

Hormones bind to receptor proteins on the surface of, or within, target cells. This triggers changes within the target cells, such as the secretion of another hormone. Insulin and hGH are examples of protein hormones. Progesterone and testosterone are examples of steroid hormones. Some actions or events (stimuli), such as stress, can initiate a chain of events in the nervous system and possibly have long-term effects on nervous system function or health.

Many hormones are regulated by negative feedback loops. For example, in response to low blood pressure, ADH secretion increases and water reabsorption by the kidneys increases. This leads to an increase in blood pressure, which shuts off ADH secretion and water reabsorption. This cycle of maintaining body fluids at a constant level is called osmoregulation.

The hypothalamus links the nervous system to the endocrine system by regulating hormone secretion by the pituitary gland. The anterior pituitary secretes human growth hormone (hGH), which stimulates fat metabolism, protein synthesis, and bone and muscle growth. Pituitary dwarfism, gigantism, and acromegaly are caused by imbalances in hGH.

The thyroid gland secretes thyroxine and other hormones, which regulate cell metabolism, growth, and development. An underactive thyroid can lead to hypothyroidism. An overactive thyroid can lead to hyperthyroidism. Insufficient iodine in the diet causes goitre.

The hypothalamus controls the secretion of thyroxine via releasing hormones, which stimulate the release of thyroid-stimulating hormone (TSH). A negative feedback loop regulates this system.

The four parathyroid glands regulate calcium levels by secreting parathyroid hormone (PTH).

In response to stressors, the sympathetic nervous system initiates stress responses. The short-term stress response (fight-or-flight response) includes increases in heart rate, blood pressure, and blood glucose. In response to a perceived threat, the hypothalamus sends nerve signals to the adrenal medulla, which releases the short-term stress hormones, epinephrine and norepinephrine.

In the long-term stress response, the hypothalamus secretes adrenocorticotropic hormone (ACTH), which triggers the adrenal cortex to secrete cortisol. The adrenal cortex also secretes aldosterone, which increases blood pressure and balances electrolytes in the blood.

The hormones of the pancreas act antagonistically to regulate blood glucose levels. The beta cells of the islets of Langerhans secrete insulin, which lowers blood glucose. The alpha cells secrete glucagons, which raise blood glucose. Type 1 diabetes causes hyperglycemia. Type 2 diabetes results from insulin-resistance of the insulin target cells.

Chapter 13 Graphic Organizer

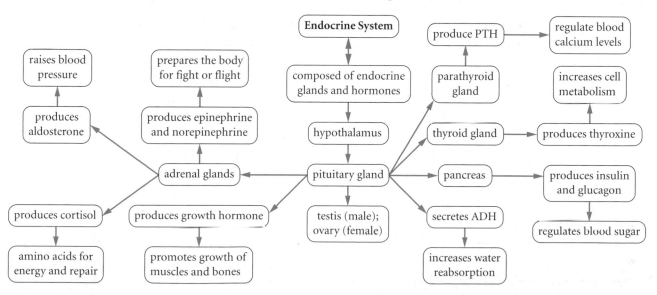

Understanding Concepts

1. Compare the general roles of the nervous system and the endocrine system in maintaining homeostasis.

2. **a)** Explain why the pituitary gland is sometimes called the "master gland."
   b) Describe how the anterior pituitary and posterior pituitary are regulated.

3. Using ACTH as an example, explain what a tropic hormone is.

4. Describe three modern methods that researchers use to learn about human endocrine glands and their hormones.

5. Suppose you are tutoring a younger student in biology. The student tells you that the beta cells of the pancreas secrete glucagon, and the alpha cells secrete a hormone that lowers blood glucose levels. Is this statement correct? If not, rewrite it to make it correct.

6. Compare how cortisol, epinephrine, insulin, and glucagon affect blood glucose levels.

7. Assuming there is adequate iodine in the diet, how would secretion of thyroid-stimulating hormone (TSH) affect the production of thyroxine by the thyroid gland? How would increased levels of thyroxine affect the production of TSH?

8. Distinguish between the structure and function of the adrenal medulla and adrenal cortex.

9. How do levels of hGH change as people age? How do the changing levels of hGH affect the body?

10. Explain why glucagon and insulin are considered antagonistic hormones.

11. **a)** Explain how the lack of dietary iodine interferes with basic cellular metabolism.
    b) What is this condition called? Why is it relatively uncommon in Canada?

12. Suppose you are lost in concentration while studying biology. Suddenly, the phone rings. Outline the physiological changes that occur in your body due to release of the stress hormones, cortisol and epinephrine. What triggers the release of each of these hormones? **ICT**

13. Compare and contrast the role of norepinephrine in the nervous system with its role in the endocrine system.

14. How does aldosterone help the body cope with an ongoing stressful situation? How is this response different from the fight-or-flight response?

15. Why are the effects of hypothyroidism different when this condition occurs in a developing child compared to when the condition occurs in adulthood?

Applying Concepts

16. Suppose an early researcher was trying to determine the function of the pituitary. The researcher removed the pituitary from a laboratory animal and observed the effects on the animal. Suggest two or more reasons why this approach probably would have given the researcher confusing results.

17. Using the headings in the example table below, make a similar table in your notebook. In your table, write the name of each endocrine gland indicated on the following diagram by a letter. Complete the table, and include the hormonal imbalances associated with each gland, including diabetes mellitus, diabetes insipidus, acromegaly, hyperthyroidism, hypothyroidism, Addison's disease, and goitre.

Letter on diagram	Name of hormonal imbalance	Endocrine gland or glands involved	Hormones involved	Symptoms of the condition

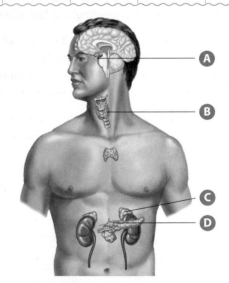

18. An individual is playing hockey without a helmet. He receives a severe blow to the head that causes severe damage to his anterior pituitary gland. In your notebook list all the hormones that might be affected, and how this might affect the body in each case.

19. A doctor has a patient with very low levels of thyroxine in the blood but high levels of TSH. Is the person's problem in the thyroid gland or the pituitary gland? Explain your answer. What condition might this hormonal imbalance cause?

20. A tumour (overgrowth of cells) in an endocrine gland can sometimes cause the gland to become overactive. What hormonal effects might occur in someone with a tumour in the adrenal gland?

21. Suppose you are a doctor. You see a patient who has symptoms of sluggishness, depression, and intolerance to the cold. After eliminating several other possible causes, you diagnose a hormonal imbalance. What condition would produce these symptoms? Infer the endocrine gland that is probably involved.

22. A man reports having extreme thirst and fatigue. He drinks water almost constantly and urinates a great deal. Name two hormonal imbalances that could produce these symptoms. How could a doctor determine what the disorder is?

23. Studies with rats suggest that overcrowding causes behaviour changes due to increased stress levels.
a) Hypothesize how overcrowding might affect people.
b) How could you investigate whether people living in cities experience more or less stress than people living in less crowded environments?
c) Supposing city dwellers were found to be more prone to stress, could you conclusively link this observation to overcrowding? Explain why or why not.

24. Based on what you know about the actions of insulin and glucagon, would a person with diabetes mellitus be more likely to require more insulin or more sugar following strenuous exercise? Explain your answer.

25. Copy the following flowchart into your notebook. Label the flowchart "Regulation of ACTH." On the flowchart, identify the following. (ICT)
a) lobe of the pituitary affected
b) hormone released from the pituitary gland
c) endocrine gland affected
d) hormone released from this endocrine gland
e) effects on the body systems and tissues
f) what regulates the hormone

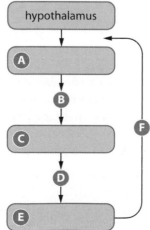

Making Connections

26. Explain why adequate lipid (fat) intake is essential for the healthy functioning of some endocrine glands and their hormones.

27. Some parents are asking their doctors to prescribe synthetic human growth hormone (hGH) treatments to their children, to improve their children's chance of winning sports scholarships for university. Based on what you know about the effects of synthetic hGH, do you think it should be prescribed in this situation? Justify your response.

28. Many types of animals (such as mice, rats, dogs, and monkeys) are sometimes used in medical research to investigate disorders of the endocrine system. How do such studies benefit human life? In your opinion, under what (if any) circumstances should animals be used for medical research? Suggest one or more effective alternative research methods that could replace some procedures involving laboratory animals.

29. There is a strong correlation between people with type 2 diabetes and obesity. What are some societal factors that might be contributing to the rise of type 2 diabetes in countries such as Canada? Suggest how one of these factors could be addressed.

30. The graph below shows the blood glucose levels of two individuals.
a) Identify what event most likely occurred at time 0.
b) Identify which of these individuals has diabetes and which does not. Explain your reasoning.
c) Explain which hormone the person with diabetes took to cause the drop in glucose from 1 to 5 h.
d) What caused the drop in glucose from 1 to 5 h in the person without diabetes?
e) If both people exercised heavily at 5 h, what would you predict would happen to their blood glucose levels?
f) Identify the hormone that would be released to regulate the blood glucose levels at 5 h.
g) Identify the substance the person with diabetes could take following exercise to restore the blood glucose to a healthy level.

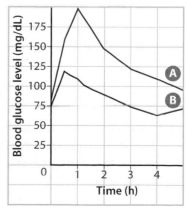

Career Focus: **Ask an Endocrinologist**

Dr. Edmond Ryan is the Medical Director of the University of Alberta Clinical Islet Transplant Program and a Professor of Medicine at the University of Alberta, in the Division of Endocrinology and Metabolism. He works alongside Program Director, Dr. James Shapiro, Islet Laboratory Director, Dr. Jonathan Lakey, and others to take people who have hard-to-manage type 1 diabetes through the islet transplant procedure known as the Edmonton Protocol.

Q What is the significance of the Clinical Islet Transplant Program?

First and foremost it gives hope to people with diabetes that there will be a treatment that doesn't involve insulin injections. The second thing is, this is the first time that cellular therapy for diabetes has been proven to be effective. Prior to this the only way of getting someone completely off insulin injections was to do a whole pancreas transplant, which is a very technical and major surgery. (The Edmonton Protocol) is relatively straightforward and people can be in and out of hospital within a day or two. Third, the fact that we can get people off insulin using the islet cells is stimulus for the whole area of stem cell research. And finally, it is an effective way of managing very difficult diabetes.

Q Who make good candidates for islet cell transplants?

The major indications for an islet transplantation at this time are people who have very labile diabetes—in other words, the glucose is swinging from high to low and there's no pattern to it. It's unpredictable and it is not responding to the standard treatment … The other major group are people who have profound problems with low blood sugar, or hypoglycemia. Most people with hypoglycemia get warning of it. They get shaky and they feel their blood glucose dropping, and they can deal with it effectively by taking some carbohydrate. But some people lose these warning signs. It becomes very precarious for them and they can pass out.

Q What is your role as Medical Director of the program?

With my colleagues, Drs. Breay Paty and Peter Senior, I evaluate patients' diabetes and put forward the pros and cons (of islet transplantation) in a fashion that they can understand to make an informed decision, and work with patients and their physicians following

treatment … The pros are that you may come off insulin, and you may have cells working for you and that will stabilize your blood glucose. The cons are that you have to undergo the procedure. You also have to take immunosuppressive drugs on a life-long basis, and these drugs carry a significant risk. My role is to be an understanding person who appreciates the difficulties of having the diabetes, but also can give perspective on treatment advances.

Q Your work sounds very demanding. What keeps you motivated?

It's busy! But diabetes in and of itself is a phenomenally interesting disease. It affects the circulation, it affects the kidneys, it affects the eyes, it affects the nerves. So the person dealing with diabetes has to treat the whole person rather than just the blood sugars … What motivates me is the strength of people who have diabetes. It's a disease that has an impact all day, every day, and my job is to help them cope with it until we have better ways of handling it—and this will ultimately lead to a cure.

Q What does the future hold for islet transplant treatment?

Huge question. There aren't easy answers. The two major hurdles are a source of cells, and to be able to give the cells either with safer immunosuppression or with no immunosuppression. The sources of the cells could either be animal sources (xenotransplantation), or a stem cell source. There is also the issue of immunity, not only the immune reaction against the foreign, transplanted cells, but also the fact that type 1 diabetes, itself, is an autoimmune condition, so that even with a perfect transplant match, the body would still attack and destroy the islet cells. This is where gene therapy could come in. Canada has been a leader in diabetes from the time that insulin was discovered. We have a strong tradition and we want to continue that.

Other Careers Related to Diabetes Management

Biomedical Engineer Engineers apply mathematical principles to design and test medical tools, such as blood glucose monitors and insulin delivery devices. Software engineers in this field write computer programs to record, analyze, and organize medical data, such as real-time measurements of blood glucose levels. An undergraduate degree in engineering or biomedical engineering is needed to work in a research laboratory or with an industrial design team.

Fitness Consultant Kinesiologists (specialists in human movement), physiologists, and fitness instructors help motivate and educate people to meet various fitness goals, including weight loss, improved cardiovascular health, or improved strength or flexibility. Certified fitness consultants are trained in cardiopulmonary resuscitation (CPR), and have relevant certificates, college diplomas, or undergraduate degrees. Exercise specialists require post-degree certification in order to assist people with chronic conditions, such as diabetes.

Foot Care Nurse Registered nurses with special training in foot care examine, clean, groom, and otherwise care for the feet of elderly patients or patients with chronic conditions. For example, people with diabetes can develop poor circulation and lose sensation in the feet, and unknowingly develop life-threatening injuries and infections. Some foot care nurses are self-employed and provide home care for patients, while other nurses work in hospitals or clinics. In Alberta, registered nurses must have a diploma or undergraduate degree in nursing.

Ophthalmologist Eye doctors are physicians with specialized training in eye health and diseases. For instance, people with type 1 or type 2 diabetes are at risk for diabetic retinopathy, which damages blood vessels in the eye, and can lead to blindness if untreated. Ophthalmologists perform eye examinations to check for signs of disease or injury, prescribe medications, and perform laser surgery to correct diabetic retinopathy and other conditions.

Pharmacist/Pharmacy Assistant Many pharmacy degree graduates work as pharmacists in community drug stores, where they dispense and sell prescription and non-prescription medications and medical supplies. In the hospital setting, pharmacists dispense medications and provide advice on disease or pain management, and may help conduct drug trials and related research. Pharmacy assistants and technicians, who require up to two years' training, answer patient and physician inquiries, input patient records, and restock medical kits, among other activities.

Registered Dietician Graduates of a four-year degree in foods and nutrition can work as registered dieticians or nutritionists to help people better manage their diets. Registered dieticians can work as consultants or with a team of health professionals, and may counsel individuals or educate groups. A Certified Diabetes Dietician Educator teaches people how to prevent or better deal with diabetes through healthy eating habits.

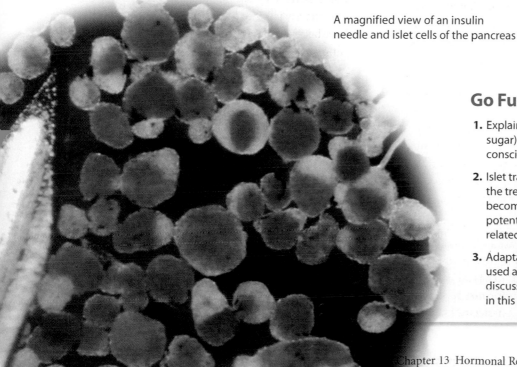

A magnified view of an insulin needle and islet cells of the pancreas

Go Further...

1. Explain why hypoglycemia (low blood sugar) could cause someone to lose consciousness.

2. Islet transplant candidates must wait for the treatment until donated organs become available. Suggest three other potential sources of islet cells, and issues related to their use.

3. Adaptations of the Edmonton Protocol are used around the world. Investigate and discuss the benefits of the latest advance in this procedure.

Understanding Concepts

1. In your notebook, draw a diagram of a neuron. Label the dendrites, cell body, axon, and synaptic terminals. Identify the location of the sodium-potassium pump.

2. Which type of glial cell is responsible for increasing the speed of nerve impulses? Identify the structure that this type of glial cell forms, and explain how the structure speeds impulse transmission.

3. The diagram below shows the nerve pathway that would be involved if you accidentally caught your finger in a door as it closed.

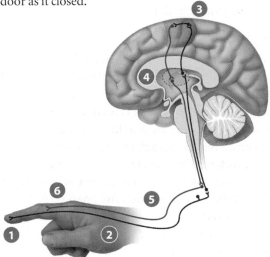

a) Name the types of neurons indicated by numbers 2, 3, and 5 on the diagram, and describe their functions.

b) Describe what is occurring at each number, from 1 through 6. Identify the stimulus and effector.

c) Identify the two brain structures at number 3, and describe their functions.

d) Name the brain structure at number 4, and describe its function.

e) Explain how this nerve pathway differs from a reflex arc.

f) Explain how using a painkiller, such as Aspirin™, would affect this nerve pathway and alleviate pain.

4. An obvious symptom of bovine spongiform encephalitis (BSE) is extreme lack of co-ordination. Infer the areas of the brain that BSE affects to cause this symptom.

5. Draw a graph that represents the change in voltage across a neuron's membrane during impulse transmission. Label the *x*-axis "Voltage" and the *y*-axis "Time." Label polarization, depolarization, repolarization, and the return to polarization on your graph. Indicate the voltage during each of these events. **ICT**

6. Identify the major divisions of the nervous system indicated by the letters in the diagram below. List the major roles of each division.

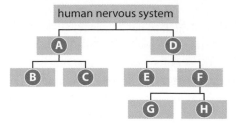

7. Name three areas of the body with specialized clusters of sensory neurons that relay information to the brain. Which structure of the brain does each cluster of sensory neurons affect?

8. As you have learned, there are four types of sensory receptors: mechanoreceptors, photoreceptors, chemoreceptors, and thermoreceptors. For each type, name **a)** the form of energy that is converted into electrochemical impulses, and **b)** the human sense(s) that rely on this type of receptor.

9. The light-detecting cells of the eye are found at the back of the retina, under several layers of cells. Identify and describe the structures of the eye that light passes through, from the outside of the eyeball to the light-detecting cells. What are the names and functions of the light-detecting cells?

10. Which structures of the ear enable a person to maintain balance while dancing? Which structures of the ear enable a person to maintain balance while standing still, watching birds fly overhead? Compare and contrast the functions of these different structures.

11. Outline the structures of the outer, middle, and inner ear. How does each structure contribute to hearing? **ICT**

12. Draw a flowchart to show how light is transformed into nerve impulses in the retina. **ICT**

13. What are the functions of the aqueous humour and vitreous humour of the eye?

14. Think about walking from a dark room to a bright room. Explain how your eyes adjust to the bright light.

15. What do neurotransmitters and hormones have in common? In general, how are they different?

16. In a table, list the ways in which the sympathetic and parasympathetic nervous systems act antagonistically to maintain homeostasis in the body. **ICT**

17. Name the human system (nervous and/or endocrine) that would be most important in each activity, and justify your choice.
  a) driving a car
  b) raising your blood glucose levels when you are hungry
  c) regulating your blood glucose levels when you are playing soccer

18. After playing a game of softball on a hot, sunny day, you are perspiring and very thirsty. List the glands and hormones that help your body maintain homeostasis in this situation. Describe the effects of these glands and hormones.

19. Describe the hormonal response that is involved in the short-term response to a stressful situation, such as being surprised by a fire alarm. What is this response called?

20. Draw and annotate a feedback loop to explain how a lack of dietary iodine can result in a goitre. **ICT**

21. Describe three challenges that were faced by the researchers who first determined the structures and functions of the major endocrine glands and hormones.

22. In general, how is a hormone able to "recognize" and stimulate its target cells?

23. Using a specific example, explain how the hormones of the adrenal medulla complement the actions of the sympathetic branch of the autonomic nervous system.

24. People with diabetes tend to avoid foods that are high in sugar. Explain why someone with type 1 diabetes would keep juice or a chocolate bar handy.

25. a) Why has the pituitary gland often been called "the master gland"?
  b) Explain how the hypothalamus controls the pituitary gland. Is "the master gland" a suitable name for the pituitary gland?

26. What causes diabetes insipidus? Describe the symptoms of this condition.

27. Various endocrine glands and their hormones regulate the concentration of glucose in the blood.
  a) List these hormones, and explain their effects on blood glucose levels.
  b) Form a hypothesis to explain why several hormones in the body, rather than just one, control blood glucose levels.

28. Use a flowchart to show why thyroid-stimulating hormone (TSH) is considered to be a tropic hormone. What regulates the release of TSH?

29. List the three hormones that are produced by the adrenal cortex. Compare and contrast the functions of these hormones and their effects on the body. **ICT**

30. Draw a concept map to organize the following endocrine structures and their functions: hypothalamus, anterior pituitary, posterior pituitary, thyroid, adrenal medulla, adrenal cortex, kidneys, pancreas, hGH, ADH, TSH, thyroxine, ACTH, cortisol, insulin, glucagon. **ICT**

Applying Concepts

31. Many people consider the Ironman Triathlon to be the most gruelling endurance event in the world. World champion contender, Chris Legh, almost died during the 1997 championship in Hawaii, when he pushed his body systems well past their homeostatic limits. He collapsed just metres before the finish line and had to be rushed to hospital. Doctors found that many of his body's systems had been damaged from severe dehydration and heat. Name five physiological conditions that were probably not operating at homeostasis in Chris Legh's body by the end of the race. Which responses of the nervous and endocrine systems would ordinarily have regulated these physiological conditions in order to restore homeostasis in his body?

32. Suppose that Alan, a six-year boy, is growing so quickly that he is 80 percent taller than his Grade 1 peers. An MRI scan reveals that he has a tumour in the anterior pituitary gland. What is most likely causing his rapid growth? What condition could Alan develop if corrective measures are not taken to deal with his hormonal imbalance?

33. Draw an outline diagram of yourself, and identify and label the major structures in your nervous system. Indicate the structures you are using to complete these questions. **ICT**

34. Suppose that you stub your foot on a chair leg. Your foot recoils before you feel any pain. Draw a flowchart of the nerve pathway that is involved in this reaction. What is this reaction called? How does this reaction protect you? When you later feel pain, what structures in your nervous system are involved? **ICT**

35. A neurosurgeon is probing a person's brain in order to map the brain's functions. The person is awake and feels no pain during the procedure. As each area of the brain is probed, the person perceives a different sensation, as described in the following table. Make a table in your notebook to list the structures of the brain that are stimulated by the probes, and the function of each structure.

Responses During Brain Probe

Area probed	Person's response
A	"I can hear a radio playing."
B	"I see a flash of bright light."
C	"I can smell the flowers in my garden."
D	"I remember a happy moment from my childhood."
E	"I can feel pain in my foot."
F	"My finger just twitched."

36. Researchers used a squid giant axon to study changes in the neuron's membrane during nerve impulse transmission. They manipulated the ion concentrations around the neuron, but kept ion concentrations within the neuron constant. Predict the results they obtained when they

a) added sodium ions to the fluid surrounding the axon

b) added potassium ions to the fluid surrounding the axon

Justify each of your predictions. Suggest a third change that the researchers could make to ion concentrations around the neuron and the effect this change would have.

37. Use the table below to answer the questions that follow.

Sodium Ion and Potassium Ion Concentrations Inside and Outside a Neuron

Ion	Concentration inside neuron (mmol/L)	Concentration in body fluid outside neuron (mmol/L)
sodium ion	12	145
potassium ion	140	4

a) What do the ion concentrations in the table suggest about the state of polarization of the neuron? Indicate the voltage across the membrane with respect to the inside of the neuron. How does a neuron establish this charge difference across the membrane?

b) How might a strong stimulus affect the state of polarization of the neuron? What would the ion concentrations and voltage across the membrane become? What would the generated response be called?

c) Qualitatively describe how the ion concentrations would change during repolarization. How would this affect the voltage across the membrane?

38. a) In your notebook, draw a simple diagram that shows a presynaptic neuron, a neuromuscular junction, and the associated facial muscle.

b) Illustrate the transmission of a nerve impulse at this neuromuscular junction. Label the synaptic vesicles, acetylcholine, cholinesterase, and receptor proteins.

c) Explain why Botox® injections around the forehead smooth facial wrinkles. On your diagram, indicate how Botox® affects the neuromuscular junction.

39. An eagle has a large number of densely packed cones in the retina. What advantages might this adaptation give the eagle?

40. Most elephants can detect sound frequencies between 1 Hz and 20 000 Hz. The following table lists the data collected when different sound frequencies were used to stimulate a single auditory neuron from an elephant and a single auditory neuron from a human. Write a paragraph that explains the results in terms of threshold potential and the all-or-none response. Note whether or not nerve activity increases as sound frequency increases.

Sound Stimulation of an Elephant Ear Neuron and a Human Ear Neuron

Frequency of sound (Hz)	Elephant ear neuron stimulated?	Human ear neuron stimulated?
0.5	no	no
1	yes	no
20	yes	yes
40	yes	yes

41. On a dare, a high-school student foolishly drinks 4 L of water in 20 min. How would this affect the concentrations of sodium in the student's blood? Describe how the endocrine system would help to return the body systems to homeostasis. Name the hormones and gland(s) that would be involved.

42. The following graph illustrates the changes in a person's blood glucose concentrations before and after a meal. Study the graph, and answer the following questions.

Relative Blood Glucose Concentrations over 12 h

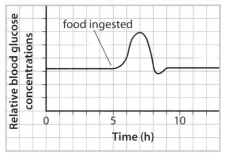

a) Describe what happened to the person's blood glucose concentration at 5 h.

b) Identify the hormone that was released at 7 h, the gland that released it, and the stimulus.

c) Identify the hormone that was released at 8 h, the gland that released it, and the stimulus.

d) Predict how the graph would look if the person engaged in strenuous exercise at 12 h. What hormone would be released during exercise?

e) Suppose that the person has type 1 diabetes. When would he have taken insulin?

43. The following data were collected from one person over 40 years as part of an experimental study. Results were always collected 3 h after a main meal.

Daily Blood Glucose Concentrations over 40 Years

Age	Average daily blood glucose concentration (mmol/L)
10	4.5
20	5.0
30	6.5
40	8.0
50	16.5

a) Why were the readings always taken 3 h after the main meal of the day?

b) The concentrations given are averages of 10 readings taken over one month. Why are averages given instead of raw data?

c) What has happened to the person's blood glucose concentrations over the 40 years?

d) What condition is associated with her symptoms? What causes this condition?

e) Suggest two things that she can do to improve her condition.

44. Your friend is frustrated in math class because his desk is at the back of the room and he cannot see the chalkboard. Other students at the back of the room say, however, that they have no trouble seeing the chalkboard. Tell your friend what kind of corrective lenses may help him. Draw a simple diagram to show him why his eyes likely have trouble focussing on distant objects. **ICT**

Making Connections

45. People who work with heavy equipment without ear protection often suffer hearing loss, but only for certain sound frequencies. Explain why.

46. When children are between six months and 10 years of age, the frontal lobe of their brain consumes twice as much energy as the frontal lobe of an adult brain. Name the major functions of the frontal lobe. Suggest why the frontal lobe of a child's brain needs more energy than the frontal lobe of an adult's brain.

47. Give two practical uses for a PET scan of the brain. If a PET scan of the brain is going to be used to gather research results, do the researchers have an ethical obligation to explain to study participants what data is being collected and how the results will be used? Justify your response in a brief paragraph.

48. The Students' Union at your school has raised $5000 for medical research. Students are being polled to determine what research they would like to support: research on multiple sclerosis, Alzheimer's disease, or Creutzfeldt-Jakob disease. Explain how each of these diseases affects the nervous system. Argue why each disease is worthy of the money for research.

49. Suggest how a medication that binds and interferes with dopamine could be used to help someone recover from a cocaine addiction. Use a diagram to show how the medication might work. Do you think that someone with a cocaine addiction should be forced to take the medication? Justify your response.

50. Suppose that you belong to a health promotion committee. The committee is preparing a campaign to teach people about treatments for cancer, high blood pressure, and heart disease. Explain to the committee how the endocrine system reacts to long-term stress and how this reaction affects the body. Explain why the campaign should also teach people ways to reduce stress.

51. Six months ago, your friend started a sodium-free diet. She has eliminated table salt, seafood, and dairy products from her diet. She tells you that recently her throat has been swollen, she has been feeling more tired and cold than usual, and she has gained weight. Based on her symptoms, what do you think has occurred in her endocrine system? Why should she see a doctor?

Reproduction and Development

General Outcomes

In this unit, you will

- explain how survival of the human species is ensured through reproduction

- explain how human reproduction is regulated by chemical control systems

- explain how cell differentiation and development in the human organism are regulated by a combination of genetic, endocrine, and environmental factors

Unit Contents

Focussing Questions

1 In what ways does a human change from conception to childhood to adulthood, and then through the senior years?

2 What are the roles of chemical control systems in regulating human reproduction?

3 How do reproductive technologies challenge the options, assumptions, and beliefs of individuals and society?

his man and his baby are biologically separate individuals. Each has completely distinct respiratory, circulatory, and other body systems. Like all human body systems, the reproductive system involves complex interactions among a variety of organs and chemical pathways. The reproductive system is unique, however, in that its organs and chemical pathways are not all contained within the body of one individual. The interactions between male and female parents, and between mother and fetus, are the basis for the continuance of human life.

The reproductive system is the only body system that functions mainly to support the continuation of the species, rather than the well-being of an individual. Knowledge and technologies that affect human reproduction have the potential to transform human societies. In this unit, you will study the structures and processes that contribute to human sexual reproduction and to the development of a new human. As well, you will consider some of the social and ethical questions associated with the science and technology of human reproduction and development.

Prerequisite Concepts

This unit draws and builds upon your understanding of various hormones of the endocrine system in relation to the maturing and function of the human reproductive systems.

The Endocrine System

The endocrine system consists of glands and tissues that secrete hormones—chemical signals that affect the activity of other glands or tissues of the body. The endocrine system interacts with the nervous system to regulate activities of other body systems and, as a result, to maintain homeostasis.

Table P6.1 reviews principle endocrine glands and some of their hormones. Figure P6.1 reviews hormones of the pituitary gland. Several of these—oxytocin, prolactin, hGH, FSH, and LH among them—play prominent roles in the development of reproductive organs as well the development of new human life.

Table P6.1 Principal Glands of the Endocrine System and Some of their Hormones

Endocrine Gland	Hormone Secreted	Effects of Hormone on Target Tissues/Organs
hypothalamus	hypothalamic releasing- and inbiting-hormones	regulates anterior pituitary hormones
anterior pituitary	human growth hormone (hGH)	stimulates cell division, bone and muscle growth, and metabolic functions
	thyroid-stimulating hormone (TSH)	stimulates the thyroid gland
	adrenocorticotropic hormone (ACTH)	stimulates the adrenal cortex to secrete glucocorticoids
	follicle-stimulating hormone (FSH)	stimulates production of ova and sperm from the ovaries and testes
	luteinizing hormone (LH)	stimulates sex hormone production from the ovaries and testes
	prolactin (PRL)	stimulates milk production from the mammary glands
posterior pituitary	antidiuretic hormone (ADH)	promotes the retention of water by the kidneys
	oxytocin (OCT)	stimulates uterine muscle contractions and release of milk by the mammary glands
thyroid	thyroxine (T_4)	affects all tissues increases metabolic rate and regulates growth and development
	calcitonin	targets bones and kidneys to lower blood calcium by inhibiting release of calcium from bone and reabsorption of calcium by kidneys
parathyroid	parathyroid hormone (PTH)	raises blood calcium levels by stimulating the bone cells to release calcium, the intestine to absorb calcium from food, and the kidneys to reabsorb calcium
adrenal cortex	glucocorticoids (e.g., cortisol)	stimulate tissues to raise blood glucose and break down protein
	mineralocorticoids (e.g., aldosterone)	promote reabsorption of sodium and water by the kidneys
	gonadocorticoids	promote secondary sexual characteristics
adrenal medulla	epinephrine and norepinephrine	fight-or-flight hormones raise blood glucose levels
pancreas	insulin	lowers blood glucose levels and promotes the formation of glycogen in the liver
	glucagon	raises blood glucose levels by converting glycogen to glucose
ovaries	estrogen	stimulates uterine lining growth and promotes development of the female secondary sexual characteristics
	progesterone	promotes growth of the uterine lining and prevents uterine muscle contractions
testes	testosterone	promotes sperm formation and development of the male secondary sexual characteristics

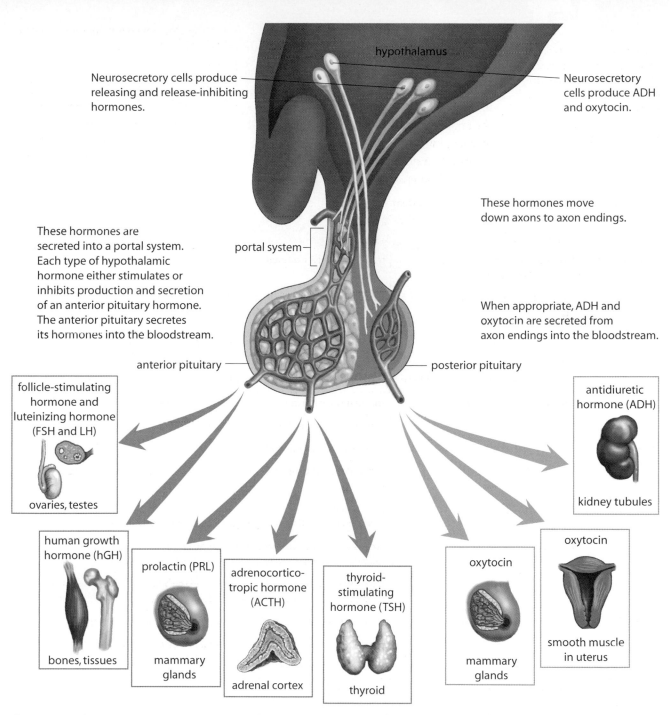

Neurosecretory cells produce releasing and release-inhibiting hormones.

hypothalamus

Neurosecretory cells produce ADH and oxytocin.

These hormones move down axons to axon endings.

These hormones are secreted into a portal system. Each type of hypothalamic hormone either stimulates or inhibits production and secretion of an anterior pituitary hormone. The anterior pituitary secretes its hormones into the bloodstream.

portal system

When appropriate, ADH and oxytocin are secreted from axon endings into the bloodstream.

anterior pituitary

posterior pituitary

follicle-stimulating hormone and luteinizing hormone (FSH and LH)

ovaries, testes

human growth hormone (hGH)

bones, tissues

prolactin (PRL)

mammary glands

adrenocorticotropic hormone (ACTH)

adrenal cortex

thyroid-stimulating hormone (TSH)

thyroid

oxytocin

mammary glands

antidiuretic hormone (ADH)

kidney tubules

oxytocin

smooth muscle in uterus

Figure P6.1 The hypothalamus produces two hormones, ADH and oxytocin, which are stored and secreted by the posterior pituitary gland. The hypothalamus also controls the secretions of the anterior pituitary, which itself controls secretions of other endocrine glands such as the gonads.

The Continuance of Human Life

Chapter Concepts

14.1 The Male and Female Reproductive Systems

- The male and female reproductive systems have features in common as well as features that distinguish one from the other.

- The reproductive cells (gametes) in males are sperm and in females are eggs (ova).

14.2 The Effect of Sexually Transmitted Infections on the Reproductive Systems

- Sexually transmitted infections may be caused by a variety of organisms, including bacteria and viruses.

- Sexually transmitted infections can harm the health of individuals as well as interfere with the proper functioning of egg and sperm cells.

14.3 Hormonal Regulation of the Reproductive Systems

- Hormonal as well as genetic (chromosomal) factors affect the formation of the gonads and reproductive organs during prenatal (pre-birth) development.

- Sex hormones help in the maintenance and function of male and female reproductive systems.

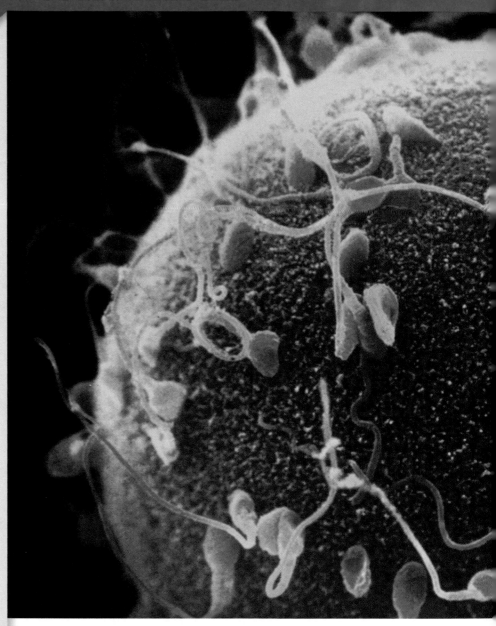

Contact between sperm and egg is the central event of human reproduction. At that moment, reproductive processes in two different individuals join together to create the single cell that will develop over a period of nine months into a new human being.

While most mammals can produce more young than humans can, humans are among the few species able to mate and produce young at any time of year. This ability helps to make human populations very mobile and adaptable to new surroundings. In association with our intelligence and technological capabilities, the ability to conceive at any time is one of the factors that has enabled our species to establish our populations almost everywhere on Earth and even to seek and create environments for ourselves beyond the confines of our planet.

Inside Story

Different species of animals have evolved a wide range of reproductive strategies. For example, in the late fall, a female salmon lays 500 to 2500 eggs in the gravel bed of a stream. At the same time, the male releases a cloud of millions of sperm over the eggs. The fertilized eggs develop through the winter, and the hatchlings emerge in the spring. Based on what you already know about human reproduction, how do the strategies of salmon and humans compare?

Procedure

1. Working in small groups, make a list of some of the main features of salmon reproductive strategies. Compare human reproduction to each of these features. Create a table or a graphic organizer to help you organize your ideas.

2. Based on this comparison, what differences would you expect to see between the reproductive organs of the two species? Record your ideas in a table or chart.

Analysis

1. What are the adaptive advantages of a reproductive strategy in which fertilization and fetal development take place within the body of the female? What are the disadvantages of this strategy?

2. Would you expect a male salmon to have a penis? Why or why not?

3. Would you expect a female salmon to have a uterus? Why or why not?

4. Human sperm are much smaller than a human egg. What other differences can you see between them? What might be the adaptive advantages of these differences?

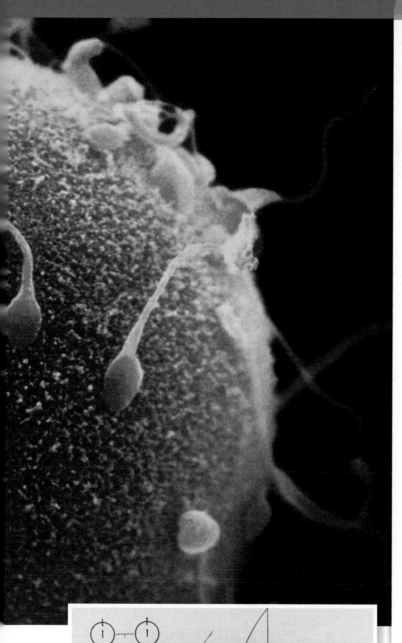

Two space probes, Pioneers 10 and 11, are carrying this plaque into deep space, awaiting possible discovery by intelligent beings from another planet. Many people on Earth expressed concern that human sexual characteristics were displayed so prominently. Why are human sexuality and reproduction such sensitive topics?

The Male and Female Reproductive Systems

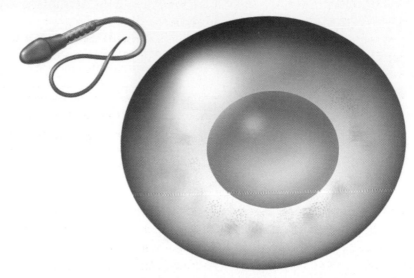

Figure 14.1 All human life begins when an egg cell that is about the size of the period at the end of this sentence is fertilized by an even smaller sperm cell. The length of an average human sperm is about one-half to one-third the diameter of an average human egg.

The human reproductive system is adapted to unite a single reproductive cell from a female parent with a single reproductive cell from a male parent (see Figure 14.1). To achieve this outcome, the male and female reproductive systems have very different structures and functions. The two systems also have many features in common.

Both the male and female reproductive systems include a pair of gonads. The **gonads** (testes and ovaries) are the organs that produce reproductive cells: sperm in males and eggs in females. The male and female reproductive cells are also called *gametes*. (You will learn more about the production of gametes in Chapter 16.)

The gonads also produce sex hormones. **Sex hormones** are the chemical compounds that control the development and function of the reproductive system.

In addition to the gonads, the human reproductive system includes internal and external sex organs, as well as ducts and glands that play a role in forming and transporting gametes. The structures (organs, ducts, and glands)

that play a direct role in reproduction are called the **primary sex characteristics**. Males and females also have a distinct set of features that are not directly related to reproductive function. These are known as **secondary sex characteristics**. Table 14.1 outlines the organs, structures, and features that comprise the primary and secondary sex characteristics of males and females.

In human societies, sexual relationships serve a range of social and emotional functions. In this chapter, however, you will examine how the male and female reproductive systems are adapted to the biological functions of creating and supporting a human embryo.

• • •

Q 1 Distinguish between primary sex characteristics and secondary sex characteristics.

• • •

Structures and Functions of the Male Reproductive System

The male reproductive system includes organs that produce and store large numbers of **sperm cells** (the male

Table 14.1 Primary and Secondary Sex Characteristics

Sex	Primary sex characteristics		Selected secondary sex characteristics (with wide variations among individuals and ethnic groups)	
male	• gonads (testes)	• penis	• facial hair	• body hair
	• scrotum	• seminal vesicles	• deeper voice, broader shoulders, narrower hips, and more obvious muscle development compared with female	
	• epididymis	• prostate gland		
	• ductus deferens	• Cowper's gland		
female	• gonads (ovaries)	• cervix	• minimal facial hair	• minimal body hair
	• oviducts	• vagina	• prominent breasts (compared with male)	
	• uterus	• vulva	• higher voice, more rounded shoulders, wider hips, and less obvious muscle development compared with male	

BiologyFile

FYI
The term *gonad* comes from a Greek word that means "procreation." The term *gamete* comes from a Greek word that means "marriage," referring to the union of a sperm and an egg.

gametes) and organs that help to deposit these sperm cells within the female reproductive tract. Some of the male reproductive structures are located outside the body, and others are located inside the body. Figure 14.2 shows the male reproductive system. Refer to this figure as you read through the following paragraphs. Table 14.2, on page 481, summarizes the functions of the male reproductive organs.

The Testes

The two male gonads are called the **testes**. The testes are held outside the body in a pouch of skin called the **scrotum**. The scrotum regulates the temperature of the testes. Sperm production is most successful at temperatures around 35 °C—that is, a few degrees cooler than normal body temperature. In cold conditions, the scrotum draws close to the body, so the testicles stay warm. In hot conditions, the scrotum holds the testicles more loosely, allowing them to remain cooler than the body.

As shown in Figure 14.3, the testes are composed of long, coiled tubes, called **seminiferous tubules**, as well as hormone-secreting cells, called interstitial cells, that lie between the seminiferous tubules. The interstitial cells secrete the male hormone testosterone. The seminiferous tubules are where sperm

BiologyFile

FYI
About 3 percent of all baby boys are born with testes that have not descended properly. This condition can be corrected surgically.

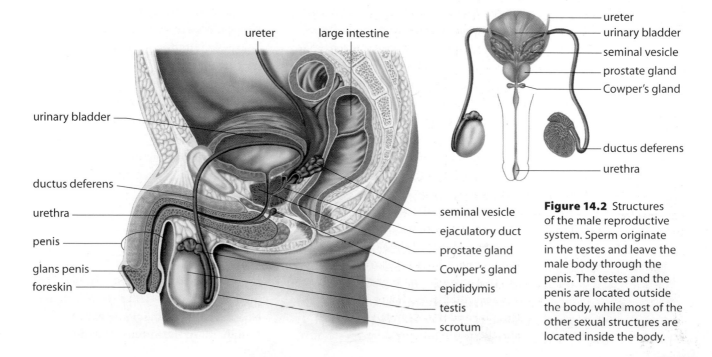

ureter — large intestine — urinary bladder — ductus deferens — urethra — penis — glans penis — foreskin — seminal vesicle — ejaculatory duct — prostate gland — Cowper's gland — epididymis — testis — scrotum

ureter — urinary bladder — seminal vesicle — prostate gland — Cowper's gland — ductus deferens — urethra

Figure 14.2 Structures of the male reproductive system. Sperm originate in the testes and leave the male body through the penis. The testes and the penis are located outside the body, while most of the other sexual structures are located inside the body.

Figure 14.3 Human testis and sperm. **(A)** Each testis contains several compartments, packed with seminiferous tubules. **(B)** This light micrograph shows a cross-section of a seminiferous tubule. Some of the cells are engaged in sperm formation (spermatogenesis). **(C)** A mature sperm has a head, a middle section, and a tail. **(D)** Sertoli cells line the inner walls of the seminiferous tubules. Sertoli cells secrete chemicals required for the nourishment and development of sperm cells.

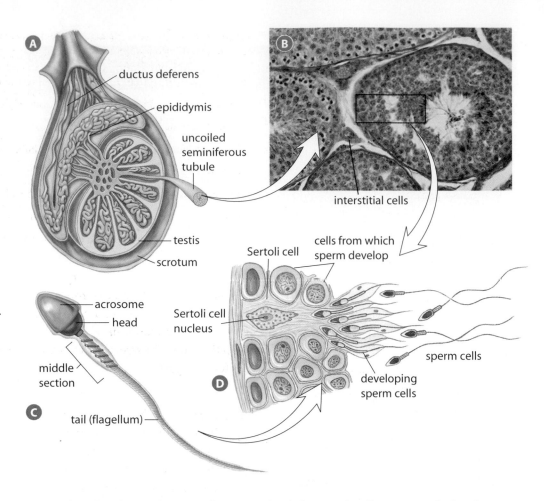

A — ductus deferens, epididymis, uncoiled seminiferous tubule, testis, scrotum

B — interstitial cells, cells from which sperm develop

C — acrosome, head, middle section, tail (flagellum)

D — Sertoli cell, Sertoli cell nucleus, sperm cells, developing sperm cells

BiologyFile

FYI
The fruitfly *Drosophilia bifurca* is about 3 mm long, yet its sperm cells are nearly 60 mm long—about 200 times larger than its body. On a similar scale, a human sperm would be as long as a blue whale—about 30 m!

are produced. (The production of sperm is called *spermatogenesis*. You will learn more about the cellular processes of spermatogenesis in Chapter 16.) Each testis contains more than 250 m of seminiferous tubules and can produce more than 100 million sperm each day.

A mature sperm is a tadpole-shaped structure, about 0.06 mm long. Each sperm cell has three parts: an oval head, a cylindrical middle piece, and an extended tail. The head contains a nucleus with 23 chromosomes. It is covered by a cap-like structure called the acrosome. The acrosome stores enzymes that are needed to penetrate the protective layer surrounding a female egg. The middle piece contains mitochondria, which provide energy for the movement of the tail. The tail propels the sperm with a lashing motion. The sperm can move at a rate of about 3 mm per hour.

Developing sperm are supported and nourished by **Sertoli cells**, which are also located in the seminiferous tubules.

(The Sertoli cells are named after the Italian physiologist Enrico Sertoli, who first described them in 1865.) From each testis, sperm are transported to a nearby duct called the **epididymis** (plural: epididymides). Within each epididymis, the sperm mature and become motile. The epididymis is connected to a storage duct called the **ductus deferens** (plural: ductus deferentia), which leads to the penis via the **ejaculatory duct**. (The ductus deferens is also known by an older term, *vas deferens*. In Latin, the term *deferens* means "to carry," referring to the role of the ductus deferens in carrying sperm to the penis.)

The Penis

The **penis** is the male organ for sexual intercourse. Its primary reproductive function is to transfer sperm from the male to the female reproductive tract. The penis has a variable-length shaft with an enlarged tip called the glans penis. A sheath of skin, called the foreskin, surrounds

2 Using sentences, a graphic organizer, or a diagram, outline the relationship among the following structures: ductus deferens, epididymis, scrotum, seminiferous tubules, testes.

3 Distinguish between interstitial cells and Sertoli cells.

Table 14.2 Functions of the Male Reproductive Organs

Organ	Function
testes	produce sperm and sex hormones
epididymides	mature and store developing sperm
ductus deferentia	conduct and store sperm
seminal vesicles	contribute fructose and fluid to semen
prostate gland	contributes alkaline and mucoid fluids to semen
Cowper's gland	contributes alkaline and mucoid fluids to semen
urethra	conducts semen through the penis
penis	carries semen into the female reproductive tract

and protects the glans penis. The foreskin does not have any reproductive function. *Circumcision*, the surgical removal of the foreskin, is a common practice in some cultures and families.

During sexual arousal, the flow of blood increases to specialized erectile tissues in the penis. This causes the erectile tissues to expand. At the same time, the veins that carry blood away from the penis become compressed. As a result, the penis engorges with blood and becomes erect. Sperm cells move out of each epididymis though the ductus deferens.

Seminal Fluid

As the sperm cells pass through the ductus deferentia, they are mixed with fluids from a series of glands. The **seminal vesicles** produce a mucus-like fluid that contains the sugar fructose, which provides energy for the sperm. The **prostate gland** and **Cowper's gland** also secrete mucus-like fluids, as well as an alkaline fluid to neutralize the acids from urine in the urethra. The combination of sperm cells and fluids is called **semen**. (The term semen comes from a Latin word that means "seed.")

If sexual arousal continues, semen enters the urethra from the ductus deferentia. The **urethra** is a duct that carries fluid through the penis. The urethra is shared by the urinary and reproductive systems. (During sexual intercourse, a sphincter tightens to prevent urine from mixing with the semen.) The movement of semen is the result of a series of interactions between the sympathetic, parasympathetic, and somatic nervous systems. Sensory stimulation, arousal, and co-ordinated muscular contractions combine to trigger the release, or **ejaculation**, of semen from the penis. The semen is deposited inside the vagina.

4 Arrange the following structures into the order in which sperm passes through them: ductus deferens; urethra; epididymis; seminiferous tubules; ejaculatory duct.

5 What is the significance of the acrosome of the sperm?

6 Name the glands that contribute fluids to semen, and list what each contributes.

Structures and Functions of the Female Reproductive System

In contrast to the male reproductive system, the female reproductive system does not mass-produce large numbers of gametes. The two female gonads, or **ovaries**, produce only a limited number of gametes. The female gametes are called *eggs*, or **ova** (singular: ovum). The other female sexual organs are adapted to provide a safe environment for fertilization, for supporting and nourishing a developing fetus, and for allowing the birth of a baby.

Most of the structures of the female reproductive system are located inside

BiologyFile

FYI
In some men, the erectile tissue does not expand enough to cause an erection. This creates a condition known as *erectile dysfunction* or *impotence*. The drug sildenafil (Viagra™) acts on the enzymes that control blood flow in the penis. Because the same enzymes are found in the retina, the potential side effects of this drug include vision problems.

BiologyFile

FYI
Several hundred million sperm cells may be released in a single ejaculation. Sperm cells make up about 1 percent of the total volume of semen released in an ejaculation.

the body. Figure 14.4 shows the main structures of the female reproductive system. Refer to this figure as you read the following paragraphs. Table 14.3 on page 484 summarizes the functions of the female reproductive organs.

The Ovaries

The two ovaries are suspended by ligaments within the abdominal cavity. The ovaries are the site of *oogenesis*— the production of an ovum. (Oogenesis comes from two Greek words that mean "egg-creation." Ova are also called oocytes. You will learn more about oocytes and the cellular processes of oogenesis in Chapter 16.) In contrast to the male reproductive system, in which both testes function at the same time, the ovaries usually alternate so that only one produces an egg each month.

The ovary contains specialized cell structures called **follicles**. A single ovum develops within each follicle. Each month, a single follicle matures and then ruptures, releasing the ovum into the oviduct. This event is called **ovulation**.

Thread-like projections called **fimbriae** continually sweep over the ovary. (The term *fimbriae* comes from a Latin word that means "threads" or "fringes.") When an ovum is released, it is swept by the fimbriae into a cilia-lined tube about 10 cm long called an **oviduct**. The oviduct carries the ovum from the ovary to the uterus. Within the oviduct, the beating cilia create a current that moves the ovum toward the uterus.

A mature ovum is a non-motile, sphere-shaped cell approximately 0.1 mm in diameter (that is, over 20 times larger than the head of a sperm cell). The ovum contains a large quantity of cytoplasm, which contains nutrients for the first days of development after fertilization. The ovum is encased in a thick membrane which must be penetrated by a sperm cell before fertilization can take place.

The Uterus and Vagina

The **uterus** is a muscular organ that holds and nourishes a developing fetus. The uterus is normally about the size and shape of a pear, but it expands to many

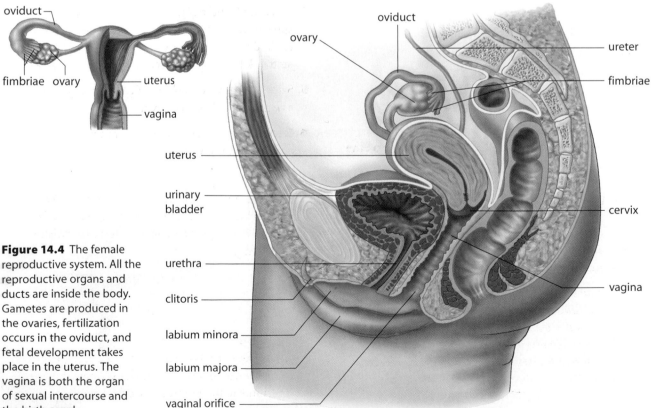

Figure 14.4 The female reproductive system. All the reproductive organs and ducts are inside the body. Gametes are produced in the ovaries, fertilization occurs in the oviduct, and fetal development takes place in the uterus. The vagina is both the organ of sexual intercourse and the birth canal.

times its size as the fetus develops. The lining of the uterus, called the **endometrium**, is richly supplied with blood vessels to provide nutrients for the fetus. (The term endometrium comes from two Greek words that mean "inner uterus.") At its upper end, the uterus connects to the oviducts. At its base, the uterus forms a narrow opening called the **cervix**. The cervix, in turn, connects to the **vagina**. The vagina serves as an entrance for the erect penis to deposit

INVESTIGATION 14.A

Target Skills

Using a microscope to **observe** prepared slides of ovarian and testicular tissues

Distinguishing and **identifying** ovarian and testicular structures

Examining Gonads and Gametes

Testicles and ovaries serve the same two basic purposes: the production of gametes and the release of sex hormones. These two organs are quite different, however. In this investigation, you will use a microscope to examine and compare testicular and ovarian tissues.

Question

How do the structures of testicular and ovarian tissues relate to their biological functions?

Safety Precautions

Handle microscopes and microscope slides with care.

Materials

- blank paper
- pencil
- prepared slides of testicular tissue
- prepared slides of ovarian tissue
- microscope

Procedure

Part 1: Testicular Tissue

1. Mount the prepared slide of testicular tissue on the microscope stage.

2. Under low power, examine the specimen. Look for several circular structures. These are the seminiferous tubules.

3. Draw and label a diagram of the specimen as it appears under low power.

4. Switch to medium and then high power to examine one seminiferous tubule. Try to identify developing sperm cells, mature sperm cells, and interstitial cells. You may want to refer to the descriptions on pages 479–480 of this textbook to help you identify these structures.

5. Draw and label a diagram of the specimen as it appears under high power.

Part 2: Ovarian Tissue

1. Mount the prepared slide of ovarian tissue on the microscope stage.

2. Under low power, examine the specimen. Look for developing follicles near the outer edge of the ovary. Try to identify immature ova within the developing follicles.

3. A mature follicle will appear as a large, fluid-filled structure that contains an ovum. How many mature follicles can you find in the specimen?

4. Create and label a diagram of the specimen as it appears under low power. You may want to refer to the descriptions on pages 481 and 482 of this textbook to help you identify the structures you see.

5. Switch to medium and then high power to examine a mature follicle with an ovum.

6. Draw and label a diagram of the specimen as it appears under high power.

Analysis

1. How does the number of sperm cells that are visible in the testicular tissue specimen compare with the number of ova that are visible in the ovarian tissue specimen?

2. How does the size of the sperm cells in the testicular tissue specimen compare with the size of the ova in the ovarian tissue specimen?

Conclusion

3. Explain how the differences in the size and quantity of the gametes in the male and female gonads contribute to their reproductive functions.

Table 14.3 Functions of the Female Reproductive Organs

Organ	Function
ovaries	produce eggs and sex hormones
fimbriae	sweep an egg into an oviduct
oviducts (Fallopian tubes)	conduct an egg from the ovary to the uterus; place where fertilization occurs
uterus (womb)	houses the developing fetus
cervix	is the opening to the uterus
vagina	receives the penis during sexual intercourse; serves as the birth canal and as the exit for menstrual flow

sperm during sexual intercourse. The vagina also serves as an exit for the fetus during childbirth.

The ovum survives in the oviduct for up to 24 hours after ovulation. If a living egg encounters sperm in the oviduct, fertilization may take place. The fertilized egg, now called a zygote, continues to move through the oviduct for several days before reaching the uterus. During this time, the endometrium thickens as it prepares to receive the zygote. The zygote implants itself in the endometrium, and development of the embryo begins. If the egg is not fertilized, it does not implant in the endometrium. The endometrium disintegrates, and its tissues and blood flow out the vagina in a process known as **menstruation**.

The vagina opens into the female external genital organs, known together as the **vulva**. The vulva includes the *labia majora* and *labia minora*, which are two pairs of skin folds that protect the vaginal opening. The vulva also includes the glans clitoris. Like the penis, the glans clitoris becomes erect during sexual arousal.

• • •

7 In which part of the female reproductive system does fertilization take place?

8 How does the path of an unfertilized ovum differ from the path of a fertilized ovum?

9 What is the endometrium?

10 What is menstruation?

• • •

Differences between Sperm Cells and Egg Cells

In Investigation 14.A, you studied some of the visible differences between sperm cells and egg cells. These gametes differ in many other significant ways, some of which are outlined in Table 14.4. All of these differences relate to the biological function of uniting one gamete from each parent to create the single cell that will develop to become a new person.

Section 14.1 Summary

• Fertilization takes place when a sperm cell, the male gamete, fuses with an ovum, the female gamete. This event follows from reproductive processes that take place within the bodies of the male and female parent.

• The male reproductive system is adapted to produce and release large quantities of motile sperm cells.

• Sperm production begins in the seminiferous tubules of the testes. Developing sperm are transported into the epididymis for maturation and storage.

• During sexual arousal, sperm move into the ductus deferens.

• Sperm are mixed with fluids from a series of glands to create semen. Semen is carried through the penis and released into the female reproductive tract.

• The female reproductive system is adapted to produce and release small numbers of ova.

• Ova are produced in follicles within the ovary.

• Each month a single ovum is released and is carried through the oviduct. If the egg encounters sperm in the oviduct, it may be fertilized.

• The fertilized egg continues through the oviduct to the uterus, which has been prepared to receive it. If the fertilized egg implants in the endometrium of the uterus, pregnancy begins.

• If the egg is not fertilized, it does not implant. Instead, the egg and endometrial tissues flow out through the vagina (menstruation).

Table 14.4 Comparing Sperm Cells and Egg Cells

Criterion for comparison	Sperm cell	Egg cell
	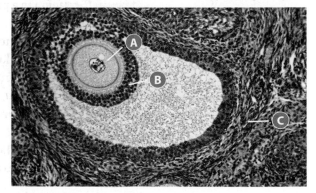	
size	The head is about 5 μm long. The middle piece is about 5 μm long. The flagellum is about 40 μm long.	An egg cell is about 100 μm in diameter.
energy reserves	Before ejaculation, the mitochondria process fat to provide energy. After ejaculation, the mitochondria process fructose (a sugar) in seminal fluid to provide energy. Inside a woman's body, sperm can live for three to five days.	An egg can only live for about one day if it is not fertilized. If it is fertilized, it will implant in the endometrium, which serves as an energy source.
mitochondria	The middle piece of a sperm cell contains about 50 to 100 mitochondria, which supply ATP to provide energy for movement.	The cytoplasm of an egg cell contains about 140 000 mitochondria.
numbers produced	Sperm are continuously produced. About 300 to 500 million sperm are produced each day in a male's lifetime.	At puberty, each ovary contains 300 000 to 400 000 egg-forming structures (follicles). Usually, one egg is released from one of the ovaries each month.
motility	Sperm are motile. A sperm cell has an undulating tail (flagellum) that enables it to swim in fluid media.	Eggs are not motile. They have no structures to propel themselves.
outer structures	The sperm head has a cap called an acrosome, which contains enzymes that help the sperm enter an egg.	An egg is covered by a specialized outer coating which, in most cases, can only be penetrated by sperm of the same species.

Section 14.1 | Review

1. What are the two main purposes of the gonads in both males and females?

2. For each of the following structures, write a short description to indicate whether it is found in the male or female reproductive system and to summarize its function:

   a) fimbriae   c) endometrium

   b) ductus deferens   d) epididymis

3. List the organs and glands that contribute to the components of semen.

4. Which structures contribute to the movement of the ovum from the ovary to the uterus?

5. Draw a labelled diagram to describe the pathway of a sperm cell through the male reproductive system, beginning from the testes. **ICT**

6. Identify the labelled structures in the following image.

7. Briefly describe the structures of a sperm cell and an ovum. How does the structure of each cell relate to its function?

8. A man who is having difficulty conceiving children with his wife is advised by his doctor to wear looser pants. How could a change in clothing make a difference to this man's reproductive system?

The Effect of Sexually Transmitted Infections on the Reproductive Systems

Section Outcomes

In this section, you will
- **identify** the risks that sexually transmitted infections present to individuals and to human reproduction
- **explain** how sexually transmitted infections can interfere with the passage of eggs and sperm
- **research** the effects of sexually transmitted infections
- **design** and **collaborate** on a plan to communicate information about these infections, including their prevention and control, to young adults

Key Terms

sexually transmitted infection (STI)
AIDS
HIV
hepatitis
genital herpes
human papilloma virus (HPV)
chlamydia
pelvic inflammatory disease (PID)
gonorrhea
syphilis

Sexual intercourse involves close physical contact and the exchange of body fluids. For this reason, sexual intercourse can transmit infections from one person to another. An infection that is transmitted only or mainly by sexual contact is generally known as a **sexually transmitted infection**, or **STI**.

STIs may be caused by viruses, bacteria, and parasites. STIs of greatest concern are those caused by viruses and bacteria. The most common viral STIs are HIV/AIDS, hepatitis, genital herpes, and human papilloma virus (HPV). The most common bacterial STIs are chlamydia, gonorrhea, and syphilis.

HIV/AIDS

The acronym **AIDS** stands for *acquired immunodeficiency syndrome*. AIDS is caused by a group of related viruses that are collectively called *human immunodeficiency virus*, or **HIV**. HIV attacks a particular form of white blood cell known as helper T cells, which form part of the immune system. As the level of helper T cells in the blood decreases, the infected person becomes more vulnerable to infections that may lead to sickness and death in people who are diagnosed with acute AIDS.

HIV is transmitted through sexual contact with an infected person. HIV can also be transmitted among intravenous drug users who share needles. Children of mothers who are infected with HIV may themselves be infected before or during birth or through breast-feeding.

According to the Centre for Infectious Disease Prevention and Control, between 1985 and 2004, approximately 57 000 people in Canada tested positive for HIV infection. (See Figure 14.5.) About 20 000 of these people have developed full-blown AIDS, and more than 13 000 have died.

There is no cure for HIV. Treatments can alleviate the symptoms of specific diseases and can extend the life expectancy of someone with AIDS. Many of these treatments have harmful side effects. While the search continues for effective treatments and for a vaccine that can help to protect against AIDS, the most effective solution is to prevent transmission.

Hepatitis

The group of diseases known as **hepatitis** includes three types of viral infections: hepatitis A, B, and C. Hepatitis A is usually contracted by drinking water that is contaminated with fecal material. As well, it can be transmitted through oral or anal contact. Hepatitis B is spread in

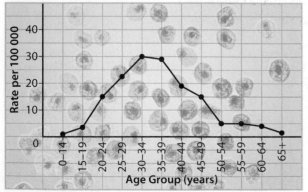

Figure 14.5 A graph of the rate of HIV infection in Alberta by age group, superimposed on a photomicrograph of the HIV virus.

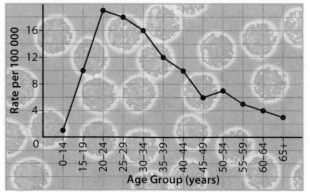

Figure 14.6 A graph of the rate of hepatitis B infection in Alberta by age group, superimposed on a photomicrograph of the hepatitis B virus.

the same way as HIV—through sexual contact or through other contact with infected body fluids or blood. For this reason, hepatitis B is considered to be an STI. (See Figure 14.6.) Hepatitis C is transmitted through blood to blood contact with infected needles or syringes.

Each year, about 3000 Canadians are diagnosed with hepatitis B. Symptoms of the initial infection are flu-like, including fever, headache, nausea, loss of appetite, and abdominal pain. The skin of an infected person may become yellowish, a condition known as jaundice. A hepatitis B infection can progress to cause infection of the liver, leading to liver failure, liver cancer, and even death. Hepatitis viruses can cross the placenta to infect an unborn child. Some people recover completely. Others become *asymptomatic*—that is, they do not show any symptoms. Asymptomatic carriers can still, however, infect other people with the virus.

Effective and safe vaccines for hepatitis A and B are available. The hepatitis B vaccine is administered routinely to babies in Canada. As well, physicians recommend vaccination for people who work in the health system and for people whose lifestyles put them at risk of infection.

• • •

11 Describe how HIV leads to sickness and death in people who have AIDS.

12 How is HIV transmitted?

13 Compare the transmission of hepatitis A, B, and C.

• • •

Genital Herpes

Genital herpes is an extremely common viral STI. The Canadian health system does not maintain statistics on rates of herpes infection. Based on international data, however, researchers estimate that almost one in three sexually active people in Canada has genital herpes and this number is rising. (See Figure 14.7.)

Genital herpes is a viral STI that is caused by one of two herpes viruses: herpes simplex 1 (HSV 1) or herpes simplex 2 (HSV 2). HSV 2 is more likely to be acquired through genital contact, causing genital herpes. HSV 1 commonly causes infections of the mouth (such as cold sores), but also causes genital infections.

Once someone is infected with herpes, the symptoms usually appear within a month. The symptoms vary widely among individuals. The most common set of symptoms includes a tingling or itching in a particular area of the body, followed by the appearances of blisters. The most common areas of infection are the genitals, buttocks, and thighs, but the blisters can form anywhere on the body, even on internal tissues such as the urethra. The blisters rupture, causing painful sores that can take 5 to 20 days to heal. The outbreak may be accompanied by flu-like symptoms, such as swollen glands, aching joints, and fatigue. After the initial outbreak, the blisters may recur with varying frequency, or not at all. Fever, stress, sunlight, intercourse, or certain foods may trigger future outbreaks.

Along with the discomfort associated with herpes outbreaks, the herpes sores mean an increased risk of HIV infection. There is also a risk of transmission from an infected mother to her baby during birth. The resulting infection in the baby may cause blindness, neurological disorders, and even death. Physicians usually recommend that a mother with genital herpes give birth by Caesarean

BiologyFile

FYI
The herpes simplex viruses are closely related to the viruses that cause chicken pox and mononucleosis.

Figure 14.7
A photomicrograph of the herpes virus infecting a cell. Genital herpes infects one in five Americans and one in two people in some less industrialized countries. Despite over 20 years of research and promising, but inconclusive, clinical trials, a successful vaccine remains elusive.

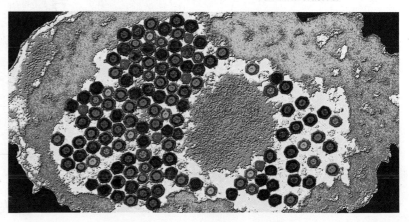

section to reduce the risk to her baby. (A Caesarean section is a surgical procedure in which a physician delivers the baby through an incision made in the abdomen and uterus.)

There is no cure for herpes. Once infected, an individual carries the virus for life and may infect others at any time. Although the risk of passing on genital herpes is greatest when the carrier has an active sore, the disease can be transmitted even when no sores are visible. Antiviral medication can help to control and diminish the severity of outbreaks. Researchers are also working to develop a herpes vaccine.

Human Papilloma Virus (HPV)

The group of viruses known as **human papilloma virus** (HPV) is responsible for a condition known as *genital warts*. Like herpes, HPV infection is very common in North America. It is transmitted by skin-to-skin contact. (See Figure 14.8.)

Many people who are infected with HPV develop flat or raised warts around the genital area. Many others, however, show no symptoms. Because the direct symptoms of an HPV infection are not always obvious, many people carry the virus without knowing it. This is a health concern because HPV can lead to more serious disorders. Some forms of HPV are linked to cervical cancer in women. As well, HPV increases the risk of tumours of the vulva, vagina, anus, and penis.

• • •

14 List the most common symptoms of genital herpes infections.

15 Why do physicians usually recommend that mothers who have genital herpes give birth by Caesarean section?

16 People who have infections caused by human papilloma virus do not always show symptoms of the infection. Explain why this is potentially dangerous.

• • •

Chlamydia

Chlamydia is a potentially dangerous infection caused by the bacterium *Chlamydia trachomatis*. It is the most common bacterial STI in Canada, with more than 55 000 new cases reported each year. As shown in Figure 14.9, people between the ages of 15 and 24 account for the majority of new cases. The rate of infection in young women is more than twice the rate in young men.

After infection with chlamydia, some people experience symptoms immediately. The symptoms may include a discharge from the penis or vagina, a burning pain while urinating, or a fever. One of the greatest dangers of chlamydia is that up to 75 percent of infected people have no obvious symptoms. These people may unknowingly pass the

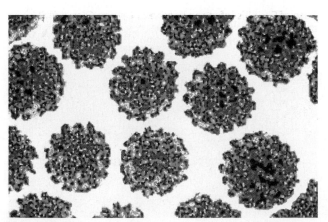

Figure 14.8 A photomicrograph of HPV. The infection can be treated but not cured.

Rate of Chlamydia infection in Alberta by Age Group, 2004

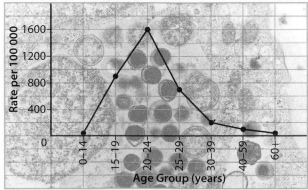

Figure 14.9 A graph of the rate of Chlamydia infection in Alberta by age group, 2004, superimposed on a photomicrograph of a cell infected with chlamydia.

infection on to others, and they may be unaware of the damage that is occurring within their own bodies.

In women, if the infection is not detected, it can spread to the cervix and the oviducts. This, in turn, can lead to **pelvic inflammatory disease** (PID). PID is painful and can result in a build-up of scar tissue in the oviducts. The oviducts may become fully blocked, causing infertility. Infection of the cervix can result in open sores that increase the risk of acquiring HIV. A baby who comes in contact with chlamydia during birth can develop infections of the eyes and respiratory tract. Fortunately, there are effective tests for chlamydia. If an infection is diagnosed early enough, treatment with antibiotics can lead to a complete cure with no permanent effects.

Gonorrhea

Gonorrhea is the second most widespread bacterial STI in Canada. Some of the effects of gonorrhea are similar to the effects of other bacterial infections, such as chlamydia. In fact, the two infections are often found together. In contrast to chlamydia, however, the reported rate of infection is almost twice as high in men as in women. As shown in Figure 14.10, young people have the highest risk of contracting gonorrhea.

Gonorrhea is caused by the bacterium *Neisseria gonorrhoeae*. It can cause infection of the urethra, cervix, rectum,

and throat. The infection often causes pain when urinating and a thick greenish-yellow discharge from the urethra. As with chlamydia, some people experience no initial symptoms. Left untreated, the disease can lead to PID and may spread through the bloodstream to the joints, heart, or brain. A baby who comes in contact with gonorrhea in the birth canal can develop a serious eye infection. Physicians routinely give eye drops to newborns to prevent this.

Like chlamydia, gonorrhea can be successfully treated with antibiotics. Although many strains of the bacterium are becoming resistant to traditional antibiotics such as penicillin, alternative antibiotics remain effective.

Syphilis

Syphilis is the least common of the three bacterial STIs. Until very recently, health practitioners thought that eliminating syphilis completely in Canada would be possible. Unfortunately, the rate of syphilis infection has increased sharply in Canada since 1997 (see Figure 14.11).

Syphilis is an infection caused by the bacterium *Treponema pallidum*. Syphilis proceeds in three stages, with each stage separated by a period of latency. During the first stage, infectious ulcerated sores called chancres (pronounced "shankers") appear at the infection site.

The second stage is characterized by a rash. The rash may appear anywhere on

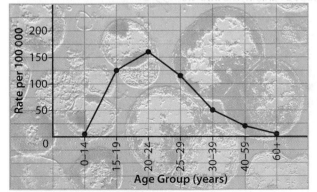

Rate of Gonorrhea infection in Alberta by Age Group, 2004

Figure 14.10 A graph of the rate of gonorrhea infection in Alberta by age group, 2004, superimposed on a photomicrograph of *Neisseria gonorrhoeae*.

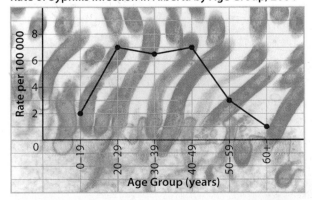

Rate of Syphilis infection in Alberta by Age Group, 2004

Figure 14.11 The rate of syphilis infection in Alberta by age group, 2004, superimposed on a photomicrograph of *Treponema* on the surface of the human duodenum.

the skin, but it generally appears on the palms of the hands and the soles of the feet. Any contact with the infected person may spread the infection.

During the third stage, the infection begins to affect the cardiovascular and nervous systems. An infected person may become mentally ill, blind, or lame, and may develop heart disease. Large, destructive ulcers called gummas may develop on the skin or internal organs.

During any stage, syphilitic bacteria can infect a developing embryo, causing birth defects or stillbirth.

If the disease is not treated early, the bacteria can cause permanent damage. Fortunately, syphilis is readily diagnosed and can be treated effectively with antibiotics, including penicillin. Health professionals are concerned, however, that both risky sexual behaviour and lack of awareness are contributing to new regional outbreaks of syphilis.

• • •

 Use a table to compare the causes and treatments for chlamydia, gonorrhea, and syphilis.

• • •

Controlling the Spread of STIs in Canada

Many cases of STIs go undiagnosed simply because people are not aware of the significance of their symptoms. When people know the symptoms of STIs, they are more likely to be tested and treated before they infect others. For this reason, health practitioners stress education and awareness programs as an essential part of controlling the spread of STIs. Since many people carry STIs without knowing it, health practitioners also stress the importance of personal responsibility for safe sex practices. Table 14.5 provides some examples of ways that people can protect themselves from STI transmission. STIs can lead to very serious diseases, but they are preventable.

Section 14.2 Summary

- Sexual intercourse can be a way of transmitting infections from one person to another.
- Sexually transmitted infections (STIs) may have a variety of effects, from temporary discomfort to permanent damage of the reproductive system and other body systems. Some STIs can be fatal.
- STIs may be caused by viral and bacterial infection.
- Common viral STIs include HIV/AIDS, hepatitis B, genital herpes, and human papilloma virus (genital warts).
- Common bacterial STIs include chlamydia, gonorrhea and syphilis. For many of these STIs, young people show the highest rates of infection.
- One of the greatest challenges in controlling the spread of STIs is that many people who are infected show no symptoms. These people may unknowingly pass the infection on to other individuals.
- Education, awareness, and responsible practices are important elements of public health strategies for prevention and treatment of STIs.

Table 14.5 Preventing Transmission of STIs

Way to prevent transmission	Description
abstinence	Not engaging in any sexual activity is the only sure protection against all STIs.
long-term monogamous relationships	Relationships with the same partner are generally safe, if neither partner has an STI. Some STIs, such as HPV, can be dormant for many years before symptoms appear, however. Many people who have STIs are not aware of their infection.
condoms	Using male or female condoms can reduce, but does not eliminate, the risk of STI transmission.
personal responsibility	Personal responsibility is crucial. Safe sexual practices include not using alcohol or drugs, which can impair self-control or personal judgment. Sexual practices that are known to increase the risk of STI transmission include having multiple partners or partners who use intravenous drugs. Any practices that involve contact between the genitals and the mouth or rectum also increase the risk of STI transmission.

Thought Lab 14.1 — STIs: What To Know and How To Know It

Target Skills

Planning a strategy to communicate effectively information about sexually transmitted infections to a teenage audience

Working cooperatively to research and communicate findings about damage to the reproductive systems caused by STIs

In Canada, the rate of infection for several STIs is highest among teenagers and young adults. In the coming years, many of these people will want to start families. What do young people need to know about how STIs can affect their bodies? What strategy would you design to reach this audience?

Procedure

1. In your group, choose one STI that will be the focus of your education program.

2. Use print and Internet resources to learn about the STI you chose. In particular, find out what effects the STI can have on the male and female reproductive systems. **ICT**

3. Organize your findings in a written report. Your report should include the following information:
   - the cause of the STI
   - the effects of the STI on the human body and, in particular, the male and female reproductive systems
   - why young adults are the age group at greatest risk for aquiring an STI
   - the issues and challenges involved in preventing and controlling the transmission of the STI

4. Using the information in your report, develop an education program aimed at young people. Decide on the two or three most important messages. Then decide how you will deliver these messages. For example, you could create print advertisements for a magazine, produce a music video, or write and perform a play. Deliver your presentation to your class. **ICT**

Analysis

1. Which STIs are most likely to disrupt the function of the human reproductive system?

2. Which STIs are most likely to cause permanent damage to the human reproductive system?

3. Which education program do you think was the most effective? What made it effective?

4. What do you think are the most serious challenges for health practitioners who want to reach young people in Canada? What could be done to meet these challenges?

Extension

5. Some strategies to control the spread of STIs raise social and ethical issues. For example, some people argue that people should be able to test themselves for STIs in the privacy of their own homes. Other people believe that tests should always be conducted in a health clinic so that the results can be recorded. Working with a partner, choose an ethical issue associated with STIs. Prepare a short debate to argue both sides of the issue. What did you conclude?

Section 14.2 Review

1. Give two examples of viral STIs and two examples of bacterial STIs.

2. What is pelvic inflammatory disease, and why is it a concern?

3. In what ways can a woman who is infected with an STI present a health risk to her baby? Give three examples.

4. Some people who become infected with an STI may show no symptoms.
   a) How does this present a risk to the health of the infected individual?
   b) How does this present a public health risk?

5. A friend says to you, "viral STIs are always more serious than bacterial STIs, because they are not curable." How would you respond? Include specific examples to support your argument.

6. Programs that are designed to teach young people about STIs are often controversial. Many people believe that young people should be taught to abstain entirely from sexual contact. Other people believe that young people should be taught about safe sex practices.
   a) List two arguments that could be made on each side of this issue.
   b) Is it possible for health practitioners to design education campaigns that respect both views? Explain your ideas in an editorial. **ICT**

Hormonal Regulation of the Reproductive System

Section Outcomes

In this section, you will
- **identify** the main reproductive hormones and **describe** how they interact
- **explain** the role of sex hormones in the development and regulation of primary and secondary sex characteristics
- **analyze** blood hormone data and associated physiological events
- **research** and **assess** the medical use of reproductive hormones in humans

Key Terms

chromosomal sex
puberty
gonadotropin releasing hormone (GnRH)
follicle-stimulating hormone (FSH)
luteinizing hormone (LH)
testosterone
inhibin
andropause
estrogen
progesterone
menstrual cycle
corpus luteum
follicular stage
luteal stage
menopause
hormone replacement therapy (HRT)

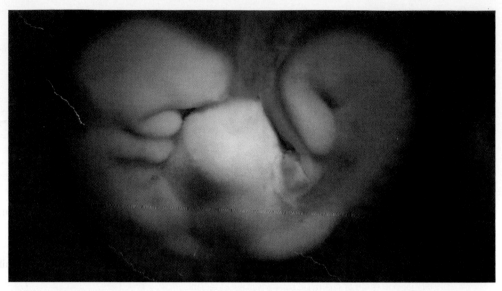

Figure 14.12 The cells of this four-week-old human are already programmed with a genetic sex. The primary sex characteristics of this embryo, however, will not be evident for several more weeks.

The **chromosomal sex**, or genetic sex, of an individual is determined at fertilization (Figure 14.12). In humans and other mammals, an embryo that carries the sex chromosome combination XY is genetically male. An embryo that carries the sex chromosome combination XX is genetically female. (You will learn more about the structure and function of chromosomes in Unit 7.)

The chromosomal sex remains constant throughout the life of an individual. The structure and function of the male and female reproductive systems, however, are more than simply a matter of genetics. Until about the seventh week of development, male and female embryos are anatomically identical. After this time, the presence or absence of specific hormones determines which sex organs develop, when the sex organs mature, and how they function.

Many of the same reproductive hormones are at work in both males and females. The interaction of genetic and hormonal factors produces different reproductive systems in each sex. The main sex hormones and their effects are summarized in Table 14.6. You may want to refer to Table 14.6 as you read through this section.

18 What chromosome combination results in an offspring that is (a) genetically male and (b) genetically female?

Sex Hormones and the Male Reproductive System

The development of the male sex organs begins before birth. In embryos that are genetically male, the Y chromosome carries a gene called the *testis-determining factor* (TDF) gene. The action of this gene triggers the production of the male sex hormones. (The male sex hormones are also known as *androgens*. The prefix *andro-* comes from a Greek word that means "man" or "male.") The presence of androgens initiates the development of male sex organs and ducts in the fetus.

As the reproductive structures develop, they migrate within the body to their final locations. For example, the testes first develop in the abdominal cavity. During the third month of fetal

Table 14.6 Summary of Key Reproductive Hormones and Their Functions

Hormone	Production site	Target organ(s)	Function in male reproductive system	Function in female reproductive system
gonadotropin releasing hormone (GnRH)	hypothalamus	anterior pituitary gland	stimulates the release of FSH and LH from the anterior pituitary	stimulates the release of FSH and LH from the anterior pituitary
follicle stimulating hormone (FSH)	anterior pituitary	ovaries and testes	stimulates the development of the sex organs and gamete production	stimulates the development of the sex organs and gamete production
luteinizing hormone (LH)	anterior pituitary	ovaries and testes	stimulates the production of testosterone	triggers ovulation, and (with FSH) stimulates estrogen production
estrogen	ovary (follicle)	entire body	minor	stimulates the development of the female reproductive tract and secondary sex characteristics
progesterone	ovary (corpus luteum)	uterus	minor	causes uterine thickening
testosterone	testes (interstitial cells)	entire body	stimulates the development of the male reproductive tract and secondary sex characteristics	minor
inhibin	testes (Sertoli cells)	anterior pituitary and hypothalamus	inhibit FSH production	inhibit FSH production

development, the testes begin to descend toward the scrotum. This process is not complete until shortly before birth.

Maturation of the Male Reproductive System

A boy's genitalia are visible at birth, but his reproductive system will not be mature until puberty. **Puberty** is the period in which the reproductive system completes its development and becomes fully functional.

Most boys enter puberty between 10 and 13 years of age, although the age of onset varies greatly. At puberty, a series of hormonal events lead to gradual physical changes in the body. These changes include the final development of the sex organs, as well as the development of the secondary sex characteristics.

Puberty begins when the hypothalamus increases its production of **gonadotropin releasing hormone (GnRH)**. GnRH acts on the anterior pituitary gland, causing it to release two different sex hormones: **follicle-stimulating hormone (FSH)** and **luteinizing hormone (LH)**. In males, these hormones cause the testes to begin producing sperm and to release

testosterone. **Testosterone** acts on various tissues to complete the development of the sex organs and sexual characteristics.

Hormonal Regulation of the Male Reproductive System

From the end of puberty, the male reproductive system is usually capable of producing millions of sperm every hour of the day, seven days a week until death. The same hormones that trigger the events of puberty also regulate the mature male reproductive system over a person's lifetime. Hormone feedback mechanisms control the process of spermatogenesis, and they maintain the secondary sexual characteristics. Refer to Figure 14.13 as you read the following paragraphs.

As you can see, the release of GnRH from the hypothalamus triggers the release of FSH and LH from the anterior pituitary. FSH causes the interstitial cells in the testes to produce sperm. At the same time, FSH causes cells in the seminiferous tubules (where sperm are produced) to release a hormone called **inhibin**. Inhibin acts on the anterior pituitary to inhibit the production of FSH. The result is a negative feedback loop. As the level of FSH drops, the testes

BiologyFile

FYI
LH and FSH are produced by both males and females, but they are named for their actions in the female. In the male, LH is sometimes called interstitial cell stimulating hormone (ICSH) because it controls the production of testosterone by interstitial cells. Chemically, however, LH (ICSH) in males is identical to LH in females.

Figure 14.13 Hormonal control of the male reproductive system. GnRH from the hypothalamus stimulates the anterior pituitary to release LH and FSH. LH and FSH act on the testes to trigger sperm production and the release of testosterone and inhibin. Testosterone and inhibin exert regulatory control over the anterior pituitary and hypothalamus.

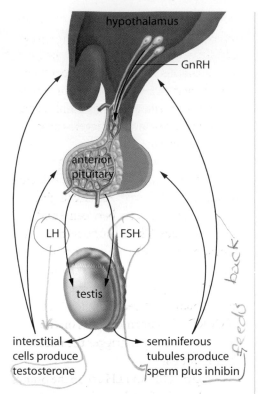

hypothalamus

GnRH

anterior pituitary

LH

FSH

testis

interstitial cells produce testosterone

seminiferous tubules produce sperm plus inhibin

feeds back

release less inhibin. A decrease in the level of inhibin causes the anterior pituitary to release more FSH. This feedback loop keeps the level of sperm production relatively constant over time.

A similar feedback loop maintains the secondary sex characteristics. LH causes the testes to release testosterone, which promotes changes such as muscle development and the formation of facial hair. As well, testosterone acts on the anterior pituitary to inhibit the release of LH. This feedback loop keeps the testosterone level relatively constant in the body.

Reproductive function and secondary sex characteristics both depend on the continued presence of male sex hormones. Substances that interfere with the hormonal feedback system can cause changes in the reproductive system. For example, anabolic steroids mimic the action of testosterone in promoting muscle development. For this reason, some athletes illegally use steroids to increase their speed or strength. Steroids, however, also disrupt the reproductive hormone feedback systems. The side effects of steroid use in men may include shrinking testicles, low sperm count, loss of body hair, and the development of breasts.

Thought Lab | 14.2 | Testosterone and Male Development

Target Skills

Analyzing blood hormone data and physiological events for a human male

Inferring the roles of male sex hormones

Selecting and **using** an appropriate mode of representation to communicate ideas and information about sex hormone levels

Blood tests of testosterone levels are sometimes used to help diagnose disorders of the male reproductive system, as well as other conditions that affect hormone balance in the body. In this activity, you will plot and analyze blood testosterone data for male children and young adult males.

Procedure

1. Examine the data in the table below. Graph these data using the type of graph you think is most appropriate.

2. Based on the data, at what age does puberty begin? Mark this on your graph.

Normal Blood Testosterone Levels in Males

Age (years)	Blood testosterone level (ng/dL)
1 to 7.9	40
8 to 10.9	42
11 to 11.9	260
12 to 13.9	420
14 to 17.9	1000
18 to 29	1100

3. Use print or Internet resources to research the physiological changes that take place during male puberty. Write a brief description of the changes that are associated with changing levels of testosterone. Identify which of these changes are directly related to reproductive function. **ICT**

Analysis

1. Is it possible to use blood hormone data to identify the end of puberty? Explain your answer.

2. In young men, the growth of facial hair begins at the same time as blood testosterone levels start to increase.

   a) From this evidence, can you conclude that testosterone causes facial hair growth? Justify your answer.

   b) Design an experiment to test the hypothesis that testosterone causes facial hair growth in men.

List five male sex hormones and briefly describe their significance.

Aging and the Male Reproductive System

A man in good health can remain fertile for his entire life. Even so, most men experience a gradual decline in their testosterone level beginning around age 40. This condition is called **andropause**. In some men, the hormonal change may be linked to symptoms such as fatigue, depression, loss of muscle and bone mass, and a drop in sperm production. However, some studies suggest that low doses of testosterone can help to counter the symptoms of andropause. Because not all men experience symptoms of andropause, and because the symptoms can vary widely, this condition is difficult to diagnose accurately.

Other hormonal changes associated with aging can also affect the male reproductive system. For example, the prostate gland often begins to grow gradually in men over age 40. This can lead to discomfort and urinary difficulties, because the prostate squeezes on the urethra as it grows. Older men have an increased risk of cancer of the prostate gland, as well. Surgery may be used to provide relief and to reduce the cancer risk. Younger men, however, are more prone to developing infections of the prostate. The resulting inflammation of the prostate (a condition called prostatitis) may cause a burning sensation when urinating or a need to urinate more frequently. Antibiotics are usually prescribed to fight the infection and reduce the inflammation.

Sex Hormones and the Female Reproductive System

Our understanding of the specific factors that trigger the development of female sex organs in a genetically female embryo is incomplete. Until recently, scientists assumed that the development of female sex organs was a "default" pattern—that is, if there is no Y chromosome, then female organs will develop. Researchers now suspect that the processes of female sex development are more complex and that specific hormonal triggers cause female sex organs to develop.

Like a baby boy, a baby girl has a complete but immature set of reproductive organs at birth. North American girls usually begin puberty between 9 and 13 years of age. The basic hormones and hormonal processes of female puberty are similar to those of male puberty. A girl begins puberty when the hypothalamus increases its production of GnRH. This hormone acts on the anterior pituitary to trigger the release of LH and FSH.

In girls, FSH and LH act on the ovaries to produce the female sex hormones **estrogen** and **progesterone**. These hormones stimulate the development of the female secondary sex characteristics and launch a reproductive cycle that will continue until about middle age.

20 What is the role of GnRH, FSH, and LH in the development of the female reproductive system?

Hormonal Regulation of the Female Reproductive System

In humans, female reproductive function follows a cyclical pattern known as the **menstrual cycle**. The menstrual cycle ensures that an ovum is released at the same time as the uterus is most receptive to a fertilized egg.

The menstrual cycle is usually about 28 days long, although it may vary considerably from one woman to the next, and even from one cycle to the next in the same woman. By convention, the cycle is said to begin with menstruation and end with the start of the next menstrual period. The menstrual cycle is actually two separate but interconnected

BiologyFile

Try This
Copy an outline of Figure 14.13 into your notebook, including the labels. Add plus signs (+) and negative signs (–) beside the arrows to show which hormones have a stimulating action and which have an inhibitory action.

BiologyFile

Web Link
Testosterone may be prescribed by a licensed physician for specific medical conditions and treatments. It may also be used illegally, in synthetic form as an anabolic steroid, by people looking for a fast, easy way to build muscle mass, reduce fat, and improve endurance. How do the legal and illegal uses of testosterone differ? What are the risks of using this hormone?

www.albertabiology.ca WWW

cycles of events. One cycle takes place in the ovaries and is known as the *ovarian cycle*. The other cycle takes place in the uterus and is known as the *uterine cycle*. Both cycles are controlled by the female sex hormones estrogen and progesterone, which are produced by the ovaries.

The Ovarian Cycle

As you saw in Section 14.1, the ovary contains cellular structures called follicles. Each follicle contains a single immature ovum. At birth, a baby girl has over 2 000 000 follicles. Many degenerate, leaving up to about 400 000 by puberty. During her lifetime, only approximately 400 of these follicles will mature to release an ovum. In a single ovarian cycle, one follicle matures, releases an ovum, and then develops into a yellowish, gland-like structure known as a **corpus luteum**. The corpus luteum then degenerates. (The term *corpus luteum* comes from two Latin words that mean "yellow body." The term *follicle* comes from a Latin word that means "small

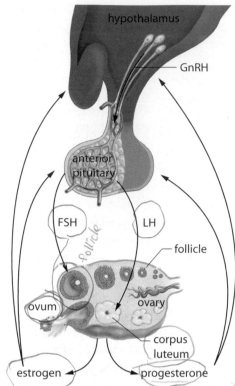

Figure 14.15 The hypothalamus produces GnRH, which stimulates the anterior pituitary to produce FSH and LH. FSH stimulates the follicle to produce estrogen. LH stimulates the corpus luteum to produce progesterone.

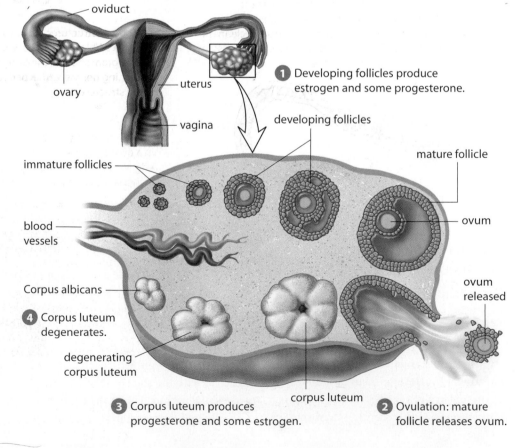

Figure 14.14 A follicle matures by growing layers of follicular cells and a central fluid-filled vesicle. The vesicle contains the maturing ovum. At ovulation, the follicle ruptures and the ovum is released into the oviduct. The follicle develops into a corpus luteum. If pregnancy does not occur, the corpus luteum starts to degenerate after about 10 days. Note that the follicle does not migrate around the ovary, as shown here for clarity, but goes through all the stages in one place.

1 Developing follicles produce estrogen and some progesterone.

4 Corpus luteum degenerates.

3 Corpus luteum produces progesterone and some estrogen.

2 Ovulation: mature follicle releases ovum.

bag.") Figure 14.14 illustrates the ovarian cycle, and Figure 14.15 illustrates the hormone systems that control this cycle.

The ovarian cycle can be roughly divided into two stages. The first stage is known as the **follicular stage**. It begins with an increase in the level of FSH released by the anterior pituitary gland. FSH stimulates one follicle to mature. As the follicle matures, it releases estrogen and some progesterone. The rising level of estrogen in the blood acts on the anterior pituitary to inhibit the release of FSH. At the same time, the estrogen triggers a sudden release of GnRH from the hypothalamus. This leads to a sharp increase in LH production by the anterior pituitary triggering ovulation— the follicle bursts, releasing its ovum.

Ovulation marks the end of the follicular stage and the beginning of the second stage. The second stage is called the **luteal stage**. Once the ovum has been released, LH causes the follicle to develop into a corpus luteum. The corpus luteum secretes progesterone and some estrogen. As the levels of these hormones rise in the blood, they act on the anterior pituitary to inhibit FSH and LH production. The corpus luteum degenerates, leading to a decrease in the levels of estrogen and progesterone. The low levels of these sex hormones in the blood cause the anterior pituitary to increase its secretion of FSH, and the cycle begins again.

If the ovum is fertilized and implants in the endometrium, blood hormone levels of progesterone and estrogen remain high under stimulus of hCG released by embryo-supporting membranes. The continued presence of progesterone maintains the endometrium to support the developing fetus. The continued presence of estrogen stops the ovarian cycle so no additional follicles mature.

Thought Lab | 14.3 | Development of the Corpus Luteum

Some structures in the ovary remain fairly constant throughout a female's lifetime. Other structures develop, change, and disappear through each menstrual cycle. In this activity, you will identify the structures that remain constant and the structures that change in the ovary.

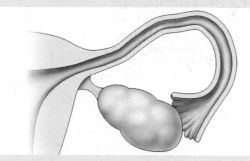

Procedure

1. Copy the outline of an ovary into your science notebook. (The fimbriae, oviduct, and a portion of the uterus have been included to help you visualize the orientation of the ovary. Do not include these structures in your copy.)

2. Using the descriptions in this textbook as a reference, sketch and label the following structures in your diagram:

- immature follicle
- developing follicle
- mature follicle
- ovum
- mature corpus luteum
- disintegrating corpus luteum

3. All of these structures are not visible in an ovary at any one time. Which structures would you expect to see if this diagram showed the ovary of a woman who was just beginning her menstrual period? Highlight the labels for these structures.

Analysis

1. If you were using a microscope to find the corpus luteum in a tissue sample, would you first look near the outer edge of the ovary or near the centre of the ovary? Explain your answer in terms of the events of the ovarian cycle.

2. Unlike most human organs, the corpus luteum is not a permanent structure in the body. What might be one adaptive advantage of having reproductive function regulated by a gland that develops and then disappears within a few weeks?

Extension

3. Use appropriate presentation software or develop and write your own code to demonstrate—for example, through animation—the development and disintegration of the corpus luteum within the ovary. **ICT**

BiologyFile

FYI

The menstrual cycles of individual women differ widely in their length and timing. When women live together, however, their menstrual cycles tend to synchronize.

21 What is the significance of the menstrual cycle?

22 Name the two stages of the ovarian cycle and briefly describe them.

23 What is the function of the corpus luteum?

hormones, each of which triggers different events in the body. In Investigation 14.B on page 500, you will synthesize what you have learned about this reproductive cycle.

24 Explain how the uterine cycle differs from the ovarian cycle.

The Uterine Cycle

The uterine cycle is closely linked to the ovarian cycle. As you have seen, ovulation takes place about halfway through the ovarian cycle, around day 14. The ovum survives for up to 24 h after ovulation.

If fertilization occurs, the fertilized egg completes the passage through the oviduct and arrives at the uterus a few days later. The timing of the uterine cycle ensures that the uterus is prepared to receive and nurture a new life. The events of the uterine cycle cause a build-up of blood vessels and tissues in the endometrium. If fertilization does not occur, the endometrium disintegrates and menstruation begins.

The uterine cycle begins on the first day of menstruation (which is also the first day of the ovarian cycle). On this day, the corpus luteum has degenerated and the levels of the sex hormones in the blood are low. As a new follicle begins to mature and release estrogen, the level of estrogen in the blood gradually increases. Beginning around the sixth day of the uterine cycle, the estrogen level is high enough to cause the endometrium to begin thickening. After ovulation, the release of progesterone by the corpus luteum causes a more rapid thickening of the endometrium. Between days 15 and 23 of the cycle, the thickness of the endometrium may double or even triple. If fertilization does not occur, the corpus luteum degenerates. The levels of the sex hormones drop, the endometrium breaks down, and menstruation begins again.

You have seen that the menstrual cycle involves a number of different

Aging and the Menstrual Cycle

After puberty, the male reproductive system can continue to produce viable sperm for a lifetime. In contrast, the number of functioning follicles in the female reproductive system decreases with age. This, in turn, leads to a gradual overall decline in the amount of estrogen and progesterone in the blood. As hormone levels drop, a woman's menstrual cycle becomes irregular. Within a few years, it stops altogether. The end of the menstrual cycle is known as **menopause**. Among North American women, the average age of menopause is approximately 50, but menopause can begin earlier or later.

A woman who has completed menopause no longer produces ova, so she is no longer fertile. As well, the decrease in the sex hormones disrupts the homeostasis of a number of hormone systems. This has a range of effects on the body. During menopause, blood vessels alternately constrict and dilate, resulting in uncomfortable sensations for some women known as "hot flashes." Some women also experience variable changes in mood. Over the longer term, menopause is associated with rising cholesterol levels, diminishing bone mass, and increased risk of uterine cancer, breast cancer, and heart disease. For these reasons, many women consider **hormone replacement therapy** (HRT) during or following menopause. Hormone replacement therapy is a prescription of low levels of estrogen with or without progesterone. However, while this therapy can ease some symptoms of menopause, the treatment also carries a number of health risks. In recent studies, hormone replacement therapy has been linked to

- an increased risk of coronary heart disease, strokes, and blood clots
- an increased risk of breast cancer and colorectal cancer
- an increased risk of dementia

For this reason, Health Canada advises that a woman should not begin hormone replacement therapy without a thorough medical evaluation and a careful assessment of her own particular needs, health, and medical history. In some cases, the benefits of the therapy may outweigh the risks. In other cases, the reverse is true. Scientists continue to search for other ways to alleviate the symptoms and long-term health effects of menopause.

Section 14.3 Summary

- Sex hormones work to stimulate the development of male and female reproductive systems and regulate the function of the mature reproductive system.

- Human babies are born with complete but immature reproductive systems. At puberty, an increase in production of GnRH by the hypothalamus stimulates the release of FSH and LH in the anterior pituitary. These hormones, in turn, trigger the development of gametes and the release of sex hormones.
- In males, the main sex hormone is testosterone. In females, the main sex hormones are estrogen and progesterone.
- In addition to their effect on the reproductive system, the sex hormones act throughout the body to cause the development of secondary sex characteristics.
- In the male reproductive system, a negative feedback hormone system maintains a relatively constant level of sperm production and testosterone.
- In females, hormone systems interact to regulate a monthly menstrual cycle.
- The menstrual cycle combines events in the ovary and in the uterus to maximize the chance of a zygote successfully implanting in the uterus for development into a fetus.

Thought Lab | **14.4** | **Therapy Options for Menopause**

Target Skills

Identifying physiological and ethical concerns about the medical use of reproductive hormones

Researching and **assessing** the medical use of reproductive hormones and their effects

For many years, doctors in North America routinely prescribed estrogen, or a combination of estrogen and progesterone, to help alleviate the symptoms of menopause. In 2000, the U.S.-based National Institutes of Health began a detailed investigation of the effects of hormone replacement therapy (HRT). Researchers stopped the study several years early, however, when they found that HRT was associated with a significant increase in the risk of strokes, heart disease, and breast cancer among their test subjects. The findings led scientists to look for a safer alternative to HRT.

Procedure

1. Using print or Internet resources, research two or three different kinds of therapies available to women who want to alleviate the symptoms of menopause. **ICT**

2. For each of the therapies you are studying, gather information about
   - how the treatment affects cells and tissues in the body
   - how the treatment affects hormone feedback systems
   - any known health risks and benefits

3. Organize the information you have gathered. Create a short report or presentation to summarize and communicate your findings. **ICT**

Analysis

1. Based on your research, is it possible to claim that one of these therapies is better than the others?

2. Many people argue that women should never have been prescribed hormone replacement therapy in the years before the NIH study was completed. Do you agree? What, if anything, should health practitioners and pharmaceutical companies have done differently?

The Menstrual Cycle

LH and FSH are *pituitary hormones* because they are produced by the pituitary gland. Similarly, progesterone and estrogen are *ovarian hormones* because they are produced in the ovaries. In this investigation, you will see how pituitary and ovarian hormones affect, and are affected by, ovarian and uterine events during the menstrual cycle.

Question

How do pituitary and ovarian hormones interact with ovarian and uterine events during the menstrual cycle?

Procedure

1. Study the graphs, and observe how the levels of hormones affect each other as well as the follicle and endometrium.

2. Use the Analysis questions to analyze and interpret the graphs.

Analysis

1. During which days of the menstrual cycle does the level of FSH increase? What happens to the follicle during this time?

2. On which day is the level of LH in the bloodstream at its highest? What event occurs immediately after this peak?

3. What event is associated with the decline of LH in the blood?

4. During which days of the cycle does the level of estrogen in the blood increase most rapidly? What happens in the uterus during this time?

5. During which days of the cycle does the level of progesterone in the blood increase most rapidly? What happens in the uterus during this time?

6. During which days of the cycle are the levels of estrogen and progesterone at their lowest? What happens in the uterus during this time?

Conclusions

7. How do increased levels of estrogen and progesterone appear to affect the level of FSH in the blood?

8. Do the names of the hormones FSH and LH correspond to their functions? Explain your answer.

9. Select and use an appropriate mode of representation to compare and contrast the functions of estrogen and progesterone in the menstrual cycle. **ICT**

10. At which time in the menstrual cycle is a woman most fertile? Explain your answer.

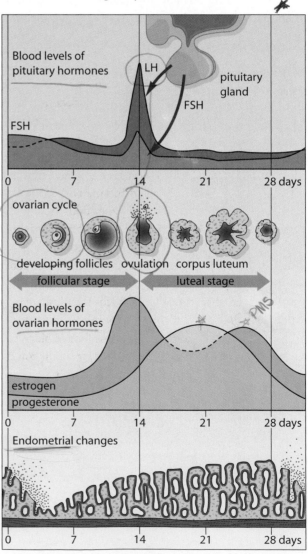

Endocrine Disruptors in the Environment

Hormones influence nearly all aspects of the body processes in animals, notably cellular development, growth, and reproduction. Thus, when people noticed that animals in areas that are contaminated by pollutants began to exhibit certain types of abnormalities, scientists began to wonder if there might be a link between certain pollutants and endocrine effects on body systems.

Examining the Evidence

Substances that interfere with the normal functions of hormones are called *endocrine disruptors*. These chemicals upset the growth, development, and reproduction of organisms by mimicking natural hormones or by blocking their effects. For example, when fish populations are exposed to reproductive endocrine disruptors, the sexual organs of young males fail to fully develop. In extreme cases, the males produce eggs! Both effects are examples of feminization. Endocrine disruptors that mimic estrogen can cause feminization. Substances that block the action of male reproductive hormones can also have feminizing effects.

While the effects of known endocrine disruptors can be demonstrated in a laboratory, it is not always easy to assess their impact in the environment. One problem is that endocrine disruptors tend to be diluted in lakes and rivers. Even so, scientists have observed effects such as the feminization of fish near sewage discharge sites. Scientists have also observed impaired reproduction and development of fish near pulp and paper mills. As shown in the table, sewage and mill wastes both contain endocrine disruptors. Even treated sewage contains obvious endocrine disruptors such as synthetic estrogen from birth control pills.

Are estrogen disruptors to blame for the increase in abnormalities in frogs in some regions and the decrease in amphibians worldwide? Why do some female black bears and polar bears develop male sexual traits? It could be that increased exposure to UV light is harming

amphibians, and that some bears simply inherit the trait of showing both male and female sexual characteristics.

Selected Products Containing Endocrine Disruptors

Source/Product	Endocrine Disruptors
flame retardants	polybrominated diphenyl ethers (PBDEs)
paint (for ships' hulls)	tributyltin
pesticides	DDT, lindane, permethrin
soft plastics	phthalates
pulp and paper mill effluent	phytoestrogens
perfumes and soaps	polycyclic musks
shampoo and other cosmetics	phthalates

Assessing the Risks

If endocrine disruptors in the environment are affecting wild animals, are they also affecting people? Scientists and representatives of industrial manufacturers continue to debate whether these chemicals pose a health risk to humans. There is evidence that endocrine disruptors are leading to lower sperm counts, reduced fertility in both men and women, and increased rates of certain types of cancers. Some studies have suggested a link between endocrine disruptors and learning and behaviour problems in children. To date, however, direct (causal) links between environmental exposure to endocrine disruptors and human health effects have not been established. Continued research that includes the cooperation of industry and financial support of governments is necessary to identify and mediate the risks that these chemicals pose to the environment and organisms.

• • •

1. Should a potential endocrine disruptor be considered "guilty until proven innocent" or "innocent until proven guilty" before being put on the market? Justify your response.

2. What would you need to know to link a particular substance to specific endocrine disrupting effects in a population, such as unusually high cancer rates?

Many cosmetics—including some, but not all, brands of nail polish—contain endocrine-disrupting chemicals in amounts that are comparable to, and sometimes greater than, hormone levels in the human body. Should this be cause for concern?

1. Distinguish between the following terms: chromosomal sex and reproductive sex.

2. Use a diagram to summarize the hormone interactions that regulate the male reproductive system. **ICT**

3. Briefly describe the main hormonal and physiological events of

 a) male puberty

 b) female puberty

 c) the ovarian cycle

 d) the uterine cycle

4. Examine the graphs and answer the following questions:

 a) Identify the hormones represented by the letters A, B, C, and D.

 b) Describe the events that are occurring in the region of the diagram labelled E.

 c) Identify what is happening at the region of the diagram labelled F.

 d) Describe the events that are occurring in the region of the diagram labelled G.

 e) Write suitable labels for the regions of the diagram labelled H and I.

 f) Write a caption that briefly and accurately summarizes what is being depicted in this whole diagram.

5. Compare and contrast the effects of testosterone on the male body with the effects of estrogen on the female body. In what ways are these effects similar? In what ways do they differ? **ICT**

6. How does the menstrual cycle contribute to successful human reproduction?

7. Assuming that all other body systems remain unaffected, what physiological effects would you expect to find in an adolescent male whose anterior pituitary produced FSH but not LH? Use a flow chart or labelled diagram to explain your reasoning. **ICT**

8. Predict what would happen to testosterone production in the testes in response to an injection of a large amount of testosterone in an adult male.

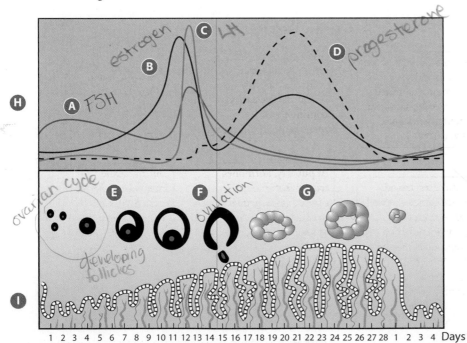

In both males and females, the reproductive system includes a pair of gonads which produce sex cells (gametes) as well as sex hormones that regulate reproductive function. Male gonads are the testes, located outside the body. The testes are adapted to produce large quantities of male gametes called sperm. The scrotum regulates the temperature of the testes. Female gonads are the ovaries, located within the body and adapted to produce a single female gamete, called an ovum, each month.

In males, developing sperm are transported from the testes to the epididymis, where they mature and are stored. Sexual stimulation causes sperm cells to move through the ductus deferens and to become mixed with other fluids to produce semen. Semen is carried through the urethra and is released from the penis into the female reproductive tract.

In females, ova develop within follicles in the ovary. Each month a single ovum matures and is swept into the oviduct. The movement of cilia in the oviduct carries the ovum toward the uterus. If the ovum is fertilized by sperm in the oviduct, it may implant in the uterus. Otherwise the ovum, along with excess uterine tissues, flow out of the body.

Sexually transmitted infections (STIs) may be primarily viral or bacterial in origin. These infections can have severe consequences and are a serious health concern. STIs include HIV/AIDS, hepatitis, genital herpes, human papilloma virus, chlamydia, gonorrhea, and syphilis.

In males, puberty begins when an increase in GnRH production in the hypothalamus triggers the release of FSH and LH from the anterior pituitary. These hormones in turn stimulate the production of sperm and a surge in testosterone. Hormone interactions maintain secondary sex characteristics along with the steady production of sperm.

In females, puberty begins when an increase in GnRH production in the hypothalamus triggers the release of FSH and LH from the anterior pituitary. These hormones in turn stimulate the production of ova and initiate the menstrual cycle.

The menstrual cycle controls the maturation of an ovum and the preparation of the uterine lining to receive a zygote. The menstrual cycle continues until middle age, at which time diminishing hormone levels lead to menopause.

Chapter 14 Graphic Organizer

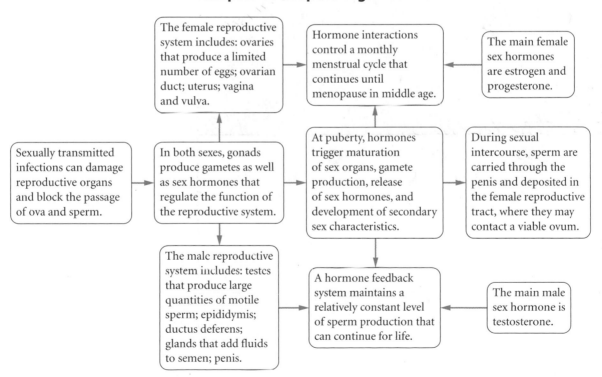

Understanding Concepts

1. Name the structures within a testis, and describe their functions.

2. In which part of the body are each of the following produced?
   a) testosterone
   b) progesterone
   c) sperm
   d) luteinizing hormone
   e) follicle stimulating hormone
   f) ovum

3. Outline, in the form of a labelled sketch or flow chart, the path of a sperm cell from its formation to the moment it reaches an ovum. In your answer, identify all the male and female structures through which the sperm travels. **ICT**

4. List three of the components of semen, and briefly explain what these fluids contribute to reproductive function.

5. Construct a table or graphic organizer to compare and contrast the source, common modes of transmission, effects, and treatments for the following sexually transmitted infections. **ICT**
   a) HIV/AIDS
   b) hepatitis B
   c) genital herpes
   d) human papilloma virus
   e) chlamydia
   f) gonorrhea
   g) syphilis

6. a) How would a newborn child acquire an infection of chlamydia, gonorrhea, syphilis, and herpes?
   b) What effects do these STIs have on infants?

7. What are the health risks and treatment options associated with each of the infections in question 5?

8. Describe the stages of development of a follicle within an ovary.

9. Describe the changes in the endometrium through the stages of the menstrual cycle.

10. Compare the levels of sex hormones in the blood of a female before and after the onset of puberty, and describe how these changes affect the reproductive system.

11. The following graph represents the average blood concentration of four circulating hormones collected from 50 healthy adult women who were not pregnant. Use the graph to answer the following questions:

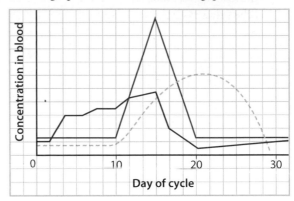

a) Which line represents luteinizing hormone?
b) Which line represents progesterone?
c) Which hormone increases during the last half of the menstrual cycle?

Applying Concepts

12. Penicillin is an antibiotic that effectively cures syphilis. Explain why penicillin would be ineffective against AIDS.

13. Describe the effect you would expect to see in a human male whose sperm cells have no acrosome.

14. Do the names "follicle stimulating hormone" and "luteinizing hormone" correspond to their function in the human reproductive system? Give examples to justify your answer.

15. Young female athletes often experience delayed puberty. What would you expect to find if you compare the blood hormone levels of a fourteen-year-old gymnast with those of less athletic girls of the same age?

16. Farmers who maintain stocks of large animals often castrate the males. Based on the hormonal control of the male reproductive system, explain the likely physiological and behavioral effects of castration. What advantages does castration offer to the farmer?

17. A young woman tells her doctor that she is experiencing irregular menstrual periods.
    a) Hypothesize some possible causes of the irregularity.
    b) Design an investigation that could test for one of these causes.

18. a) Two main events of the menstrual cycle are the release of an egg from an ovary and the build-up of the uterine lining. Use the data table to predict which of the hormones A, B, or C would be associated with each of these two events. Assume the cycle length is 28 days.

Day of menstrual cycle	Relative hormone concentration		
	A	B	C
1	12	5	10
5	14	5	14
9	14	5	13
13	70	10	20
17	12	60	9
21	12	150	8
25	8	100	8
1	12	5	10

b) A woman is having difficulty becoming pregnant. For the last month, her hormone levels have been measured on each of the eight days listed in the data table. Hormone A remained steady at 12. Hormone B remained steady at 5. Hormone C had the levels shown in the data table. How could these hormone levels explain her fertility difficulties?

19. Imagine that you are a government official in a health department. In response to pressure from community groups, your department has created a new, $10 million program to fight the spread of STIs. The program includes work in two different areas: education and awareness campaigns; and scientific research on treatment and vaccines. How would you divide the funding between these two program areas? Explain your reasoning.

Making Connections

20. An individual whose chromosomal (genetic) sex is XX has inherited a genetic defect so that cellular receptors for estrogen are lacking.
  a) Would you expect this person to have testes or ovaries? Explain why.
  b) Can this person respond to estrogen? Why or why not, and what effects will this have on the body?
  c) The adrenal cortex produces some testosterone. Is it possible that this person could have the secondary sex characteristics of a male? Explain.
  d) Predict whether this individual is fertile and give reasons for your answer.

21. The mortality rate of sperm is high compared to the mortality rate of eggs. Suggest reasons why this might be the case.

22. Chlamydia can be readily cured with antibiotics. Why then are there so many new cases of chlamydia reported each year? Give three reasons.

23. When a woman becomes pregnant, menstruation stops for the duration of the pregnancy.
  a) Explain how menstruation is prevented if pregnancy occurs.
  b) Explain why menstruation begins again after the pregnancy.

24. Some male athletes take anabolic steroids to enhance their performance. These substances mimic the action of testosterone, but are not identical to testosterone. The side effects of steroid use can include changes that might be associated with an increase in sex hormones in the body, such as increased muscular development and aggressiveness. However, side effect can also include changes that might be associated with a decrease in sex hormones, such as the shrinking of testicles and the loss of facial hair. Using hormone feedback systems, explain how a drug that mimics the effect of testosterone could have these apparently contradictory effects on the male body.

Human Development

Chapter Concepts

15.1 Fertilization and Embryonic Development

- Fertilization results in a zygote, which goes through several stages of development before implantation.

- An implanted embryo undergoes significant stages of development and differentiation in the first eight weeks after fertilization.

- Extra-embryonic membranes, some of which develop into the placenta and umbilical cord, provide support, protection, and nourishment for the developing life.

15.2 Fetal Development and Birth

- Fetal development occurs over about the last 30 weeks of pregnancy.

- Parturition is the process leading up to and including birth.

- Hormones play an important role during pregnancy, birth, and lactation following birth.

- Environmental factors, including teratogens, have an effect on embryonic and fetal development.

15.3 Development, Technology, and Society

- Reproductive technologies include technologies to enhance reproductive potential and technologies to restrict reproductive potential.

- The use of reproductive technologies leads to ethical, moral, legal, and personal issues.

The process of human development and birth inspires awe and wonder in both scientists and non-scientists alike. Over a period of about 38 weeks—266 days—a single fertilized egg cell undergoes a staggeringly complex sequence of changes as it multiplies, modifies, develops, and grows to form the hundreds of billions of cells that make up the tissues, organs, and systems of the infant human body. In this chapter, you will follow the processes and events that lead to the development and birth of a human child. As well, you will consider the role that technology increasingly plays in these processes and events. In addition, you will examine some of the challenges that reproductive technology presents to individuals, families, and other segments of society.

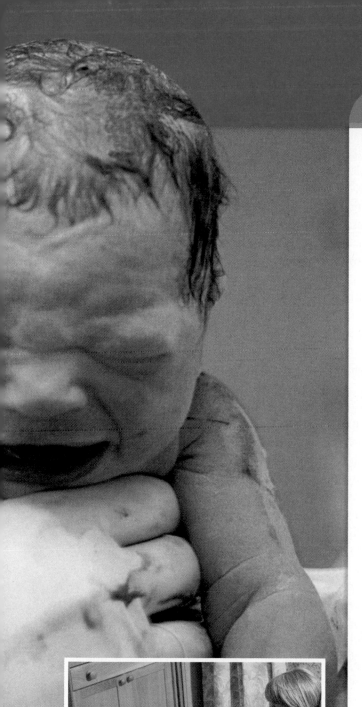

Visualizing Early Human Development

The first 56 days (two months) are the most crucial period during human development. Among the many changes that occur during this time is an astonishing increase in size. What else might be changing during this time?

Procedure

1. Graph the data in the data table. Consider designing a three-dimensional bar-type graph, either with a computer or using concrete objects, to help you visualize the sizes.

Human Embryo Size (Length) during the first 56 Days of Development

Day	Approximate Length (mm)
1	0.1
7	0.1
14	0.2
21	1
28	3
35	8
42	13
49	20
56	30

Analysis

1. In terms of size, over what period of time is the *least* amount of change occurring?

2. How does the change in size in the first four weeks of development compare with the change in size during the second four weeks?

3. Sketch or describe what you think the developing human embryo looks like at four weeks. Then do the same for the embryo at eight weeks.

4. The first eight weeks is the most significant period of time during human development. What types of changes do you think occur during the remaining 30 weeks? List at least five and when you think they occur.

5. Substances consumed by or exposed to the mother during pregnancy can harm the baby as it develops.

   a) List at least four substances that you think are harmful to the developing baby.

   b) During which period of time do you think a baby is most sensitive to harm from these substances?

Carrying on a tradition that is perhaps as old as the oldest human societies, a midwife (meaning literally "with woman") provides care and advice to a woman during her pregnancy and the birth of her baby. The midwife also helps to provide care for the newborn child in the weeks, and sometimes months, that follow.

Fertilization and Embryonic Development

Biologists commonly divide prenatal (prebirth) development into three three-month periods called *trimesters*. Biologists also use a complementary system to organize and describe developmental events before birth. This system uses two main periods of prenatal development:

- The *embryonic period of development*: This period of development takes place over the first eight weeks, or the first two thirds of the first trimester. During this time, tremendous change takes place. Cells divide and become redistributed. Tissues and organs form, as do structures that support and nourish the developing embryo.

- The *fetal period of development*: This period of development takes place from the start of the ninth week through to birth. It corresponds to the remaining third of the first trimester and all of the second and third trimesters. During the fetal period, the body grows rapidly and organs begin to function and coordinate to form organ systems.

In this section, you will learn about key developments that take place during the embryonic period. In Section 15.2, you will examine key developments that take place during the fetal period.

Fertilization

Human development begins with fertilization. **Fertilization** involves the joining of male and female gametes (sperm and egg) to form a single cell that contains 23 chromosomes from each parent, for a total of 46 chromosomes.

Several events lead up to the moment of fertilization (also called conception). In the female body, an egg is released from an ovary and swept into an oviduct. The egg is carried toward the uterus by muscular contractions and the wavelike actions of cilia, which line the walls of the oviduct. The passage of the egg is slow—it takes about four days to reach the uterus. It must be fertilized, however, within 12 to 24 h of its release, or it will lose its capacity to develop further. For a sperm and egg to join, the sperm must reach the egg during the early part of its movement through the oviduct.

Several hundred million sperm cells exit the male's urethra during each ejaculation. Once they enter the female's vagina, they must make their way to the cervix, then through the uterus, and finally to the oviduct into which the egg was released. Most sperm do not survive this journey. Many are destroyed by the naturally acidic environment of the vagina. Other sperm go the "wrong way"—that is, they enter the oviduct that does not have the egg. From the millions of sperm released, only a few dozen to a few hundred survive to reach the egg.

The plasma membrane of the egg is surrounded by a thin, clear layer of protein and carbohydrates called the *zona pellucida*. This layer, in turn, is surrounded by several jelly-like layers of follicle cells that loosely adhere to one another, called the *corona radiata*. These cells were a source of nourishment for the egg when it was in an ovarian follicle.

When a sperm meets the corona radiata, the sperm's enzyme-containing acrosome (the "cap" surrounding the nucleus) releases its contents. The enzymes digest a path through the corona and zona pellucida. Meanwhile, the sperm advances farther by means of the lashing actions of its tail. As shown in Figure 15.1, many sperm are involved in this activity. The action of hundreds of sperm may be necessary to clear a path for the one sperm that is able to successfully enter the egg. Once a sperm enters the egg, the egg's plasma membrane depolarizes, preventing other sperm from binding with and entering it.

Within about 12 h of the sperm's nucleus entering the egg, the membranes of the sperm nucleus and the egg nucleus disappear. The 23 chromosomes in the

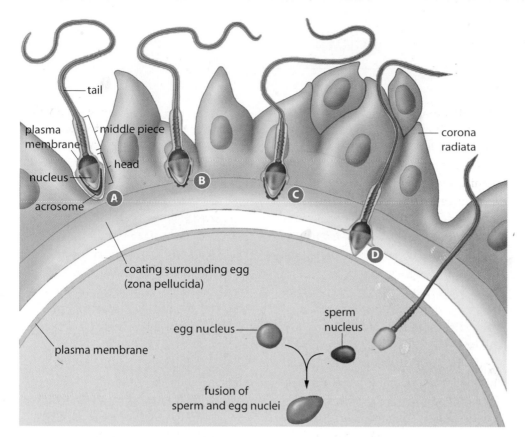

Figure 15.1 During fertilization, sperm cells reach the jelly-like coating surrounding the egg (**A**) and release enzymes that digest a path through the coating. The path allows other sperm cells to go farther through the coating and move toward the plasma membrane of the egg (**B, C, D**). Eventually, the head of one sperm cell might successfully enter the egg. When this happens, the sperm nucleus and the egg nucleus fuse, completing fertilization.

ovum are joined with the 23 chromosomes in the sperm. Fertilization of the egg is now complete. The resulting single cell—the first cell of a new life—is called a **zygote** (from a Greek word that means "joined"). The zygote has 23 *pairs* of chromosomes—one chromosome from each pair in each parent for a total of 46 chromosomes.

1. How many chromosomes are there in a human egg once it has been fertilized?

2. Why must the egg be fertilized within 12 to 24 hours of its release?

3. Why do so few sperm arrive in the oviduct where the egg is?

4. Why is the first sperm that reaches the egg unlikely to be the sperm that enters and joins with it?

Cleavage and Implantation

When the egg is fertilized, it is still moving through the oviduct and is several days away from entering the uterus. During this journey, tremendous activity can be observed in the zygote, as shown in Figure 15.2 on page 510. (Unfamiliar terms in this diagram are explained in the paragraphs below.)

Within 30 h of being fertilized, the 0.1 mm zygote divides by mitosis for the first time, giving rise to two new cells. These cells also divide, forming four cells. The four cells, in turn, divide to form eight cells, and so on. This process of cell division occurs quickly, with little time for the individual cells to grow. As a result, the cells become smaller and smaller with each division. The overall size of the zygote, however, remains about 0.1 mm. This process of cell division without enlargement of the cells is called **cleavage**. Figure 15.3 shows the zygote during several stages of cleavage. By the time the zygote is a sphere of 16 cells, it is called a *morula*. (The term *morula* comes from a Latin word that means "mulberry.")

The morula reaches the uterus within three to five days after fertilization. During this time, it begins to fill with fluid that diffuses from the uterus. As the fluid-filled space develops, two different

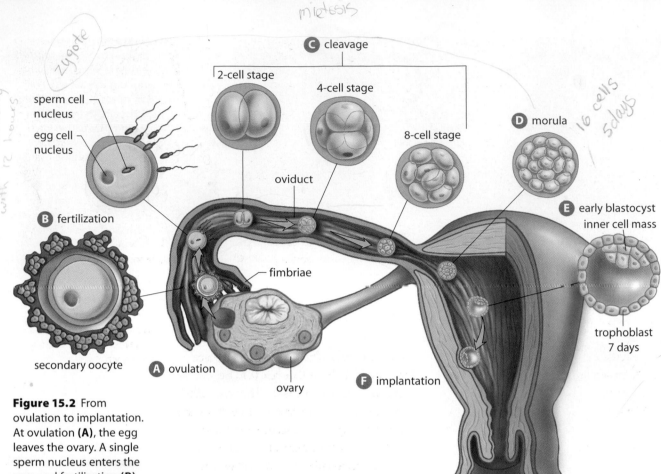

handwritten annotations: zygote; mitosis; 16 cells 5 days; Start dividing with 12 hours

C cleavage

2-cell stage

4-cell stage

8-cell stage

D morula

sperm cell nucleus

egg cell nucleus

oviduct

B fertilization

E early blastocyst inner cell mass

fimbriae

secondary oocyte

A ovulation

ovary

trophoblast 7 days

F implantation

Figure 15.2 From ovulation to implantation. At ovulation (**A**), the egg leaves the ovary. A single sperm nucleus enters the egg, and fertilization (**B**) occurs in the oviduct. As the zygote moves along, it undergoes cleavage (**C**) to produce a morula (**D**). The blastocyst forms (**E**) and implants in the lining of the uterus (**F**).

groups of cells form. The entire spherical structure is now called a **blastocyst** (Figure 15.4). The term *blastocyst* comes from two Greek words that mean "germ pouch." Here, the word "germ" refers to cells from which new cells or tissues can develop. Thus, the blastocyst is a hollow structure—a "pouch"—from which new cellular structures can develop.

One group of cells, called the *trophoblast* (meaning "nourishment of the germ"), forms the outer layer of the blastocyst. The trophoblast will develop into a membrane called the chorion. (The term *chorion* comes from a Greek word that refers to the region surrounding a city. In more modern terms, *chorion* means "membrane.") The chorion, in turn, will develop to form part of the placenta. The placenta is a structure that provides nutrients and oxygen to, and removes wastes from, the developing offspring. (You will learn more about the placenta on page 516.) The other group

of cells come together within the blastocyst to form the **inner cell mass** (also called the embryoblast). The inner cell mass develops into the embryo itself.

Between the fifth and seventh day after fertilization, the blastocyst attaches to the endometrium (the outer lining of the uterus), with the inner cell mass positioned against the endometrium. The trophoblast cells secrete enzymes that digest some of the tissues and blood vessels of the endometrium, and the blastocyst slowly sinks into the uterine wall. This nestling of the blastocyst into the endometrium is called **implantation**. Implantation is complete by the tenth to fourteenth day. With successful implantation, the woman is now said to be pregnant.

About the time that implantation begins, the trophoblast starts to secrete a hormone called **human chorionic gonadotropin (hCG)**. hCG has the same effects as luteinizing hormone (LH), so

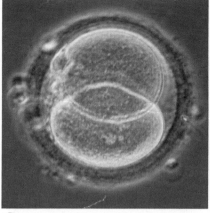

A First division (two cells produced)

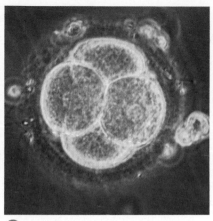

B Second division (four cells produced)

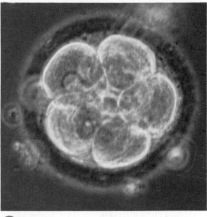

C Third division (eight cells produced)

Figure 15.3 The zygote at several stages of early cell division. Notice that the overall size (volume) of the zygote remains the same with each division.

it maintains the corpus luteum past the time when it would otherwise degenerate. As a result, the secretion of estrogen and progesterone continues, maintaining the endometrium and preventing menstruation. The secretion of hCG continues at a high level for about two months. Then it declines to a low level by the end of four months. Although the corpus luteum remains intact throughout pregnancy, its function as a source of hormones is less important after the first trimester. By this time, the placenta secretes sufficient estrogen and progesterone to maintain the endometrium (see Figure 15.5 on page 512).

• • •

5 Explain what the process of cleavage is.

6 How does a morula differ from a blastocyst?

7 From which group of cells, the trophoblast or the inner cell mass, does the embryo develop?

8 Explain what implantation is.

9 What is hCG, and how long is it secreted?

• • •

Gastrulation and the Start of Tissue Formation

During the second week, as the blastocyst continues and completes the process of implantation, the inner cell mass

changes. A space begins to form between the inner cell mass and the trophoblast. This space, called the amniotic cavity, will soon fill with fluid and is the place where the baby will develop. (The amniotic cavity forms within a sac called the amnion. The amnion is one of several embryo-supporting structures that you will learn about later in this section.)

As the amniotic cavity forms, the inner cell mass flattens into a disk-shaped structure called the *embryonic disk* (see Figure 15.6). The embryonic disk is supported by a short stalk that connects the blastocyst with the endometrium. At first, the embryonic disk consists of two layers: an outer *ectoderm*, which is closer to the amniotic cavity, and an inner *endoderm*. Shortly after, a third layer, called the *mesoderm*,

Figure 15.4 At the time of implantation, the blastocyst is about the size of the period at the end of this sentence.

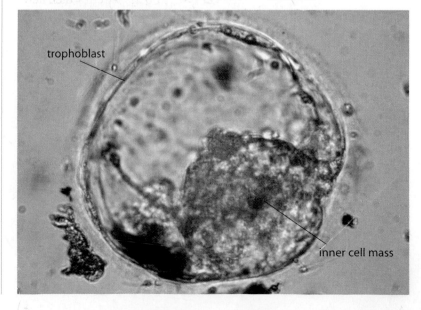

trophoblast

inner cell mass

Figure 15.5 hCG, progesterone, and estrogen are secreted from various sources during pregnancy. Early in pregnancy, estrogen and progesterone are secreted by the corpus luteum. During mid-pregnancy, there is a shift toward secretion of these hormones by the placenta. Late in pregnancy, these hormones are secreted solely by the placenta. (The thickness of the arrows represents the relative concentrations of these hormones.)

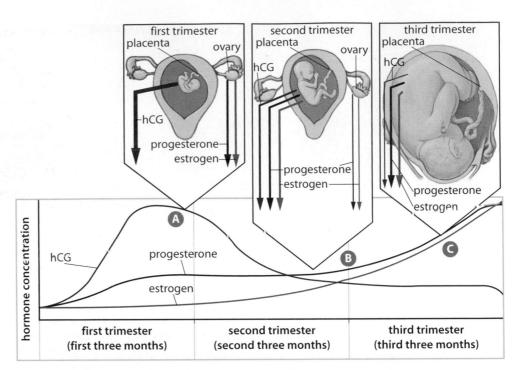

A Human chorionic gonadotropin (hCG) increases until it reaches a maximum concentration near the end of the first trimester. Then it decreases to a low level for the remainder of the pregnancy.

B Progesterone continues to increase until it levels off near the end of the pregnancy. Early in the pregnancy, progesterone is produced by the corpus luteum in the ovary. By the second trimester, its production shifts to the placenta.

C Estrogen levels increase slowly throughout the pregnancy, but they increase more quickly as the end of the pregnancy approaches. Early in the pregnancy, estrogen is produced only in the ovary. By the second trimester, its production shifts to the placenta.

forms between the endoderm and the ectoderm. The process of forming these three layers is called **gastrulation**, and the three layers are called the **primary germ layers**. The developing embryo is now called the *gastrula*.

Gastrulation marks the start of **morphogenesis**—the series of events that form distinct structures of the developing organism. (*Morphogenesis* comes from two Greek words that mean "shape creator" or "producer of forms.") Morphogenesis depends on the ability of early embryonic cells to become different types of cells—that is, to differentiate. **Differentiation** is the cellular process that enables a cell to develop a particular shape and to perform specific functions that are different from the functions of other cells. The development of the three primary germ layers is especially important because all the cells, tissues, and organs of the body are derived from the primary germ layers through differentiation (see Figure 15.7).

BiologyFile

FYI

The term *gastrulation* comes from Greek words that mean "stomach forming." It refers to one of the early structures formed during the process, the archenteron (or gastrocoel), from which the digestive system will develop.

- - -

Q 10 What is the amniotic cavity, and where does it form?

Q 11 Name each of the three layers of the embryonic disk.

Q 12 Name the process that results in the formation of the primary germ layers.

Q 13 What is morphogenesis?

Q 14 Explain how the development of the primary germ layers is related to differentiation.

- - -

Neurulation and Organ Formation

Between the third and eighth weeks, the organs form. With each passing day, different rates of cell division in the primary germ layers cause tissues to fold into distinct patterns. Gradually, the three-layered embryo is transformed

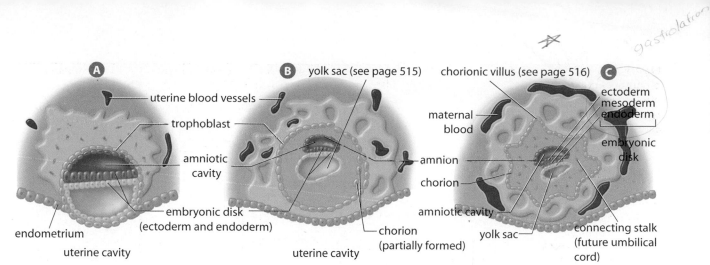

gastrolation

A
uterine blood vessels
trophoblast
amniotic cavity
endometrium
embryonic disk
(ectoderm and endoderm)
uterine cavity

B
yolk sac (see page 515)
maternal blood
amnion
chorion
amniotic cavity
chorion
(partially formed)
uterine cavity

C
chorionic villus (see page 516)
ectoderm
mesoderm
endoderm
embryonic disk
yolk sac
connecting stalk
(future umbilical cord)

Figure 15.6 The changes that are illustrated in these diagrams take place over a period of about one week. Gastrulation—the formation of the three primary germ layers—is a pivotal event in embryonic development. All future tissues, organs, and organ systems of the body will develop from the cells of the germ layers.

into a body with separate organs and, by about the eighth week, a shape that is recognizably human.

During the third week, a thickened band of mesoderm cells develops along the back of the embryonic disk. These cells lie along what will become the baby's back and come together to form a rod-like structure called the notochord. (The *noto-* part of this term comes from a Greek word that means "back.") The notochord will form the basic framework of the skeleton. The nervous system develops from ectoderm that is located just above the notochord (Figure 15.8). First, cells along the surface above the

Figure 15.7 Organs and body systems that develop from the three primary germ layers

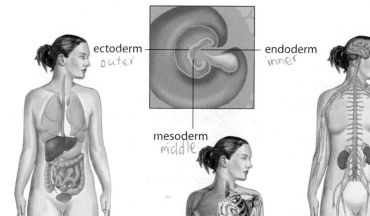

ectoderm
outer

endoderm
inner

mesoderm
middle

Ectoderm (Outer Primary Germ Layer)
- outer skin (epidermis) and associated structures (hair, nails, sweat glands, mammary glands)
- nervous tissue and sense organs
- pituitary gland   • tooth enamel
- adrenal medulla   • eye lens

Mesoderm (Middle Primary Germ Layer)
- dermis of skin
- cellular lining of blood vessels, lymphatic vessels, body cavities
- muscle tissue
- connective tissue (including bone, cartilage, blood)
- adrenal cortex   • kidneys and ureters
- heart   • spleen
- internal reproductive organs

Endoderm (Inner Primary Germ Layer)
- cellular lining of respiratory tract, digestive tract, urinary bladder, urethra
- liver (most)   • tonsils (partial)
- gallbladder   • parathyroid glands
- pancreas   • thyroid glands
- thymus

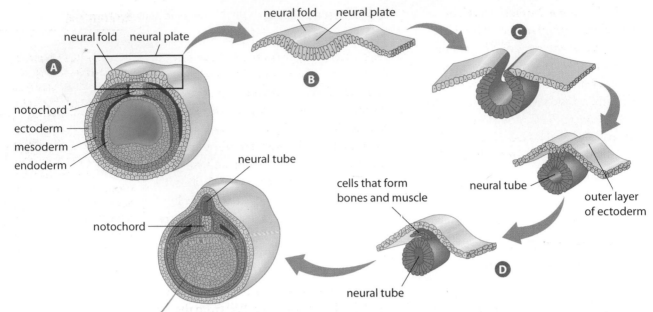

Figure 15.8 The process of neurulation. **(A)** The notochord forms from mesoderm on the dorsal (back) side of the embryo. **(B)** The neural tube starts as a plate of ectoderm just above the developing notochord. **(C)** The edges of this plate fold inward, meeting to form a hollow tube surrounded by cells. The neural tube pinches off from the ectoderm and develops into the spinal cord and brain. **(D)** Cells migrate from the meeting margins of the neural tube and eventually form other organs, bone, and muscles.

notochord begin to thicken. Folds develop on each side of a groove along this surface. When the folds fuse, they become a tube, called the neural tube, which develops into the brain and spinal cord. The process of forming this tube is called **neurulation** and marks the start of organ formation. Soon after neurulation begins, a reddish bulge that contains the heart forms. By about the eighteenth day, the heart starts beating.

The fourth week of prenatal development and on is a time of rapid growth and differentiation (Figure 15.9). Blood cells start to form and fill developing blood vessels. Lungs and kidneys take shape. Small buds, which will develop into arms and legs, appear. A distinct head is visible, as well as early evidence of eyes, ears, and nose. The embryo is about 0.6 cm long at this point. The mother might now suspect that she is pregnant, because her menstrual period is about two weeks late.

During the fifth week, the embryo's head is very large compared with its body. The eyes open, but they do not yet have eyelids or irises. Cells in the brain are differentiating very quickly. The embryo is about 1.3 cm long now.

In the sixth week, the brain continues its rapid development. The limbs lengthen and flex slightly. The gonads are starting to produce hormones that will influence the development of the external genitalia.

During the seventh and eighth weeks, the embryo has distinct human characteristics. The organs are formed, and the nervous system is starting to coordinate body activity. A skeleton of cartilage has formed. (Bone will not begin to replace the cartilage until about the ninth week.) Eyes are well developed, but the lids are now closed, stuck together to protect them against random movements of fingers from the still-elongating arms. The nostrils are developed, but are plugged with mucus. (Breathing will not be required until the baby emerges from the uterus.) The external genitalia are still forming, but they are undifferentiated. That is, the physical sex of the embryo is not yet apparent, even though its genetic sex has already been determined.

By the end of the eighth week of prenatal development, the embryo is about the size and mass of a paper clip. Approximately 90 percent of the organs and other structures that make up the adult human body are established. From this time on, as the organs enlarge and mature, until birth, the developing life is called a fetus (Latin for "offspring").

• • •

15. What is neurulation?

16. Other than neurulation, identify two events that occur during the third week of development.

17. Identify three events that occur during the fourth week of development.

18. Identify four events that occur between the fifth and eighth week and when they occur.

19. At what point is the embryo termed a fetus?

• • •

Structures That Support the Embryo

The internal organs of the embryo form between the third and eighth weeks. At the same time, an intricate system of membranes that are external to the embryo are also forming. Figure 15.10 shows these **extra-embryonic membranes**: the **allantois**, **amnion**, **chorion**, and **yolk sac**. The extra-embryonic membranes, along with the placenta and umbilical cord that develop from some of them, are responsible for the protection, nutrition, respiration, and excretion of the embryo (and, later, the fetus). During birth, these membranes—as well as the placenta and umbilical cord—are expelled from the uterus. The expelled membranes and structures are collectively and commonly referred to as the *afterbirth*.

The Placenta and Umbilical Cord

By the end of the second week after fertilization, finger-like projections from

BiologyFile

FYI
The amniotic fluid initially forms by filtration of the mother's blood plasma. By about the eighth or ninth week, the fetus urinates into the amniotic fluid about once an hour, adding to the volume of the fluid. The volume increases slowly because the fetus swallows amniotic fluid at nearly the same rate. By the time of birth, the amnion contains 700 mL to 1000 mL of fluid.

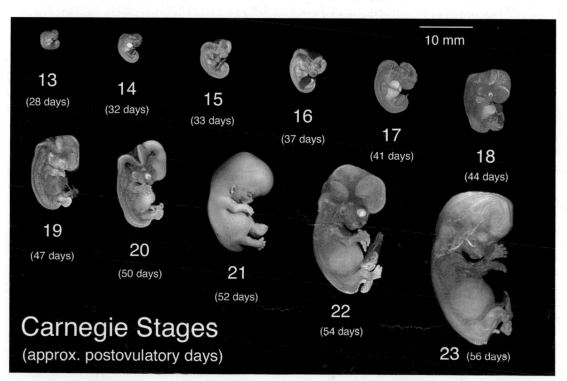

10 mm

13 (28 days)
14 (32 days)
15 (33 days)
16 (37 days)
17 (41 days)
18 (44 days)
19 (47 days)
20 (50 days)
21 (52 days)
22 (54 days)
23 (56 days)

Carnegie Stages
(approx. postovulatory days)

Figure 15.9 During the first eight weeks (56 days) after ovulation, the appearance of various internal and external features may be used to describe the development of the embryo. The eight weeks are divided into 23 embryonic stages, also known as Carnegie stages. Embryologists use the Carnegie stages to make statements about development that are more specific than reference to size or age allow, since the moment of conception cannot be determined precisely.

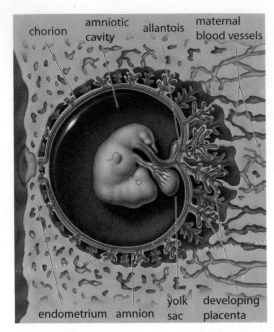

chorion amniotic cavity allantois maternal blood vessels

endometrium amnion yolk sac developing placenta

Amnion (AM-knee-on): a transparent sac that develops from cells of the embryonic disk. It grows to enclose the embryo completely. It is penetrated only by the umbilical cord. The amnion becomes filled with fluid (amniotic fluid), which protects the embryo from trauma and temperature fluctuations, allows freedom of movement, and prevents limbs from sticking to the body. (The term *amnion* comes from a Greek word that means "lamb." It refers to the membrane that is often observed clinging to the head of a lamb when it is born.)

Yolk sac: a small sac that is suspended from the abdominal area of the embryo. It contributes to the formation of the digestive tract and produces the first blood cells and the future egg or sperm cells. Unlike the yolk sac in many other vertebrates, the yolk sac in humans serves no nutritive function.

Allantois (uh-LAN-toe-iss): forms the foundation for the umbilical cord. During the second month, most of the allantois degenerates. The remainder becomes part of the urinary bladder. (The term *allantois* comes from a Greek word that means "sausage," referring to the shape of this structure.)

Chorion (KOR-ee-on): the outermost membrane. It encloses all the other extra-embryonic membranes, as well as the embryo. The chorion forms the fetal portion of the placenta.

Figure 15.10 The extra-embryonic membranes are structures that are external to (*extra-*) the embryo.

the chorion extend into the uterine lining. These projections, called chorionic villi, establish the beginnings of the placenta. The **placenta** is a disk-shaped organ that is rich in blood vessels. The embryo (or fetus) is attached to the uterine wall by the placenta, and metabolic exchange occurs through it (see Figure 15.11). The placenta is fully developed by about 10 weeks, with a mass of about 600 g. (The term *placenta* comes from a Greek word that means "flat cake.")

One part of the placenta—the chorion tissue—comes from the embryo. The other part consists of blood pools from the mother's circulatory system. The blood systems of the mother and embryo are separate, but they lie very close to each other. This proximity permits nutrients and oxygen to diffuse from the mother's circulatory system to the developing baby and for wastes to leave the baby's circulation and enter the mother's for excretion. Table 15.1 outlines the functions of the placenta.

Note that the placenta does not filter out substances such as alcohol, drugs, and nicotine, which can diffuse across membranes. If these substances are present in the mother's blood, they will diffuse into the developing baby's blood. Exposure to these substances while pregnant can have severe negative effects on the embryo and fetus. (Refer to the section called "The Effects of Teratogens on Development" on page 521 for more information.)

Near the end of the eighth week, as the yolk sac shrinks and the amniotic sac enlarges, the umbilical cord forms. The **umbilical cord** is a rope-like structure that averages about 60 cm long and 2 cm in diameter. (It can, however, be as long as 300 cm or as short as a few millimetres.) It leads from the navel area of the fetus

Table 15.1 Functions of the Placenta

Nutritional functions	• transports nutrients (for example, glucose, amino acids, fatty acids, minerals, and vitamins) from the mother's blood to the fetus's blood
	• stores nutrients, such as carbohydrates, proteins, iron, and calcium, in early pregnancy and releases them to the fetus later, when fetal demand is greater than the mother can absorb from her diet
Excretory functions	• transports wastes (such as urea, ammonia, and creatinine) from the fetal blood to the mother's blood
Respiratory functions	• transports oxygen from the mother to the fetus and carbon dioxide from the fetus to the mother
Endocrine functions	• secretes hormones, such as estrogen, progesterone, and human chorionic gonadotropin
	• allows hormones from the fetus to diffuse into the mother's blood and hormones from the mother to diffuse into the fetus's blood
Immune functions	• transports antibodies from the mother into the fetus's blood to provide passive immunity

to the centre of the placenta. (The term *umbilical* comes from a Latin word that means "navel.") The umbilical cord contains two arteries, which transport oxygen-depleted blood from the fetus to the placenta. It also contains one vein, which brings oxygen-rich blood to the fetus.)

The umbilical cord has natural twists because the umbilical vein is longer than the arteries are. In about 20 percent of all deliveries, the umbilical cord is looped once around the baby's neck. Usually, this poses no problem for the baby's health or the delivery. The doctor or midwife can easily slide the umbilical cord over the baby's head before delivery.

• • •

20 Name the extra-embryonic membranes.

21 From which extra-embryonic membranes do the placenta and umbilical cord develop?

22 Summarize the role of the placenta.

23 Summarize the role of the umbilical cord.

• • •

Section 15.1 Summary

- Fertilization occurs in the oviduct and results in a zygote.
- Cleavage of the fertilized egg occurs within 30 h and continues until a morula forms.
- The morula enters the uterus around the third day.

BiologyFile

Web Link
Potential complications that involve the umbilical cord are surprisingly numerous. What types of complications can occur? How serious are they? What percentage of babies are affected?

www.albertabiology.ca
WWW

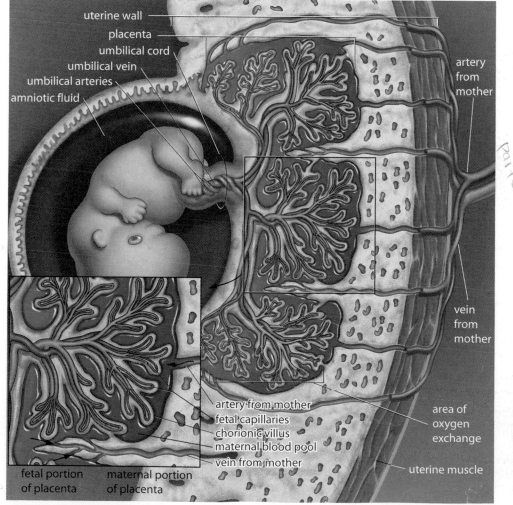

uterine wall
placenta
umbilical cord
umbilical vein
umbilical arteries
amniotic fluid

artery from mother

vein from mother

area of oxygen exchange

uterine muscle

artery from mother
fetal capillaries
chorionic villus
maternal blood pool
vein from mother

fetal portion of placenta
maternal portion of placenta

Figure 15.11A In the placenta, chorionic villi that extend from the embryo are in contact with pools of blood from the mother. Nutrients and oxygen pass by diffusion from the maternal blood to the embryo, and wastes diffuse in the opposite direction.

Figure 15.11B The pancake-like placenta

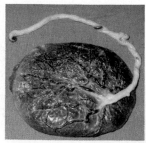

- The still-dividing morula begins to fill with a fluid and is now called a blastocyst.
- The blastocyst is bounded by a thin layer of cells, called the trophoblast, and has a group of cells, called the inner cell mass, within it.
- The inner cell mass develops into the embryo.
- The blastocyst implants in the uterine wall around the seventh day after fertilization.
- During the second week, cells begin to specialize.
- During gastrulation, which marks the start of morphogenesis, the embryo's cells become arranged into three distinct primary germ layers (ectoderm, mesoderm, and endoderm), which develop from the embryonic disk within the blastocyst.

- During neurulation, the embryo's nervous system begins to develop.
- By the third week, the extra-embryonic membranes begin to form. These membranes provide support, nourishment, and protection for the embryo. Some of them will become the placenta and umbilical cord, which continue to provide nourishment for the fetus until birth.
- By the fourth week, the embryonic heart is beating, the arm and leg buds are recognizable, and the tissues that will form the eyes, brain, spinal cord, lungs, and digestive organs are in place.
- By the eighth week, all the body organs are formed (although they will continue to develop) and the embryo's features are distinctly recognizable as human.

Section 15.1   Review

1. List at least three events that must occur for fertilization to take place.

2. Describe three ways that a fertilized egg is different from the two cells that combined to form it.

3. Describe what happens during implantation.

4. Arrange the following in order, from youngest to oldest: morula, zygote, blastocyst, gastrula. Give reasons for your order.

5. Identify the three primary germ layers, and explain their significance.

6. Following implantation, the trophoblast begins to secrete hCG (human chorionic gonadotropin hormone).
   a) Describe the effect of hCG secretion on the mother's reproductive system.
   b) Pregnancy tests are designed to detect higher-than-normal concentrations of hCG in the mother's blood or urine. Explain why you would expect to be able to find hCG in these two body fluids.

7. Using a table, concept map, or labelled diagram, outline the six structures that support the developing embryo (and, later, the fetus) and briefly describe the function of each. ICT

8. The following diagram outlines the timetable of trophoblastic and placental nutrition.
   a) Approximately when does trophoblastic nutrition reach its peak, and when does it end?
   b) Approximately when does placental nutrition begin?
   c) Infer the significance of the shape of the placental nutrition element in the diagram.
   d) According to the diagram, at what times do the two modes contribute equally to prenatal nutrition?

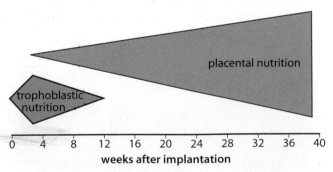

9. Developing human embryos do not have a significant amount of yolk as part of their supporting tissues, but chick embryos do. Explain why.

10. Design a table to summarize the major events that occur from fertilization to the end of eight weeks of human prenatal development. Your table should include at least these headings: Time period, Place of occurrence, Major events. ICT

Comparing Embryonic Structures

Question

How do embryonic structures of humans and other animals compare?

Safety Precautions

Handle microscope equipment and slides carefully.

Materials

- prepared slides showing stages of development of an animal from zygote to embryo (e.g., sea star or sea urchin)
- microscope or microviewer

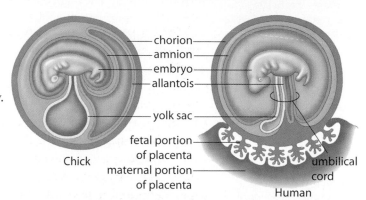

Chick

chorion
amnion
embryo
allantois

yolk sac

fetal portion of placenta
maternal portion of placenta

umbilical cord

Human

Procedure

Part 1: Observing Embryonic Structures

1. Obtain and set up a microscope or microviewer and the slides you will be viewing.

2. Sketch the main features that you observe in each slide. Add labels to identify all the features that you recognize.

3. Answer Analysis questions 1–4.

Part 2: Comparing Extra-embryonic Structures

1. Examine the diagrams of extra-embryonic membranes of an embryonic chick and an embryonic human.

2. **a)** In your notebook, identify the extra-embryonic membranes that human and chicken embryos have in common.

   b) What similarities and differences do you observe in the structure of these membranes? Describe or sketch your observations.

3. Answer Analysis questions 5 and 6.

Analysis

1. On which slide or slides do you observe evidence that cleavage has occurred?

2. Identify changes in the embryo that indicate that a blastocyst has formed.

3. Identify changes that indicate a gastrula has formed.

4. Describe any recognizable tissues in the last phase of development that you observed.

5. In birds, the extra-embryonic membranes have the following functions:

   - allantois: transports, in combination with the chorion, oxygen to the embryo and removes carbon dioxide produced by the embryo; also stores nitrogenous wastes and absorbs calcium from the shell to make it available for bone formation

   - amnion: a fluid-filled sac that provides protection from physical shock and enables the embryo to move freely and safely

   - chorion: see allantois

   - yolk sac and yolk: stores nutrient-rich yolk and absorbs nutrients from it so that they are available for nourishing the embryo via blood vessels in the sac membrane

   How do the functions of the extra-embryonic membranes in birds compare with their function in humans?

6. **a)** Think about the place (the environment or location) in which human development takes place. Based on the place (environment or location) in which the following animals develop, predict whether they would form a placenta, and give reasons to justify your prediction.

   - frog   - turtle   - sea star   - pike   - crow

   b) Identify the extra-embryonic membranes from which the placenta forms and explain how their function, modified in humans, relates to their function for chicken embryos.

Fetal Development and Birth

Section Outcomes

In this section, you will
- **trace** the processes and key events that occur during fetal development (the last thirty weeks of prenatal life)
- **describe** and **investigate** the effect of teratogens and other environmental factors on the development of prenatal body structures and systems
- **trace** the processes of parturition and lactation, and **outline** their control mechanisms

Key Terms

teratogen
fetal alcohol spectrum
   disorder (FASD)
parturition
lactation

The fetal period of development starts during the ninth week and lasts until birth. During this period, the fetus looks obviously human. The main difference between the embryonic and the fetal periods relates to the organs. In the embryo, most of the organs are taking shape. In the fetus, the organs are present and continue to develop. The embryonic period is a time of morphogenesis. The fetal period, on the other hand, is a time of growth and "refinement" of the existing structures.

First Trimester Developments (Weeks 1 to 12)

In Section 15.1, you examined the embryonic period of development, which takes place in the first eight weeks after fertilization. During the next four weeks—the last month of the first trimester—growth in the length of the body accelerates, but growth of the head slows. The cartilage-based skeleton begins to harden, with the development of bone. By the end of the twelfth week, the external reproductive organs are distinguishable as male or female.

Second Trimester Developments (Weeks 13 to 24)

By the fourth month, the heartbeat of the fetus is strong enough to hear with a stethoscope. The bones of the skeleton begin to form. The brain grows rapidly, and the nervous system starts to function. As the fetal legs grow and develop, the mother begins to feel movement.

During the fifth month, the fetus becomes covered with fine, soft hair and an oily substance to protect the still-developing skin. The hair, called lanugo (from a Latin word that means "wool") is usually shed before birth.

In the sixth month, the skin appears wrinkled because there is very little fat

beneath it. The skin becomes more pink as blood-filled capillaries extend into it. If the fetus is born at this stage, it is unlikely to survive. It certainly would not survive without medical intervention.

Third Trimester Developments (Weeks 25 to 38)

In the third and final trimester, fetal brain cells form rapidly (by the tens of thousands per minute), connecting to form more and more intricate networks. The testes of males descend into the scrotum. A layer of fat develops beneath the skin. The digestive and respiratory systems are usually the last to mature, which is why infants that are born prematurely often have difficulty digesting milk and breathing.

Proper nutrition is important during all of pregnancy, for both the mother and the fetus. Nutrition is especially important during the third trimester. Poor nutrition damages the placenta, which can lead to low birth weight, short stature, delayed sexual development, and learning disabilities.

About 266 days (approximately 40 weeks) after the formation of a single fertilized cell, a multi-trillion-celled being is ready to be born. Table 15.2 lists major monthly events in the development of this new life.

• • •

24 What is the main difference between the embryonic and fetal periods of development?

25 Identify three events or characteristics of fetal development during the second trimester.

26 Identify three events or characteristics of fetal development during the third trimester.

• • •

Biology File

Try This
Plan, design, and create a multimedia presentation to show development through the embryonic and fetal periods. What images will you use? Will your information be text-only or can you include audio? What sources of information will you use for your images and script?

The Effects of Teratogens on Development

In addition to the nutrients and other beneficial substances that a mother transfers to the embryo and fetus, she can transfer harmful substances. Whatever the mother ingests or inhales can end up in her circulating blood. Some of these substances pass through the placental system to the fetus's blood. This is especially significant during the first nine weeks, when developing organs are highly sensitive to environmental factors, as shown in Figure 15.12 on page 522.

Many substances and conditions can affect the normal development of the embryo and fetus. The term **teratogen**

Follic acid is not a teratogen

Table 15.2 Major Events, by Month, in Prenatal Development

Month	Length* at end of month (cm)	Mass at end of month (g)	Significant developmental events
1	0.4	less than 1	• Spinal column and central nervous system start to form. • Appendages are represented by small limb buds. • Heart begins beating (around day 22).
2	3	1	• Eyes form, but eyelids are fused shut. • Nose is flat. • Head is nearly as large as rest of body. • Nostrils are evident, but plugged with mucus. • Limb buds form paddle-like hands and form ridges (which later separate into distinct fingers and toes). • Brain waves are detectable. • Bone growth begins. • Blood cells and major blood vessels form. • Genitals are present, but sexes are not yet distinguishable.
3	9	30	• Eyes are well developed, but eyelids are still fused. • Nose develops bridge. • Fetus swallows amniotic fluid and produces urine. • Sexes can be distinguished visually. • Limbs are well-formed, with nails on fingers and toes. • External ears are present. • Fetus moves but too weakly for mother to feel it.
4	14	100	• Face looks more distinctly human. • Body is larger in proportion to head. • Skin is bright pink. • Scalp has hair. • Joints are forming. • Lips exhibit sucking movements. • Heartbeat can be heard with a stethoscope.
5	19	200–450	• Body covered with fine hair (lanugo). • Skin has oily secretion to protect it from amniotic fluid. • Fetus is now bent forward into "fetal position" because it is beginning to outgrow the amniotic sac. • Mother can feel fetal movements. • Skin is bright pink.
6	27–35	550–800	• Eyes are open. • Eyelashes form. • Skin is wrinkled, pink, and translucent.
7	32–42	1100–1350	• Skin is wrinkled and red. • Fetus turns to an upside-down position. • Bone marrow is now the only site for red blood cell formation. • Testes descend into scrotum. • Fetus can usually survive if born prematurely.
8	41–45	2000–2300	• Fatty tissue deposition gives fetus a more plump, "babyish" appearance, with lighter, less wrinkled skin. • Twins are usually born now.
9	50	3200–3500	• More fat deposition occurs. • Lanugo is shed. • Nails extend to or beyond fingertips. • Birth is imminent.

* Length is measured from the top of the head to the bottom of the buttocks (often referred to as the crown-to-rump, or CR, length).

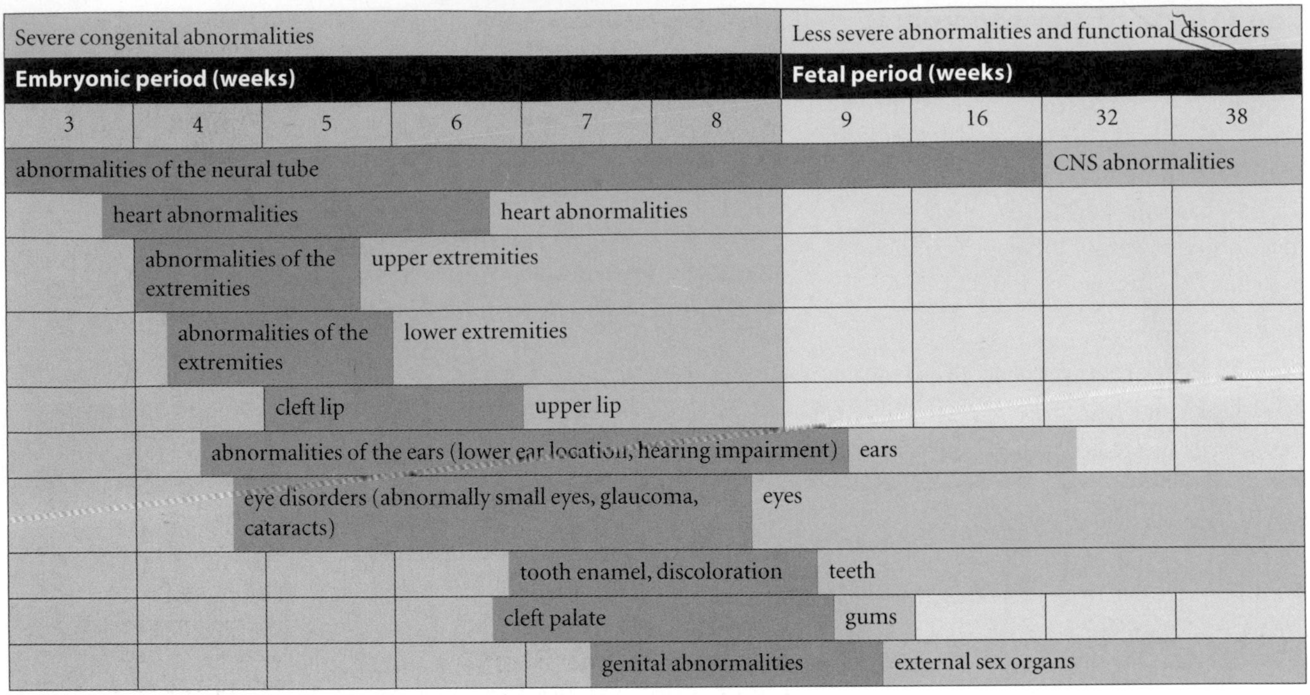

Severe congenital abnormalities						Less severe abnormalities and functional disorders			
Embryonic period (weeks)						**Fetal period (weeks)**			
3	4	5	6	7	8	9	16	32	38
abnormalities of the neural tube									CNS abnormalities
heart abnormalities				heart abnormalities					
	abnormalities of the extremities		upper extremities						
		abnormalities of the extremities	lower extremities						
		cleft lip		upper lip					
	abnormalities of the ears (lower ear location, hearing impairment)					ears			
	eye disorders (abnormally small eyes, glaucoma, cataracts)				eyes				
			tooth enamel, discoloration		teeth				
			cleft palate		gums				
				genital abnormalities		external sex organs			

Legend:
■ highly sensitive phase
■ less sensitive phase

Figure 15.12 This graph shows the critical phases of prenatal development. The darker portions correspond to periods when organs are most sensitive to teratogens.

refers to any agent that causes a structural abnormality due to exposure during pregnancy. Cigarette smoke, for example, can constrict the fetus's blood vessels, preventing the fetus from getting enough oxygen. Mothers who smoke or who are exposed to second-hand smoke during pregnancy tend to have babies that are underweight. Cigarette smoke during pregnancy also increases the risk of premature births, stillbirths, and miscarriages. As well, there is mounting evidence of behavioural problems and reduced intellectual ability in children of smoking mothers.

One of the most damaging teratogens is also the most avoidable: alcohol. Alcohol can affect the fetus's brain, central nervous system, and physical development (see Figure 15.13). Babies who are affected by alcohol consumption during pregnancy are likely to have decreased weight, height, and head size, as well as malformations of the face and head. In addition, these children show varying degrees of learning and memory difficulties and often exhibit unusual aggression or personality disorders. Because each woman metabolizes alcohol slightly differently, physicians advise that all women avoid alcohol when pregnant, when trying to become pregnant, and when breast-feeding.

The term that is used to describe all the disorders related to alcohol consumption during pregnancy is **fetal alcohol spectrum disorder (FASD)**. This includes the more commonly known clinical disorder called fetal alcohol syndrome (FAS).

Many prescription and over-the-counter medications have teratogenic properties. Examples of medications that are known to have dangerous effects on a fetus include some antibiotics (such as tetracycline), some acne medications, anti-thyroid drugs (for treating hypothyroid and hyperthyroid conditions), and some anti-cancer drugs. The most notorious prescription drug with teratogenic effects is thalidomide, which was first prescribed in the 1950s to reduce morning sickness. Its use for pregnant women was discontinued when doctors discovered that an alarming number of babies were being born with missing and deformed limbs. Thalidomide is still available under tightly controlled regulations. In the United States, it is approved for treating skin conditions associated with leprosy. As well, it is being studied for its potential to treat cancers of the bone marrow (myeloma).

Certain nutrients ingested in large amounts, particularly vitamins, can have teratogenic effects. One example is vitamin C. The fetus becomes accustomed to the large doses and, when the supply drops after birth, the baby develops symptoms of vitamin C deficiency (scurvy), bruising easily and being prone to infection. Other teratogenic agents include radiation, such as X-rays, and pollutants, such as PCBs and organic mercury compounds.

Good judgment and decision making play key roles during pregnancy. Sometimes, however, the mother cannot control her exposure to teratogens. For example, people in many northern Aboriginal communities rely heavily on fish and wildlife in their traditional diet. The presence of environmental contaminants in the food chain, due to industrial discharges and run-off from contaminated land, is a great concern for those who rely solely or partly on traditional foods. There is ongoing research, and much debate, about the effects of exposure to elevated levels of environmental contaminants (such as mercury, lead, cadmium, DDT, and PCBs) in fish and wildlife for pregnant and nursing women. Contaminants have been found in pregnant women, the umbilical cord, and the breast milk of nursing mothers in northern Aboriginal communities. Women with these contaminants in their blood are reported to have a higher number of miscarriages, lower birth-weight babies, babies who have difficulty fighting infections and disease, and children who are developmentally delayed, compared with women who have limited or no exposure to these contaminants.

• • •

27 What are teratogens?

28 Give three examples of dangers that teratogens pose to the developing baby.

• • •

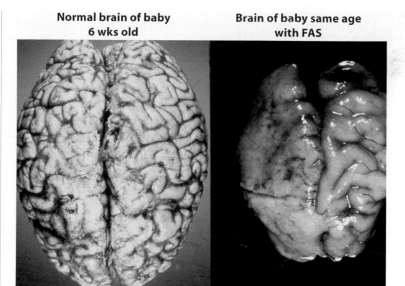

Normal brain of baby 6 wks old **Brain of baby same age with FAS**

Figure 15.13 This photograph provides dramatic evidence of the damaging effects of alcohol on brain development.

Parturition: Delivery of the Baby

The birthing process is called **parturition**, and all the events associated with parturition are commonly referred to as *labour*. These events typically begin with uterine contractions.

The uterus experiences contractions throughout pregnancy. At first, these are light, lasting about 20 to 30 seconds and occurring every 15 to 20 minutes. Near the end of pregnancy, the contractions become stronger and more frequent. The onset of labour is marked by uterine contractions that occur every 15 to 20 minutes and last for 40 seconds or longer.

The onset of labour includes both hormonal and neural components (Figure 15.14). A positive feedback mechanism can explain the onset and

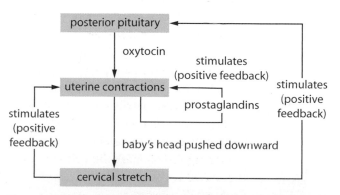

Figure 15.14 This diagram outlines positive feedback mechanisms that are hypothesized to control parturition. In fact, despite advances in technology, our understanding of the factors that initiate and control parturition in humans remains incomplete.

Teratogens are agents that cause developmental or physical abnormalities through ingesting (or inhaling) them or through exposure to them. In some cases, however, not being exposed to a substance or receiving inadequate amounts of it can also result in physical or developmental abnormalities. This is certainly true of nutrition during (as well as before and after) prenatal development. Inadequate intake of one nutrient in particular, folic acid (vitamin B9, also called folate), can have devastating consequences for embryonic development. In this investigation, you will use an abstract from a medical journal as the starting point for further study on the impact of folic acid on neural tube defects. (Neural tube defects, or NTDs, result when the neural tube—refer to page 514—does not close by about the twenty-eighth day. This leaves open an area of the spine from which nervous tissue protrudes, usually causing paralysis from the site downward.)

Procedure

1. Read the abstract below, which was published in *Clinical and Investigative Medicine* in 1996. You may need to look some words up in a print or electronic dictionary. Even if you do not understand every word or some of the sentences, you should still be able to "pick out" the general meaning or significance of what the authors of the journal article are saying. **ICT**

2. Using print or electronic resources, conduct further research on neural tube defects to find out the following. **ICT**

- what kind of defects can occur, how often they occur statistically in Alberta and/or Canada, their characteristics/symptoms, and what, if any, treatments are available for them
- why Canada's health agency was reluctant to advise fortifying foods with folic acid, and the current status of folic-acid fortification
- actions taken on the part of Health Canada to inform the public about folic acid and NTDs

Analysis

1. What is the recommended daily amount of folic acid for women who could become pregnant?

2. When should women who could become pregnant start taking folic acid?

3. Why is dietary (unsupplemented) intake of folic acid considered to be inadequate to prevent NTDs?

4. What other risk factors are involved in having a baby with an NTD?

5. In your opinion, based on what you have discovered through your research, should the Canadian government have acted more quickly when the link between folic acid and neural tube disorders was established and communicated in the scientific community? Give reasons to justify your opinion.

Abstract

Objectives: To determine the diffusion of information about preventing neural tube defects (NTDs) through folic acid consumption by examining whether mothers of Canadian children born with spina bifida, who had become pregnant at least a year after evidence of the preventive effect of folic acid had been published, had taken sufficient amounts of folic acid in the periconceptional period [that is, the first few weeks of pregnancy] and were aware of this important new information.

Design: Validated food-frequency questionnaire to assess folate intake.

Setting: The Hospital for Sick Children in Toronto between Jan. 4 and Aug. 16, 1994.

Participants: Thirty mothers whose infants were being treated for spina bifida.

Main outcome measures: The mothers' mean folate intake and knowledge about the protective effect of folic acid; demographic and health information.

Results: The mothers' mean folate intake was 0.182 mg/d (standard deviation 0.076 mg/d, range 0.02 to 0.53 mg/d), less than half the protective dose. Only 4 (13%) of the mothers had been aware of the relation between nutritional folate and NTDs when they conceived, but even they did not supplement their diets with sufficient folic acid. The medical data showed that, in addition to the failure of primary prevention of NTDs, secondary prevention through diagnostic tests during pregnancy were also inadequate.

Conclusions: Our study, one of the first to be conducted after the role of folate in preventing NTDs was confirmed, reveals that, in one of the most advanced countries in the world, this new information has had no effect on patients' folate intake. Unless food is fortified with folate, the estimated 400 to 800 annual cases of NTDs in Canada will not be prevented.

Source: *Clin Invest Med* 1996; 19 (3): 195–201

continuation of labour. <u>Uterine contractions are induced by a stretching of the cervix, which also brings about the</u> release of oxytocin from the posterior pituitary gland. Oxytocin stimulates the uterine muscles, both directly and through the action of prostaglandins. Uterine contractions push the fetus downward, and the cervix stretches even more. This cycle keeps repeating itself until birth occurs.

Figure 15.15 illustrates the three stages of parturition. Although the diagrams show the birthing mother in a horizontal position, some mothers may choose to give birth from a squatting or partially upright position so that gravity can help with the delivery. Other mothers prefer to give birth in water,

to lessen the shock of the baby's entry into an atmospheric environment.

For several reasons, it may not be safe or possible to deliver a baby in the usual way. For example, the baby may be in a rump-first position. It is difficult for the cervix to expand enough to accommodate this type of birth (called a breech birth), and the baby or mother could be harmed. Instead, the baby is usually delivered by a Caesarean section. In this procedure, a physician makes an incision in the mother's abdomen and uterus, and delivers the baby through the incision. A mother with a sexually transmitted infection, such as herpes, or a mother with a small pelvis may also have her baby delivered by Caesarean

BiologyFile

Web Link
Some women elect to give birth to a baby at home ("home birth"), rather than in a hospital setting. In either case, a woman may prefer the services of a midwife to that of a physician. What are the roles and responsibilities of a midwife? What is the current status of midwives in Alberta as compared with the rest of Canada?

www.albertabiology.ca
WWW

Figure 15.15 Three stages of parturition (birth)

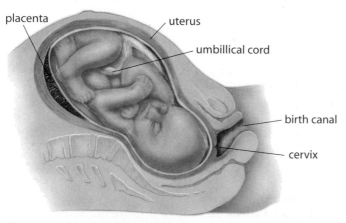

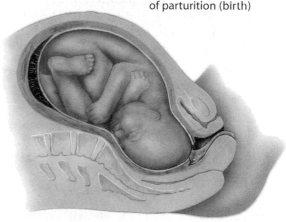

A **Dilation stage** Uterine contractions and oxytocin cause the cervix to open, or dilate. During this stage, the amniotic sac breaks and the amniotic fluid is released through the vagina. The dilation stage usually lasts from 2 to 20 hours.

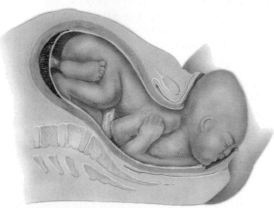

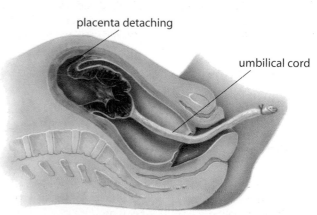

B **Explusion stage** Forceful contractions push the baby through the cervix to the birth canal. As the baby moves through the canal, the head rotates, making it easier for the body to pass through the birth canal. This stage usually lasts from 0.5 to 2 hours.

C **Placental stage** About 10 to 15 minutes after the baby is born, the placenta and umbilical cord are expelled from the uterus. The expelled placenta is called the afterbirth.

Web Link
Alberta is home to the only public, not-for-profit Cord Blood Bank in Canada. Why do some people choose to collect and save ("bank") the blood that remains in the umbilical cord after birth? Who can benefit from this choice?

www.albertabiology.ca
WWW

section to protect herself and her baby from injury or infection.

Once the baby is breathing normally, the umbilical cord is clamped, cut, and tied. (There are no nerves in the umbilical cord, so no pain is felt.) The baby is now cut off from the source of protection and nutrients it has depended on for nine months. It must breathe, ingest food, and eliminate wastes on its own. The cord eventually shrivels, and the place where the cord was attached to the fetus becomes the navel.

> **29** What hormones are involved during parturition (birth)?
>
> **30** What is a Caesarean section?

Lactation and the Suckling Reflex

Hormones control the onset of **lactation**—the secretion and formation of breast milk in the mother. Prolactin, the hormone that is needed for milk production, is not secreted during pregnancy. High levels of estrogen and progesterone suppress its production in the anterior pituitary. Once the mother has given birth, however, the anterior pituitary begins to produce and secrete prolactin. Milk production starts within a few days. Before then, the breasts secrete colostrum, a thin yellowish fluid that is similar to milk but contains more protein and less fat. Colostrum and milk also contain antibodies from the mother, providing the baby with protection from various infectious agents.

Figure 15.16 shows how a suckling baby stimulates the release of milk from the mother's breast. When a baby suckles, it stimulates nerve endings in the nipple and areola (circular area of different-coloured skin around the nipple). The nerve impulses travel to the hypothalamus, which, in turn, stimulates the posterior pituitary to release oxytocin. Oxytocin causes contractions within the mammary lobules. The mammary lobules contain alveoli, which are sacs with cells that produce milk. The lobules end in mammary ducts at the nipple. Contractions within the lobules cause milk to flow to the ducts, where the infant can draw it out by suckling. If suckling does not occur, or if it stops, milk production stops within a few days. Conversely, increased suckling stimulates increased milk production which can continue for several years.

> **31** What is lactation?
>
> **32** Describe the role of oxytocin in lactation.

Figure 15.16 A suckling baby initiates the events that lead to milk secretion as well as milk production.

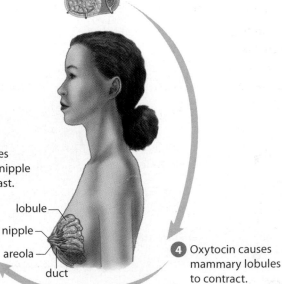

2 Neural pathways carry stimuli to hypothalamus.

3 Hypothalamus produces oxytocin that is released by posterior pituitary.

1 Suckling stimulates nerve endings in nipple and areola of breast.

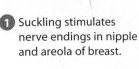

lobule
nipple
areola
duct

5 Milk letdown occurs.

4 Oxytocin causes mammary lobules to contract.

Section 15.2 Summary

- Body growth is the main characteristic of the fetal stage, which extends from the ninth week until birth.
- During the third and fourth months, the skeleton is forming bone, and the sex of the fetus becomes distinguishable.
- From the fifth month through the ninth month, the fetus continues to grow and to gain in body mass. Fat is

Stem Cells

Imagine being able to repair human body parts with tissue grown especially for the purpose. For instance, people who have had heart attacks could receive new cardiac (heart) cells. Instead of waiting for organ transplants, people with failing livers, kidneys, or lungs could have healthy new organs grown for them. People who have lost the use of their legs through paralysis might be able to walk again with new nerve cells growing in their spinal cords. The key to these technological feats is stem cells.

What are Stem Cells?

Stem cells are unspecialized or undifferentiated cells. This means that they have not yet begun to develop into red blood cells, muscle cells, or any other of the 200 or so cell types that make up the human body.

Stem cells have two important features. First, they can replicate (make copies of themselves) for a long time by dividing. Second, under suitable laboratory conditions, stem cells can be coaxed to give rise to cells with special functions, such as heart muscle cells and neurons (nerve cells).

There are two main types of stem cells: adult stem cells (also called somatic stem cells) and embryonic stem cells. In spite of their name, adult stem cells are found in humans of all ages. In fact, one source of adult stem cells for medical use is the umbilical cords of newborns. Small numbers of these stem cells have now been found in many different human organs and tissues.

Embryonic stem cells, as their name implies, come from embryos—about four or five days after fertilization. The source of embryonic stem cells has been an assisted reproduction technique called *in vitro* fertilization. In this process, embryos are produced in a lab; more are produced than are implanted in the woman who wishes to become pregnant. Scientists now also have the ability to create embryos solely for research, but many countries, including Canada, have banned this technique as unethical.

Embryonic stem cells are pluripotent, which means that they can become many different types of cells in the human body. Until very recently, it was thought that adult stem cells could only give rise to the different types of cells in the tissues where they were found. For example, basic blood stem cells found in bone marrow could become red blood cells, white blood cells, and so on. However, recent research has shown that many adult stem cells can be made to develop into a wider range of specialized cells. For instance, in the laboratory, blood stem cells have yielded muscle cells, including heart muscle cells, and nerve cells. This is an exciting area of research for two reasons: first, it would avoid the ethical issues of embryonic stem cell research, and second, it could produce repair tissues from a person's own body cells that would be a perfect match.

Stem Cell Research in Canada

Working together, Alberta-born biophysicist James Till and Toronto physician Ernest McCulloch discovered stem cells in 1960. In 1992, neuroscientist Samuel Weiss of the University of Calgary was the first to show that adult stem cells exist in the human brain. Today, Canada is still in the forefront of stem cell research. Dr. Weiss, for example, is now researching how the brain's stem cells could be used to help people who have had strokes. Meanwhile, researchers at the University of Alberta are working on a stem cell treatment for Type 1 Diabetes, while an Ottawa scientist is working with heart stem cells that could be used in the treatment of heart attacks.

Many important questions about stem cells still remain to be answered. Among them: how many different types of adult stem cells can be found in the human body, and in what tissues? What is the purpose of adult stem cells in the body? Why do they remain in an undifferentiated state, when all the cells around them have differentiated?

• • •

1. One of the first diseases to be treated with stem cells was leukemia. Research what this treatment was and why it worked. How has the treatment changed today?

2. Depending on their source, stem cells may be referred to as totipotent, pluripotent, and multipotent. What are the differences among these types of stem cells, and where are they found in the body?

3. Some people (including some scientists) consider stem cell research and use objectionable. What is the foundation of the controversies surrounding stem cells? What steps has Canada taken to restrict the ways in which stem cell research can be performed?

deposited beneath the skin to help insulate the newborn, and the fetus kicks, stretches, and moves freely within the amniotic sac.

- Teratogens are factors that can adversely affect the health of a fetus.
- Examples of teratogens include alcohol, tobacco, illegal drugs (such as cocaine), environmental toxins (such as pesticides), maternal infections (such as chicken pox and measles), lack of nutrients (especially folic acid), and too much of certain nutrients (such as vitamin C).

- The hormones oxytocin and prostaglandins help to stimulate uterine contractions, assisting the movement of the fetus in the process of parturition.
- The stimulus of suckling results in the secretion of oxytocin from the posterior pituitary, stimulating the contraction of the milk glands and ducts for lactation.

Section 15.2   Review

1. In what ways does the fetal period of development differ from the embryonic period of development?

2. During which trimester do the following events occur?
   a) heart starts beating
   b) the body is larger in proportion to the head
   c) fatty tissues are deposited beneath the skin
   d) brain cells are connecting to form more intricate networks
   e) external reproductive organs are distinguishable as male or female
   f) eyelashes form
   g) contractions felt by the mother signal the onset of labour
   h) skin appears wrinkled
   i) nervous system starts to function
   j) external reproductive organs are present but not distinguishable as male or female
   k) the fetus produces urine
   l) the fetus adopts the "fetal position"
   m) blood cells and major blood vessels start to form
   n) the head is larger in proportion to the body

3. a) Which of the following is not a teratogen: x-rays, folic acid, alcohol, mercury, HIV, nicotine, tetracycline (an antibiotic), vitamin C?
   b) Explain why the answer you chose in (a) is not a teratogen and why the others are.

4. What is parturition?

5. a) How many stages of parturition are there?
   b) Describe what occurs during each of these stages.

6. Describe two hormonal changes that occur in the mother's body as parturition occurs.

7. Outline how hormones are involved in lactation and the suckling reflex. ICT

8. In the traditional birthing practices of Inuit women, the women increased their consumption of caribou, char, muktuk (whale blubber and skin), and seal, and they limited their intake of berries. They did not eat any aged food. (Source: *Midwifery and Aboriginal Midwifery in Canada*, National Aboriginal Health Organization, 2004, p. 24.) Infer at least two reasons for these food choices and omissions.

Reproduction, Technology, and Society

Section Outcomes

In this section, you will
- **describe** different reproductive technologies
- **evaluate** various reproductive technologies based on their effectiveness and safety, and **justify** your evaluation

Key Terms

reproductive technologies
in vitro fertilization (IVF)
sterile
infertile
artificial insemination
surrogate mother
superovulation
abstinence
tubal ligation
vasectomy
contraceptive technologies

On July 25, 1978, Leslie Brown made history by giving birth to a healthy baby girl. Louise Joy Brown, born in Great Britain, was the world's first "test tube baby." Her life began in a laboratory. Scientists removed an egg from her mother and mixed it with sperm from her father. After two and a half days, scientists placed the fertilized egg in Leslie's uterus. Almost nine months later, Louise was delivered by Caesarean section.

The success of the first test-tube baby gave many infertile couples hope that they, too, could have a child. Over 1.5 million test tube babies have been born since 1978. The new technology stimulated, and continues to stimulate, controversy, however. Is it ethical? Will people find ways to abuse the technology? In the decades since Louise's birth, many new forms of **reproductive technologies**—technologies that enhance or reduce reproductive potential—have been developed. And many of the same social and ethical questions are still being asked.

The technology used in the conception of Louise Brown is called **in vitro fertilization**, or **IVF**. (*In vitro* is Latin for "in glass," referring to the Petri dish in which fertilization takes place.) IVF is one example of a technology that was designed to enhance the reproductive potential of couples who wish to have children but are unable to conceive. Other reproductive technologies are designed for couples who are physically able to conceive children but do not wish to do so. In this section, you will consider a range of reproductive technologies within each of these two broad categories.

Technologies That Enhance Reproductive Potential

The term **sterile** is used to describe men and women who are unable to have any children. Men and women who have difficulty conceiving children are described as infertile. Couples are considered to be **infertile** when they have been trying unsuccessfully to become pregnant for a year or more. Researchers have identified some causes of infertility and sterility. The precise cause of a couple's infertility cannot always be identified or explained, however.

A man may be infertile or sterile for any of the following reasons:
- obstruction in the ductus deferens or epididymis, which may be caused by complications arising from STIs or from other blockages in the testicles
- low sperm count, caused by numerous factors including overheated testicles, smoking, and alcohol intake
- high proportion of abnormal or non-viable sperm, caused by factors including overheated testicles, exposure to toxic chemicals or radiation, and infections such as STIs
- inability to achieve an erection or ejaculation (also known as erectile dysfunction or impotence), caused by factors including vascular disease, nervous system injury, stress, hormonal imbalance, medication, smoking, and alcohol intake.

A woman may be infertile or sterile for any of these reasons:
- blocked oviducts, often an effect of STIs
- failure to ovulate, caused by hormonal imbalances that occur for a variety of reasons, including being malnourished
- endometriosis, a painful condition in which endometrial tissues grow outside the uterus
- damaged eggs, which may be caused by environmental factors such as exposure to toxic chemicals or radiation

Some causes of infertility can be corrected with medical treatment or a healthier lifestyle. Couples who remain unable to have children, however, may consider one of the following technologies to increase their chances of having a child.

BiologyFile

Web Link
The space age and the continued presence of humans in space have spawned questions that would not have occurred to early researchers of reproduction. For example, how do sperm behave in microgravity conditions? In what ways could their behaviour and movement affect fertility? What role might gravity play in human development?

www.albertabiology.ca
WWW

Artificial Insemination

Artificial insemination (AI) has been used for decades as a way to promote breeding success among domestic animals. It had also been used by human couples for years, before the first success of IVF. Artificial insemination continues to be refined and is still useful when the man is sterile or infertile. In **artificial insemination**, sperm are collected and concentrated before being placed in the woman's vagina. In some cases, the sperm are donated by the woman's male partner. In other cases, the sperm are from a stranger. Sperm banks provide a source of sperm samples that have been gathered for this purpose.

In Vitro Fertilization

As in the case of Leslie Brown, IVF offers a solution for women with blocked oviducts. Today, ultrasound machines are used to identify specific follicles that are close to ovulation. Immature eggs can be retrieved directly from these follicles. The eggs are combined with sperm in laboratory glassware (see Figure 15.17). After fertilization, the developing embryo is placed in the uterus. A slight variation on IVF is Gamete Intrafallopian Transfer (GIFT), in which the eggs and sperm are brought together in the oviduct rather than *in vitro*. This procedure has a higher success rate than IVF.

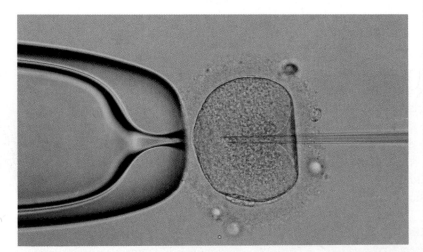

Figure 15.17 In a variation of *in vitro* fertilization, performed when a sperm is unable to penetrate the egg *in vitro*, sperm may be injected into the egg—a technique called intracytoplasmic sperm injection. It is used to help men with very low sperm counts, high numbers of abnormal sperm, or injuries or illnesses that prevent men from providing a sperm sample through ejaculation.

Surrogate Mothers

Sometimes, an infertile couple contracts another woman to carry a baby for them. The woman who carries the baby is called the **surrogate mother**. Using AI or IVF, one or both gametes may be contributed by the contracting couple.

Superovulation

Superovulation is the production of multiple eggs as a result of hormone treatment. Women who ovulate rarely or not at all may receive treatment with hormones that stimulate follicle development and ovulation. Superovulation is also often used in conjunction with other artificial reproductive technologies.

• • •

33 Give two reasons that a man might be infertilie or sterile, and identify two reproductive technologies that could help.

34 Give two reasons that a woman might be infertile or sterile, and identify two reproductive technologies that could help.

• • •

Technologies That Reduce Reproductive Potential

Sometimes, couples who are fertile wish to avoid or delay conceiving a child. Any behaviour or technology that prevents conception is a form of contraception, or birth control. There are several different forms of contraception, each with its own advantages and disadvantages. Some examples are described briefly below.

Abstinence

The surest way to avoid conceiving a child is simply not to have sexual intercourse. Complete **abstinence** also has the important advantage of ensuring almost total protection from STIs. Not all couples, however, are willing to abstain entirely from a sexual relationship.

Surgical Sterilization

As shown in Figure 15.18, both men and women can have surgery to make them infertile or sterile. In women, a procedure called a tubal ligation is used. **Tubal ligation** involves cutting the oviducts and tying off the cut ends. This ensures that the ovum never encounters sperm and never reaches the uterus. The ovum disintegrates in the oviduct. The equivalent procedure in men is called a **vasectomy**. The ductus deferens is cut and tied. The man is still able to have an erection and ejaculate, but his semen does not contain any sperm. Effectiveness of the procedure at preventing conception is nearly 100 percent for both men and women.

Hormone Treatments

Several **contraceptive technologies** work by changing the balance of reproductive hormones within a woman's body. Hormone medications may be taken orally (through an oral contraceptive or birth control pill), by injection, or by implants inserted under the skin. The artificial hormones mimic the effect of progesterone and inhibit the release of FSH and LH from the anterior pituitary.

As a result, the woman does not ovulate. While hormone treatments are a very reliable form of contraception, with effectiveness ranging from 90 to 99 percent, they do have some side effects. Common side effects include an increased risk of blood clots, strokes, and breast cancer.

A more intensive hormone treatment can also be taken for emergency use. It is not a form of contraception. A woman may use an emergency hormone treatment to reduce the risk of conception following unprotected sexual intercourse. The most commonly used type is known as the "morning-after pill," although in fact it is a treatment of several pills taken within three days after intercourse. The pills deliver high doses of synthetic estrogen and progesterone. These hormones disrupt the ovarian cycle and can prevent or delay ovulation. If fertilization has already taken place, these hormones can also prevent the embryo from implanting in the uterus. The most common side effects of this treatment include vomiting and painful cramps. Effectiveness ranges from about 95 percent if taken within 24 hours after unprotected intercourse to 85 percent if

Figure 15.18 Surgery can be used to render men (**A**) and women (**B**) sterile.

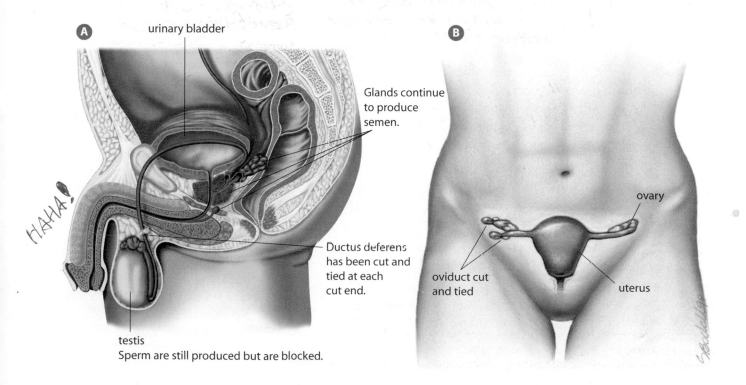

A urinary bladder

Glands continue to produce semen.

Ductus deferens has been cut and tied at each cut end.

testis
Sperm are still produced but are blocked.

B

ovary

oviduct cut and tied

uterus

taken within 24 to 48 hours. Effectiveness drops significantly to about only 5 percent if taken within 48 to 72 hours.

Physical or Chemical Barriers

Many contraceptive technologies are designed to prevent sperm from reaching the ovum. Physical barriers include male or female condoms (effectiveness about 85 percent), a latex cap—called a diaphragm—that fits over the cervix (effectiveness about 90 percent), and the contraceptive sponge (effectiveness ranging from about 70 to 90 percent depending on whether the woman has given birth and the care taken in using it). Spermicides—chemical barriers that kill sperm—include jellies, foams, and creams. Effectiveness is about 75 percent. Chemical barriers and physical barriers can be used together, which increases their effectiveness. Condoms have the additional advantage of offering some protection against the transmission of STIs.

Natural Family Planning

Some couples refrain from sexual intercourse during the time of the woman's cycle when she is most fertile (that is, from a week before her ovulation to a day or two afterward). This is known as natural family planning or the rhythm method. Because a woman's cycle can vary from month to month, the couple must pay careful attention to the subtle signals of the woman's body, such as body temperature and the properties of the cervical mucus. This method is among the least reliable forms of birth control, with an effectiveness estimated at about 70 percent.

• • •

35 What is the most effective method to avoid conceiving a child?

36 Which technology for preventing conception also protects against the transmission of sexually transmitted infections?

• • •

Social and Ethical Questions

When Louise Joy Brown was born, there was a wave of public concerns about the prospect of IVF being used in "baby factories" to mass-produce new humans. These concerns have proven to be unfounded. Many people, however, remain uncomfortable with technologies that interfere with the natural processes of conception and childbirth. Individual reproductive technologies also raise a number of difficult questions, including the questions below:

• What rights should a zygote have? Many reproductive technologies involve the gathering and fertilization of several eggs. Only one or a few of the resulting zygotes may be implanted and carried to term. The rest are destroyed before being implanted. Although this practice is legal in Canada, many people see the deliberate creation and destruction of human zygotes as immoral. A related issue is the commercialization of reproduction. What happens to the way we value human life if we buy and sell human gametes?

• What rights should gamete donors and surrogate parents have? Should a man or woman who has donated gametes to an infertile couple have any rights as a parent? On the other hand, should a gamete donor have the right to remain anonymous even if the child wants to meet his or her biological parent? If a surrogate mother decides that she wants to keep the baby she has carried for another couple, should she have the right to break her contract? Should the answer be the same if her own ovum is used in the procedure? These and other legal questions continue to be tested in courts around the world.

• How far should reproductive technologies go? It is already simple to sort sperm into those that are likely to carry an X chromosome and those that are likely to carry a Y chromosome. This means that couples using artificial insemination, *in vitro* fertilization, or gamete intrafallopian transfer technologies can select the sex of their babies. As well, zygotes can be tested for a number of genetic disorders before being implanted. As genetic screening becomes ever more sophisticated, ethical and moral questions arise about the extent to which people should be able to "design" their children. (You will explore some of these questions in more depth in Chapter 18.)

- Does everybody have the right to be a parent? Should reproductive technologies (which can be very expensive) be available only to individuals who are able to pay for them, or should they be funded by the

---

Thought Lab 15.2 — Evaluating Reproductive Technologies: Safety and Effectiveness

People who seek to enhance their ability to conceive or to prevent it require advice from qualified health professionals to determine the best course of action for their particular situations. Many factors are involved in making this determination. Two of these factors are the safety of any given available technology and its effectiveness.

These two factors, safety and effectiveness, require further elaboration to clarify their meaning. For example, to what or to whom does safety refer: the person undergoing treatment, the embryo/fetus, or both? What does effectiveness mean, and how is it to be quantified? How reliable is the method used to quantify it?

In this Thought Lab, you will gather information and data to assess and evaluate the safety and effectiveness of various technologies for enhancing and preventing conception. Based on your findings, you will offer and justify an opinion about the effectiveness and safety of these technologies.

Procedure

1. Working in small groups, select at least three of the technologies from each column of the following lists. (Therefore, you will select a minimum of six technologies.)

Selected Technologies for Enhancing Conception	Selected Technologies for Preventing Conception
• artificial insemination (AI) • assisted hatching (also called laser assisted hatching) • gamete intrafallopian transfer (GIFT) • in vitro fertilization (IVF) • intracytoplasmic sperm injection (ICSI) • surrogacy • tubal embryo transfer (TET) • zygote intrafallopian transfer (ZIFT)	• condoms • fertility awareness methods • intrauterine device (IUD) • lactational amenorrhea (LAM) • oral contraceptives (pills containing both estrogen and progestin (synthetic progesterone)) • progestin-only contraceptives • spermicides • tubal ligation • vasectomy

2. With the members of your group, discuss the meanings of the terms "safety" and "effectiveness" as they apply to reproductive technologies. Develop preliminary definitions for these terms.

3. Conduct research to find data or information about the safety and effectiveness of each of the technologies you have selected. **ICT**

4. In the course of your research, you may find that your definitions of the terms "safety" and "effectiveness" require modification or replacement. Redefine these terms with the members of your group. Then consult with other groups to compare definitions. As a class, develop definitions that everyone can agree to use. **ICT**

5. Reexamine the information and data you have gathered in light of the class definitions of safety and effectiveness. As necessary, conduct additional research to refine your findings. **ICT**

6. Consult with other groups to prepare a master chart that summarizes findings for all the technologies investigated.

Analysis

1. Based on your research, what key factors influenced your definitions of "safety" and "effectiveness"? List them in order of priority. What seems to be considered an acceptable risk to take to conceive or prevent conception of a child?

2. Based on your research and the summary in the master chart, decide which conception-enhancing and which conception-preventing technology is the most safe and effective technology. Use clear and logical arguments to justify your opinion. (You may answer this question as a group, as an individual, or both.)

Extension

3. List three other factors that you think would affect a person's or a couple's determination of the best course of action for enhancing or preventing conception.

Canadian health-care system? Should a mother who has completed menopause but wants another child have the same access to reproductive technologies as a young woman who wants to start a family? Should access to reproductive technologies be limited to individuals or couples who meet certain criteria, such as age, marital status, income, and health? Would limiting access be unfair discrimination, since fertile individuals and couples do not have to meet similar criteria in order to become parents?

These are only a few of the legal, moral, and ethical questions that surround reproductive technologies. In the coming years, Canadian governments, courts, spiritual leaders, families, and individuals will continue to debate these and similar reproduction-related questions.

Section 15.3 Summary

- Reproductive technologies have been developed to assist couples in conceiving a child as well as assist couples in preventing conception.

- People who are sterile or infertile may be helped by reproduction-enhancing technologies and practices such as artificial insemination, *in vitro* fertilization (IVF), surrogate motherhood, and superovulation.

- People who wish to reduce the likelihood of conception may benefit from technologies and practices such as abstinence, surgical procedures that prevent eggs from entering the uterus (tubal ligation) or sperm from being a component of semen (vasectomy), hormone treatments, physical barriers such as condoms and diaphragms, chemical barriers such as spermicides, and natural family planning (also called the rhythm method).

- The ability to enhance and prevent conception raises social and ethical issues that challenge individuals, courts, and governments to critically examine their views and beliefs about the value of human life and when that life begins.

- These issues have been debated for decades, and they continue to be debated.

| Section 15.3 | Review |

1. For each of the following situations, suggest a reproductive technology that might be appropriate. Briefly explain your suggestion.

  a) The male has a low sperm count. The female is reproductively healthy.

  b) The male has a healthy sperm count. The female rarely ovulates but is otherwise reproductively healthy.

  c) The male has a healthy sperm count. The female has blocked oviducts.

  d) A male is about to undergo radiation therapy. He currently has no female partner, but he wants to have children in the future.

  e) A female has no male partner but wants to conceive.

2. Design a table to summarize at least three methods for enhancing reproductive potential. Your summary table should include the following information: name and description of each method, how it works, and who would use it. **ICT**

3. Design a table to summarize at least five common methods for reducing reproductive potential (contraception). Your summary table should include the following information: name and description of each method, its effectiveness, how it works, and safety concerns. **ICT**

4. Explain how *in vitro* fertilization is different from artificial insemination.

5. Briefly describe three examples of issues that have been raised over the technologies used to enhance and reduce reproductive potential.

Human prenatal development begins at fertilization. A single sperm joins with an egg to form a zygote.

The embryonic period occurs during the first two months of the first trimester. Cleavage follows, with successive mitotic cell divisions, leading to the formation of a morula. The morula arrives at the uterus and hollows to form a blastocyst consisting of an outer trophoblast layer and an inner cell mass. The blastocyst implants in the uterine wall, and trophoblast cells secret human chorionic gonadotropin, which prevents menstruation.

During the second week, the amniotic cavity forms as the inner cell mass flattens, forming the embryonic disk. Through gastrulation, ectoderm and endoderm form, followed by the formation of mesoderm, establishing the three primary germ layers. Through morphogenesis, cells in a particular germ layer differentiate and develop into specific organs and organ systems.

During the third week, the extra-embryonic membranes form, some of which will eventually develop into the life-supporting placenta and umbilical cord. Gradually, structures appear, including the notochord, neural tube, arm and leg buds, heart, facial structures, skin specializations, and skeleton.

The fetal period occurs during the last month of the first trimester and over the remaining two trimesters. In the fetal period, existing structures formed via morphogenesis are elaborated and refined. Throughout prenatal development, teratogens exposed to or ingested by the mother can affect the health of the embryo and fetus.

During parturition, uterine contractions expel the baby, the placenta, and the umbilical cord.

Some reproductive technologies (such as *in vitro* fertilization and superovulation) are designed to enhance reproductive potential. Some reproductive technologies (such as condoms and surgical sterilization) are designed to restrict or suppress reproductive potential.

Issues surround the use of reproductive technologies.

Chapter 15 Graphic Organizer

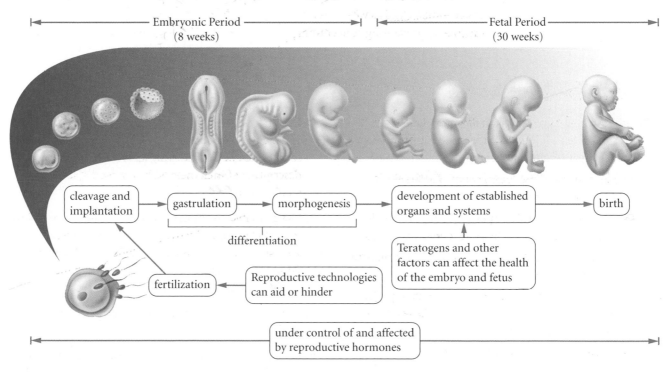

Understanding Concepts

1. In terms of embryonic and fetal changes, explain how the following terms are related: development, growth, differentiation.

2. List the sequence of events that occur during the process of fertilization.

3. Distinguish between a morula and a blastocyst.

4. a) What is the significance of the inner cell mass?
b) How is the inner cell mass different from the trophoblast?

5. Describe the functions of hCG (human chorionic gonadotropin).

6. What is the relationship between the embryonic disk and the primary germ layers?

7. a) List at least three major body parts or organs that are derived from ectoderm.
b) List at least three major body parts or organs that are derived from endoderm.
c) List at least three major body parts or organs that are derived from mesoderm.

8. Describe the formation of the placenta, and explain its main functions.

9. Distinguish between the chorion and the amnion.

10. Describe the function of amniotic fluid.

11. Explain how the yolk sac and the allantois in humans are related, and list the functions of each.

12. List five major changes that occur during the embryonic period of development and five major changes that occur during the fetal period of development.

13. Explain the term morphogenesis.

14. a) Describe the role of progesterone in initiating parturition.
b) Describe the events that occur during parturition.

15. Explain how chemical teratogens can end up in the blood system of the embryo or fetus.

16. List two beneficial health habits and two detrimental health habits during pregnancy and their consequences for the health of the embryo or fetus.

17. Name five hormones that are associated with prenatal development, parturition, and lactation and use a table or concept map to outline their relationship and functions. (ICT)

Applying Concepts

18. Some scientists distinguish between morphogenesis and organogenesis. Infer what the term organogenesis refers to and how it might differ from morphogenesis.

19. Translate the significance of the data and information conveyed in the following graph into words. Record your answer in a maximum of three paragraphs, with full sentences.

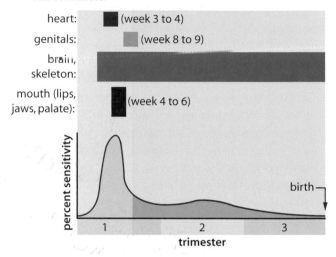

20. During the menstrual cycle, the endometrium thickens. A friend explains that this happens to prepare the uterus for sperm to fertilize an egg. How accurate is this explanation? Give reasons to justify your answer.

21. An ectopic pregnancy occurs when the blastocyst implants outside the uterus or in an abnormal site within the uterus. (The term ectopic comes from a Greek word that means "out of place.") The letters in the diagram on the next page show, in order of frequency of occurrence, various sites of ectopic pregnancies. How likely is it that an embryo or fetus would survive an ectopic pregnancy? Explain your answer.

22. You hear that there is a drug that stops the production of milk in the breast after a few days. Which hormone does the drug affect, and does the drug increase or inhibit secretion of the hormone?

23. Only one sperm is needed to fertilize an egg, and yet a man who ejaculates fewer than 10 million sperm is considered to be infertile. Explain why.

Making Connections

24. A woman has been told by her physician that her pregnancy has progressed 44 days since her last menstrual period. Approximately how many days has the embryo been developing, and what developmental events are occurring at this time?

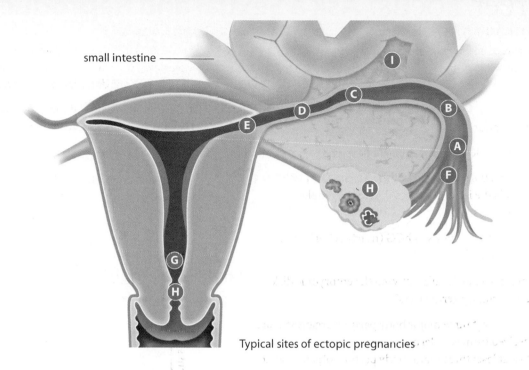

small intestine

Typical sites of ectopic pregnancies

25. For some women, secretion of GnRH (gonadatropin-releasing hormone) is inadequate, and they are considered to be sterile. They may be treated for their sterility with drugs that mimic the action of this hormone. Suggest one possible reason that such treatment is often associated with multiple births.

26. The diagram below outlines the early-development events that lead to dizygotic (fraternal) twins. Such twins are not identical and may be different sexes. In the uterus, each twin has its own chorion, its own amnion, and its own placenta. (The placentas may be separate or fused.) Monozygotic twins, on the other hand, are identical. They are always the same sex and are genetically identical. They develop from a single zygote. Such twins have two amnions but only one chorion, and they share the placenta. Based on this information and details provided in the diagram, predict the early-development events that lead to the formation of monozygotic twins. Record your prediction in the form of a sketch modelled after the diagram. **ICT**

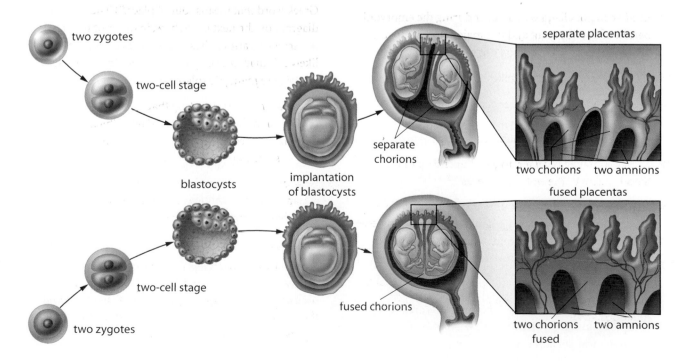

two zygotes

two-cell stage

blastocysts

implantation of blastocysts

separate chorions

separate placentas

two chorions   two amnions

two-cell stage

two zygotes

fused chorions

fused placentas

two chorions   two amnions
fused

Career Focus: Ask a Sexual and Reproductive Health Coordinator

Wendi Lokanc-Dilizio firmly believes that sexual health is a positive part of general well-being, not simply the absence of illness or disease. Her goal is to provide the information, motivation, and personal insight people need in order to develop personal skills that will support their positive sexual health. How to accomplish this goal is the challenge. "Even though Canadians have diverse values and opinions on human sexuality, sexual health education needs to be accessible to all people and it should be provided in an age-appropriate, culturally sensitive manner that is respectful of an individual's right to make informed choices about sexual and reproductive health. That is my job."

Q How do you define sexual and reproductive health?

First and foremost, sexual health is part of personal health and healthy living. It involves emotional, physical, mental, and social well-being. Here at the Calgary Health Region, our approach is two-fold: first, we want to work towards the positives such as the ability to develop rewarding personal relationships and the joy of desired parenthood; second, we want to help people avoid the negatives such as unwanted pregnancy and sexually transmitted infections.

Q Are sexually transmitted infections a significant problem?

Unfortunately they are, and they pose a particular threat to the health of specific groups. The rates of infections such as chlamydia and gonorrhea are highest among teens and young adults, so the need for knowledge and information for this group is urgent. Neglecting to provide this education can have significant consequences. For example, untreated chlamydia infection could lead to pelvic inflammatory disease and infertility, chronic pelvic pain, ectopic pregnancy, and increased susceptibility to HIV infection.

Q What would a typical day at work look like for you?

The appeal of this job for me is that there is no typical day. My mornings often begin with a brief meeting with colleagues. When I turn to the day's email, it can be a bit daunting to see the lack of basic sexual health knowledge that is demonstrated in the questions I receive through the website. The questions are often complex and can involve biological, emotional, psychological, social, economic, political, cultural, ethical, legal, religious, and even spiritual elements. It can take quite a bit of research and work on my part to provide the best response.

Q What motivated you to enter this field?

As a nurse, I always had an interest in community development and health promotion, if not specifically sexual health promotion. I was fortunate to find a role model in this field who was absolutely passionate about what he did, and that had a big influence on me.

Q What qualities do you think a person needs to do this kind of work?

Well, truthfully, this is not for everyone. Sexual health can be sensitive and controversial, so it requires people who have the personal qualities, training, and professional preparation that includes:
- biological knowledge of human sexuality and reproductive functions
- knowledge of general sexual health issues
- teaching and clinical skills
- an ability to respond respectfully to the sexual health education needs of diverse groups
- a capacity to discuss sexual health in a positive and sensitive manner
- conflict management and resolution skills
- an understanding of issues surrounding sexual orientation and gender
- insight to help people evaluate the ways that media can affect sexual health
- a commitment to a professional code of ethics on sexual health education, counselling and clinical services

Other Careers Related to Sexual and Reproductive Health Promotion

Teachers and Other Educators People from a variety of educational backgrounds provide sexual health education through schools, colleges, universities, health care settings, public health programs, social service agencies, as well as community and religious organizations. Whether in an academic or a community setting, educators provide students with information, motivation and self-esteem, and teach them the skills necessary to maintain sexual health.

Community and Public Health Workers Practitioners in community and public health work to promote positive lifestyles and create a supportive environment for prevention of disease and protection of health. Sexual health education is an integral part of public health and addresses the broader environmental and lifestyle factors that can impact public health. A degree in social work, nursing, or a relevant college certificate of diploma is generally required to work in the community health field.

Clinical Counsellor or Therapist Counsellors and therapists teach individuals to feel positive about themselves by providing them with the opportunity to develop the knowledge, personal insight, motivation and behavioural and decision making skills that are consistent with each individual's personal values. Some therapists are self-employed practitioners, while others work in hospitals or clinics. A graduate degree is generally required to work as a clinical counsellor or therapist.

Peer education and counselling Peers can have a significant influence on behaviour. Trained volunteers in the high school, university and college setting are an effective source of sexual health education. Individuals involved in peer education are trained specifically for their role and are carefully supervised by professionals. No formal degree or certificate is required to be a peer counsellor.

Go Further...

1. Discuss how socio-economic or environmental factors such as income, social environment, education levels, and access to services affect sexual health.

2. What segments of our society might require specific sexual health education? Discuss the challenges and issues and suggest ways in which society could meet their needs.

3. Mass media exerts a strong influence on sexual behaviour. How can individuals critically evaluate what they see, hear, and read in the media about sexual norms and practices?

Understanding Concepts

1. How is the human reproductive system different from all other systems of the human body?

2. Describe three ways in which the male and female reproductive systems are similar and three ways in which they are different.

3. Compare and contrast the female and male sex cells. **ICT**

4. Identify the three primary germ layers, and name the cellular body in which they first appear.

5. Describe the menstrual cycle.

6. Distinguish among the following structures: seminiferous tubules, Sertoli cells, interstitial cells. Use a sketch to record your answer. **ICT**

7. **a)** List the components of semen.
   b) Identify the structures that contribute to semen.
   c) Semen is mainly an alkaline fluid. Explain why.

8. Name the structures of the male and female reproductive systems indicated by the letters in the diagrams below.

9. Briefly describe the functions of each structure you identified in question 8.

10. Describe the role that hormones play in regulating primary and secondary sex characteristics in females and in males.

11. Which of these hormones—estrogen, GnRH, progesterone, FSH, and LH—is the correct match for the following statements:
    a) secreted by the follicular cells
    b) stimulates maturing of female sex organs
    c) maintains the uterine lining during pregnancy
    d) secreted by the corpus luteum
    e) stimulates development and function of the corpus luteum
    f) promotes thickening of the endometrium
    g) stimulates development of ovarian follicles
    h) high concentrations inhibit GnRH secretion

12. Describe the relationship between internal feedback mechanisms and the regulation of male reproductive hormones.

13. Distinguish between the inner cell mass and the trophoblast.

14. Name the three primary germ layers, and list two organs or systems that develop from each layer.

15. Identify the extra-embryonic membranes that form in support of a human embryo, and briefly describe their function.

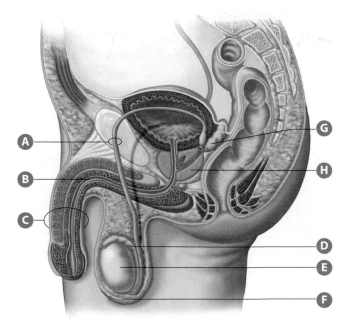

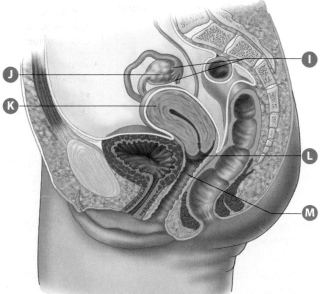

16. What is the function of the seminiferous tubules?

17. a) Is the acrosome part of the male or female reproductive system?
b) Describe the function of the acrosome.

18. What prevents an egg from being fertilized by more than one sperm?

19. Name two methods that are effective at preventing fertilization *and* protecting against sexually transmitted infections.

20. Distinguish between a morula and a blastocyst.

21. Can women become pregnant after menopause? Why or why not?

22. Which hormone or hormones prepare the mammary glands for lactation?

23. Make a sketch to show where fertilization usually takes place in the female reproductive system. **ICT**

24. Copy the following table into your notebook and complete it.

Hormone	Produced by	Target organ(s)	Effect(s)
Testosterone			
	• hypothalamus		• stimulates release of FSH and LH
		• ovaries, uterus	• inhibits ovulation • stimulates thickening of endometrium
			• stimulates development of sex organs • stimulates gamete production

25. Describe how chromosomal factors and hormones each influence the development of the male and female reproductive systems.

26. Contrast the means by which male and female gametes are transported from their site of origin to the site of fertilization. In what ways do these different transportation mechanisms contribute to reproductive function?

27. Identify at least one hormone associated with each of the following, and briefly describe the effect of the hormone(s).
a) fertilization
b) development of the placenta
c) parturition

28. Outline, in the form of a diagram, the feedback mechanism involved in the control of the ovaries. **ICT**

Applying Concepts

29. Most of the organs of the adult human are present by the end of the first eight weeks of prenatal development. Use paragraphs or point form notation to list at least eight key events that occur during this period of time.

30. Eggs and sperm are genetically very similar, but structurally they are very different. Explain why this is the case.

31. Failure of the testes to descend into the scrotum causes sterility in males. Explain why.

32. Most reptiles—for example, crocodiles, alligators, and turtles—develop in hard-shelled eggs. Scientists hypothesize that birds share the same evolutionary lineage as reptiles. Based on this hypothesis, infer the extra-embryonic structures you would expect to observe in a reptile egg, and explain your reasoning.

33. Why is it necessary for human gametes to have 23 chromosomes rather than 46?

34. Describe the function of the corpus luteum (a) if an egg is fertilized and implants in the endometrium and (b) if an egg is unfertilized.

35. If several different methods of enhancing reproductive potential are used at the same time, a baby could have as many as five "parents." Explain how this is possible.

36. Which of the following would be an indication that ovulation is soon to occur: the cervical mucus is becoming thick and sticky, an increase in body temperature, or a marked rise in the level of LH in the blood? Explain your answer.

37. If a male's testes were removed, would he still be able to produce male sex hormones? Explain.

38. Suggest one possible interpretation for the following graph.

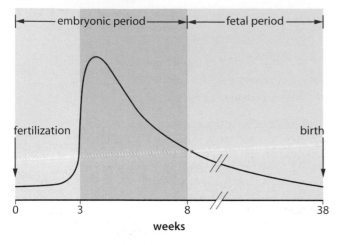

Making Connections

39. A 35-year-old female long-distance runner wants to have children with her male partner, but they have been unable to conceive for over one year. Tests on her partner's semen reveal that his sperm count is at a healthy level, and his sperm are in good condition.

   a) Based on the above information, suggest at least two reasons that may explain why the couple has been unable to conceive.

   b) Suggest a course of action the couple could try before they turn to reproductive technologies. Explain why your suggestions might help.

   c) If the couple remains infertile, what reproductive technologies might help them to conceive?

40. As the fetus grows, the uterus enlarges greatly. Instead of being confined to its usual location in the pelvic cavity, it extends upward and may eventually reach the level of the ribs. The organs of the abdominal region are displaced upward and are compressed against the diaphragm. The enlarging uterus also presses on the urinary bladder. Based on this information, infer three likely effects of the expanding uterus on the mother's body.

41. If a woman has one ovary surgically removed, can she still become pregnant? Why or why not?

42. If a male has a vasectomy, is he still able to produce sperm? If so, what happens to those sperm? How is the composition of semen changed in a person who has had a vasectomy?

43. Use a table to compare the roles of FSH in males and in females. **ICT**

44. Imagine that you have been commissioned to plan, write, and produce a pamphlet for a public health organization to demonstrate the effects of teratogens and other environmental factors on the development of an embryo and fetus. Create an outline that shows the main points that your pamphlet will cover and emphasize. Also describe two visuals that you will include in the pamphlet. (The visuals can be photographs, illustrations, graphs, or data tables.) Note: Read this question carefully to determine exactly what you are being asked to provide as an appropriate response.

45. If parents do no have access to genetic testing methods and wish to know the sex of their unborn baby, they usually have to wait until between the eighteenth and twenty-second week of development to find out. Based on your knowledge of reproductive development, explain why the sex of the unborn baby cannot be determined easily before this time.

Use the following information to answer the next question.

Amenorrhea is the absence of menstruation. (The term comes from Greek words that literally mean "absence of monthly flow".) Amenorrhea is not a disorder. Rather, it is a symptom that reflects a condition that usually is not serious. Nevertheless, any condition in which menstruation does not occur requires evaluation to determine the cause.

Amenorrhea is categorized as two types. Primary amenorrhea is the absence of menstruation by age 16. (**Note:** The onset of menstruation varies widely, commonly occurring between the ages of 11 and 16.) Secondary amenorrhea is the absence of three or more menstrual periods in a row.

Causes of primary amenorrhea include low levels of FSH, a pituitary tumour, anorexia nervosa, thyroid disorders, GnRH deficiency, Cushing's disease, genetic abnormalities, and obstructions of the vagina. Causes of secondary amenorrhea include the use of oral contraceptives (birth control pill), certain medications, thyroid disorders, excessive exercise, stress, and low body weight. Treatment, if deemed necessary, depends on the cause.

46. Infer three other common, logical causes of amenorrhea, either primary or secondary.

Use the following information to answer the next questions.

A pregnant thirty-one-year-old Chilean woman with normal menstrual history and two previous, uneventful pregnancies was seen by her doctor at eight weeks gestation. She had a single, intrauterine pregnancy. A pelvic ultrasound showed multicystic ovaries measuring 5 cm × 3.5 cm each and containing many fluid-filled sacs. Two weeks later she was admitted to the hospital complaining of abdominal pain. This time a pelvic ultrasound showed her right ovary was 13.2 cm × 8.0 cm, and the left was 13.4 × 9.7 cm. The patient was discharged when the pain settled and advised to rest at home.

At 16 weeks gestation she was admitted again, due to acute abdominal pain, nausea, and vomiting. Physical examination revealed a very large abdominal mass, extending from her pelvis to her ribs. The abdominal ultrasound showed giant, tumor-filled ovaries, approximately 19 cm × 15 cm each, and a normal fetus and placenta. Both ovaries were removed (a bilateral oophorectomy). After the operation the woman was fine, and she spontaneously delivered a 3.8-kg, 52-cm male infant at 39 weeks. The placenta weighed 600 g and was of normal macroscopic appearance. Lactation commenced spontaneously. She fully breastfed for ten days; she then maintained partial breastfeeding until 10 weeks after the birth.

Hormone replacement therapy (HRT) was started two months after the baby's birth. The woman's doctor had taken blood samples to measure her hormone levels at 37 weeks gestation and then at 8 hours, 4 days, 5 weeks, and 2 months post-partum (after the delivery). The results of these blood tests are presented in the two tables (37 weeks) and (post-partum) below. In the first table, the blood test results for eight Chilean women with normal pregnancies are shown as the control. In the second table, results for 25 women who breastfed and maintained amenorrhoea (lack of a menstrual period) for more than 6 months post partum are provided as the control.

Hormonal profile at 37 weeks of gestation in an oophorectomized pregnant woman compared to non-oophorectomized pregnant women at 38 weeks.

Group	FSH (IU/L)	Estrogen (nmol/L)	Progesterone (nmol/L)	Prolactin (μg/L)
Patient	6.1	78.2	1256	251
Controls	NM	39–114	328–897	120–457

Post-partum hormonal profile of an oophorectomized nursing woman

Time post-partum	FSH (IU/L)	Estrogen (pmol/L)	Progesterone (nmol/L)	Prolactin (μg/L)
8 h	<4.0	4864	NM	235
4 days	5.9	202.2	4.3	229
5 weeks				
Patient	31.4	239	<1.6	162
Controls	0.9–6.9	73–426	0.4–3.2	159
2 months				
Patient	68.0	136	NM	123
Controls	1.2–8.1	51–360	0.4–2.7	NM

NM = not measured   nmol = nanomole (10^{-9}) pmol = picomole (10^{-12})

47. The woman's doctor did not to remove her ovaries when she first presented with abdominal pain at 10 weeks gestation and an ultrasound showed that her ovaries were full of cysts. Explain why you think this decision was made.

48. Identify an important reproductive hormone that the doctors did not measure in these tests, and explain why it wasn't necessary to test for this hormone.

49. a) Analyze the change in follicle stimulating hormone (FSH) level from the end of gestation to two months post-partum for both the oophorectomized, nursing woman and the control women.

    b) Explain why there is a difference.

50. Why was HRT given to the patient at 2 months post-partum?

51. Why is the concentration of estrogen similar at the end of gestation for both the patient and the controls?

52. Why was the woman able to deliver her baby normally and spontaneously breastfeed afterwards?

UNIT
7

Cell Division, Genetics, and Molecular Biology

General Outcomes

In this unit, you will

- describe the processes of mitosis and meiosis

- explain the basic rules and processes associated with the transmission of genetic characteristics

- explain classical genetics at the molecular level

Unit Contents

Focussing Questions

1 What processes contribute to genetic variation?

2 Why do you and other organisms inherit some characteristics and not others?

3 How did scientists discover the structure of DNA, and how do they use technology to change that structure to produce new varieties of organisms?

Unit PreQuiz ?
www.albertabiology.ca

T he peregrine falcon is one of the world's swiftest predators. Its curved wings allow it to maneuver quickly in flight. A band of dark feathers under each eye cuts the glare of the Sun. The falcon's vision is adapted to spot a small bird more than a kilometre away—and to keep this prey in precise focus during a dive that can reach a speed of more than 300 km/h. During the mating season, the male falcon shows off his hunting skill by offering gifts of food to the female. All of these characteristics are hereditary traits that the adult bird will pass on to its chicks. How can mating behaviour, or the colour of a feather, be programmed into an egg? What natural and human-induced means are there for changing that programming? What are the ramifications of these changes?

In this unit, you will examine the cellular processes that store, transmit, and express hereditary information. Beginning with a study of the life cycles of cells and organisms, you will learn to analyze and predict patterns of inheritance. You will become familiar with the range of events—from random mutations to careful genetic engineering—that can give rise to new traits, deadly diseases, or entirely new organisms. Perhaps more than any other scientific discipline, the fast-changing field of genetics promises to change human society. In this unit you will encounter some of the challenging social and ethical issues that accompany this promise.

Prerequisite Concepts

This unit draws and builds upon your understanding of biodiversity from Chapter 3 as well as from earlier studies.

The Chemical Codes of Cells

Nucleic acids are biological chemicals that direct the growth and development of every single-celled and multi-celled organism by means of a chemical code. These chemicals determine how the cell functions and what characteristics it has. The cell contains two types of nucleic acid: RNA (ribonucleic acid) and DNA (deoxyribonucleic acid). DNA is the main component of the genes (hereditary material) in all cells. Each gene contains instructions for making RNA, which contains the instructions for making proteins. These proteins make up much of the structure of a cell and control how it functions.

Prokaryotes and Eukaryotes

The smallest cells with the simplest type of internal organization lack a nucleus. That is, they lack an enclosed region inside of the cell where the DNA is separated from the rest of the cell. Instead, the DNA in these cells is concentrated in one region inside the cell. Such cells are called prokaryotes ("pro" meaning before and "karyon" meaning nucleus). Prokaryotic organisms are divided into two domains—Bacteria and Archaea— as shown in Figure P7.1.

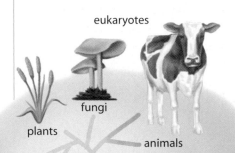

eukaryotes

plants

fungi

animals

Eukarya
- Eurkaryotic, unicellular to multicellular organisms
- Membrane-bounded nucleus
- Sexual reproduction
- Phenotypes and nutrition are diverse
- Each kingdom has specializations
- Flagella, if present, have a 9 + 2 organization

protists

cyanobacteria

Bacteria
- Prokaryotic, unicellular organisms
- Lack a membrane-bounded nucleus
- Reproduce asexually
- Heterotrophic by absorption
- Autotrophic by chemosynthesis or by photosynthesis
- Move by flagella

heterotrophic bacteria

Archaea
- Prokaryotic, unicellular organisms
- Lack a membrane-bounded nucleus
- Reproduce asexually
- Many are autotrophic by chemosynthesis; some are heterotrophic by absorption
- Unique rRNA base sequence
- Distinctive plasma membrane and cell wall chemistry

prokaryotes

common ancestor

Figure P7.1 Two of the three domains of life contain prokaryotic organisms. The remaining domain contains eukaryotic organisms, including humans.

The cells of all other organisms are larger than prokaryotes and have a more complex structure that includes a nucleus. Such cells are called eukaryotes ("eu" meaning true, as in "true nucleus").

The organelles of a eukaryotic cell divide its interior into compartments. This allows the many different chemical reactions constantly taking place within the cell to proceed at the same time without interfering with one another. Many organelles contain highly folded membranes that increase the surface area on which chemical reactions can be co-ordinated as well as the overall rate of reactions within the cell.

The Nucleus and Ribosomes

The genetic information stored in the DNA (Figure P7.2) determines the structural characteristics of the cell and how it functions. Unless a cell is in the process of dividing or preparing to divide, the DNA exists in a network of strands called chromatin.

The nucleus has at least one area of chromatin, called a nucleolus, that is dedicated to producing a special type of RNA that is used to construct the many ribosomes required by the cell.

Ribosomes are tiny organelles that are the sites of protein synthesis in cells. Ribosomes are found in both eukaryotic and prokaryotic cells. In eukaryotes, ribosomes are 20 nm to 30 nm in diameter; they are slightly smaller in prokaryotes. In both types of cells, ribosomes are made up of two subunits, one large and one small, each with its own mix of proteins and RNA.

The nucleus is separated from the cytoplasm by a double membrane called the nuclear envelope. This membrane has nuclear pores about 100 nm in diameter that permit the passage of proteins into the nucleus and ribosomal subunits of the nucleus.

Figure P7.2 The cell nucleus and related structures. Continuous with the outer membrane of the nuclear envelope is a system of flattened membrane-bound sacs, the endoplasmic reticulum, studded with protein-synthesizing ribosomes. Some ribosomes also float freely in the cytoplasm.

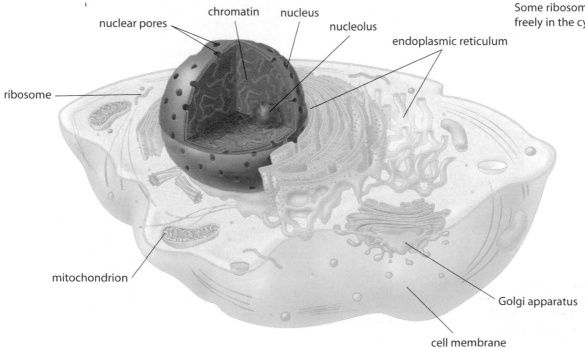

nuclear pores · chromatin · nucleus · nucleolus · endoplasmic reticulum · ribosome · mitochondrion · Golgi apparatus · cell membrane

Cellular Reproduction

Chapter Concepts

16.1 The Cell Cycle

- Multicellular organisms grow by adding new cells through the process of cell division.

- The cell cycle is the continuous sequence of growth and division that gives rise to all cells.

- The cells of each species have a characteristic number and arrangement of chromosomes.

16.2 The Reproduction of Somatic Cells

- Mitosis involves a precise sequence of events, which can be grouped into four phases.

- The cell cycle is carefully regulated.

16.3 The Formation of Gametes

- Meiosis involves two nuclear divisions to create haploid gametes from diploid parent cells.

- Human gametes form by the processes of spermatogenesis and oogenesis.

- Meiosis contributes to genetic variation.

16.4 Reproductive Strategies

- Different species have life cycles that include different reproductive strategies.

- Many species are capable of both sexual and asexual reproduction.

In the late fall, the foothills of the Rocky Mountains ring with the clash of antlers as male elk challenge one another. An elk's antlers, which may span up to 2 m, take less than one year to grow. Antler tissue is one of the fastest-growing animal tissues. As each antler grows, millions of genetically identical antler cells are produced every day. When the elk breed, however, their offspring will have a variety of genetic characteristics. Some of these characteristics will be similar to those of their parents. Other characteristics will be quite different. In this chapter, you will investigate the cellular processes that allow for these different outcomes. You will also learn how an understanding of cell division helps scientists explore the important mechanisms of heredity.

Cell Division

In order for most organisms to grow, to repair damaged cells, and maintain their life functions, new cells are needed. Each new cell, or daughter cell, must contain the same genetic information as the original cell, or parent cell. How are these new, genetically identical cells produced?

Procedure

1. The diagrams show onion root-tip cells before and after the cells have divided to form new cells. The tip of an onion root-tip is an active growing region. The cells in this region are actively dividing to produce new cells.

2. Study the diagrams. Compare the number and characteristics of the chromosomes in the parent cell to the number of chromosomes in the two daughter cells.

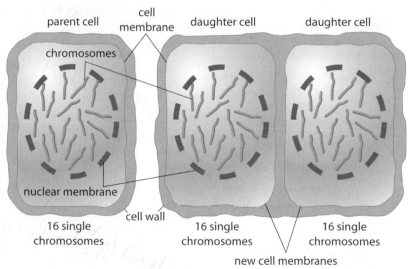

Analysis

1. What do you notice about the number of chromosomes in the parent cell compared to the number of chromosomes in the two daughter cells?

2. What do you notice about the characteristics of each chromosome in the three cells?

3. How do you think it is possible to start with 16 chromosomes in the parent cell and end up with 16 chromosomes in each of the two daughter cells?

4. A somatic cell in humans contains 46 chromosomes. If this cell divides, how many chromosomes do you think will appear in the two new daughter cells?

This microscope image shows an animal cell dividing to produce two new somatic (body) cells. In what way would this image look different if the cell were dividing to produce sperm or egg cells instead of body cells?

The Cell Cycle

Imagine that you are a scientist who is studying plants and animals in the mid-1800s. Until the early 1800s, the best commonly available microscopes could reach a magnification of about 270×. By 1840, however, advances in lens technologies have led to the manufacture of microscopes that can magnify up to about 1200×. When you use one of these new microscopes to study plant and animal tissues, you are among the first scientists to observe that all living things are made up of cells. As well, you observe that cells of different tissues are different shapes and sizes, but almost all cells are microscopic in size. You conclude that as an organism grows, new cells are added. Perhaps you wonder why individual cells do not keep growing.

As a cell grows in size, the volume of its cytoplasm increases at a faster rate than the surface area of its plasma membrane. Recall that a cell absorbs nutrients and excretes wastes through its plasma membrane. As the volume of the cytoplasm increases, more materials must pass through this membrane. If a cell continued to grow, its plasma membrane would be too small to meet its metabolic needs (see Figure 16.1). Thus, a cell must stop growing once it reaches a certain size. New growth, therefore, must come from the addition of new cells.

Until the mid-1800s, most scientists accepted the theory of *spontaneous generation*. According to this theory, living organisms could arise from non-living matter. Observations of cell division led scientists to propose an alternative theory of how living cells originate. In 1855, Rudolph Virchow (1821–1902) became the first scientist to publish the conclusion that new cells arise *only* from the division of other cells. This conclusion became an important part of the argument against spontaneous generation, and it inspired many scientists to turn their attention to the study of cell division.

Cell Division and the Cell Cycle

The life cycle of the cell is called the **cell cycle**. The lives of **somatic cells** (body cells) vary, based on their type and their environment. For example, blood cells and skin cells are replaced frequently, so the cells that produce them divide frequently. Nerve cells, on the other hand, divide infrequently or not at all. For the many somatic cells that divide, the cell cycle consists of a maintenance period during which a cell seems to be resting and a period during which it divides. A single cell cycle is defined as the sequence of events from one cell division to the next. For a growing organism to develop properly, new cells that arise through cell division must be able to carry on the same function as the original cell.

While some scientists in the 1800s had begun to explore heredity, the mechanisms of heredity were not yet understood. Although researchers had begun to identify some cell structures,

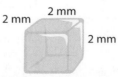
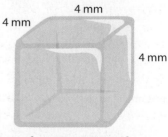

Figure 16.1 The ratio of surface area to volume is a key factor that limits cell size. In these model cells, an increase in the length of the cell from 1 mm to 4 mm causes the ratio of surface area to volume to decrease from 6:1 to 1.5:1.

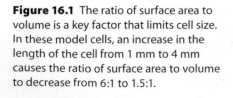

surface area = 6 mm²
volume = 1 mm³
ratio = 6:1

surface area = 24 mm²
volume = 8 mm³
ratio = 3:1

surface area = 96 mm²
volume = 64 mm³
ratio = 1.5:1

many others—including genetic material—appeared transparent under a microscope. These structures were impossible to differentiate, even at high magnifications. Although scientists could observe the division of cells, they could not infer how distinct cellular processes work.

A significant technological boost came from an unexpected source—the clothing industry. In the mid-1800s, the first synthetic dyes were produced. In 1879, the German biologist Walther Flemming (1843–1903) used one of these new dyes to stain a specimen of tissue. The stain was picked up by a substance in the nucleus, which Flemming called *chromatin* (meaning "coloured matter"). Within a few years, Flemming had observed that chromatin is made up of a set of individual coloured structures. As well, he had offered the first accurate description of the cell cycle and the process of cell division in plant and animal cells. Flemming coined the word *mitosis*—from Greek, meaning "thread"—to describe his observations of thread-like structures dividing in the cell nucleus. (You will learn about mitosis in Section 16.2.)

Flemming had no idea there was a connection between the coloured substance he was studying and the processes of heredity. Even so, the fact that this substance behaved in predictable ways during cell division, and that its behaviour was similar in both plant and animal cells, indicated that it was important to the life of all cells. The systematic study of cell division began in earnest in the late 1800s.

Today, scientists know that the structure and function of a cell are determined by its genetic material. Therefore, the central feature of the cell cycle is the way that genetic material is duplicated and then passed from the original cell, called the **parent cell**, to each new cell, called a **daughter cell**. This process is made possible by the highly organized arrangement of genetic material within a cell.

• • •

1. Explain why there is a limit to how large a cell can grow.

2. Define the term "cell cycle."

3. Briefly summarize how advances in technology led to the new theories about the origin of cells.

4. What is the central feature of the cell cycle?

• • •

Organization of Genetic Information in the Eukaryotic Cell

The genetic information of a cell is contained in its **DNA** (deoxyribonucleic acid), a molecule of nucleic acid that governs processes of heredity in the cells of organisms. DNA is found in each **chromosome** of a cell. A chromosome is a length of DNA and its associated proteins.

In eukaryotic cells, the chromosomes are found in the nucleus. (Eukaryotic cells are those that make up protists, fungi, plants, and animals. These cells have a membrane-bound nucleus.) If you lined up all the DNA found in the nucleus of a single human cell, it would reach about 3 m. The diameter of a nucleus, however, is only about 5 μm. (As a comparison, imagine stuffing a piece of string about 150 km long into a lunch box.) A highly organized arrangement of proteins, known as **histones**, and DNA compacts this material within the cell.

For most of a cell's life cycle, its genetic material appears as a mass of long, intertwined strands known as **chromatin**. As the genetic material is reorganized during the processes of cellular division, the threads of chromatin condense and become visible under a light microscope as distinct chromosomes. Figure 16.2 shows the levels of organization of genetic material within a eukaryotic cell. The constricted (pinched-in) region in the condensed chromosome is a specialized region called a **centromere**.

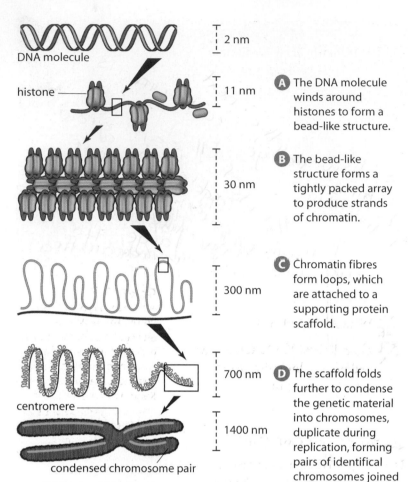

DNA molecule — 2 nm

histone — 11 nm

A The DNA molecule winds around histones to form a bead-like structure.

30 nm

B The bead-like structure forms a tightly packed array to produce strands of chromatin.

300 nm

C Chromatin fibres form loops, which are attached to a supporting protein scaffold.

700 nm

D The scaffold folds further to condense the genetic material into chromosomes, duplicate during replication, forming pairs of identical chromosomes joined by a centromere.

1400 nm

centromere

condensed chromosome pair

Figure 16.2 The levels of organization of genetic material in a eukaryotic cell

⑤ In what structures is the genetic information of a cell contained? Where are these structures located?

⑥ What is a centromere and where would you find it?

Chromosome Number

The levels of organization of genetic material shown in Figure 16.2 are much the same in all eukaryotic cells. However, the number of individual chromosomes each cell contains varies from one species to another. Human somatic cells have 46 chromosomes. These can be organized into 22 pairs of **homologous chromosomes** (similar-looking chromosomes) known as **autosomes**. Each somatic cell also has two **sex chromosomes** that may or may not be a homologous pair. The autosomes are numbered 1 through 22. The sex chromosomes are called X and Y.

The sex chromosomes determine the sex of an individual. A human female has two X chromosomes, and a human male has one X and one Y chromosome. By convention, the sex chromosomes are counted as a pair even though X and Y are not homologous.

Homologous chromosomes carry the same **genes**—areas of DNA that contain specific genetic information—at the same location, or **locus**. Despite appearing similar, homologous pairs are not identical to each other. Instead, they carry different forms, or **alleles**, of the same gene (Figure 16.3).

A cell that contains pairs of homologous chromosomes is said to be **diploid** (from a Greek word meaning "double"). The diploid number in humans is 46, or 23 pairs. A cell that contains unpaired chromosomes is said to be **haploid** (from a Greek word meaning "single"). Human **gametes**, or reproductive cells (egg and sperm cells), are haploid. The haploid number of chromosomes in a species is designated as n. In humans, $n = 23$, and a diploid cell has $2n$ chromosomes ($2n = 46$). n varies from species to species. In corn plants (*Zea mays*), $n = 10$. In fruit flies (*Drosophila* sp.), $n = 4$. Some organisms are **polyploid**, which means they have sets of more than two homologous chromosomes. For example, some plants are *tetraploid* ($4n$, or four homologous chromosomes of each type), *triploid* ($3n$), or even *octoploid* ($8n$).

⑦ How many chromosomes are there in the somatic cells of humans?

⑧ What are homologous chromosomes?

⑨ Why are the X and Y chromosomes known as the sex chromosomes?

⑩ Write a sentence that clearly differentiates these terms: diploid, haploid, polyploid.

BiologyFile

FYI
The total length of the DNA in all of your cells is about 2×10^{10} km—about twice the distance between Earth and the Sun.

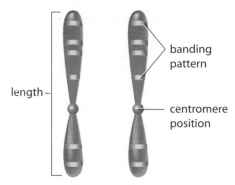

length — banding pattern

centromere position

Figure 16.3 Homologous chromosomes are not identical to one another, because they carry different forms, or alleles, of the same genes. They have several other characteristics in common, such as their length, centromere location, and banding pattern.

Examining Chromosomes: The Karyotype

Autosomes 1 to 22 and chromosomes X and Y are distinct from one another in several ways. For example, they vary in their overall length, the location of their centromere, and their staining properties. (Each chromosome has a distinct pattern of banding when stained.) These three characteristics are the same in homologous chromosomes, however (see Figure 16.3). Therefore, scientists can use these characteristics to identify individual chromosomes and to match pairs of homologous chromosomes.

The particular set of chromosomes that an individual possesses is called the individual's **karyotype** (see Figure 16.4).

To prepare a karyotype, scientists collect a cell sample and use chemicals to stop the cell cycle when the condensed chromosomes are most clearly visible under a light microscope. Then they stain the cells to help them identify the individual chromosomes. Usually, they photograph the stained chromosomes and transfer the images onto a new background. They complete the karyotype by organizing the images into a series of homologous pairs. In the next investigation, you will model the process of preparing a karyotype by hand. (In the past, karyotypes were prepared by hand. Now this is usually done on a computer.)

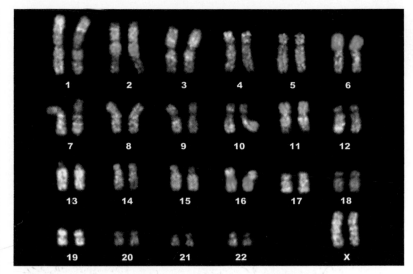

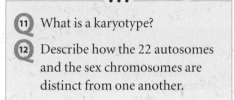

11 **Q** What is a karyotype?

12 **Q** Describe how the 22 autosomes and the sex chromosomes are distinct from one another.

Figure 16.4 A human karyotype. The chromosome pairs are arranged and numbered in order of their length, from longest to shortest. The sex chromosomes appear last. Karyotypes are helpful in diagnosing conditions such as Turner syndrome, where one X chromosome is partly or totally missing, and Down syndrome, where there is an extra chromosome 21.

Stages of the Cell Cycle

The cell cycle is made up of two main stages: a growth stage and a division stage. Each of these stages includes a series of distinct events, as shown in Figure 16.5.

Growth Stage

Most of the somatic cell's life is spent in the growth stage, which is called **interphase**. During interphase, the cell carries out its regular metabolic functions and prepares for its next division. There are three phases in interphase: G1, S, and G2.

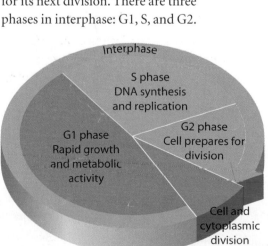

Interphase
S phase
DNA synthesis and replication
G1 phase
Rapid growth and metabolic activity
G2 phase
Cell prepares for division
Cell and cytoplasmic division

Figure 16.5 The cell cycle. Interphase, the stage of growth and metabolic activity, occupies most of the cell cycle. The division stage involves the reproduction of the nucleus and the division of the cell contents.

- **G1 phase:** Early scientists could not identify any specific activities taking place during this phase, so they called it "Gap 1" or "G1." Scientists now know that important growth processes are occurring, so more recent work usually refers to this phase as "Growth 1." The cell grows quickly during the G1 phase.
- **S phase:** About midway through interphase, the cell's DNA is copied exactly. That is, the DNA in the chromatin *replicates* to create a second identical set of DNA. (You will learn more about DNA replication in Chapter 18.) These two identical chromosomes, called **sister chromatids**, are joined at the centromere, as shown in Figure 16.6. Because new genetic material is synthesized during this phase, it is known as the *synthesis* or S phase.
- **G2 phase:** Cells that have completed the S phase then enter the last segment of interphase, called "Gap 2" or "Growth 2." DNA replication in the S phase has consumed a great deal of energy, so this second growth stage lets the cell rebuild its reserves of energy to prepare for division. As well, the cell manufactures proteins and other molecules to make structures required for division of the nucleus and cell.

INVESTIGATION 16.A

Target Skills

Preparing and **interpreting** models of a human karyotype

Modelling a Karyotype

A karyotype provides information about the number and organization of chromosomes in an individual. Karyotypes are used most often by geneticists to determine the presence of particular genetic conditions. In this investigation, you will simulate the preparation of a karyotype and analyze your results.

Question

How can you prepare and interpret a karyotype?

Safety Precautions

- Use care when handling scissors.

Materials

- image of the chromosomes in a human somatic cell
- blank karyotype form
- scissors
- tape

Procedure

1. Work with a partner. Your teacher will provide an image of chromosomes in a human somatic cell. Examine the chromosomes. How many chromosomes can you count? What similarities and differences can you see? Record your observations.

2. Carefully cut out each chromosome.

3. Match the homologous pairs of chromosomes. Remember to match the length, location of the centromere, and banding pattern of the chromosomes in each pair.

4. Tape the pairs of autosomes 1 to 22 on the karyotype form in order, from longest to shortest. Place the sex chromosomes with each other, at the end of the karyotype. **Note:** The X and Y chromosomes are not a homologous pair. The length of the X chromosome is between the lengths of chromosome 4 and chromosome 5. The Y chromosome is much shorter, about the same length as chromosome 14.

5. Examine your finished karyotype, and record your observations.

Analysis

1. How many chromosomes does this cell have? How would you write the chromosome number to show the haploid chromosome number?

2. How would the karyotype differ if this were a gamete? What would its chromosome number be?

3. Did these chromosomes come from a male or a female? How can you tell?

Conclusion

4. What kind of information can you infer from a karyotype?

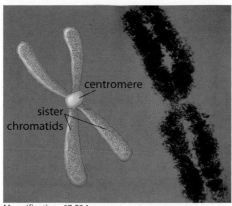

Magnification: 67 534 ×

Figure 16.6 During the S phase of the cell cycle, each chromosome is copied. The resulting sister chromatids are held together at the centromere.

Interphase ends when the cell begins the process of nuclear division: mitosis.

Cell Division

There are two main processes in cell division:

- **mitosis**, the division of the genetic material and the contents of the nucleus into two complete and separate sets
- **cytokinesis**, the division of the cytoplasm and the organelles into two separate cells

Together, mitosis and cytokinesis form two new daughter cells with the same genetic information as the parent cell. In the next section, you will examine these processes in more detail.

13 What are the main phases of the cell cycle?

14 Briefly describe each phase.

Section 16.1 Summary

- Multicellular organisms grow by adding new cells through the process of cell division.
- The cell cycle is the continuous sequence of growth and division that gives rise to all cells.
- A highly organized arrangement serves to compact genetic material within a eukaryotic cell.
- Each eukaryotic cell contains chromosomes. The number and arrangement of these chromosomes varies from species to species. For example, a human somatic cell contains 23 pairs of chromosomes.
- The cell cycle ensures that the diploid parent cell provides an identical set of chromosomes to each of its daughter cells.
- The cell cycle is made up of two main stages: interphase and division.
- These stages can be organized into five general phases or processes: a first growth stage, called the G1 phase; a period of DNA synthesis, called the S phase; a second growth stage, the G2 phase; the division of the nucleus (mitosis); the division of the cytoplasm (cytokinesis).

Section 16.1 | **Review**

1. Give two reasons that cell division is necessary for a plant to grow from a seedling into a tree.

2. What two main technological advances enabled scientists to observe cell division?

3. What are the five general phases or processes of the cell cycle?

4. Contrast the two terms in each pair of terms.
   a) haploid and diploid
   b) chromatin and chromosome
   c) XX and XY

5. What three characteristics are the same in each chromosome of a homologous pair?

6. During what phase of the cell cycle are chromosomes replicated?

7. Suppose that you are examining a human cell with 22 pairs of autosomes, one X chromosome, and one Y chromosome. Did this cell come from a male or a female? Is the cell somatic or a gamete? Diploid or haploid? Explain.

The Reproduction of Somatic Cells

Section Outcomes

In this section, you will
- **identify** the phases of mitosis and describe their significance
- **assess** the similarities and differences between mitosis in plant cells and mitosis in animal cells
- **calculate** the duration of individual phases of the cell cycle

Key Terms

prophase
centrioles
spindle apparatus
metaphase
anaphase
telophase
cell plate
cancer

Figure 16.7 If a sea star (*Asterias vulgaris*) is attacked by a predator and loses one or more arms, new arms are regenerated through the processes of mitosis and cytokinesis. Four arms are regenerating here. What applications could the study of these processes have for humans?

Each cell that undergoes mitosis will divide to produce two new cells. The linked processes of mitosis and cytokinesis have three important functions:
- Growth: They enable organisms to grow from a single-celled zygote into a mature organism that may contain hundreds of trillions of cells.
- Maintenance: They produce new cells to replace worn out or dead cells.
- Repair: They can regenerate damaged tissues. If you cut your finger, skin cells reproduce so that new skin can grow over the injured area. Some organisms are able to regenerate entire body parts that have been lost (see Figure 16.7).

To accomplish each of these functions, each daughter cell must have the correct genetic information. This means that several cellular events must take place:
- The genetic material of the parent cell must be replicated.
- The replicated chromatin must be condensed and organized as chromosomes in the nucleus.
- One complete set of chromosomes must be divided into each of two new nuclei.

- The cell cytoplasm must divide to produce two complete and functional daughter cells.

In this section, you will study the cellular events that achieve these outcomes.

• • •

15 Name the three important functions of mitosis and cytokinesis.

16 Why must each daughter cell have the correct genetic information?

• • •

Phases of Mitosis

Recall, from Section 16.1, that DNA replication takes place during the S phase of interphase. In G2, the cell begins manufacturing or assembling other materials it will require for mitosis and cytokinesis. At the end of interphase, the chromatin consists of two identical sets of DNA. The cell is ready to begin mitosis.

Mitosis consists of a precise sequence of events. In a living cell, this sequence is continuous. That is, there are no clear dividing lines between one event and the next. To facilitate description and communication, cell biologists have grouped the events into four main phases. Each phase is identified by a characteristic arrangement of chromosomes and by the appearance or disappearance of other cell structures. Study Figure 16.8 as you read through the following description of the phases of mitosis in animal cells.

Prophase

Prophase is the first of the four phases of mitosis. During prophase, the chromatin condenses into tightly packed chromosomes.

Other structures in the cell also change during prophase. The nuclear membrane breaks down, releasing the

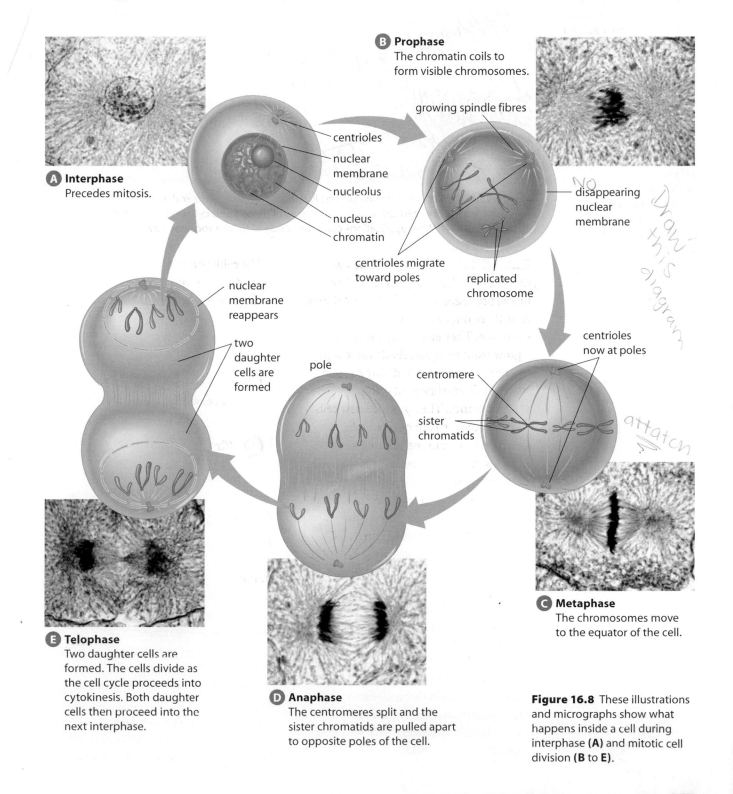

A **Interphase**
Precedes mitosis.

centrioles
nuclear membrane
nucleolus
nucleus
chromatin

B **Prophase**
The chromatin coils to form visible chromosomes.

growing spindle fibres

disappearing nuclear membrane

centrioles migrate toward poles

replicated chromosome

centrioles now at poles

centromere

sister chromatids

pole

nuclear membrane reappears

two daughter cells are formed

C **Metaphase**
The chromosomes move to the equator of the cell.

D **Anaphase**
The centromeres split and the sister chromatids are pulled apart to opposite poles of the cell.

E **Telophase**
Two daughter cells are formed. The cells divide as the cell cycle proceeds into cytokinesis. Both daughter cells then proceed into the next interphase.

Figure 16.8 These illustrations and micrographs show what happens inside a cell during interphase (**A**) and mitotic cell division (**B** to **E**).

chromosomes into the cytoplasm. The nucleolus disappears. One pair of cylindrical organelles, called **centrioles**, moves apart to opposite poles of the cell. As the centrioles move apart, a network of fibres called the **spindle apparatus** forms between them. Each *spindle fibre* is made of microtubules—hollow tubes of protein that facilitate movement of chromosomes within a cell. A spindle fibre lengthens with the addition of microtubule subunits. The removal of these subunits causes a spindle fibre to shorten.

Metaphase

The second phase of mitosis is called **metaphase**. During metaphase, the spindle fibres guide the chromosomes to the equator, or centre line, of the cell. The spindle fibres from opposite poles attach to the centromere of each chromosome. The spindle fibres attach in such a way that one sister chromatid faces one pole, while the other sister chromatid faces the opposite pole. (By convention, each pair of sister chromatids is considered to be a single chromosome as long as the chromatids remain joined at the centromere.)

Anaphase

The third phase of mitosis is called **anaphase**. During anaphase, each centromere splits apart and the sister chromatids separate from one another. The spindle fibres that link the centromeres to the poles of the cell shorten. As these fibres shorten, sister chromatids are pulled to opposite poles. At the same time, other microtubules in the spindle apparatus lengthen and force the poles of the cell away from one another. At the end of anaphase, one complete diploid set of chromosomes has been gathered at each pole of the elongated cell.

Telophase

The fourth and final phase of mitosis is called **telophase**. Telophase begins when the chromatids have reached the opposite poles of the cell. The chromatids begin to

unwind into the longer and less visible strands of chromatin. The spindle fibres break down. A nuclear membrane forms around each new set of chromosomes, and a nucleolus forms within each new nucleus.

Cytokinesis

Mitosis is the process of nuclear division. It is followed by cytokinesis, which is division of the cytoplasm to complete the creation of two new daughter cells. During cytokinesis in animal cells, an indentation forms in the cell membrane along the cell equator. This indentation deepens until the cell is pinched in two. The cytoplasm and organelles divide equally between the two halves of the cell. Cytokinesis ends with the separation of the two genetically identical daughter cells. The daughter cells are now in G1 of interphase.

> • • •
>
> **17** What are the four phases of mitosis?
>
> **18** List the key events that happen to chromosomes in each phase.
>
> • • •

Mitosis and Cytokinesis in Plant Cells

In the mid-1800s, scientists observed that the phases of cell division are very similar in plants and animals. The observation that plants and animals share this basic process of life caused a philosophical shift toward recognizing the unity of living things. At the same time, however, scientists recognized that the structural differences between plant cells and animal cells lead to some differences in cell division:

• Plant cells do not have centrioles, but they do form a spindle apparatus.

• The rigid cell wall of a plant cell is much stronger than the membrane of an animal cell. The cell wall does not furrow and pinch in during cytokinesis. Instead, a membrane called a **cell plate** forms between the two daughter nuclei (see Figure 16.9). This cell plate extends across the diameter of the cell, and it is then reinforced by the addition of cellulose and proteins to create a new cell wall.

Q 19 How do mitosis and cytokinesis differ in plant cells and animal cells?

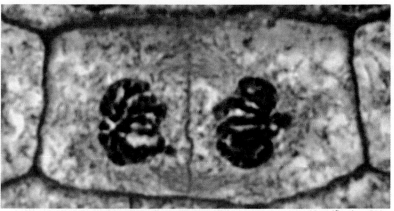

Figure 16.9 Cytokinesis in a plant cell. A new cell wall is forming between the two daughter cells.

Magnification: 514 ×

INVESTIGATION 16.B

Observing the Cell Cycle in Plant and Animal Cells

In this investigation, you will observe and compare the stages of the cell cycle in prepared slides of onion root tip cells and in whitefish embryo cells.

Question

What stages of the cell cycle can you recognize and identify in plant and animal cells?

Safety Precautions

• Be sure that the microscope is turned off and your hands are dry when you plug in or disconnect the cord.

• Handle the microscope slides with care.

Materials

• microscope
• prepared slide of onion root-tip cells
• prepared slide of whitefish embryo cells

Procedure

1. Place the onion root-tip slide on the microscope stage, and observe it under low power. Focus on the area just behind the tip of the root.

2. Carefully shift to medium power, focus, and then go to high power to observe the cells. Try to find cells in the different phases of mitosis, and draw a cell in each phase. Also find and draw a cell in interphase and a cell undergoing cytokinesis. Label as many features as you can.

3. Move the slide to concentrate your attention on the root tip. Note any differences between the root tip and the area you observed in step 2.

4. Change back to lower power, and remove the onion root tip slide. Place the whitefish embryo slide on the stage, and observe it under low power.

5. Find an area of dividing cells. Change to medium power, focus, and then shift to high power. As you look at each cell, determine which phase of mitosis it is in.

6. Draw one cell in interphase, one cell in each phase of mitosis, and one cell in cytokinesis. Label as many parts as you can. Note any difference between mitosis in animal cells and mitosis in plant cells.

7. Copy the data table on the next page. Switch back to the onion slide and, working in pairs, observe every onion root-tip cell in one high power field of view and identify its phase of the cell cycle. Have one partner observe the slide and call out the phase of each cell while the other partner records the observations. After you do one full field of view, choose another

continued on next page

and switch roles. If you have not counted at least 200 cells, then count a third field of view.

8. Calculate the percentage of cells found in each stage by dividing the number of cells in a given stage by the total number of cells in the sample and then multiplying by 100:

$$\frac{\text{number in a stage}}{\text{total sample number}} \times 100$$

Enter your calculated values in the data table.

9. Assuming that it takes about 24 h (1440 min) for onion root-tip cells to go through one full cell cycle, you can calculate the amount of time the cells spend in each phase from the percentage of the cells in that stage: percent of cells in a stage × 1440 min. Enter your calculated values in the data table.

10. Change back to lower power, and remove the slide. Turn off and unplug the microscope.

Analysis

1. What differences did you notice between the cells in the onion root tip and the cells farther away from the root tip? Consider

   a) the size of the cells   b) the shape of the cells

   c) the number of dividing cells

2. What differences did you notice between the onion root-tip cells and the whitefish embryo cells? Consider

   a) the size of the cells   b) the shape of the cells

   c) the arrangement of chromosomes in the cells

3. Draw a pie graph using the data you collected in steps 8 and 9.

4. Do you think that your observations and calculations in steps 7–9 are representative of the cell division taking place in the entire root? Explain your answer.

Conclusion

5. Prepare a table that compares and contrasts the events of the cell cycle in plant cells and animal cells.

Data table for determining timing of cell division

	Number of Cells				Percent of total counted	Time in each stage
	Field 1	Field 2	Field 3 (optional)	Total		
Interphase						
Prophase						
Metaphase						
Anaphase						
Telophase						
Total cells						

Regulation of the Cell Cycle

You know that mitosis and cell division govern the growth, repair, and maintenance of plant and animal tissues. In your own body, about 150 billion cell divisions take place each day. What would happen if the wrong cells were dividing?

For any organism to develop properly and to remain healthy, its cells must divide only at certain times and they must stop dividing at the correct time. This requires a delicate balance among many different regulatory signals. Within a cell, specific protein interactions serve as "start" or "stop" signals for cell division. External factors such as the presence of particular hormones, the availability of nutrients, and contact with other cells also play a role.

Anything that interferes with regulatory signals can cause the cell cycle to proceed at an uncontrolled rate. The group of diseases that are associated with uncontrolled, rapid cell division are known as **cancer**. Rather than spending much of their cell cycle as functioning tissue cells in interphase, cancerous cells move quickly from one cell division to the next. The result is a fast-growing mass of non-functional cells, called a *tumour*. In Chapter 18, you will learn more about some of the specific genetic events that can lead to cancer.

Applying Knowledge of Mitosis

Many of the studies of cell division have used tissues from non-human organisms, such as yeasts, frogs, and fruit flies. Because the processes of cell division are similar in all eukaryotes, these studies have applications for human cells as well. Many non-human tissues offer important advantages for laboratory investigations. The embryo cells of some species of frog, for example, are large enough that researchers can micro-inject proteins and other substances directly into the dividing cells to study the effects. In more recent years, the study of cell division has shifted to the roles of individual genes in triggering specific events. The fruit fly, *Drosophila melanogaster*, has proven to be a useful model organism for these studies because its genetic material contains counterparts to many of the human genes involved in regulating the cell cycle.

Since the first observations of dividing cells in the late 1800s, new microscopes and staining techniques have advanced our understanding of the cell cycle. For example, scientists can now tag individual protein molecules with fluorescent dyes to track the movements and reactions of proteins at different stages of the cell cycle. New types of light microscopes provide improved live images of cell division at work. These technologies have helped researchers learn more about the complex interactions of signals and processes that are involved in the cell cycle.

Section 16.2 Summary

- Mitosis involves a precise sequence of events.
- These events are grouped into four phases: prophase, metaphase, anaphase, and telophase.
- Each phase is defined by a particular arrangement of chromosomes within the dividing cell. Telophase is followed by cytokinesis.
- The cell cycle is carefully regulated by specific regulatory signals. Interference with these signals can result in uncontrolled cell division and the development of cancer.

| Section 16.2 | Review |

1. What three functions does mitosis serve in your body?

2. In which phase of mitosis does each of the following events occur?
   a) migration of sister chromatids to opposite poles
   b) condensation of chromatin into compact chromosomes
   c) formation of a nuclear membrane
   d) alignment of chromosomes along the cell equator

3. Sketch the four phases of mitosis. Include labels to explain what is happening in each phase.

4. What role does the spindle apparatus play in cell division?

5. Briefly explain the link between cell cycle regulation and cancer.

6. The scientists in a lab have isolated a substance that prevents cells from synthesizing microtubules. What impact would this substance have on cell division? Explain.

7. A scientist studying a group of somatic cells notices that upon the completion of the cell cycle half of the daughter cells have no chromosomes and the other half have 92 chromosomes. In what phase of mitosis did an error most likely occur? Explain your reasoning.

Regenerating the Sense of Hearing?

Nerve deafness, the most common form of hearing loss, is caused by damage or loss of hair cells in the inner ear. Until recently, scientists assumed that hearing loss due to nerve deafness was irreversible. Treatments to aid the hearing impaired, such as hearing aids and cochlear implants, are not designed to re-grow hair cells.

The discovery in 1986 that birds could regenerate hair cells in their ears after trauma—and thus could regain hearing—gives hope that deafness in humans can be reversed.

The organ of Corti is located in the cochlea of the inner ear and contains two types of cells: hair cells, and supporting cells, which nourish hair cells. Outer organ of Corti hair cells detect sound. In the innermost part of the organ of Corti, hair cells turn auditory input into an electrical signal, which is then sent to the brain via the auditory nerve.

In birds, remaining support cells receive a signal to divide into daughter cells by mitosis and cytokinesis after hair cells die. Brain-derived neurotrophic factor (BDNF) molecules that encourage the survival of nervous tissue are understood to promote this process in birds. After cell division, support daughter cells receive a signal to change into hair cells by transdifferentiation—a process whereby a non-stem cell develops into another kind of cell.

Initially, scientists doubted this kind of regeneration could occur in mammals. However, laboratory studies on pigs, mice, rats, guinea pigs, and humans have shown that when hair cells are destroyed, a small amount of support cells grew in the tissue of the inner ear. This offers hope that human hearing loss can one day be reversed, if the mechanism that causes support cells to grow into hair cells can be further manipulated.

One method that has been used to support cell regeneration involves the use of growth factors. These are hormone-like chemicals that control the growth of cells. Another method of support cell regeneration is gene therapy, which introduces specialized growth genes into the support cell through a specially made virus. The reasoning is that if a growth factor or gene therapy is successful, it will trigger cell division. Then, support cells will regenerate into hair cells and potentially restore hearing.

While progress so far is encouraging, barriers remain. Scientists are only beginning to identify and test growth factors that may play a role in regeneration. Furthermore, hair cells must "know" where and how much to grow. Cell growth must be controlled, since uncontrolled growth could result in tumors. Finally, for a hair cell to be useful, it must connect with the auditory nerve.

• • •

1. Research and describe three common causes of non-congenital (not present at birth) hearing impairment. What steps can you take to prevent hearing loss?

2. Retinoblastoma (Rb) is a protein that prevents cells from multiplying. Research with Rb with respect to support cell regeneration. How could an understanding of retinoblastoma contribute to a cure for nerve deafness?

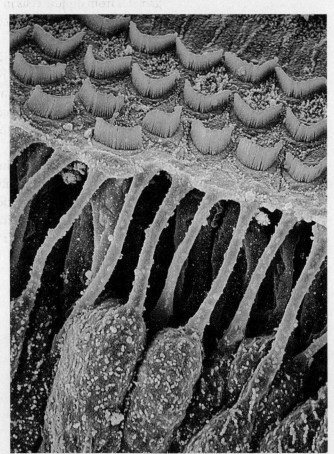

Magnification: 2905 ×

This colourized scanning electron micrograph of a healthy human inner ear shows hair cells (brownish-pink) and the feathery projections, called stereocilia (pink) at their ends. Unlike hair cells in some other animals, human hair cells are unable to regenerate naturally if they are damaged.

SECTION 16.3

The Formation of Gametes

Key Terms

meiosis
reduction division
recombination
meiosis I
meiosis II
germ cells
synapsis
tetrad
non-sister chromatids
crossing over
nondisjunction
spermatogenesis
oogenesis
spermatogonium
primary spermatocyte
secondary spermatocyte
spermatids
oogonium
primary oocyte
secondary oocyte
first polar body
second polar body

Figure 16.10 The union of two haploid gametes forms a diploid zygote. The zygote contains chromosomes from each parent. The chromosomes that are donated from the ovum are of *maternal origin* and those from the sperm cell are of *paternal origin*.

Each species has a unique set of genetic information in its chromosomes. When the somatic cells reproduce, the new cells have the same genetic information and the same number of chromosomes as the parent cells. During sexual reproduction, however, a gamete from the male organism and a gamete from the female organism fuse to create a new cell (see Figure 16.10). The resulting zygote has genetic information from both parents and the same number of chromosomes as its parents. For this to be possible, the gametes of an organism must contain half the number of chromosomes as the somatic cells of the organism.

The process that produces haploid gametes from diploid cells in the ovaries and testes is called **meiosis**. Meiosis has two key outcomes:

- **Reduction division**: Meiosis is sometimes referred to as a reduction division because it is a form of cell division that produces daughter cells with fewer chromosomes than the parent cells.
- **Recombination**: The products of meiosis have different combinations of genes. Genetic recombination gives rise to offspring that are genetically distinct from one another and their parents.

Q 20 Describe the two key outcomes of meiosis.

Q 21 In what ways does meiosis serve a different function than mitosis?

Q 22 Where does meiosis take place?

Phases of Meiosis

Like mitosis, meiosis involves a precise sequence of events that can be grouped into four distinct phases: prophase, metaphase, anaphase, and telophase. Meiosis, however, involves two complete rounds of these phases, called **meiosis I** and **meiosis II**. Refer to Figure 16.11 on page 564 as you read through the following descriptions of the phases.

Interphase

Like somatic cells, **germ cells** (gamete-producing cells) proceed through the growth and synthesis phases of interphase before dividing. Recall, from Section 16.1, that chromosomes are replicated during the S phase of interphase. This also occurs before a germ cell begins meiosis. At the start of meiosis, therefore, a germ cell contains duplicated chromosomes. Each chromosome is made up of a pair of identical sister chromatids held together at the centromere.

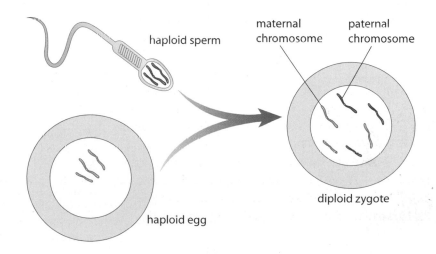

haploid sperm

maternal chromosome   paternal chromosome

diploid zygote

haploid egg

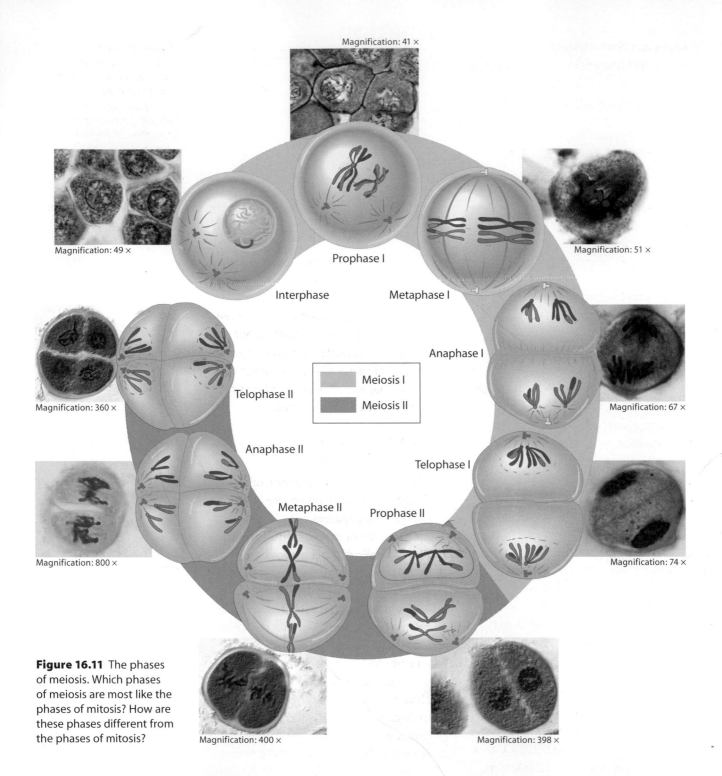

Magnification: 41 ×

Magnification: 49 ×

Magnification: 51 ×

Prophase I

Interphase   Metaphase I

Anaphase I

Magnification: 67 ×

Meiosis I

Meiosis II

Telophase II

Magnification: 360 ×

Anaphase II   Telophase I

Metaphase II   Prophase II

Magnification: 800 ×

Magnification: 74 ×

Figure 16.11 The phases of meiosis. Which phases of meiosis are most like the phases of mitosis? How are these phases different from the phases of mitosis?

Magnification: 400 ×

Magnification: 398 ×

Prophase I

In prophase I, each pair of homologous chromosomes align side by side. This aligning of homologous chromosomes is called **synapsis**. Recall that homologous chromosomes are not identical. Although they contain the same genes, the homologues carry different alleles of these genes. (You will learn more about alleles in Chapter 17.) At synapsis, homologous

chromosomes pair up. Because each consists of two chromatids, a pair of homologous chromosomes is made up of four chromatids and is called a **tetrad**.

As shown in Figure 16.12, each tetrad is made up of a pair of sister chromatids synapsed with another pair of sister chromatids. In the middle of a tetrad, two homologous but non-identical chromatids, which are called

non-sister chromatids, lie side by side. As you will find out later, this alignment of non-sister chromatids plays an important role in genetic recombination.

Metaphase I

Following prophase I, a spindle fibre attaches to the centromere of each chromosome. A spindle fibre from one pole attaches to one pair of sister chromatids in the tetrad, and a spindle fibre from the opposite pole attaches to the other pair of sister chromatids. The spindle fibres guide each tetrad to the equator of the cell. The chromosomes, however, do not line up in single file as they do in mitosis. Instead, they line up as homologous pairs. In each pair, one homologous chromosome is positioned on one side of the cell's equator, and the other homologous chromosome is positioned on the other side of the cell's equator.

Anaphase I

During anaphase I, the spindle fibres shorten. This causes the homologous chromosomes to separate from one another. The homologues move to opposite poles of the cell. Because the sister chromatids are still held together, the centromeres do not split as they do in mitosis. The result is that a single chromosome (made up of two sister chromatids) from each homologous pair moves to each pole of the cell.

Telophase I

Some cells move directly from anaphase I to meiosis II (described below). Other cells go through telophase I following anaphase I. In telophase I, the homologous chromosomes begin to uncoil and the spindle fibres disappear. The cytoplasm is divided, the nuclear membrane forms around each group of homologous chromosomes, and two cells are formed. Each of these new cells contains one set of sister chromatids and is now haploid. Chromosome replication *does not* take place before the next phase of meiosis.

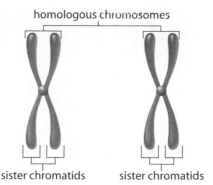

Meiosis II

The phases of meiosis II are similar to the phases of mitosis. Each cell proceeds through prophase II, metaphase II, anaphase II, and telophase II. Each cell that enters meiosis II is haploid but consists of replicated chromosomes. At the end of meiosis II, the daughter cells are still haploid, but they contain single unreplicated chromosomes.

Sources of Genetic Recombination

Mitosis results in the creation of daughter cells that are precise genetic copies of their parent cells. In contrast, the outcome of meiosis is the formation of genetically distinct haploid gametes. What processes create new combinations of genetic material in meiosis?

Remember that each diploid germ cell has two copies of each chromosome. One copy of this homologous pair was contributed by the female gamete (egg), so it is of maternal origin. The other chromosome was contributed by the male gamete (sperm), so it is of paternal origin. During meiosis, genetic variation is ensured in two ways: by the creation of gametes that carry different combinations of maternal and paternal chromosomes, and by the exchange of genetic material between maternal and paternal chromosomes.

Independent Assortment

During metaphase I, chromosomes are arranged in homologous pairs along the equator of the cell. In each pair, the chromosome of maternal origin is

Figure 16.12 A chromosome tetrad is made up of two pairs of non-sister chromatids arranged side by side. Homologous chromosomes carry the same genes at the same locations, but may carry different alleles of these genes. Sister chromatids, in contrast, are identical to each other.

BiologyFile

FYI
In early studies of meiosis, crossing over during meiosis was considered to be an "error." Scientists now know that it is a common event and an important contributor to genetic diversity.

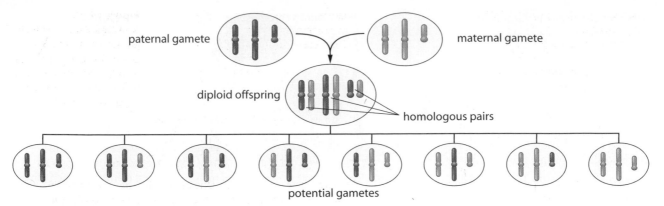

paternal gamete   maternal gamete

diploid offspring   homologous pairs

potential gametes

Figure 16.13 The diploid offspring has three chromosome pairs. The potential combinations of chromosomes produce eight genetically different gametes. A cell that has seven chromosome pairs can give rise to 2^7 or 128 different gametes.

oriented toward one pole of the cell while the chromosome of paternal origin is oriented toward the other pole. This orientation of each pair of homologous chromosomes is independent of the orientation of the other pairs. Therefore, some maternal homologues and some paternal homologues face each pole of the cell. As shown in Figure 16.13, the resulting gametes have different combinations of parental chromosomes.

Crossing Over

You have seen that homologous chromosomes synapse, or pair up, during prophase I. While they are lined up side by side, non-sister chromatids may exchange pieces of chromosome in a process known as **crossing over**. The process of crossing over is illustrated in Figure 16.14.

A section of chromosome that is crossed over may contain hundreds or even thousands of genes. As a result of crossing over, individual chromosomes contain some genes of maternal origin and some genes of paternal origin. Although only one example of crossing over is shown in Figure 16.14A, crossing over can occur at several points along non-sister chromatids, as shown in Figure 16.14B.

• • •

23 Describe the phases of meiosis I and meiosis II.

24 How is the outcome of meiosis different from the outcome of mitosis?

25 Distinguish independent assortment from crossing over.

• • •

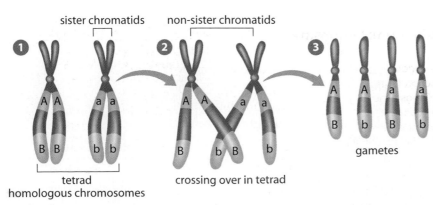

sister chromatids   non-sister chromatids

tetrad
homologous chromosomes

crossing over in tetrad

gametes

Figure 16.14 (A) Crossing over occurs at random between pairs of homologous chromosomes. In these chromosomes, upper-case and lower-case letters denote different alleles, or different versions of the same gene. **(1)** During prophase, homologous chromosomes form pairs. **(2)** Non-sister chromatids cross over each other and exchange segments of chromosomes. As a result, chromosomes in the gametes **(3)** contain new combinations of genetic material.

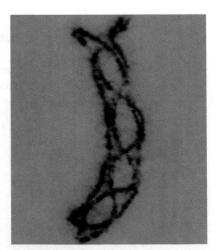

Figure 16.14 (B) Crossing over between non-sister chromatids can occur at several points simultaneously.

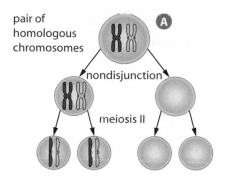

Figure 16.15
Nondisjunction results in gametes with too many or too few chromosomes. Nondisjunction may take place during anaphase I **(A)** or anaphase II **(B)**.

pair of homologous chromosomes

nondisjunction

meiosis II

Abnormal gametes: two gametes have one extra and two gametes have one fewer chromosome than normal.

pair of homologous chromosomes

normal meiosis I

normal meiosis II

nondisjunction

Gametes have usual number of chromosomes.

One gamete has one extra and the other has one fewer chromosome.

Nondisjunction

Sometimes chromosomes or chromatids do not separate as they should during meiosis. This phenomenon is called **nondisjunction**. Nondisjunction occurs in anaphase I and II of meiosis.

- In anaphase I, nondisjunction occurs when homologous chromosome pairs do not separate to opposite poles; instead, one entire pair is pulled toward the same pole together.
- In anaphase II, nondisjunction occurs when sister chromatids do not separate to opposite poles; instead, both sister chromatids are pulled toward the same pole together.

As a result, nondisjunction produces gametes that have either too few or too many chromosomes (see Figure 16.15).

When one chromosome is lost due to nondisjunction, it is called *monosomy*. In this case, the gamete is missing one chromosome of a homologous pair. For example, individuals with Turner syndrome are missing an X chromosome. Individuals who have this disorder have female sexual characteristics which are underdeveloped.

Conversely, nondisjunction can also result in *trisomy*—the gain of an extra chromosome. Trisomy occurs in Down syndrome, a condition in which individuals are born with an extra chromosome 21. The characteristics of Down syndrome include impairment of physical growth, below-average cognitive ability, and the development of certain physical features such as almond-shaped eyes and an enlarged tongue. Infants with Down syndrome are also more likely to have congenital (present at birth) heart defects. The incidence of nondisjunction increases with age. For example, the chance of conceiving a child

BiologyFile

Try This
Down syndrome results from nondisjunction of chromosome 21. Use Figure 16.15 to determine the ways in which trisomy could occur in a zygote.

Thought Lab | **16.1** | **Nondisjunction Syndromes**

Target Skills

Working co-operatively for a presentation of nondisjunction syndromes

The table shows the chromosomal basis for various syndromes (disorders) involving nondisjunction. Most of these are rare in the human population. Choose one syndrome that you have not read about and conduct research about it using the library or the Internet. Present your findings in a print or electronic multimedia format. **ICT**

Analysis

1. What is the frequency of the syndrome you studied?

2. How does the syndrome occur?

3. Describe the technologies that are used to diagnose the syndrome. What, if any, treatments are there? What is involved in the treatment?

Syndrome	Sex	Chromosomes
Down	M or F	trisomy 21
Patau	M or F	trisomy 13
Edward	M or F	trisomy 18
Turner	F	XO
Triplo-X	F	XXX (or XXXX)
Klinefelter	M	XXY (or XXXY)
Jacobs	M	XYY

with Down syndrome is 1 in 1490 between ages 20 to 24 and increases to 1 in 106 at age 40. At age 49, the chance increases to about 1 in 11.

• • •

 Describe nondisjunction, and outline the difference between monosomy and trisomy.

• • •

Gamete Formation in Animals

The products of meiosis are haploid gametes. In many organisms, the gametes are sperm and eggs. The process of sperm production is called **spermatogenesis**, and the process of egg production is called **oogenesis**. While both of these processes involve meiosis, they take place in slightly different ways, as illustrated in Figure 16.16.

INVESTIGATION | 16.C

Modelling to Compare Meiosis and Mitosis

You have seen that meiosis and mitosis have many similarities. They also have important differences. In this investigation, you will create a model of a cell that undergoes mitosis and meiosis. Then you will use your model to describe the different phases of each type of cell division.

Problem

How can you design a model to show a cell that is undergoing mitosis and meiosis?

Design Specifications

1. Work in a small group. With your group, examine the following design specifications:

   • You are modelling a germ cell from the testes of a male diploid organism. The haploid number of chromosomes in this organism is 4 (that is, $2n = 8$).

   • Your model must be able represent the changes that take place in the germ cell and in its chromosomes as it divides to produce two identical germ cells, one of which then divides to produce four non-identical gametes.

   • Your model must be able to represent at least one mechanism that ensures genetic variation among the gametes.

Plan and Construct

1. Brainstorm options for a model that meets the design specifications. Be creative—for example, your group could build a clay model, create a computer simulation, or perform a play. Make a list of your ideas, and decide on the model you will use.

2. Design your model.

3. Prepare an assessment plan for your model. That is, how will you know if your model is successful at meeting the design specifications? What features will make it a useful model for explaining cell division?

4. Review your model design and assessment plan with your teacher. Then assemble the materials you will need, and create your model.

5. Present your model to your class.

Evaluate and Communicate

1. Using the assessment plan you prepared, evaluate your model and presentation. How effectively do you think your model and presentation described mitosis and meiosis?

2. Evaluate the presentations by other groups in your class. What are the features of the most effective models?

3. After seeing all the presentations, what changes (if any) would you make to your own model? Explain your reasons.

4. In what ways are the outcomes of meiosis suited to the production of gametes, but not to the purposes of the cell cycle? Explain your answer using your model as a reference. How is mitosis better suited for these purposes?

Spermatogenesis

In most male animals, meiosis takes place in the testes. As you can see from Figure 16.16, the process of spermatogenesis starts with a diploid germ cell called a **spermatogonium**. Beginning at puberty, spermatogonia are stimulated to divide by mitosis to form two daughter cells. One of these cells replenishes the spermatogonia cell population, and the other develops into a **primary spermatocyte**. The primary spermatocyte undergoes meiosis I to form two **secondary spermatocytes**. The secondary spermatocytes then undergo meiosis II to form four **spermatids**.

Following meiosis II, the spermatids go through a final set of developmental stages in order to develop into mature sperm. The nucleus and certain enzymes are organized into a "head" region. The midsection holds many mitochondria, which serve as an energy resource for the cell. Finally, a long tail-like flagellum develops for locomotion.

Some animals, including most mammals, produce sperm throughout the year. Other animals produce sperm only during a specific breeding season. Hundreds of millions of sperm are released in a single ejaculation, so meiosis is constantly occurring. Mitosis is also occurring regularly to keep a supply of germ cells for gamete production.

Oogenesis

In female animals, meiosis takes place in the ovaries. As shown in Figure 16.16, oogenesis starts with a diploid germ cell called an **oogonium**. Each oogonium undergoes mitosis to form two primary oocytes. About three months after conception, two million primary oocytes can be found in the ovaries. They are arrested in prophase I and remain that way until puberty. Every month after puberty, one **primary oocyte** undergoes meiosis. In contrast to spermatogenesis, however, oogenesis involves an unequal division of cytoplasm, known as

Figure 16.16 The processes of spermatogenesis and oogenesis in mammals. This illustration is not drawn to scale. In reality, the diameter of the egg is about 20 times greater than the length of the sperm head.

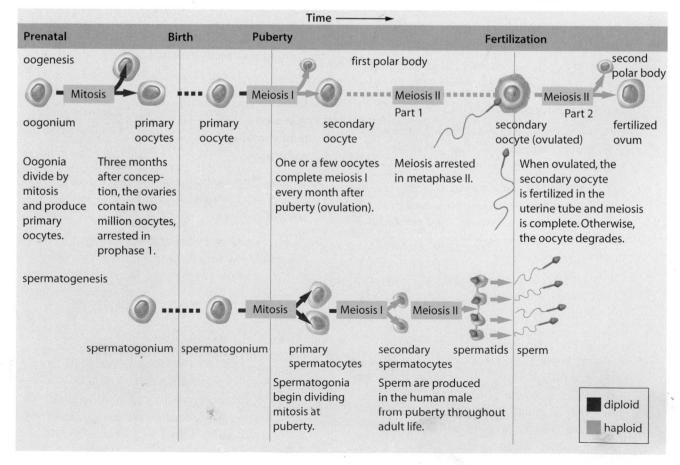

asymmetrical cytokinesis. At the end of meiosis I, the cytoplasm is not equally divided between the two daughter cells. The cell that receives most of the cytoplasm is called the **secondary oocyte**. The other cell is called the **first polar body**. The first polar body may or may not go through a second division to produce a pair of second polar bodies. In either case, the polar bodies are not functional and soon degenerate.

When the secondary oocyte undergoes meiosis II, the cytoplasm is again unequally divided. The cell that contains most of the cytoplasm will eventually become a mature egg, or ovum. The other cell, another **second polar body**, is not a viable gamete.

The unequal division of cytoplasm means that only one egg cell is produced from the division of the secondary oocyte. This egg cell, however, contains a large quantity of nutrients that the zygote can use prior to implantation.

The processes of meiosis I and meiosis II are not always continuous. In human females, more than a decade separates the events of meiosis I and meiosis II. The primary oocytes begin meiosis I before birth, but cell division stalls in prophase I. The cells remain in this suspended state until puberty. At puberty, a hormone signal triggers a single primary oocyte to resume meiosis. The primary oocyte completes meiosis I. The secondary oocyte is then released from the ovary and travels down the Fallopian tube.

The secondary oocyte is arrested at metaphase II until fertilization occurs. If the secondary oocyte does not come into contact with a sperm cell, it will not complete a second meiotic division. If it does come into contact with a sperm cell and fertilization occurs, it will complete meiosis II. The product of this second meiotic division is the ovum, or egg cell, and a second polar body. The haploid nucleus of the egg cell then fuses with the haploid nucleus of the sperm cell to complete fertilization and create a diploid zygote.

As you know from your study of the menstrual cycle (see Chapter 14), in most cases only one primary oocyte undergoes this process each month. The production of egg cells continues at a rate of about one per month from the start of puberty until menopause, which usually occurs between 40 and 50 years of age. Thus, a human female will produce about 400 gametes in her lifetime.

• • •

27 Identify key similarities and differences between spermatogenesis and oogenesis.

28 How does the process of asymmetrical cytokinesis help to ensure a healthy zygote?

29 How does the timing of spermatogenesis differ from the timing of oogenesis? In what way is the timing of these processes suited to their functions?

• • •

Cell Division and the Conception of Twins

As you know, the fusion of one ovum and one sperm creates a single zygote. Sometimes, however, a woman gives birth to more than one baby at once. In humans, twins occur in slightly more than one percent of all births. As you can see in Figure 16.17, *fraternal twins* are no more alike than any other siblings, while *identical twins* are genetically identical to one another (but not to either parent).

While most women release only a single secondary oocyte at each ovulation, occasionally more than one secondary oocyte may be released. If both of these oocytes are fertilized and successfully implant in the uterus, fraternal twins may be born. On the other hand, if a single zygote or blastocyst divides into two separate bodies in the first few days of embryonic development, identical twins may be

Figure 16.17 Fraternal twins **(A)** and identical twins **(B)**

born. About 30 percent of all human twins are identical.

30 Explain how the development of fraternal twins is different from the development of identical twins.

Applying Knowledge of Meiosis

An understanding of meiosis is clearly important to the study of reproduction and development. As shown in Figure 16.18, cell biologists can put their understanding of meiosis to work in the field—literally.

Animal cells do not usually survive if they contain extra chromosomes. In contrast, polyploidy is common in plants. Polyploid plants often produce larger flowers or fruit than their diploid counterparts do. As well, they may have other commercially valuable features, such as the "seedless" fruit of the watermelon shown in Figure 16.18.

An ordinary watermelon (*Citrullis lanatus*) is diploid (2*n*), and its gametes are haploid (*n*). Using chemicals that cause nondisjunction, biologists can create tetraploid (4*n*) watermelons, which produce diploid (2*n*) gametes. A cross between a 4*n* watermelon and a 2*n* watermelon produces a triploid (3*n*)

watermelon zygote. This zygote divides by mitosis to form an adult watermelon plant. The 3*n* plant develops fruit, but the extra pair of homologous chromosomes means that the required synapsis of homologous chromosomes cannot take place at metaphase I. Meiosis does not proceed, so the watermelon does not create viable seeds.

Section 16.3 Summary

- The process of meiosis involves two nuclear divisions, which create haploid gametes from diploid parent cells.

Figure 16.18 If a watermelon plant does not complete meiosis, it will produce only rudimentary seeds. "Seedless" fruit, such as this watermelon, are popular consumer products. In what other ways could scientists apply their understanding of meiosis?

- Two key features of meiosis contribute to genetic variation: (1) The pairing of homologous chromosomes allows for crossing over, which results in the exchange of chromosome sections between non-sister chromatids. (2) The independent assortment of homologous chromosomes during metaphase I results in gametes that have different combinations of parental chromosomes.

- Nondisjunction occurs when chromosomes fail to separate correctly during one of the anaphase divisions of meiosis.
- Different meiotic processes result in the production of human sperm and eggs.
- An understanding of meiosis can be applied to develop modified forms of living organisms with useful attributes.

Section 16.3 | Review

1. What two main functions does meiosis accomplish?

2. Where does meiosis take place?

3. At the end of meiosis II, how many haploid cells have been formed from the original parent cell?

4. A diploid organism has four pairs of chromosomes in each somatic cell. Assuming that no crossing over occurs, how many genetically distinct gametes can this organism produce?

5. Explain what you think is happening in the following image. Why is this significant?

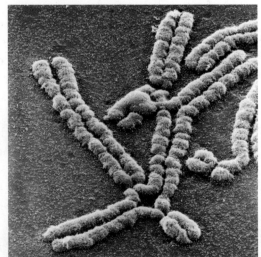

Magnification: 5187 ×

6. Compare and contrast the two terms in each pair of terms.

   a) nondisjunction and crossing over

   b) primary oocyte and secondary oocyte

   c) spermatid and sperm cell

   d) oocyte and polar body

7. A human germ cell in interphase has 23 pairs of chromosomes. If this cell undergoes cell division, how many chromosomes are found in each of the following phases? Indicate whether the chromosomes are found as linked sister chromatids, single chromatids, or homologous pairs.

   a) metaphase (mitosis)

   b) metaphase I (meiosis)

   c) metaphase II (meiosis)

8. Is it possible for identical twins to be different sexes? Explain in terms of the cellular processes that result in identical twins.

9. In what stage of meiosis do chromosome tetrads align at the cell equator? What feature of this alignment contributes to genetic diversity?

10. The karyotype of a young woman shows that she is missing one X chromosome. Draw or describe the sequence of events that made this occur.

Reproductive Strategies

Section Outcomes

In this section, you will
- **describe** the diversity of reproductive strategies among living organisms
- **evaluate** the advantages and disadvantages of sexual and asexual reproduction
- **research** and **present** information about contrasting reproductive strategies
- **assess** how research on plant and animal reproduction has affected the development of new reproductive technologies

Key Terms

asexual reproduction
sexual reproduction
binary fission
conjugation
pilus
budding
vegetative reproduction
fragmentation
parthenogenesis
spore
alternation of generations
sporophyte
gametophyte

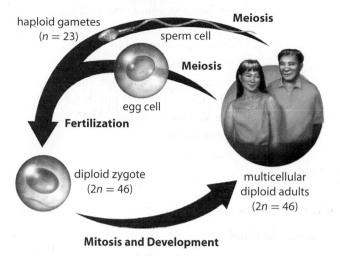

Figure 16.19 The human life cycle is based on a regular pattern of meiosis and mitosis.

In the preceding sections, you learned how mitosis and meiosis work as separate processes in individual cells. In this section, you will learn how these two forms of cell division operate within the life cycle of different organisms. In general, mitosis is the key mechanism involved in **asexual reproduction**, the reproductive process in which a parent organism produces genetically identical offspring. **Sexual reproduction** involves the production of gametes by meiosis, followed by fertilization between genetically distinct parental gametes to produce genetically distinct offspring.

The life cycle of many organisms includes a regular sequence of both forms of cell division. Figure 16.19 illustrates how mitosis and meiosis alternate in the human life cycle. Humans can only reproduce sexually, and the diploid individual is the only life stage that has the capacity for independent existence. While most animals have a similar life cycle, other organisms have a wide variety of life cycles.

• • •

31 Distinguish asexual reproduction from sexual reproduction.

• • •

Reproduction in Prokaryotes

Like a human somatic cell, a bacterial cell reproduces by replicating its DNA and then distributing one complete copy of its DNA into each of two identical daughter cells. Bacteria and other prokaryotes, however, have a single, circular chromosome and no nucleus. Therefore, a bacterial cell does not undergo mitosis. Instead, it reproduces through a form of cell division called **binary fission**. The stages of binary fission are illustrated in Figure 16.20.

In favourable conditions, a bacterial cell can divide in as little as 20 min. Each new cell can then grow and produce two more cells 20 min later. This sequence of repeated doubling is called *exponential growth*. It allows bacteria to produce huge populations in a fairly short time. However, these populations are genetically identical. If one cell is vulnerable to a particular toxin or virus, then every cell in the colony will also be vulnerable to the same toxin or virus.

Some bacteria are able to reproduce by a process called **conjugation**. Conjugation involves the transfer of genetic material from one cell to another by cell-to-cell contact through a bridging structure called a **pilus** (plural: pili), as shown in Figure 16.21.

Figure 16.20 Binary fission in a bacterial cell. Binary fission begins with the attachment of the circular bacterial chromosome to the cell wall. As the chromosome replicates, the new chromosome also attaches to the cell wall. The elongation of the cell and the formation of a septum then separates the two chromosomes. Cell division results in two genetically identical daughter cells.

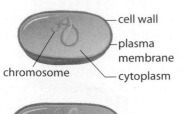
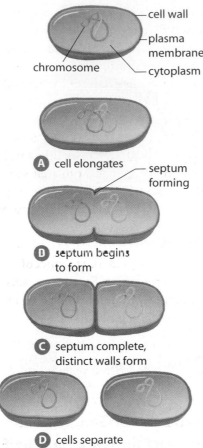

cell wall
plasma membrane
cytoplasm
chromosome

A cell elongates

septum forming

B septum begins to form

C septum complete, distinct walls form

D cells separate

Conjugation creates cells with new genetic combinations, and thereby provides a chance that some cells may be better adapted to changing conditions. It can only take place between non-identical bacterial cells, however. It creates only a single genetically unique daughter cell, but this new cell can undergo binary fission to create a colony of cells. Later, you will see how the processes of genetic recombination and reproduction in bacteria can be used as a tool in genetic engineering.

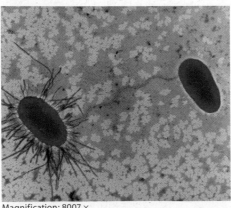

Figure 16.21 During conjugation, one bacterium transfers all or part of its chromosome to another bacterium. The receiving bacterium then undergoes binary fission. Some eukaryotes, including certain algae and fungi, are also capable of conjugation.

Magnification: 8007 ×

Figure 16.22 This *Hydra* is reproducing by budding. The species can also reproduce sexually.

32 In what ways does the asexual reproduction of prokaryotic cells differ from mitosis?

33 In what ways does conjugation differ from sexual reproduction?

Asexual Reproduction

Some organisms can reproduce asexually by budding. **Budding** is a form of asexual reproduction in which a complete but miniature version of the parent grows out from the parent's body. The new organism then separates to become an independent organism. Figure 16.22 shows an example of budding in *Hydra*.

A similar form of asexual reproduction, called **vegetative reproduction**, takes place in many plants. For example, strawberry plants can spread across a garden by extending thin creeping stems. A new strawberry plant develops at the end of each stem. Once the new plant has taken root, the stem disintegrates, separating the new plant from its parent.

Another form of asexual reproduction involves the creation of new plants from a fragment (portion) of a parent plant. This process is called **fragmentation**. In the cultivation of potatoes, for example, entire new plants are grown from a fragment, or tuber, of a parent plant. Gardeners rely on fragmentation to propagate new garden plants from cuttings (see Figure 16.23).

Figure 16.23 In many plant species, even a small fragment of a leaf can develop roots and grow into a complete new plant.

• • •

34 Describe two ways that plants can reproduce asexually.

• • •

Parthenogenesis

Asexual reproduction is less common in animals than in plants. Many animals, however, are capable of some forms of asexual reproduction. Some animals, such as sea stars, can reproduce by fragmentation. Other animals can reproduce through **parthenogenesis**, a form of asexual reproduction in which an unfertilized egg develops into an adult. In honeybees, for example, the queen bee lays both fertilized and unfertilized eggs. The fertilized eggs develop into female worker bees, while the unfertilized eggs develop into male drones. The whiptail lizard (*Cnemidophorus neomexicanus*), is another animal that reproduces by parthenogenesis.

• • •

35 Why is parthenogenesis a form of asexual reproduction?

• • •

Spores

Many forms of asexual reproduction require that the offspring develop close to or in contact with the parent. While this enables the offspring to take advantage of a favourable environment, it limits the organism's ability to spread quickly to more distant environments. Several different species have evolved a mechanism to reproduce asexually and disperse their offspring long distances. A **spore** is a structure that contains genetic material and cytoplasm surrounded by a protective sheath or wall. The wall protects the contents until conditions are favourable, at which point the spore wall opens and the organism begins to develop. Because spores tend to be very small, they are readily dispersed in water and by the wind (see Figure 16.24).

Spores may be haploid or diploid, and not all spores are the product of asexual reproduction. Some organisms produce spores by meiosis, resulting in an alternation of generations.

• • •

36 What are spores?

• • •

Alternation of Generations

Imagine what the world might be like if humans gave birth to sperm and eggs, which then grew up and had lives of their own before mating to create a new diploid baby. Something much like this is happening in fields, forests, and gardens all around you. The life cycle of plants consists of two generations: a haploid generation and a diploid generation that alternate. This is called **alternation of generations**. Figure 16.25 illustrates the

Figure 16.24 The spores released by this puffball mushroom can be carried long distances by the wind.

BiologyFile

Web Link
Some species of reptiles, amphibians, and fish are able to reproduce naturally by parthenogenesis. As well, biologists can induce parthenogenesis in some species, including some mammals. What new fields of research have opened up as a result of research on parthenogenesis? Which field do you think is the most interesting?

www.albertabiology.ca
WWW

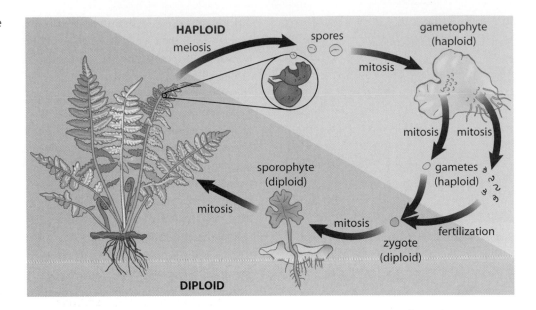

Figure 16.25 The life cycle of a fern, like all plants, consists of the alternation of generations of diploid sporophytes and haploid gametophytes.

basic components of the alternation of generations.

The diploid generation of a plant is called the **sporophyte** (spore-making body). Through the process of meiosis, the sporophyte produces one or more haploid spores. These spores develop without fertilization. Each haploid spore grows into a plant body called the **gametophyte** (gamete-making body). Gametophytes produce male and female gametes, which fuse at fertilization and develop into another sporophyte. The cycle then repeats.

Although all plant life cycles include a sporophyte generation and a gametophyte generation, one generation or the other is characteristically dominant in different plant groups. The non-dominant generation is often either a temporary structure or a much smaller component attached to the dominant generation. As described below, the dominant generation in vascular plants (plants that have a transport system of conducting tubes) is the diploid sporophyte. The dominant generation in non-vascular plants, such as mosses, is the haploid gametophyte.

Mosses

The alternation of generations is easy to observe in mosses (Figure 16.26). The leafy green mat that is characteristic of mosses is the gametophyte. At certain times of the year, a stalk grows up from this mat. This stalk is the sporophyte, and spores are cast from its cap. These spores fall on the ground and develop into the leafy gametophyte. Special structures within the gametophyte produce sperm and eggs. The sperm swim to the eggs and fertilize them. Each fertilized egg then develops into a new stalk. Because the sperm must swim to the eggs, mosses can only grow in environments that are moist for at least part of the year.

Conifers

In conifers, such as a pine tree (*Pinus* sp.), the tree itself is the diploid sporophyte (Figure 16.27 on page 578). The haploid gametophyes are microscopic structures within the male and female cones that are produced by the tree. The single-celled female gametophyte develops from a spore that is produced by a specialized structure at the top of each scale of the female cone. (The female cone is the larger, woody cone that most people think of as the pine cone.) The female gametophyte remains inside the spore-producing structure.

The male gametophyte is produced by a structure that is found on the male cone. (The male cone is much smaller than the female cone.) The male gametophyte is released in the pollen that is cast by the male cones. The pollen is dispersed by the wind. If the pollen reaches a female cone, sperm from the gametophyte will grow and fertilize the egg within the female gametophyte. The fertilized zygote forms a seed that is attached to the scale of the female cone.

Alternation in Sexual Cycles

Strictly speaking, the term "alternation of generations" refers to the alternation of diploid and haploid generations. This reproductive strategy is found only in plants. Some animal life cycles, however, alternate between asexually-reproducing and sexually-reproducing phases. For example, the phylum Cnidaria includes jellyfish, sea anemones, and corals. Most of the animals in this phylum alternate reproductive phases. The life cycle of

these organisms is characterized by two distinct adult forms: a non-motile *polyp* and a free-swimming *medusa*. The characteristic cnidarian life cycle is illustrated in Figure 16.28.

The cnidarian life cycle varies from species to species within this class. In jellyfish, the medusa stage is dominant or exclusive. In sea anemones, the polyp stage is dominant or exclusive. The species *Obelia* alternates regularly between an asexual polyp form and a sexual medusa form.

• • •

37 What is the difference between the alternation of generations and the alternation of reproductive cycles?

• • •

Figure 16.26 The life cycle of moss. The moss gametophyte produces gametes that join to form a zygote. The zygote develops into the sporophyte that produces spores. Spores can germinate and grow into a gametophyte, completing the life cycle.

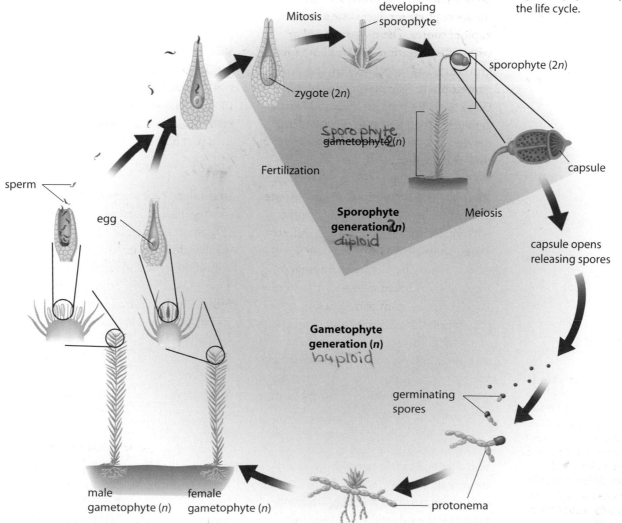

Mitosis
developing sporophyte
zygote (2n)
sporophyte (2n)
Sporophyte gametophyte (n)
Fertilization
capsule
sperm
Sporophyte generation (n)
diploid
Meiosis
capsule opens releasing spores
egg
Gametophyte generation (n)
haploid
germinating spores
male gametophyte (n)
female gametophyte (n)
protonema

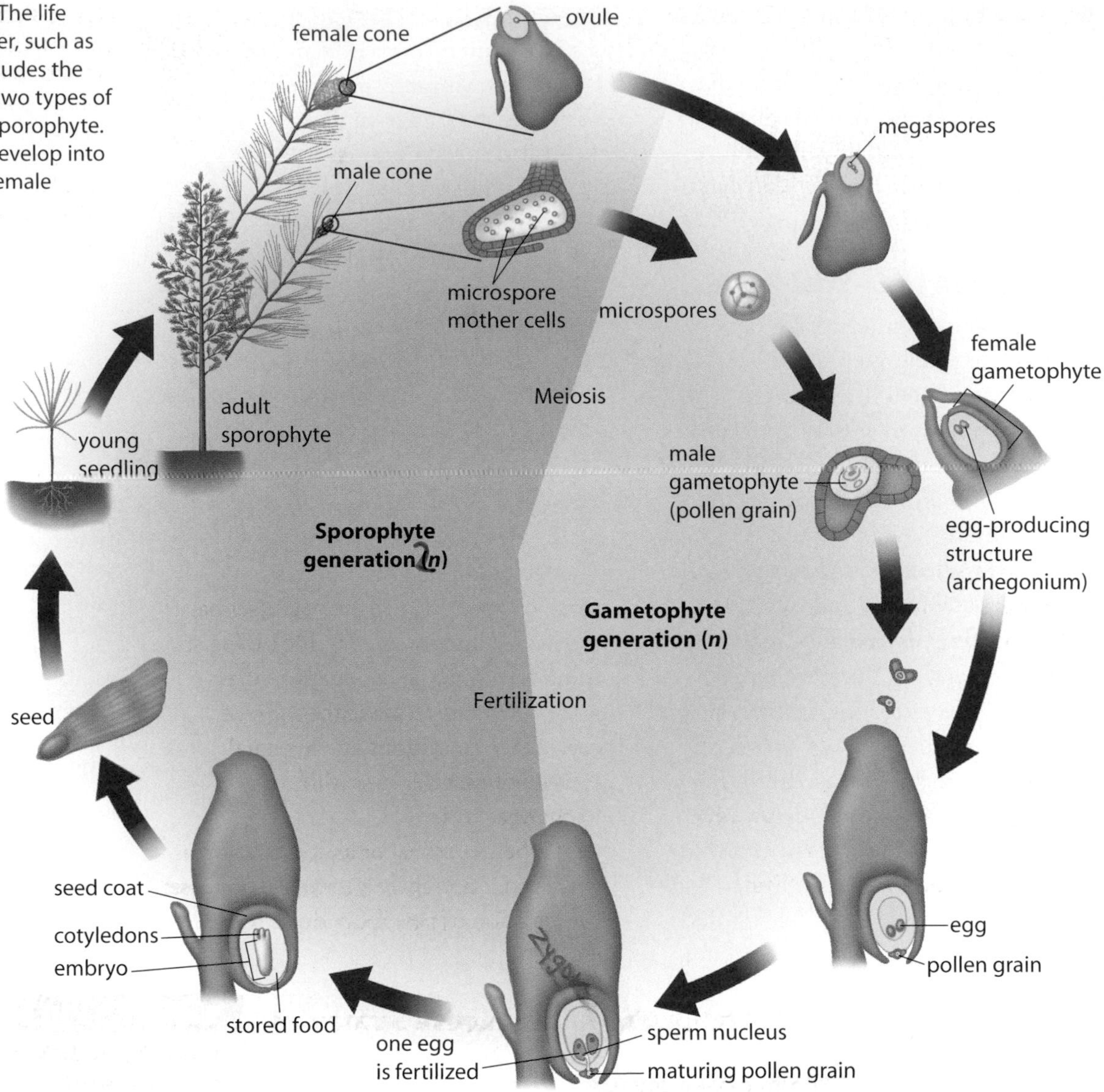

Figure 16.27 The life cycle of a conifer, such as a pine tree, includes the production of two types of spores by the sporophyte. These spores develop into the male and female gametophytes.

female cone — ovule
megaspores
male cone
microspore mother cells
microspores
female gametophyte
Meiosis
male gametophyte (pollen grain)
egg-producing structure (archegonium)
adult sporophyte
young seedling
Sporophyte generation (n)
Gametophyte generation (n)
Fertilization
seed
egg
pollen grain
seed coat
cotyledons
embryo
stored food
one egg is fertilized
sperm nucleus
maturing pollen grain

Advantages and Disadvantages of Reproductive Strategies

Almost all organisms are capable of some form of sexual reproduction. There is no consensus among evolutionary biologists, however, on how sexual reproduction first arose. While sexual reproduction offers an opportunity for genetic variation, this variation may not always be helpful to a well-adapted organism. If an organism is well-suited to its environment, there is always the possibility that offspring with new characteristics may, in fact, be less well-adapted to this environment than its parents are.

There are three potential advantages of sexual reproduction:

- Sexual reproduction offers a population a way to adapt to a changing environment. At least some offspring, for example, may have a greater ability to resist parasites or toxins in the environment or to take advantage of new food sources.
- Competition among siblings may be reduced if they are genetically diverse.
- Pairing of homologous chromosomes and crossing over offer opportunities to replace or repair damaged chromosomes.

Asexual reproduction also offers certain advantages:

- Asexual reproduction often proceeds more quickly than sexual reproduction, and it does not require the presence of a second parent organism.

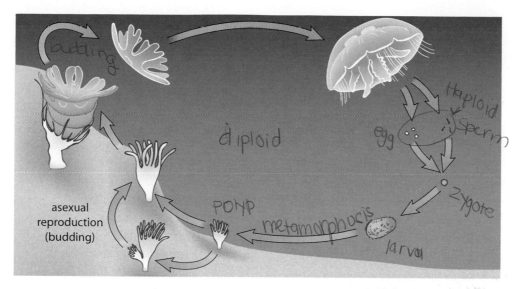

Figure 16.28 A generalized representation of the cnidarian life cycle. Not all cnidarians alternate adult forms like this, but most cnidarians can reproduce both sexually and asexually.

(handwritten labels on figure: budding, Haploid, egg, sperm, diploid, zygote, POLYP, metamorphosis, larva)

asexual reproduction (budding)

- Asexual reproduction usually requires less energy than sexual reproduction.
- Many forms of asexual reproduction, such as vegetative reproduction and budding, help to maximize the chances that individual offspring will survive. In these forms of asexual reproduction, the daughter organism does not fully separate from the parent until it is capable of independent survival.

Do organisms that alternate generations or reproductive phases have the best of both worlds? Some biologists think so. Asexual reproduction offers an opportunity to make the most of favourable conditions, while sexual reproduction offers a way to adapt to change.

Whether sexual or asexual, all forms of reproduction share a common purpose: the addition of new individuals to a

---

Thought Lab | 16.2 | Comparing Reproductive Strategies

Target Skills

Researching reproductive strategies in a variety of organisms

Presenting research results in a suitable form (such as a chart, table, or diagrams)

As you have seen, there are many different forms of reproduction. In this Thought Lab, you will create a table or another form of concept organizer to describe, analyze, and communicate the advantages and disadvantages of two different strategies.

Procedure

1. In small groups, select two organisms that have different forms of reproduction. You can select two organisms described in this textbook, or use a library or the Internet to select two organisms.

2. Write brief descriptions or draw simple diagrams to illustrate the life cycles of these organisms. Then brainstorm a list of potential advantages and disadvantages of each strategy. Try to think of the advantages and disadvantages for an individual organism and for the population as a whole.

3. Prepare a table or another form of concept organizer to present your findings.

4. Summarize your findings in a brief concluding statement. Then present your concluding statement to the class.

Analysis

1. Did all groups come to similar conclusions? How could you account for any differences?

2. Is there one reproductive strategy that is clearly better than the others? Explain your answer.

3. Suppose that you wanted to create a new species (plant or animal) that would live in your classroom.

   a) What form of reproduction would you choose for your species?

   b) Prepare a description or illustration that shows how the life cycle of your species works. Make sure that this life cycle can carry on over time.

   c) Explain how the form of reproduction you chose would benefit your organism, given the environment in which it will exist.

population. Each of these new individuals carries a set of genetic instructions that determines how members of the species will grow and develop. This set of instructions is passed from one generation to the next in an unbroken line that extends back to the origins of life on Earth. In the next chapter, you will study the patterns of inheritance that maintain the continuity of life.

Section 16.4 Summary

- Prokaryotes reproduce through a form of cell division called binary fission.
- Asexual reproduction is the creation of offspring through the mitosis. Examples of asexual reproduction include budding, fragmentation, and parthenogenesis.
- Offspring that arise from asexual reproduction are genetically identical to the parent organism.
- Conjugation in bacteria produces organisms with new genetic combinations.
- Sexual reproduction involves meiosis to create haploid gametes, followed by fertilization to produce a new and genetically unique diploid organism.
- Many organisms are capable of both sexual and asexual reproduction.
- Plants reproduce vegetatively and have a sexual life cycle that features the alternation of haploid and diploid generations.
- Some animals are capable of both asexual and sexual reproduction, and may shift strategies in response to changing environmental conditions.
- Sexual reproduction and asexual reproduction have different advantages and disadvantages. One of the key advantages of sexual reproduction is the creation of genetic variation.

Section 16.4   Review

1. Give two examples of different forms of asexual reproduction.

2. What form of reproduction is shown in the following image? In what kind of organism would you expect to see this form of reproduction?

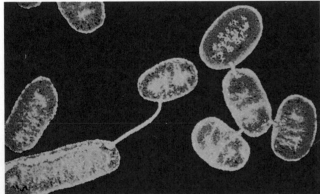

Magnification: 14700 ×

3. In what way is fragmentation similar to budding? In what way are the two forms of reproduction different?

4. In one species of fish, the females lay eggs that are not fertilized. The eggs hatch and develop into adult fish.

    a) What is the name of this form of reproduction?

    b) What proportion of the offspring are likely to be male? Explain.

5. Draw a diagram that illustrates the life cycle of a mammal. Use the following terms to label your diagram: haploid phase, diploid phase, meiosis, mitosis, fertilization, zygote. (You may need to use some of these terms more than once.)

6. How are the life cycle of a moss and the life cycle of a pine tree similar? How are they different?

7. What reproductive advantage does a spore offer over vegetative reproduction?

8. Briefly explain two advantages and two disadvantages of a life cycle that requires sexual reproduction.

9. Sea anemones can reproduce asexually by budding and sexually by means of fertilized eggs, which hatch into larvae. Adult sea anemones exist only as polyps, which remain fixed in one location. Their larvae, however, are free-swimming. Explain how sexual reproduction could help a population of sea anemones overcome a toxic-waste spill.

Many somatic cells go through a continuous sequence of growth and division: the cell cycle. New cells have the same structure and function as their parent cells. Cell structure and function are determined by genetic information carried on the chromosomes in the cell nucleus.

Each species has a characteristic number and arrangement of chromosomes: the karyotype. Each diploid human somatic cell contains 22 pairs of autosomes and a pair of sex chromosomes. Human females have two X chromosomes; human males have one X and one Y chromosome.

The cell cycle can be broken into a phase of growth and metabolic activity called interphase and a phase of division. The reproduction of somatic cells takes place through mitosis: a single parent cell gives rise to two new daughter cells that are genetically identical to the parent cell. Before a cell begins mitosis, all its genetic information is duplicated. Each chromosome replicates to form a pair of identical sister chromatids joined at the centromere. The process of mitosis can be broken into four general phases: prophase, metaphase, anaphase, and telophase. Mitosis is followed by cytokinesis, the division of the cytoplasm to produce two separate cells.

Meiosis is the cellular process that produces haploid gametes from diploid somatic cells. Meiosis proceeds through two complete rounds of nuclear division. Meiosis provides for two different sources of genetic recombination: crossing over between non-sister chromatids and the independent assortment of maternal and paternal chromosomes. Meiosis takes place only in specialized germ tissues within the gonads. In the ovaries, each complete meiotic sequence produces one haploid secondary oocyte and two or more non-functional polar bodies. In the testes, each complete meiotic sequence produces four haploid spermatids.

Some organisms reproduce asexually, and other organisms reproduce sexually. Some plants and animals can reproduce both sexually and asexually. The life cycle of plants includes a regular alternation of haploid and diploid generations. Sexual reproduction and asexual reproduction each have advantages and disadvantages. One characteristic of sexual reproduction is genetic variation among offspring.

Chapter 16 Graphic Organizer

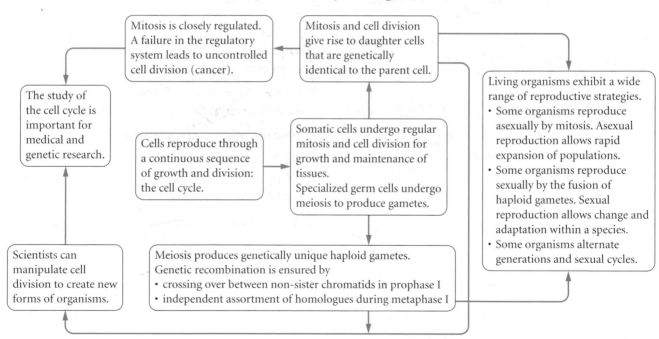

Understanding Concepts

1. Describe one advance in technology between 1800 and 1900 that helped biologists understand the process of cell division.

2. Define and distinguish among chromatin, chromatids, and chromosomes.

3. Describe the three stages of interphase, and explain their importance.

4. The following diagram shows a cell in early prophase of mitosis. Copy this diagram into your notebook, and label it.

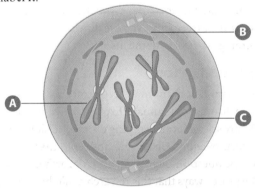

5. Why does the number of chromosomes in gametes need to be less than the number of chromosomes in somatic cells?

6. Which kind of cell division, mitosis or meiosis, is involved in each of the following functions?
   a) tissue renewal
   b) growth of an embryo
   c) production of gametes

7. Which plant tissue would be best to use for studying each of the following processes? Explain your answer.
   a) mitosis
   b) meiosis

8. At which point in the cell cycle does the replication of chromosomes take place?

9. One of the following diagrams represents metaphase I of meiosis. Which diagram is it? How do you know?

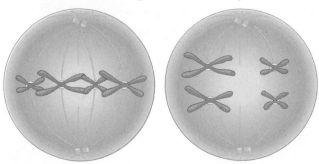

10. a) Copy the following diagram into your notebook, and complete the labels.
    b) What is the significance of the arrangement shown?

11. A diploid germ cell is undergoing meiosis. Is the product of telophase I haploid or diploid? Explain.

12. Describe two means of asexual reproduction, and identify one organism that can reproduce by each.

13. Explain why crossing over between non-sister chromatids does not occur during mitosis. Why is this important?

14. Use the chromosome numbers in the first table to complete the second table. (Do not write in this book.)

Chromosome Numbers of Some Common Organisms

Organism	Diploid body cell (2n)
fruit fly	8
garden pea	14
leopard frog	26
pine tree	24

Cell type and phase	Number of chromosomes	State of chromosomes (duplicated or unduplicated)
fruit fly germ cell after telophase I of meiosis		
garden pea germ cell after telophase II of meiosis		
leopard frog somatic cell in interphase		
pine tree gametophyte cell in prophase of mitosis		

15. Describe what is occurring in the two processes shown below. Copy the diagrams into your notebook and use proper labels to explain your answer.

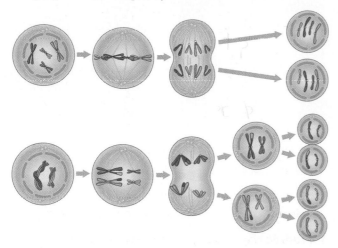

Applying Concepts

16. Which individual is more likely to be seriously affected by the same exposure to radiation: an embryo in the first four weeks of development or a 10-year-old child? Explain.

17. The cell cycle of a cancerous skin cell takes place at a faster rate than the cell cycle of a normal skin cell.
   a) Which phase(s) of the cell cycle is (are) likely to be most shortened in the cancerous skin cell? Explain.
   b) Design a procedure you could use to test your hypothesis. Write the steps in your procedure and a list of the materials you will need.

18. What would happen if a chromosome synapsed with a non-homologous chromosome during meiosis, rather than with its homologue?

19. Create a table or diagram that compares and contrasts the processes and timing of spermatogenesis and oogenesis in humans.

20. How many different gametes could a human germ cell produce? If a man and a woman already have one child, what is the possibility that their second child will be genetically identical to their first child? (Assume that no crossing over takes place.)

21. Draw a labelled diagram to illustrate a life cycle that includes the alternation of generations. Write a brief description to communicate three important features of this life cycle.

22. Create a table that clearly outlines the advantages and disadvantages of asexual reproduction.

23. Your orchard has become infested by a species of insect that devours the blossoms before any fruit can develop. The insects are damaging the trees as well, and some trees appear to be dying.
   a) How could an understanding of the insects' life cycle help you combat the infestation? Give examples.
   b) Your neighbour tells you, "I hope this species of insect reproduces asexually. That would help to keep the insects from spreading to my orchard." Is your neighbour's assumption correct?
   c) What can you do to make sure that you do not lose your fruit trees while you are developing your strategy to deal with the insects?

Making Connections

24. a) Does mitosis occur more frequently in a 5-year-old or a 40-year-old human? Explain your answer.
   b) Many scientists are working on ways to slow the effects of aging. Given your answer to the first part of the question, suggest an area for further research. List three ways that this research could be applied.

25. Imagine that you have been asked to explain cell division to a junior class. You know that many people learn best when they can use their bodies as well as their minds, so you decide to have the class put on a 15 min "mitosis play." Create a list of characters and the dialogue for this play. Include a props list and production directions.

26. Geneticists can use the frequency of crossing over as a way to map the relative locations of genes on chromosomes. Describe, in general terms, how you think this could be done. In what ways could mapping the relative locations of genes be useful?

27. You have discovered a new species of insect that reproduces both sexually and asexually. Design an experiment to test the effects of two different environmental factors on this insect's reproduction. Be sure to include a control.

28. Some genetic researchers are developing artificial chromosomes. What features would these chromosomes need to have for them to behave appropriately during cell division?

Patterns and Processes in Inheritance

Chapter Concepts

17.1 Laying Foundations: Peas, Patterns, and Probabilities

- All somatic cells of diploid organisms have two alleles (copies) of each gene. When a gamete forms, it receives only one of these two alleles.

- The distribution of alleles in gametes is random.

- The inheritance of characteristics follows predictable patterns.

17.2 Extending Mendel's Laws: More Patterns and Probabilities

- Genes are arranged in a linear manner along chromosomes.

- Alleles for genes that are close together on the same chromosome do not assort independently.

- The probability of recombination of linked genes increases with the map distance between these genes.

- Genes that are located on sex chromosomes have a distinct pattern of inheritance.

- The expression of certain genes may be influenced by other genes and by environmental factors.

17.3 Genetics and Society

- Deliberate selection of particular traits can lead to the development of new breeds of plants and animals.

- The pattern of inheritance of human traits is usually studied through the analysis of pedigrees.

- Genetic screening and diagnosis can determine whether an individual carries genes for a particular genetic condition.

Admired for its speed, stamina, and good nature, the Appaloosa is one of the many gifts Aboriginal peoples have bestowed on the world. Horses (*Equus conversidens*) were once native to North America, but they became extinct about 10 000 years ago, likely as a result of environmental change and overhunting. Spanish explorers reintroduced horses to North America in the 1500s. Many First Nations peoples quickly became expert horse handlers. The Nez Perce became, and remain, famous for their selective breeding of horses. Living by the Palouse River near the Rocky Mountains, the Nez Perce carried out a very successful breeding program, selecting only the best and strongest horses for mating. Originally called the Palouse horse, after the Palouse River, this breed soon became known as the Appaloosa.

Coin Toss

The Nez Perce developed their selective breeding prowess through skills such as observation and patience. Modern geneticists use these same skills and others, as well as knowledge from biochemistry, statistical analysis, and other fields of inquiry. Geneticists analyze the data they collect, and they may use the results to formulate or to test a hypothesis.

How well can you predict results based on a hypothesis? How close to the predicted results must the data be for you to be confident that they support the hypothesis? A coin toss is a good way to make and test predictions. You and a partner will each toss a coin. Then you will record the results to show whether or not either of the two coins has turned up heads. Either two heads or a combination of a head and a tail will be considered "heads." Two tails will be considered "no heads." You will repeat the coin toss 10 times.

Materials

2 coins

Procedure

1. Determine the probability that any toss of two coins will result in "heads" or "no heads." Use a table, such as the one below, to determine the probability. For 10 pairs of coin tosses, how many "heads" do you expect? How many "no heads" do you expect?

2. Toss your coins 10 times, and record your results.

Results	Prediction "Heads" (Head–Head or Head–No head)	Prediction "No Heads" (No head–No head)	Actual "Heads" (Head–Head or Head–No head)	Actual "No Heads" (No head–No head)
Toss Results				
Total				

Analysis

1. Calculate your percent error in the number of "heads" by using the formula below.

$$\text{percent error} = \left| \frac{\text{observed} - \text{expected}}{\text{expected}} \right| \times 100\%$$

2. Do your data support your hypothesis? Why or why not?

3. Combine the data obtained by the entire class. Calculate the percent error in the number of "heads." How does the percent error for the combined data compare with yours?

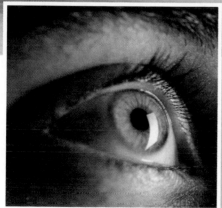

The genetic information that is responsible for eye colour only codes for the presence or absence of a pigment called melanin. Melanin produces either brown or blue colouring. What could be responsible for other eye colours in humans?

Laying Foundations: Peas, Patterns, and Probabilities

Eurasian wolf
(*Canis lupus lupus*)

Great Pyrenees
(*Canis familiaris*)

Dachshund
(*Canis familiaris*)

Toy poodle
(*Canis familiaris*)

Figure 17.1 The Great Pyrenees is one of the oldest-known dog breeds, bred several thousand years ago to protect sheep herds from wolves and bears. The dachshund was bred about 600 years ago to hunt badgers in their underground dens. The toy poodle, a product of the mid-twentieth century, was bred to provide dog lovers with the intelligence and sensitivity of the large poodle in a much smaller form.

For thousands of years, humans have recognized that offspring resemble their parents. People have used this observation to their advantage by choosing and breeding specific plants and animals for particular physical features or behaviours—a process called **selective breeding**. Beginning with wild canines, such as the Eurasian wolf (*Canis lupus lupus*), humans have used centuries of selective breeding to develop, gradually, hundreds of breeds of dogs with specific attributes (see Figure 17.1).

Early Theories of Inheritance

People bred animals and plants for thousands of years without understanding the mechanisms of inheritance. Many people were curious about these mechanisms, however, and tried to explain them. The Greek philosopher Aristotle (384–322 B.C.E.) proposed the first widely accepted theory of inheritance, called *pangenesis*. According to this theory, egg and sperm consist of particles, called pangenes, from all parts of the body. Upon fertilization of the egg by a sperm, the pangenes develop into the parts of the body from which they

were derived. The theory of pangenesis was accepted for hundreds of years although no experiments were done to test its assumptions or results.

In 1677, the amateur scientist Antony van Leeuwenhoek (1632–1723) discovered living sperm in semen with his exquisitely designed single-lens microscopes. He believed that he saw a complete, miniature person, called a homunculus, in the head of sperm (see Figure 17.2). Leeuwenhoek believed that the homunculus came from the father but developed in the mother. A contemporary of Leeuwenhoek, Regnier de Graaf, proposed that the egg, not the sperm, contained the entire person. He argued that the sperm only stimulated the egg to develop.

During the 1800s, when the breeding of ornamental plants was becoming popular, scientists observed that the offspring had characteristics of *both* parent plants. The idea of blending became the working theory of inheritance. Scientists believed that characteristics of the parents blended in the offspring in a way that was irreversible. In other words, scientists

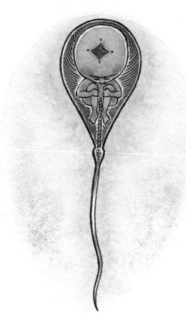

Figure 17.2 Even with microscopes as powerful as those made by Antony van Leeuwenhoek, able to magnify up to 500 times, details of the human sperm cell left much to the imagination of the observer.

believed that the original parental characteristics would not reappear in future generations.

None of the explanations of inheritance proposed prior to the 1850s stood the test of time.

Q1 What is selective breeding? Give an example.

Q2 Briefly describe two early explanations of inheritance.

Developing a Theory of Inheritance: Gregor Mendel's Experiments

Great scientific discoveries are sometimes made in the most unexpected places. No one would have expected a great discovery to be made in a monastery garden by an Augustinian monk in Brunn, Austria (now in the Czech Republic), in the 1860s. The scientists of the time certainly did not expect it. In fact, they ignored the scientific paper describing this discovery until 1900, when supporting evidence began to emerge. Nevertheless, the work of a monk and teacher named Gregor Mendel (1822–1884) laid the foundation for the field of genetics, the science of inheritance (see Figure 17.3).

Between the years 1856 and 1863, Mendel bred, tended, and analyzed over 28 000 pea (*Pisum sativum*) plants in the monastery garden. He observed many different traits, or characteristics. He chose seven traits that were expressed in two easily distinguishable forms. These traits are shown in Figure 17.4. Before

Figure 17.3 In this garden, Gregor Mendel planted and tended the pea plants that helped to establish the field of genetics.

doing any experiments, Mendel let the plants self-pollinate to ensure that they were true breeding. **True breeding** plants exhibit the same characteristics generation after generation.

Mendel called the true breeding plants the *parental*, or P, generation. He started his experiments by crossing true breeding plants for each characteristic with true breeding plants having the opposite characteristic. For example, he bred plants that produced purple flowers with plants that produced white flowers. He called the offspring the first *filial*, or F₁, generation. Mendel let the F₁ plants self-pollinate and then observed the characteristics of their offspring, which he called the second filial, or F₂, generation. Mendel identified the characteristics of the F₁ and F₂ generation plants and counted how many plants produced which characteristics. Since only one trait is involved in this type of cross, it is called a **monohybrid cross**. (A *hybrid* is the offspring of a cross between two parent organisms with different inheritable traits.)

Figure 17.4 Each of the seven traits that Mendel chose to study had two clearly distinguishable forms.

Characteristics	Contrasting traits	
stem length	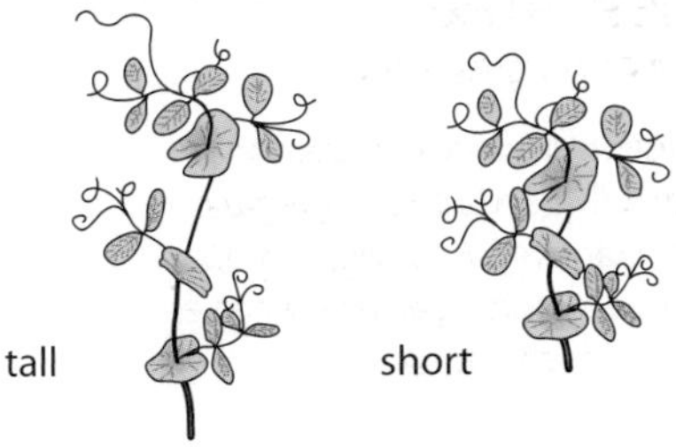 tall	short
pod shape	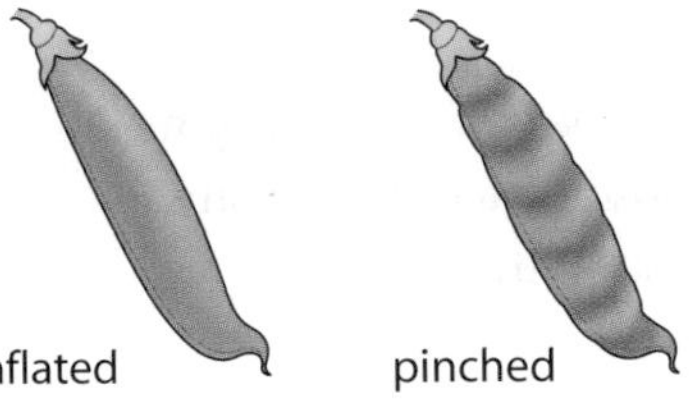 inflated	pinched
seed shape	round	wrinkled
seed colour	yellow	green
flower position	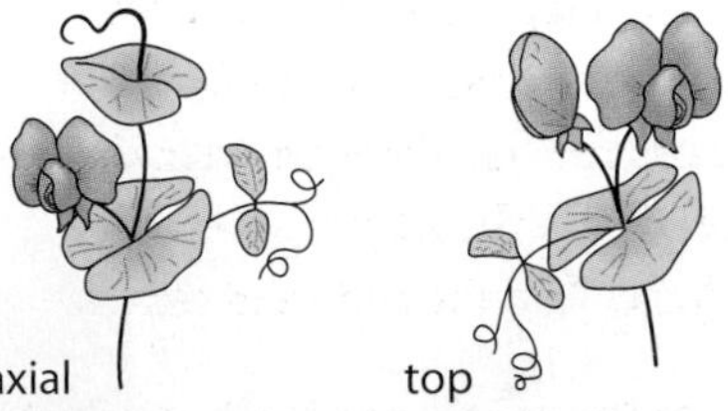 axial	top
flower colour	purple	white
pod colour	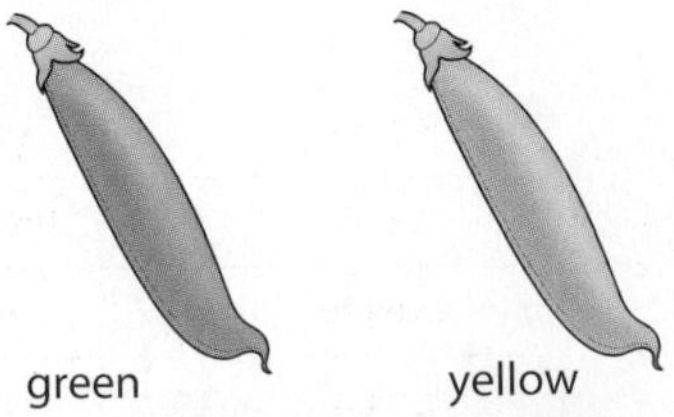 green	yellow

Dominant   Recessive

---

3 Explain how a hybrid plant is different from a true breeding plant.

4 Explain the difference between P, F₁, and F₂ generations in a cross.

Dominant and Recessive Genes

Mendel observed that, for every trait, the F₁ plants showed only one of the two parental characteristics. For example, in the cross between plants with round seeds and plants with wrinkled seeds, all the seeds in the F₁ generation were round. Although all the F₁ plants had a copy of each form of the factor for seed shape, only one form was shown, or *expressed*. Mendel called the characteristic that was expressed in the F₁ generation **dominant**. He called the characteristic that was not expressed **recessive**. Mendel concluded that one form showed **complete dominance** over the other form. That is, an individual with one recessive and one dominant form had the same observable physical characteristic as an individual with two dominant forms.

Table 17.1 summarizes the dominant and recessive forms of each of the seven traits that Mendel tested. If you compare Table 17.1 with Figure 17.4, you will see that the forms on the left side of the second column are dominant and the forms on the right are recessive.

The Law of Segregation

When Mendel analyzed the data from his monohybrid crosses, he saw very clear patterns. For each of the seven traits he analyzed, each F_1 plant exhibited the trait of only one of the two parental plants. For example, when he crossed plants that produced round seeds with plants that produced wrinkled seeds, the F_1 plants all produced round seeds. When the F_1 plants self-pollinated, however, some of their offspring (the F_2 generation) had wrinkled seeds.

In repeated experiments, Mendel found that traits that had not appeared in the F_1 plants reappeared in the F_2 plants, but in smaller numbers than in the P generation. Figure 17.5 summarizes the results of one of Mendel's experiments, in which he crossed parental plants with different seed shapes. Notice that the ratio of F_2 plants with round seeds to F_2 plants with wrinkled seeds is about 3:1. Mendel observed similar ratios in the F_2 generation for monohybrid crosses involving each of the seven traits.

From these data for monohybrid crosses, Mendel inferred the following generalizations:

- Discrete factors determine individual traits. (**Note:** Mendel used the term "factors" to describe what are now called genes.)

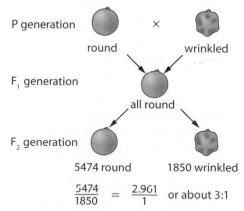

P generation   round × wrinkled

F_1 generation   all round

F_2 generation   5474 round   1850 wrinkled

$$\frac{5474}{1850} = \frac{2.961}{1} \quad \text{or about 3:1}$$

Figure 17.5 The ratio of plants with round seeds to plants with wrinkled seeds in the F_2 generation is 5474:1850 or 2.96:1. This is very close to a 3:1 ratio.

- Each individual organism has two copies of each factor.
- When gametes (eggs and sperm) are formed, the copies of the factors segregate so that each gamete receives one copy of each factor.
- Eggs and sperm fuse randomly. The embryo that develops into a new individual has two copies of each factor—one copy from each parent.

Mendel's first law, also called the **law of segregation**, is a summary of these concepts.

Mendel's First Law: The Law of Segregation

All individuals have two copies of each factor. These copies segregate (separate) randomly during gamete formation, and each gamete receives one copy of every factor.

Q 5 State Mendel's first law in your own words, and use an example to illustrate it.

Representing Genetic Crosses

In 1909, Danish botanist and geneticist, Wilhelm Ludwig Johannsen, coined the term gene for Mendel's factors. The different forms of each gene are now called alleles. That is, you would say that the *gene* is seed shape, and the *allele* for round seeds is dominant to the *allele* for wrinkled seeds (or the *allele* for wrinkled seeds is recessive to the *allele* for round seeds). To symbolize the different alleles,

homozygous.
heterozygous

Table 17.1 The Seven Traits of Pea Plants Studied by Mendel

Trait	Dominant	Recessive
stem length	tall	short
pod shape	inflated	pinched
seed shape	round	wrinkled
seed colour	yellow	green
flower position	axial	terminal
flower colour	purple	white
pod colour	green	yellow

BiologyFile

FYI
Before Mendel did his experiments, heredity had been a descriptive science. No one had ever applied mathematical methods or statistical analysis to the study of inheritance.

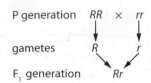

P generation   RR   ×   rr

gametes   R   r

F₁ generation   Rr

Figure 17.6 Representation of a monohybrid cross between two true breeding parent plants. One parent plant is homozygous for round seeds (*RR*), and the other parent plant is homozygous for wrinkled seeds (*rr*). The F₁ generation is heterozygous for round seeds (*Rr*).

Figure 17.7 Using a Punnett square to analyze a cross between F₁ plants, producing an F₂ generation assessed for seed shape

geneticists use a system that Mendel devised. They use the first letter in the description of the dominant allele, in upper case, to represent the dominant allele. They use the *same* letter in lower case to represent the recessive allele.

According to this system, the allele for round seeds is represented by *R* and the allele for wrinkled seeds is represented by *r*. Since each individual has two alleles for every gene, a pea plant could have the allele combination *RR*, *Rr*, or *rr* (see Figure 17.6). Johannsen called the combination of alleles for any given trait the individual's **genotype**. He called the outward expression of the trait—the physical form that you can observe—the **phenotype**. For example, an individual with genotype *RR* would have the phenotype of round seeds. Since *R* is dominant to *r*, individuals with genotype *Rr* would also have the phenotype of round seeds. Only individuals with genotype *rr* would have wrinkled seeds.

An individual with two identical alleles for a trait, such as *RR* or *rr*, is **homozygous** for the trait. An individual with two different alleles for a trait, such as *Rr*, is **heterozygous** for the trait.

You can use these symbols and concepts to represent Mendel's crosses

of plants with round and wrinkled seeds in a condensed form. Since the parental plants were true breeding, they had to have identical alleles. You would write the cross as shown in Figure 17.6.

• • •

6 State the meanings of the terms dominant and recessive.

7 Distinguish between the terms gene and allele.

8 Distinguish, using an example, between the terms genotype and phenotype.

9 What does it mean to be homozygous for a trait? How is this different from being heterozygous for a trait?

• • •

Analyzing Genetic Crosses

How did the recessive characteristic reappear in the F₂ generation? When F₁ plants produce gametes, the alleles segregate randomly and each gamete receives only one allele. There is an equal chance that any gamete will receive *R* or *r*. To analyze the results of crosses, British geneticist Reginald Punnett (1875–1967)

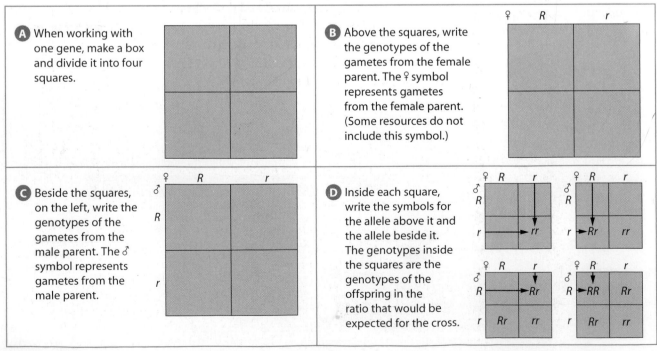

A When working with one gene, make a box and divide it into four squares.

B Above the squares, write the genotypes of the gametes from the female parent. The ♀ symbol represents gametes from the female parent. (Some resources do not include this symbol.)

C Beside the squares, on the left, write the genotypes of the gametes from the male parent. The ♂ symbol represents gametes from the male parent.

D Inside each square, write the symbols for the allele above it and the allele beside it. The genotypes inside the squares are the genotypes of the offspring in the ratio that would be expected for the cross.

devised a visual technique that is now called the **Punnett square**. This technique, applied to the F_1 cross, is shown in Figure 17.7.

After drawing a Punnett square, you can analyze the genotypes to determine the phenotypes. In Figure 17.7, for example, all the *RR* and *Rr* plants will produce round seeds, and all the *rr* plants will produce wrinkled seeds. The ratio of the phenotypes, round to wrinkled, is 3:1. This is the ratio that Mendel found in his data. As noted in Figure 17.8, Mendel worked backward to formulate a hypothesis that could explain the data. His law of segregation explains the data very well. In the Practice Problems below, you will see this for yourself. Then, in the investigation that follows, you will assess the law of segregation.

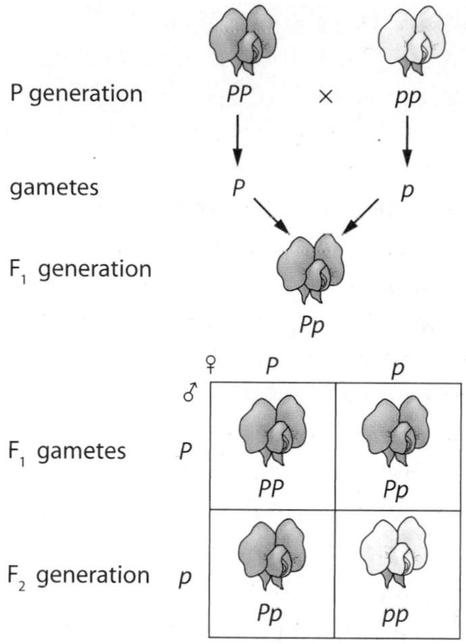

Test Cross

When geneticists want to know if a phenotypically dominant individual is homozygous or heterozygous, they do a test cross. A **test cross** is a cross between the organism of unknown genotype and a homozygous recessive organism. In mice, for example, a condition called waltzer is recessive. A waltzer mouse has a defect in the region of the inner ear that interferes with its balance. Consequently, waltzers run in circles. A mouse that runs normally might be homozygous dominant for this gene, or it might be heterozygous. If geneticists had several mice that walk normally, and wanted to know if any of these mice were heterozygous for the waltzer mutation, they would do a test cross.

You can use Punnett squares to predict the genotypes and phenotypes of

the offspring of the test crosses as shown in Figure 17.9. In these examples, *N* represents normal (non-waltzer), and *n* represents the recessive waltzer mutation. The genotypes of the gametes for homozygous recessive are on the top of each Punnett square. One of the two possible genotypes of the mouse being tested is on the side of each Punnett square.

If the mouse being tested is homozygous normal, all the offspring will be phenotypically normal. If the mouse being tested is heterozygous for waltzer, half the offspring will be phenotypically normal and half will be waltzers. As you can see, test crosses are an important tool for geneticists, particularly in cases where reproduction is frequent and multiple offspring are produced.

The Law of Independent Assortment

Mendel did more than conduct experiments to test single traits. He

Figure 17.8 For each trait that he tested, Mendel observed the same types of results and inferred the same pattern. This illustration shows a cross between true breeding purple-flowered plants and true breeding white-flowered plants. The ratio of phenotypes in the F_2 generation is 3:1.

Figure 17.9 Predicting phenotypes of a test cross

Practice Problems

1. Mendel crossed true breeding plants that had yellow pods with true breeding plants that had green pods. Using the information in Table 17.1, predict and write down the genotypes and phenotypes of the F_1 and F_2 generations. Predict the ratio of F_2 plants with green pods to F_2 plants with yellow pods.

2. In one of his experiments, Mendel counted 6022 yellow seeds and 2001 green seeds. Write the genotypes and phenotypes of the plants in all the crosses he did in order to get these results. How well did his data fit the predicted ratios?

Chapter 17 Patterns and Processes in Inheritance • MHR **591**

Testing the Law of Segregation

In this investigation, you will work with plants called Wisconsin Fast Plants™ (*Brassica rapa*). They germinate and mature quickly, so you can grow your own plants, tend them, pollinate the flowers, and harvest and plant the seeds. Your goal is to collect evidence to explain how stem colour in *Brassica rapa* is inherited. You will use your evidence to predict the phenotype of the male parental generation (P_M). The trait you are focussing on, stem colour, is controlled by a gene that regulates whether or not anthocyanin (a purple pigment) is expressed.

Hypothesis

Each group will formulate a testable hypothesis to explain how the stem colour phenotypes of *Brassica rapa* reflect their genotypes. Your hypothesis will form the basis of your experimental design.

Safety Precautions

Wash your hands whenever you handle any of the materials in this Investigation.

Materials

- *Brassica rapa* seeds and growing systems
- potting mix
- fertilizer
- stakes and ties
- labels
- instructions for growing, tending, pollinating, and harvesting

Procedure

1. One group will plant seeds from the female parental generation (P_F). All the other groups will plant seeds from the first-generation offspring (F_1). Use the instructions provided by your teacher to germinate the seeds and tend the developing plants.

2. After about four days, observe the stem colour and all other phenotypes of the young P_F and F_1 plants. Record your observations in a suitable table.

3. Return the P_F plants to your teacher. Continue to tend the F_1 plants by thinning the plants to two per pot. Refer to the instructions provided by your teacher.

4. In your group, discuss how you think stem colour is inherited in *Brassica rapa*. State a hypothesis and use it to predict the stem colour of the male parental generation plants (P_M) from which the F_1 offspring came.

5. After about a week and a half, pollinate the F_1 plants over three days. Be sure that all the flowers receive pollen from several different plants. (Refer to the instructions provided by your teacher.)

6. Based on your hypothesis, predict the stem colour of the second-generation offspring (F_2) that will result from the pollination you have done.

7. Over the next several days, cut off any new flower buds that developed after you pollinated the plants.

8. After about two weeks, stop watering the plants. Let them dry for a full week.

9. After about one week, harvest the seeds from the pods of the F_1 plants. (Refer to the instructions.) These are your seeds for the F_2 generation. Plant the seeds.

10. After about four days, observe the stem colour and other phenotypes of the young F_2 plants. Design a table to record your observations.

11. Return the F_2 plants to your teacher.

12. After you complete Analysis questions 1 and 2, plant the P_M seeds supplied by your teacher. About four days later, record your observations of stem colour and other phenotypes of the young P_M plants in a suitable table.

13. Return all the plants and other materials to your teacher.

Analysis

1. Think about what you know of Mendel and his experimental procedures. In what ways are your experiences similar? In what ways are they different?

2. Explain the purpose of cutting off new flower buds in step 7 of the Procedure.

3. Examine your hypothesis and your results. How accurate was your hypothesis? Identify any sources of error.

4. Draw a Punnett square and a diagram showing the P, F_1, and F_2 generations to record the results of your investigation.

---

also conducted experiments to find out whether the pattern of segregation of the alleles for one gene has any influence on the pattern of segregation of the alleles for another gene. He crossed plants that were true breeding for two different traits with plants that were true breeding for the opposite form of the same two traits. Since two genes are involved in this type of cross, it is called a **dihybrid cross**.

In one dihybid cross, for example, Mendel crossed true breeding tall plants that had green pods (*TTGG*) with true breeding short plants that had yellow pods (*ttgg*). This produced an F_1 generation of plants that were all heterozygous for both traits (*TtGg*). Mendel allowed the F_1 plants to self-pollinate and then analyzed the traits of the F_2 plants.

The cross *TtGg* × *TtGg* produced F_2 plants with the phenotypes of tall with green pods, tall with yellow pods, short with green pods, and short with yellow pods in a ratio of 9:3:3:1. For every dihybrid cross that Mendel carried out and analyzed, he found the same pattern in the F_2 generation. Mendel did a statistical analysis to compare this 9:3:3:1 ratio to the ratio that would be expected if the segregation of alleles for one gene had *no influence* on the segregation of alleles for another gene.

You can use a Punnett square to test Mendel's ratio (see Figure 17.10). All the individuals in the F_1 generation receive one allele for each gene from each parent. The genotype of all F_1 plants is therefore *TtGg*. If the alleles for the two genes segregate independently of each other, the gametes will have an equal chance of carrying any one of the four genotypes, *TG, Tg, tG, tg*. You can use these gametes to construct a Punnett square. As shown in Figure 17.10, the ratio of 9:3:3:1 is obtained when the alleles segregate

randomly among the gametes. Mendel based his second law, the **law of independent assortment**, on results such as these.

Mendel's Second Law: The Law of Independent Assortment

The two alleles for one gene segregate (assort) independently of the alleles for other genes during gamete formation.

Q 10 What is a Punnett square?

Q 11 What is a test cross?

Q 12 State Mendel's second law in your own words.

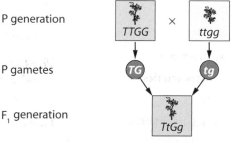

P generation — TTGG × ttgg

P gametes — TG, tg

F_1 generation — TtGg

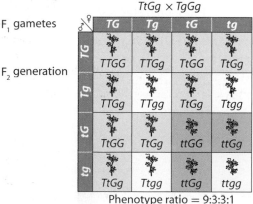

TtGg × *TgGg*

F_1 gametes

F_2 generation

	TG	**Tg**	**tG**	**tg**
TG	TTGG	TTGg	TtGG	TtGg
Tg	TTGg	TTgg	TtGg	Ttgg
tG	TtGG	TtGg	ttGG	ttGg
tg	TtGg	Ttgg	ttGg	ttgg

Phenotype ratio = 9:3:3:1

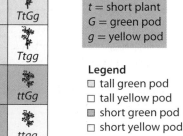

Key:
T = tall plant
t = short plant
G = green pod
g = yellow pod

Legend
☐ tall green pod
☐ tall yellow pod
■ short green pod
☐ short yellow pod

Figure 17.10 For any dihybrid cross, individuals in the largest group (9) have at least one dominant allele for each gene (*T_G_*), where the underscore represents any one of the four alleles. In the intermediate groups (3), the individuals have at least one dominant allele for one gene but two recessive alleles for the other gene (*T_gg* or *ttG_*). The smallest group (1) is homozygous recessive for both traits (*ttgg*).

Incomplete Dominance and Co-dominance

Since Mendel's work became recognized, geneticists have studied a number of traits that do not appear to follow the same pattern of inheritance that Mendel observed. These patterns can also be explained in terms of Mendel's laws, however.

Incomplete dominance describes a condition in which neither of two alleles for the same gene can completely conceal the presence of the other. One example is the flower colour of the four-o'clock plant (*Mirabilis jalapa*). As you can see in Figure 17.11, a cross between a true-breeding red-flowered plant and a true-breeding white-flowered plant produces offspring with pink flowers. When representing incomplete dominance, upper-case and lower-case letters are not generally used to represent the alleles. Some geneticists use all upper-case letters, with subscripts to denote the alleles, as shown in the key in Figure 17.11.

The fact that the alleles segregate just like the alleles for a completely dominant trait is supported by the pattern observed when the pink flowers are self-pollinated. The Punnett square in Figure 17.11 shows that the ratio of red (R_1R_1) to pink (R_1R_2) to white (R_2R_2) flowers should be 1:2:1. The experimentally observed ratios are close enough to the expected ratio of 1:2:1 to support the theory of incomplete dominance.

Two genetic conditions in humans exhibit incomplete dominance: sickle cell anemia and familial hypercholesterolemia.

Sickle cell anemia is caused by a specific form of the gene that directs the synthesis of hemoglobin, the molecule that carries oxygen in the blood. Slightly lowered oxygen concentrations in the blood cause the hemoglobin in the red blood cells to form needle-like crystals that distort the shape of the cells. The misshapen cells cannot pass through small capillaries and cause blockages that result in tissue damage to the local area as well as intense pain. Geneticists believe that this form of the gene arose in Africa centuries ago.

The allele for normal hemoglobin is represented as Hb^A, and the allele for sickle cell hemoglobin is represented as Hb^S. As shown in Figure 17.12, individuals who are homozygous (Hb^SHb^S) have sickle cell disease.

Individuals who are heterozygous for the gene (Hb^AHb^S) are said to have the sickle cell trait. Their blood cells are much less likely to become sickle-shaped, and they rarely experience any symptoms. In fact, having the sickle cell trait can be an advantage because heterozygotes are resistant to malaria. This is very beneficial in certain parts of Africa, where deadly malaria epidemics can occur. The sickle cell trait is an example of the principle of *heterozygote advantage*—heterozygous individuals having an advantage over homozygous dominant or homozygous recessive individuals.

Familial hypercholesterolemia is a genetic condition that prevents the tissues from removing low-density lipoproteins (LDL, commonly known

Figure 17.11 The allele for red flowers in the four o'clock plant directs the synthesis of red pigment. When only one allele is present, the flower cannot make enough pigment to make the flowers red, resulting in incomplete dominance (pink flowers).

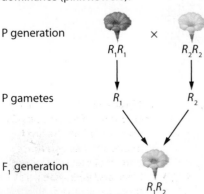

P generation R_1R_1 × R_2R_2

P gametes R_1 R_2

F₁ generation R_1R_2

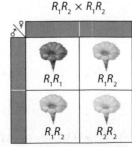

F₁ gametes

F₂ generation

$R_1R_2 \times R_1R_2$

R_1R_1	R_1R_2
R_1R_2	R_2R_2

Phenotype ratio =
1 red : 2 pink : 1 white

Key:
R_1R_1 = red
R_1R_2 = pink
R_2R_2 = white

as "bad cholesterol") from the blood. People who are homozygotes for the trait have six times the normal amount of cholesterol in their blood and may have a heart attack by the age of 2. Heterozygotes have about twice as much cholesterol in their blood and may have a heart attack by the age of 35.

Co-dominance is a situation in which both alleles are fully expressed. A roan horse or cow is an excellent, visible example of co-dominance. A roan animal is a heterozygote in which both the base colour and white are fully expressed. If you look closely at the individual hairs on a blue roan, such as the horse in Figure 17.13, you will see a mixture of black hairs and white hairs. One allele is expressed in the white hairs, and the other allele is expressed in the black hairs. A red roan has a mixture of chestnut-coloured hairs and white hairs.

• • •

13 Explain what incomplete dominance is.

14 Give two examples of genetic conditions in humans that exhibit incomplete dominance, and briefly describe what they are.

15 Explain how co-dominance is different from incomplete dominance.

16 Explain why the roan colouring of a horse is an example of co-dominance.

• • •

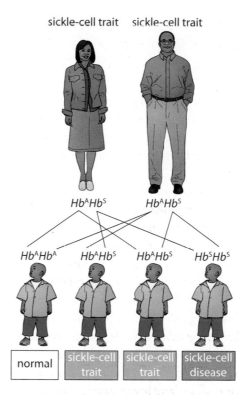

Figure 17.12 When a man and a woman are both heterozygous for the sickle cell gene, there is a one in four chance that they will have a child with sickle cell disease.

Genes and Chromosomes

Throughout his research, Mendel made no attempt to determine the chemical or physical nature of his factors (now called genes). He accepted that they must be present in order to cause the results he observed. This way of thinking was uncommon for the biologists of his time, and it is one reason why his published work went almost unnoticed for many years. It was not until about 1900, about 16 years after Mendel's death, that other biologists began to perform experiments similar to Mendel's experiments with garden peas. Three scientists, working independently, rediscovered Mendel's

Figure 17.13 The roan colouring of a horse usually does not affect the head, mane, and tail. This horse's body looks blue because black and white hairs are thoroughly mixed.

Handwritten notes (left margin):

3. White × yellow
WW   w
Ww
Test cross

4. TTRR × ttrr
tall red   short yellow
  ↓   ↓
  TR   tr

F1 TR [TtRr] all TtRr tallred
                tr

TtRr × TtRr

[TTRR grid/Punnett square]

Printed text (column 1):

publication. Dutch plant physiologist Hugo de Vries (1848–1935), German botanist Carl Erich Correns (1864–1933), and Austrian agronomist Tschermak von Seysenegg (1871–1962) were all performing crosses with plants. As part of their research, each of them searched the scientific literature for any similar work that had been published. They all found Mendel's publication, and they all realized that their own work was in agreement with Mendel's proposed laws.

Then, in 1902, Walter Sutton (1877–1916), a graduate student at Columbia University in New York, studied sperm development in grasshoppers. Sutton examined the processes of synapsis (segregation of homologous chromosomes) and migration of sister chromatids during meiosis I and meiosis II. Sutton realized that the distribution of chromosomes into developing gametes follows the pattern for two alleles of a gene, according to Mendel's law of segregation. Genes come in pairs, as do chromosomes. During gamete formation, alleles segregate just as homologous chromosomes do (see Figure 17.14). Sutton published a paper proposing

Printed text (column 2):

that genes are carried on chromosomes. Sutton's theory became known as the **chromosome theory of inheritance**.

As you saw in Chapter 16, there is no apparent interaction between non-homologous chromosomes during meiosis. The movement of each pair of homologous chromosomes is independent of the movement of all the other pairs of homologous chromosomes. This agrees with Mendel's law of independent assortment; however, Sutton recognized an important implication of his research: genes that are carried on the same chromosome do not assort independently. This means that they do not follow Mendelian inheritance patterns.

• • •

17 Give two examples of how the movement of alleles is consistent with the movement of chromosomes during meiosis.

• • •

Objections to Sutton's Theory

Sutton's theory—that Mendel's "factors" are located on chromosomes—was not widely accepted at first. Many scientists

Handwritten notes (center-bottom):

6. red × white
P RR × WW
Incomplete dominance

F1 RW | pink | R [RR|RW]
    RW × RW   W [RW|WW]

genotype	phenotype
1 RR	1 red
2 RW	2 pink
1 WW	1 white

Practice Problems

Handwritten notes (left margin):

F2 genotypes
1 TTRR
2 TTRr
1 TTrr
2 TtRR
4 TtRr
2 Ttrr
1 ttRR
2 ttRr
1 ttrr

Phenotypes
9 tall red
3 tall yellow
3 short red
1 short yellow

9:3:3:1

3. In zucchini (*Cucurbita pepo*), yellow-coloured flesh is recessive to white-coloured flesh. You are plant breeder and would like to know if any of the white-fleshed zucchini you have are heterozygous for the yellow-fleshed allele. How would you determine this? Describe the procedure you would follow.

4. In tomatoes (*Lycopersicon esculentum*), red fruit (*R*) is dominant to yellow fruit (*r*), and tall (*T*) is dominant to short (*t*). True-breeding tall plants that produced red fruit were crossed with true-breeding short plants that produced yellow fruit.

  a) State the genotype and phenotype of the F_1 generation plants.

  b) List the genotypes of the gametes produced by the F_1 plants.

  c) List the genotypes and phenotypes of the F_2 generation plants. Include the genotypic and phenotypic ratios of the F_2 generation plants.

5. In mice, black fur (*B*) is dominant to brown fur (*b*), and non-waltzer mice (*N*) are dominant to waltzers (*n*). Two mice that are heterozygous for both traits are crossed. Draw a Punnett square for the F_1 generation, and determine the phenotype ratio for these offspring.

6. The gene that codes for colour in snapdragons (*Antirrhinum majus*), exhibits incomplete dominance. A true-breeding red snapdragon is crossed with a true-breeding white snapdragon. What is the phenotype ratio of the F_1 generation? The F_1 offspring are then crossed to produce an F_2 generation. Draw a Punnett square for this generation and determine the phenotypic ratio.

7. Two blue roan horses are bred together. What is the chance that the colt will be white?

Handwritten notes (bottom):

blue roan × blue roan
BW   ×   BW
codominant → ½ blue
              ½ white

BW × BW
B [BB|BW]
W [BW|WW]

genotype	phenotype
1 BB	1 blue
2 BW	2 blue + white
1 WW	1 white

prophase

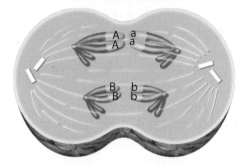

or

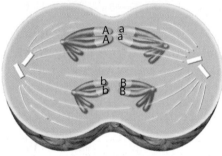

anaphase I

Figure 17.14 Alleles and chromosomes both segregate during meiosis. During anaphase I, the homologous chromosomes segregate (separate) and migrate to opposite ends of the cell. After telophase I, the homologous chromosomes are in separate cells. The resulting gametes are equally likely to contain each possible combination of alleles.

still believed in the blending of hereditary information. Many also believed that the environment, or events in the parents' lives, played the main role in determining which parental traits would be expressed in the offspring. Objections to Sutton's theory included the lack of convincing evidence linking Mendel's factors to any cellular structure and the absence of any studies that could account for more complex inheritance patterns. The path to the resolution of these objections, and to the affirmation of a chromosomal theory of heredity, leads back to Columbia University, to a laboratory room buzzing

with intellectual and experimental excitement—and with fruit flies, *Drosophila melanogaster*. You will learn about the important work that occurred in this laboratory in the next section.

Section 17.1 Summary

- Gregor Mendel used pea plant crosses to follow the transmissions of one or two traits at a time. The genes for the traits he studied were carried on different chromosomes, and each gene had two alleles.
- Mendel's law of segregation states that inherited factors (genes) separate in meiosis. Each individual receives one copy of each gene from each parent.
- An allele whose expression masks another is dominant. An allele whose expression is masked by a dominant allele is recessive.
- An individual who has two identical alleles for a trait (for example, *rr*) is homozygous for that trait. An individual who has two different alleles for a trait (for example, *Rr*) is heterozygous for the trait. A heterozygote has two different alleles of a gene. A homozygous recessive individual has two recessive alleles. A homozygous dominant individual has two dominant alleles.
- The combination of alleles is the genotype. The expression of a genotype of an individual is its phenotype.
- The parental generation is designated P_1. The next general is the first filial generation and is designated F_1. The next generation is the second filial generation and is designated F_2.
- A monohybrid cross yields a phenotype ratio of 3:1. A test cross breeds an individual of unknown genotype to a homozygous recessive individual.
- Punnett squares are based on the principles of probability and can be used to predict the outcomes of genetic crosses.
- Mendel's law of independent assortment was derived by observing the transmission of two or more characters whose genes are on different

chromosomes. Because maternally and paternally derived chromosomes (and their genes) assort randomly in meiosis, different gametes receive different combinations of genes.

- A dihybrid cross yields a 9:3:3:1 phenotype ratio.
- Different dominance relationships influence phenotype ratios. Heterozygotes of incompletely dominant alleles have phenotypes intermediate between those of the two homozygotes. Co-dominant alleles are both expressed.
- The chromosome theory of inheritance states that genes are located on chromosomes, and chromosomes provide the basis for the segregation and independent assortment of genes.

Section 17.1 Review

1. Explain how the Launch Lab: Coin Toss applies to making predictions about the genotypes and phenotypes of the F_2 generation of a monohybrid cross.

2. Describe two aspects of Mendel's experiments that were unusual for biology experiments in the 1800s.

3. Compare and contrast the following terms: selective breeding and true breeding. How does each term relate to the field of genetics?

4. Explain the meaning of the law of segregation.

5. If you did not know whether green or yellow was dominant for the gene for pod colour in peas, how would you determine this experimentally? Describe your experiment in detail, and explain how you would interpret the results.

6. In the garden pea, inflated pod shape (I) is dominant to constricted shape (i). Axial flower position (A) is dominant to terminal flower position (a). Start with the cross $IIAA \times iiaa$ from the parental generation.
   a) State the genotype and phenotype of the F_1 plants.
   b) List all of the genotypes and phenotypes of the F_2 plants, and determine the genotypic and phenotypic ratios.
   c) Explain how experimental data and your ratios in part (b) support the law of independent assortment.

7. In fruit flies, long wings (L) are dominant to short wings (l) and gray body colour (G) is dominant to black body colour (g). If flies that are heterozygous for both traits are crossed and 256 offspring are produced, how many of these offspring would you predict to have each phenotype below?
   a) long, gray
   b) long, black
   c) short, gray
   d) short, black

8. Imagine that you randomly select one of the long-winged gray-bodied flies from the offspring described in question 7 and perform a test cross with a fly that is homozygous recessive for both traits. What is the probability that the offspring will be produced in the ratio 1:1:1:1 for long, gray : long, black : short, gray : short, black?

9. Now imagine that you performed the cross described in question 8. Your results were 139 flies with long wings and gray bodies, 49 flies with long wings and black bodies, 53 flies with short wings and gray bodies, and 15 flies with short wings and black bodies. Are these the results you would expect? Explain your reasoning.

10. Explain how incompletely dominant and co-dominant alleles differ from dominant and recessive alleles. What type of observation would indicate that alleles are co-dominant?

11. A farmer crosses a black rooster with a white hen. Of the seven offspring, three are black, three are speckled black and white, and one is white.
   a) What could you infer about the black and white alleles?
   b) Do the ratios of characteristics among the offspring follow the pattern you would expect? Why or why not? What further information would you need in order to draw conclusions about the inheritance of this trait?

12. Describe the observations that suggested to scientists that genes might be carried on chromosomes.

Extending Mendel's Laws:
More Patterns and Probabilities

A few years after Sutton suggested that genes are located on chromosomes, an American biologist named Thomas Hunt Morgan (see Figure 17.15) moved his research team into another laboratory at Columbia University. Morgan did not accept Sutton's arguments and intended to collect evidence for an alternative theory. For his research, he required an organism that was economical to maintain, could be raised in his small laboratory, and would reproduce rapidly. He chose the fruit fly, *Drosophila melanogaster*, and his laboratory became known as "the fly room." Morgan's research was characterized by rigorous experimental procedures and careful statistical analysis. His results soon convinced him of Sutton's chromosome theory and established much of the framework for today's genetic research.

In 1910, Morgan discovered an unusual white-eyed male among his fly population. He crossed the white-eyed male with a normal red-eyed female. All the F_1 generation had red eyes. This seemed to indicate that normal red eyes are dominant to the white-eye mutation. When Morgan crossed a male and female from the F_1 generation, however, the results surprised him. All the females of the F_2 generation had red eyes, while half the F_2 males had red eyes and half had white eyes. The discovery that eye colour was connected to gender led Morgan to deduce that the gene for eye colour is located on the X chromosome. This was the first gene to be mapped to a specific chromosome. Morgan went on to uncover additional experimental evidence for the chromosome theory.

Linked Genes and Chromosome Maps

In Section 17.1, you learned that the movement of chromosomes follows the pattern that Mendel predicted for genes

Figure 17.15 Thomas Hunt Morgan (1866–1945) sought to disprove the chromosome theory of inheritance. Like all good scientists, he reconsidered his position when his experimental evidence did not support his initial hypothesis. In 1933, Morgan received the Nobel Prize for his work.

(what he called "factors"). This observation led to the chromosomal theory of inheritance: genes are carried on chromosomes, and chromosomes segregate independently into gametes during meiosis.

Sutton predicted that when alleles of two different genes are on the same chromosome they do not assort independently. For this reason, genes that are found on the same chromosome are sometimes called **linked genes**. Experimental data show, however, that linked genes segregate on a regular basis. How can alleles of two genes on the same chromosome be found in different gametes? The answer is found in the process of crossing over.

Crossing Over and Inheritance

In Chapter 16 you saw that crossing over occurs in prophase I of meiosis, when the non-sister chromatids in a tetrad exchange pieces of chromosomes. (Turn to page 564 and 566 for review.) Suppose that you are studying two genes. If the point at which a crossover occurs is between these genes, the alleles will be on separate chromosomes and will therefore migrate into different gametes.

Crossing over is a random event and occurs, with equal probability, at nearly any point on the sister chromatids, except near the centromere. This means that a crossover is more likely to occur between genes that are farther apart on a chromosome than between genes that are closer together.

In repeated experiments, Morgan and his students found that any given pair of linked genes would separate with a predictable frequency. They also found that this frequency varied among different pairs of linked genes. One of Morgan's students, Alfred Sturtevant, was the first to demonstrate that these results could be explained by assigning each gene a specific position along a linear chromosome. Because of Sturtevant's work, Morgan and his team amended the chromosome theory of inheritance. The *gene-chromosome theory* now states that *genes exist at specific sites arranged in a linear manner along chromosomes.*

Chromosome Mapping

The concept of crossing over is used to determine the relative positions of genes on a chromosome in a process called **chromosome mapping**. One **map unit** is defined as the distance between points on a chromosome where a crossover is likely to occur in 1 percent of all meiotic events. The *map distance* is the distance between genes on a single chromosome.

Imagine that you are a biologist working with Morgan in the famous "fly room" at Columbia University. As a researcher, you decide to perform a cross with *Drosophila melanogaster*. You cross a homozygous recessive purple-eyed, vestigial-winged fly (*ppvv*) with a heterozygous dominant normal-eyed, normal-winged fly (*PpVv*). You expect

the phenotype ratio for the cross to be 1:1, because both genes are found on chromosome 2. To your surprise, you find that 45 percent of the flies have normal eyes and normal wings, 45 percent have purple eyes and vestigial wings, 5 percent have normal eyes and vestigial wings, and 5 percent have purple eyes and normal wings. After discussing your results with your colleagues, you realize that for a fly in the F_1 generation to have the phenotypes purple eyes and normal wings, or normal eyes and vestigial wings, a crossover must have occurred during meiosis. Since the chromosomes of these F_1 flies have a different combination of alleles than the chromosomes of the P generation, these flies are called **recombinant types**, or recombinants. The F_1 flies with the phenotypes normal eyes and normal wings or purple eyes and vestigial wings are called **parental types** because their chromosomes are identical to those of the P generation.

As you know, the greater the distance is between linked genes, the more likely they are to cross over during meiosis. In fact, the percentage of recombinant types in the F_1 generation is directly proportional to the distance between the genes. The percentage of flies that are recombinant types corresponds to the **recombination frequency**—that is, the percentage of times that a crossover occurred as P gametes were formed.

Now imagine that your cross produces 1000 offspring. Of these offspring, 450 of have normal eyes and normal wings, 450 have purple eyes and vestigial wings, 50 have normal eyes and vestigial wings, and 50 have purple eyes and normal wings. The recombination frequency would be determined as follows:

$$\text{Recombination frequency} = \frac{50 + 50}{1000} \times 100\% = 10\%$$

$$\text{Recombination frequency} = \frac{\text{number of recombinant types}}{\text{total number of offspring}} \times 100\%$$

Thus, in your cross, 10% of the F₁ generation were recombinant types. Because the recombination frequency is directly proportional to map distance (1% = 1 map unit), you can use this value to create a chromosome map showing the relative distances between the linked genes. For example, in your cross, the genes for eye colour and wing type are 10 map units apart.

After conducting further crosses, you discover that the map distances between three different genes on chromosome 2 are as follows:
- The distance between the genes for eye colour and wing type is 10 map units.
- The distance between the genes for eye colour and body colour is 4 map units.
- The distance between the genes for body colour and wing type is 6 map units.

How does this information help you determine the order in which the genes are found on chromosome 2? In order to fit the data, the gene for eye colour must be 4 map units from the gene for body colour and 10 map units away from the gene for wing type. Thus, in order for the gene for body colour to be 6 map units away from the gene for wing type, it must fall between the other two genes as shown in Figure 17.16.

• • •

18 Differentiate between the chromosome theory of inheritance and the gene-chromosome theory.

19 What is chromosome mapping?

20 What is a map unit?

21 Distinguish between the terms recombinant types and parental types.

• • •

Sex-Linked Inheritance

As you know, the first gene to be mapped to a specific chromosome was the gene coding for white eye colour in *Drosophila melanogaster*. Once Morgan realized that this gene is located on the X chromosome,

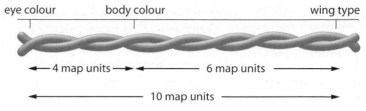

eye colour | body colour | wing type

◄— 4 map units —► ◄— 6 map units —►

◄———— 10 map units ————►

Figure 17.16 Mapping chromosomes. Genes are arranged linearly on the chromosome at specific gene loci.

he found that the unusual inheritance pattern could be explained by simple Mendelian genetics.

Like humans, female fruit flies have two X chromosomes, while males have one X chromosome and one Y chromosome. The F₁ data indicated that the white-eye trait is recessive. Therefore, to have white eyes, a female fruit fly must inherit an X chromosome with the recessive allele from each parent. A male fruit fly, however, has to inherit only a single recessive allele from the female parent to display the white-eye trait because it has only one X chromosome. (The male parent donates the Y chromosome, which does not carry the allele.)

Traits that are controlled by genes on either the X or Y chromosome are called **sex-linked traits**. Punnett squares can be used to predict the outcome of crosses that involve sex-linked traits. Figure 17.17 shows a cross between a wild-type female and a white-eyed male.

In humans, a common form of colour blindness is the result of a recessive trait that is carried on the X chromosome. This trait makes it difficult to distinguish between reds and greens.

BiologyFile

Try This
Use a Punnett square to predict the genotype and phenotype ratios of the F₂ generation of fruit flies, crossing a male and a female from the F₁ generation.

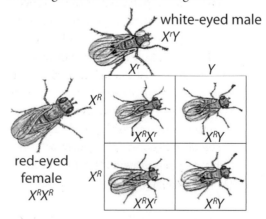

Figure 17.17 A cross of fruit flies, showing the inheritance of alleles on the X chromosome. What is the expected ratio of male to female offspring from this cross?

In Part A of this activity, you will follow a procedure to construct a chromosome map. In preparation for future studies of genetics, your teacher may choose to assign Part B to expose you to the special notation geneticists use for analyzing linked genes.

Part A: Constructing a Chromosome Map

Procedure

1. Using the table below as a guide, determine the map distance between the linked genes for eye colour and wing type in the following experiment.

   You perform the following cross: $PpVv \times ppvv$. You count 1000 offspring in the F_1 generation. You find that 406 of the flies have normal eyes and normal wings, 398 have purple eyes and vestigial wings, 96 have normal eyes and vestigial wings, and 100 have purple eyes and normal wings.

2. From previous research findings, you know that the distance between the gene for eye colour and the gene for body colour is 12.2 map units, and the gene for body colour is 7.4 map units away from the gene for wing type. All three genes are on the same chromosome. Draw a chromosome map showing the relative distances between the three linked genes.

Analysis

1. You conduct the same cross again, but this time you get an almost exact 1:1 ratio of flies with normal eyes and normal wings to flies with purple eyes and vestigial wings. There are no recombinant types. Provide two explanations that might account for these results.

2. Linkage data has been used to map genes on the chromosomes of *Drosophila melanogaster*. Do you think such data could be used to map human chromosomes? Explain your reasoning.

Part B: Using Linked Gene Notation

In order to describe linked genes, fruit fly geneticists developed a different notation for genes. The normal allele—the allele that is nearly always found in natural populations—is called the *wild type* allele. The wild type allele is represented with a plus sign (+). The mutant allele for a gene is represented with lower-case italic letters. Linked genes are represented with a horizontal line or a slash.

For example, the gene for purple eyes (*pr*) and the gene for vestigial wings (*vg*) are on chromosome number 2. The homozygous recessive genotype is represented as $\frac{prvg}{prvg}$ or $pr\,vg\,/\,pr\,vg$ to indicate that these genes are on the same chromosome. The homozygous dominant genotype is represented as $\frac{+\ +}{+\ +}$ or $+ +\,/\,+ +$.

Procedure

1. Create a chromosome map of three linked genes based on the research presented below.

   a) In fruit flies, the mutant gene *d* causes short legs and the mutant gene *pr* causes purple eyes. A geneticist performs the following cross: $pr\,d\,/\,+ + \times pr\,d\,/\,pr\,d$. She counts 1000 offspring and finds 391 wild type, 115 purple-eyed and normal-legged, 105 normal-eyed and short-legged, and 389 purple-eyed and short-legged. What is the map distance between the genes for leg length and eye colour?

   b) The same geneticist then performs the following cross: $vg\,d\,/\,+ + \times vg\,d\,/\,vg\,d$. She counts 1000 offspring and finds 350 wild type, 154 vestigial-winged and normal-legged, 153 normal-winged and short-legged, and 343 vestigial-winged and short-legged. What is the map distance between the genes for leg length and wing type?

   c) The recombination frequency for the gene for eye colour and the gene for wing type is 8.7%. What is the map distance between these two genes? Draw a chromosome map showing the relative distances between all three linked genes studied in Part B.

Analysis

1. Do you think the linked gene notation used by geneticists simplifies or complicates linked gene analysis? Explain your reasoning.

Steps to determine map distance

Step	Example
Perform a cross between a fly that is known to be heterozygous for both traits and a fly that is homozygous recessive for both traits.	$PpVv \times ppvv$
Collect a large number of F_1 flies from the cross. Determine the number of flies with each of the possible phenotypes.	Possible non-recombinant phenotypes: • purple eye, vestigial wing • normal eye, normal wing Possible recombinant phenotypes: • purple eye, normal wing • normal eye, vestigial wing
Calculate the total number of recombinant F_1 phenotypes as a percentage of the total number of F_1 flies. This gives you the recombination frequency and the number of map units separating the two genes.	$\dfrac{\text{number of recombinant types}}{\text{total number of offspring}} \times 100\%$

For example, people who are red-green colour blind cannot see the number in Figure 17.18. About 8 percent of men and 0.4 percent of women have this form of colour blindness. Figure 17.19 shows how this trait is passed on in families.

In humans and most other animals, only the male carries a Y chromosome. In these species, Y-linked traits are passed only from males to their sons. A female cannot be a carrier of a Y-linked trait. There are relatively few Y-linked traits. The gene for hairy ears is found on the Y chromosome.

Barr Bodies

An extra chromosome or a missing chromosome can result in a serious and even lethal genetic disorder. How, then, is it possible for females to carry two X chromosomes and males only one,

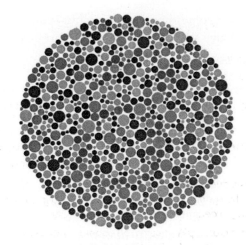

Figure 17.18 Can you see the number hidden in the dots? What can you conclude about your own genotype?

without any apparent difference in the expression of X-linked genes? The answer is that every cell has only one functioning X chromosome. In every female cell, one of the X chromosomes is inactive. The inactive X chromosome is condensed tightly into a structure known as a **Barr body**. Either of the two

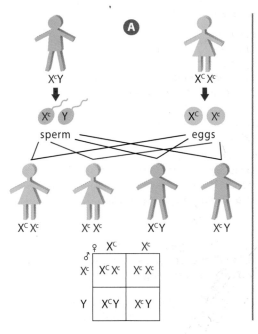

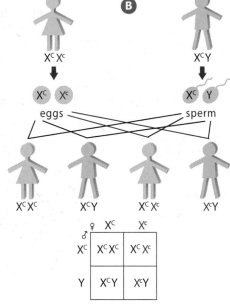

Figure 17.19 An allele for sex-linked colour blindness is passed to the next generation. Males can pass the X-linked recessive trait only to their daughters (**A**). Females who are heterozygous for the condition have a 50 percent chance of passing the recessive allele to a child (**B**). Can a man with normal vision have a child who is colour blind?

Practice Problems

8. A woman who has normal vision and the heterozygous genotype $X^C X^c$ marries a man who is colour-blind ($X^c Y$). What is the expected ratio of genotypes and phenotypes among their children?

9. Suppose that you have one wild-type female fly and one white-eyed male fly. What steps would you follow to produce a white-eyed female fly? Illustrate your steps with Punnett squares.

10. In a species of dog, a mutant gene that causes deafness is found on the Y chromosome. Draw a Punnett square to show the outcomes of a cross between

a) a male dog whose father is deaf and a female dog whose father is not deaf

b) a female dog whose father is deaf and a male dog whose father is not deaf

Figure 17.20 Male tortoiseshell cats are very rare. Why is this not surprising?

X chromosomes can be inactive—and which X chromosome forms a Barr body is random.

A visible effect of the inactivation of one X chromosome is the calico, or tortoiseshell, coat colour in cats, such as the type shown in Figure 17.20. The tortoiseshell coat colour is the result of a random distribution of orange and black patches. The gene that codes for coat colour (orange or black) is located on the X chromosome. (Some tortoiseshell cats also have white patches, but a different gene codes for these.) A tortoiseshell cat is heterozygous for the coat colour allele. That is, one X chromosome carries the allele for black fur, and the other X chromosome carries the allele for orange fur. At an early stage of the cat's embryonic development, one X chromosome in each cell is deactivated. The descendants of these cells have the same inactive X as their parent cells. When the kitten is born, patches of orange show collections of cells in which the X chromosome that is carrying the black allele is deactivated, and patches of black show collections of cells in which the X chromosome that is carrying the orange allele is deactivated.

• • •

22 What are sex-linked traits?

23 Explain why the formation of a Barr body means that human females have only one functioning X chromosome in each somatic cell.

24 Explain how the formation of a Barr body accounts for the coat colour of a tortoiseshell cat.

• • •

Multiple Alleles

You know that a maximum of three genotypes can be produced by one gene with two alleles. Two of the genotypes are homozygous for one of the two alleles, and the third genotype is heterozygous. Only one gene, however, is responsible for all the patterns on the leaves of the white clover (*Trifolium repens*) shown in Figure 17.21. How is this possible?

In clover, as in most other organisms, many genes have more than two alleles. A gene with more than two alleles is said to have **multiple alleles**. Any individual organism has only two alleles for each gene (one allele on each homologous chromosome), but many different alleles exist within the population as a whole. If you examine the genotypes below each phenotype in Figure 17.21, you can see that there are seven different alleles for cloverleaf patterns.

In humans, a single gene determines a person's ABO blood type. This gene determines the type of antigen, if any, that is attached to the cell membrane of red blood cells. The gene is designated I, and it has three common alleles: I^A, I^B, and i. The different combinations of the three alleles produce four different phenotypes, which are commonly called blood types: A, B, AB, or O. (Refer to Figure 17.22.) The I^A allele is responsible for the presence of

Figure 17.21 A single gene is responsible for each of the 22 patterns that can be expressed in clover leaves.

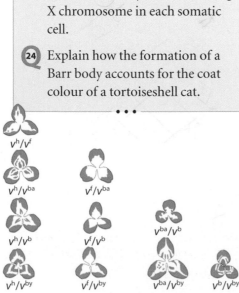

possible alleles from female

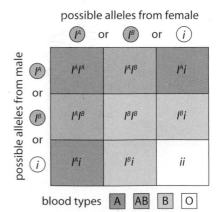

Figure 17.22 Different combinations of the three I gene alleles result in four different blood type phenotypes: type A (either I^AI^A homozygotes or I^Ai heterozygotes), type B (either I^BI^B homozygotes or I^Bi heterozygotes), type AB (I^AI^B heterozygotes) and type O (ii homozygotes).

Table 17.2 ABO Blood Types

Genotype	Phenotype	Antigen
ii	O	none
$I^A i$	A	A
$I^A I^A$	A	A
$I^B i$	B	B
$I^B I^B$	B	B
$I^A I^B$	AB	A and B

an A antigen on the red blood cells. The I^B allele is responsible for the presence of the B antigen, and the i allele causes there to be no antigen. Of the three possible alleles that determine blood type, one (i) is recessive to the other two, and the other two (I^A and I^B) are co-dominant with each other. Table 17.2 shows blood genotypes, along with their phenotypes and the antigens on the red blood cells.

Another well-researched example of multiple alleles involves coat colour in rabbits, as shown in Figure 17.23. The gene that controls coat colour in rabbits has four alleles: agouti (C), chinchilla (c^{ch}), Himalayan (c^h), and albino (c). In the order given, each allele is dominant to all the alleles that follow. The **order of dominance** sequence can be written as $C > c^{ch} > c^h > c$, where the symbol $>$ means "is dominant to."

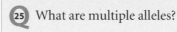

25 What are multiple alleles?

The Sample Problem on page 606 will help you learn how to analyze crosses that involve multiple alleles. Study the problem-solving strategy carefully, and then use it to solve the Practice Problems that follow.

Polygenic Inheritance

Plant height was one of the traits that Mendel studied. He carefully selected plants that had strikingly different heights so there would be no question about phenotypes when he counted offspring. After Mendel worked out the basic mechanisms of inheritance, other people began to look at **continuous traits**—traits for which the phenotypes vary gradually from one extreme to another. Some examples of continuous traits include height in humans, ear length in corn, kernel colour in wheat, and weight of beans. Continuous traits cannot be placed into discrete categories (such as "colour blind" and "not colour blind"). Instead, they vary over a continuum. For example, humans cannot simply be categorized as "short" and "tall." Instead, height in humans

BiologyFile

Try This
Recall your studies of evolution and speciation in Chapter 4. How could polygenic inheritance contribute to the processes of evolution and speciation?

Figure 17.23 The agouti rabbit **(A)** could have genotypes CC, Cc^{ch}, Cc^h, or Cc. The chinchilla rabbit **(B)** could have genotypes $c^{ch}c^{ch}$, $c^{ch}c^h$, or $c^{ch}c$. The Himalayan rabbit **(C)** could have genotypes $c^h c^h$ or $c^h c$. The albino rabbit **(D)** must have the genotype cc.

Human Blood Types

Problem

If a man has type O blood and a woman has type B blood, what possible blood types could their children have? If this couple has six children, all with type B blood, what could you state about the woman's genotype?

What Is Required?

Possible blood types of children
Statement about woman's genotype

What Is Given?

The man has type O blood.
The woman has type B blood.

Plan Your Strategy

Step 1 Determine the possible genotypes of the man and the woman.
Step 2 Make Punnett squares for all the possible combinations of genotypes.
Step 3 List all the possible genotypes of the children.
Step 4 State all the possible phenotypes (blood types) produced by these genotypes.

Act on Your Strategy

Step 1
The man must have the genotype *ii*.
The woman could have genotype $I^B i$ or $I^B I^B$.

Step 2

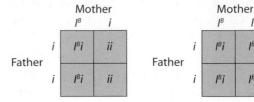

Step 3
Children could have genotypes $I^B i$ or *ii*. These genotypes produce type B and type O blood, respectively.

Step 4
If the couple has six children with type B blood, you would suspect that the woman's genotype is $I^B I^B$. You could not be certain, however, because the processes involved in gamete formation are random. The woman could have the genotype $I^B i$, but none of the children received the *i* allele. (If the woman has the genotype $I^B i$, the chances of all six children receiving her I^B allele are 1 in 64, or about 1.6 percent.)

Check Your Solution

The only genotype that produces type O blood is *ii*. To produce type B blood, the woman must have at least one I^B allele. Her second allele could be *i* or I^B. All the children had to receive an *i* allele from their father. They could receive either an *i* or an I^B allele from their mother.

---

11. If a man has type AB blood and a woman has type A blood, what possible blood types could their children have?

12. In one family, all three siblings have type B blood.

   a) Use Punnett squares to show how two different sets of parent genotypes could produce this result.

   b) Which of the two sets of potential parents in your answer to (a) is more likely to be the parents of these siblings?

13. A couple just brought home a new baby from the hospital. They begin to believe that the hospital switched babies, and the baby they brought home is not theirs. They check the hospital records and find that the man's blood type is B, the woman's blood type is AB, and the baby's blood type is O. Could the baby be theirs?

14. A chinchilla rabbit with genotype $c^{ch}c^h$ is crossed with a Himalayan rabbit with genotype $c^h c$. What is the expected ratio of phenotypes among the offspring of this cross?

15. Some of the offspring of a chinchilla rabbit and a Himalayan rabbit are albino. What must be the genotypes of the parent rabbits?

16. Could a mating between a chinchilla rabbit and an albino rabbit produce a Himalayan rabbit? Explain your reasoning, with reference to the genotypes and phenotypes of the parents and possible offspring.

17. Four children have the following blood types: A, B, AB, and O. Could these children have the same two biological parents? Explain.

varies over a wide range of values. Thus, it is a continuous trait. How is it possible for discrete elements, such as genes, to control a gradually changing trait?

Continuous traits are usually controlled by more than one gene. It is often difficult to determine the precise number of genes that control a given trait, but there could be as many as five or more for some traits. Traits that are controlled by many genes are called **polygenic traits**. A group of genes that all contribute to the same trait is called a *polygene*. Each dominant allele contributes to the trait—for example, adds to a person's height. Recessive alleles do not contribute to the trait.

To see how polygenes generate offspring with a continuous trait, consider ear length in corn. Assume that ear length is controlled by two genes, *A* and *B*. In true-breeding corn with the genotype *AABB*, four dominant alleles contribute to ear length. As a result, this genotype has the longest ears. True-breeding corn with the genotype *aabb* has four recessive alleles, none of which

contribute to ear length. Thus, this genotype has the shortest ears. If true-breeding lines for shortest ears of corn and longest ears of corn are crossed, the F$_1$ generation will have medium-length ears (*AaBb*) where two dominant alleles contribute to ear length.

P   *AABB* × *aabb*

F$_1$ *AaBb*

The Punnett square for the F$_2$ generation is shown in Figure 17.24. With just two genes, creating a range of zero to four contributing alleles, you start to see a distribution of ear lengths. If there are three genes (*A*, *B*, and *C*) creating a range of zero to six contributing alleles, the ratio of phenotypes is 1:6:15:20:15:6:1, as shown in bar graph C in Figure 17.24. As you can see, when more genes contribute to ear length, the curve representing ear length becomes more gradual. Environmental conditions, such as temperature, precipitation, and soil composition, also influence ear length in corn. The overall result is a very gradual curve representing ear length.

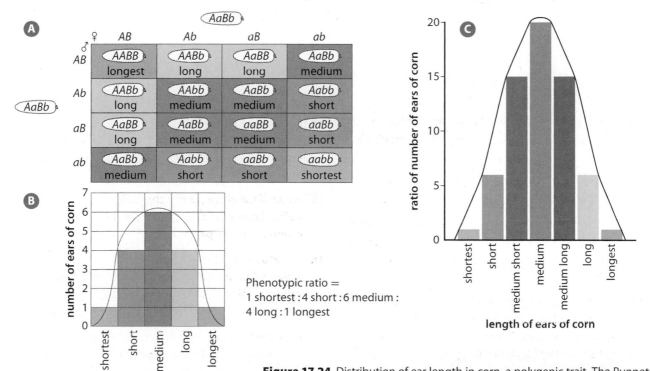

Phenotypic ratio =
1 shortest : 4 short : 6 medium :
4 long : 1 longest

Figure 17.24 Distribution of ear length in corn, a polygenic trait. The Punnett square **(A)** shows a cross between corn with medium-length ears (*AaBb*). The resulting phenotype ratio of 1:4:6:4:1 is graphed in **(B)**. In graph **(C)**, three genes control ear length, resulting in a more gradual-length distribution curve.

Target Skills

Designing and **performing** an experiment to demonstrate a causal relationship between an environmental factor and the expression of genetic information in plants

Environmental Influences on Gene Expression

As you know, chlorophyll is the molecule that allows plants to capture energy from sunlight and use this energy to produce nutrients. Chlorophyll is also the pigment that gives leaves their green colour. Plants that produce chlorophyll appear green, while plants that do not produce chlorophyll appear pale yellow.

You will work in small groups for this investigation. Using the materials provided, your group will design and conduct an experiment to test the influence of light on the production of chlorophyll. Your experiment must enable you to draw conclusions about

- the minimum duration of exposure to light required to trigger the production of chlorophyll
- whether the triggering event is reversible (that is, whether chlorophyll production starts and stops as environmental conditions change)

Question

How does light influence the production of chlorophyll in germinating plants?

Hypothesis

Formulate a hypothesis to explain how light influences the expression of the genes responsible for chlorophyll production. You will use this hypothesis as the basis of your experimental design.

Safety Precautions

Wash your hands after handling materials in the laboratory.

Materials

- seeds (All seeds carry the same genes for chlorophyll production.)
- petri dishes
- shoe boxes
- graduated cylinder
- labels
- water
- light source
- paper towels

Experimental Plan

1. Brainstorm several methods you could use to test your hypothesis. As a group, select one method for your experimental design.

2. Your experimental design should include the collection of qualitative and quantitative data.

3. Identify the responding and manipulated variables. Which variables do you need to control?

4. As you prepare your procedure, be sure to consider the time required for each step.

5. Prepare the data table you will use to record your observations. Decide what form (such as a chart or graph) you will use to present your results.

6. Review your procedure with your teacher. When your procedure has been approved by your teacher and all the members of your group, you are ready to begin.

Data and Observations

7. Record your observations in your table. Make notes about any findings that do not fit in your data table. Record any questions that come up as you conduct your experiment.

Analysis

1. Did your observations support your hypothesis? Explain.

2. Did your experiment allow you to draw conclusions about the inheritance of chlorophyll-producing genes? Why or why not?

3. Identify the variables you considered when designing your experiment. Explain why you needed to consider each variable to obtain scientifically valid results.

Conclusions

4. State your conclusions about the relationship between exposure to light and expression of chlorophyll-producing genes.

5. Could a different hypothesis also explain the results of your experiment? How could you design an experiment to test this different hypothesis?

Extensions

6. What social benefit could come from understanding the effect of light on chlorophyll production?

26 What is the difference between a trait that has multiple alleles and a trait that is controlled by multiple genes? Give an example of each.

27 What is a continuous trait?

28 Give an example of one way (other than the ways described above) that environment can influence the expression of genetic traits.

Figure 17.25 Siamese and Burmese cats have an allele that produces a dark fur colour. All the cells have the same allele, but it is expressed only in cells whose temperature is lower than about 33 °C.

Genes and the Environment

Environmental conditions often affect the expression of genetic traits. For example, some genes are influenced by temperature. The colour pattern of Himalayan rabbits (Figure 17.23) is similar to the colour pattern of Siamese cats (see Figure 17.25). Their fur is pigmented on the cooler parts of their bodies: the face, ears, tails, and feet. In these animals, dark colouring is the result of a gene that is only active below a certain temperature. Another effect of a gene influenced by temperature can be seen in fruit flies. The expression of a mutant form called curly wings depends on temperature. If flies that are homozygous for curly wings are raised at 25 °C, their wings will be curly. If they are raised at 16 °C, their wings will be straight.

Section 17.2 Summary

- Several variables that extend classical Mendelian genetics.
- These variables produce patterns of inheritance and phenotypes that do not, at first, appear to be consistent with Mendel's laws. Each is consistent, however, with the gene-chromosome theory.
- Sex-linked traits are expressed in different ratios by male and female offspring, because they are governed by the segregation of X and Y chromosomes.
- Linked genes do not segregate independently. Instead, the probability of recombination is determined by the relative positions of the alleles on the chromosome.
- The frequency of recombination can be used to construct a chromosome map.
- Other inheritance patterns that extend Mendel's laws are those for traits that are influenced by more than one gene or by environmental conditions, as well as those with multiple alleles.

Section 17.2 Review

1. Describe how the process of crossing over of non-sister chromatids led to an understanding of linked genes.

2. A woman with normal vision marries a man with normal vision. They have three children, and one is colour blind.

   a) What can you conclude about the genotypes of the parents?

   b) What sex is the child who is colour blind? How do you know?

3. Could a person with type AB blood have a child with type O blood? Explain.

4. Your friend keeps rabbits as pets. She has bred her female albino rabbit with her male Himalayan rabbit. "I'm hoping I'll get some agouti rabbits," she says. What are her chances of getting an agouti rabbit? Explain.

5. In one species of bean plant, weight is influenced by two different genes.

   a) How many weight classes would you expect to find in this plant population? Explain using a Punnett square or another visual representation.

   b) When you analyze the weights of several beans from the same cross, you find that many beans have weights between the predicted weight classes. Identify two other factors that could influence the bean phenotypes.

6. Siamese cats that spend their lives indoors tend to have lighter-coloured fur than Siamese cats that live outdoors. What genetic process could account for this change?

Genetics and Society

Figure 17.26 Farmers in all three Prairie provinces grow large quantities of canola (*Brassica napus*). In Alberta, close to one million hectares of cropland are seeded with canola each year.

The field of genetics, as it is known today, is a relatively recent scientific discipline, originating with Gregor Mendel. However, genetics is rooted—literally—much farther in the past, in the earliest practices of agriculture. Traditional agriculture involves the controlled breeding of plants and animals with specific combinations of useful or desirable inherited phenotypes. Traditional agriculture is often imprecise, because it combines many genes (and, therefore, many traits) at a time. Nevertheless, in the hands of skillful, observant, and patient farmers and breeders, selective breeding has resulted in the Appaloosa (recall the chapter introduction) and many of the plant and animal products on which modern society depends.

Breeding Plants

About 7000 years ago, in the area that is now southern Mexico, Native American peoples were breeding maize (more commonly called corn, *Zea mays*). The evolution of maize, which became a staple in their diet, required thousands of generations of selecting and breeding the plants that produced the largest grains and the most clusters of grain. For years, biologists thought that maize was descended from a plant called teosinte (*Zea mexicana*). Studies involving both genetics and archeology now cast doubt on this hypothesis. Maize is related to teosinte, but may have resulted from a cross involving another source of genes from gamagrass (*Tripsacum* sp.). In either case, modern maize is the product of thousands of years of careful breeding.

The development of canola (see Figure 17.26) by plant breeders at Agriculture Canada's Research Centre in Saskatoon is a more recent example of a success story involving selective breeding. Oil from the oilseed plant, also called rapeseed, was long used as a lubricant. Since two chemicals that are found in rapeseed oil—erucic acid and glucosinolates—are toxic to laboratory animals, rapeseed oil was banned for human consumption. In the 1970s, plant scientists in Saskatoon carried out a breeding program that successfully developed a variety of rapeseed with such low levels of erucic acid and glucosinolates that the oil has been approved for human consumption.

The new variety was named *canola*, in recognition of its Canadian origin. Canola is considered to be one of the healthiest vegetable oils available because it is high in monounsaturated and polyunsaturated fats—factors that decrease the likelihood of plaque-forming deposits in arteries. Canola is now grown and used worldwide.

Breeding Animals

Historical records show that the Shorthorn cow, shown in Figure 17.27, first became a recognized breed about 400 years ago in Northern England. This makes the Shorthorn one of the world's oldest established breeds of domestic cattle. Shorthorn cows were first imported to North America in the mid-1800s, and they quickly became popular as both dairy and beef cattle.

Research teams continue to study ways to improve the Shorthorn's traits. Some estimates suggest that the average milk production of Canadian Shorthorn herds increased by almost 30 percent between 1990 and 2000. Successful breeding programs such as this rely on an understanding of Mendelian genetics. For example, although bulls do not produce milk, they can carry genes that make their female offspring good milk producers. Animal breeders can use the characteristics of offspring to deduce which bulls carry these genes.

Similar breeding programs have been used in the Canadian beef industry. At one time, a steak was considered to be good if it had a lot of "marbling" of fat. With current knowledge that animal fat is not as healthy for the diet as lean meat, cattle have been bred to be leaner. Pigs have also been bred to produce leaner meat. When nutritionists began to emphasize the dangers of consuming too much cholesterol, chicken breeders developed chickens that produce eggs with less cholesterol. Thus, knowledge of both nutrition and animal genetics has made it possible to breed animals that provide larger amounts of healthier products.

29 Give an example (other than those provided in the textbook) of how selective breeding has developed a new species of plant or animal.

Figure 17.27 The Canadian Milking Shorthorn is found on many dairy farms on the Prairies. What steps would you take to find out if this bull's female offspring are likely to be good milk producers?

Human Genetics

In the previous two sections, you have learned that the controlled breeding of plants and animals was the basis for many breakthroughs in genetics research. This kind of approach, however, does not work in the study of human genetics. It is clearly impossible for researchers to perform experimental crosses between selected men and women. As well, researchers cannot accumulate large numbers of offspring from the same parents in order to improve the statistical reliability of their data. Instead, when geneticists want to learn about the inheritance of human traits, they collect as much information about a family's history as they can and use this information to create a diagram called a pedigree. A **pedigree** is a type of flowchart that uses symbols to show the patterns of relationships and traits in a family over many generations (see Figure 17.28 on the next page).

Analyzing a Human Pedigree

You can use a pedigree to determine the pattern of inheritance of a particular trait. Examine the pedigree in Figure 17.29 on the next page.

BiologyFile

Web Link
The Newfoundland Pony is a breed of horse that arose during the history of settlement in Newfoundland. What horses are part of the genetic heritage of this breed? What environmental factors influenced the development of this breed? What factors led to its decline, and what is its current population?

www.albertabiology.ca
WWW

Figure 17.28 To make comparisons between different pedigrees as easy as possible, geneticists use several symbols to prepare a pedigree.

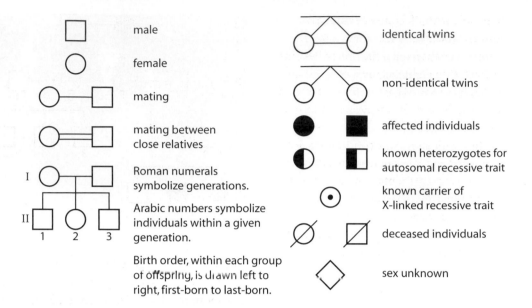

male

female

mating

mating between close relatives

I

II

1   2   3

Roman numerals symbolize generations.

Arabic numbers symbolize individuals within a given generation.

Birth order, within each group of offspring, is drawn left to right, first-born to last-born.

identical twins

non-identical twins

affected individuals

known heterozygotes for autosomal recessive trait

known carrier of X-linked recessive trait

deceased individuals

sex unknown

Autosomal Dominant Inheritance

Autosomes are any chromosomes other than sex chromosomes. *Autosomal inheritance* refers to traits—dominant and recessive—that are coded for by genes on autosomes. Figure 17.29 shows a human pedigree for an autosomal dominant condition called polydactyly—the occurrence of extra fingers or toes. Notice that both parents in the first generation are polydactylous. Two of their three children are also polydactylous. One child is not. Whenever a recessive phenotype occurs in a child of parents who exhibit the dominant trait, the parents must be heterozygous for that trait. Therefore, the normal allele must be recessive, which means that polydactyly is the dominant allele.

Huntington's disease is another autosomal dominant condition. It is a lethal disorder in which the brain deteriorates over a period of about 15 years. Its symptoms usually first appear after age 35, which is often after the affected individual has already had children. Early symptoms include irritability and memory loss, along with involuntary muscle movements. Over time, these symptoms become more severe, resulting in dementia and loss of muscle control.

Marfan syndrome is an autosomal dominant condition that affects the connective tissues. Because these tissues are found throughout the body, the disorder can affect all of the body's systems. Some common symptoms are unusually long bones, which can lead to abnormal curvature of the spine; eye problems, such as glaucoma, and an increased risk of retinal detachment; faulty heart valves; and respiratory problems. Symptoms tend to be mild in young people, but they become increasingly severe over time.

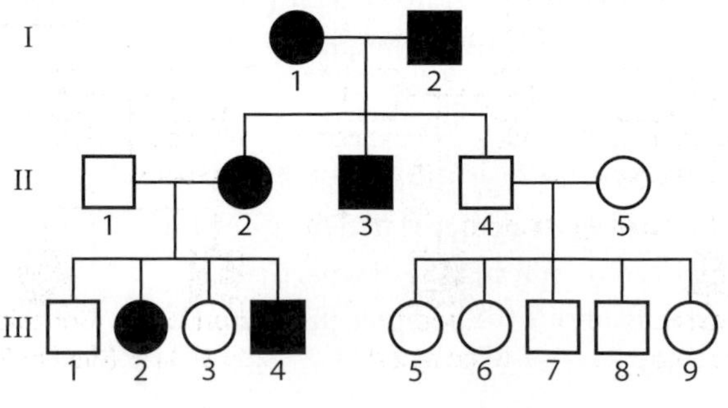

• • •

30 Distinguish between the meaning of roman numerals and arabic numerals in a pedigree.

31 What is autosomal inheritance?

• • •

Autosomal Recessive Inheritance

Figure 17.30 shows a pedigree for an autosomal recessive disorder called phenylketonuria (PKU), which affects the development of the nervous system.

Figure 17.29 This pedigree shows the inheritance of polydactyly—an autosomal dominant trait. Notice that heterozygotes are affected by the trait, and that an affected child must have at least one affected parent. How do you know that individual II 2 is heterozygous?

I

1   2

II

1   2   3   4   5

III

1   2   3   4   5   6   7   8   9

In people with PKU, an enzyme that converts phenylalanine to tyrosine is defective or absent, causing phenylalanine to convert to phenylpyruvic acid, which builds up to toxic levels. (Tyrosine is used by the body to make melanin and certain hormones.) Babies with PKU appear healthy at birth. If their condition is not diagnosed and treated, however, they will become severely mentally handicapped within a few months. Newborns are routinely tested for PKU. If they test positive for the disorder, they are placed on a very restrictive, phenylalanine-free diet. The dietary restrictions can be eased later in life, once the nervous system is more fully developed.

Another autosomal recessive disorder is cystic fibrosis. Cystic fibrosis causes a buildup of thick mucus in the lungs and digestive system. People with cystic fibrosis have an increased risk of pneumonia and respiratory failure, as well as difficulty digesting their food. The treatment includes a combination of physical therapy, nutritional supplements, and antibiotics. An estimated one in 2500 Canadian children is born with cystic fibrosis, making this the most common lethal genetic condition affecting young Canadians. Scientists estimate that one in 25 Canadians carries the recessive gene.

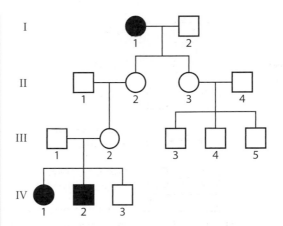

Figure 17.30 A pedigree showing the inheritance of PKU, an autosomal recessive trait. Notice that affected children may have unaffected parents, and that heterozygotes are not affected by the trait. How do you know that individual III 1 is heterozygous?

Sex-Linked Traits

The pedigree in Figure 17.31 shows the inheritance of hemophilia in the European royal families. Hemophilia is a condition that affects the body's ability to produce the proteins involved in blood clotting. People with hemophilia can suffer serious blood loss from simple cuts and bruises. The pedigree shows that males are at a much greater risk of being affected by hemophilia than females. It also shows that women who do not have the condition can pass on the trait to their children. From this information, you can deduce that hemophilia is an X-linked recessive trait.

You have already studied colour blindness, which is an X-linked recessive trait. Duchenne muscular dystrophy is another X-linked recessive trait. People

BiologyFile

FYI
People with PKU must not eat diet foods or drink diet soft drinks that contain the sugar substitute aspartame. Aspartame contains phenylalanine.

Figure 17.31 Pedigree showing the inheritance of hemophilia, an X-linked recessive trait, in the European Royal families. Males are much more likely to have hemophilia than females. Females who are heterozygous for the condition (carriers) can pass the trait on to their children. Note that only offspring that are either affected or carriers are shown in this pedigree.

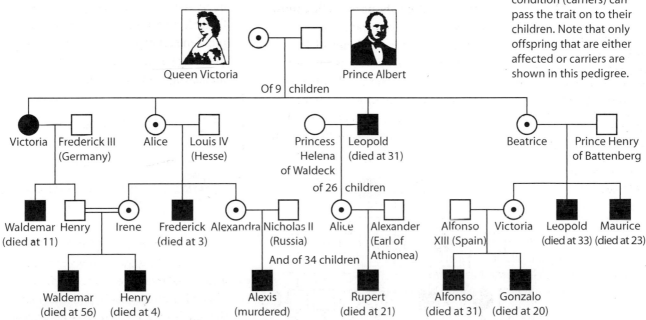

with this disorder cannot manufacture the muscle protein dystrophin. As a result, their muscle tissues weaken and degenerate over time. The symptoms usually appear within the first three to five years of life and become increasingly severe with age. Because the muscles of the heart and respiratory system are also affected, the life expectancy of people with muscular dystrophy is only about 20 years.

• • •

32 How do pedigrees for autosomal recessive and X-linked recessive traits differ?

33 Can a female have hemophilia? Explain.

• • •

Human Genetic Analysis

In 1902, an English physician named Sir Archibald Garrod (1857–1936) coined the phrase "inborn errors in metabolism" to describe four conditions that he realized were inherited: alkaptonuria, albinism, cystinuria, and pentosuria. Garrod also realized that these conditions were caused by the absence of specific enzymes. A few years later, he wrote a book called *Inborn Errors in Metabolism*. Although the field of genetics was in its infancy, Garrod saw patterns of inheritance in the four conditions.

Since Garrod's time, many more genetic conditions have been identified and mapped to specific chromosomes. Table 17.3 lists a few examples. Chromosome mapping helps geneticists develop new ways to identify people

---

Sample Problem

Problem

The following pedigree shows the inheritance of cystic fibrosis, an autosomal recessive trait, in a family. Identify the genotypes of each family member represented in the pedigree.

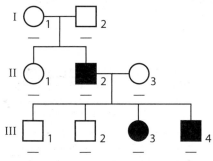

What Is Required?

The genotype of each individual in the pedigree.

What Is Given?

The pedigree is given.

Plan Your Strategy

Step 1 Look for an individual with a phenotype that differs from the corresponding phenotype in both parents. This phenotype must result from a homozygous recessive phenotype.

Step 2 Write the symbol for the dominant allele below every individual who does not show the trait.

Step 3 Both parents of the individuals showing the trait must have at least one recessive allele. All the children of a person showing the trait had to receive one recessive allele from this parent.

Act on Your Strategy

Step 1 Individual II 2 has a different phenotype. Write a homozygous recessive genotype (*aa*) below the symbol for all the individuals who show the trait (II 2, III 3, and III 4).

Step 2 Write the symbol for the one dominant allele (*A*) below all open symbols.

Step 3 Write "*a*" beside "*A*" for I 1, I 2, and II 3.

Step 4 Write "*a*" beside "*A*" for III 1 and III 2.

Step 5 You cannot determine whether II 1 is heterozygous or homozygous dominant.

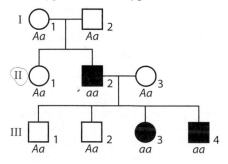

Check Your Solution

Upon checking the pedigree, all genotypes are correct.

18. A curved "hitchhiker's thumb" is recessive to a straight thumb. The following pedigree traces the presence of hitchhiker's thumb in a family. Identify the phenotypes and genotypes of all the people shown in the pedigree. Whose genotypes can you not be certain of?

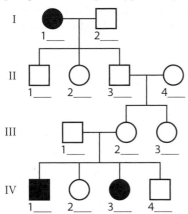

19. In certain families in Norway, woolly hair (hair that looks like sheep's wool) is passed down through the generations. In order for children to have this trait, at least one of their parents must have woolly hair. How is this trait most likely inherited? Draw a pedigree for a family where one of three children and both parents have woolly hair. Identify the genotypes and phenotypes for each individual in the family. Whose genotype can you not be certain of?

20. This pedigree traces tongue rolling in a family. The ability to roll your tongue is controlled by a dominant allele; people with the recessive allele cannot roll their tongue. Identify the phenotypes and genotypes of all the people shown in this pedigree.

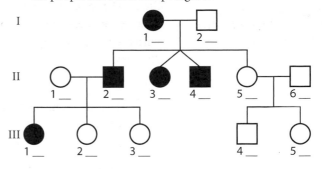

21. Duchenne muscular dystrophy is an X-linked recessive trait. The following pedigree shows the occurrence of this disorder in an extended family. Provide the phenotypes and genotypes of all the individuals in the pedigree.

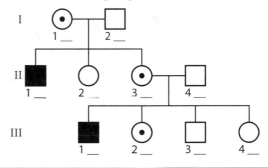

Thought Lab | 17.2 | Creating a Pedigree

Although most characteristics in humans are influenced by more than one gene, some are controlled by single genes. Each of the following is a single-gene trait.
- shape of hairline peaked or smooth
- clasped hands left thumb on top or right thumb on top
- hair on middle segment of fingers or no hair on middle segment of fingers
- tongue rolling ability or inability to roll tongue
- thumb straight or bent back
- earlobe detached or attached

Procedure

1. Work with a partner. Choose a single-gene human trait. Then choose a family to interview. This can be your family or your partner's family, or another family if you know a large number of family members.

2. Interview family members, including grandparents, aunts, uncles, and cousins. Find out which phenotype each person exhibits for your chosen trait.

3. Using the symbols in Figure 17.28 create a pedigree for the trait.

Analysis

1. From the pedigree, determine whether the trait is due to a dominant or recessive allele.

2. Fill in as much of each genotype as you can with the data you have.

3. Do all the data fit the patterns you might expect? If not, what factors could explain the difference?

Table 17.3 Examples of Single-Gene Conditions Mapped to Chromosomes

Chromosome	Condition	Description
4	Huntington's disease	degenerative neurological disease that results in loss of muscle control and dementia
7	cystic fibrosis	condition that causes thick, sticky mucus to build up in the lungs, making breathing difficult and leading to infection; also blocks the pancreas, stopping digestive enzymes from reaching the intestines
12	phenylketonuria (PKU)	condition that prevents breakdown of phenylalanine, causing an accumulation of phenylpyruvic acid, which results in developmental delays in cognitive function
13	retinoblastoma	tumour development on the retina of young children, which is usually fatal if not treated
15	Marfan syndrome	disorder of the connective tissues, causing weakness in the heart, blood vessels, and skeleton, as well as very long limbs
	Prader-Willi syndrome	developmental disorder, causing decreased muscle tone, short stature, and an insatiable appetite; can lead to life-threatening obesity
16	alpha thalassemia	condition in which defective hemoglobin binds oxygen poorly
18	Nieman-Pick disease	brain and nervous system impairment due to accumulation of lysosomes filled with cholesterol
19	maple syrup disease	inability to break down three amino acids, causing an accumulation of by-products and nerve degeneration; usually fatal if untreated
20	severe combined immunodeficiency disease (SCID)	a deficiency in one enzyme, resulting in minimal immune response and susceptibility to all diseases; bone marrow transplant used to replace immune system

who are at risk of developing particular genetic conditions or of passing these conditions to their children. This process is called **genetic screening**. *Drosophila* research has been very helpful in this work, since many human genetic disorders have counterparts in the fruit fly.

Conditions such as alkaptonuria (which causes the affected individual to produce black urine) and albinism (which is a lack of the skin pigment melanin) are rare, but not life threatening. As you have seen, other genetic conditions can cause severe—even fatal—health problems. For this reason, geneticists and medical scientists around the world invest a great deal of effort and money into researching new methods of genetic diagnosis and screening. Every advance brings new questions, however.

If you have the allele for Huntington's disease, for example, would you want to know that you will eventually develop this degenerative neurological disease? If you could find out whether you are a carrier for a disease such as cystic fibrosis, would it make a difference in your decision about having a family? If you were expecting a baby, would you want to know that the baby had a serious inherited condition?

Many people who grapple with questions such as these seek advice from **genetic counsellors**. Genetic counsellors can estimate the risk of inheriting a particular genetic condition. As well, they can explain the symptoms of genetic conditions and the available treatments, provide other information, and, equally importantly, give emotional support.

Section 17.3 Summary

- Although selective breeding has been practiced for centuries, an understanding of Mendelian genetics enables modern scientists to be very selective in the development of new plant and animal breeds.
- A pedigree is a key tool for geneticists who study the inheritance of human traits.
- Analysis of a pedigree indicates whether a trait is autosomal dominant, autosomal recessive, or sex-linked.
- A pedigree can provide information about the genotypes and phenotypes of previous generations, and it can be used to predict the genotypes and phenotypes of future offspring.
- Other methods of genetic screening and diagnosis can also provide information about human genotypes.

Procedure

You have seen a pedigree can be used to trace the inheritance pattern of a single-allele trait. A pedigree can also be used to study multiple-allele traits. In the pedigree below, different blood types are identified by the letters A, B, AB, and O. Examine the pedigree, and then answer the questions that follow.

Analyze

1. Neither individual I 4 or I 6 has ever had their blood tested. What are their blood types?

2. Write the genotypes of as many individuals as you can. Whose genotypes can you not be sure of? Explain.

3. Individual III 3 marries a man with blood type AB, and they have four children. Will any of these children have blood type O? Explain.

4. Individuals II 1 and II 2 have a second child. After you see the child's blood-test results, you know that both parents have the genotype I^Ai. What blood type is the child?

5. Using examples from the pedigree, describe some of the limitations that apply to human genetic analysis. In what ways could these limitations affect genetic research?

6. Blood typing has often been used as an aid in paternity disputes. Can a blood test ever prove that a man is definitely the father of a particular child? Explain.

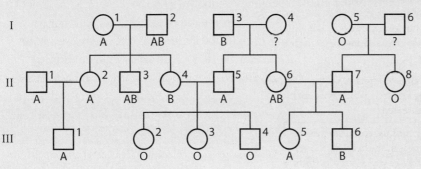

Section 17.3 | Review

1. Give two examples of plants that have been developed through selective breeding techniques.

2. In what ways do the methods of researchers studying human genetics differ from the methods of researchers studying *Drosophila*? Explain.

3. Examine the following pedigree.

   a) What can you deduce about the pattern of inheritance of the trait?

   b) Give one example of a human genetic condition that is passed on in this way.

   c) What is the genotype of individual I 1?

   d) How do the phenotypes of individuals III 1, III 2, and III 3 differ from the predicted ratios? What might account for this difference?

4. You have discovered a new autosomal recessive genetic condition. Individuals with this condition do not survive long after birth, and so do not have children of their own. Will the trait be eliminated from the population over time? Explain.

5. You suspect that you may be a carrier for a serious genetic condition, and you decide to consult a genetic counsellor. What three characteristics would you want the genetic counsellor to have?

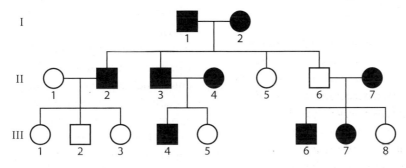

Biobanks

Stored within the cellular fabric of your body tissues and fluids are the biochemical "bytes" that define and comprise your genetic identity. Do your genes belong to you and to no one else?

The Canadian Biotechnology Advisory Committee defines a biobank as "a collection of physical specimens [from a wide sampling of individuals] from which DNA can be derived and the data that can be derived from these DNA samples." A primary goal of biobanking is to "open source" millions of high-quality samples collected from a diverse group of world citizens for the medical benefit of humanity.

Some Key Questions

Human biological materials are routinely obtained during diagnosis and surgery. When diseased tissue is removed, part of the specimen is frequently retained for future clinical, research, or legal purposes. As well, volunteers often donate their bodies, organs, or blood for educational purposes, transplantation, or research. Unlike other information that is used for health purposes, however, genetic information is not just *about* us. Because of its uniqueness, it *is* us. In the future, who will have access to this information and what safeguards will be required? Will this information be available to insurance companies, employers, law enforcement agencies, or marketers of products and services?

Genes hold information not only about the donor, but also about other family members. While welcoming the potential health benefits of genetic research, many people have reservations about possible infringements on their privacy and human rights. One purpose of establishing large-scale human genetic research databases is to create research resources for the future. This raises other questions. Should individuals be contacted for each new use of their data? Should they be financially compensated if the use of their data results in the production of a life-saving drug?

Canada's Plan

Population biobanks are already established or being planned in Sweden, Iceland, Estonia, Tonga, the United Kingdom, and several other countries. Canada is developing a comprehensive position on biobanking, which will be followed by appropriate legislation to outline, delimit, and regulate the activities of institutions or companies that conduct biobank research.

In a background paper called *Survey of National Approaches to the Development of Population Biobanks*, prepared for the Canadian Biotechnology Advisory

Committee in 2003, nine major challenges were put forward for Canada to consider when developing biobanking policies. These challenges are listed below.

Biobanking challenge for Canadians	Example of an associated question or issue
consultation	What steps are necessary to obtain and maintain the public trust?
recruitment	Which individuals, from which segments of the population, will be sampled?
consent	How will the approval of individuals, and Canadian society as a whole, be obtained?
governance	Who's in charge?
commercialization	What rights of ownership do sampled individuals give up—and to whom?
privacy	How will privacy be ensured, and who will be accountable?
communication of research results	Should individuals have access to their personal results or only to those of the aggregate (that is, the population)?
contribution to the welfare of the population	What constitutes a benefit in terms of a population, and how is this to be measured?
contribution to the welfare of humanity	How will all humanity share in and have access to the benefits of biobank research?

• • •

1. Find out how one of the countries that has already established biobanking addresses the moral, social, and legal issues.

2. Biobanking in Canada will be a reality in your lifetime. What opinions do you have and how can you voice them, now and in the future? What questions do you need answered to help you inform and clarify your opinions? What are the possible consequences of "passing the buck" where this particular issue is concerned?

Gregor Mendel was the first person to apply statistical methods to the study of inheritance. Mendel observed that heterozygotes do not express recessive traits, but can pass on these traits to their offspring.

Mendel's law of segregation states that all individuals have two copies of each factor (gene). These copies segregate randomly during gamete formation, and each gamete receives one copy of every factor.

Mendel's law of independent assortment states that the two alleles for one gene assort independently of the alleles for other genes during gamete formation. Parental genotypes can be inferred from the ratio of phenotypes among offspring.

Dominant traits mask recessive traits in heterozygotes. When alleles are co-dominant or incompletely dominant, heterozygotes have a different phenotype from both the homozygous dominant and the homozygous recessive.

Sutton observed that the pattern of Mendelian inheritance follows the movement of chromosomes during meiosis. He proposed the chromosome theory of inheritance. Morgan found that his experimental results could be explained if genes were arranged in a linear manner along chromosomes. He proposed the gene-chromosome theory.

Linked genes do not assort independently. Instead, the probability of recombination among linked genes increases with the distance that separates the two genes. Phenotype ratios can be used to calculate the map distance between linked genes.

Not all traits follow the same patterns of inheritance. Polygenetic traits, and the presence of multiple alleles all result in genotype ratios that differ from Mendelian ratios in offspring.

Sex-linked traits have distinct patterns of inheritance. Recessive traits that are carried on the X chromosome are expressed far more frequently in men than in women. Environmental factors also can influence the expression of certain traits.

An understanding of the mechanisms and patterns of inheritance allows humans to develop new breeds of plants and animals that have desired traits.

Human inheritance follows the same principles as inheritance in other organisms. Different approaches are required to study human genetics, however. A pedigree is a tool that is used to trace patterns of inheritance of particular human traits. Pedigrees show distinct patterns for the inheritance of autosomal dominant traits, autosomal recessive traits, and sex-linked traits.

Chapter 17 Graphic Organizer

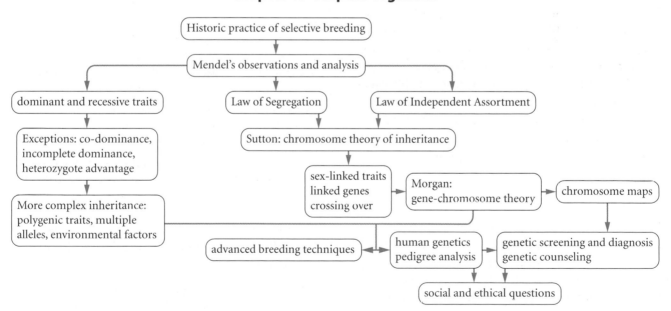

Understanding Concepts

1. Give three reasons that pea plants were an excellent choice for Mendel's research.

2. What is Mendel's law of segregation?

3. In humans, drooping eyelids are dominant to non-drooping eyelids.
   a) What are the two possible genotypes that a person with drooping eyelids might have?
   b) A man who is heterozygous for both alleles marries a woman with non-drooping eyelids. Use a Punnett square to show the expected genotypes and phenotypes of their children.
   c) A man with non-drooping eyelids and a woman with drooping eyelids have three children, all with non-drooping eyelids. How can you explain this outcome?

4. In humans, the gene for albinism is recessive to the gene for normal pigmentation. Your friends Milan and Aila both have normal pigmentation. They have one child who is an albino and are expecting a second child. Milan tells you, "We knew that our chance of having one albino child was 1:4. This means our chance of having *two* albino children is only 1:16, so we can be very sure that our next baby will not be albino." How would you respond? Using a specific example, explain to Milan whether or not his reasoning is correct.

5. A cross of true-breeding purple-flowered and true-breeding white-flowered plants results in F_1 plants that are all lavender (light purple). A cross of two F_1 plants results in an F_2 generation with the following numbers of phenotypes: 28 purple, 52 lavender, and 19 white.
   a) What were the genotypes of the F_1 generation? Explain.
   b) Use a Punnett square to show the predicted phenotypes and genotypes of the F_2 generation.
   c) Describe the type of inheritance that this cross reveals.

6. What is a test cross, and when is it used?

7. In what way does the chromosome theory of inheritance require a revision to Mendel's law of independent assortment?

8. A male mouse with a grey coat is mated with an albino female. Their six offspring all have grey fur. The albino female is then mated with a second grey male mouse. Four of the seven offspring in this litter are albino.
   a) What are the probable genotypes of the three parent mice?
   b) A male from the first litter is mated with a grey female from the second litter. What is the expected ratio of phenotypes among the offspring?

9. A man with type B blood marries a woman with type AB blood. What blood types would you expect to find among their children? What would tell you that the man is heterozygous for type B blood?

10. A woman with type AB blood has a child with the same blood type. What are the possible genotypes of the father?

11. Explain the significance of the Barr body in the expression of sex-linked traits.

12. A breeder of show horses finds that one of his stallions has a genetic defect that affects the production of sperm. The gene associated with this trait is located on the Y chromosome. What is the possibility that the stallion's female offspring could pass on this trait to their sons? Explain.

13. The following diagram shows the results of two crosses. Explain the results and the genetic principle that is illustrated.

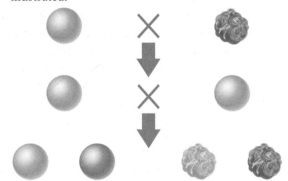

Applying Concepts

14. In foxes, a pair of alleles, *P* and *p*, interact as follows: *PP* is lethal, usually during the embryonic stage; *Pp* produces platinum-coloured fur; and *pp* produces silver foxes. Could a fox breeder establish a true-breeding variety of platinum foxes? Explain.

15. Rudy and Sinead are expecting a baby. They have normal vision, but both of their fathers are colour blind. Determine the chance that the baby will be
   a) a colour-blind girl
   b) a boy with normal vision

16. Fruit flies can have normal wings or stunted wings. In an experiment, you mate several normal-winged females with a male that has stunted wings. In the F_1 generation, only the males have stunted wings.
   a) What can you conclude from this experiment?

b) Design an experiment to demonstrate whether or not females in the F₁ generation can also have stunted wings.

17. Imagine that the first dihybrid crosses Mendel performed had involved traits controlled by closely linked genes.

a) How would Mendel's results have differed from the results of a dihybrid cross involving non-linked genes?

b) What hypothesis might Mendel have developed to explain his results?

c) What experiment could Mendel have performed to test this hypothesis? What would he have observed?

18. Among some breeds of cattle, there is a trait called *polled*. Polled individuals do not develop horns. Suppose that a farmer breeds the same two polled individuals several times and five calves are born. Three of these calves are polled, and two are not. Is this an example of dominant or recessive inheritance? Explain.

19. A farmer wants to breed a variety of taller corn.

a) How can the farmer use variation in the height of the current corn plants to produce taller corn plants?

b) Will the farmer's work be most effective if height in corn plants is determined by polygenic inheritance, multiple alleles, or co-dominant alleles? Explain.

c) The farmer finds that many of the tallest corn plants are also very susceptible to a particular disease. How could the farmer design an experiment to find out if the genes for height are linked to the genes for resistance to the disease?

d) If these genes are linked, what steps could the farmer take to create a breed of corn that is taller and more disease-resistant than the current corn crop?

20. Explain why genes that are more than 50 map units apart on a single chromosome may behave as though they are on different chromosomes.

21. Osteogenesis imperfecta (OI), also known as brittle bone disease, results in extremely fragile bones that tend to break for no apparent reason. The following pedigree traces OI in a family. Based on the pedigree, what sort of inheritance pattern does OI display? Identify the phenotypes and genotypes of all the people shown in this pedigree. Whose genotype can you not be sure of?

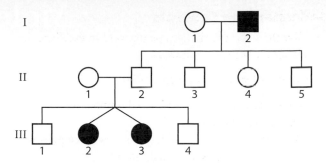

Making Connections

22. Imagine that you are a genetic counsellor. Brian and Sarah come to see you. They are planning to start a family, but they want to know if their children are at risk for cystic fibrosis. Brian's sister has cystic fibrosis. Brian does not have the disease, nor do his parents.

a) What kind of questions do you think Brian and Sarah will ask?

b) How would you answer these questions?

c) What other information could you gather to help you define the risk?

23. Certain populations and cultural groups interest genetic researchers because they may have unique genetic characteristics. The study of these characteristics can contribute to the development of genetic tests and treatments that advance medical research. Who should have access to the genetic information of individuals from these populations and groups? Is this private information, or does it belong to all humanity? Discuss this question with a partner, and brainstorm your ideas. Prepare a presentation that outlines ideas on both sides.

24. People who are heterozygous for a recessive trait do not express the trait, but may pass it on to their children. Do we have a responsibility to inform our children of certain recessive traits they may have inherited from us? Present your thoughts in a short essay.

25. Many breeds of dogs are known for a high incidence of genetic disorders. German Shepherd and Saint Bernard dogs, for example, are predisposed to develop a crippling condition called hip dysplasia. Why are purebred dogs more at risk for such conditions than mixed breeds are? What advice would you give to dog breeders who want to maintain their dogs' purebred pedigrees, but also want their dogs to be as healthy as possible?

Molecular Genetics

Chapter Concepts

18.1 DNA Structure and Replication

- A molecule of DNA is made up of two long strands of nucleotides wound around each other in the shape of a double helix.

- During DNA replication, complementary base pairing ensures that each daughter molecule is identical to the original DNA molecule.

18.2 Protein Synthesis and Gene Expression

- Gene expression involves two basic steps: transcription of genetic information from DNA to RNA, then translation from RNA to protein.

- The genetic code is made up of nucleotide triplets called codons. Each codon corresponds to a specific amino acid.

18.3 Mutations and Genetic Recombination

- Permanent changes in DNA give rise to genetic variation and may also cause hereditary disorders or cancer.

18.4 Genetics and Society

- Genetic technologies have many useful applications but can also give rise to challenging social and ethical questions.

The genetic information that is encoded in this DNA filament might define the colour of flower petals, the antibiotic resistance of a bacterial cell, the mating behaviour of a water bird, or even a child's chance of developing a deadly disorder. How does this kind of information find its way into—and out of—a series of biochemical reactions? Molecular genetics is the study of how DNA stores and transmits genetic information and how that information is expressed phenotypically in the world. This involves studying the unique molecular properties of DNA and the complex interactions between DNA and proteins. Increasingly, molecular genetics also involves confronting difficult moral and ethical questions and even questioning our definition of life itself.

Within the cell, specialized structures called ribosomes (colourized blue) use genetic information (colourized pink) to construct proteins (green).

DNA Extraction

A powerful microscope is needed to observe the shape of a DNA molecule. What does DNA look like to the unaided eye?

Materials

- mortar and pestle
- graduated cylinder
- 250 mL beaker
- small piece of animal tissue
- 50 mL beakers (2)
- 0.9% NaCl solution
- glass stirring rod
- 10% detergent solution
- cheesecloth
- 95% ice-cold ethanol solution

Procedure

1. Place the sample of animal tissue in the mortar. Add 10 mL of the 0.9% NaCl solution, and grind thoroughly with the pestle for 2 to 5 min.

2. Strain the solution through three layers of cheesecloth. Collect the liquid in the 250 mL beaker.

3. Pour the liquid into a 50 mL beaker. Add 1.5 mL of the 10% detergent solution.

4. Estimate the volume of the fluid in the beaker. Then measure approximately twice as much of the ice-cold 95% ethanol into the other 50 mL beaker.

5. Slightly tilt the beaker holding the tissue extract. Gently add the ethanol by pouring ethanol down the inside of the beaker.

6. Gently stir the mixture with the stirring rod. When you see a precipitate form at the boundary of the two liquids, twirl the rod to wind the DNA sample onto the glass rod.

Analysis

1. Describe the DNA you extracted.

2. What kinds of studies and observations do you think researchers would have made as they worked from a description like yours to create a molecular model of DNA? List your ideas. Review and modify your ideas as you work through this chapter.

DNA Structure and Replication

In 1869, a young Swiss physician named Friedrich Miescher coined the term "nucleic acid" to describe a weakly acidic, phosphorus-containing substance that he had isolated from the nuclei of white blood cells. Miescher reported his findings only four years after Mendel had published his research on heredity in garden peas. Almost a century passed, however, before a series of studies and experiments—along with an occasional stroke of luck—led scientists to establish the connection between nucleic acid and Mendel's factors of inheritance.

Today, scientists know that **deoxyribonucleic acid (DNA)** is the nucleic acid molecule that governs the processes of heredity in all plant and animal cells. **Ribonucleic acid (RNA)**, a nucleic acid that plays a role in gene expression and protein synthesis, shares a similar structure with DNA. In the next few pages, you will examine some of the research that led to this knowledge and enabled scientists to deduce the molecular structure of DNA.

Isolating the Material of Heredity

In the early 1900s, a Russian-born American biochemist named Phoebus Levene isolated two types of nucleic acid. He called them *ribose nucleic acid (RNA)* and *deoxyribose nucleic acid (DNA)*. Levene went on to show that chromosomes are made up of a combination of DNA and proteins. Within a few years, Morgan and his team provided the first experimental evidence that genes are located on chromosomes. At this time, scientists did not know whether the DNA or the proteins in chromosomes served as the physical basis for genes. Research to determine the physical structure and function of genes began in earnest after Morgan's work. The first evidence that DNA played a role in heredity came by accident.

The Transforming Principle

In 1928, Frederick Griffith, an English medical officer, designed an experiment to study the pathogenic (disease-causing) bacteria that were responsible for a pneumonia epidemic in London. Griffith set up his experiment using dead *Streptococcus pnemoniae* bacteria as a control. To his surprise, he discovered that the dead pathogenic bacteria had somehow passed on their disease-causing properties to live, non-pathogenic bacteria (see Figure 18.1). Griffith called this phenomenon the **transforming principle**, because something from the heat-killed pathogenic bacteria must have transformed the living non-pathogenic bacteria to make them disease-causing.

Griffith died during World War II, but several scientists built on his work, attempting to identify the agent of transformation. In 1944, the team of Oswald Avery, Colin MacLeod, and Maclyn McCarty, at Rockefeller University in the United States, conducted a series of experiments and discovered the following:
- When they treated heat-killed pathogenic bacteria with a protein-destroying enzyme, transformation still occurred.
- When they treated heat-killed pathogenic bacteria with a DNA-destroying enzyme, transformation did not occur.

These results provided strong evidence for DNA's role in transformation. Even so, most scientists still were not prepared to view DNA as the likely source of hereditary material. Instead, they thought that DNA might activate gene-carrying proteins.

Hershey and Chase: Evidence in Favour of DNA as the Hereditary Material

Convincing evidence that DNA, not proteins, carried genetic information was finally provided in 1952. The American research team of Alfred Hershey and

Griffith's discovery of transformation

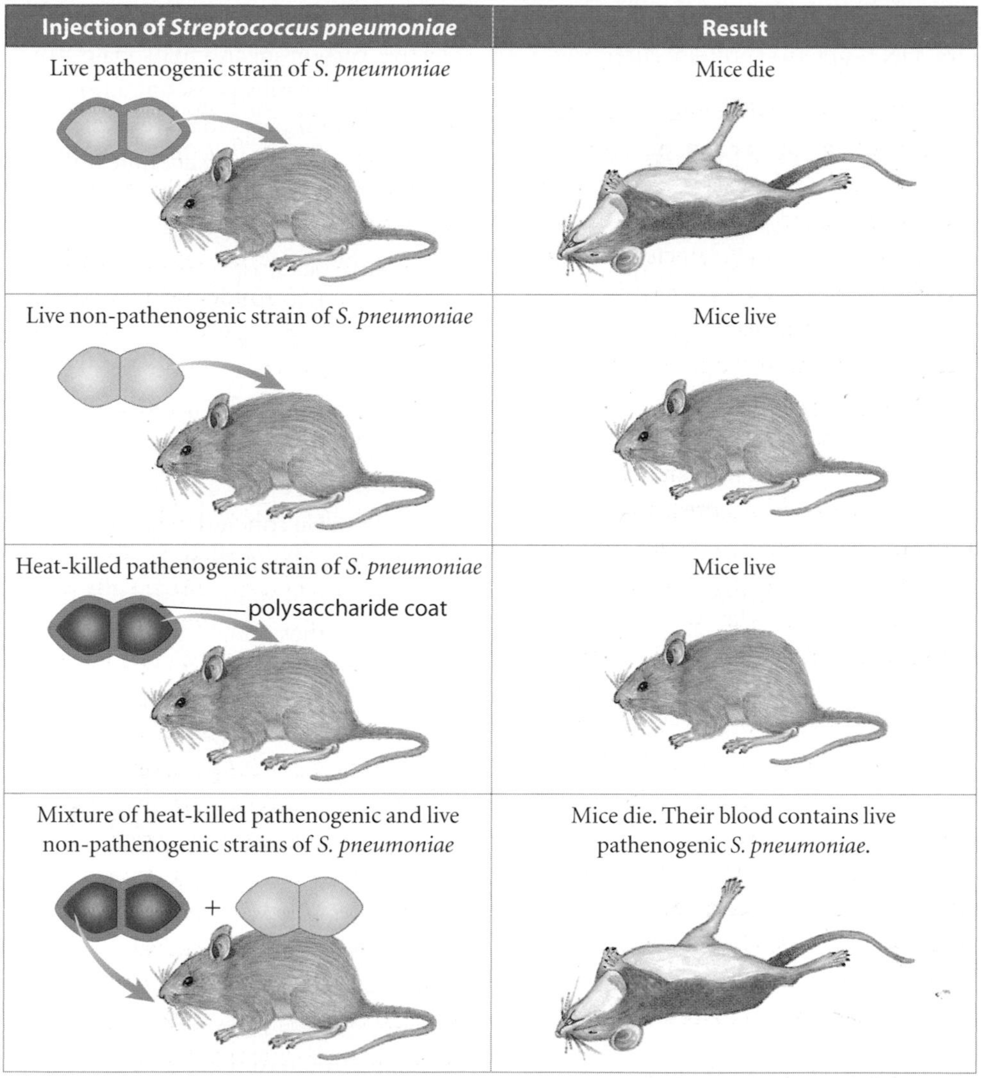

Injection of *Streptococcus pneumoniae*	Result
Live pathenogenic strain of *S. pneumoniae*	Mice die
Live non-pathenogenic strain of *S. pneumoniae*	Mice live
Heat-killed pathenogenic strain of *S. pneumoniae* — polysaccharide coat	Mice live
Mixture of heat-killed pathenogenic and live non-pathenogenic strains of *S. pneumoniae*	Mice die. Their blood contains live pathenogenic *S. pneumoniae*.

Figure 18.1 Frederick Griffith found that hereditary information passed from dead bacterial cells to live bacterial cells. The live cells were transformed from a harmless form into a disease-causing form.

Martha Chase used a new technology, radioactive labelling, to show that genes are made of DNA. Their experiment is illustrated in Figure 18.2 on the next page.

Hershey and Chase used a strain of virus known as a T2 bacteriophage, which consists of a protein coat surrounding a length of DNA. This virus attaches to a bacterial cell and injects genetic information into the cell. The infected cell manufactures new viruses, and then it bursts. The newly released viruses go on to infect other cells. To determine whether viral protein or viral DNA was responsible for taking over the genetic machinery of the host cell, Hershey and Chase created two batches of the virus. In one batch, they labelled the protein coat using radioactive sulfur. In the other

batch, they labelled the DNA with radioactive phosphorus. The labelled viruses were allowed to infect bacterial cells. The cells were then agitated in a blender to separate the viral coats from the bacterial cells. Each medium was

• • •

Q1 What was Miescher's contribution to the study of hereditary material?

Q2 What conclusion did Avery, MacLeod, and McCarty draw from their study of the transforming principle?

Q3 What conclusion did Hershey and Chase draw from their study of the transforming principle?

• • •

tested for radioactivity. The results, shown in Figure 18.2, demonstrated that viral DNA, not viral protein, enters the bacterial cell.

The Structure of DNA

While some scientists were trying to identify the physical agent of heredity, other scientists were studying the structure of DNA. In the early 1900s, Phoebus Levene, a biochemist working at the newly established Rockefeller Institute in New York, contributed the first information about the molecular structure of DNA.

The Chemical Composition of DNA

After isolating DNA and RNA, Levene determined that both molecules are made up of long chains of individual units he called **nucleotides**. Both DNA and RNA contain a combination of four different nucleotides. As shown in Figure 18.3, each DNA nucleotide is composed of a five-carbon sugar, a phosphate group, and one of five nitrogen-containing bases. The four bases that are found in DNA nucleotides are adenine (A), guanine (G), cytosine (C), and thymine (T). RNA has the base uracil (U) instead of thymine. Scientists often identify the nucleotides simply by referring to their bases: A, G, C, T (for DNA) and A, G, C, U (for RNA).

Levene also determined that nucleic acids are made up of long chains of nucleotides, strung together as shown in Figure 18.4. He concluded incorrectly, however, that the nucleotides were present in equal amounts and that they appeared in these chains in a constant and repeated sequence, such as ACTGACTGACTG. This was the main reason why most scientists looked to proteins, rather than DNA, as the hereditary material. Scientists assumed that the molecular structure of DNA was just too simple to provide the tremendous variation in inherited traits.

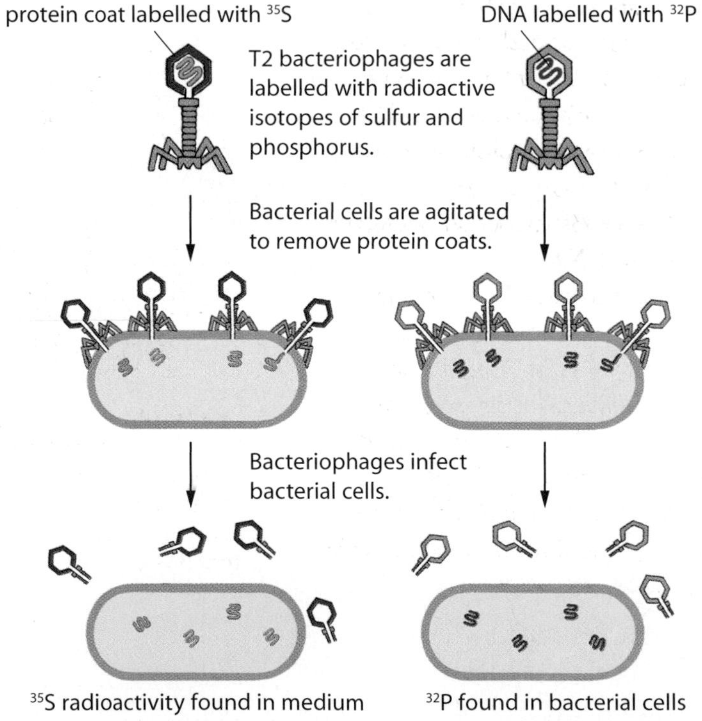

Chargaff's Rule

In the late 1940s, an important series of studies by Ukrainian-American biochemist Erwin Chargaff overturned Levene's incorrect conclusion about the

protein coat labelled with ^{35}S

DNA labelled with ^{32}P

T2 bacteriophages are labelled with radioactive isotopes of sulfur and phosphorus.

Bacterial cells are agitated to remove protein coats.

Bacteriophages infect bacterial cells.

^{35}S radioactivity found in medium

^{32}P found in bacterial cells

Figure 18.2 The Hershey-Chase experiment. The scientists knew that virtually all of the phosphorus present in the T2 virus is in its DNA, while sulfur is found only in its protein coat. Thus, they prepared two different samples of the T2 virus: one tagged with radioactive phosphorus (^{32}P) and the other tagged with radioactive sulfur (^{35}S). Bacterial cells that were infected by viruses with radioactive DNA were radioactive, indicating that the viral DNA entered the host cell. In contrast, bacterial cells that were infected by viruses with radioactive protein coats were not radioactive, indicating that no viral protein entered the host cell. Therefore, DNA must direct the cell to produce new viruses.

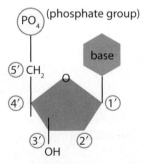

Figure 18.3 The general structure of a DNA nucleotide. An RNA nucleotide has an additional oxygen molecule in the five-carbon sugar ring. Notice the numbering of the carbon atoms on the sugar molecule. The five carbon atoms of the sugar of the nucleotide are numbered 1′ to 5′, and they proceed clockwise from the oxygen atom. The prime symbol (′) indicates that the carbon belongs to the sugar rather than to the base.

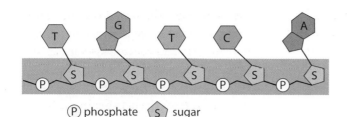

Figure 18.4 Nucleotides are joined together in a long chain. The "backbone" of the chain is made up of alternating sugar and phosphate groups that are joined by chemical bonds. The nitrogenous bases project out from the sugar-phosphate backbone.

(P) phosphate (S) sugar

four nucleotides in DNA. Chargaff found that the nucleotides are not present in equal amounts. Instead, the nucleotides are present in varying, but characteristic, proportions. Most significantly, as shown in Table 18.1, Chargaff found that the amount of adenine in any sample of DNA is always approximately equal to the amount of thymine, and the amount of cytosine is always approximately equal to the amount of guanine. This constant relationship became known as **Chargaff's rule**.

The Three-Dimensional Structure of DNA

Early in the 1950s, British scientist Rosalind Franklin used X-ray photography to analyze the structure of DNA. Her observations provided crucial new information about the molecular structure of DNA.

One of Franklin's images is shown in Figure 18.5. From images like this, she was able to conclude that DNA has a helical structure with two regularly repeating patterns—one recurring at intervals of 0.34 nm, and the other recurring at intervals of 3.4 nm.

As Franklin prepared her samples for photography, she observed how DNA

Table 18.1 Relative Proportions (Percent) of Bases in DNA of Several Organisms

Organism	A (Adenine)	T (Thymine)	G (Guanine)	C (Cytosine)
Mycobacterium tuberculosis	15.1	14.6	34.9	35.4
Escherichia coli	26.0	23.9	24.9	25.2
Yeast	31.3	32.9	18.7	17.1
Herring	27.8	27.5	22.2	22.6
Rat	28.6	28.4	21.4	21.5
Human	30.9	29.4	19.9	19.8

reacted with water. From her observations, she concluded that the nitrogenous bases were located on the inside of the helical structure, and the sugar-phosphate backbone was located on the outside, facing toward the watery nucleus of the cell. Franklin's observations and her detailed X-ray work, along with the work done by Chargaff, proved to be important keys for understanding the structure of DNA.

The partnership between the American geneticist James Watson and the British physicist Francis Crick was the first to produce a structural model of DNA that could account for all the experimental evidence. In 1953, Watson and Crick published a two-page paper describing a double-helix model. This

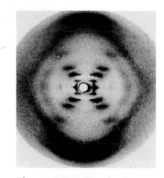

Figure 18.5 Rosalind Franklin's work with X-ray diffraction images provided several important clues about the molecular structure of DNA.

Practice Problems

1. A sample of DNA contains A and C nucleotides in the following proportions: A = 34% and C = 16%. What are the proportions of G and T nucleotides in this sample? (Assume that the characteristic proportions are exactly equal.)

2. Use Chargaff's rule to complete the following table. (Assume that the characteristic proportions are exactly equal.)

Nucleotide Composition of DNA in Sample X

Nucleotide	Proportion (%)
A	24
C	26
G	26
T	24%

FYI
Watson attended a lecture by Rosalind Franklin in 1951. In this lecture, Franklin described her findings in some detail, including her inference about the helical shape of DNA. Watson did not take notes, however, and incorrectly remembered important points of the lecture. His inattention likely cost him and Crick two extra years of work.

model soon became accepted as the molecular structure of DNA.

The Double Helix Structure of DNA

DNA is a thread-like molecule, made up of two long strands of nucleotides that are bound together in a spiral shape called a *double helix*. If the helix were unwound, as shown in Figure 18.6, the DNA molecule would look something like a ladder. The "handrails" of the ladder are the sugar-phosphate backbones of the two nucleotide strands. The "rungs" are the bases that protrude inward at regular intervals along each strand.

From Franklin's images, Watson and Crick knew that the distance between the sugar-phosphate handrails remained constant over the length of the molecule. The nitrogenous bases are different sizes, however. Adenine and guanine are derived from the family of compounds known as purines, which have a double-ring structure. Thymine and cytosine are derived from pyrimidines, which have a single-ring structure. Using Chargaff's rule, Watson and Crick hit upon the idea that an A nucleotide on one chain always sits across from a T nucleotide on the other chain, while a C nucleotide on one chain always sits across from a G nucleotide on the other chain. Thus, the two handrails maintain a constant total distance of three rings. The A-T and C-G pairs are called **complementary base pairs**. The complementary base pairs are held together by hydrogen bonds.

As you can see in Figure 18.6, the two strands of DNA that make up the double helix are not identical. They are complementary to each other. You can always deduce the base sequence on one strand from the base sequence on the other strand. The two strands are **antiparallel**, as well. That is, the phosphate bridges run in opposite directions in the two strands. Each end of a double-stranded DNA molecule contains the 5′ end of one strand and the 3′ end of the complementary strand. These two

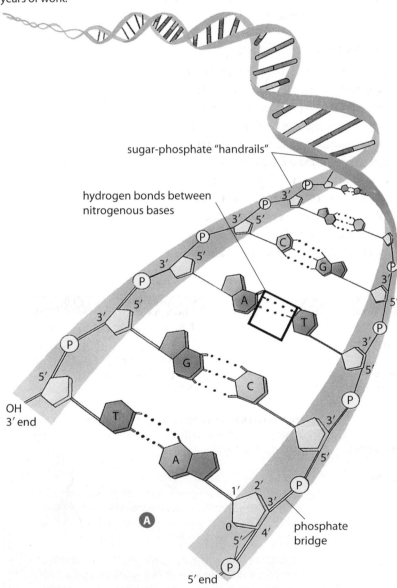

sugar-phosphate "handrails"

hydrogen bonds between nitrogenous bases

OH
3′ end

phosphate bridge

5′ end

A

Figure 18.6 A DNA molecule is made up of two strands of nucleotides that are wound around each other (**A**). The two strands are held together by hydrogen bonds between complementary base pairs. C-G pairs are held together by three hydrogen bonds, and A-T pairs are held together by two hydrogen bonds. Notice that the chains are antiparallel—the 5′ to 3′ orientation runs in the opposite direction on each strand. Another example of antiparallelism is represented by M.C. Escher's sketch, "Drawing Hands" (**B**).

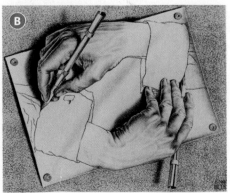

properties have important implications for DNA replication and protein synthesis, as you will see later in this chapter.

• • •

4 What was the contribution of each of the following researchers to the study of DNA?

    a) Chargaff

    b) Franklin

    c) Watson and Crick

5 Explain how complementary base pairing maintains a constant width in a DNA molecule.

• • •

RNA

Like DNA, ribonucleic acid (RNA) is a nucleic acid. Both DNA and RNA are found in most bacteria and in the nuclei of most eukaryotic cells. The molecular structure of RNA is similar to the molecular structure of DNA, with three key differences:

• The sugar component of RNA is ribose rather than deoxyribose.

• RNA does not have the nucleotide thymine (T). In its place is the nucleotide uracil (U).

• RNA remains single-stranded, although the single strand can sometimes fold back on itself to produce regions of complementary base pairs.

The RNA molecule can assume different structures, which result in several different types of RNA, each serving a particular function. The specific structures and functions of some of these types of RNA are described in more detail later in this chapter.

Genes and the Genome

As scientists have learned more about the structure and function of DNA, they have developed new definitions to describe genetic material. For example, a gene was once described as an inheritable trait. Today, a **gene** is defined as a functional sub-unit of DNA that directs the production of one or more polypeptides (protein molecules).

The **genome** of an organism is the sum of all the DNA that is carried in each

---

Thought Lab | **18.1** | **DNA Deductions**

Target Skills

Constructing a model of a portion of a DNA molecule

Analyzing data and **applying** a conceptual model to infer the structure of a DNA molecule

As you have seen, Edwin Chargaff discovered that the nucleotide composition of DNA varies from one species to another. The nucleotide composition always follows certain rules, however. You can use these rules to make deductions about the structure of a particular DNA molecule.

Procedure

1. Imagine that you are analyzing a DNA sample from the liver tissue of a newly discovered species of mouse. Use the information in the table below to complete the nucleotide composition of your sample.

Nucleotide	Presence in DNA sample (percent)
adenine	31
cytosine	
guanine	
thymine	

2. Draw a linear stretch of a double-stranded DNA molecule about 20 base pairs long, with a nucleotide composition that corresponds (as closely as you can)

to the nucleotide composition of your sample. Use solid lines to show chemical bonds and dotted lines to show hydrogen bonds.

Analysis

1. Explain what you would expect to find if you compared the nucleotide composition of your DNA sample with the nucleotide composition of a second DNA sample from the muscle tissue of the same mouse.

2. Would the nucleotide composition of your original DNA sample be different from the nucleotide composition of a tissue sample from the gametes of the same mouse? Explain your answer.

3. Would the nucleotide composition of your original DNA sample be different from the nucleotide composition of a tissue sample from the liver of a deer? Explain your answer.

BiologyFile

BiologyFile

FYI

When scientists first discovered non-coding DNA in the 1970s, it was often referred to as "junk DNA" because scientists hastily assumed that it had no function. Many "junk" sequences have since been shown to serve a variety of important developmental and regulatory functions. Approximately 90 percent of human DNA is "junk."

cell of the organism. This DNA includes genes as well as regions of non-coding DNA, which may play various roles in gene expression. (You will learn more about gene expression later in this chapter.)

Genes are not spaced regularly along chromosomes. In humans, for example, chromosome 4 is about 200 000 000 bases long and has about 800 genes, while chromosome 19 is only 55 000 000 bases long but has almost 1500 genes. Similarly, there is no set relationship between the number of genes in an organism and the total size of its genome. The total human genome is about three billion base pairs, and it includes an estimated 20 000 to 25 000 genes. The single-celled protozoan *Amoeba dubai* has an enormous genome of over 650 billion bases but fewer than 7000 genes. The roundworm *Caenorhabditis elegans* (*C. elegans*), shown in Figure 18.7, has almost as many genes as a human, but its total genome is almost 30 times smaller.

> • • •
> **6** Explain the difference between the terms gene and genome.
> • • •

DNA Replication

Replication is the process of creating an exact copy of a molecule of DNA. As you know from Chapter 16, a cell replicates all of its DNA—its entire genome—once,

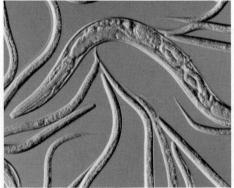

Magnification: 133 ×

Figure 18.7 *C. elegans* has been, and continues to be, an important organism in the study of genetics. Its genome is fairly small, and about one-third of *C. elegans* genes are very similar to those found in humans.

and only once, in the cell cycle, during S phase of interphase. A human cell can copy all of its DNA in a few hours, with an error rate of about one per one billion nucleotide pairs. As a comparison, imagine typing one letter for each base pair in the human genome. Working non-stop at a rate of one letter per second, this would take you close to 100 years to complete. To match the accuracy of a cell, you could make no more than a single one-letter error every 30 years. The speed and accuracy of the replication process relies on both the structural features of DNA and the action of a set of specialized proteins.

Semi-Conservative Replication

Watson and Crick's landmark paper on the structure of DNA concludes with this remark: "It has not escaped our notice that the specific pairing we have postulated immediately suggests a possible copying mechanism for the genetic material." Each strand of DNA serves as a template for the creation of its complementary strand. As illustrated in Figure 18.8, replication is **semi-conservative**—each new molecule of DNA contains one strand of the original complementary DNA molecule and one new parent strand. Thus, each new DNA molecule conserves half of the original molecule.

The main events of replication are described in the remainder of this section. They are presented as a sequence. In reality, however, all of these events take place simultaneously on the same molecule of DNA.

Initiation

Replication starts at a specific nucleotide sequence, called the **replication origin**. The small circular chromosome of a prokaryote contains a single replication origin, while the linear chromosome of a eukaryote may contain thousands of replication origins. A group of enzymes, called **helicases**, bind to the DNA at the replication origin. The helicases cleave and unravel a segment of the double

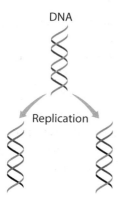

DNA

Replication

Figure 18.8 During DNA replication, two molecules of DNA are made from one. The original double helix unwinds. Two new strands of DNA are assembled using the original strands as templates. The resulting new molecules are identical to the original molecule. Each new molecule contains one original strand of DNA (shown here in blue) and one new strand (shown in red).

helix. This opening up of a region of DNA creates two Y-shaped areas at each end of the unwound area. The oval-shaped unwound area is called a **replication bubble**. Each Y-shaped area is called a **replication fork**. (See Figure 18.9.) The replication fork consists of two unwound DNA strands that branch out into unpaired (but complementary) single strands. These single strands serve as the templates for fashioning new strands of DNA. The molecule is now ready for replication to occur.

Elongation and Termination

An enzyme called **DNA polymerase** inserts into the replication bubble and begins to add nucleotides, one at a time, to create a strand of DNA that is complementary to the existing strand. The process of joining nucleotides to extend a new strand of DNA is called **elongation**, and it is the heart of replication. Elongation relies on the action of DNA polymerase. This enzyme attaches new nucleotides to the free 3' hydroxyl end of a pre-existing chain of nucleotides. There are two conditions for elongation. First, elongation can only take place in the 5' to 3' direction. Second, a short strand of RNA, known as a **primer**, must serve as a starting point for the attachment of new nucleotides.

The fact that DNA polymerase can only catalyze elongation in the 5' to 3' direction means that replication occurs in a slightly different way along each strand of the parent DNA. As shown in Figure 18.10 on the next page, one strand is replicated continuously in the 5' to 3' direction. This strand is known as the **leading strand**. The other strand, known as the **lagging strand**, is replicated in short segments. Nucleotides are still added in the 5' to 3' direction on the lagging strand, but the new DNA is synthesized in short

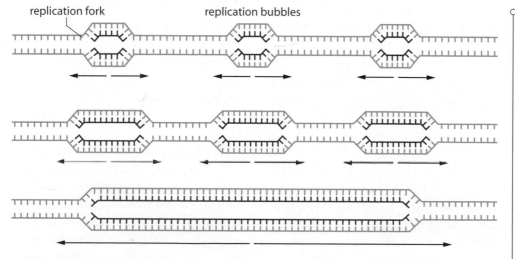

replication fork   replication bubbles

Figure 18.9 Replication takes place at several locations simultaneously. Each replication bubble represents two replication forks moving in opposite directions along the length of the chromosome. As replication proceeds along the strand, the bubbles grow until they meet. The parent strand of DNA is shown in blue. The new complementary strand is shown in red.

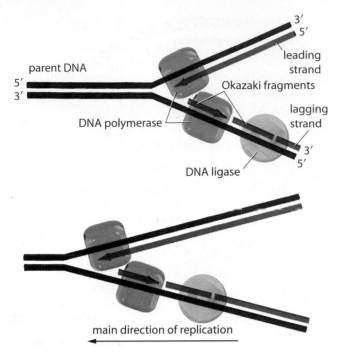

parent DNA
5′
3′

3′
5′
leading strand

Okazaki fragments

DNA polymerase

lagging strand

3′
5′

DNA ligase

main direction of replication

Figure 18.10 During DNA synthesis, the overall direction of elongation is the same along both strands, but elongation occurs differently. On the leading strand, DNA synthesis takes place along the DNA molecule in the same direction as the movement of the replication fork. On the lagging strand, DNA synthesis proceeds in the opposite direction to the movement of the replication fork. As well, the lagging strand is synthesized in short fragments.

BiologyFile

FYI

Okazaki fragments are named in recognition of Japanese molecular biologist, Reiji Okazaki, who— aided by his colleagues, including his wife, Tsuneko Okazaki—demonstrated experimentally how DNA is replicated along each strand. Okazaki's death in 1975 resulted from leukemia brought on by his exposure to high levels of radiation; he was in Nagasaki when the second atomic bomb was dropped during World War II.

segments called **Okazaki fragments**. The Okazaki fragments are then spliced together by an enzyme called **DNA ligase**.

Since DNA polymerase cannot synthesize new DNA fragments, an RNA primer serves as the starting point for the elongation of each new DNA strand. An enzyme called **primase** is required to construct the primer. Once the primer is in place, DNA polymerase extends each fragment by adding new nucleotides. Then DNA polymerase removes the RNA primer by eliminating the nucleotides in a 5′ to 3′ direction and fills in the space by extending the neighbouring DNA strand.

DNA polymerase has an important proofreading function, as well. After each nucleotide is added to a new DNA strand, DNA polymerase can recognize whether or not hydrogen bonding is taking place between the new base and its complement on the original strand. The absence of hydrogen bonding indicates a mismatch between the bases. When this occurs, DNA polymerase excises the

incorrect base from the new strand and adds the correct base using the parent strand as a template.

Along with polymerase, primase, ligase, and helicase, the coordinated activity of several other proteins and enzymes is required to accomplish DNA replication. These proteins and enzymes include enzymes that relieve torsion in the unwinding DNA helix and proteins that bind to exposed segments of single-stranded DNA to keep the unstable molecule from denaturing. Altogether, the complex of polypeptides and DNA that interact at the replication fork is known as the **replication machine**.

As the replication fork progresses along the replicating chromosome, only a very short region of DNA is found in a single-stranded form. As soon as the newly formed strands are complete, they rewind automatically into their chemically stable helix structure. Replication proceeds until the new strands are complete and the two new DNA molecules separate from one another. The completion of the new DNA strands and the dismantling of the replication machine is called **termination**.

Figure 18.11 shows the replication machine at work, and Table 18.2 summarizes the roles of the key enzymes. In Investigation 18.A, you will build a model to simulate DNA replication.

⋯

7 What is meant by the term "semi-conservative replication?"

8 Why does replication take place in a slightly different way on each DNA strand?

9 Explain how the leading and lagging strands of a DNA molecule are replicated.

10 Describe the components of the replication machine.

⋯

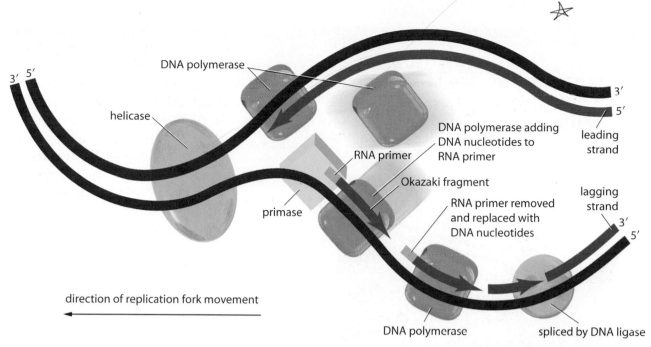

DNA polymerase

helicase

3′ 5′

direction of replication fork movement

primase

RNA primer

DNA polymerase adding
DNA nucleotides to
RNA primer

Okazaki fragment

RNA primer removed
and replaced with
DNA nucleotides

DNA polymerase

leading
strand

3′
5′

lagging
strand

3′
5′

spliced by DNA ligase

Figure 18.11 This simplified illustration of the replication machine shows how a loop in the lagging strand allows a single polymerase complex to replicate both DNA strands simultaneously.

Table 18.2 Key Enzymes in DNA Replication

Enzyme group	Function
helicase	cleaves and unwinds short sections of DNA ahead of the replication fork
primase	synthesizes an RNA primer to begin the elongation process
DNA polymerase	adds new nucleotides to the 3′ OH group of an existing nucleotide strand; dismantles the RNA primer; proofreads base pairing
DNA ligase	splices together Okazaki fragments in the lagging strand

Sequencing Genomes

DNA sequencing is the process of identifying the precise nucleotide sequence of a DNA fragment. Researchers began sequencing DNA fragments more than 30 years ago. In 1977, the genome of the virus θX174 became the first entire genome to be sequenced. At that time, the sheer size of eukaryotic genomes made it impossible for scientists to sequence these genomes using the same techniques. In the years since then, gene sequencing techniques have been refined and computer technology has advanced so that enormous databases of information can be quickly analyzed.

As a result, it is now routine for researchers to sequence genes, as well as the entire genomes of organisms.

In 2003, an international team of researchers completed the **Human Genome Project**, a monumental effort to sequence the entire human genome. The Human Genome Project is a landmark in the field of human genetics, and it has important applications in medicine and other sciences. Why? How does knowing the nucleotide sequence in a particular stretch of DNA contribute to our understanding of cell function? In the next section, you will examine how the information encoded in DNA molecules is expressed in living organisms.

Section 18.1 Summary

- Over a period of more than 50 years, various researchers conducted a series of experiments that identified DNA as the material of heredity and determined the properties of DNA.
- This research culminated in 1953, when Watson and Crick published a paper describing the molecular structure of DNA.
- DNA is made up of two strands of nucleotides, bound together to form a double helix.

BiologyFile

Try This
Many people confuse the terms "gene mapping" and "DNA sequencing." Write two definitions or a single paragraph to clear up this confusion.

Modelling DNA Structure and Replication

Watson, Crick, and the model of DNA that they constructed

Watson and Crick did not conduct any experiments to determine the structure of DNA. Instead, they worked as synthesizers, examining and interpreting the research and discoveries made by other scientists. As well, Watson and Crick used a technique that was used previously by the chemist Linus Pauling to visualize and determine the helical structure of proteins by building physical models. Watson and Crick tried different arrangements until they created one model that could account for all the evidence. In this investigation, you will work in a group to design and build a model that can be used to simulate the structure and replication of DNA.

Question

How can you design a working model of a short strand of DNA (eight to ten base pairs) that can be used to simulate the molecular structure of DNA and the process of DNA replication?

Experimental Plan

1. Brainstorm ideas for designing and constructing a model.

2. Use your ideas to develop a plan. List the materials and equipment you will need.

3. When all the members of your group have approved the plan, write it down and review it with your teacher.

4. Create your model. Keep a written record of the steps you followed and any changes you made to your plan.

Data and Observations

5. Record the nucleotide sequences for each strand of DNA in your molecule, using the correct conventions.

6. Use your model to simulate the process of DNA replication. Keeping in mind the action of DNA polymerase, use your model to demonstrate

   a) replication along the leading strand

   b) replication along the lagging strand

   c) the actions of primase, helicase, DNA polymerase, and DNA ligase

Analysis

1. In what ways is your model useful for explaining the structure and replication of DNA? What are the limitations of your model?

2. List the key replication enzymes in the order in which they are involved. For each enzyme, briefly describe what would happen if it were not present in the replication medium. (Assume the absence of any one enzyme does not affect the activity of others.)

3. In an early model tested by Watson and Crick, the sugar-phosphate handrails were on the inside of the helix and the nitrogenous bases protruded outward. How is this model inconsistent with experimental evidence about the structure of nucleic acids?

- Chemical bonds between sugar and phosphate molecules make up the backbone of each strand.
- Nitrogenous bases project out from the backbone.
- Hydrogen bonds between pairs of complementary bases hold the two strands together.
- Each DNA nucleotide carries one of four bases: adenine (A), guanine (G), cytosine (C), or thymine (T). A and T are complementary, and C and G are complementary.

- During DNA replication, the double helix opens. Each strand of the DNA molecule serves as a template for the creation of a complementary strand.
- DNA polymerase catalyzes the formation of new DNA molecules.
- Replication takes place in slightly different ways on the leading and lagging strands of the DNA molecule.
- The events of DNA replication show the close interaction of proteins and DNA in genetic processes.

Section 18.1 Review

1. Describe one of the experiments that contributed to the study of DNA. How were the results of this experiment used by other researchers in subsequent work?

2. For many years, scientists assumed that proteins rather than DNA made up the material of heredity.
   a) What were some of the factors behind this assumption?
   b) What experimental results provided strong evidence that genetic information was carried on DNA?

3. Draw a single DNA nucleotide, and label its main parts.

4. One strand in a stretch of DNA has the base sequence CCTGA. Draw this stretch of DNA, showing both strands. Label the sugar-phosphate backbone, the 5′ and 3′ ends of each strand, and the regions of hydrogen bonding.

5. Lacking knowledge of Rosalind Franklin's X-ray analysis of the DNA molecule, Linus Pauling proposed a structure for DNA in which the phosphate groups were tightly packed on the inside of the molecule, thus leaving the nitrogenous bases projecting outward. If DNA replication occurred in this structure, how do you think it would differ from what you know is the actual process of DNA replication?

6. Your research team is studying a virus that infects tomato plants. The genetic material of this virus is a single-stranded form of DNA. You extract two samples of DNA from an infected cell: one is the viral DNA and the other is the DNA of the plant cell. The table below shows the results of your analysis of the nucleotide composition of each sample. Which sample is the viral DNA? Explain.

Nucleotide	Presence in sample A (%)	Presence in sample B (%)
adenine	30.3	38.5
cytosine	19.7	10.7
thymine	30.3	13.3
guanine	19.7	37.5

7. Create a table to show the similarities and differences between RNA and DNA.

8. Explain what is meant by semi-conservative replication as it applies to DNA.

9. Summarize the steps that are involved in the synthesis of the DNA molecule.

10. What was the objective of the Human Genome Project?

Protein Synthesis and Gene Expression

Section Outcomes

In this section, you will
- **explain** how genetic information is encoded in DNA molecules
- **describe** the processes through which genetic information is expressed in living cells
- **design** and **perform** a simulation to illustrate the steps of protein synthesis

Key Terms

amino acids
genetic code
gene expression
transcription
messenger RNA (mRNA)
transfer RNA (tRNA)
translation
codon
RNA polymerase
promoter
anticodon
ribosomal RNA (rRNA)
genomics
proteomics

In the same year that Watson and Crick published their model for the structure of DNA, in a laboratory at the same university, biochemist Frederick Sanger established that proteins consist of a sequence of molecules called **amino acids**. The specific sequence of amino acids determines the chemical properties of each protein. In turn, the specific proteins that are produced by a cell determine the structure, function, and development of the cell.

Once scientists understood that a given set of amino acids, arranged in a particular order, could produce the proteins that are responsible for inherited traits, they began to consider a new idea: Perhaps there was a connection between the sequence of nucleotides along a DNA molecule and the sequence of amino acids in a protein. Scientists soon showed that there is, in fact, a connection. The order of the base pairs in a DNA molecule makes up the **genetic code** of an organism. The genetic code determines how the amino acids are strung together and how the proteins are made. In other words, the order of the nucleotides in a gene provides the information, written in genetic code, that is necessary to build a protein.

Figure 18.12 summarizes the path of **gene expression**. The theory that genetic information flows from DNA to RNA to protein is often referred to as the "central dogma" of gene expression. During gene expression, DNA is copied into an RNA molecule in a process called **transcription**.

In a eukaryotic cell, transcription takes place in the nucleus and involves a special type of RNA molecule called **messenger RNA (mRNA)**. The mRNA molecule moves into the cytoplasm of the cell, where the mRNA nucleotide sequence directs the synthesis of a polypeptide (a chain of amino acids) with the aid of another RNA molecule, **transfer RNA (tRNA)**. This process is known as **translation**. Over the next few pages, you will examine the genetic code and gene expression in more detail.

• • •

11 In what way is the structure of a protein related to the structure of DNA?

12 What are the two basic steps involved in gene expression?

• • •

The Genetic Code

In a gene, each set of three bases (for example, ACC or GAA) is known as a **codon**. By convention, the genetic code is always interpreted in terms of the mRNA codon rather than the nucleotide sequence of the original DNA strand. Table 18.3 lists all of the mRNA codons and their corresponding amino acids. To read the table, find the first letter of the mRNA codon in the column titled "First base." Then read across the rows in the column titled "Second base" to find the second letter of the codon. This will take you to four possible amino acids. Finally, read down the column titled "Third base" to find the last letter of the codon. The last letter of the codon, combined with the previous two letters, identifies the amino acid that corresponds to the codon.

For example, the three nucleotides UAU code for the amino acid tyrosine. The first letter, U, is in the "First base" column. The second letter, A, is in the "Second base" column. The third letter,

Figure 18.12
The path of gene expression. The "central dogma" proposes that genetic information passes (via transcription) from the genes (DNA) to an RNA copy of the gene, and the RNA copy directs the sequential assembly of a chain of amino acids to produce a protein (via translation).

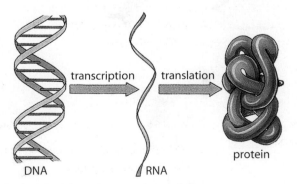

DNA → transcription → RNA → translation → protein

Table 18.3 Messenger RNA Codons and Their Corresponding Amino Acids

First base	Second base				Third base
	U	**C**	**A**	**G**	
U	UUU phenylalanine UUC phenylalanine UUA leucine UUG leucine	UCU serine UCC serine UCA serine UCG serine	UAU tyrosine UAC tyrosine UAA stop** UAG stop**	UGU cystcine UGC cysteine UGA stop** UGG tryptophan	U C A G
C	CUU leucine CUC leucine CUA leucine CUG leucine	CCU proline CCC proline CCA proline CCG proline	CAU histidine CAC histidine CAA glutamine CAG glutamine	CGU arginine CGC arginine CGA arginine CGG arginine	U C A G
A	AUU isoleucine AUC isoleucine AUA isoleucine AUG methionine*	ACU threonine ACC threonine ACA threonine ACG threonine	AAU asparagine AAC asparagine AAA lysine AAG lysine	AGU serine AGC serine AGA arginine AGG arginine	U C A G
G	GUU valine GUC valine GUA valine GUG valine	GCU alanine GCC alanine GCA alanine GCG alanine	GAU aspartate GAC aspartate GAA glutamate GAG glutamate	GGU glycine GGC glycine GGA glycine GGG glycine	U C A G

* AUG is an initiator codon. It also codes for the amino acid methionine.
** UAA, UAG, and UGA are terminator codons.

U, is in the "Third base" column. Notice that the three nucleotides UAC also code for this same amino acid.

The genetic code has three important characteristics.

1. As you can see from Table 18.3, the genetic code is *redundant*—that is, more than one codon can code for the same amino acid. Only three codons do not code for any amino acid. As you will learn, these codons serve as "stop" signals to end protein synthesis.

2. The genetic code is *continuous*. That is, the genetic code reads as a series of three-letter codons without spaces, punctuation, or overlap. Knowing exactly where to start and stop translation is therefore essential. A shift of one or two nucleotides in either direction can alter the codon groupings and result in an incorrect amino acid sequence.

3. The genetic code is nearly *universal*. Almost all living organisms build proteins with the genetic code shown in Table 18.3. As you will learn, this has important implications for gene technology, since a gene that is taken from one kind of organism and inserted into another kind of organism will produce the same protein.

• • •

13 How many bases make up each codon?

14 Describe each characteristic of the genetic code.
a) redundant
b) continuous
c) universal

• • •

Transcription

During transcription, the information in a segment of DNA is copied into messenger RNA (mRNA). Messenger RNA is a linear strand of RNA that carries

Practice Problems

3. Use Table 18.3 to find the amino acid that corresponds to each of the following codons.
a) CCA   b) AUG   c) GCA

4. What three RNA codons serve as "stop" signals?

5. Write three different codons that correspond to the amino acid arginine.

information from DNA in the nucleus to the protein synthesis machinery in the cytoplasm of the cell. For each gene, only one strand of the double-stranded DNA molecule is transcribed. This strand is called the *sense strand*. The other strand, which is not transcribed, is called the *anti-sense strand*. In a single DNA molecule, either strand can serve as the sense strand for different genes.

The main enzymes that catalyze the synthesis of RNA are the **RNA polymerases**. (In eukaryotes, each RNA polymerase has a specific function.) A sequence of nucleotides on the DNA molecule serves as a **promoter** region that tells the RNA polymerase complex where to bind (Figure 18.13).

Once the RNA polymerase complex has bound to the sense strand of the DNA molecule, it opens a section of the double helix. The enzymes then work their way along the DNA molecule and synthesize a strand of mRNA that is complementary to the sense strand of DNA. In the mRNA strand, however, the base thymine is replaced with uracil. Like DNA polymerase, RNA polymerases work in the 5′ to 3′ direction, adding each new nucleotide to the 3′-OH group of the previous nucleotide. RNA polymerases transcribe only one strand of the template DNA, however, so there is no need for Okazaki fragments.

A specific nucleotide sequence in the template DNA serves as a signal to stop transcription. When the RNA polymerases reach this signal, they detach from the DNA strand. The new mRNA strand is released from the transcription assembly, and the DNA double helix reforms.

Translation

For a cell to create the proteins it needs, it must translate the codons along a stretch of mRNA into amino acid sequences. This process requires both a chemical translator and a set of cellular protein synthesis equipment. Once the mRNA reaches the cytoplasm, the translator and protein synthesis equipment work together to assemble the proteins.

The molecule that links each mRNA codon to its specific amino acid is another form of RNA, called transfer RNA (tRNA). Transfer RNA is made up of a single strand of RNA that folds into the characteristic shape shown in Figure 18.14. One lobe

Figure 18.13 During transcription, a complex of RNA polymerases track along the DNA molecule, synthesizing a single-stranded mRNA molecule that is complementary to the sense strand of DNA. The DNA helix reforms behind the RNA polymerases complex.

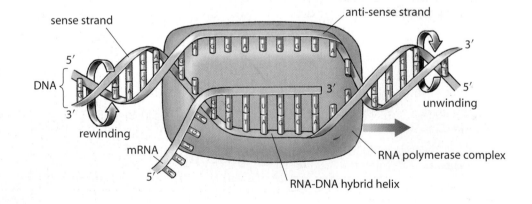

Practice Problems

6. An mRNA strand contains the following nucleotide sequence: AUGCCCACUACAUAG. What amino acid sequence does this mRNA code for?

7. A DNA strand contains the following nucleotide sequence: TACTGCCTCCCCATAAGAATT.

   a) What is the nucleotide sequence of the mRNA strand that is transcribed from this DNA template?

   b) What is the amino acid sequence of the polypeptide that is produced from this mRNA strand?

contains the **anticodon**, a stretch of three nucleotides that is complementary to the mRNA codon. At the opposite end of the molecule is a binding site for the amino acid that corresponds to the codon. The binding is accomplished by a specialized set of enzymes.

The main structures of the protein synthesis equipment are ribosomes. The ribosomes bring together the mRNA strand, the tRNA molecules carrying the amino acids, and the enzymes needed to build the polypeptides. The ribosomes also contain a third kind of RNA, known as **ribosomal RNA (rRNA)**. Ribosomal RNA is a linear strand of RNA that remains associated with the ribosomes.

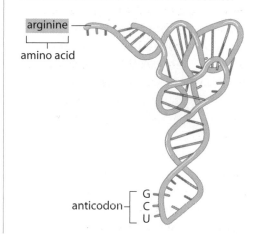

Figure 18.14 Each tRNA molecule is about 80 nucleotides long. The tRNA molecule shown here has the anticodon GCU, which pairs with the mRNA sequence CGA. This tRNA molecule carries the amino acid arginine.

Thought Lab | 18.2 | Transcription in Reverse

Target Skills

Constructing a model of a portion of a DNA molecule

Performing a simulation to demonstrate the transcription of a stretch of DNA

The analysis of DNA can help researchers determine which polypeptides are produced by particular genes. Similarly, but in reverse, the analysis of polypeptides can provide information about the genes that are associated with them. In this activity, you will work backward from a polypeptide chain to construct a stretch of DNA that might code for it.

Procedure

1. The illustration shows an imaginary polypeptide produced by a bacterial cell. Using Table 18.3 (on page 633), and the table below, draw one possible nucleotide sequence for the DNA molecule that contains the gene for this polypeptide.

2. Draw a labelled diagram to show the mRNA molecule being transcribed from the DNA strand.

Analysis

1. Compare DNA molecules with your class. How many different sequences could code for the same polypeptide product? What advantage might this give a living cell?

2. The processes of transcription and translation consume a great deal of cellular energy. Why do you think the cell does not simply translate proteins directly from DNA? Brainstorm some ideas, and discuss your ideas with your classmates.

Amino acid	Three-letter abbreviation
alanine	ala
arginine	arg
asparagine	asn
aspartate	asp
cysteine	cys
glutamate	glu
glutamine	gln
glycine	gly
histidine	his
isoleucine	ile

Amino acid	Three-letter abbreviation
leucine	leu
lysine	lys
methionine	met
phenylalanine	phe
proline	pro
serine	ser
threonine	thr
tryptophan	trp
tyrosine	tyr
valine	val

Figure 18.15 The translation cycle involves the base pairing of a new tRNA, the transfer of a growing polypeptide chain, and the movement of the ribosome along the mRNA molecule. The complete cycle occurs about 15 times per second in a prokaryotic cell.

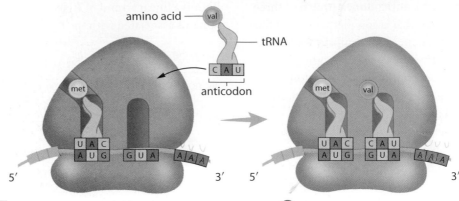

A When translation is initiated, a single tRNA molecule carrying the amino acid methionine sits on the first exposed codon, the start codon AUG. A second tRNA, carrying a second amino acid, approaches the adjacent codon.

B The anticodon of the second tRNA pairs with the mRNA codon at a site next to the first tRNA.

Translation is activated when an mRNA molecule binds to an active ribosome complex. The mRNA binds in such a way that two adjacent codons are exposed. The first tRNA molecule carrying the amino acid methionine, base-pairs with the first exposed mRNA codon—the start codon, AUG. Once the tRNA and mRNA are in place, translation follows a cycle of three steps:

1. A second loaded tRNA molecule arrives at the codon adjacent to the first tRNA.

2. Enzymes catalyze the formation of a chemical bond that joins the amino acid carried by the first tRNA to the amino acid carried by the second tRNA. At the same time, the amino acid chain is transferred from the first tRNA to the second tRNA.

3. The ribosome moves a distance of one codon along the mRNA strand.

The first tRNA molecule detaches from the mRNA and picks up another amino acid. The second tRNA now holds a growing amino acid chain. A third tRNA molecule arrives at the newly-exposed codon next to the second tRNA, and the cycle repeats.

The translation cycle continues until a stop codon is reached. The completed polypeptide chain is then released, and the ribosome assembly comes apart. Figure 18.15 summarizes the steps in translation. Table 18.4 compares and contrasts the structures and functions of the different nucleic acids involved.

⋯

15 Describe the role of RNA polymerase complex in transcription.

16 What is the role of tRNA in translation?

⋯

Genomics and Proteomics

Since the late 1990s, progress in the field of genetics—the study of inheritance and the functions of genes—has opened up the field of genomics. **Genomics** is the study of entire genomes, including the interactions among multiple genes. Genomics is closely associated with **proteomics**, the study of all the proteins that are produced by a given genome.

Table 18.4 Nucleic Acids Involved in Gene Expression

Nucleic acid	Structure	Function
DNA	double helix	stores genetic information
messenger RNA (mRNA)	linear single strand	carries genetic information from DNA to the protein synthesis equipment; in eukaryotes, mRNA is processed before it moves to the cytoplasm for translation
transfer RNA (tRNA)	lobed shape	carries a particular amino acid to the correct codon site in the protein synthesis equipment
ribosomal RNA (rRNA)	linear single strand	combines with a complex of proteins to form a ribosome, the main structure of protein synthesis

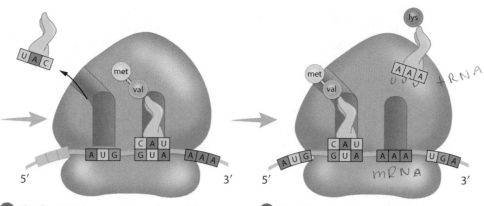

C The first tRNA passes its amino acid to the second tRNA and leaves its binding site. A chemical bond is catalyzed between the two amino acids.

D The ribosome moves forward, exposing a new mRNA codon for a third tRNA. The cycle continues until the ribosome reaches the stop codon UGA. The polypeptide is released, and the assembly comes apart.

INVESTIGATION 18.B

Target Skills

Performing a simulation to demonstrate the replication of DNA and the transcription and translation of its information

Working cooperatively with team members to communicate information and ideas about DNA replication

Simulating Protein Synthesis

During the 1950s and 1960s, scientists developed several models to simulate and explain the steps in protein synthesis, even though they could not see most of the processes taking place at the cellular level. Today, researchers can use electron microscopes to observe and analyze molecular processes. Large-scale models, however, are still important tools in scientific research. In this investigation, you will work in a group to develop a model of protein synthesis.

Question

How can you use materials available in your home or classroom to simulate the processes of transcription and translation?

Experimental Plan

1. As a group, list the steps that are involved in transcription and translation. For each step, note the structures, molecules, and events involved.

2. Discuss how you might simulate transcription and translation in your classroom. Your simulation could take any form. For example, you could prepare an interactive computer program, write and perform a play, or construct a physical model.

3. Once you have agreed on a plan, list the materials and equipment you will need to carry out your simulation. Assign responsibilities to each member of your group. Then assemble your materials and prepare your simulation.

Data and Observations

4. Present your simulation to the class. Record any comments you receive from your classmates.

Analysis

1. Which parts of your presentation seemed to be the most effective at simulating protein synthesis? Now that you have seen what other groups did, how would you revise your own simulation?

2. Explain how a stop codon triggers the termination of the translation cycle. How does your simulation illustrate this?

Conclusion

3. What are some advantages and disadvantages of simulating molecular processes? What characteristics help to make a simulation effective?

Together, genomics and proteomics are influencing the research in many fields of biology, including medicine. For example, rather than targeting only the action of individual genes and proteins, scientists now study the interactions among genes and regulatory proteins that contribute to particular disorders. This, in turn, enables scientists to develop new treatments.

Key tools in these fields are computerized databases of the DNA sequences and associated proteins that are found in different organisms. Comparisons among different organisms are proving to be extremely valuable to scientists who are studying interactions between different genes, between genes and proteins, and between different proteins. You will learn more about the methods and applications of this research later in the chapter. In the next section, you will see how changes in genetic information can alter gene expression—and how such changes can be deliberately engineered.

Section 18.2 Summary

- In gene expression, the particular sequence of nucleotides in a stretch of DNA directs the sequence of amino acids in a polypeptide.
- The "central dogma" of gene expression states that genetic information is first transcribed from DNA to RNA, and then translated from RNA to protein.
- During transcription, the sense strand of a gene is used as a template to synthesize a strand of messenger RNA (mRNA). (In eukaryotes, transcription takes place in the nucleus.) The mRNA transcript is then transported to the cytoplasm.
- During translation, the mRNA binds to a ribosome assembly. A tRNA carrying methionine binds with the start codon sequence exposed in the first binding site. Another tRNA molecule then recognizes the codon sequence at the next exposed binding site on the mRNA, and brings the corresponding amino acid to this site. Enzymes bind the amino acids held by adjacent tRNA molecules. As the ribosome progresses along the mRNA, the amino acid chain grows until a stop codon is reached and the new polypeptide is released.
- The processes of gene expression govern the development of living organisms.

Section 18.2 Review

1. What is the "central dogma" of gene expression?

Use the information in Table 18.3 to answer questions 2 and 3.

2. What amino acid corresponds to each of the following mRNA codons?
   a) UCC
   b) ACG
   c) GUG
   d) CAC

3. What codons could code for the amino acid serine?

4. Which characteristic of the genetic code provides evidence that all organisms have a common origin? Explain.

5. Use a labelled diagram to illustrate the process of transcription.

6. As you have learned, gene expression involves transcribing information from only one strand of the DNA molecule. What could be some of the biological advantages of double-stranded DNA?

7. What cellular structure provides the machinery for translation? Where is this structure located in a eukaryotic cell?

8. Use labelled diagrams to illustrate the three-step cycle in the elongation phase of translation.

9. Describe the structures and functions of the three main forms of RNA that are involved in gene expression.

10. In bacterial cells, transcription and translation can take place at the same time on the same strand of mRNA.
    a) Why is this not possible in a eukaryotic cell?
    b) In what ways could this have both advantages and disadvantages for bacterial cells?

Mutations and Genetic Recombination

Much of what you have learned about genetics so far depicts hereditary information as relatively stable. You have seen, for example, how pedigrees trace the inheritance of a single trait through many generations. When Mendel first published his laws of inheritance, one of the objections was that these laws could not account for the newly emerging theory of evolution. If the factors of inheritance remain constant, how can species become adapted to new environments over time?

In fact, genomes are far from stable. In the dynamic environment of a cell, the structure of DNA is constantly changing. Some of these changes are quickly repaired by enzymes in the cell. Other changes are not. A permanent change in the genetic material of an organism is called a **mutation**. All mutations are inheritable. They are copied during DNA replication and passed on to daughter cells. Not all mutations are passed on to future generations, however. Only mutations that affect the genetic information in the gametes of an organism are passed on to the organism's offspring. Mutations that occur in the body cells are called **somatic cell mutations**. As you will learn later in this section, somatic cell mutations are a key cause of cancer. Mutations that occur in reproductive cells are called **germ line mutations**. These mutations are passed on from one generation to the next.

Types of Mutations

Most mutations involve small changes in nucleotide sequence. A chemical change that affects just one or a few nucleotides is called a **point mutation**. A point mutation may involve the *substitution* of one nucleotide for another, or the *insertion* or *deletion* of one or more nucleotides.

A point mutation that involves a nucleotide substitution may have a relatively minor effect on the metabolism of the cell. One reason for this minor effect is the redundancy of the genetic code. A change in the coding sequence of a gene does not always result in a change to the polypeptide product of the gene. For example, a change in the DNA sense strand sequence from CCT to CCC will not alter the polypeptide produced, since the associated mRNA codons (GGA and GGG, respectively) both code for the same amino acid, glycine.

Even when a point mutation involves the substitution of one amino acid for another, this substitution may not have a significant effect on the final structure or function of the polypeptide produced. A mutation that has no effect on the cell's metabolism is called a **silent mutation**.

In comparison, other substitutions may lead to a slightly altered but still functional polypeptide. A mutation that results in an altered protein is called a **mis-sense mutation**. Mis-sense mutations can be harmful. For example, a change in a single amino acid in one of the polypeptides that makes up hemoglobin is responsible for the genetic blood disorder known as sickle cell disease, which you studied in Chapter 17. On the other hand, mis-sense mutations may help organisms develop new forms of proteins that can meet different requirements. For example, mis-sense mutations may play an important role in generating the enormous variety of antibodies that your body requires to fight new infections.

Unfortunately, some substitutions can have severe consequences. If a change in a gene's coding sequence deletes a start signal or results in a premature stop signal, the gene may be unable to produce a functional protein. Similarly, a nucleotide substitution that affects a *regulatory sequence* may result in the cell being unable to respond properly

BiologyFile

FYI
More than one trillion changes occurred in your DNA during the time it took you to read this sentence. Most—but not all—of these changes will be repaired before they are passed on to daughter cells. Some will remain as mutations in your DNA.

to metabolic signals. A mutation that renders the gene unable to code for a functional polypeptide is called a **nonsense mutation**. Figure 18.16 illustrates how a nucleotide substitution in a single coding sequence can result in a silent, mis-sense, or nonsense mutation.

Nucleotide substitutions do not affect neighbouring coding sequences. The insertion or deletion of one or two nucleotides, however, results in a **frameshift mutation**. A frameshift mutation causes the entire reading frame of the gene to be altered, as shown in Figure 18.17. A shift in the reading frame usually results in a nonsense mutation.

Chromosomal Mutations

Point mutations usually affect only one gene. Mutations that involve a rearrangement of genetic material may affect several genes, including genes located on different chromosomes. One example of a chromosomal mutation is crossing over. As you have seen, crossing over recombines genetic material from different chromosomes. Another example is the loss or duplication of portions of chromosomes during DNA replication. This can result in changes to structural or regulatory DNA sequences.

Causes of Mutations

Many mutations are caused by molecular interactions that take place naturally within cells. These mutations are known as *spontaneous mutations*. One source of spontaneous mutations is incorrect base

GUU–CAU–UUG–ACU–CCC–GAA–GAA
val – his – leu – thr – pro – glu – glu

A The normal coding sequence, with the codons in the top row and the resulting amino acids below them.

GUU–CAU–UUG–ACC–CCC–GAA–GAA
val – his – leu – thr – pro – glu – glu

B This mutation is silent, since the change in nucleotide sequence has no effect on the polypeptide product.

GUU–CAU–UUG–ACU–CCC–GUA–GAA
val – his – leu – thr – pro – val – glu

C This is a mis-sense mutation, since it causes the amino acid valine to be inserted in the place of glutamate within the polypeptide chain. The resulting protein is unable to transport oxygen effectively and produces a disorder known as sickle cell disease.

GUU–CAU–UAG
val – his – stop

D This substitution causes a nonsense mutation by changing the codon for the amino acid leucine (UUG) into a premature stop codon. No functional polypeptide will be produced from this gene.

Figure 18.16 A nucleotide substitution can have varied effects, as shown on this portion of the gene that codes for human beta-globulin, one of the two polypeptides in the blood protein hemoglobin.

GUU–CAU–UUG–ACU–CCC–GAA–GAA
val – his – leu – thr – pro – glu – glu

A The normal coding sequence, with the codons in the top row and the resulting amino acids below them.

GUU–CAU–GUU–GAC–UCC–CGA–AGA A
val – his – val – asp – ser – arg – arg

B The insertion of a single nucleotide, in this case guanine, results in a frameshift mutation.

A
GUU–CAU–UUG–CUC–CCG–AAG–AA
val – his – leu – leu – pro – lys

C Similarly, a deletion of even a single nucleotide, in this case adenine, also results in a frameshift mutation.

Figure 18.17 Frameshift mutations are usually nonsense mutations.

17. What feature of the genetic code helps to protect a cell from the effects of nucleotide substitution?
18. What is a frameshift mutation?
19. Why is a mutation caused by an insertion or a deletion more likely to have serious consequences for a cell than one caused by a substitution?

pairing by DNA polymerase during the process of DNA replication. The rate of spontaneous mutations varies among organisms and even among different genes within a single cell.

While every cell undergoes spontaneous mutation, exposure to certain factors in the environment can increase the rate of mutation. Mutations that are caused by agents outside the cell are said to be *induced*. A substance or event that increases the rate of mutation in an organism is called a **mutagen**. Mutagens fall into two general categories: physical and chemical.

Physical Mutagens

Morgan studied the genetics of fruit flies for more than 20 years. During this time, he observed about 400 visible mutations in the tens of millions of fruit flies in his laboratory. In 1926, the American researcher Hermann Muller (one of Morgan's students) bombarded a population of fruit flies with X rays and produced several hundred mutants in a single day. X rays are a form of high-energy radiation. They tear through DNA molecules, causing random changes that range from point mutations to the loss of large portions of chromosomes. Because these mutagens cause physical changes in the structure of DNA, they are known as **physical mutagens**. High-energy radiation, such as that from X rays and gamma rays, is the most damaging form of mutagen known.

Ultraviolet (UV) radiation, which is present in sunlight, has a lower range of energy levels than X rays, but it is still a powerful mutagen. UV radiation can cause a chemical reaction between adjacent pyrimidine (C and T) bases. The result is a distortion in the DNA molecule that interferes with replication. Damage from UV radiation, as a result of exposure to sunlight, is a known cause of melanoma, a form of skin cancer. A single sunburn doubles a light-skinned person's chances of developing skin cancer.

Chemical Mutagens

A **chemical mutagen** is a molecule that can enter the nucleus of a cell and induce mutations by reacting chemically with the DNA. A chemical mutagen may act by inserting itself into the DNA molecule in a manner that causes a nucleotide substitution or a frameshift mutation. Other chemical mutagens have a structure that is similar to the structure of ordinary nucleotides but with different base-pairing properties. When these mutagens are incorporated into a DNA strand, they can cause incorrect nucleotides to be inserted during DNA replication. Examples of chemical mutagens include nitrites (which are sometimes used as a food preservative), gasoline fumes, and more than 50 different compounds found in cigarette smoke.

Most chemical mutagens are **carginogenic**—that is, they are associated with one or more forms of cancer. As you saw in Chapter 16, cancer is characterized by uncontrolled cell division in somatic cells. In molecular terms, cancer is the result of somatic cell mutations that disrupt the expression of genes involved in the regulation of the cell cycle. While carcinogens are present throughout the environment, personal choices can increase or decrease a person's risk of developing cancer. In Thought Lab 18.3 on the next page, you will examine the relationship between human activities, mutations, and cancer.

• • •

 Distinguish between the two terms in each pair of terms.

a) induced mutation and spontaneous mutation

b) chemical mutagen and physical mutagen

• • •

Mutations and Genetic Variation

A single mutation often has little or no effect on a living cell. Over time, however,

BiologyFile

FYI
Genetic material can be rearranged by the activity of transposable elements, also known as jumping genes or *transposons*. Transposable elements are short strands of DNA that are capable of moving from one chromosome to another.

a series of spontaneous and induced mutations can add up to more serious damage in a cell. Most cancers are caused by combinations of mutations. Some of these mutations may be inherited, while others may occur as a result of exposure to mutagens in the environment. The fact that mutations accumulate within a cell helps to explain why exposure to carcinogenic factors does not always result in cancer, and why cancer can occur without exposure to any known carcinogens.

The accumulation of mutations over time also gives rise to the tremendous genetic variation among organisms. The study of DNA sequences extracted from different organisms—including organisms that have been extinct for thousands of years—enables scientists to gather information and make hypotheses about the evolution of different species.

Tracing Ancestry Through Mitochondrial DNA

Earlier in this chapter, you read that almost all organisms have the same genetic code. A significant exception to this universality is the DNA of mitochondria and chloroplasts. These cellular organelles have their own DNA, and their genome is replicated, transcribed, and translated independently from the DNA in the nucleus of the cell in which

---

Thought Lab 18.3 Investigating Cancer Genes

Lung cancer is the most preventable of all cancers, and yet it is the leading cause of cancer deaths in Canada. In 2005, almost 20 000 Canadians died of lung cancer. Lung cancer is the result of somatic mutations in the cells of the lungs. What can the data indicate about the relationship between human activities and mutation rates?

The changing rates of lung cancer in men and women between 1900 and 1990

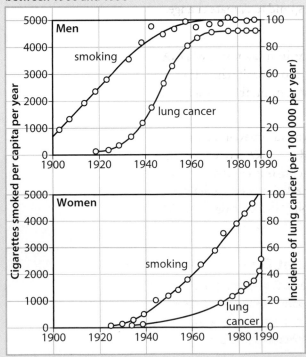

Procedure

1. Study the graphs. Write a brief summary of the relationships shown in the graph.

2. Record your ideas about the molecular reactions that may be occurring, based on what you have learned in this chapter.

3. Conduct research to describe one of the molecular reactions that might contribute to the relationship you see in the graph. You may find the following keywords helpful to guide your research:

   - oncogenes
   - tumour-suppressor genes
   - stability genes
   - p53 gene

Analysis

1. Write a brief report to describe how your personal choices can affect the chemical reactions that take place in your cells. How can these reactions in individual cells result in changes to your health and well-being?

2. Compare your research on the molecular reactions related to smoking with your classmates' research. How many different mutagens did your class find?

3. Suppose that you are a communications officer for the Canadian Lung Association. Your job is to help youth between the ages of 10 and 15 understand the risks of smoking. How would you reach this audience? What would your main messages be?

---

they are found. The expression of their DNA relies on a genetic code that is slightly different from the genetic code shown earlier in Table 18.3. The different genetic code of mitochondria and chloroplasts (along with evidence related to their structures and functions) supports the theory that these organelles were once independent prokaryotic cells. This theory, known as the *endosymbiont theory*, proposes that eukaryotic cells arose through a process in which one species of prokaryote was engulfed by another.

In addition to providing evidence about the origins of eukaryotic organisms, the study of **mitochondrial DNA (mtDNA)** is being used to gather information about the more recent history of individual species. Recall, from Chapter 16, that the cytoplasm in a zygote is donated by the ovum. The sperm cell contributes essentially no cytoplasm, and therefore no cytoplasmic organelles, to its offspring. While the DNA in the nuclei of your cells is made up of an equal combination of DNA from your mother and your father, your mtDNA is genetically identical to the mtDNA of your mother. Her mtDNA, in turn, is identical to the mtDNA of her own mother.

Over the countless generations of human history, mutations have arisen in mtDNA just as they have in nuclear DNA. Therefore, if two people have identical mtDNA sequences, they likely share a relatively recent maternal ancestor. By comparing the nucleotide sequences of the mtDNA of different living people, scientists can deduce lineage patterns that reveal prehistoric relationships among different human populations. Similarly, a comparison of the DNA of mitochondria and chloroplasts can provide information about the evolutionary path of animal and plant species.

Genetic Variation Within Species

The study of biological diversity and evolution usually involves examining genetic variations among different species. DNA analysis allows scientists to study genetic variations among individuals of the same species, as well. This helps scientists develop an understanding of ancient ecosystems and track the evolution of a species through time.

A crucial tool in the study of biological diversity and evolution is the analysis of non-coding stretches of DNA. These non-coding stretches tend to have a higher mutation rate than the DNA within genes. The higher mutation rate leads to extensive genetic variations among individuals of the same species. These variations, in turn, can be interpreted to deduce patterns of mutations over time. Scientists can extract DNA from ancient plant and animal tissues that have been preserved in the soil. Comparing the DNA of ancient plants, animals, and even bacteria with the DNA of their modern counterparts (using computerized genome databases) can reveal such varied information as the ancestry of modern organisms, the movement of populations through time, the evolution of particular disease-causing bacteria, and the way that ecosystems respond to climate change.

• • •

21 Why is your mitochondrial DNA identical to the mitochondrial DNA of your mother, rather than father?

22 Give two examples of ways that the study of DNA sequences can help scientists learn about genetic relationships, genetic variations, or evolution.

• • •

Recombinant DNA

As you have seen, DNA mutations can arise spontaneously or be induced by a variety of environmental factors. Working in a laboratory, researchers can manipulate genetic material to alter genes and blend plant, animal, and bacterial DNA—a process known as **genetic engineering**. A molecule of DNA

BiologyFile

FYI
In 2005, scientists successfully sequenced the genome of a cave bear (*Ursus spelaeus*) that has been extinct for more than 10 000 years. This was the first sequencing of the DNA of a long-extinct organism.

that includes genetic material from different sources is called **recombinant DNA**. The pace of change in the field of genetic engineering is rapid. Even so, many of the enzymes and processes that were used in the 1970s still provide the basic tools for genetic engineering today.

Restriction Endonucleases

To defend themselves against infection by foreign DNA, most prokaryotic organisms manufacture one or more enzymes known as restriction enzymes. **Restriction enzymes** catalyze the cleavage of DNA at specific nucleotide sequences. Genetic engineers are especially interested in a specific group of these enzymes called

restriction endonucleases. The term endonuclease refers to a restriction enzyme that cuts within the interior of a DNA molecule, rather than at the ends.

Restriction endonucleases recognize a short sequence of nucleotides (called the *target sequence*) within a strand of DNA and cut the strand at a particular point within the sequence. This point is known as a *restriction site*. Many different endonucleases have been isolated, and each recognizes a different target sequence. For any given endonuclease, its target sequence will occur by chance in one or more locations in almost any fragment of DNA.

Figure 18.18 illustrates a typical restriction endonuclease reaction. Two characteristics of this reaction makes it useful to genetic researchers:

- Specificity: The cuts made by an endonuclease are specific and predictable. That is, the same enzyme will cut a particular strand of DNA the same way each time, producing an identical set of small DNA fragments. These small fragments are called **restriction fragments**.

- Staggered cuts: Most restriction endonucleases produce a staggered cut that leaves a few unpaired nucleotides on a single strand at each end of the restriction fragment. These short strands, often referred to as *sticky ends*, can then form base pairs with other short strands that have a complementary sequence. For example, they can base-pair with a restriction fragment produced by the action of the same restriction endonuclease on a different strand of DNA.

Once the sticky ends have formed base pairs with one another, the action of another enzyme, *DNA ligase*, splices them together. The result is a stable recombinant DNA molecule.

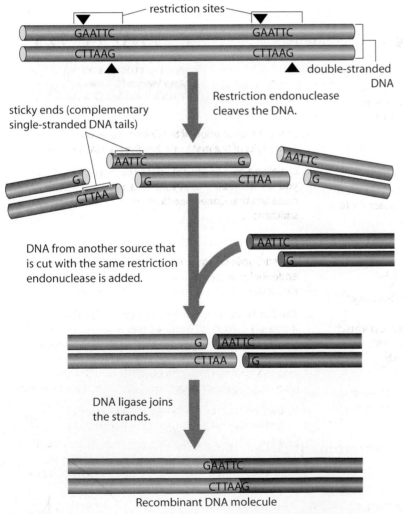

Figure 18.18 The target sequence of the restriction endonuclease known as EcoR1 is GAATTC. Wherever this sequence appears on one strand of a DNA molecule, the same sequence will appear running in the opposite direction on the complementary DNA strand. The result is a set of fragments with exposed complementary nucleotide sequences. These "sticky ends" may base-pair with one another. DNA ligase will then seal the break between them.

23
Explain why these characteristics of restriction endonucleases makes these enzymes useful to genetic engineers.

a) specificity

b) staggered cuts

Sorting and Analyzing DNA

Genetic researchers use many different tools to sort and analyze DNA samples. One of these tools is a process called **gel electrophoresis**. Gel electrophoresis is used to separate molecules according to their mass and charge. It can be used to separate fragments of DNA.

The process of gel electrophoresis is illustrated in Figure 18.19. To begin, a solution that contains DNA fragments is applied at one end of a gel. An electric current is then passed through the gel. This causes one end of the gel to develop a positive electric charge and the other end to develop a negative electric charge. Because DNA has a negative charge, the DNA fragments tend to move toward the gel's positive end. The smaller fragments move more quickly. After a period of time, the fragments separate into a pattern of bands. This pattern is called a **DNA fingerprint**.

Together, restriction enzymes and gel electrophoresis help researchers analyze and compare DNA samples. For

BiologyFile

FYI

Before a small DNA sample can be analyzed, it must be *amplified*. That is, the DNA must be copied many times to produce a large number of identical DNA molecules. An automated process called the *polymerase chain reaction* can quickly generate billions of copies of a DNA sequence for analysis.

Thought Lab | 18.4 | Recreating the First Chimera

Target Skills

Performing a simulation to demonstrate the use of restriction endonucleases and DNA ligases

In genetic engineering, a chimera is a genetically engineered organism that contains DNA from unrelated species. The first chimera was created in 1973 by the American team of Stanley Cohen and Herbert Boyer. Bacteria were then exposed to the recombinant plasmid. Those bacteria that displayed tetracycline resistance had taken up the plasmid.

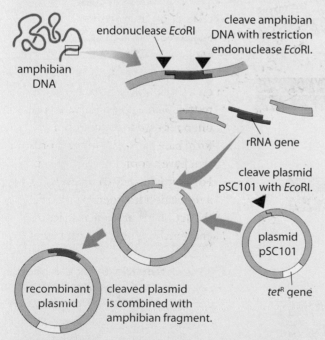

amphibian DNA

endonuclease *Eco*RI

cleave amphibian DNA with restriction endonuclease *Eco*RI.

rRNA gene

cleave plasmid pSC101 with *Eco*RI.

plasmid pSC101

tet^R gene

recombinant plasmid

cleaved plasmid is combined with amphibian fragment.

In Cohen and Boyer's experiment, the amphibian gene coded for the production of rRNA. The bacterial gene tet^R conferred resistance to the antibiotic tetracycline. They used the restriction endonuclease *Eco*R1 and DNA ligase to splice (insert) a gene from a toad into a molecule of bacterial DNA plasmid pSC101.

Procedure

1. Study the illustration of the Cohen-Boyer experiment. Make a list of the materials that the researchers used.

2. Develop a plan to simulate the experiment. Show how you will use materials in your classroom to represent the materials that Cohen and Boyer used. Then perform your simulation.

Analysis

1. How did your simulation illustrate the action of an endonuclease and a ligase? In what ways was your simulation effective? What were its limitations?

2. The Cohen-Boyer experiment was important because it created a colony of bacterial cells that were resistant to the antibiotic tetracycline and produced amphibian rRNA. What other bacterial phenotypes would have resulted from this experiment? What would each phenotype indicate about events at the molecular level?

3. a) Give one example of how you might use this technology for a social or industrial purpose.

   b) What environmental, social, or ethical issues would your experiment raise? Make a list of these issues, and discuss them with other students in your class.

example, investigators at a crime scene might find a small sample of blood or skin tissue. The DNA from this sample can be cut with a restriction enzyme and run on a gel to create a DNA fingerprint. This can be compared with the DNA fingerprint of a suspect in the crime. Since no two people (other than identical twins) have the same DNA fingerprint, a match is very strong evidence that the suspect was present at the crime scene.

Similarly, DNA fingerprints can be used to solve disputes over parentage. Because DNA is inherited equally from both parents, a child's DNA fingerprint will show some matches with the DNA

Figure 18.19 Gel electrophoresis

A **Restriction enzymes** Either one or several restriction enzymes are added to a sample of DNA. The enzymes cut the DNA into fragments.

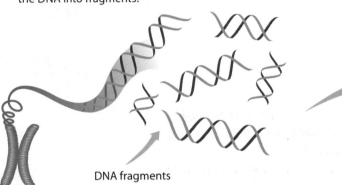

DNA fragments

B **The gel** A gel, with a consistency similar to gelatin, is formed so small wells are left at one end. Small amounts of the DNA sample are placed into these wells.

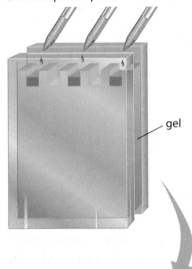

gel

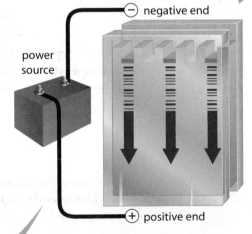

⊖ negative end

power source

⊕ positive end

C **The electrical field** The gel is placed in a solution, and an electrical field is set up so one end of the gel is positive and the other end is negative.

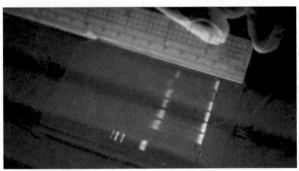

E Before the DNA fragments are added to the wells, they are treated with a dye that glows under ultraviolet light, allowing the bands to be studied.

completed gel

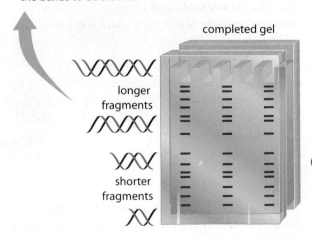

longer fragments

shorter fragments

D **The fragments move** The negatively charged DNA fragments travel toward the positive end. The smaller the fragment, the faster it moves through the gel. Fragments that are the farthest from the well are the smallest.

Target Skills

Analyzing DNA fingerprints

The following diagram shows the results of a gel electrophoresis analysis of one child and four different sets of parents. Use these DNA fingerprints to answer the Analysis questions and identify the child's biological parents.

Analysis

1. Which parental DNA matches the child's DNA? How do you know?

2. Try to determine the percentage of the father's DNA that matches the child's DNA. Can you do the same for the mother's DNA? Explain why or why not.

3. Describe other situations in which DNA fingerprinting might be useful.

---

fingerprint of each parent. A comparison of the DNA fingerprints of different people can help researchers identify the relationships among them.

Section 18.3 Summary

- Mutations are permanent changes in DNA. They may involve the insertion, deletion, or substitution of individual nucleotides, or larger-scale rearrangements of portions of chromosomes.

- Mutations may be spontaneous, or they may be induced by exposure to physical or chemical mutagens. Mutations may be harmful to cells. For example,

mutations that disrupt gene expression or the cell cycle may result in disorders, such as cancer.

- Mutations are also the source of genetic variations among organisms. Researchers can trace patterns of mutations through time to learn about the history of ecosystems and the evolution of species.

- Genetic engineering techniques allow researchers to manipulate the DNA of living organisms.

- Using restriction endonucleases and DNA ligases, researchers can splice genes from one organism into the genome of another organism to create organisms with recombinant DNA.

Section 18.3 | Review

1. Explain the difference between a germ line mutation and a somatic cell mutation. Which type of mutation contributes more to the variations among organisms?

2. Describe the difference between a mutation that occurs due to a nucleotide substitution and one that occurs as a result of an insertion or deletion (a frameshift mutation). Which is likely to be more harmful to a cell? Explain your answer.

3. Older people are at a higher risk of developing most cancers than younger people. Why?

4. Explain how random spontaneous mutations can help to reveal the relationship between two species of plants.

5. Describe the action of a restriction endonuclease. What two features of this action make restriction endonucleases useful to genetic engineers?

6. One mutation results in the replacement of a G nucleotide with a T nucleotide in the sense strand of a DNA molecule. Under what circumstances will this substitution produce each of the following mutations?

   a) a silent mutation

   b) a mis-sense mutation

   c) a nonsense mutation

7. Use labelled diagrams to illustrate the steps involved in creating a bacterial cell that can produce human insulin.

Genetics and Society

Section Outcomes

In this section, you will
- **explain** how the insertion of new DNA sequences into cells can transform organisms
- **describe** some of the social, environmental, and ethical issues associated with genetic technologies

Key Terms

biotechnology
DNA microarray
copy DNA (cDNA)
transgenic
bioremediation
clone
ultrasound
amniocentesis
chorionic villi sampling
genetic marker
DNA probe
gene therapy
DNA vector
somatic gene therapy
germ-line therapy

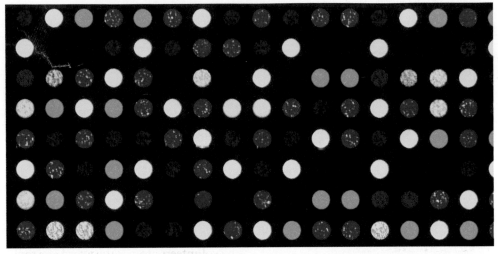

Figure 18.20 The results of a DNA microarray analysis comparing gene expression in two different cell samples. The red spots indicate genes that are expressed only by cells in the first sample, and the green spots indicate genes that are expressed only by cells in the second sample. The yellow spots indicate genes that are expressed by cells in both samples.

Biotechnology is the use of natural biological systems to create new technologies and products. Few sciences have as much potential as biotechnology to change the way we live—from the way we diagnose and treat diseases to the food we eat, the industries we work in, the air we breathe, and even the way we define life itself. Few technologies raise as broad a range of challenging social, ethical, and legal questions. Genetic engineering is one of the fastest-growing areas of biotechnology.

Gathering and Managing Genetic Information

As you have learned, one of the most important tools in the development of genetic engineering has been computers that are capable of handling the enormous amounts of information encoded in a eukaryotic genome. Genetics researchers use computerized gene banks and DNA libraries to store and organize genetic information.

Another important tool is a **DNA microarray**. A DNA microarray is a chip (usually a glass microscope slide or a polymer membrane) that contains a grid

of thousands of microscopic cells. Each cell contains a nucleic acid sequence that can bind with one of the mRNA molecules transcribed during gene expression. A typical microarray experiment includes the following steps:

1. mRNA is extracted from the cell or cells to be studied.

2. mRNA from each cell sample is used as a template to synthesize an artificial form of DNA, called **copy DNA (cDNA)**. The cDNA from each sample is marked by a fluorescent tag for later identification.

3. The labelled cDNA samples are incubated with the microarray. The cDNA binds to the microarray at locations that correspond to individual genes in the cell genome.

4. The microarray is scanned and analyzed to compare the patterns of gene expression in each cell sample.

The results of a typical microarray experiment are shown in Figure 18.20. A DNA microarray allows scientists to analyze the activity of thousands of genes at once. For example, a microarray can be used to compare the genes expressed by the same cell in different environments, or to compare the genes expressed by healthy and cancerous cells. The results of a microarray allow scientists to pinpoint the genes that are responsible for particular functions or conditions, to study the interactions among genes, or to gather information about the relationship between environmental conditions and gene expression.

 What is a DNA microarray, and for what purpose is it used?

Public Benefits of Genetic Research

Technologies such as DNA microarrays, and similar protein microarrays, enable scientists to analyze the enormous quantity of information that is gathered through studies such as the Human Genome Project. Some of the most important benefits of these technologies are in the area of human medicine. Studying the human genome, as a whole, offers the potential for developing drugs that are tailored not only to the expression of individual genes associated with particular disorders, but also to the unique genome of a patient. Studying the differences in gene expression among individuals can help medical researchers understand why certain drugs work better in some people than in others, and why certain people experience side effects from medications. The findings support the development of new techniques for predicting risks and diagnosing medical conditions.

All the research gathered through the Human Genome Project is publicly available. By making this a condition of the project, the scientists were able to share much of what they learned about human genetics. In other areas of genetic research, however, the relationship between public and private information is more complex.

 What kind of information can a DNA microarray analysis provide?

 How would medical researchers benefit from studying the human genome as a whole, rather than studying individual genes? Give an example.

Ownership of Genetic Information

In 2005, the National Geographic Society and the company IBM jointly launched the *Genographic Project*, a five-year venture to use DNA samples provided by volunteers around the world as a tool to learn more about the migrations of ancient peoples. Projects such as this can contribute valuable information to researchers in many fields. Who owns the genetic information, however? For example, should companies have the right to sell DNA information to other companies without the permission of the people who provided the samples? Should companies that use DNA in medical research be required to share the results of their work with the individuals or communities whose genetic information was used?

Many people argue that genetic information is a natural resource that belongs to everyone. Other people believe that an individual's genetic information belongs only to this individual. On the other hand, if companies cannot earn a profit from their research, there is little incentive for them to invest in genetic studies. In the world of genetics, where is the boundary between public and private property?

Patenting Organisms and Genes

When Saskatchewan farmer Percy Schmeizer met the international biotechnology corporation Monsanto in court, the case revolved around Monsanto's right to control how farmers use its products. Monsanto is the developer of

BiologyFile

Web Link

Different countries have developed different laws related to patenting genetic information. How do the laws in Canada compare with the laws in the United States, Europe, or Japan? Which country's laws do you think are more effective?

www.albertabiology.ca
WWW

Roundup-Ready™ Canola, a genetically-engineered form of canola that is resistant to the herbicide Roundup™ (also produced by Monsanto).

This genetically modified plant has helped farmers increase their crop yields and save money on herbicide applications. Its use is also changing farming practices, however. Traditionally, farmers save seeds from one year's crop to plant the following year. Farmers also exchange seeds with one another. When plants appear by chance in a farmer's field—for example, as a result of seeds blown by the wind or dropped by passing birds—the farmer has had the opportunity to decide whether to keep or remove them. Farmers who buy seeds from Monsanto must agree not to save any seeds from their crop, but to buy fresh seeds every year. The farmers are not permitted to exchange Monsanto seeds with other farmers. If Roundup-Ready™ Canola appears by accident in their fields, they must remove and destroy the plants. These regulations provide a way for Monsanto to earn a profit from its work.

In the end, the Canadian courts upheld Monsanto's right to patent the Roundup-Ready™ gene and to control the use and distribution of its seeds. Many people remain skeptical about the growing role of global biotechnology companies in the production of crop plants. Some people are concerned about the loss of traditional ways of life and the increasing dependence of farmers on the corporations that patent seeds. Others are concerned about world food production becoming concentrated in the hands of private companies. These companies, however, play an important role in genetics research and in the development of gene technologies and products that have important public benefits. Gene patents offer a way to reward their investment and innovation.

The issue of gene patents extends to other fields, including medicine. For example, imagine that a company has identified the location and function of a gene associated with breast cancer. Should the company be allowed to patent the gene? What if this means that the company then has control over all the treatments that affect the function of the gene? Governments, companies, and individuals around the world are grappling with the legal and ethical questions associated with the ownership of genetic information.

Biotechnology Products

Earlier in this chapter, you learned how genetic engineers insert foreign DNA into bacteria. Genetic engineers have also refined techniques for importing foreign DNA into plants and animals. The result of a procedure like this is a **transgenic** organism. A transgenic organism, such as the one shown in Figure 18.21, is an organism whose genetic material includes DNA from a different species. Below are just a few examples of some of the ways in which transgenic organisms are being used.

Medicinal Bacteria

In 1982, human insulin synthesized by transgenic bacteria was approved for

Figure 18.21 Pigs are often used as laboratory models in the study of human disorders and diseases. The embryos of these pigs, bred by Taiwanese researchers studying stem cells, were injected with green, fluorescent proteins from jellyfish. The pigs' internal organs are green, while external features such as eyes, mouths, and knuckles are a lighter, greenish tint.

medical use in the United States. This was the first example of a genetically engineered pharmaceutical product. Because bacteria can be cultured in large quantities at a relatively low cost, researchers are studying ways to use bacterial colonies to produce the polypeptides that form the basis for many medicines. This work can help to make medicines available at a lower cost.

Genetically-modified bacteria can support human health in other ways, as well. Some bacteria naturally degrade toxic substances, such as polychlorinated biphenyls (PCBs). Genetic engineering can enhance these metabolic functions, creating colonies of bacteria that can be used to clean up soils polluted with PCBs. The use of living cells for environmental remediation is known as **bioremediation**. Other examples of bioremediation include bacteria that have been designed to clean up oil spills, to filter air from factory smokestacks, or to remove heavy metals from water.

Transgenic Plants

Crop plants that contain recombinant DNA now account for over half the corn and canola produced in North America. Many of these plants have been modified to increase their resistance to herbicides, insect pests, or viruses. Genetic engineering has made it possible for crops to be grown in new places, as well, by creating transgenic plants that are tolerant of drought or that can be grown in colder climates.

Some people argue that the real promise of plant genetic engineering is in the production of plants with increased nutrition value. Around the world, millions of people suffer from malnutrition because they lack access to sufficient food and balanced diets. In many developing countries, where rice is the main staple food, symptoms of iron and vitamin A deficiencies affect hundreds of thousands of people. In 2000, Swiss researchers developed a genetically modified strain of rice known as golden rice. As shown in Figure 18.22, this rice has been genetically engineered to increase its iron and vitamin A content. Golden rice is now available as a staple part of the food aid delivered to many developing countries.

Cloned and Transgenic Animals

Organisms that are genetically identical are said to be **clones** of one another. As you learned in Chapter 16, identical twins form when a single zygote develops into two fetuses. Identical twins are clones that arise naturally in animal populations. For many years, researchers

BiologyFile

Web Link
Golden rice has wide-ranging humanitarian benefits, but it is not without controversy, both scientific and social. What concerns have been raised about this genetically modified food? How have those concerns been responded to, and what questions still remain?

www.albertabiology.ca
WWW

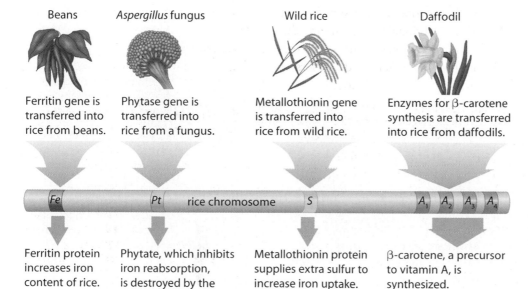

Beans	*Aspergillus* fungus	Wild rice	Daffodil
Ferritin gene is transferred into rice from beans.	Phytase gene is transferred into rice from a fungus.	Metallothionin gene is transferred into rice from wild rice.	Enzymes for β-carotene synthesis are transferred into rice from daffodils.

rice chromosome — Fe | Pt | S | A₁ A₂ A₃ A₄

Ferritin protein increases iron content of rice.	Phytate, which inhibits iron reabsorption, is destroyed by the phytase enzyme.	Metallothionin protein supplies extra sulfur to increase iron uptake.	β-carotene, a precursor to vitamin A, is synthesized.

Figure 18.22 The transgenic product, golden rice, contains four different foreign genes. Three of these genes come from other plants, and one comes from a fungus.

believed that animals could not be cloned artificially. In the 1990s, however, researchers were successful in using the cells of mouse embryos to produce cloned mice. In 1997, the Scottish researcher Ian Wilmut and his team created the cloned sheep Dolly. They were the first scientists to clone a mammal successfully, using a cell from an adult donor. Figure 18.23 shows the basic steps in their cloning procedure.

Since the "invention" of Dolly, researchers have successfully used similar techniques to clone other mammals. Cloned offspring suffer from a high mortality rate, however, as well as a high incidence of disease. Many also show signs of metabolic disorders, such as premature aging. Outcomes such as these reflect the need for ongoing research into the complexities of gene expression in animals.

Other forms of animal genetic engineering have been more successful. Researchers have been able to create new varieties of animals with useful traits. For example, transgenic milk-producing animals, such as goats, are being used to produce pharmaceutical products. Figure 18.24 shows the main steps in creating a herd of goats that are genetically modified to secrete a human polypeptide in their milk.

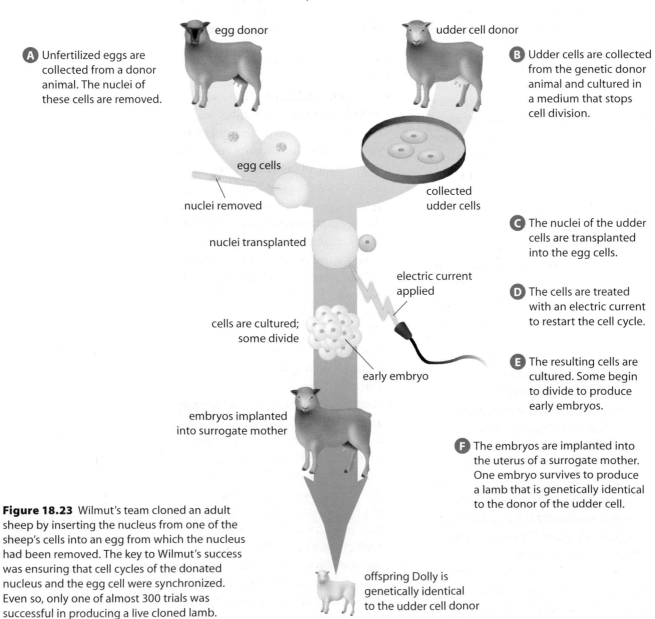

A Unfertilized eggs are collected from a donor animal. The nuclei of these cells are removed.

egg donor

egg cells

nuclei removed

nuclei transplanted

cells are cultured; some divide

embryos implanted into surrogate mother

udder cell donor

B Udder cells are collected from the genetic donor animal and cultured in a medium that stops cell division.

collected udder cells

C The nuclei of the udder cells are transplanted into the egg cells.

electric current applied

D The cells are treated with an electric current to restart the cell cycle.

early embryo

E The resulting cells are cultured. Some begin to divide to produce early embryos.

F The embryos are implanted into the uterus of a surrogate mother. One embryo survives to produce a lamb that is genetically identical to the donor of the udder cell.

offspring Dolly is genetically identical to the udder cell donor

Figure 18.23 Wilmut's team cloned an adult sheep by inserting the nucleus from one of the sheep's cells into an egg from which the nucleus had been removed. The key to Wilmut's success was ensuring that cell cycles of the donated nucleus and the egg cell were synchronized. Even so, only one of almost 300 trials was successful in producing a live cloned lamb.

Similar steps have been used by a Canadian research company to insert a spider gene into goats. The transgenic goats secrete spider silk in their milk. The silk can be extracted and spun into lightweight, strong fibres with many uses.

Another area of research involves developing transgenic animals that can serve as organ donors for humans. Usually, the transplantation of organs from animals, such as pigs, into human patients has very limited success because an antigen that is produced by the animal cells causes a serious immune response. Some genetic engineering research teams are conducting work to develop transgenic pigs that produce a human version of the antigen, or no antigen at all. These pigs could become a source of organs that are more compatible to the human body. Research such as this also raises some difficult issues, however. Some people are concerned about the risk of transferring diseases from pigs to humans. Other people ask whether it is ethical to create new kinds of animals purely for the purpose of harvesting their organs.

Assessing the Risks

In Canada, proposals for the development and use of transgenic products are reviewed by government agencies, such as Health Canada and the Canadian Food Inspection Agency. When deciding whether or not to approve a transgenic product for use in Canada, these agencies consider a number of criteria, including

- the potential social, economic, and environmental costs and benefits
- the process by which the product was made, including the source of the genetic material
- the biological characteristics of the transgenic product, compared with the characteristics of the natural variety
- the potential health effects, including the possibility that the product may contain toxins or allergens

Despite the review process, many organizations and citizen groups have opposed the use of transgenic organisms.

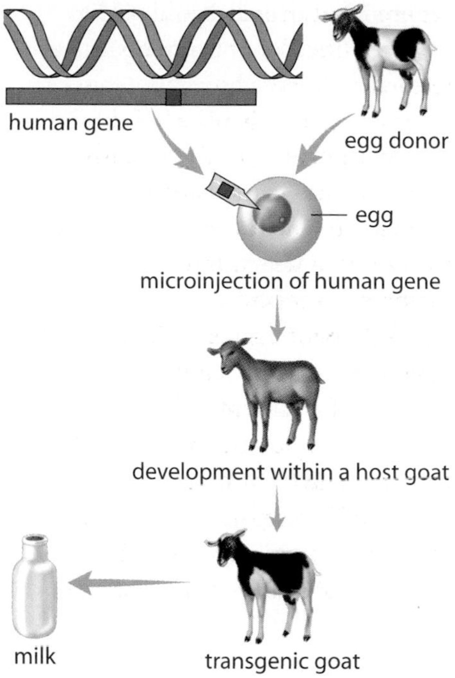

Figure 18.24 Genetic engineering can create transgenic mammals that secrete human proteins or other substances in their milk.

Below are some of the risks cited by these groups.

- Environmental threats: The use of herbicide-resistant plants could encourage farmers to use higher levels of herbicides. This, in turn, could lead to a buildup of herbicide chemicals in water supplies and neighbouring ecosystems. As well, there is evidence that engineered genes can be transferred to wild plants and other organisms, raising concerns about the emergence of "superweeds" and "superbugs." More generally, ecosystems involve complex and delicate balances among many different organisms. The introduction of transgenic bacteria, plants, or animals could upset these balances, with unknown results.
- Health effects: Many consumer groups argue that not enough is known about the long-term effects of consuming transgenic products, including genetically modified foods and medicines. The complex processes of gene regulation are not well understood, so it is difficult to predict potential health risks.
- Social and economic issues: Advocates of genetically modified foods argue that these foods will help to improve

human health and alleviate world hunger. Their opponents argue that genetic research absorbs millions of dollars, which would be better spent directly helping people in need. In addition, as mentioned earlier, many people are concerned about the growing influence of private corporations over global food production. The treatment of plants and animals as commodities to be manipulated and patented also raises questions about our relationships with—and responsibilities to—other living organisms.

• • •

27 How can transgenic organisms help to achieve social, economic, or environmental goals? Give one example of a transgenic bacterium, transgenic plant, and transgenic animal designed for one of these goals.

28 Give two examples of social, legal, or moral issues that are associated with the development of transgenic organisms.

• • •

The Diagnosis and Treatment of Genetic Disorders

Geneticists have identified the genes associated with more than 2000 human disorders, ranging from prostate cancer to insomnia. In some cases, a single defective gene is responsible for a particular disorder. In other cases, a certain gene may put an individual at a higher risk for developing a disorder. A number of technologies offer different ways to diagnose and treat genetic conditions.

Prenatal Diagnosis and Genetic Screening

In Chapter 17, you learned how to predict the chance that a child might inherit a particular genetic condition from his or her parents. If a woman has already conceived, several tests can be done to find out whether the fetus has an

inheritable disorder. Figure 18.25 shows an **ultrasound** image of a developing fetus. During an ultrasound procedure, sound waves beyond the limit of human hearing are sent through the amniotic fluid. The sound waves bounce off the developing fetus and are used to create a cross-sectional image of the fetus. This image can reveal physical abnormalities, such as a missing limb, malformed heart, or cleft palate. Many other genetic conditions, however, can be identified only by analyzing a tissue sample from the fetus.

In Chapter 17, you also learned how a karyotype can be used to identify chromosomal disorders, such as Down syndrome. The risk of having a baby with Down syndrome increases if the mother is over 40 years old. To find out whether her developing fetus is affected, a woman may choose to have an **amniocentesis**. As shown in Figure 18.26, in an amniocentesis, a needle is used to withdraw a small sample of amniotic fluid from the uterus. The extracted fluid is placed in a special nutrient-rich medium and the cells are allowed to multiply. When the cell sample is large enough, researchers can prepare a karyotype or another genetic analysis.

Due to the risk of injuring the fetus, an amniocentesis cannot be done before the fourteenth week of pregnancy. After that, weeks may pass before the results

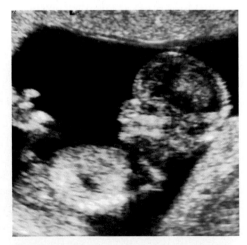

Figure 18.25 An ultrasound image like this one can provide information about genetic conditions that have visible effects.

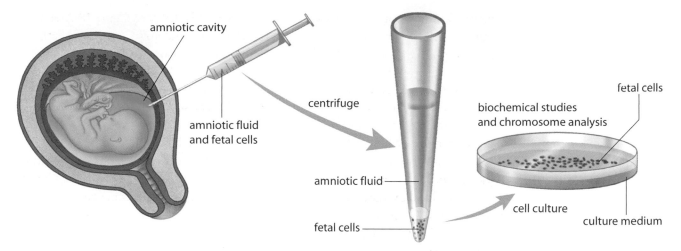

amniotic cavity

amniotic fluid
and fetal cells

centrifuge

amniotic fluid

fetal cells

biochemical studies
and chromosome analysis

fetal cells

cell culture

culture medium

are available. A woman who is interested in obtaining results sooner may opt for a procedure called **chorionic villi sampling** (see Figure 18.27). Around the ninth week of pregnancy, cells can be removed from the chorion, a tissue that surrounds the amniotic sac. The chorion is one of the tissues that make up the placenta. The chorionic cells are fetal cells, and therefore they carry the same genetic information as the developing fetus. A sample of chorionic cells can be used to prepare a karyotype.

Genetic material from a fetal tissue sample—or from a child or adult—can also be screened for specific **genetic markers**. A genetic marker is a characteristic that provides information about the genotype of an individual. Think about Mendel's pea plants, for example. The white flowers were a genetic marker

indicating the homozygous recessive genotype *rr*. Genetic markers for many human genetic disorders have also been identified at the molecular level. For example, a genetic marker may be a nucleotide sequence that is known to be associated with, or even part of, the gene of interest.

A genetic marker can be found using a **DNA probe**. A DNA probe consists of a molecule of DNA with a nucleic acid sequence that is complementary to the marker sequence, "marked" with a radioactive or fluorescent chemical tag. DNA from the tissue sample is placed in a suspension with the DNA probe. If the DNA sample contains the gene of interest, the probe will bind to the marker sequence. Using the tag, researchers can verify the presence of the gene of interest.

Figure 18.26
Amniocentesis enables analysts to perform about 40 tests for different genetic problems. Because few cells are available in the amniotic fluid, up to four weeks may be needed to wait for sufficient numbers to develop in the culture medium.

Figure 18.27 Chorionic villi sampling provides sufficient numbers of cells to perform tests and analysis immediately.

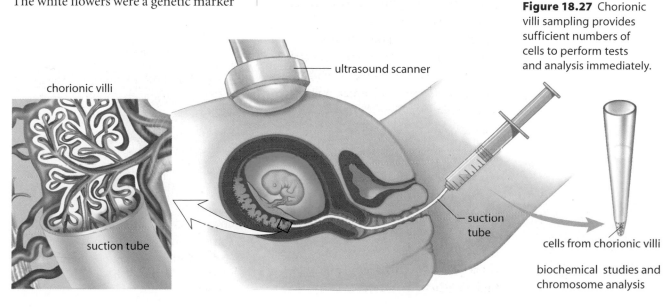

chorionic villi

ultrasound scanner

suction tube

suction tube

cells from chorionic villi

biochemical studies and chromosome analysis

29 What kind of genetic information can be obtained from each of the following procedures?
   a) ultrasound   **c)** DNA probe
   b) amniocentesis

Treating Human Genetic Disorders

Since the 1990s, researchers have been exploring ways to treat genetic conditions by correcting the functions of the defective genes. The process of changing the function of a gene in order to treat or prevent a genetic disorder is called **gene therapy**. The results of gene therapy trials show that some disorders, such as diabetes and Parkinson's disease, can be combated by targeting their genetic causes, rather than simply treating their symptoms.

In gene therapy, a molecule called a **DNA vector** carries foreign DNA into target cells in the patient. One type of DNA vector commonly used in gene therapy trials is a modified form of virus. Viruses are well-suited to gene therapy because most have the ability to target certain types of living cells and to insert their DNA into the genomes of these cells. Using restriction endonucleases, viruses can be genetically altered to carry a desired gene. Figure 18.28 shows the basic steps in creating a viral vector.

The benefits of using viruses in gene therapy are countered by some risks. Even though disease-causing genes are first spliced out of the viral genome, the remaining viral protein coat can trigger an immune response, including high fever and organ failure. Several deaths in clinical trials have been attributed to an immune response. As well, some researchers are concerned that a disarmed virus in the body might be able to regain its pathogenic properties if it comes in contact with other viruses. Because of the risks associated with viral vectors, researchers are exploring other forms of vectors, including artificial chromosomes.

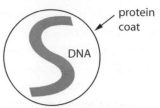

A The intact virus is made up of a protein coat containing a strand of DNA.

B The viral DNA is isolated and the disease-causing portion of the viral genome (red) is spliced out. Genes coding for the enzymes that allow the virus to insert its DNA into the genome (blue) of its host cell are left intact.

C A working human gene (green) is inserted into the viral genome. The modified viruses are then cultured with human cells. Some of the viruses will transfer the new gene into the cells' genome.

Figure 18.28 Viruses can be modified and used as vectors to carry new genes into a human cell. The human immunodeficiency virus (HIV)—one of the deadliest viruses known—has the potential to be a very powerful viral vector. The viruses that cause common colds are also useful vectors.

As researchers strive to make gene therapy an effective medical tool, some individuals and organizations are raising concerns about the ethical and moral aspects of manipulating the human genome. So far, all gene therapy trials in humans have focused on **somatic gene therapy**—that is, therapy aimed at correcting genetic disorders in somatic cells. While somatic gene therapy can improve the health of a patient, it does not prevent the disorder from being passed on to the patient's children.

One of the most controversial types of gene therapy is **germ-line therapy** gene therapy used to modify the genetic information carried in egg and sperm cells. In theory, this kind of therapy could eliminate inherited genetic disorders. In reality, however, it could have many unforeseen effects on future generations. Human germ-line therapy research is currently banned in Canada and in many other countries.

Like other genetic technologies, genetic screening and gene therapy research raise difficult ethical issues. For example, what genetic conditions should be considered "disorders" that deserve treatment? How much control should parents have over the "design" of their babies? The potential benefits of all biotechnologies must constantly be balanced by public interests and beliefs. Governments, companies, communities, and individuals all play a role in the lively debate that is helping to chart the future course of genetic research.

Section 18.4 Summary

- Tools such as DNA microarrays enable researchers to examine the expression and interaction of thousands of genes at once. This provides a way to study the genetic processes that underlie many diseases and offers the possibility of developing individually tailored treatments.

- The development of transgenic organisms that contain recombinant DNA is changing agriculture, industries, and society.
- Many people have concerns about the risks associated with genetic research. Among the concerns are the potential environmental, health, social, and ethical impacts of creating new organisms and releasing them into the world.
- Gene therapy experiments and clinical trials in humans have had some success, but they also carry some risks.
- Gene therapy involves inserting new genes into human cells.
- Geneticists distinguish between somatic gene therapy (which changes the genetic information in somatic cells) and germ-line therapy (which alters the genetic information carried in reproductive cells, and therefore influences the genetic make-up of future generations).
- Although gene therapy is likely to become a powerful treatment for disorders such as cancer, its applications raise difficult social and ethical issues.

Section 18.4 | **Review**

1. Describe two of the potential applications of the genetic research conducted through the Human Genome Project.

2. What is a DNA microarray? Why is it a useful tool for genetic research?

3. Imagine that you have been hired as an advisor to an international body that establishes conventions for genetic research. Your job is to develop a policy on the collection and ownership of genetic information.

　a) What are some of the issues you will consider?

　b) Briefly summarize how your policy will balance public and private interests.

4. A private company has developed a transgenic carrot that secretes its own pesticide. This carrot is therefore resistant to the insects and worms that often damage root crops.

　a) What are some of the risks and benefits that the Canadian government will consider when deciding whether to approve this plant for agricultural use?

　b) If approved, what advantages will this transgenic carrot offer to farmers? What are some potential drawbacks for farmers?

　c) Do you believe that foods produced with genetically modified ingredients (such as this carrot) should be labelled for consumers? List your arguments. Then list some of the arguments you could make to support the other side.

5. Briefly describe how each of the following procedures can contribute to the diagnosis of genetic conditions.

　a) ultrasound

　b) chorionic villi sampling

6. What is a DNA probe? How is it used to screen for genetic conditions?

7. Describe the difference between somatic gene therapy and germ-line therapy. How could each be used in the treatment of cancer?

Biotechnology: Assessing Unintended Consequences

Would you approve of a new technology that could lead to the death of hundreds of thousands of people every year and drastically alter the environment around the world? If not, you would not have welcomed the automobile.

We are living during the early years of a developing biotechnology industry. Like the automobile industry, biotechnology is certain to have a widespread impact on society. Few people in the 1920s foresaw how vehicle exhausts would eventually contribute to air pollution and global warming. Similarly, the long-term effects of biotechnology are unpredictable. How can society balance the benefits and risks of new technologies when some of their outcomes are uncertain?

Predicting Complex Systems

Is genetically modified (GM) food harmful or beneficial? Research data supports both sides. To understand why, consider the following characteristics of any complex system, such as food production:

- A complex system has many components, which are interconnected.
- The components of a complex system are dynamic. That is, they can change independently of control by a central agent.
- Some components are not easily observed or measured, but nevertheless affect the operation of the system.
- Our ideas and models of systems may be incorrect due to lack of knowledge and incorrect hypotheses.

These four characteristics mean that we can never be certain about the results of altering a complex system. The results that we intend by adding something new to a system may not be the results that actually occur.

Speed of Change

Another difficulty of controlling the impact of biotechnology is the speed with which new technologies spread. Genetic engineering passed from laboratories to farms and hospitals before governments fully studied its implications. GM foods were on store shelves while people still debated issues of safety, regulation, and labelling.

The Precautionary Principle

In Europe, in the 1960s and 1970s, groups concerned about the potential impacts of new technologies developed an idea called the *precautionary principle*. Various versions of this idea have since been included in many international treaties. A key point of the precautionary principle is that governments should act in advance, as a precaution, to prevent potential harm from new technologies. Furthermore, governments should act even when neither danger nor the effectiveness of the preventive measures have been demonstrated scientifically.

Although the precautionary principle appears to be a reasonable approach to reducing unknown risks, it has also had unintended consequences. For example, during 2002, millions of people in southern Africa were at risk of famine as a result of severe droughts that had reduced crop yields in several countries. The United States offered corn and soybean products to these countries, but the aid was initially rejected because of concerns that the food included GM plants. These countries had to choose between certain widespread starvation or uncertain, unproven, and even undefined future risks from GM crops.

Making an Analysis

The difficulty of predicting the effects of a new technology does not mean that we must reject the technology or give up the effort to control or reduce its risks. Consider automobiles, for example. Over time, governments have developed regulations governing speed limits, emission controls, fuel efficiency, safety design, and seat-belt use to reduce the harm from automobiles.

• • •

1. Do you think government regulations are the best way to protect people from the potential risks of biotechnology? Explain why or why not.

2. Do the risks and benefits of a new technology affect everybody in society equally? Do you think they should? What is your opinion?

Research to determine the physical basis of heredity and the molecular structure of DNA involved many different teams over several decades. Watson and Crick were the first scientists to prepare a physical model of DNA that could account for all the experimental evidence.

DNA is made up of two strands of nucleotides. These two strands wind around one another to form a double helix. The two strands of the double helix are complementary and antiparallel. The base-pairing properties of DNA provide a mechanism for accurate replication.

The nucleotides along a strand of DNA make up three-letter codons in the genetic code. Each codon corresponds to one amino acid. The genetic code is nearly universal among living organisms.

The path of gene expression involves two processes: the transcription of DNA into RNA, and the translation of RNA into protein. These processes involve several types of RNA, as well as enzymes.

A mutation is a permanent change in the DNA sequence in a cell. Mutations that affect genetic material in gametes can contribute to genetic variation within species. Mutations can be spontaneous or induced. Several factors contribute to the severity of a mutation.

Using restriction endonucleases and DNA ligase, genetic engineers can splice genes from one organism into the genome of another. The development of this technology has led to the development of transgenic organisms which have benefits and costs for humans and the environment.

Researchers can use a variety of techniques to diagnose and screen for genetic conditions, both before and after birth. Gene therapy offers an avenue for the treatment of many disorders, but it raises some difficult moral and ethical questions.

Chapter 18 Graphic Organizer

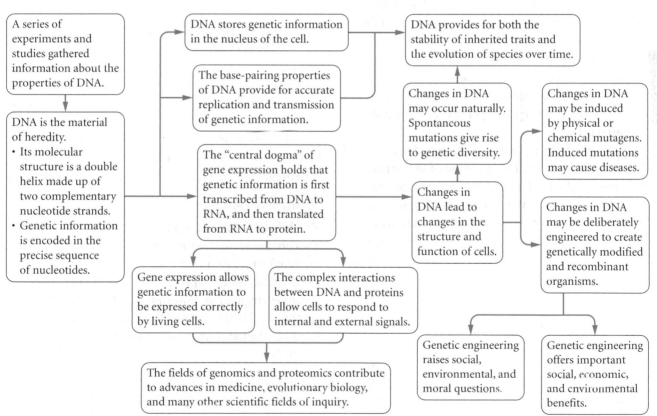

Understanding Concepts

1. Describe the main steps in the 1952 experiment by Alfred Hershey and Martha Chase. What was the significance of their experiment?

2. Define Chargaff's rule. How did Chargaff's findings overturn earlier beliefs about DNA?

3. Using symbols to represent the different nucleotides, illustrate the molecular structure of a portion of a double-stranded DNA molecule.

4. What is the base sequence of a DNA strand that is complementary to a strand with the sequence TTCGAATCGA?

5. DNA can only be synthesized in one direction. The replication of DNA strands, however, proceeds in two directions at once. Use a labelled diagram to show how this is possible.

6. Arrange the following events in the order in which they occur during the replication of a single portion of a DNA molecule:
   • Primase synthesizes a new RNA strand.
   • Helicases cleave DNA.
   • Ligase binds nucleotides together.
   • DNA polymerase adds nucleotides to a fragment of DNA.

7. How does the base-pairing property of DNA contribute to the proofreading function of DNA polymerase?

8. Name three characteristics of the genetic code, and explain why they are significant.

9. Define the following terms, and explain their significance with respect to gene expression.
   a) codon
   b) anticodon
   c) ribosome

10. Create a table that compares the various types of RNA and their roles in gene expression.

11. Using examples, explain the difference between a physical mutagen and a chemical mutagen.

12. Explain what a restriction endonuclease does. What two features of this action are particularly useful for genetic engineers?

13. Would restriction endonucleases still be of use in genetic engineering if DNA ligase were not available? Explain.

14. Three different adult sheep were involved in the cloning process that led to the birth of the lamb Dolly.
   a) What were their roles?
   b) Which one was Dolly's clone?

15. Briefly explain how each of the following procedures could be used to diagnose or treat a genetic condition.
   a) ultrasound
   b) fetoscopy
   c) chorionic villi sampling
   d) amniocentesis

Applying Concepts

16. Imagine that you have isolated the genetic material of a particular strain of virus. Your analysis of the genetic material indicates the following base composition:

Nucleotide	Presence in (%)
A	36
C	24
G	18
U	22
T	0

Is the genetic material of this virus likely to be made up of RNA or DNA? Explain your reasoning.

17. In the following image, the pale linear strand is a molecule of DNA. The red bodies are ribosomes.

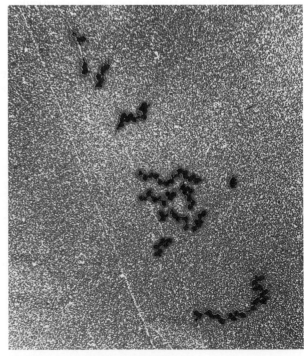

   a) What processes are occurring?
   b) Are these processes occurring in a prokaryotic or eukaryotic cell? Explain.

18. A dog breeder wants to develop a breed of dog with fur colour that changes according to the season. She establishes a partnership with a furrier who breeds stoats (animals with a coat that is white in winter and brown in summer).
    a) Develop an experimental plan that would enable the two researchers to develop a breed of transgenic dog.
    b) Briefly describe one social or ethical issue the researchers should consider before they begin their experiment.

19. Suppose that you have samples of DNA from two different plants. You want to find out whether these plants are clones. Your laboratory is equipped with DNA ligase, restriction enzymes, and gel electrophoresis equipment.
    a) Outline the steps you would take to analyze the DNA samples.
    b) Use a labelled diagram to show the results you would expect if the plants are clones.

20. You are working in a lab that is trying to find a gene associated with stunted growth in mice. You know that the gene contains the sequence GGCATTATCCG on one strand of DNA. Explain how you could use a DNA probe to determine which chromosome carries this gene.

Making Connections

21. A certain species of invertebrate has a genome that is 6000 times larger than the genome of a particular yeast cell.
    a) What conclusions, if any, could you make about the relative complexities of the two organisms?
    b) What practical applications could result from a study that compared the genomes of the two organisms?

22. A given organism has many different tissues, but its cells all carry the same genetic information. Explain how this is possible.

23. DNA is sometimes said to be like a language. Explain whether you think this comparison is valid.

24. Working with a partner, debate the following statement: "Human cloning should never be permitted." Then list what you think are the best arguments on each side of the debate.

25. At a school career fair, you tell a career counsellor that you plan to become a molecular geneticist and study viral genomes. The career counsellor asks, "Don't you think it would be more useful to study human genetics?" What points would you make in your response?

26. Many nitrites are known to be mutagenic, yet they are still commonly used as preservatives in processed foods. Describe some of the costs and benefits to society of permitting the use of mutagens in industry and food production.

27. An aquaculture research corporation based in Prince Edward Island has created a variety of transgenic salmon that grows ten times faster than normal salmon.
    a) What are the potential advantages of this transgenic fish?
    b) What are the potential risks associated with this fish?
    c) What regulations would you recommend to govern the use of this fish in commercial fish-farming operations?

28. Using examples, briefly describe two ethical dilemmas that arise from our ability to detect genetic disorders before or after birth.

Career Focus: Ask a Cancer Geneticist

Motivation comes naturally to Dr. Juliet Daniel. As an internationally recognized biology professor, she teaches students about cell development at McMaster University in Ontario, and she conducts research on proteins that are involved in normal cell growth and the spread of cancer in the body— a process called metastasis. She hopes that her research will lead to life-saving cancer treatments.

Q What made you want to study cancer genetics?

I wanted to study cancer. While I was an undergraduate student, the first discoveries were made regarding *oncogenes* and the role they played in promoting cancer. My instructor was pretty excited about the whole thing, and her enthusiasm got to most of us. With this discovery the general feeling was that now we might actually make some progress in understanding cancer, and hopefully develop treatments for it. In fact, the majority of treatments have come from those kinds of studies.

Q What have we learned about cancer and how to treat it since Terry Fox started his Marathon of Hope in 1980?

Many of the oncogene discoveries were being made around that time. Since then, we've advanced quite a lot. For example, the success rate for treating childhood leukemia is about 80 percent. For some of the other cancers, such as breast cancer, there's still a lot of work to be done. There are now some therapies that are working, and they're a result of our understanding of oncogenes, as well. We also understand more about how proteins work and what processes they regulate in the cell. This has given us more and more insight into how the body works normally. And that's going to help us understand how to treat not just cancer, but many other diseases.

Q How do genes and the proteins they encode play a role in cancer?

Basically most proteins that are linked to cancer all have normal functions in the cell, but can contribute to cancer in one of two main ways: Either they are over-expressed, and then they're what we call tumour-promoting, or *oncoproteins*. Or, if they're under-expressed, absent, or non-functional, they are considered tumour-suppressors. That means their normal role was to prevent tumour progression by keeping the cell in check.

Q You discovered a protein called Kaiso. What does this protein do?

Kaiso is a transcription factor. Transcription factors are proteins that regulate the expression of *other* proteins. Transcription factors are usually localized in the nucleus, and they bind to the DNA. As you know, the DNA contains the gene, and the gene encodes the protein, and it's the protein that performs the function. So the transcription factor regulates genes, and therefore ultimately regulates the expression of other proteins that have roles in cells.

Q Is Kaiso an oncoprotein or a tumour suppresser protein?

This is what we're working on right now. Some proteins can play both roles, depending on the situation. We know that Kaiso is over-expressed in some breast, colon, and skin cancers, and under-expressed in other breast, colon, and skin cancers. Basically, it's misregulated.

Q Where does the name "Kaiso" come from?

It's a Caribbean word for a type of music, called calypso. I'm from Barbados originally, and when I identified the gene I had a chance to name it, so I wanted to name it something to reflect my heritage. And also, when my colleagues and I were doing the experiments we listened to lots and lots of calypso music!

Other Careers Related to Genetics

Animal Breeder Breeders specialize in raising livestock (such as poultry or cattle), working animals (such as police dogs), or pets. Livestock breeders can acquire the skills they need through work experience, a two-year diploma in livestock production or agriculture technology, or a bachelor's degree in agriculture, biology, or genetics. People who breed fish, birds, cats, dogs, and other companion animals have informal training or a combination of on-the-job training and post-secondary education in animal care. Breeders associated with kennel clubs or similar organizations must abide by a code of practice and ethics.

Bioethicist Some geneticists and social scientists study the implications of genetic testing on society and individuals, or the societal perceptions of genetic engineering, mammalian cloning, or other genetics-related issues. These bioethicists may require graduate training. Lawyers may specialize in bioethics, as well, to address issues such as genetic testing in the workplace or to help form policies about the use of transgenic organisms.

Biotechnologist Biotechnology is the study of making useful products from living organisms, such as using bacteria to make insulin. Biotechnologists often use genetic engineering to develop micro-organisms that will produce tailor-made antibiotics, vitamins, food additives, bleaching agents, and other products. Biotechnologists take various educational routes. In general, a bachelor's degree in a relevant science is required for work in an industrial setting.

Forensic Laboratory Analyst Analysts work with police services to examine evidence from crime or accident scenes. Forensic technologists have a diploma in biological or chemical science technologies, and forensic scientists have a bachelor's degree in forensic science or related disciplines. Some analysts work specifically in biology. Their job includes analyzing blood and other samples, and producing genetic fingerprints.

Genetic Counsellor Genetic counsellors have a nursing degree or a master's degree in genetic counselling. They help families and other health professionals understand genetic tests, disorders, and possible treatments. For example, a genetic counsellor may meet with a family to discuss appropriate treatments for a child's genetic condition or to explain the significance of test results. In addition to having a solid understanding of genetics, a genetic counsellor must be able to communicate and interact well with people.

Microbial Geneticist Some microbial geneticists specialize in comparing rRNA sequences among micro-organisms to establish their evolutionary relationships. Others identify gene sequences or functions, or study how microbial genes are regulated in specific situations, such as when bacteria cause a disease. To work at research institutions, most microbial geneticists have a doctorate degree and post-doctoral training.

Go Further...

1. *Proto-oncogenes* are normal genes that code for proteins that stimulate cell division. Mutated proto-oncogenes can become oncogenes. List and describe three types of mutations that could convert a proto-oncogene into an oncogene.

2. Some tumour suppressor genes regulate apoptosis (programmed cell death) in unhealthy cells. What might trigger the apoptosis of a cell?

3. Certain viruses can cause proto-oncogenes to become oncogenes. Hypothesize how this might occur. Research this topic to confirm your hypothesis.

Understanding Concepts

1. Explain what is meant by the term "cell cycle."

2. Arrange the following events into the order in which they take place during mitosis: anaphase; metaphase; prophase; telophase.

3. A diploid plant cell contains 54 chromosomes ($2n = 54$). Describe the number and arrangement of chromosomes in each of the following:
   a) a leaf cell immediately following cytokinesis
   b) a gametophyte cell at the conclusion of the S phase of mitosis
   c) a sporophyte cell at the conclusion of anaphase I

4. Explain how Mendel's laws derive from events that take place during meiosis.

5. Distinguish between the following:
   a) genotype and phenotype
   b) homozygote and heterozygote
   c) recessive and dominant

6. Assume that no crossing over takes place. What is the possibility that a woman's egg cell contains only chromosomes that the woman inherited from her father? Explain the significance of your answer.

7. Nondisjunction and crossing over are two events that may take place in a reproducing cell.
   a) Use labelled diagrams to illustrate each event.
   b) Which event is more likely to result in non-viable daughter cells? Explain.

8. Compare and contrast the life cycles of humans and ferns. What reproductive advantages does each life cycle offer?

9. For each of Mendel's laws of heredity, provide
   a) an explanation in terms of classical (Mendelian) genetics
   b) an explanation in terms of molecular genetics

Use the following information to answer questions 10 to 13. In a particular breed of fly, black eyes (B) are dominant to grey eyes (b); normal wings (W) are dominant to short wings (w); and hairy legs (H) are dominant to smooth legs (h).

10. What ratio of phenotypes would you expect to find in
    a) the F_1 generation of a cross between a true-breeding normal-winged fly (*WW*) and a true-breeding short-winged fly (*ww*)?
    b) the F_2 generation of the cross in (a)?

11. Describe a procedure you could use to find out the genotype of a black-eyed fly.

12. A cross between a normal-winged fly and a short-winged fly resulted in the following F_1 offspring: 489 normal-winged; 511 short-winged. What can you infer about the genotypes of the P_1 generation?

13. You cross two flies that are both heterozygous for both traits. Assume that the genes are not linked. Of 1000 offspring, how many would you expect to have
    a) normal wings?
    b) black eyes and short wings?
    c) grey eyes and short wings?

14. A couple has three children, two of whom have hemophilia. What is the probability that their next child will have hemophilia? Use a Punnett square to explain your reasoning.

15. Examine the following figure.
    a) What process does A represent?
    b) What process does B represent?

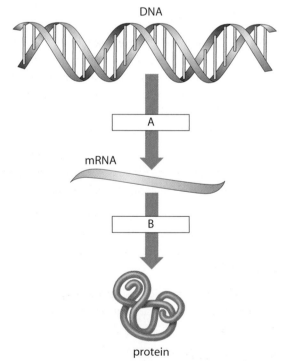

16. The coding strand of a segment of DNA in a bacterial chromosome has the following base sequence: 5'-TACACATGCATC-3'. Refer to Table 18.3 to answer these questions.
    a) Draw a section of the double-stranded DNA molecule that includes this segment.

b) Which end of the segment has a free –OH group?

c) What is the amino acid sequence of the polypeptide product of this gene?

d) Show how a nucleotide substitution could result in a silent mutation of this gene.

17. Describe the function(s) of each of the following enzymes:
   a) DNA polymerase
   b) DNA ligase
   c) RNA primase
   d) RNA polymerase
   e) helicase

18. Identify three different types of RNA and describe their roles in gene expression.

19. For each of the following terms, provide a brief definition and a description of its significance in the field of genetic engineering:
   a) restriction endonuclease
   b) DNA microarray
   c) DNA vector
   d) recombinant DNA

20. A species of grass has four chromosomes. In this grass, the gene for bunched seeds (*S*) is dominant to the gene for loose seeds (*s*). As well, the gene for long stems (*L*) is dominant to the gene for short stems (*l*). Use a labelled diagram to show how these genes assort independently in the gametes of a heterozygote plant.

21. "In an organism that reproduces asexually, there is no difference between a somatic cell mutation and a germ line mutation." Is this statement true? Explain.

22. Describe two features that are characteristic of the action of restriction endonucleases. How do these features make restriction endonucleases useful to genetic engineers?

23. Explain why DNA fragments migrate in a gel electrophoresis. Which fragments migrate farthest: large or small?

Applying Concepts

24. "Every cell is haploid for at least part of its life cycle." Explain whether or not this statement is true.

25. Explain why a karyotype is a useful research tool, and describe how you would prepare a karyotype.

26. A researcher in your lab has created a chemical that prevents microtubules from attaching to centromeres. "We can use this to stop the spread of cancerous tumours," the researcher claims. Is the researcher right? Why or why not?

27. A scientist creates a substance that denatures the enzyme DNA ligase. What impact will this substance have on the cell cycle? Explain.

28. Familial Mediterranean Fever (FMF) results in short but reoccurring episode of fever, as well as pain in the chest, joints, and abdomen. The disease occurs most frequently in individuals of Mediterranean descent. The gene responsible for FMF was discovered on chromosome 16 in 1997. The following pedigree shows the occurrence of this disorder in one family. How is FMF inherited? Provide the phenotypes and genotypes of all the individuals in the pedigree. Whose genotype can you not be sure of?

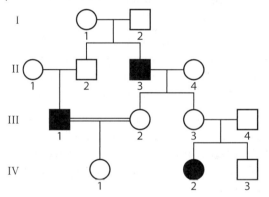

29. Lesch-Nyhan sydrome is an X-linked recessive disorder caused by a deficiency of a certain enzyme known as HPRT. Lack of HPRT leads to a build up of uric acid in the body, resulting in moderate mental retardation, poor muscle control, and the formation of crystals in the joints, kidneys, and nervous system. The following pedigree shows the occurrence of this disorder in a family. Provide the phenotypes and genotypes of all the individuals in the pedigree.

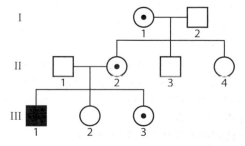

30. In humans, the allele for normal hearing (*H*) is dominant over the allele for a particular form of congenital deafness (*h*). The trait is not sex-linked. Interpret the pedigree shown here in order to answer the following questions.

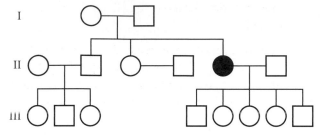

a) Explain how it is possible for individual II 5 to be congenitally deaf if neither parent has the condition.

b) Individual II 5 has five children, none of whom are congenitally deaf. What can you infer about the genotype of individual II 6? Can you be certain of this conclusion? Explain why or why not.

c) You are a genetic counselor. One of II 5's children comes to see you. She and her husband, whose sister is congenitally deaf, are planning to start a family. Using a Punnett square, explain what you will tell this couple about the likely phenotypes and genotypes of their children.

31. Frieda breeds her black rooster with Elsie's white hen. The offspring are all evenly speckled black and white. Elsie keeps all the chicks and adds them to her flock of white chickens. "I want to breed chickens that look like Dalmation dogs: mostly white, but with some black speckles," says Elsie. Will Elsie be able to do this? Use Punnett squares to explain your answer.

32. An attendant in a hospital accidentally mixes up the name tags on the four babies in the nursery. "Don't worry," says her partner. "We can use the blood type charts to match the babies to their parents." The blood type information is summarized below. Which baby belongs to which parents?
Baby A: blood type A
Baby B: blood type B
Baby C: blood type AB
Baby D: blood type O
Parents 1: blood types A and B
Parents 2: blood types O and O
Parents 3: blood types AB and O
Parents 4: blood types B and B

33. A farmer wishes to create a variety of lemon that will grow in Alberta and starts by collecting seeds from varieties of lemon trees that grow naturally in cooler climates.

a) How might the farmer use artificial selection to create the new variety of lemon?

b) How might the farmer use genetic engineering to create the new variety of lemon?

c) What is one advantage and one disadvantage of each method?

34. Slipper limpets are a species of shellfish. They live together in stacked colonies. If no female limpets are present in the colony, some male limpets will turn into females.

a) What genetic process can account for this?

b) State a hypothesis about how the absence of a female limpet triggers a change in the male limpet. Then outline an experiment you could conduct to test your hypothesis. Describe the results you would expect if your hypothesis is correct.

35. Ainslie and Josh are expecting a baby. They know there is a chance that their child may have inherited a genetic condition that causes achondroplasia (unusually short stature). The condition is caused by a single gene.

a) Identify and describe one prenatal screening technique that might enable Ainslie and Josh to know whether their child has this condition.

b) Give an example of a broader ethical or moral question that accompanies this kind of prenatal screening.

36. Will cells from your liver and your brain have the same DNA fingerprint? Explain.

Making Connections

37. Create a flow chart or graphic organizer that describes how smoking can lead to the formation of a cancerous tumour of the lung.

38. Your community is hosting a series of public information meetings about health issues. The objective of the series is to teach people about the science behind healthy lifestyle choices. You are asked to make a 10-minute presentation on the topic "DNA and Mutations."

a) Write a one- or two-sentence key message you would want your audience to remember.

b) Outline your presentation under five main headings, beginning with "Introduction" and ending with "Conclusion."

c) Under each heading list three points you would want to cover, and describe each in a few sentences.

39. A farmer plants a strain of transgenic corn in her fields. The corn carries a recombinant gene that confers resistance to a common herbicide. The next year, a species of weed growing near the corn fields is found to be herbicide-resistant. A study shows that the weed is expressing the recombinant gene. You are a journalist assigned to report on the story.

a) What is the significance of the discovery of the herbicide-resistant weed?

b) Write two main points that you would expect to hear from each of the following individuals you interview: the farmer; an official from the genetic engineering corporation that created the transgenic corn; the owner of a nearby organic farm; a consumer organization opposed to the development of genetically modified organisms; a genetics researcher.

40. Mendel conducted ground-breaking genetics research using pea plants. What might have been the impact on the field of genetics if Mendel had instead studied patterns of inheritance in cats? Explain.

41. Many conservation programs use scientific research to help protect endangered animals. Some programs breed animals in captivity, and then release the offspring into the wild. Give two specific examples of ways that a knowledge of genetics could contribute to the success of a conservation program like this.

42. a) Give three examples of the ways in which the development of technology in fields unrelated to genetics helped to advance genetic research in the period between 1800 and 2000.

b) What new breakthrough in an unrelated field might advance genetic research in this century?

43. Explain how the study of genomics differs from the study of genetics. For each field of research, give one example of how this study can be used to benefit human societies.

44. A team of researchers announces that it has identified a gene associated with high IQ. They then develop a form of gene therapy that can insert this gene into the genome of an infant.

a) What do you think might be some of the social effects of this discovery?

b) What regulations (if any) do you think should be applied to the use of this gene therapy procedure?

c) What are some steps that could be taken now to prepare society for this kind of discovery in the future?

45. Imagine that you are an official in the government of Canada. Your job is to support research that will contribute to human health. You must decide how to allocate $100 million in research funding among the following three areas: development of transgenic crops; development of techniques for somatic cell gene therapy; research into the molecular processes involved in regulation of the cell cycle. How much funding will you allocate to each area? Justify your decision.

46. Copy the following table into your notebook. Using the example of transgenic pigs that have been engineered for the purpose of serving as donors for organ transplants in humans, fill in the benefits and risks that you forsee.

Using transgenic pigs as organ donors	Benefits	Risks
To individual people		
To society		
To the economy		
To other species		
To the environment		

47. The experiments that enabled scientists to infer and model the structure and function of DNA used a variety of organisms. How can such species diversity demonstrate the same genetic principle?

48. The introduction to Chapter 18 noted that molecular genetics involves confronting difficult questions, including the question of the very definition of life itself. Write a paragraph that summarizes your opinions about how the investigations and applications of molecular genetics leads us to question what life is.

Population and Community Dynamics

General Outcomes

In this unit, you will

- describe a community as a composite of populations in which individuals contribute to a gene pool that can change over time

- explain the interaction of individuals in populations with each other and with members of other populations

- explain, in quantitative terms, the changes in populations over time

Unit Contents

Focussing Questions

1 How is population change detected and measured over time?

2 What factors influence the degree and rate of growth or decline in a population's size?

3 In what ways do individual members of a population interact with one another and with members of other populations?

I n 2003, Traditional Leaders of the Wechiau area in Ghana, West Africa visited Alberta on a conservation mission. The Wechiau Traditional Area along the Black Volta River harbours a natural community of rare species of plants, birds, monkeys, bats, various reptiles, and one of Ghana's only two remaining hippo (*Hippopotamus amphibious*) populations. These species have a long history together. Their populations' interactions have helped shaped the tremendous biodiversity of the current community. Farming, fishing, and hunting have taken a toll on these wild populations, though, especially the hippos. Therefore, with the help of Conservation Outreach at the Calgary Zoo, and other international partners, the human population of the Wechiau community has established the Wechiau Community Hippo Sanctuary.

Why was it important to people from around the world to protect the Wechiau hippo population? What would it mean for this population if it were to shrink any further? In this unit, you will consider how and why populations change over time and how their interactions shape ecological communities.

Prerequisite Concepts

This unit draws and builds upon your understanding of genetics (from Unit 7), factors that affect populations (from Unit 4, Chapter 3), and the theory of evolution by natural selection (from Unit 4, Chapter 4).

Heredity and Evolution

In the theory of evolution by natural selection, new variants of species arise continually in populations. Some variants thrive and produce more offspring, thus slowly leading to change in a population, which may even lead to the development of new species over time. Other variants die off because they cannot thrive in their environment.

As scientists in the 1930s began to broaden their understanding of genetics, they demonstrated that there is substantial genetic variation within populations. These variations can arise in populations through mutations—permanent changes in the genetic material of an organism. Evolution, therefore, depends on both random genetic mutation (with provides variation) and mechanisms such as natural selection.

Reviewing the Language of Genetics

To understand and discuss genetic variation, it is helpful to review certain terms. Alleles are alternate forms of a gene. In humans, for example, there are three alleles—I^A, I^B, and i—that determine whether an individual has A, B, AB, or O blood type. Since individuals generally have two sets of chromosomes, one received from the male parent and one from the female parent, there are two alleles for each gene at each locus. A locus (plural loci) is the location of a gene on a chromosome. So humans could be $I^A I^A$, $I^A I^B$, $I^A i$, $I^B I^B$, $I^B i$, or ii at the locus for blood group. If the two alleles at a locus are identical (for example, $I^A I^A$ or ii), the individual is called homozygous for that characteristic. An individual with two different alleles at the locus (for example, $I^A I^B$) is called heterozygous. The three blood type alleles, I^A, I^B, or i,

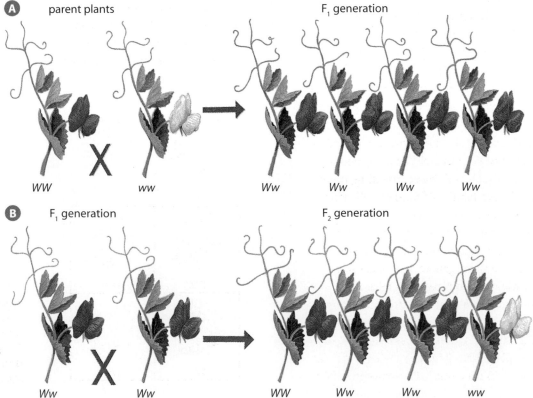

Figure P8.1 Two generations (**A** and **B**) resulting from the cross of a purple-flowered pea plant and a white-flowered pea plant.

exist in the population, but no single person can have all three. In some populations, the allele possibilities are even greater, and they far exceed the two possible alleles any human can have.

If the two alleles inherited from parents are different, one of them—the dominant allele—will be fully expressed in the individual's appearance and therefore will become the phenotype. The other allele, the recessive allele, has no noticeable effect on the organism's appearance, but it remains as part of the genotype of the organism. Figure P8.1 shows a cross between a pure purple-flowered pea plant and a pure white-flowered pea plant. The alleles for colour are represented by the letters W (for the dominant allele) and w (for the recessive allele). Since W is the dominant allele, the flowers can only be white when the two alleles are both recessive (that is, ww).

The genotype, or genetic makeup, of an individual remains constant throughout its life. However, over time, the alleles within a population may change. New alleles may arise and may be recombined, thus producing individuals with novel phenotypes. Phenotypes are the physical and physiological traits of an organism. A phenotype of an individual can be the product of both the environment and heredity. For example, environmental factors such as disease, crowding, injury, or the availability of food can all affect the appearance of an individual. But these acquired characteristics are not heritable; that is, they are not passed on to the next generation. Because of dominant and recessive alleles, an organism's appearance does not always reflect its genetic makeup. For example, Figure P8.2 shows a cross between two pea plants that have the alleles W or w at the locus for colour. The genotypes WW

and Ww both result in a purple flower, while the genotype ww results in a white flower. Table P8.1 summarizes how genotype is related to phenotype.

Table P8.1 Genotype versus Phenotype

Genotype	Genotype	Phenotype
WW	homozygous dominant	purple flowers
Ww	heterozygous	purple flowers
ww	homozygous recessive	white flowers

Not all traits are totally dominant or totally recessive. Sometimes neither allele controlling a trait is dominant. In this case, blending of the two traits can occur—a situation called incomplete dominance. Occasionally both alleles for a trait may be dominant. These alleles are said to be co-dominant, and both alleles are expressed in the heterozygous individual. In some varieties of chickens, for example, two alleles for a trait may be expressed equally. A black rooster crossed with a white hen produces offspring that have some black feathers and some white feathers.

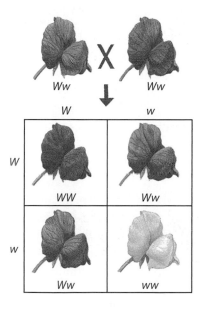

Figure P8.2 This cross between heterozygous pea plants (the same as the $F_1 \times F_1$ cross in Figure P8.1) is shown in a Punnett square.

CHAPTER
19

Genetic Diversity in Populations

Chapter Concepts

19.1 The Hardy-Weinberg Principle

- A gene pool is the sum of all the alleles for all the genes in a population. Population geneticists study gene pools.

- The Hardy-Weinberg principle is a mathematical model that is used to determine allele frequencies and genotype frequencies in a population.

- Sexual reproduction does not, by itself, cause allele frequencies to change from one generation to the next.

- Allele frequencies change over time in populations that are undergoing microevolution. The Hardy-Weinberg equation can be used to detect these changes.

19.2 The Causes of Gene Pool Change

- Genetic mutations, gene flow, non-random mating, chance events followed by genetic drift, and natural selection can lead to changes in gene pools.

- The formation of small isolated populations leads to inbreeding and a potential loss of genetic diversity from gene pools.

- Recessive alleles that are harmful in the homozygous state may remain in a gene pool if the heterozygous genotype provides a selective advantage.

Sage grouse (*Centrocercus urophasianus*, shown here), wood bison (*Bison bison athabascae*), and peregrine falcons (*Falco peregrinus*) were once abundant in the Prairies. As the human population in Canada grew and spread out, however, the habitats of many species became fragmented or polluted, and their populations declined. Ecologists are concerned about the lack of genetic diversity in these small populations. Small populations are more susceptible to disease, sudden changes in the environment, and competition from invasive non-native species.

In this chapter, you will learn how population genetics—the study of genetic diversity in populations—can be used to assess changes in populations over time. You will consider the factors that influence genetic diversity in populations, and learn why scientists consider these factors in order to develop effective conservation programs.

Pick Your Plumage

The greater sage grouse is a subspecies of sage grouse that lives in the prairies of Canada and the United States. During mating season, groups of these ground-dwelling birds gather at breeding areas, called leks, where the males strut across bare ground in full view of the females. The males display their tail feathers and inflate their yellow air sacs, which are otherwise concealed under white chest feathers. Which males do the females choose? How does the selection of mates affect the next generation?

Materials

- paper silhouette of a greater sage grouse
- coloured felt pens
- paper tail feathers of different lengths
- stapler or clear tape
- paper air sacs of different colours

Procedure

1. Choose a paper silhouette of a greater sage grouse. Also choose five to ten paper tail feathers and a pair of paper air sacs. Attach the tail feathers and air sacs to the silhouette. Use a felt pen to add markings to the tail feathers.

2. Hold up your model bird so the other students can see it. At the same time, observe your classmates' model birds. Notice the variations among the model birds.

3. Your teacher will announce which greater sage grouse will reproduce and pass on their traits to the next generation.

Analysis

1. Identify three variations among the tail feathers and air sacs that you observed.

2. a) In step 3, what determined which male birds will reproduce? Which gender—male or female—influenced this more?

   b) What will the next generation of male birds look like?

3. In this activity, the selection of mates was based on two traits. In nature, many traits and other factors influence mate selection. Suggest three traits (not necessarily obvious to the human eye) that female greater sage grouse might use to select a mate.

4. Some of the male birds in this activity did not mate and pass on their genes to the next generation. Explain how that could be both an advantage and a disadvantage to the next generation.

A male greater sage grouse inflates his air sacs to attract a female.

The Hardy-Weinberg Principle

Figure 19.1 The California ground squirrel is related to the Richardson's ground squirrel (*Spermophilus richardsonii*), also called a gopher in the Canadian Prairies. Both types of ground squirrel are small (less than 50 cm long), but dig extensive underground tunnels and mounds.

The California ground squirrel (*Spermophilus beecheyi*) may escape from predators by hiding in its burrows (Figure 19.1). While it has a key role in its ecosystem, humans often consider it to be a pest because of the digging it sometimes does in golf courses and farm fields. One of its ecological roles is as a food source for other species in the community. Scientists have observed that some populations of California ground squirrels are resistant to the venom of the northern Pacific rattlesnake (*Crotalus oreganus*), a ground squirrel predator. The venom-resistant ground squirrels are found in habitats where there are many northern Pacific rattlesnakes. Where the snakes are rare, the ground squirrels are less resistant to the snakes' venom. Are these populations of ground squirrels evolving?

As you may recall from Chapter 4, Charles Darwin and Alfred Wallace explained the mechanism by which species change over time as follows: *Individuals* with variations that make them better suited to their environment are more likely to survive and reproduce, and thereby pass on their favourable variations to the next generation.

Darwin and Wallace could not explain the source of these variations, however, or the way that traits were passed on from parents to offspring. The two naturalists were not aware of the work of Gregor Mendel, and other geneticists after him, who developed a basic understanding of inheritance. When scientists integrated the concepts of natural selection and inheritance, they were able to explain that evolution occurs when there are genetic changes in a population over time.

Thus, populations of venom-resistant ground squirrels would arise when ground squirrels with genes for venom-resistance pass on these genes to their offspring. In this section, you will learn how scientists measure changes in populations at the molecular level.

Describing Genetic Diversity in Populations

A **population** is a group of organisms of the same species that live together in a defined area and time. Thus, a group of ground squirrels that inhabit a particular field one summer make up a population, as do the Alberta wild rose bushes (*Rosa acicularis*) that grow in a particular valley over one summer (Figure 19.2). Although the individuals in a population sometimes interbreed with members of a different population nearby, they usually breed among themselves. When a population becomes fragmented—for example, when a new road creates a barrier through a habitat—the individuals on either side of the barrier may form separate populations.

As you learned in Chapter 17, **genes** are carried on chromosomes and control the inheritance of traits such as flower colour in plants and fur colour in animals. A gene can have more than one form. Each form of a gene is called an **allele**. For example, one of the genes for coat colour in mice (*Mus musculus*) can take the form of either the black coat allele (*B*) or the white coat allele (*b*). The alleles that are carried by the sperm and the egg combine during fertilization to produce a genotype. Thus, three genotypes of coat colour are possible: *BB*, *Bb*, or *bb*.

A **gene pool** is the sum of all the alleles for all the genes in a population. In other words, a gene pool is the sum of all the genetic variation that can be passed on to the next generation. In general, the more variety there is in a

Figure 19.2 The wild roses growing in a specific area during a particular time frame are an example of a population. Together, the alleles of all the plants in the population make up the population's gene pool.

gene pool, the better the population can survive in a changing environment.

Population geneticists study gene pools. As shown in Figure 19.3 on the next page, gene pools can be described in terms of genotypes and alleles. A **genotype frequency** is the proportion of a population with a particular genotype. It is usually expressed as a decimal. Suppose, for example, that a sample of a mouse population includes 72 black mice with the genotype *BB*, 96 black mice with the genotype *Bb*, and 32 white mice with the genotype *bb* (Figure 19.3). In this case, the allele for black coat colour is dominant to the allele for white coat colour. The genotype frequency of the *bb* genotype can therefore be determined by calculating the fraction of homozygous recessive mice in the sample. Since there are 200 mice in the sample, the genotype frequency of the *bb* genotype is $\frac{32}{200}$, or 0.16. The genotype frequency can also be expressed as the percentage of individuals with a particular genotype: $\frac{32}{200} \times 100 = 16$ percent.

Since the numbers of mice with *BB* and *Bb* genotypes are given, the frequencies of these genotypes can also be determined. The frequency of the *BB* genotype is $\frac{72}{200}$, or 0.36 (36 percent). The frequency of the heterozygous (*Bb*) genotype is $\frac{96}{200}$, or 0.48 (48 percent). Notice that the sum of all three genotype frequencies is 1.00, or 100 percent.

Similarly, a **phenotype frequency** is the proportion of a population with a particular phenotype, expressed as a decimal or percent. For the black and white mice, the phenotype frequency for white coat colour is the same as the genotype frequency for the *bb* genotype. This is because white coat colour is a recessive trait.

An **allele frequency** is the rate of occurrence of a particular allele in a population, with respect to a particular gene. An allele frequency is usually expressed as a decimal. Since diploid

BiologyFile

FYI
German-born scientist Ernst Mayr (1904–2005) was one of the first scientists to integrate the concepts of Mendelian genetics and Darwinian natural selection into a modern theory to explain evolutionary change. This theory became known as the theory of modern synthesis, or the synthetic theory of evolution. Mayr used this theory to explain how new species originate, a problem that Darwin and others had been unable to explain.

BiologyFile

Try This
Given the genotype frequencies for the *BB* and *Bb* genotypes, how would you calculate the phenotype frequency for black coat colour in a mouse population? How would you check your results?

Figure 19.3 Determining the genotype and allele frequencies in a population sample by counting

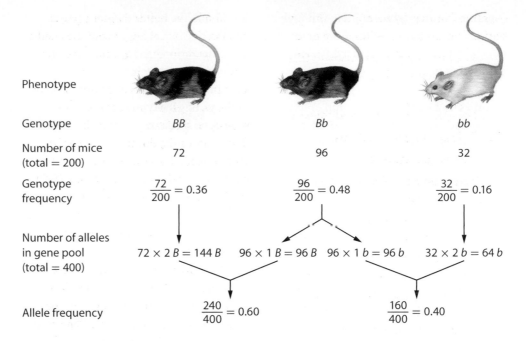

Phenotype			
Genotype	*BB*	*Bb*	*bb*
Number of mice (total = 200)	72	96	32
Genotype frequency	$\frac{72}{200} = 0.36$	$\frac{96}{200} = 0.48$	$\frac{32}{200} = 0.16$
Number of alleles in gene pool (total = 400)	$72 \times 2\,B = 144\,B$	$96 \times 1\,B = 96\,B$ $\quad$ $96 \times 1\,b = 96\,b$	$32 \times 2\,b = 64\,b$
Allele frequency	$\frac{240}{400} = 0.60$		$\frac{160}{400} = 0.40$

organisms have two possible alleles for every gene, the total number of alleles in a population is twice the number of individuals. The sample of 200 mice, for example, has a total of 400 coat colour alleles.

The number of *B* or *b* alleles in the mouse population can be found by simply counting these alleles:

72 *BB* mice with $72 \times 2 = 144\ B$ alleles
and $0 \times 72 = 0\ b$ alleles

96 *Bb* mice with $96 \times 1 = 96\ B$ alleles
and $96 \times 1 = 96\ b$ alleles

32 *bb* mice with $32 \times 0 = 0\ B$ alleles
and $32 \times 2 = 64\ b$ alleles

Totals: $144 + 96 + 0 = 240\ B$ alleles
and $0 + 96 + 64 = 160\ b$ alleles

The frequency of each allele is found by dividing the incidence of the allele by the total number of alleles in the sample. Thus, the frequency of the *B* allele is $\frac{240}{400} = 0.60$, or 60 percent. The frequency of the *b* allele is $\frac{160}{400} = 0.40$, or 40 percent. This also means that 0.60 (60 percent) of the gametes produced will carry the *B* allele and 0.40 (40 percent) will carry the *b* allele. Because there are only two versions of the coat colour gene, the allele frequencies add up to 1.00—that is, $0.60 + 0.40 = 1.00$ (100 percent).

1. What makes up a population's gene pool?

2. Distinguish among genotype frequency, phenotype frequency, and allele frequency.

Introducing the Hardy-Weinberg Principle

It might seem logical to assume that a recessive allele, such as the allele for albinism (lack of pigmentation), would eventually be eliminated from a population. This was the prevalent thinking among biologists in the early 1900s. In many populations, however, some recessive alleles are more common than the corresponding dominant alleles. Human blood type O, for example, is a recessive blood type, but it is the most common blood type among Albertans. How is this possible?

In 1908, two scientists, working independently, provided a mathematical model for studying population genetics. Godfrey Hardy, an English mathematician, and Wilhelm Weinberg, a German physician, each showed that allele frequencies in a population will remain the same from one generation to the next, as long as five conditions are met:

1. The population is large enough that chance events will not alter allele frequencies.
2. Mates are chosen on a random basis.
3. There are no net mutations.
4. There is no migration.
5. There is no natural selection against any of the phenotypes.

The prediction based on these conditions is known as the **Hardy-Weinberg principle**.

The Hardy-Weinberg principle allows us to study one trait at a time. Consider the simplest case, a trait that is controlled by a dominant allele and a recessive allele. In this case, the letter p represents the frequency of the dominant allele in the population. The letter q represents the frequency of the recessive allele. Thus, p and q represent the proportion of these alleles in the population. Since there are only two alleles, when their frequencies are added together, the sum must be 1.00, or 100 percent of the alleles.

$$p \quad + \quad q \quad = \quad 1.00$$

p	q	1.00
frequency of dominant allele	frequency of recessive allele	all the alleles (100 percent)

These allele frequencies also represent the genetic contribution that the population can make to the next generation. The Punnett square in Figure 19.4 on the next page shows the proportions of the two alleles in the gametes that can be produced by a population of black (Bb or BB) and white (bb) mice. Remember that each sperm and each egg is haploid and therefore carries only one of the alleles, dominant or recessive. In this example, the allele frequencies, p and q, are 0.70 and 0.30, respectively. This provides a general equation that can be used to determine the frequencies of different genotypes in a population. This equation, known as the **Hardy-Weinberg equation**, is highlighted to the right.

You know that the inner squares of a Punnett square represent the results of fertilization—the diploid offspring. Thus, a Punnett square takes into account all the possible recombinations of the given alleles. According to the product rule, if p represents the frequency of the dominant allele (B), then p^2 represents the frequency of the homozygous dominant offspring (BB). Similarly, if q represents the frequency the recessive allele (b), then q^2 represents the frequency of the homozygous recessive offspring (bb).

As shown in the Punnett square in Figure 19.4, there are two possible recombinations that will result in the heterozygous genotype (Bb). Therefore, the frequency of the heterozygous genotype is $pq + pq = 2pq$.

Given the allele frequencies, $p = 0.70$ and $q = 0.30$, we can calculate the frequencies of the different genotypes: p^2 is 0.49, q^2 is 0.09, and $2pq$ is 0.42. Thus, 49 percent of the individuals in the next generation will be homozygous for the dominant allele, 42 percent will be heterozygous, and 9 percent will be homozygous recessive.

Notice that the sum of all the genotypes is equal to 1.00, or 100 percent:

$$0.49 \quad + \quad 0.42 \quad + \quad 0.09 \quad = \quad 1.00$$
$$49 \text{ percent} + 42 \text{ percent} + 9 \text{ percent} = 100 \text{ percent}$$
$$p^2 \quad + \quad 2pq \quad + \quad q^2 \quad = \quad 1.00$$

In other words, 70 percent of the mice in the study population have at least one dominant allele (B), while the other 30 percent have at least once recessive allele (b). Again, the sum of these allele frequences is 1.00, or 100 percent.

p^2	$2pq$	q^2	1.00
frequency of homozygous dominant genotype	frequency of heterozygous genotype	frequency of homozygous recessive genotype	all the individuals in the population (100 percent)

The Hardy-Weinberg equation can be used to calculate the proportion of a population that carries recessive alleles for genetic conditions, such as sickle cell anemia or cystic fibrosis. It can also

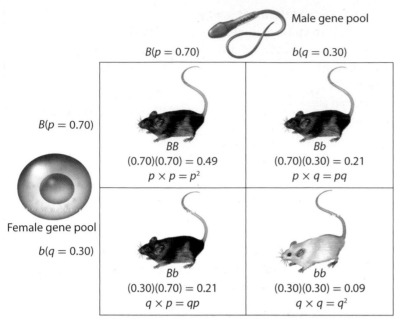

Male gene pool

$B(p = 0.70)$ $b(q = 0.30)$

$B(p = 0.70)$

Female gene pool

$b(q = 0.30)$

BB $(0.70)(0.70) = 0.49$ $p \times p = p^2$	**Bb** $(0.70)(0.30) = 0.21$ $p \times q = pq$
Bb $(0.30)(0.70) = 0.21$ $q \times p = qp$	**bb** $(0.30)(0.30) = 0.09$ $q \times q = q^2$

Figure 19.4 A Punnett square can be used to determine the expected genotype frequencies in the next generation. This Punnett square has been scaled up to represent the genotype frequencies for the gametes in an entire gene pool. In generic terms, p^2 represents the homozygous dominant offspring, $2pq$ represents the heterozygous offspring, and q^2 represents the homozygous recessive offspring.

be used to calculate the number of individuals with a specific genotype, such as the number of carriers of a genetic condition. To calculate the number of individuals, however, you need to know the population size, N:

$$p^2(N) + 2pq(N) + q^2(N) = N$$

Study the Sample Problems that follow. Then complete the Practice Problems and the Investigation that appear afterward.

• • •

(3) What are the conditions of the Hardy-Weinberg principle?

(4) Using the Hardy-Weinberg equation, distinguish between p and p^2 as used to describe a population.

(5) How is it possible to find the number of heterozygotes in a sample population, given the allele frequencies?

• • •

Sample Problems

Sample Problem 1

Albinism in a Snake Population

In a randomly mating population of snakes, one out of 100 snakes counted is albino, a recessive trait. Determine the theoretical percentage of each of the genotypes in the population.

What Is Required?

To determine the values for p^2, $2pq$, and q^2, which represent the frequencies of the AA, Aa, and aa genotypes in the population

What Is Given?

The value of q^2: The proportion of snakes that are albino and thus have the aa genotype is $\frac{1.00}{100.00}$.

$p + q = 1.00$

Plan Your Strategy

Change the value of q^2 to a decimal.

Take the square root of the value of q^2 to find the value of q.

Subtract q from 1.00 to find the value of p.

Find the values of p^2 and $2pq$.

Express p^2 and $2pq$ as percents.

Act on Your Strategy

Step 1

$q^2 = \dfrac{1.00}{100.00}$

$= 0.0100$, or 1.00 %

Step 2

$\sqrt{q^2} = \sqrt{0.0100}$

$q = 0.100$

Step 3

$p + q = 1.00$

$p = 1.00 - q$

$= 1.00 - 0.100$

$= 0.900$

Step 4

$p^2 = (0.900)(0.900)$

$= 0.810$, or 81.0 %

$2pq = 2(0.900)(0.100)$

$= 0.180$, or 18.0 %

The theoretical percentages of the genotypes are 81.0 percent AA, 18.0 percent Aa, and 1.00 percent aa.

Check Your Solution

$p^2 + 2pq + q^2 = 1.00$, or 100 %

$81.0\ \% + 18.0\ \% + 1.00\ \% = 100\ \%$

$100\ \% = 100\ \%$

Sample Problem 2

Wing Length in Fruit Flies

A single pair of alleles codes for one of the genes that controls wing length in fruit flies (*Drosophila melanogaster*). The long wing allele (L) is dominant to the short wing allele (l). If 40 fruit flies out of 1000 that are counted have short wings, how many fruit flies out of 1000 would be expected to be heterozygotes?

What Is Required?

To determine the number of fruit flies that are heterozygous (Ll) for the wing length gene, given a population sample (N) of exactly 1000

What Is Given?

The proportion (q^2) of homozygous recessive (ll) fruit flies in the sample, $\dfrac{40}{1000}$

Plan Your Strategy

Change the frequency of q^2 to a decimal.
Take the square root of the value of q^2 to find the value of q.
Subtract q from 1.00 to find the value of p.
Find the value of $2pq$.
Multiply the population size (N) by the frequency of the heterozygous genotype ($2pq$).

Act on Your Strategy

Step 1
$$q^2 = \frac{40.0}{1000}$$
$$= 0.040$$

Step 2
$$\sqrt{q^2} = \sqrt{0.0400}$$
$$q = 0.200$$

Step 3
$$p + q = 1.00$$
$$p = 1.00 - q$$
$$= 1.00 - 0.200$$
$$= 0.800$$

Step 4
$$2pq = 2(0.800)(0.200)$$
$$= 0.320$$

Step 5
$$\text{number of heterozygotes} = (2pq)(N)$$
$$= (0.320)(1000.0)$$
$$= 3.2 \times 10^2$$

The population sample would be expected to contain exactly 320 fruit flies that are heterozygous (Ll) for the wing length gene.

Check Your Solution
$$p^2 + 2pq + q^2 = 1.00$$
$$(0.800)^2 + 0.320 + 0.0400 = 1.00$$
$$0.640 + 0.320 + 0.0400 = 1.00$$
$$1.00 = 1.00$$

Fruit fly with long wings

Fruit fly with short wings

Practice Problems

1. Suppose that in a fruit fly population the frequency of the recessive allele that codes for short wings (l) is 0.30. What would be the expected genotype frequencies in the next generation?

2. In a pea plant population, the dominant allele for tallness (T) has a frequency of 0.64. What percent of the population would be expected to be heterozygous (Tt) for the height alleles?

3. In a randomly mating population of mice, 25.0 out of every 100.0 mice born have white fur, a recessive trait.

   a) Calculate the frequency of each allele in the population.

   b) Calculate the genotype frequencies for the population.

4. A dominant allele, T, codes for the ability to taste the compound phenylthiocarbamide (PTC). People who are homozygous for the recessive allele, t, are unable to taste PTC. In a genetics class of 125 students, 88 students can taste PTC and 37 cannot.

   a) Calculate the expected frequencies of the T and t alleles in the student population.

   b) How many students would you expect to be heterozygous for the tasting gene?

   c) How many students would you expect to be homozygous dominant for the tasting gene?

   d) How could you check your answers for parts (b) and (c)?

5. In the Caucasian population of North America, one out of every 10 000 babies is born with a recessive condition known as phenylketonuria (PKU). This condition is controlled by a single pair of alleles. People who are homozygous recessive for the PKU gene completely lack the enzyme that is necessary to metabolize the amino acid phenylalanine into harmless by-products. The presence of this amino acid in a baby's diet can slow the development of the baby's brain. What percentage of the Caucasian population of North America would you expect to be heterozygous for the PKU allele?

Minding *p* and *q*

The Hardy-Weinberg principle not only provides a method for measuring the amount of variation within a gene pool, but also allows geneticists to compare allele frequencies in a population at different times. If there is no change in allele frequencies over time, then the population is said to be at **genetic equilibrium** (also called *Hardy-Weinberg equilibrium*). A population at genetic equilibrium is not changing or evolving. If, on the other hand, there *is* a change in allele frequencies over time, then one of the conditions of the Hardy-Weinberg principle is not being met and the population may be evolving. For example, if the first four conditions are being met, then we can conclude that natural selection is occurring.

The gradual change in allele frequencies in a population is called **microevolution**. An example of microevolution is the development of DDT-resistance in *Anopheles* mosquito populations. The females of 30 to 40 species of *Anopheles* mosquitoes carry the parasitic protozoan, *Plasmodium*. This single-celled parasite causes malaria, a disease responsible for at least one million deaths worldwide annually. The pesticide DDT has been used successfully for decades in tropical and subtropical countries to reduce *Anopheles* numbers in the past, but resistance in some species has limited the effectiveness of DDT over time. Look for signs of microevolution in two populations as you complete Investigation 19.B.

6 How can you tell if a population is at genetic equilibrium or undergoing microevolution?

INVESTIGATION 19.A

Target Skills

Asking questions about genotype frequencies based on observable phenotypes, and **investigating** these frequencies

Applying, quantitatively, the Hardy-Weinberg principle to observed data

Interpreting data, and **communicating** results and ideas

Applying the Hardy-Weinberg Equation

Some human traits are controlled by a single gene, with one pair of alleles. These traits can easily be studied to measure genetic variability in a population. The presence of freckles, for example, is generally dominant to the absence of freckles. Unattached earlobes are dominant to attached earlobes. A pointed hairline on the forehead when the hair is pulled back is dominant to a straight hairline. What are the frequencies of the various genotypes in your class?

Procedure

1. Work with a partner. Your teacher will tell you which three single-gene traits to investigate.

2. Survey the class to find out the number of students with each phenotype for the traits you are investigating. For example, survey the class to find out how many students have attached earlobes and how many do not. Alternatively, your teacher will provide you with data to use.

Analysis

1. Using the Hardy-Weinberg equation, determine the frequency of the dominant and recessive alleles for each trait in the class.

Conclusions

2. Determine the frequency of each genotype in the class. (Remember that there are three genotypes for each trait that you investigated.)

3. How closely would you expect your class results to match the genotype frequencies for the population of North America? Explain your answer.

Expanding the Hardy-Weinberg Equation

You have learned how to use the Hardy-Weinberg equation to study pairs of dominant and recessive alleles. The Hardy-Weinberg equation can also be used to study co-dominant alleles, alleles that show incomplete dominance, or alleles that do not produce observable phenotypic differences.

Population ecologists often use DNA testing to find out which allele an individual carries. They can test DNA from several individuals in a population to determine allele frequencies for the sample. Then they can use these frequencies to predict the allele frequencies for the total population. For example, DNA testing was used to find the allele frequencies in the gene pool of a collared pika population (*Ochotona collaris*) over time (Figure 19.5).

In addition, the Hardy-Weinberg equation can be expanded to study genes with multiple alleles. Examine Figure 19.5, for example. Each line in Figure 19.5 represents the frequency of an allele at different points in time, and all the alleles are for the same gene. The sum of the frequencies for all the alleles at any point in time equals 1.00, or 100 percent of the alleles. Changes in the frequencies over time indicate that something is happening to cause microevolution in this vulnerable population.

• • •

 ⑦ Describe how the two equations based on the Hardy-Weinberg principle can be used to detect gene pool changes over time.

• • •

Section 19.1 Summary

• A gene pool contains all the alleles for all the genes in a population that can be passed on to the next generation.
• The Hardy-Weinberg principle provides a basis for studying allele frequencies and genotype frequencies in a gene pool.

Change in allele frequencies in a collared pika population 1998–2005

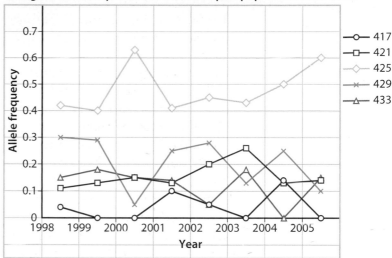

Figure 19.5 The change in frequencies of five alleles (identified by different numbers in the legend) in a collared pika population over eight years. This population, which has been declining in size, appears to be undergoing microevolution. The sum of the allele frequencies estimated for each year of the study is 1.00 (or very close to 1.00 due to rounding and estimation). (Data provided by Jessie Zgurski, University of Alberta.)

• According to the Hardy-Weinberg principle, a population can be at genetic equilibrium only if the population is large enough that chance events do not alter allele frequencies, there is random mating among all individuals in the population, there are no net mutations, there is no migration, and natural selection is not occurring. If any of these conditions are not met, microevolution will occur.
• The total of the allele frequencies, p and q, for one gene locus always equals 1.00, or 100 percent of the alleles.
• According to the Hardy-Weinberg equation, $p^2 + 2pq + q^2 = 1.00$. The letters p and q represent the frequencies of the dominant and recessive alleles, respectively.
• The genotypes in the gene pool are represented by p^2 (frequency of homozygous dominant genotype), $2pq$ (frequency of heterozygous genotype), and q^2 (frequency of homozygous recessive genotype).
• If the population size, N, is known, the number of individuals with a particular genotype can be calculated using the equation, $p^2(N) + 2pq(N) + q^2(N) = N$.

Testing the Hardy-Weinberg Principle

The Hardy-Weinberg principle states that the allele frequencies in a population will not change from generation to generation, as long as five conditions are met. In this investigation, you will focus on the first two conditions:

- The population is large enough that chance events will not alter allele frequencies.

- Mates are chosen on a random basis.

Part 1 of this investigation involves simulating the effect of random mating on allele frequencies in a large population. Part 2 involves testing to find out if a model population is at genetic equilibrium. You will work with a partner. One of you will carry out the procedure for Part 1, while the other carries out the procedure for Part 2. You will work together to complete the hypothesis and prediction for each part, and the analysis and conclusions.

Question

What processes affect the genetic equilibrium of a population?

Part 1: Demonstrating Genetic Equilibrium

Hypothesis

Make a hypothesis about the effects of random mating on allele and genotype frequencies in a population over time.

Prediction

In a model simulation using 80 beads, the proportion of corresponding alleles in a population undergoing random mating are $\frac{48}{80}$ for D, the dominant allele, and $\frac{32}{80}$ for L, the recessive allele. Calculate the allele frequencies for L and D. Use the Hardy-Weinberg equation to predict the expected frequency of each genotype DD, DL, and LL. Then predict the allele and genotype frequencies for future generations.

Materials

- 2 paper cups (or similar containers)
- 48 dark-coloured beads
- 32 light-coloured beads

Procedure

1. Prepare two data tables like the following one. Use one table for your data and the other table for class data.

Number of Each Genotype in a Population Undergoing Random Mating

Generation	Number of *DD*	Number of *DL*	Number of *LL*	Total number of individuals

2. Label one paper cup "male gene pool" and the other paper cup "female gene pool." Put 24 dark-coloured (*D*) and 16 light-coloured (*L*) beads in each cup. The beads represent the alleles for a specific trait.

3. Gently shake the cups to mix the beads. To simulate random mating, without looking, select one bead (allele) from each cup. Place the pair of beads (the genotype of the offspring) on the table. Repeat this process, lining up the genotypes (*DD*, *DL*, and *LL*) in separate columns until you have used all the beads.

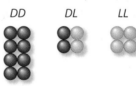

DD   *DL*   *LL*

4. In your data table, record the number of offspring with each genotype for this generation.

5. To establish the gene pool for the next generation, assume that half the population in each column of beads is male and the other half is female. Place the beads representing the male genotypes in the male gene pool and the beads representing the female genotypes in the female gene pool. Remember that genotypes are made up of two alleles, so each male and female must contribute two beads to the gene pool. (You should end up with an equal number of alleles in each gene pool. If there is an odd number of genotypes in a column, assume that the last genotype belongs to a male. The next time this happens, assume that the last genotype belongs to a female. Switch from male to female every time there is an odd number of genotypes in a column.)

6. Repeat steps 3 to 5 three more times to obtain data for a total of four generations.

7. Pool your data with the data obtained by the rest of the class and record the class data.

Part 2: Testing for Genetic Equilibrium

Hypothesis

Make a hypothesis about the effects of a recessive lethal allele on allele frequencies and genotype frequencies in a population over time.

Prediction

The proportions of corresponding alleles in a population are $\frac{48}{80}$ for D (the dominant allele for a healthy phenotype) and $\frac{32}{80}$ for L (the recessive lethal allele). Calculate the allele frequencies for L and D. Use the Hardy-Weinberg equation to predict the expected frequency of each genotype DD, DL, and LL. Then predict the allele and genotype frequencies for future generations.

Materials

- 3 paper cups (or similar containers)
- 48 dark-coloured beads
- 32 light-coloured beads

Procedure

1. Prepare a data table like the one below. Use one table for your data and the other table for class data.

Number of Each Genotype in a Population with a Lethal Allele, L

Generation	Number of DD	Number of DL	Number of LL	Total number of individuals

2. Complete steps 2 to 4 as described in Part 1.

3. Assume that the light bead (L) is the recessive lethal allele. Therefore, none of the organisms with the LL genotype will survive to reproduce. Remove the LL genotypes from the population on the table, and place them in a separate cup. You now have two columns of beads on the table: DD and DL.

4. Complete step 5 as described in Part 1.

5. Repeat steps 2 to 4 three more times to obtain data for a total of four generations.

6. Pool your data with the data obtained by the rest of the class and record the class data.

Analysis

1. **a)** Use the class data from Part 1 to graph the genotype frequencies over four generations. Compare your results with your prediction.

   b) Use the class data from Part 1 to determine the allele frequencies for the fourth generation. (**Hint:** Use the Hardy-Weinberg equation and the equation $p + q = 1.00$.) Compare your results with your prediction.

2. **a)** Use the class data from Part 2 to graph the genotype frequencies over four generations. Compare your results with your prediction.

   b) Use the class data from Part 2 to determine the allele frequencies for the fourth generation. Compare your results with your prediction.

   c) What happened to the total number of alleles in the population over the course of the investigation? Did this affect the results of the investigation? Explain your answer.

3. Explain why data from the whole class were pooled.

4. In reality, each individual contributes one allele to the next generation. Identify any false assumptions that were made when choosing alleles in this investigation.

Conclusions

5. Account for the allele and genotype frequencies observed over time in Part 1. Were the conditions of the Hardy-Weinberg principle met in this population? Explain your answer.

6. Account for the allele and genotype frequencies observed over time in Part 2. Were the conditions of the Hardy-Weinberg principle met in this population? Explain your answer.

1. Is the frequency of a homozygous dominant genotype equal to the proportion of individuals that show the dominant trait? Explain your answer.

2. Suppose that the frequency of a recessive allele is found to be 0.30. When the same population is sampled five years later, the frequency of the recessive allele is found to be 0.20. Do these findings indicate that the Hardy-Weinberg principle is false? Justify your response.

3. Cystic fibrosis is an inherited recessive disorder that causes especially thick mucus to build up in the lungs and digestive tract. The mucus makes it difficult to clear micro-organisms from the airways, so people with cystic fibrosis are prone to dangerous respiratory infections. Among Caucasians, about one in every 3000 newborns is affected by this condition. Determine the frequency of the cystic fibrosis allele among Caucasians. What proportion of this population would you expect to be heterozygous carriers of the cystic fibrosis allele? Express your answers as decimals.

4. The M and N factors are glycoproteins that are found on the surface of red blood cells. Unlike other types of red blood cell antigens, the M and N factors do not cause antibody reactions in human blood transfusions. People with type M blood are homozygous for the M allele, and people with type N blood are homozygous for the N allele. Heterozygous individuals have type MN blood. In a study of a population of Inuit living in the Northwest Territories, 512 people had blood type M, 256 had blood type MN, and 32 had blood type N.

   a) Calculate the frequency of each allele, M and N, in the population studied.

   b) What would be the expected frequency of each genotype in the next generation, assuming that this population is in genetic equilibrium for the trait.

   c) In a second study group, the frequencies of the genotypes were 0.306 MM, 0.491 MN, and 0.203 NN. Could this second study group have, in fact, come from the previously described Inuit population? Explain your answer.

5. In Japan, the incidence of recessive homozygosity for PKU is one in every 119 000 newborns. What percent of the Japanese population is heterozygous for this allele?

6. If 85 percent of the population of Alberta has Rh$^+$ blood, a dominant trait, what percentage of Albertans would you expect to be heterozygous for this trait?

7. A farmer planted some bean seeds. When the seeds germinated, 192 of the seedlings were albino, a recessive trait, and 2880 were green.

   a) Determine the proportion of the seedlings that you would expect to be homozygous for the production of chlorophyll. Express your answer as a decimal.

   b) Determine the number of seedlings that you would expect to be carriers of the albino allele.

8. The following graph shows the frequency of a recessive allele in the parental generation (0 on the x-axis) of a hypothetical fruit fly population and throughout 10 subsequent generations.

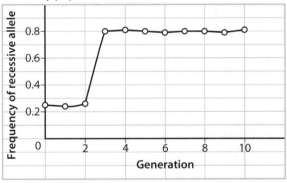

Frequency of recessive allele in fruit fly population over time

   a) Based on the graph, determine whether or not the fruit fly population is evolving. Justify your response.

   b) Describe the frequency of the recessive allele over time. Make a hypothesis to explain what has affected the frequency of the recessive allele over time.

The Causes of Gene Pool Change

Figure 19.6 Although most mallard ducks migrate south for the winter, some populations stay in Alberta and even Alaska as long as they can find open water and enough food. Male mallard ducks are recognizable by their green heads. Female mallard ducks are brown with white spots.

To most people, the mallard ducks (*Anas platyrhynchos*) shown in Figure 19.6 look much the same as mallards always have. Over time, however, the population these mallards belong to has probably undergone microevolution. For example, a mallard population that stays in Alberta year-round will have occasionally been joined by migrating mallards, which have contributed to the gene pool. On the other hand, an especially cold winter a few years ago might have killed many of the less resilient ducks, reducing **genetic diversity**, the degree of genetic variation within a species or population. Clearly, the conditions of the Hardy-Weinberg principle do not hold true in this population.

The conditions of the Hardy-Weinberg principle represent an ideal situation that rarely, if ever, occurs in natural populations. The principle is valuable, however, because the Hardy-Weinberg equation can be used to measure the amount of change in the allele frequencies of a population over time. Processes such as genetic mutations, gene flow, non-random mating, genetic drift, and natural selection all cause changes in

gene pools (Figure 19.7 on page 688). These processes are discussed separately in this section, but they tend to be interacting. Together, over a few generations, they can expand or limit genetic variation in a population.

> **Q 8** What is the relationship between the conditions of the Hardy-Weinberg principle and gene pool change?

Mutations

A **mutation** is a change that occurs in the DNA of an individual. An inheritable mutation, however, has the potential to affect an entire gene pool. While most mutations are neutral, some are harmful and a few are even beneficial. A small number of people, for example, have a rare mutation in a gene that codes for a protein receptor on the surface of the white blood cells. In people without the mutation, HIV can use the protein receptor to enter the white blood cells. Some people who are homozygous for the mutation lack the functioning

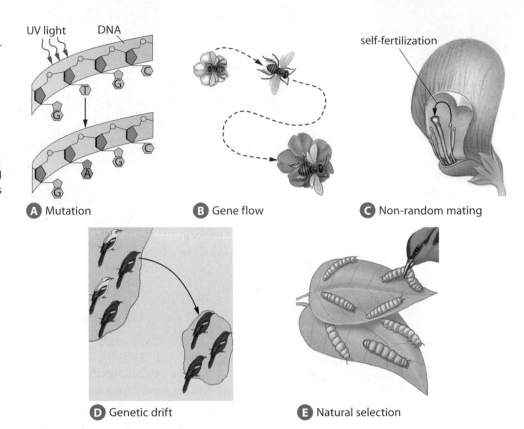

A Mutation **B** Gene flow **C** Non-random mating

D Genetic drift **E** Natural selection

Figure 19.7 The five agents of evolutionary change are **(A)** mutation, a change in DNA; **(B)** gene flow, the migration of alleles from one population to another; **(C)** non-random mating, such as self-fertilization in flowers; **(D)** genetic drift, a change in allele frequencies in a small population due to a chance event; and **(E)** natural selection for favourable variations.

receptor and are therefore resistant to HIV infection (Figure 19.8).

Sometimes *back mutations* occur. These mutations reverse the effects of former mutations. If the number of mutations from *A* to *a* are equal to the number of back mutations from *a* to *A*, then there are no net mutations.

Initially, however, inheritable mutations may diversify a gene pool. The more genetic variation there is in a population, the greater the chance that a variation will be present and provide a selective advantage in a changing environment. Resistance to HIV might be considered an example of a selective advantage.

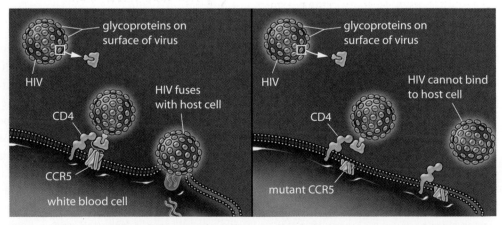

Figure 19.8 In healthy white blood cells, CCR5 is a receptor for chemical messages of the immune system. Along with the receptor CD4, CCR5 acts as a receptor for HIV. Some people who are homozygous for a mutation in the CCR5 gene are resistant to HIV infection.

Another example is poison resistance in the Norway rat (*Rattus norvegicus*). The compound Warfarin has been widely used to control rat populations since the 1950s. Warfarin is a blood thinner, which means that it prevents the blood from clotting and can therefore cause internal bleeding. Before Warfarin was introduced as a rat poison, it is likely that a few rats already had a mutation that made them resistant to Warfarin's effects. These rats survived applications of Warfarin, mated, and passed on the mutation for Warfarin resistance to their offspring. By the 1960s, there were many Warfarin-resistant rat populations in Europe.

> 9 Explain how inheritable mutations may add to the diversity of a gene pool.

Gene Flow

Gene flow describes the net movement of alleles from one population to another due to the migration of individuals (Figure 19.9). Grey wolves (*Canis lupis*), for example, have large territories. In addition, a lone grey wolf may travel over 800 km in search of a new territory or breeding partner. Very often, a grey wolf from one population will mate with members of a nearby population and may bring new alleles into the gene pool of the nearby population (Figure 19.10). As a result, genetic diversity in the nearby population may increase. Having greater genetic diversity may help this population survive.

Wolf conservationists considered the importance of genetic diversity when they reintroduced the grey wolf to Yellowstone National Park in the United

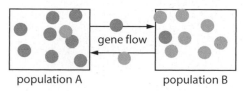

Figure 19.9 Gene flow between nearby populations

Figure 19.10 Gene flow between grey wolf populations is quite common because individuals travel long distances. Why might scientists have difficulty in defining distinct grey wolf populations in North America?

States in the mid-1990s. Grey wolves from different populations in Alberta, and later British Columbia, were captured and brought to Yellowstone. These 32 wolves formed the basis of a new, successful population that grew to 148 individuals by 2003.

While gene flow increases genetic diversity in one population, it reduces genetic differences among populations. As a result, adjacent populations tend to share many of the same alleles. In the past, for example, local human populations tended to be isolated from one another and probably had distinct gene pools. As cultural and geographic barriers have dissolved, gene flow between human populations has increased. This has reduced genetic differences between local human populations.

> 10 How does gene flow into a population affect the population's gene pool?
>
> 11 Describe the outcomes of two situations that result in gene flow between populations.

Non-Random Mating

Random mating in a population means that there is no way to predict which males will mate with which females, or which females will mate with which males. The probability of any individual with a specific genotype mating with another

Biology File

Web Link
The Yukon to Yellowstone Conservation Initiative (Y2Y) combines land stewardship with scientific research to protect habitat within the numerous mountain corridors spanning these two regions. How does the preservation of critical mountain corridors influence gene flow within the Yukon to Yellowstone region?

www.albertabiology.ca
WWW

FYI
Scientists estimate that everyone carries four to six lethal recessive alleles. When close relatives have children together, the likelihood that these children will receive two copies of the same lethal allele is higher than it is in the general population, resulting in above average rates of infant mortality.

individual with a specific genotype depends on the allele frequencies in the population. Random mating is much like a lottery in which breeding partners are randomly selected by drawing names out of a hat. Unrestricted random mating is probably uncommon in natural populations for two main reasons: preferred phenotypes and inbreeding.

In animal populations, individuals may choose mates based on their physical and behavioural traits. Female greater sage grouse, for example, choose mates based on their phenotypes. In caribou (*Rangifer tarandus*) herds, males compete for mates by using their antlers to spar against other males, chasing one another, and fighting. This is a form of **non-random mating** because it prevents

individuals with particular phenotypes from breeding. Only the individuals that mate will contribute to the gene pool of the next generation.

Inbreeding is another example of non-random mating. Inbreeding occurs when closely related individuals breed together. An extreme example of inbreeding is the self-fertilization of some flowers (Figure 19.7). Since close relatives share similar genotypes, inbreeding increases the frequency of homozygous genotypes. Although inbreeding does not directly affect allele frequencies, as homozygous genotypes become more common, harmful recessive alleles are more likely to be expressed. The negative effects of inbreeding are sometimes seen in purebred

---

Thought Lab 19.1 The Spirit Bear

Target Skills

Describing the factors that cause gene pool diversity to change

Applying, quantitatively, the Hardy-Weinberg principle to published data, and **inferring** the significance of the results

Assessing the role of the Hardy-Weinberg principle in explaining natural phenomena

A Kermode black bear mother and her cubs

The Kermode bear (*Ursus americanus kermodei*) is a white variety of black bear that is found only in small island populations and in populations on the coastal mainland of British Columbia. Known to local Aboriginal peoples as the spirit bear, the Kermode is rare and people are unclear about how best to ensure its survival. Scientists know that its white coat colour is due to a recessive allele. They rely on bear counts and DNA testing of hair samples to estimate the frequency and distribution of this allele.

Estimated Frequency of White Kermode Bears on Two British Columbia Islands

Location	Gribbell Island	Princess Royal Island
Frequency of white bears	0.3	0.1

Procedure

Use the information and preceding table to answer the following Analysis questions.

Analysis

1. Predict the frequency of the white coat allele in the Kermode bear population of
   a) Gribbell Island
   b) Princess Royal Island

2. Predict the frequency of the heterozygous genotype for coat colour in the Kermode bear population of
   a) Gribbell Island
   b) Princess Royal Island

3. Suggest why the frequency of the white coat allele is different on Gribbell Island and Princess Royal Island.

4. Suggest why some conservationists are concerned about inland black bears having access to the coastal bears' territories.

5. Scientists are unsure if Kermode bears select mates based on coat colour. Suggest how this form of non-random mating might affect coastal black bear populations.

Figure 19.11 A domestic goat (*Capra aegagrus hircus*) with an underbite. Underbites in goats are commonly due to inbreeding.

farm animals and pets, which tend to have a higher incidence of deformities and health problems compared to out-bred animals (Figure 19.11). For some purebred animals, fertility rates are very low and offspring die at a young age.

Inbreeding can also have a positive effect on a population, however. If homozygous recessive individuals fail to breed, and there are fewer heterozygous individuals each generation, harmful recessive alleles will be eliminated from the gene pool over time. In wild plant populations, self-fertilization may allow individual plants to reproduce even when they are isolated from one another or there are few pollinators in the area. In addition, artificial selection is often used to produce varieties of crops that consistently express desirable traits.

• • •

(12) Why is most mating in populations non-random?

(13) Describe one effect of non-random mating in plants and one effect in animals.

• • •

Genetic Drift

In moments of frustration, older siblings may sometimes say that they are "never going to have children." In biological terms, this means that they will not contribute genetic material to the next generation. Any unique alleles they may have will therefore be lost from the gene pool.

A small population is more likely to lose alleles from its gene pool than a large population is. A change in allele frequencies due to chance events in a small breeding population is called **genetic drift**. The roses (*Rosa* sp.) shown in Figure 19.12 form a small population, and, in each generation, only a few individuals reproduce. Due to random chance, none of the light pink roses (*aa*) or roses heterozygous for this colour (*Aa*) in the second generation reproduced. As a result, the pink petal allele was lost from the population in only three generations.

In general, large populations do not experience genetic drift, because chance events are unlikely to affect overall allele frequencies. For example, in a large population of ground squirrels, predators are unlikely to kill all the ground squirrels with a particular allele. If the population size decreases relatively quickly, however, due to disease, climatic change, or extensive habitat fragmentation, genetic drift can occur.

BiologyFile

Web Link
Africa's Ngorongoro Crater in Tanzania is home to a population of lions (*Panthera leo*) that exhibit little genetic variation. Although the steep crater walls prevent easy movement of animals in and out, migrations of lions have occured over time. Why is there so little genetic diversity in this lion population and what is the population's current status?

www.albertabiology.ca
WWW

Figure 19.12 In every generation, only some of the plants in this population reproduce. When the light pink and heterozygous roses in the second generation did not reproduce, the allele for light pink petals was quickly lost from the gene pool.

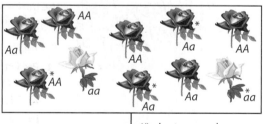

First generation
p (frequency of *A*) = 0.6
q (frequency of *a*) = 0.4

4* plants reproduce

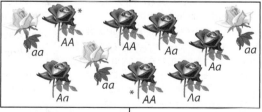

Second generation
p = 0.5
q = 0.5

2* plants reproduce

Third generation
p = 1.0
q = 0.0

14 Why are small populations more susceptible to genetic drift than large populations are?

The Founder Effect

Often, new populations are formed by only a few individuals, or *founders*. For example, strong winds may carry a single, pregnant fruit fly to a previously unpopulated island, where the fruit fly and her offspring may found a new colony. The founders will carry some, but not all, of the alleles in the original population's gene pool. Diversity in the new gene pool will therefore be limited. Furthermore, the founders may not be typical of the population they came from, and so previously rare alleles may increase in frequency. The gene pool change that occurs when a few individuals start a new, isolated population is called the **founder effect**. The founder effect occurs frequently on islands, and probably occurred when various plants, insects, birds, and reptiles first colonized the islands of Hawaii and the Galápagos.

The founder effect also occurs in human populations, and the lack of genetic diversity in these populations can be a medical concern. Due to the founder effect, the incidence of inherited health conditions in these populations is much higher than average. The Amish population of Philadelphia, Pennsylvania, for example was founded in the 1700s by just a few families. One of the couples carried a recessive allele for Ellis Van Creveld syndrome, a form of dwarfism that also causes bone and heart malformations. This syndrome is nearly 300 times more common in the current Pennsylvania Amish population than in the general U.S. population.

15 Describe two possible gene pool changes that could result from the founder effect.

16 Why might the founder effect cause inbreeding?

The Bottleneck Effect

Starvation, disease, human activities, or natural disasters, such as severe weather, can quickly reduce a large population. Since the survivors have only a subset of the alleles that were present before the population declined, the gene pool will lose diversity. Gene pool change that results from a rapid decrease in population size is known as the **bottleneck effect** (Figure 19.13).

This phenomenon is often seen in species driven to the edge of extinction. By the 1890s, overhunting had reduced the number of northern elephant seals (*Mirounga angustirostris*) to as few as 20 (Figure 19.14). Today, there are tens of thousands of northern elephant seals, but, due to the bottleneck effect followed by genetic drift, their genetic diversity is very low. Similarly, DNA analysis of cheetahs (*Acinonyx jubotus*) shows little to no genetic variation among individuals. This evidence suggests that their populations declined dramatically in the past, and all the cheetahs that are alive today are descendants of the survivors. As a result, the fertility rates of cheetahs are extremely low, making the work of conservationists very difficult.

17 Describe two situations that might result in the bottleneck effect.

Figure 19.13 Modelling the bottleneck effect. The parent population contains roughly equal numbers of yellow and blue alleles. A catastrophe occurs and there are only a few survivors. Most of these survivors have blue alleles. Due to genetic drift, the gene pool of the next generation will contain mostly blue alleles.

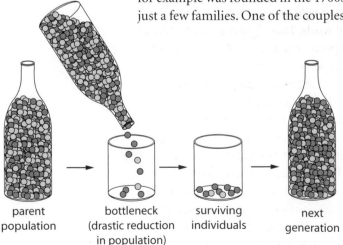

parent population → bottleneck (drastic reduction in population) → surviving individuals → next generation

Natural Selection

Natural selection is the only process that leads directly to evolutionary adaptation. In a given environment, some individuals are better able to survive and reproduce than others are. Those individuals with greater fitness breed and pass on their favourable variations to the next generation.

The environment is what makes certain mutations relatively beneficial, neutral, or detrimental. Natural selection occurs when a mutation produces a phenotype that gives one individual a survival advantage over another. Ultimately, if a population's gene pool is small and lacks diversity due to genetic drift, the population may not be able to adapt to environmental change and may become extinct.

You learned about various examples of natural selection in Chapter 4. With the use of antibiotics, a few bacterial cells with genes for antibiotic-resistance had a *selective advantage* over other bacterial cells, resulting in new populations of bacteria that were antibiotic resistant. The frequency of the allele for dark wings in the peppered moth changed as levels of air pollution changed. It is possible that human resistance to HIV, the Ebola virus, the West Nile virus, and other viruses will increase in frequency as these viruses become more widespread in the population.

Sexual selection, which results from a form of non-random mating, is related to natural selection. If a male greater sage grouse can attract more mates as a result of his bright air sacs and extravagant tail feathers, then his phenotype gives him a reproductive advantage over the other males in his population. Furthermore, scientists hypothesize that female greater sage grouse may associate his looks and behaviour with being strong and healthy—both important survival advantages.

Survival advantages also explain why some lethal recessive alleles remain in the human gene pool rather than being eliminated over time. Several alleles that

Figure 19.14 The northern elephant seal became protected in the early 20th century, and, since then, its populations have recovered. Why might the lack of genetic variation in current northern elephant seal populations put them at risk once again?

are related to genetic health conditions are thought to provide a **heterozygote advantage**. For example, an allele for cystic fibrosis may help carriers better resist diarrheal diseases such as cholera. The allele for Tay-Sachs disease may protect against tuberculosis, a bacterial infection of the lungs, while the allele for PKU may protect against miscarriages caused by fungal toxins.

• • •

18 What is the relationship between mutations and natural selection?

19 Define heterozygote advantage.

• • •

Human Activities and Genetic Diversity

Human activities can affect the genetic diversity of populations in various ways. Habitats may become fragmented when people convert large stretches of wilderness into croplands or when they develop wild areas, construct dams, or build roads. These human-made barriers may prevent gene flow between the split populations. Over time, the isolated populations may undergo adaptive radiation if their environments are very different. Due to genetic drift, however, each population will likely have little genetic diversity within it.

Unregulated hunting, habitat removal, and other human activities that cause populations to decline abruptly can cause a bottleneck effect followed by genetic drift. The sudden large-scale loss of genetic diversity results in inbreeding, which may cause fertility rates to decline. Populations that lack genetic diversity are more susceptible to new diseases and other environmental changes, too (Figure 19.15). As you will learn in Thought Lab 19.2, conservation and wildlife management programs must take into account the processes affecting gene pools in order to ensure that wild populations remain large enough and have sufficient genetic diversity to survive.

 20 In what ways can habitat fragmentation affect gene pools of natural populations?

Thought Lab 19.2 — Maintaining Genetic Diversity in the Whooping Crane

Target Skills

Describing the factors that affect the genetic diversity of an endangered species

Assessing the value of captive breeding programs in preserving the genetic diversity of an endangered species

Whooping cranes

The whooping crane (*Grus americana*) is the tallest bird in North America. Standing 1.5 m high, this graceful white bird has a wingspan of 2.5 m. The whooping crane—affectionately referred to as the whooper—lives and breeds in shallow wetlands surrounded by bulrushes (*Scirpus* sp.) and other sedges. Its diet includes plant roots, crustaceans, mollusks, and insects. At age 3 to 4, it reaches sexual maturity. The adult whooper is known for its magnificent mating behaviour, which involves displays of plumage, courtship dances, and synchronized honking to signal its choice of a life mate. The female lays two eggs a year, but the couple will raise only one, usually the first to hatch, and may push the other from the nest.

The largest current population of whooping cranes migrates between Wood Buffalo National Park in northern Alberta and Aransas National Wildlife Refuge in southern Texas. Scientists estimate that there were 1400 migrating whooping cranes in the late 1800s. The total population fell to about 15 in the 1940s. Loss of habitat, excessive hunting, avian disease, and lead poisoning were some of the factors that contributed to their decline. The discovery and preservation of the whoopers' nesting and over-wintering grounds has helped to reverse this trend. The introduction of hunting regulations and the establishment of captive breeding programs, one of which is at the Calgary Zoo, has also helped. The world population of whoopers has now increased to over 300.

Procedure

Use the preceding information to answer the following Analysis questions. You may also use library, Internet, or other resources to help you answer the questions.

Analysis

1. All the whooping cranes that are alive today are descendants of the 15 or so that remained in the 1940s. Make a hypothesis about the degree of genetic diversity within current whooping crane populations, and justify your thinking.

2. Does the fact that pairs bond for life help or hinder captive breeding programs? Explain your answer.

3. DNA technologies, such as DNA sequencing, are being used to determine the relatedness of all the whooping cranes in the main migrating population. How could conservationists use this information to assess the vulnerability of the population to environmental change?

4. To re-establish another wild population of whooping cranes, conservationists placed whooping crane eggs in the nests of sandhill cranes (*Grus canadensis*). The whooping cranes reared by the sandhill cranes feed normally and migrate, but are not breeding. Suggest a reason why the breeding program has not been successful.

5. Suggest a method, other than captive breeding programs, that could be used to protect wild whooping cranes. Explain how this method works and how it would affect the world's population of whooping cranes.

Extensions

6. Evaluate the role of gene banks in helping to preserve endangered species, such as the whooping crane, and in helping to maintain genetic diversity within populations.

7. Identify and describe technologies that are being used by whooping crane breeders to improve the success of captive egg hatching and chick rearing.

Figure 19.15 During the last century, the chestnut blight fungus (*Cryphonectria parasitica*), an introduced species, decimated populations of the American chestnut tree (*Castanea dentate*). As a result, the current populations of American chestnut trees have little genetic variation.

Section 19.2 Summary

The Hardy-Weinberg equation is used to detect microevolution (changes in the diversity of a gene pool). Microevolution in a population is caused by one or more of the following five processes:

1. Inheritable mutations that arise may be beneficial, neutral, or detrimental in a given environment.

2. Gene flow due to the emigration and immigration of individuals increases the genetic diversity of a population that receives new members, but decreases the genetic diversity among populations.

3. Non-random mating can result in sexual selection for preferred phenotypes, or inbreeding. Inbreeding can severely limit genetic diversity in gene pools, making populations more vulnerable to environmental change.

4. Genetic drift can result in the loss of alleles from small populations, and an increase in the frequency of previously rare alleles. The founder effect and the bottleneck effect are two extreme causes of genetic drift.

5. Natural selection for favourable phenotypes interacts with the other microevolutionary processes and leads to the evolution of adaptations. Various human activities can affect the amount of gene flow and genetic drift in natural populations.

BiologyFile

Web Link
What do you do when you re-establish a bird population that migrates, but has no parents to learn from? Whooping crane conservationists have become very creative!

www.albertabiology.ca
WWW

Section 19.2 | **Review**

1. Draw a two-column table. In the first column, list the five conditions that are associated with the equilibrium of allele frequencies, as identified by the Hardy-Weinberg principle. In the second column, describe the possible effects on a population's genetic diversity if each condition is not met.

2. How can mutations help populations survive?

3. Predict what might happen to the diversity of a gene pool if individuals with rare alleles emigrated from the population.

4. Compare and contrast the founder effect with the bottleneck effect. Specifically, how do these effects occur and how can they change a gene pool?

5. In what ways might the lack of genetic diversity in cheetahs put their populations at risk? Provide an example of a human action that could be taken to increase the genetic diversity of cheetahs.

6. What could prevent a lethal recessive allele from being entirely eliminated from a population?

7. Why is inbreeding in animals unlikely to lead to evolutionary adaptations?

8. HIV mutates and reproduces faster than the body can produce antibodies against it. Some antiviral medications slow HIV's reproductive rate. This changes the environment in favour of the immune system, allowing it time to produce antibodies against HIV before it mutates. As a result, these medications can help to delay the progression of HIV to acquired immunodeficiency syndrome (AIDS). Explain how anti-HIV medications impede microevolution of the virus.

Biotechnology and Gene Pools

Genetic variation is the raw material of evolution. Natural sources of variation include genetic mutations, the recombination of alleles during sexual reproduction, gene flow, genetic drift, and various methods of gene transfer between bacteria. Biotechnology now adds genetic engineering to this list of processes. Will biotechnology result in the evolution of new species? Can biotechnology help us preserve species?

Engineering New Species?

Biotechnology—the use of organisms to benefit humanity—includes methods as old as artificial selection and as current as genetic engineering. Modern artificial breeding techniques have been used to develop plant crosses, such as triticale, which is a hybrid of wheat (*Triticum aestivum*) and rye (*Secale cereale*). Genetic engineering allows scientists to combine traits from different species that are incapable of breeding with one another. A gene from a bacterium, for example, can be made to function in a corn (*Zea mays*) plant. This does not mean that bacteria and corn share a breeding population, nor that the transgenic organism is a hybrid. But is the transgenic corn a different species because it has characteristics that are not shared by other corn plants?

All members of a species—interbreeding populations of similar organisms—share a common gene pool. By altering a gene pool, is biotechnology altering the course of evolution? Unlike biotechnology, natural selection acts on individuals, not on isolated genes, and it results in adaptive traits. Genes function in interlocking relationships with other genes in a cell. As a result, biotechnology—in particular, genetic engineering— can have unexpected effects on non-target genes. For example, adding a trait, such as herbicide resistance, to a plant may produce offsetting physiological changes in the plant that will reduce its overall survival rate. For this reason, engineering a transgenic organism that will be useful in industry or agriculture can be a challenge.

Some forms of biotechnology have the potential to affect wild populations, as well. In Canada, nearly 90 percent of the field tests of genetically engineered plants involve crop plants with introduced genes for herbicide tolerance. Studies show that the added genes can spread to populations of related wild plants by cross-pollination. Should cross-pollination occur, it could result in new populations of herbicide-tolerant weeds.

This baby gaur was the first endangered species to be cloned. It died a few days after birth. Scientists continue their work to clone mammals, such as the gaur, successfully.

Cloning to Save Species

Although the tools of biotechnology can change gene pools in both intended and unintended ways, some of these tools can also be used to preserve gene pools. Cloning is one method that may help reverse the threat to endangered species. The first endangered animal to be cloned was the Asian gaur (*Bos gaurus*), a rare, ox-like mammal native to India and Southeast Asia. The animal was cloned from a dead gaur's skin cells, which were fused with a domestic cow's egg cell from which the nucleus had been removed. The egg was then transplanted into a surrogate mother, also a domestic cow (*Bos taurus*). The cloned gaur was born in November 2000, in Iowa in the United States. The same technique may one day be used to resurrect species that have already become extinct.

• • •

1. Are transgenic organisms new species? Explain your answer.

2. How might genetic engineers prevent the spread of introduced genes into wild populations?

3. How might the release of transgenic organisms into the wild affect natural populations?

4. Discuss the benefits and disadvantages of using cloning as a method for protecting endangered species.

A gene pool contains all the alleles for all the genes in a population that can be passed on to the next generation. Population geneticists study gene pools. The Hardy-Weinberg principle is a mathematical model that population geneticists use to determine allele frequencies and genotype frequencies in a population. According to the principle, allele frequencies in a population will remain constant in succeeding generations unless acted upon by outside forces.

The total of the allele frequencies, p and q, for one gene always equals 1.00, or 100 percent of the alleles. A change in the allele frequencies over time indicates that a population is undergoing microevolution. The Hardy-Weinberg equation is $p^2 + 2pq + q^2 = 1.00$, in which the letters p and q represent the frequencies of the dominant and recessive alleles, respectively. The frequency of the homozygous dominant genotype is represented by p^2, the frequency of the heterozygous genotype is represented by $2pq$, and the frequency of the homozygous recessive genotype is represented by q^2. If the population size (N) is known, the number of individuals with a particular genotype can be calculated using the equation, $p^2(N) + 2pq(N) + q^2(N) = N$. The more diverse the gene pool of a population, the better is the population's chance of survival should the environment change.

Inheritable mutations can be neutral, beneficial, or detrimental, depending on the environment. Mutations that provide a selective advantage will increase in frequency due to natural selection.

Gene flow due to emigration and immigration of individuals increases the genetic diversity of a population that receives new members, but decreases the genetic diversity among populations.

Non-random mating due to mate selection based on phenotypic differences leads to sexual selection. Inbreeding, another form of non-random mating, increases the frequency of homozygous genotypes in a gene pool.

Genetic drift can result in the loss of alleles from small populations due to chance events, as well as an increase in the frequency of previously rare alleles. The formation of an isolated population from a small founding population or population bottleneck may lead to inbreeding and a loss of genetic diversity in the population.

The process of natural selection selects for favourable variations and directly leads to the adaptation of species to their environments. Harmful recessive alleles may be maintained in a population by heterozygous carriers, particularly if the carrier state has greater fitness (called heterozygote advantage) compared with homozygous individuals, under certain environmental conditions.

Human activities can affect the amount of gene flow between and genetic drift within natural populations.

Chapter 19 Graphic Organizer

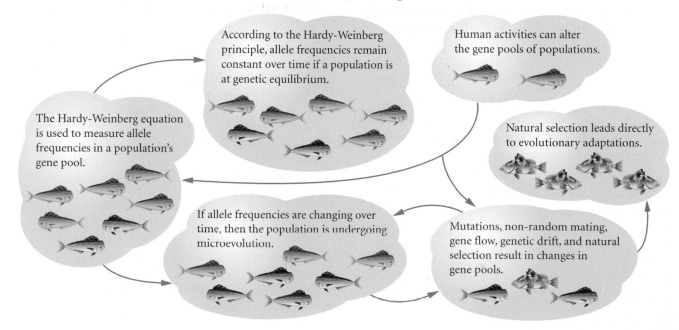

According to the Hardy-Weinberg principle, allele frequencies remain constant over time if a population is at genetic equilibrium.

Human activities can alter the gene pools of populations.

The Hardy-Weinberg equation is used to measure allele frequencies in a population's gene pool.

Natural selection leads directly to evolutionary adaptations.

If allele frequencies are changing over time, then the population is undergoing microevolution.

Mutations, non-random mating, gene flow, genetic drift, and natural selection result in changes in gene pools.

Chapter 19

Understanding Concepts

1. An individual fly has a mutation that allows it to survive being sprayed by an insecticide. Is the mutation itself an example of microevolution? Justify your answer.

2. A population has two alleles for a particular gene (*B* and *b*), and the allele frequency of *B* is 0.70. Calculate the frequency of the heterozygous genotype, assuming that the population is at genetic equilibrium.

3. If 16 out of 100 people in a population have a recessive trait, calculate the frequency of the dominant allele in the population. Assume that the population is at genetic equilibrium. Express your final answer as a decimal.

4. About 11 percent of Canadians have a recessive condition called lactose intolerance, which makes it difficult for them to digest milk and milk products. Calculate the percentage of heterozygous carriers of the lactose intolerance allele and the percentage of individuals homozygous for lactose tolerance. Assume that the population is at genetic equilibrium.

5. In a species of salamander, yellow tail colour (*Y*) is dominant to brown tail colour (*y*). In a sample of 400 of these salamanders, 44 percent are homozygous dominant, 38 percent are heterozygous, and 18 percent are homozygous recessive.
   a) Calculate the frequency of each tail colour allele in the population.
   b) Calculate the number of salamanders with each genotype in the sample.

6. In a population of ferns at genetic equilibrium, 0.60 of all the gametes carry the dominant allele for curly leaves (*C*). In recessive homozygotes, the recessive allele (*l*) produces straight leaves. Calculate the frequency of the recessive allele in the population and the expected frequency of each genotype in the next generation.

7. Why does genetic drift occur more frequently in small populations than in large populations?

8. If a human population has a higher-than-usual percentage of individuals with a genetic health problem, is the most likely explanation gene flow or genetic drift? Explain your answer.

9. Recall from your studies of Mendelian genetics that the sickle cell allele shows incomplete dominance when inherited with the allele for healthy red blood cells. The incidence of sickle cell anemia was estimated in two human populations, both of which were at genetic equilibrium for this trait. The condition occurred in one out of every 1000 births in the first population, and in three out of every 1000 births in the second population.
   a) Determine the expected frequency of the heterozygous genotype in each population.
   b) Infer which population most likely originated in Africa. Explain your answer.
   c) Sickle cell anemia is often fatal. What accounts for the higher incidence of the condition in the second population?

Applying Concepts

10. Use the following table to answer the questions below.

Change in Genotype Frequencies for a Single Gene in a Collard Pika (*Ochotona collaris*) Population

| Year | Number of pikas with each genotype | | |
	170/170	170/172	172/172
1998	9	6	0
1999	16	6	0
2000	6	6	0
2001	no data	no data	no data
2002	28	4	0
2003	4	0	1
2004	27	6	1
2005	42	9	1

Note: The alleles for the gene under study are called 170 and 172.
Source: Data provided by Jessie Zgurski, University of Alberta

   a) Based on the 1998 data, calculate the expected frequencies of the 170 and 172 alleles.
   b) Based on the 2005 data, calculate the expected frequencies of the 170 and 172 alleles.
   c) Does this collard pika population appear to be at genetic equilibrium? Explain your answer.
   d) No individuals that were homozygous for the 172 allele were detected between 1998 and 2002. How did the 172 allele remain in the population?
   e) Populations of collard pika in Canada have been declining since 1995. How would you expect this to affect genetic diversity in collard pika populations?

11. In Eastern grey squirrels (*Sciurus carolinensis*), the allele for black fur is dominant to the allele for grey fur. One afternoon, a student observed 10 Eastern grey squirrels in the school yard, and counted eight black squirrels and two grey squirrels.
   a) Based on the student's data, calculate the frequency of each fur colour allele in the local Eastern grey squirrel population.

b) Based on the student's data, calculate the percentage of the local squirrel population that you would expect to be heterozygous for fur colour.

c) A credible Internet source stated that the frequency of the grey fur allele is 0.80. How does this value compare with the value you calculated in part (a), based on the student's data?

d) How could the student's sampling method be improved?

e) Account for any differences between the student's data and the other source.

12. In a sample of 1100 Japanese people from Tokyo, 356 individuals belonged to blood group M, 519 belonged to blood group MN, and 225 belonged to blood group N.
   a) Calculate the frequency of each allele in the population.
   b) Calculate the expected frequency of each genotype in the next generation.
   c) Suppose that a small group of people, mostly with blood group N, emigrated from Tokyo to a distant island, where they founded a new colony. Predict how the gene pool for the new population might change.

13. Six out of 2400 babies that were born at a maternity hospital died shortly after birth from colonic obstruction due to a recessive allele.
   a) Determine the frequency of the lethal allele in the population, expressed as a percent.
   b) What percent of the population would you expect to be carriers of the lethal allele?
   c) The population is closely knit and isolated. Explain why the incidence of infant mortality due to the recessive lethal allele is relatively high.

14. A recessive lethal allele in domestic chickens (*Gallus domesticus*) causes circulatory failure and death of the embryo within 70 h. A commercial hatchery finds that a hatching failure greater than 4 percent due to this allele is commercially unacceptable. What is the upper limit of the frequency of this allele that would be acceptable to the hatchery managers? Express your answers as percents.

15. The process of natural selection leads to adaptive phenotypic changes in populations. Compare and contrast the process of natural selection with the process of genetic drift.

16. Draw a pedigree to show how inbreeding could lead to the elimination of the heterozygous genotype for an allele and increase the homozygous genotypes in a small population.

Making Connections

17. Scientists have been using DNA testing to determine the lineage of wild polar bears (*Ursus maritimus*). Their research is helping them learn how far polar bears range and what type of males are most successful at breeding. Because some polar bear populations are declining, the polar bears in these populations are probably becoming less selective about the mates they choose. Suggest how genetic analysis of polar bear populations could be used to help preserve the species. What microevolutionary processes are likely to be occurring in the current populations of polar bears?

18. Phenylketonuria (PKU) is a condition of newborns caused by a recessive allele. The incidence of PKU is one in 160 000 births in China, one in 2600 births in Turkey, and one in 119 000 births in Japan.
   a) Calculate the frequency of carriers of the PKU allele in each population. Express your answer as a decimal.
   b) There is evidence that the PKU allele is advantageous in the heterozygous state, because it seems to offer protection against miscarriage caused by certain fungal toxins. Make an hypothesis about the relative amounts of the toxin-producing fungi in various regions of the world.

19. Advances in medical technology have greatly improved the quality of life for people with inherited conditions, such as cystic fibrosis, as well as their ability to have children. Over time, what might happen to the frequency of the alleles for such conditions? Justify your answer.

20. A Russian geneticist, Sergi Tshetverikov had this to say about mutations: "Mutations can provide the raw material for evolution but do not constitute evolution itself." Evaluate his comment in the light of what you have learned in this chapter.

Population Growth and Interactions

Chapter Concepts

20.1 Population Growth

- The density of a population is the average number of individuals in a given area or volume.

- Changes in a population over time can be described quantitatively.

- A J-shaped growth curve is characteristic of a population that is growing at its biotic potential. An S-shaped growth curve is characteristic of a population whose growth is limited by the carrying capacity of its environment.

20.2 Interactions in Ecological Communities

- Intraspecific and interspecific competition may limit the sizes of populations within a community.

- Predator-prey interactions may limit the sizes of producer and consumer populations.

- Mutualism, commensalism, and parasitism are types of symbiosis.

- Succession is a gradual change in community structure over time, due to biotic and abiotic factors.

20.3 Sharing the Biosphere

- Sustainability has social, economic, and environmental dimensions.

- The age structure of a population can be used to predict trends in the growth of the population.

- Earth's carrying capacity for the human population is affected by variables such as trends in birth rates and consumption.

After a long, cold winter in Alberta's wilderness, an abundance of wild grasses and sedges means plenty of food for bison (*Bison bison*) and other herbivores. The warm weather and just the right amount of rain have created ideal growing conditions for flies and mosquitoes. These biting insects have short life cycles, so their populations grow rapidly. The bison have shed their protective winter coats, leaving their skin bare and vulnerable to the insects, which are out for blood and may carry diseases. When the insects die off in the fall, the bison will be more comfortable. Until then, the bison will try to rid themselves of these pests by rolling in marshes or soil. In Chapter 20, you will examine the interactions among populations of different species and discover how different populations change over time. You will also examine the factors that limit the growth of populations, including our own.

Reproductive Strategies and Population Growth

The female *Aedes* sp. mosquito uses blood sucked from vertebrate animals to nourish her developing eggs. In her lifetime, she may lay up to 600 eggs. These eggs will remain dormant until conditions are favourable for their growth. Once an *Aedes* sp. egg hatches, the larva takes about a week to develop into an adult mosquito, which will live about another 14 days. The bison, on the other hand, is North America's largest mammal and may live up to 40 years. A female bison does not reach sexual maturity until two to three years of age. Then she will give birth two times in three years, usually to only one calf at a time.

Procedure

Use the data in the tables to create two graphs (one for each population) showing population size over time. Then answer the Analysis questions.

Size of a Hypothetical *Aedes* sp. Mosquito Population over One Growing Season

Day	Number of adult mosquitoes
0	20
6	40
12	80
18	160
36	320
42	640
48	1280
54	2560
60	5120
66	10240

Number of Individuals in the Plains Bison (*Bison bison*, subspecies *bison*) Population of Pink Mountain, British Columbia

Year	Estimated number of plains bison
1988	447
1989	494
1990	546
1991	603
1992	666
1993	693
1994	765
1995	845
1996	934
1997	929

Analysis

1. Compare the shapes of your two graphs. Describe the growth of both populations during the given time intervals.

2. Make and record a hypothesis to account for the shape of your graph for the mosquito population and the bison population.

An uncomfortable bison rolls on the ground to try to rid itself of mosquitoes.

Population Growth

Figure 20.1 Spring is a time of growth for many populations in a community. Hungry bears awaken from their hibernation-like slumber, and plants that have been dormant throughout the winter rapidly reproduce. Herbivores eat the fresh, green shoots, and pollinating insects feed on the flower nectar. The seasons are a source of one constant in ecological communities—change. What else causes change in communities? How does change manifest itself over time?

Quantitative measurements of ecological communities are like snapshots of moments in time. Put together, these snapshots reveal change over time—the one constant in all communities (Figure 20.1). As populations change, so do the communities they comprise. In Chapter 19, you looked at the causes and consequences of genetic changes in populations. In this chapter, you will explore the growth and decline of populations, the distribution of their members, and the mathematical models that are used to create stories from quantitative "snapshots" of their numbers. You will also explore interactions among populations and among members of populations in various environments, and the influence of these interactions on the direction of population change. In addition, you will consider the human activities that, whether intended or unintended, influence the type and degree of change in ecological communities throughout the biosphere.

Density and Distribution of Populations

All populations can be described in terms of two fundamental characteristics: density and distribution. Ecologists use various sampling methods to estimate the density of a population. Then they use their estimate to determine the number of individuals in, and thus the size of, the population. **Population density (D_p)** is defined as the number of individual organisms (N) in a given area (A) or volume (V). As an equation, population density is expressed as

$$D_p = \frac{N}{A} \quad \text{or} \quad D_p = \frac{N}{V}$$

For example, suppose that you sample a population of gophers (Richardson's ground squirrels, *Spermophilus richardsonii*) living in a field one summer. Based on several samples, you find an average of 12 gophers living in an area of 10.0 m². The density of the population can be calculated as

$$\frac{12 \text{ gophers}}{10.0 \text{ m}^2} = 1.2 \text{ gophers/m}^2$$

If you know that the field is 200.0 m², you can estimate the size of the population:
$(1.2 \text{ gophers/m}^2)(200.0 \text{ m}^2) = 240 \text{ gophers}$

Similarly, suppose that a 200.0 mL sample of stagnant pond water contains 54 wrigglers (mosquito larvae). The density of the sample is

$$\frac{54 \text{ wrigglers}}{200.0 \text{ mL}} = 0.27 \text{ wrigglers/mL}$$

This information can be used to estimate the size of a mosquito population in an aquatic community at a given time. Since mosquitoes can carry various infectious diseases, large numbers can pose a threat to health. Based on the size of the population, local authorities need to consider controls to keep the mosquitoes in check.

Although one pond-water sample may contain numerous wrigglers, other samples from the same pond may not contain any wrigglers. As you may recall from your field study in Unit 2, you need to know how a population is distributed within its habitat before taking samples to determine the population size. For example, one count of the endangered snail *Physella johnsoni*, which lives only in the hot springs of Banff National Park, indicated that there were 2500 snails/m². Since the study area was 9.0 m², the population size was estimated to be (9.0 m²)(2500 snails/m²) = 23 000 snails. This appeared to be good news. On further study, however, researchers noted that the snails were not evenly distributed throughout their habitat. Instead, they were clumped around the areas where the spring water came out of the ground. Thus, the size of the snail population was much lower than initially predicted.

There are three theoretical *distribution patterns* for populations: *uniform*, *random*, and *clumped* (Figure 20.2). In Thought Lab 20.1, you will explore how population distribution affects population density estimates.

· · ·

1 Define population density
   a) in words
   b) in the form of an equation

· · ·

Figure 20.2 Patterns of population distribution. **(A)** Golden eagles (*Aquila chrysaetos*) are territorial, and so pairs are distributed uniformly over a suitable habitat. **(B)** In summer, female moose (*Alces alces*) with calves tend to be distributed randomly over a suitable habitat. **(C)** Soapweed yucca (*Yucca glauca*) can reproduce sexually or asexually by sprouting new plants from the rhizomes (underground stems) of older plants. Therefore, soapweed yucca plants that have reproduced asexually grow in patches, resulting in their clumped pattern of distribution.

Factors That Affect Distribution Patterns

Distribution patterns are influenced by the distribution of resources in a habitat and the interactions among members of a population, or members of a community. For example, *random distribution* can occur when resources are very abundant and population members do not have to compete with one another or, conversely, group together for survival. When a population exhibits random distribution, individuals or pairs of organisms are distributed throughout a suitable habitat with no identifiable pattern. In summer, individual bull moose or female moose

BiologyFile

Web Link
The city of Calgary controls adult mosquito populations by targeting their larvae through a process called larvaciding. What agents are used in the process, and how effective is it?

www.albertabiology.ca
WWW

Moose (*Alces alces*) tend to be solitary. During the winter, however, moose may congregate in small groups near food and for shelter. In summer, individual bull moose and mothers with their calves may be distributed randomly throughout their habitat. The typical distribution pattern of moose in one habitat compared to another gives scientists clues about the behaviour and ecology of the species. It also helps scientists choose an accurate sampling method for estimating population density. In this activity, you will see how transects (long, narrow areas of land used for ecological study) might be used to sample different moose populations.

Procedure

1. Examine the three diagrams of hypothetical moose populations. What are the two different distribution patterns shown?

2. The shaded parts of the diagrams represent the transects that were used to sample each population. Calculate the area per transect. (In these diagrams, 1.0 cm represents 1.0 km.)

3. For each hypothetical population, count the moose within each transect.

4. For each hypothetical population, calculate the average number of moose per transect.

5. Calculate the average density of each hypothetical moose population.

6. Calculate the total study area that is inhabited by one moose population. Estimate the total number of moose in each hypothetical population.

Analysis

1. The actual numbers of moose in the three populations are 60, 133, and 133, respectively. How close were your estimates to the actual sizes of the populations?

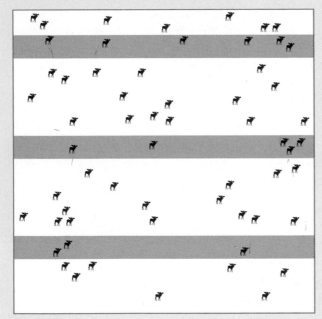

Distribution pattern 1

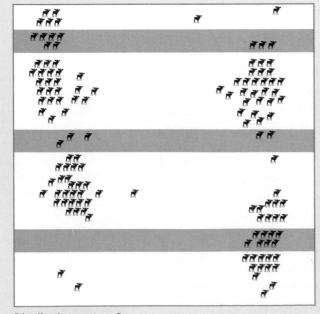

Distribution pattern 2

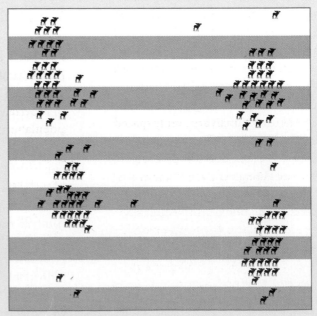

Distribution pattern 3

2. Explain the difference, if any, between your estimate and the actual size of the first population.

3. Explain any differences between your estimates and the actual sizes of the second and third populations.

4. How would you design a sampling experiment on a real population of wild moose? (**Note:** In real life, the time and expenses involved usually restricts the proportion sampled to between 10 and 20 percent of the total area of interest.)

Extension

5. There is concern that an introduced population of moose may deplete the resources in its home range. Why would scientists want to know the density of this population? If you were given the size of this population, how would you calculate its population density?

(*Alces alces*) with calves sometimes exhibit a random distribution pattern. Generally, however, random distribution in nature is rare.

More common is *clumped distribution*, in which members of a population are found in close proximity to each other in various groups within their habitat. Most populations, including humans, exhibit a clumped pattern of distribution, congregating in an area where food, water, or shelter is most abundant. Another example of a species that exhibits clumped distribution is aspens (*Populus tremuloides*). Because aspens reproduce asexually by sprouting new trees from the roots of older trees, they grow in groves, resulting in their clumped pattern of distribution. The Banff springs snail also exhibits clumped distribution. Rather than being evenly distributed throughout their habitat, the snails clump around the areas where the spring water emerges from the ground.

Artificial populations, such as plants growing in orchards or agricultural fields, often exhibit *uniform distribution*, in which individuals are evenly spaced over a defined area. This pattern of distribution is also seen in birds of prey and other organisms that behave territorially to defend their resources and protect their young. The golden eagle (*Aquila chrysaetos*) is an example of a species that exhibits uniform distribution.

In nature, most populations do not perfectly fit any one pattern of distribution. Or, a particular pattern of distribution may be characteristic of a given population, but only at a particular

time. Mosquito larvae, for example, tend to exhibit clumped distribution. When they mature into adult mosquitoes, however, they are likely to fly away and distribute randomly. Similarly, moose may congregate in small groups near food and shelter for periods of time during the winter.

• • •

2 List two factors that influence the distribution patterns of populations.

3 Use examples (one for each population distribution pattern) to explain how random distribution is different from clumped distribution and uniform distribution.

• • •

Population Growth

A population's size directly depends on how much and how fast it grows. What are the factors that influence population growth? In 2003, the human population of Alberta was 3.2 million. In 2004, the population had increased to about 3.5 million. This means that, compared with 2003, there were 300 000 more births and new residents in Alberta than there were deaths and residents that left the province.

There are four processes that can change the size (number of individuals) of a population (ΔN). Births (b) and immigration (i) (the movement of individuals into a population) cause increases in population size. Deaths (d) and emigration (e) (the movement of individuals out of a population) cause decreases in population size. Therefore, change in population size can be calculated using the following equation:

$$\Delta N = [b + i] - [d + e]$$

change in population size = births + immigration − deaths + emigration

Both immigration and emigration affect the sizes of human populations. In nature, these processes can result in gene flow between populations, but they often occur in equal amounts or in such low numbers that they are difficult to measure or do not significantly affect the sizes of the populations. There are exceptions, however. Some butterflies, for example, form many interconnected populations that exchange members quite frequently. In comparison, the migration of an *entire* population between its wintering and breeding grounds does not, of itself, change the size of the population.

• • •

4 Name the four basic processes that cause changes in population size, and write the equation that summarizes their relationship.

• • •

The Rate of Population Growth

Just as important as the change in the size of a population is the speed at which the change occurs. An invasive species, for example, may form a population that grows so rapidly that it spreads before it can be contained. Such an increase in population size is called a *population explosion*. Another population may decrease so rapidly and by so much that its decline is referred to as a *population crash*. The change in the number of individuals in a population (ΔN) over a specific time frame (Δt) is known as a population's **growth rate (gr)**:

$$gr = \frac{\Delta N}{\Delta t}$$

The formula for growth rate can be used to measure increases or decreases in population size over time. For example, in January 1997, the population of Banff Springs snails in the Lower Cave and Basin springs in Banff National Park was estimated to be 3800. Two years later, the population was estimated to be 1800. Therefore, the change in population size was

1800 snails − 3800 snails = −2000 snails

Note that the final value is negative because the population size decreased. Since the change occurred within two years, the growth rate (gr) was

$$\frac{-2000 \text{ snails}}{2 \text{ years}} = -1000 \text{ snails/year}$$

In other words, the population decreased at a rate of 1000 snails per year.

The calculation of growth rate does not take into account the initial size of the population. A large population includes more individuals that can reproduce, compared with a small population. Thus, the amount of increase in a large population will be greater than the amount of increase in a comparable small population, as long as nothing limits the growth of either population (Figure 20.3). To compare populations of the same species that are different sizes

Bacterial growth over time

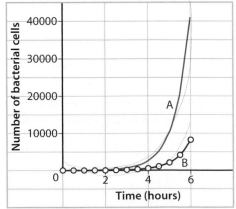

Figure 20.3 Suppose that the same type of bacteria contaminates equal portions of custard in two separate bowls. Initially, there are 10 bacterial cells in bowl A and 2 bacterial cells in bowl B. The bacterial populations double every 30 min. After 6 h at room temperature, the population in bowl A contains nearly 33 000 more bacterial cells than the population in bowl B.

or live in different habitats, the change in population size can be expressed as the rate of change per individual. This measurement, the **per capita growth rate** (*cgr*), can be determined by calculating the change in the number of individuals (ΔN) relative to N (the original number of indiviuals), and then dividing this change in the number of individuals by the original number in the population (N):

$$cgr = \frac{\Delta N}{N} \text{ or } cgr = \frac{N_{\text{final}} - N}{N}$$

Suppose that, in a town of 1000 pcople, there are 50 births, 30 deaths, and no immigration or emigration in a year. During this time interval, the per capita growth rate (*cgr*) for the population is

$$\frac{50 - 30}{1000} = 0.02$$

Like the growth rate, the per capita growth rate can be negative if deaths and emigration outnumber births and immigration. Study the Sample Problems on page 710, and then do the Practice Problems that follow.

• • •

Q **5** Explain the difference between the growth rate of a population and the per capita growth rate of a population.

Q **6** A deer population increases in size from 2000 to 2300 individuals over one year. Calculate the growth rate of the population during this time interval.

Q **7** Determine the per capita growth rate of the deer population in question 6.

• • •

Factors That Affect Population Growth

As you may recall from Chapter 3, both biotic and abiotic factors limit the growth of a population. One category of biotic limiting factors includes the physiological and physical characteristics of a species that determine how fast and how often it can reproduce. The ability of a habitat to support a population, due to abiotic and biotic factors, also limits the size of a population.

Biotic Potential

Each species has an intrinsic rate of growth that is possible given unlimited resources and ideal living conditions. The highest possible per capita growth rate for a population is called its **biotic potential** (*r*). Factors that determine a species' biotic potential include

- the number of offspring per reproductive cycle
- the number of offspring that survive long enough to reproduce
- the age of reproductive maturity and the number of times that the individuals reproduce in a life span
- the life span of the individuals

As shown in Figure 20.4, a population that is growing at its biotic potential would be expected to grow exponentially. The brief lag phase, followed by a steep increase in the growth curve—called an **exponential growth pattern**—can be described as a J-shaped curve. The biotic potentials of micro-organisms, small animals, and certain plants are relatively easy to assess in a laboratory. The exponential growth rate of these types of organisms under ideal conditions can be observed in micro-environments, such as broth cultures of bacteria. The biotic potentials of other species are harder

Change in number of organisms over time in a population growing at its biotic potential

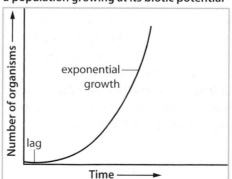

Figure 20.4 Any population, whether plankton, insects, or whales, growing at its biotic potential will grow exponentially, resulting in a J-shaped growth curve.

Sample Problem 1

A collared pika (*Ochotona collaris*) population dropped from exactly 25 individuals in 1998 to 5 individuals in 2000. Calculate the growth rate of this population from 1998 to 2000.

What Is Required?

To determine the growth rate (*gr*) of the collared pika population from 1998 to 2000

What Is Given?

The values needed to calculate the change in the number of individuals in a population size (ΔN): The original number of individuals is 25.0. The final number of individuals is 5.00.

The values needed to calculate the change in time (Δt): The beginning of the time frame is 1998. The end of the time frame is 2000.

Plan Your Strategy

Calculate ΔN.

Calculate Δt.

Calculate $gr = \dfrac{\Delta N}{\Delta t}$.

Act on Your Strategy

Step 1

$$\Delta N = \text{final number} - \text{original number}$$
$$\qquad\text{of individuals} \qquad \text{of individuals}$$
$$= 5.00 - 25.0$$
$$= -20.0 \text{ individuals}$$

Step 2

$$\Delta t = \text{final time} - \text{initial time}$$
$$= 2000 - 1998$$
$$= 2 \text{ years}$$

Step 3

$$gr = \frac{\Delta N}{\Delta t}$$
$$= \frac{-20.0 \text{ individuals}}{2 \text{ years}}$$
$$= -10 \text{ individuals/year}$$

The growth rate of the collared pika population was -10 individuals per year. In other words, the population dropped at a rate of 10 individuals per year.

Check Your Solution

$$gr = \frac{\Delta N}{\Delta t}$$
$$(gr)(\Delta t) = \Delta N$$
$$(-10 \text{ individuals/\cancel{year}})(2 \text{ \cancel{years}}) = -20 \text{ individuals}$$
$$-20 \text{ individuals} = -20 \text{ individuals}$$

Sample Problem 2

A population of 26 caribou (*Rangifer tarandus*) was introduced onto a predator-free island in Alaska in 1910. For the next 25 years, the per capita growth rate of the population was 75.9. In about 1935, resources became limited and the population crashed. Calculate the number of caribou on the island just before the population crashed.

What Is Required?

To determine the size of the island caribou population after the given time interval

What Is Given?

The value of the original number of individuals in the population (*N*): 26 caribou

The per capita growth rate (*cgr*) for the population over 25 years: 75.9

Plan Your Strategy

Rearrange the formula for per capita growth rate (*cgr*) to solve for ΔN.

Find the value of ΔN.

Add the original number of individuals in the population (*N*) to the change in the number of individuals (ΔN). Round the answer to the correct number of significant digits.

Act on Your Strategy

Step 1

$$cgr = \frac{\Delta N}{N}$$
$$\Delta N = (cgr)(N)$$

Step 2

$$\Delta N = (75.9)(26 \text{ caribou})$$
$$= 1973.4 \text{ caribou}$$

Step 3

$$\text{Final number of} \qquad = \Delta N + N$$
$$\text{individuals in population}$$
$$= 1973.4 \text{ caribou} + 26 \text{ caribou}$$
$$= 1999.4 \text{ caribou}$$

Step 4

$1999.4 \text{ caribou} \approx 2.0 \times 10^3 \text{ caribou}$

There were about 2000 caribou on the island.

Check Your Solution

$$\Delta N - N = 2000 \text{ caribou} - 26 \text{ caribou}$$
$$= 1974 \text{ caribou}$$
$$cgr = \frac{\Delta N}{N}$$
$$= 1974 \text{ \cancel{caribou}} /26 \text{ \cancel{caribou}}$$
$$= 75.9$$

1. Suppose that a sample of beef broth initially contains 16 bacterial cells. After 4.0 h, there are 1.6×10^6 bacterial cells in the sample. Assuming that the bacteria reproduce at a constant rate, calculate the growth rate of the bacterial population for the given time interval.

2. The Alberta greater sage grouse population was about 4375 in 1970. By 2002, the population was estimated to be only about 350 birds. Assuming that the population decreased at a constant rate, calculate the growth rate for the population from 1970 to 2002.

3. *Lemna minor*, a species of duckweed, can reproduce to form new plants very quickly. Suppose that a small backyard pond contains 25 *L. minor* plants, and the expected growth rate of the population is 1.0×10^2 plants per day. Predict how many *L. minor* plants the pond will contain after 31 days.

4. According to population surveys of piping plover (*Charadrius melodus*), there were 34 of these birds on Dowling Lake, Alberta, in 1992. The next year, the population of piping plover on Dowling Lake was 39. Calculate the per capita growth rate for the piping plover population during the entire survey period.

5. Between 1996 and 2001, Cochrane, Alberta, was the fastest growing municipality in Canada, with a per capita growth rate of 0.589. There were about 7424 people living in Cochrane in 1996. How many people lived there in 2001?

6. The experimentally re-introduced grey wolf population of Idaho was 310 at the beginning of 2004. Over the year, 112 pups were born and 49 individuals died or were removed from the study area. Calculate the per capita growth rate of this grey wolf population during the study period.

to assess because their ideal growth conditions are more difficult to create. Scientists can make only hypothetical estimates of their biotic potentials.

• • •

8. Define biotic potential, and give its symbol.

9. Name four factors that determine the biotic potential of a species.

10. What is an exponential growth pattern? What is its shape in a graph?

11. Explain how biotic potential and exponential growth are related.

• • •

Carrying Capacity

In the beginning, the growth of a small population is slow, since there are only a few individuals to reproduce (Figure 20.5). This initial stage is called the *lag phase*. As the numbers of individuals in the population increase, the population will experience an exponential rate of growth. The birth rate during the exponential growth phase is much greater than the death rate, so the population size will increase rapidly. Under natural conditions, however, this rapid growth rate cannot continue indefinitely. Eventually, competition for resources and other limiting factors will slow the rate of growth. Lack of food, for example, will limit the energy that is available for reproduction. At this stage, called the *stationary phase*, the birth rate and death rate are equivalent. This pattern is comparable to filling an unplugged sink with water. The sink fills slowly at first, and then faster and faster. When the level of water reaches a certain point, a much smaller amount of water can be added to keep the sink full.

The pattern of population growth that is illustrated in Figure 20.5 is an S-shaped (sigmoidal) curve known as the **logistic growth pattern**. The green line running through this curve represents the habitat's **carrying capacity** (*K*)—the theoretical maximum population size that the environment can sustain over an extended period of time. In other words, the carrying capacity represents the number of individuals in a population that can live in a given environment without depleting the resources they need or harming their habitat or themselves. As a habitat changes from season to season,

Effect of environmental resistance on population growth

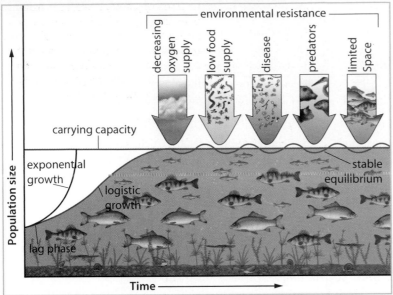

Figure 20.5 As a population increases in size, limiting factors such as disease, predation, and competition for limited resources reduce the amount of energy that is available for reproduction. This causes the growth rate of the population to decrease.

or from year to year, the carrying capacity also changes. Over time, population size may fluctuate around the carrying capacity of the habitat in a *stable equilibrium*.

The factors that limit a habitat's carrying capacity can be categorized as density-dependent or density-independent. **Density-dependent factors** are biotic. When a population is small and well below the carrying capacity of the habitat, density-dependent factors do not limit growth. The impact of density-dependent factors on a population increases with the density of the population. For example, parasites and disease spread more easily in dense populations. Also, predation becomes a more important limiting factor for prey populations as they get larger and denser.

abiotic← **Density-independent factors** are abiotic and include harsh weather, drought, floods, and forest fires. Density-independent factors limit the growth of a population, regardless of its size or density. A cold snap, for example, kills all or most of the mosquitoes in a streambed whether the population is small or large.

The combined effects of various, interacting limiting factors is described

as the **environmental resistance** to population growth. Environmental resistance prevents a population from growing at its biotic potential and determines the carrying capacity of the habitat. The arrows in Figure 20.5 illustrate how limiting factors such as predation and disease apply environmental resistance to population growth, maintaining growth at or near the carrying capacity of the habitat. (In Section 20.2, you will learn more about the effects of some limiting factors.)

• • •

12 Define carrying capacity, and give its symbol.

13 Explain, using at least two examples, the differences between density-dependent factors and density-independent factors.

14 What is environmental resistance? How does it affect populations?

• • •

Life Strategies

In an unstable environment, it can be advantageous to expend energy in order to reproduce rapidly while conditions are favourable. The growth of infectious bacteria that multiply rapidly once they enter the body, is an example. In contrast, the long life span of the wood bison and the small number of offspring per parent may be more useful adaptations in a relatively stable environment. These adaptations of the wood bison are two of many factors that can permit a population to exist close to the carrying capacity of its habitat without crashing.

The different *life strategies* of rapidly growing bacteria and wood bison can be used to represent two extremes along a continuum. The bacteria, and other species that reproduce close to their biotic potential (r), represent one end of the continuum. Such species are said to have **r-selected strategies**. Species with *r*-selected strategies have a short life span and an early reproductive age, and they

Figure 20.6 Since 1986, ecologists with La Trobe University in Australia have been tagging Antarctic fur seal pups similar to this one from separate populations at Macquarie Island in the sub-Antarctic. The scientists are trying to determine if the length of time that pups nurse affects their survival.

produce large broods of offspring that receive little or no parental care. Insects, annual plants, and algae typically have *r*-selected strategies. They take advantage of favourable environmental conditions, such as the availability of food, sunlight, or warm summer temperatures, to reproduce quickly. In Alberta's climate, for example, these organisms experience exponential growth in the summer, but die in large numbers as the summer ends.

At the other end of the continuum are populations that live close to the carrying capacity (*K*) of their habitats, and thus are described as having **K-selected strategies**. Mammals such as wood bison, northern fur seals (*Callorhinus ursinus*), and eurasian badgers (*Meles meles*), and birds such as tawny owls (*Strix aluco*), exhibit typical *K*-selected life strategies. They have few offspring per reproductive cycle, and one or both parents care for the offspring when young. The offspring take a relatively long time to mature and reach reproductive age, and they live a relatively long time. Also, they tend to have large bodies, compared with organisms that have *r*-selected strategies. A typical *K*-selected life strategy is to produce few offspring, but to invest a large amount of energy into helping the offspring reach reproductive age.

In reality, most populations have a combination of *K*-selected strategies and *r*-selected strategies. Consider, for example, any species of coniferous tree. Coniferous trees are large and can live many years, but they produce hundreds of gamete-bearing seeds. In addition, a population can only be properly described as *K*-selected or *r*-selected when it is compared to another population. A gopher population, for instance, could be described as being a *K*-selected population compared to a mosquito population. On the other hand, compared to a bison population, a gopher population would be better described as being *r*-selected. Gophers live for only three to six years and females produce one litter of about seven pups per year.

Recognizing the various *K*-selected and *r*-selected strategies of a species can be used to predict the success of a population in a particular habitat. For example, scientists who are studying two populations of Antarctic fur seals (*Arctocephalus gazella*) on the same island have observed that mother seals nurse their pups for 10 months in one population, while pups are weaned at four months in the other population. The scientists would like to find out if the greater investment of time and energy given to lactation influences the survival and reproductive success of the seal pups (Figure 20.6).

In Thought Lab 20.2, you will consider the impact of *K*-selected strategies on the survival of grizzly bear populations.

- - -

 Create a table to compare the characteristics of populations with typical *r*-selected and *K*-selected life strategies.

- - -

What Limits the Growth of Grizzly Bear Populations?

Records indicate that in the 1800s grizzly bears (*Ursus arctos*) occupied most of the region encompassed by the province of Alberta. As settlers moved west, however, hunting and the development of land for agriculture and, later, industry and recreation led to the decline of the grizzly bear population. In the 1960s, scientists concluded that conservation action was needed to preserve Alberta's grizzly bear population, which is now limited to the western edge of the province.

Statistics show that over 80 percent of all bear deaths are related to human activities. Humans present two threats to the grizzly bear population: disruption of habitat and grizzly bear mortality. The bears require a wide home range—up to 500 km² for females and more for males—to meet their dietary needs. They have large energy requirements, which they fulfill by eating grasses, sedges, berries, ants, and ungulates. Fragmentation of their habitat due to the building and use of new roads, or industrial or recreational facilities, is detrimental to their population. Like other large mammals, grizzly bears do not adapt well to major changes in their environment. Can humans and grizzly bears share the same environment?

Procedure

Using the data in the first table, draw a graph that shows the change in size of the Alberta grizzly bear population outside the National Parks over time. Then complete the following Analysis questions.

Analysis

1. To manage the grizzly bear population better, the government of Alberta introduced a hunting lottery that awards a limited number of grizzly bear hunting licenses. Predict the year that this regulation was introduced.

Number of Grizzly Bears in Alberta, Outside the National Parks

Year	Population size
1988	575
1989	536
1990	547
1991	638
1992	669
1993	686
1994	700
1995	735
1996	765
1997	776
1998	807
1999	833
2000	841

Source: Alberta Wildlife Status Reports, Alberta Sustainable Resource Development, 2002

2. The number of grizzly bear deaths in Alberta from 1976 to 1988 was estimated to be 581. Only 281 deaths were recorded from 1988 to 2000. How does this information affect the prediction you made in question 1? Explain your answer.

3. Determine the per capita growth rate (*cgr*) for each of the following time intervals: 1991 to 1992, 1997 to 1998, and 1998 to 1999. Suggest why the *cgr* has changed over time.

4. Population counts were made in several bear-management regions around the province. Some of the data are shown in following table.

   a) For each region, determine the number of grizzly bears per 1000 km².

   b) Compare the densities for the three regions. Suggest three reasons for the differences, if any. Explain your thinking.

Grizzly Bear Population Sizes in Alberta

Region	Area (km²)	Bear population
A	14 128	31
B	6 089	44
C	22 840	168

Source: Alberta Wildlife Status Reports, Alberta Sustainable Resource Development, 2002

5. Very few grizzly bears die of old age. What are two other possible causes of death, not associated with human activities?

6. Studies have shown that male grizzly bears will cross roads and use underpasses to forage in a better environment. Females tend to remain in more restricted areas.

  a) How might the movement of male and female grizzly bears in their habitat affect genetic diversity in the population?

  b) How would this behaviour influence the per capita growth rate of the population?

7. Grizzly bears reach sexual maturity at five years of age. When food is abundant, females average two cubs per litter every other year. With inadequate nutrition, females produce fewer cubs.

  a) Compared with mosquitoes, how would you describe the life strategy of grizzly bears?

  b) Explain why the biotic potential of grizzly bears is relatively low.

  c) How might grizzly bears' low biotic potential present challenges for people who are working to conserve the grizzly bear population?

8. Near Lake Louise, Alberta, there is a road sign that asks drivers on the highway to reduce their speed from 90 to 70 km/h along a 15 km stretch where grizzly bears are known to forage for food, especially at dusk and dawn.

  Do you think that lowering the speed limit along this stretch of highway is a reasonable action? Would the installation of underpasses along this stretch of highway be a better alternative? Compare the advantages and disadvantages of each option. What questions might you want answered before making a decision about this issue?

9. One report concluded that people must "find a way" to prevent the Trans-Canada highway from being a barrier to grizzly bear migration. List the stakeholders in this issue. Based on the point of view of one of these stakeholders, suggest what actions could be taken to overcome the fragmentation of the grizzly bear's habitat. Share your ideas on this issue in a class discussion.

Section 20.1 Summary

- The density of a population can be described and estimated quantitatively.
- Population density is defined as the number of organisms that make up a population in a given area or volume at a particular time: $D_p = \dfrac{N}{A}$ or $D_p = \dfrac{N}{V}$.
- There are three theoretical patterns of distribution: random, clumped, and uniform. These patterns are influenced by the distribution of resources in a population's habitat, as well as by the interactions among members of different communities in this habitat.
- Four processes that cause changes in population size are births, immigration, deaths, and emigration: $\Delta N = (b + i) - (d + e)$. Births and immigration increase the size of a population, while deaths and emigration decrease its size.

- The rate at which the size of a population changes is called the growth rate (*gr*) of the population. It can be described using the equation $gr = \dfrac{\Delta N}{\Delta t}$.
- Because the growth rate does not take the initial number of individuals in a population into account, the per capital growth rate (*cgr*) may be used to compare populations of the same species by describing the change in the number of individuals of a population in terms of the rate of change per individual: $cgr = \dfrac{\Delta N}{N}$ or $cgr = \dfrac{N_{final} - N}{N}$.
- The environment limits population growth by changing birth and death rates.
- Factors that affect population size and growth include biotic factors such as resources, disease, and predators, and abiotic factors such as floods, temperature, and hurricanes.

- Because the effects of biotic factors are often influenced by population density, biotic factors are described as being density-dependent.
- The effects of abiotic factors are not influenced by population density, so they are called density-independent factors.
- Given unlimited resources and ideal living conditions, the highest possible per capita growth rate for a population is referred to as its biotic potential (r).
- A population growing at its biotic potential grows exponentially, which can be represented graphically as a J-shaped curve.
- Since unlimited resources and ideal living conditions are rare in nature for any length of time, populations are bound by a theoretical maximum size that their habitat can support for an extended period of time. This is the carrying capacity of the habitat.
- Populations that grow in an environment where food or other resources are limited can be represented graphically with an S-shaped curve, called a logistic growth pattern. The combined effect of these limiting factors is described as environmental resistance to population growth.
- A population in a given environment can be described as r-selected or K-selected in comparison to another population.
- K-selected populations typically consist of individuals living close to the carrying capacity of their habitat, with long life spans, later reproductive ages, and small numbers of offspring.
- r-selected populations typically consist of individuals growing close to their biotic potential, with short life spans, early reproductive ages, and large numbers of offspring.
- The concepts of r-selection and K-selection are two extremes of a continuum. Most populations appear somewhere between these two extremes.

Section 20.1 Review

1. Why do scientists often need to estimate the size of a population, rather than counting each member individually?

2. Define population density.

3. Explain why population density is not always a reliable tool for estimating the number of individuals in a population.

4. How might the abundance and distribution of food in a habitat influence how a species is dispersed in this habitat?

5. Compare birth rates and death rates for a population during the lag, exponential, and stationary phases of a logistic growth pattern.

6. List three limiting factors that would be part of the environmental resistance in a forested habitat. Explain how each factor could limit the growth of a population.

7. List three factors that determine the biotic potential of a particular species. Explain how each factor affects the biotic potential of this species.

8. On the same graph, draw a typical exponential growth curve and a typical logistic growth curve. On the correct curve, label the point at which the growth of the population has begun to slow down and the point at which the population has reached the carrying capacity of its habitat.

9. Scientists refer to populations with r-selected life strategies as opportunistic populations and populations with K-selected life strategies as equilibrium populations. Use the characteristics of each type of strategy to explain how scientists came up with these terms.

Interactions in Ecological Communities

Figure 20.7 Following a flood, some of the cottonwood tree seeds on the forest floor will germinate. Only a few of the seedlings will mature into trees.

An *ecological community* is an association of interacting populations that inhabit a defined area. The plant community in a boreal forest, or the algal, bacterial, insect, and fish populations in a stream are examples of ecological communities. In any community, individuals of many populations may compete for limited resources. Members of some species may prey on members of other species. On the other hand, members of one species may be adapted to live closely with members of another species, improving the chances of survival for both species. The interactions among individuals, within the same population or from different populations, are a driving force behind population dynamics—the changes that occur in populations over time.

Intraspecific Competition

With sufficient moisture, the seeds on the floor of a cottonwood (*Populus* sp.) forest will begin to germinate (Figure 20.7). Even a small area of the forest will contain thousands of seeds. Each seed requires water, nutrients, sunlight, and sufficient space to grow, mature, and survive. Only a few of the seedlings will

be able to compete successfully to obtain what they need from the limited resources that are available to them. The competition for limited resources among members of the same species is called **intraspecific competition**.

Intraspecific competition is a density-dependent factor that limits the growth of a population. Intraspecific competition plays an important role in natural selection, as well. For example, some individuals may have a competitive advantage, such as being able to grow longer roots to absorb more water. These individuals will be more likely to survive long enough to reproduce, thereby passing on this competitive trait to their offspring. Similarly, members of an animal population may compete with one another for food or shelter.

When individuals are in competition for limited resources, why is it that parents do not out-compete their offspring? In fact, in many species, if the offspring did not disperse away from their parents, the offspring and parents would be in competition. Many fungi, for example, produce spores that can be carried on the wind to faraway locations.

You may be unfamiliar with the notation "sp.," which can be used when providing the name of a species. When the specific name of a species is not known or has not yet been determined, biologists use the abbreviation "sp." For example, "*Felis* sp." refers to a species that belongs to the genus *Felis* (a genus of cats).

Figure 20.8 The light, fluffy seeds of the aspen poplar tree are easily carried by the wind to locations far away from the parent.

Similarly, plants such as the aspen poplar (*Populus tremuloides*) produce wind-borne seeds (Figure 20.8). Some plants produce fleshy fruit around their seeds. Animals that eat the fruit digest the fleshy part but release the seeds in their feces, sometimes kilometres away from the parent plants.

Developing insect offspring undergo a complete metamorphosis. This means that the offspring go through a larval stage, in which they look completely different from the adults. The cabbage white butterfly (*Pieris rapae*), shown in Figure 20.9, begins life as a caterpillar that feeds on the leaves of plants from the mustard family, such as broccoli and cauliflower. The adult butterfly of this species feeds on flower nectar from plants such as clover, mustards, and dandelions. Since the adults and young have different needs, competition between them is reduced.

Interspecific Competition

Competition also occurs between members of different species in the same community. For example, white spruce (*Picea glauca*) may compete with lodgepole pine (*Pinus contorta*) for light and living space. Eventually, the white spruce may take over. Competition between two or more populations for limited resources, such as nutrients, light, or living space, is referred to as **interspecific competition**.

Due to interspecific competition, no two species can share the exact same ecological niche. As you may recall from Chapter 3 (see page 97), an organism's ecological niche is defined by its habitat and role within the community. An organism's ecological niche includes all the biotic and abiotic factors that are required for the organism to survive, as well as the organism's interactions with other species. When populations share overlapping niches, they compete for limited resources. Interspecific competition is less fierce, however, if the populations have even slightly different niches. For example, five species of warbler can successfully forage in the same species of spruce tree, because each species of warbler tends to feed on insects that are found in a different part of the tree. As well, each species flies in a different pattern to catch insects.

Often, when a non-native species is introduced into an environment, it competes with the native species. Sometimes, the native species compete

Figure 20.9 Larval (**A**) and adult (**B**) forms of the cabbage white butterfly, *Pieris rapae*. This insect was introduced to Quebec from Europe in the mid-1850s, and it is now found throughout much of North America.

successfully against the introduced species, which dies out. Other times, however, the introduced species takes over the niches of the native species, thereby changing the structure of the ecological community. For example, the wetlands in Canada and the United States are particularly vulnerable to varieties of reed canary grass (*Phalaris arundinacea*) that have been introduced since the 1800s (Figure 20.10). Although there are varieties of reed canary grass that are native to North America, the introduced varieties are extremely invasive. These invasive species frequently out-compete many native species, thus reducing plant diversity in the wetlands. Stands of the invasive reed canary grass are thought to make poor nesting and feeding sites for wetland animals.

• • •

16 Distinguish between intraspecific competition and interspecific competition.

17 Explain how intraspecific competition limits the growth rate of a population.

18 State what can happen when a non-native (introduced) species competes with native species.

• • •

Producer-Consumer Interactions

Not all interspecific interactions in a community are competitive. Primary producers have a direct relationship with the primary consumers that eat them. Primary consumers, in turn, have a direct relationship with their predators, the secondary consumers. **Predators** are organisms that kill and consume other organisms, known as **prey**.

The producer-consumer relationship puts selective pressure on both partners, with the more successful consumers driving the natural selection of the producers. In other words, producers that are more difficult to catch or less desirable to consume are more likely to

Figure 20.10 Eurasian varieties of reed canary grass sometimes take over areas that have been cleared of another, more readily identifiable invasive species—purple loosestrife (*Lythrum salicaria*). Purple loosestrife (shown here) is considered an ornamental grass in Asia and Europe, from where it was introduced. Often, both introduced species grow together, making the reed canary grass difficult to detect.

survive. In addition, like any important food source, the scarcity of a producer species is a factor that can limit a consumer species' population. On the other hand, a dense population of consumers may control the growth of producer populations.

For example, some grey wolves prey mainly on elk (*Cervus elaphus*). Following the extirpation of grey wolves from Banff National Park in the 1970s, the elk population of the park soared. With the increased presence of elk in and around the town of Banff, conflicts between the elk and humans became more common. In addition, ecologists found that the elk were overgrazing and damaging willow (*Salix* sp.) and aspen trees. Ecologists linked the loss of these trees, in turn, to declines in local populations of songbirds and beavers (*Castor canadensis*). To help limit the Banff elk population, grey wolves were encouraged back into the area. By 2003, the elk population had declined significantly, indicating that, along with re-conditioning elk to be wary of people, the strategy of bringing back the elk's major predator was working.

Predator-prey interactions are one factor in the *boom or bust* cycles observed in populations of some northern species. Figure 20.11 on page 719 shows two such population cycles. Hypothetically, the larger a prey population is, the more food that is available to its predators. Thus, the predators have more energy to reproduce

BiologyFile

Web Link

Russian scientist Georgyi F. Gause found that if two species of *Paramecium* occupied the same niche, eventually one would out-compete the other, resulting in the loss of one of the populations. How does this evidence support the concept of *competitive exclusion*?

www.albertabiology.ca
WWW

Interspecific and Intraspecific Competition Among Seedlings

Both *intra*specific competition and *inter*specific competition limit the growth of populations. Gardeners consider the effects of both kinds of competition when planning out garden plots. In this investigation, you will design two experiments. One will demonstrate the effects of intraspecific competition, and the other will demonstrate the effects of interspecific competition.

Part 1: Intraspecific Competition

Question

How does intraspecific competition affect the growth of individuals in a population?

Safety Precautions

The sprouts may become contaminated. Do not eat them.

Hypothesis

Make and record a hypothesis about how increasing intraspecific competition will affect the growth of individuals in a population.

Materials

- seeds (such as basil, marigold, radish, grass, lettuce, bean, or clover seeds)
- scissors
- vermiculite or potting soil
- ruler
- flower pots
- balance

Experimental Plan

1. With your group, establish the manipulated and responding variables.

2. State and record your hypothesis.

3. Using some of the listed materials as a starting point, design a procedure for your experiment. Be sure to include controlled variables in your procedure. Also include the criteria you will use to measure your experimental results.

4. Create a data table for your results. Decide how you will later present the data.

5. Once your group has agreed on the plan, have your teacher approve it.

Data and Observations

Conduct your investigation, and record your results. Then present the data in a graph.

Part 2: Interspecific Competition

Question

How does interspecific competition affect the growth of individuals in different populations?

Safety Precautions

The sprouts may become contaminated. Do not eat them.

Hypothesis

Make and record a hypothesis about the effect of interspecific competition on the growth of individuals in different populations.

Experimental Plan

Using some of the suggested materials listed in Part 1, design an experiment to demonstrate interspecific competition among populations of seedlings. Follow the same steps to plan your investigation that you followed in Part 1.

Data and Observations

Conduct your investigation, and record your results. If possible, present the data in a graph.

Analysis

1. How did you manipulate the degree of intraspecific competition in your experiment in Part 1?

2. Were the criteria you used to measure your experimental results and evaluate the differences in the seedlings' growth effective? Explain.

3. Consult with your classmates to see which procedures provided the most effective demonstrations of

   a) intraspecific competition

   b) interspecific competition

4. Critique your experimental plans for Part 1 and Part 2. What changes would you make if you could conduct this investigation again?

Conclusions

5. How did the intraspecific competition in Part 1 affect the growth of individual seedlings?

6. In Part 1, were you able to detect the effect of intraspecific competition on the entire population that you planted? If so, explain how and describe your results. If not, how would you expect intraspecific competition to affect a population?

7. In Part 2, how did interspecific competition affect the growth of the seedlings in the competing populations? Provide an explanation for these results.

8. In Part 2, did one population compete better overall? If so, which one? Provide an explanation for this result.

9. Your results were based on the germination of seeds. The death rate of plants is highest at this stage. Hypothesize how your results might have been different if you had used adult plants in both Part 1 and Part 2. How could you test your hypotheses?

---

and care for their young. This allows the predator population to increase. With a greater number of predators, the prey population will decline, resulting in more intense competition among the predators for food, which becomes a limiting factor. The predator population therefore declines, and, with fewer predators, the prey population increases.

The results of extensive, long-term ecosystem studies suggest, however, that predator-prey interactions do not fully explain population cycles. Populations of snowshoe hare (*Lepus americanus*) and Canada lynx (*Lynx canadensis*) follow boom or bust cycles that each last about 10 years. Figure 20.12 shows the number of Canada lynx and snowshoe hare pelts from the Canadian Arctic that were traded to the Hudson Bay Company over 100 years. The number of pelts would

have been affected by the demand for pelts, the number of trappers, and the location of the traps. Nevertheless, the hare and lynx populations fluctuated in cycles that were too regular to be due to abiotic factors. Furthermore, the increases and decreases in the lynx population closely followed increases and decreases in the hare population. This observation

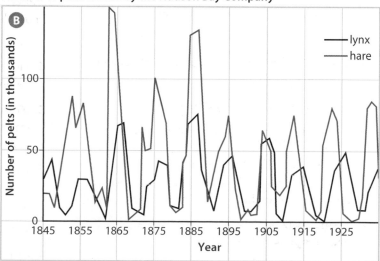

Predator-prey population cycles

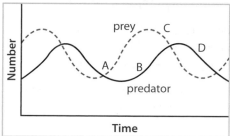

Figure 20.11 A simplified graph of predator-prey population cycles. An increase in prey increases the resources that are available to the predators **(A)**, so the predator population increases **(B)**. This leads to a reduction in the prey population **(C)**, followed by a reduction in the predator population **(D)**. And the cycle continues.

Number of pelts traded by the Hudson Bay Company

Figure 20.12 (A) The Canada lynx has strong forelimbs with sharp claws, which it uses to catch its main prey, the snowshoe hare. **(B)** Population estimates of snowshoe hare and Canada lynx show a pattern of 10-year cycles in population size. The hare population usually peaks about a year before the lynx population peaks.

led scientists to hypothesize that predator-prey interactions were causing the population cycles.

Another hypothesis to explain the cycling of snowshoe hares was that at higher population numbers, the hares were depleting their food supply. The reduction in the quantity and quality of the vegetation they browsed on therefore caused the snowshoe hare population to crash. An eight-year experiment to test the two hypotheses showed that snowshoe hare populations did, in fact, increase when more food was available to them. Test populations that were protected from predators increased, as well. With both abundant food and protection from predators, the snowshoe hare populations did even better. Based on these results, scientists have concluded that the periodic dips in snowshoe hare populations are probably due to a combination of food shortages and increased predation (Figure 20.13).

Predator-prey interactions also influence natural selection for adaptive traits. Individual lynx that are more successful hunters, for example, are more likely to survive and reproduce, and thus pass on their traits to the next generation. Snowshoe hares that are faster or better at hiding are also more likely to pass down their successful traits.

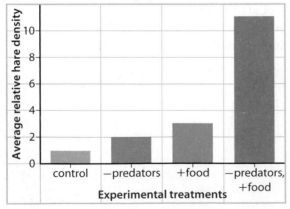

Effects of changes in food and predation levels on snowshoe hare populations

Average relative hare density vs. Experimental treatments (control, −predators, +food, −predators, +food)

Figure 20.13 The results of a field experiment on snowshoe hare populations. Plots in which either the hares had unlimited food, or were safe from ground-dwelling predators, or both were compared to control plots, which were undisturbed sections of boreal forest.

19 How do producer-consumer relationships put selective pressure on both partners?

20 Describe two hypotheses to explain the population cycles of the snowshoe hare and the Canada lynx.

Defenses Against Consumers

Producers and consumers typically *co-evolve* as a result of their interactions. Many primary producers, for example, have adaptations that help to protect them from their consumers. Some plants, such as the milkweed plant (*Asclepias* sp.), produce bitter-tasting chemicals that discourage many herbivores—although some herbivores are able to adapt. Other plants, such as the cactus (family Cactaceae), have protective thorns, spines, or hairs. Some prey animals—the porcupine (*Erethizon dorsatum*), for instance—are similarly protected by their sharp quills. Many prey species are camouflaged, making them difficult for predators to find. For example, inchworm caterpillars (such as *Necophora quernaria*) and short-horned lizards (*Phyrnosoma hernandesi*) have different forms of cryptic coloration that allow them to blend in with their surroundings (Figure 20.14). By staying still, they may escape the detection of potential predators.

Cryptic coloration is a type of **protective coloration**, or body colour as a natural defense mechanism. In nature, black, yellow, and red are typical warning colours that predators come to associate with dangerous or unpalatable animals. The highly venomous eastern coral snake (*Micrurus fulvius fulvius*), for example, has red and black stripes. Some of the most poisonous frogs of South America are red or yellow. Stinging bees and yellowjacket wasps—members of the Hymenoptera order of insects—are black and yellow.

(A)

(B)

Figure 20.14 Cryptic coloration. **(A)** An inchworm caterpillar closely resembles the twig that it hangs from. **(B)** The short-horned lizard of North America lives in sparsely vegetated areas of mixed-grass prairie. The lizards blend in so well with their environment that researchers have difficulty finding and counting them.

The syrphid fly (family Syrphidae) has the distinctive warning coloration of a yellow-jacket wasp, but no stinger (Figure 20.15). Thus, the syrphid fly is said to be a mimic. It relies on looking like a well-defended model to deter predators. This form of mimicry is known as *Batesian mimicry*.

Two or more species that are poisonous, harmful, or unpalatable may also benefit by mimicking each other. For example, the monarch butterfly (*Danaus plexippus*) closely resembles its co-mimic, the viceroy butterfly (*Limenitis archippus*). While a caterpillar, the monarch feeds on milkweed leaves and stores the milkweed poison in its body for life. When a bird learns by trial and error that eating monarch butterflies makes it sick, it will avoid all butterflies that look like monarchs, including viceroy butterflies. Scientists hypothesize that the converse is also true: when a bird finds that viceroy butterflies are distasteful, it will avoid all butterflies that look like viceroys. This co-evolved defense mechanism is known as *Müllerian mimicry*.

• • •

21 The snowshoe hare is difficult to spot. During the winter it has a white coat, which it sheds in the spring for a brown coat that also provides camouflage. What is the name of this natural defense mechanism?

22 Explain the difference between Batesian and Müllerian mimicry.

• • •

Symbiotic Relationships

Populations that have lived in association for millions of years have often co-evolved to develop even closer relationships. The direct or close relationship between individuals of different species that live together is called **symbiosis**. Symbiotic relationships usually involve an organism that lives or feeds in or on another organism, sometimes called the *host*. Three forms of symbiosis are mutualism, commensalism, and parasitism.

Mutualism

When both partners in a symbiotic relationship benefit from the relationship, or depend on it in order to survive, their relationship is called **mutualism**. Lichen, for example, is actually a combination of an alga (or cyanobacterium species) and a fungus. In some cases, their mutualistic relationship allows them to grow on exposed, bare rock, where neither one would survive on its own. The algal partner photosynthesizes, which provides food for both organisms. The fungal

BiologyFile

Web Link
Various types of fish feed on guppies (*Poecilia reticulata*). Scientists have found that the number and types of predators in a stream influence the natural selection of guppies. Conduct an online simulation of evolution in guppy populations. In what ways do the populations change over time?

www.albertabiology.ca

WWW

Figure 20.15 Mimics, such as the syrphid fly, have evolved to look like harmful or unpalatable species as a defense mechanism against predators.

partner protects the alga from drying out or blowing away. As well, it produces an acid that dissolves rock, releasing minerals that are needed by the alga.

Animal behaviour is important in some cases of mutualism. In Latin America, for example, certain species of *Acacia* tree have a mutualistic relationship with stinging ants of the genus *Pseudomyrmex* (Figure 20.16). The leaves of the *Acacia* produce protein containing structures and a sugary liquid, which the stinging ants consume. The stinging ants live, protected, inside the tree's hollow thorns. The ants benefit the tree by attacking any other herbivores that land on it and by providing organic nutrients. The ants also cut down the branches of other plants that come in contact with the *Acacia*, which ensures that the *Acacia* has adequate light for photosynthesis.

Commensalism

Commensalism is a symbiotic relationship in which one partner benefits and the other partner neither benefits nor is harmed. For example, a shark does not appear to benefit or suffer from its relationship with suckerfish (*Remora* sp.), which use their sucker-like dorsal fins to hold fast to the shark's body. The suckerfish, however, receive protection and bits of food from the shark.

It may be difficult to determine whether both partners benefit from a symbiotic relationship. Why do brown-headed cowbirds (*Molothrus ater*) spend so much time hovering around the hooves

Figure 20.16 Stinging ants live in the hollow thorns of certain species of the *Acacia* tree in Latin America. The tree provides food for the ants in the form of a sweet nectar and proteins. The ants protect the tree from herbivores and, as shown here, from being shaded by other plants.

Figure 20.17 The brown-headed cowbird benefits from the insects that are flushed out of the grass by bison and domestic cattle as they graze. Is this an example of commensalism?

of grazing bison and domestic cattle (Figure 20.17)? Scientists have discovered that as the large animals walk through the grass, they flush out insects, which are eaten by the birds. The relationship between the cowbirds and the cattle appears to be an example of commensalism. The cowbirds, however, sometimes pick flies and other parasites from the cattle's skin, which benefits the cattle. Is this relationship really an example of mutualism? There are probably few true cases of commensalism. Both partners in symbiosis are usually affected in some way, although how they are affected may not be clear.

Parasitism

Mistletoes are a group of related plant families that live on trees and shrubs. Some mistletoes have flowers but no developed leaves, and obtain food by growing roots directly into the bark and phloem of conifer trees. The interaction weakens the trees and predisposes them to disease. This relationship is an example of **parasitism**, a form of symbiosis in which one partner, the parasite, benefits at the expense of its host.

Parasites are among the most successful species in the world—they thrive in most parts of the biosphere. Parasites include viruses and various types of worms, unicellular organisms, and insects. They affect almost all species of wild and domesticated plants and animals (Figure 20.18). Internal parasites usually depend on their interaction with their host to survive. Some internal parasites, such as the protist *Plasmodium falciparum* which causes malaria, have evolved unique survival strategies, such as wrapping themselves in their host's liver cell membranes, to escape detection by the host's immune system.

Parasites have a large impact on our global economy and quality of life. The World Health Organization estimates that over 1.4 billion people are infested with parasites. Malaria affects more than 500 million people and results in 2 to 3 million deaths annually. In Alberta, cold weather kills off some, but not all, potential parasites. Almost 3 percent of Albertans are affected by *Giardia* sp., a protozoan that invades the large intestine, causing diarrhea.

In nature, parasites are an important factor in limiting the growth of host populations. When individuals succumb to parasites, this may help the host population as a whole, because it reduces the density of the population and thus reduces competition for limited resources. In addition, weakened hosts may become prey for other animals. Why, however, do parasites not kill all their potential hosts? If the host population went extinct, then, presumably, so would its parasites. If a few hosts survive, the parasites will also survive.

- - -

23. Define symbiosis.

24. Give one example of mutualism, and explain how the partners in the relationship benefit.

25. Define commensalism.

26. Explain how parasitism is different from mutualism and commensalism.

- - -

Succession: Community Change over Time

Following a forest fire, an area may appear barren. Within months, however, new vegetation may sprout, and then animals may repopulate the area. Years later, the same area will likely be thick with life. This process is known as **succession**, the sequence of invasion and replacement of species in an ecosystem over time. Succession is driven by both abiotic factors, such as climate, and biotic factors, such as interspecific competition for changing available resources.

BiologyFile

Web Link
Parasitoids, such as braconid wasps, are organisms that lay their eggs in the larvae of other insects, effectively killing the larvae. The wasp shown here has just emerged from a hole in the aphid's abdomen. Parasitoids can be used for the biological control of insect pests. How are parasitoids being used in Alberta?

www.albertabiology.ca
WWW

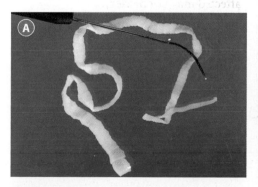 

Figure 20.18 **(A)** Tapeworms (*Taenia* sp.) are transferred from livestock to humans when people eat infected and undercooked beef or pork. The adult tapeworm's tough cuticle protects it from the digestive enzymes in the small intestine, where it attaches and absorbs nutrients. A tapeworm can lay up to 10 000 eggs each day. The eggs, which are shed in infected individuals' feces, enter the environment where they can be picked up by another host. **(B)** *Giardia* sp. infections are sometimes referred to as beaver fever. A large outbreak in Banff, Alberta, in the 1980s may have resulted from infected beavers shedding *Giardia* sp. into the water supply in their feces. The contamination of drinking-water intake supplies with sewer water is the likely cause of other *Giardia* sp. outbreaks.

Figure 20.19 Succession is a gradual change in community structure, beginning with a pioneer community and leading towards a climax community.

grass | low shrub | high shrub | shrub tree | low tree | high tree

pioneer community   climax community

Primary succession begins when there is no soil present, such as on bare rocks left behind by a retreating glacier or on a hardened lava bed. According to the classical model of succession, species populate an area in a specific chronological order (Figure 20.19). The first species to colonize an area and initiate succession form the **pioneer community**. The first species are organisms such as lichens that tend to be small and opportunistic, and able to grow in harsh conditions. Soil starts to form as some of these organisms die. As the soil builds up, its nutrient content, moisture content, and pH change (Figure 20.20). This allows larger species, such as mosses, to grow in the area. Grasses, annual herbs, shrubs, and trees follow, and the diversity of species expands (see Figure 20.21). The plants compete for light and living space. Due

to interspecific competition and the changing habitat, some populations are better able to survive. These populations replace those that are not able to survive. Animals may join the community and, as the species of plants change, so do the species of animals. The latecomers in the process of succession form a **climax community**. This community may remain relatively stable if there are no major environmental changes.

Succession also occurs in microbial communities. As you may recall from Chapter 2, each type of micro-organism in a community plays a particular role. In Investigation 20.B, you will explore the process of microbial succession.

Disturbing Events

An event that changes the structure of a community—sometimes destroying all actively growing organisms—is called

Changes in soil nitrogen during primary succession

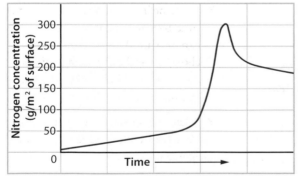

Figure 20.20 Nitrogen content of soil based on samples from Glacier Bay, Alaska. When primary succession begins, there is no soil and very few nutrients available to the organisms. As the organisms die and soil builds up, so do soil nutrients, such as nitrogen. Organisms from different species can then use the nutrients from the soil. They may also change the composition of the soil.

Changes in number of plant species during primary succession

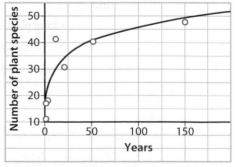

Figure 20.21 Plant succession in Glacier Bay, Alaska. By studying different sites where a glacier had retreated, ecologists found that plant diversity increased in the first 200 years of primary succession, and then levelled off.

Target Skills

Designing and **performing** an experiment to demonstrate succession in a micro-environment

Designing and **performing** an experiment to demonstrate the effect of an environmental factor on population growth rates

Communicating ideas and results

Celebrate the Small Successions

Ducks are not the only inhabitants of the local pond. Protozoans, such as *Paramecium* sp., and microscopic algae may be found swimming in the water where oxygen is available. The oxygen-poor mud at the bottom of the pond likely contains methane-producing bacteria or sulfate-reducing bacteria. What happens to populations of these micro-organisms when they are contained in a micro-environment?

Questions

How can you demonstrate microbial succession over time using everyday materials? What factors influence succession in a microenvironment?

Safety Precautions

- To avoid creating completely anaerobic conditions in the jars and to prevent gases from building up in the jars, leave the lids on the jars loose.

- Do not leave the micro-environments near open flames. Gases that are produced in the micro-environments may ignite.

- Be careful not to smell the micro-environments or the bleach solution directly. Breathing in either hydrogen sulfide gas or chlorine gas is dangerous.

- Wash your hands after working with the micro-environments.

Materials

- container of 10 % bleach (for used microscope slides, cover slips, and pipettes)
- pond water (supplied by your teacher)
- wood shavings or dried grass
- paper towels
- pH paper
- microscope slides
- cover slips
- long plastic pipettes
- 2 mason jars with lids
- microscope
- laboratory fridge

Experimental Plan

1. Use Chapter 2 and library or Internet resources to refresh your memory about the role of micro-organisms in the carbon cycle.

2. Using the listed materials as a starting point, with your group, decide what environmental factor your group will manipulate. Will you examine the effect of temperature on succession in the micro-environments? Will you examine the effect of frequent aeration on succession in the micro-environments?

3. Decide exactly how you will set up each micro-environment. Also decide how and when you will observe the micro-environments. How will you detect changes in the microbial community? How will you detect population growth in a specific population?

4. Write a step-by-step procedure for your experiment. Be sure to include safety precautions in your procedure.

5. Once your group has agreed on the procedure, have your teacher approve it.

Data and Observations

Set up your micro-environments, and take your initial observations. Make periodic observations throughout the duration of the experiment.

Analysis

1. What environmental factor did you test?

2. How were you able to identify changes in the microbial community over time?

Conclusions

3. Describe how the microbial communities in each micro-environment changed over the course of the experiment. Which micro-organisms were most abundant at the beginning, middle, and end of the experiment? Which micro-organisms were least abundant at these three times?

4. What interspecific interactions might account for the succession of micro-organisms in the micro-environments?

5. How did the environmental factor that you tested affect the growth of particular populations in the micro-environments?

6. What abiotic factors might account for the succession of micro-organisms in the micro-environments?

an **ecological disturbance**. **Secondary succession** is the recolonization of an area after an ecological disturbance, such as a forest fire or flood, or agricultural activity. The soil, which contains nutrients and organic matter, is not usually destroyed in an ecological disturbance. Seeds and the roots of vascular plants remain buried in the soil, as do the spores of ferns and mosses. In fact, some plant species produce seeds that will germinate only after they are exposed to the extreme heat of a forest fire. The giant sequoia (*Sequoiadendron giganteum*) of the Pacific Northwest and the lodgepole pine (*Pinus contorta*, the provincial tree of Alberta) are two examples. This adaptation ensures that there will be plenty of light and nutrients available for new seedlings.

Like primary succession, secondary succession includes changes in the composition and number of species over time. The stages of succession may occur over weeks in an area recovering from a flood. In other areas, such as a new forest, succession may continue for 150 years. According to the classical model of succession, once the climax community has developed, it will remain stable unless there is a major ecological disturbance.

Ecologists now think that ecological disturbances are the norm rather than the exception in many communities. Even a tree falling in a rain forest creates a small ecological disturbance. This, and larger disturbances, such as clear cutting a forest, open a space in the canopy, allowing light to hit the ground and secondary succession to occur. Thus, ecological disturbances are important for many plants. Research shows that the magnitude of a disturbance affects the types of organisms that will inhabit an area. Spruce (*Picea* sp.), a shade-tolerant plant, does well following a small ecological disturbance in a forest. A large disturbance in a forest provides plenty of light and allows shade-intolerant plants, such as the lodgepole pine, to flourish. Ecological disturbances are also

important for animals. The berry bushes that grow up a few years after a forest fire are an important food for grizzly bears as they gain body mass in preparation for hibernation.

Ecologists must therefore consider how ecological disturbances affect different species when trying to establish—or preserve—healthy natural communities. Understanding the role of ecological disturbances in structuring communities is currently an important area of investigation in ecology.

• • •

27 What is succession?

28 Distinguish between
   a) primary succession and secondary succession
   b) pioneer community and climax community

• • •

Section 20.2 Summary

- Population dynamics refers to changes that occur in a population over time, such as population growth.
- Population dynamics are influenced by biotic and abiotic factors.
- Density-dependent limiting factors on population growth include disease and intraspecific competition for limited resources, such as food, living space, and light.
- Interspecific competition is the competition among members of different populations for limited resources.
- Producer-consumer interactions may impact the growth of both the producer population and the consumer population, since the consumer population depends on the producer population for survival. Also, the consumer population may deplete the producer population.
- A predator is a consumer that kills and consumes other organisms, known as prey.

On average, fires in the boreal forest of Alberta occur every 50 years. The life span of a lodgepole pine is 220 years. Many lodgepole pines do not have a chance to live to "old age" because of the frequency of these fires.

The classical model of succession came out of an explorer's observations of a glacial valley in the late 1800s. Because succession is such a long process, however, early ecologists had difficulty testing this model of succession. In fact, no studies have lasted the hundreds of years required to observe the entire life cycle of certain types of trees. Nevertheless, with the development of new technologies and long-term studies of model forests, ecologists are able to gather and assess new information.

Suppose that you are studying the impact of a wild land fire in an area of Alberta's boreal forest. All the above-ground vegetation in the area was destroyed. Suppose that you visit the area 20 years after the fire and see a layer of small white spruce trees growing below a layer of tall lodgepole pines. You hypothesize that this community is following the classical model of succession. If your hypothesis is correct, then presumably the pine trees are being replaced by the spruce trees, which are characteristic of climax communities in this area.

Procedure

Use the information above to answer the following Analysis questions.

Analysis

1. What type of succession—primary or secondary—is taking place in the area? Explain your answer.

2. You hypothesized that the community is following the classical model of succession, with one species replacing another. If your hypothesis is correct, what would you predict about the ages of the pine trees relative to the spruce trees? Explain your answer.

3. How could you determine the ages of the trees in the area?

4. Analysis of the trees in the area indicates that both populations are about 20 years old. How does this information affect your original hypothesis?

5. Scientists have studied the birth rate and death rate of each species of tree. They have used their data to create the following survivorship curves, which show the proportion of individuals in a population that survive over time.

Number of seeds germinating after a disturbance

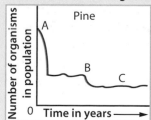

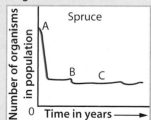

As shown in section A on the graphs, both populations have a great decline in numbers after the seeds started germinating. List three factors that might cause the young seedlings to die.

6. Compare the rate of death of lodgepole pine trees with the rate of death of spruce trees in section A of the graphs.

7. Section B of the graphs represents a natural process called density thinning. It occurs in dense populations, when resources are very limited. Some of the population dies, which leaves more resources for the remaining population. Suggest a reason why density thinning affects the lodgepole pine population more than the spruce population.

8. Lodgepole pines are shade intolerant. When their seeds germinate, the seedlings grow very tall very quickly. In contrast, spruce trees are shade tolerant and grow more slowly than lodgepole pines. Would you expect the taller or shorter lodgepole pines to die during density thinning? Explain your answer.

9. Consider again your hypothesis that the community is following the classical model of succession and, therefore, the spruce trees are replacing the lodgepole pine trees. Based on your hypothesis, sketch a graph of the number of individual trees in each population versus time. Compare your graph to the survivorship curves. Formulate an alternative hypothesis about how succession is occurring in the community under study.

10. Which type of competition—interspecific or intraspecific—is more important to the pattern of succession in the study area? Explain your answer.

Extensions

11. Explain how the trees came to grow in the study area in the first place.

12. Some plants need more light than others to survive. Knowing this, explain how the following factors might affect the type of plants that will start the process of secondary succession after an ecological disturbance. Then identify the factor that is probably the most important in determining which species will be the first to repopulate an area after an ecological disturbance. Explain your reasoning.

   a) the type of ecological disturbance (for example, a forest fire versus a fallen tree)

   b) the types of seeds left in the soil after the disturbance

   c) the availability of moisture in the soil

   d) the availability of nutrients in the soil

- With natural selection for more successful producers and more successful consumers, producers and their consumers co-evolve.
- Producer defenses against consumers include toxin production and protective coloration, such as cryptic coloration and mimicry.
- Co-evolution may result in symbiosis—the close or direct association of individuals of separate species.
- Symbiosis in which both partners benefit is called mutualism. Symbiosis in which one partner benefits and the other partner does not benefit nor is harmed is called commensalism. This form of symbiosis is probably rare, however.

- Symbiosis in which an organism benefits at the expense of the host that it lives with is considered parasitism.
- An ecological community is comprised of interacting populations.
- A new community may form in an area, resulting in a sequence of invasion and replacement of species known as succession.
- Primary succession begins on bare rock or hardened lava with the formation of a pioneer community.
- Secondary succession occurs where there has been an ecological disturbance, such as a forest fire or a fallen tree, in a previously existing community.
- A climax community is a theoretical end point late in the process of succession.

Section 20.2 Review

1. White spruce (*Picea glauca*) may compete with lodgepole pine (*Pinus contorta*) for light and living space. Eventually, the white spruce may take over. What kind of competition is taking place? Provide two reasons why the white spruce may out-compete the lodgepole pine.

2. Many species have developed specific coloration that protects them from predators.

   a) Explain the relationship between warning coloration and Batesian mimicry.

   b) Why might it be important for the mimic to learn how to mimic the behaviour of its model?

   c) Predict what would happen to the population of a mimic species if its model species were eliminated from the area? Justify your prediction.

3. Explain the role of natural selection in intraspecific competition.

4. Identify the symbiotic relationship demonstrated in each of the following situations:

   a) Tapeworms live in the small intestine of animals, including humans, and absorb the available nutrients. They lay about 10 000 eggs a day. In extreme cases, tapeworms have been known to reach a length of 30 m.

   b) Some members of the orchid family grow on the branches of trees where they receive plenty of light. They absorb all their necessary nutrients directly from the atmosphere.

   c) Some coral reef fish and shrimp obtain energy by eating parasites from the scales and gills of larger fish. These "cleaners" are suitable prey for the larger fish, but they are not eaten.

   d) Nitrogen-fixing bacteria receive protection and nutrients from their host plant. In return, they provide their host with nitrogen compounds in a form that their host can use.

5. Define succession, and describe its importance to community dynamics.

6. Envision a neighbourhood where no one has touched a front lawn in 10 years. Describe any changes that you think might have occurred over the 10 years. What do the lawns now look like? What do you see in the neighbourhood?

Sharing the Biosphere

You have learned how genetic changes are passed from one generation to the next and how genetic changes affect future populations. You have also learned that ecological communities are in constant flux and that organisms and the non-living environment change in response to each other.

How, then, do we know when there is too much change—in individual organisms, in natural populations and communities, or in the abiotic environment? How can we reach consensus about the amount of change that is acceptable? Even when we reach consensus on one of these issues, what is the most effective way to act? In this section, you will consider the role of *Homo sapiens*—you—in the biosphere.

Assessing the Significance of Population Changes

For many Canadian Inuit, the polar bear (*Ursus maritimus*) is a vital resource. When Inuit hunters kill a polar bear, they share the meat with their families and with other members of their community. The skin and fur are used to make their traditional cold-weather clothing. The Inuit greatly respect the intelligence and hunting skills of *Nanuq* (Inuktitut for "polar bear"), which is a top predator in Arctic food webs. A decline in polar bear populations would mean significant changes to the traditional Inuit way of life, as well as to the Arctic ecosystem.

Polar bear counts indicate that the polar bear population of M'Clintock Channel in Nunavut is less than half of what it was in the 1970s. On the other hand, people living near Hudson Bay are encountering polar bears more often than they did in the past—so much so that people are concerned for their safety. One explanation for the observed increase is that the polar bears are emigrating from areas where the sea ice has become too thin to live on. Conversely, the M'Clintock Channel population could be losing bears to emigration. Over-hunting (including sport hunting) during the last century may have also contributed to the population's decline. Many scientists predict that, overall, polar bear populations will decrease as the melting pattern of Arctic sea ice changes. Other threats to polar bear populations may include the increased presence of snowmobiles, aircraft, and construction projects (such as the construction of radar stations), as well as the contamination of polar bear prey by environmental pollutants.

Given the threats faced by polar bear populations, many people wish to act to limit these threats. Deciding *how* to act is complicated, requiring input from various stakeholders in order to establish a course of action.

Establishing a Course of Action

At the end of Unit 1 you read about **sustainability**—the concept of living in a way that meets our needs without compromising the health of future generations or the health of the planet. For people who hunt or grow their own food, the connections between society, the economy, and the environment may be easier to see. Even for city dwellers, however, the practice of sustainability includes all three elements.

The most effective way to practise sustainability is not always clear. Separate lines of scientific evidence can help us make decisions. Even so, as you will discover in Thought Lab 20.4, careful consideration is needed to sort out, organize, analyze, interpret, and evaluate the evidence.

• • •

 Define sustainability.

• • •

Target Skills

Summarizing and **evaluating** an interspecific relationship

Developing, presenting, and **defending** a position on whether organisms should be deliberately introduced into a new environment

The cassava plant (*Manihot esculenta*) was introduced to Africa in the sixteenth century. Today, it is a dietary staple in many African countries. Around 1970, the cassava mealybug (*Phenacoccus manihoti*) was unintentionally introduced into Western Africa. It had no natural predators on the continent and, by 1973, was devastating cassava crops. Within a decade, researchers discovered a tiny wasp from Paraguay whose larvae specifically parasitized the cassava mealybug. The wasp, *Epidinocarsis lopezi*, was introduced into the cassava growing regions of Africa and soon brought cassava mealybug infestations under control.

Procedure

Your group will be assigned one example of biological control from the table. Use the information in the table to answer the Analysis questions that follow. You may wish to do further research. Your group will then present your findings to the class, using appropriate visual aids.

Analysis

1. Describe the interaction between the biological control agent you are studying and its target species.

2. Describe the benefits and disadvantages of introducing this biological control agent to new environments.

3. Present and justify your position on whether or not this biological control agent should be used to control invasive or pest species.

4. After all the presentations, compare the different examples of biological control to determine why some had successful outcomes and some did not.

Examples of Biological Control Using Introduced Species

Location of introduction	Invasive or pest species	Species introduced for biological control	Relationship between invasive or pest species and biological control agent	Outcomes of biological control
Australia	sugar-cane pests from the Scarabaeidae beetle family	cane toad (*Bufo marinus*)	Predatory: It was believed that the cane toads would eat the sugar cane beetles.	The cane toads have had little to no effect on the sugar cane beetles because the toads and beetles do not come in contact with each other very often. The toads are extremely invasive. They are poisonous and are a danger to children, pets, and wild animals that eat them. As well, they prey on many native animal species, including snakes.
Canada, United States of America	cabbage seedpod weevil (*Ceutorhynchus obstrictus*), which damages canola and other *Brassica* species	two species of wasp (*Microctonus melanopus* and *Trichomalis perfectus*)	Parasitic: *M. melanopus* attacks adult weevils and *T. perfectus* attacks weevil larvae.	The parasitic wasps have successfully suppressed cabbage seedpod weevil populations in Europe, but so far have had only limited success in North America.
Canada, United States of America	musk thistle (*Carduus nutans*), an introduced plant that is a noxious weed in North America	seed-head weevil (*Rhinocyllus conicus*)	Parasitic: The weevils lay eggs on the buds of thistle plants, and the larvae feed on the plants and prevent the development of new seeds.	The weevils are now well-established in North America and have greatly helped to reduce musk thistle populations. The weevils also attack *Cirsium canescens*, a thistle that is native to North America, and have reduced populations of these thistles in the Nebraska sandhills of the United States.
United States of America (Hawaii)	southern green stinkbug (*Nezara viridula*), an introduced pest that damages macadamia-nut trees	species of the *Trichopoda* fly and the *Trissolcus basalis* wasp	Parasitic: The flies lay eggs on adult stinkbugs. The fly maggots then penetrate and eat the stinkbugs. The wasps deposit their eggs inside stinkbug eggs, where the wasp larvae develop.	Introducing the flies and wasps has helped to control the invasive stinkbugs, but may have contributed to the decline of the native koa bugs (*Coleotichus blackburniae*).

Growth of the Human Population

The human population is currently in a state of exponential growth. How close is the human population to reaching its carrying capacity? Species with typical *r*-selected strategies, such as some insects, often have boom or bust population cycles. In comparison, species with typical *K*-selected strategies have populations that grow exponentially for a while, and then fluctuate in size close to the carrying capacity of their habitat. Humans have many *K*-selected life strategies, such as long life spans, a relatively low reproductive rate, and parental care of their young. How is the human population affected by density-dependent limiting factors? How might intraspecific competition and disease affect the human population? What will happen to the human population as resources become scarce?

Determining the exact number of people in early times is not an easy task. Estimates made before 1650 are crude. However, demographers (people who study populations) generally think that the human population remained fairly stable until the beginning of the Industrial Revolution, with one exception. During the fourteenth century, a bacterial infection known as the Black Death killed millions of people (Figure 20.22).

From the mid-eighteenth century on, living conditions for many people began to improve. As new understandings about hygiene were put into practice, and medical and agricultural technologies were developed and refined, the death rate slowed and the rate of population growth accelerated immensely. Recall that an exponentially growing population grows faster as it gets larger. As Figure 20.22 shows, it took 130 years for the global human population to grow from 1 billion (in 1800) to 2 billion individuals (in 1930). It took only 12 years, however, for the population to increase from 5 billion (in 1987) to 6 billion (in 1999).

The growth rate has not been the same for all human populations. Britain, Japan, and more industrialized countries in Europe and North America were the first to experience a drop in death rate, especially among infants and children. As a result, after a few generations, people in these countries began to have fewer children, and the birth rate of these populations dropped. Less industrialized nations in Africa, Asia, and Latin America began to move through the same stages in the twentieth century. Human population growth rates are still changing in the twenty-first century. In Thought Lab 20.5, you will explore this idea by comparing population growth in different countries.

Population Age Structure

As the growth curves you made in Thought Lab 20.5 show, the population growth rates (*gr*) in some countries are slowing down. Keep in mind that just because a population's growth rate is slowing, this does not mean that the population is shrinking. A positive,

Biology File

FYI
In 1918, an outbreak of a highly lethal strain of influenza (dubbed the Spanish Flu) claimed the lives of an estimated 2.5–5 percent of the global population. The virus killed adults mainly between 20 and 40 years of age. In the first 25 weeks of this global pandemic, up to 25 million lives were lost. Conservative estimates place the total number killed at about 50 million.

Estimated global population 5000 B.C.E–2000 C.E.

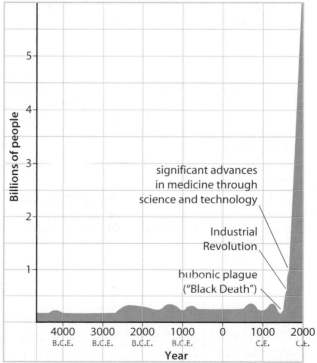

Figure 20.22 For most of its history, the human population has been stable or has grown very slowly. Explosive growth began after the Industrial Revolution in the eighteenth century, when the death rate in more industrialized countries dropped dramatically. The growth rate accelerated even more after World War II (1939–1945).

Although people may not have unlimited resources, many human populations appear to be growing exponentially. Since human populations in different parts of the world live in different environments, where people have different degrees of access to food, clean water, technologies, and medical aid, their per capita birth rates and death rates—and thus their growth rates—also vary. In this activity, you will compare the growth rates for several different human populations to see the effect of population growth rates on the shape of the growth curves.

Procedure

Use the table below to answer the following Analysis questions.

Human Demographic Information for Selected Countries in 2001

Country	Population size (millions) (N)	Number of births (b) per 1000 individuals	Number of deaths (d) per 1000 individuals
Canada	32.2	10	7
Ethiopia	77.4	41	16
Finland	5.2	11	9
Germany	82.5	9	10
Greece	11.1	9	10
India	1103.6	25	8
Nigeria	131.5	43	19

Source: 2005 World Population Data Sheet of the Population Reference Bureau

Analysis

1. Create a data table or computer spreadsheet with the following headings:

Predicted Population Growth from 2001 to 2011 in Selected Countries

Country	Annual per capita growth rate (cgr)	Population size (N) at one-year intervals										
		2001	2002	2003	2004	2005	2006	2007	2008	2009	2010	2011

2. The table of demographic information on this page shows the total population size and the number of births and deaths that occur annually per 1000 people in different populations. In other words, the table shows birth and death *rates* for each population. Subtract the deaths per 1000 individuals from the births per 1000

individuals each year to calculate the annual per capita growth rate (cgr) for each population:

$$cgr = \frac{b}{1000} - \frac{d}{1000}$$

Note that this estimate of cgr does not take into account emigration or immigration.

3. Use Canada's 2001 population size and annual cgr to calculate the predicted population size for 2002:

$$N_{(\text{Canada in 2002})} = N_{(\text{Canada in 2001})} + (cgr)(N_{(\text{Canada in 2001})})$$
$$= (1 + cgr)(N_{(\text{Canada in 2001})})$$
$$= (1 + cgr)(32.2 \times 10^6)$$

Then use Canada's 2002 population size and annual cgr to calculate the predicted population size for 2003. Repeat this step for the rest of the years listed in your data table.

4. Repeat the calculations in step 3 for each country listed in your data table.

5. Using a full sheet of arithmetic graph paper (or a computer graphing program), graph the size of Canada's population from 2001 through 2011. This graph is a hypothetical population growth curve for Canada for 2001 through 2011. Remember to label each axis and include a title for your graph.

6. Graph population growth curves for the six other countries listed in your data table. You can use the same piece of graph paper (or plot area) for all the growth curves, as long as you use a different symbol or colour for each growth curve and provide a legend.

7. Compare the steepness of the different growth curves. Describe how annual cgr affects the steepness of a growth curve.

8. Describe the effect of a population's initial size on the steepness of its growth curve.

9. Why is the annual cgr negative for some populations? Describe the growth curve for a population with a negative cgr.

10. Based on your graph, which populations are currently undergoing exponential growth?

11. Based on your graph, for which populations is the growth rate (gr) slowing? (Recall that $gr = \frac{\Delta N}{\Delta t}$.)

12. Classify the countries in your data table into countries that you would consider to be more industrialized and countries that you would consider to be less industrialized. Compare the growth curves that are typical of each group. Explain the differences between the two types of curves.

though slower, growth rate means that a population will still grow, just not as quickly as it used to. You have also seen that per capita growth rates (*cgr*) vary among countries. What factors account for these differences?

Age pyramids are tools that demographers use to help them assess a population's potential for growth (Figure 20.24). An age pyramid shows the percent of males (on the left) and the percent of females (on the right) in different age categories (usually five-year intervals). Thus, an age pyramid can be used to see the proportion of a population in each of the following three stages of development: the pre-reproductive stage (0 to 14 years), the reproductive stage (14 to 44 years), and the post-reproductive stage (45 years and older).

An upright triangle-shaped age pyramid indicates that there are more births than deaths in the population, and that the population is therefore growing rapidly. The age pyramid for the Democratic Republic of Congo, for example, shows that the population was growing rapidly in 2000 (Figure 20.23). Because a large proportion of this population is young, the population will increase substantially when the current youth reach their reproductive years and have children of their own.

A rectangle-shaped pyramid represents a stable population. As you can see in the age pyramid for Sweden in 2000, a stable population has roughly the same proportion of people in each stage of development, with the number of births roughly equal to the number of deaths. An inverted triangle-shaped pyramid indicates that the population is declining, as in Germany in 2000.

• • •

30 What is an age pyramid?

31 Describe the structure of an age pyramid.

• • •

What Does Our Future Hold?

Given that age structure is a key predictor of a population's potential for growth, what are the implications for the global human population? The global human population doubled in the last half of the twentieth century. Most likely, this will not happen again over the course of a human life span. The twenty-first century will mark the first time that the elderly will out number the youth of the world. The global birth rate is expected to fall from 2.1 percent to 1.1 percent—the first time that it will drop because people are choosing to

Figure 20.23 Age pyramids for the Democratic Republic of Congo, Sweden, and Germany in 2000. Predicted per capita growth rates based on age pyramids do not take into account emigration and immigration.

Three patterns of population change, 2000

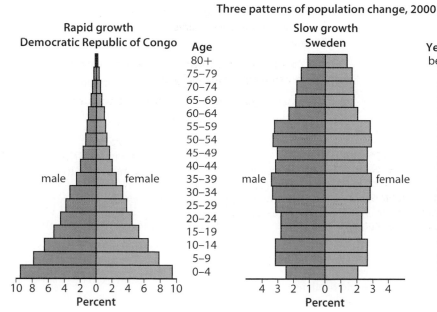

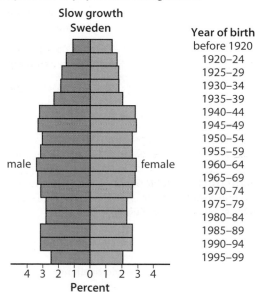

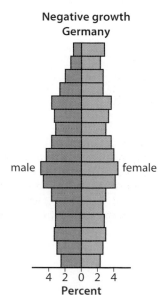

BiologyFile

Web Link
How quickly is the global population growing? Check out a world population clock on the Internet. On average, by how much does the global population increase in one day? How about in one minute?

www.albertabiology.ca
WWW

have fewer children. The high prevalence of HIV/AIDS in some populations means that fewer children are living to adulthood and more adults are dying at a younger age, which will decrease the growth rate of these populations.

Furthermore, in the twenty-first century, the number of people living in urban areas will outnumber the number of people living in rural areas for the first time. How will this affect Earth's carrying capacity?

Based on population growth rates and age structures, the state of the environment, and possible technological developments, many demographers predict that the global human population will level off at 9 billion, although estimates range from 7 billion to 14 billion (Figure 20.24).

Earth's Carrying Capacity

Advances in construction, medicine, sanitation, and agriculture have increased Earth's carrying capacity for the human population. In addition, some forms of biotechnology have improved crop yields, without taking up more space. Even so, scientists estimate that the world

Human population growth projections to 3000 C.E.

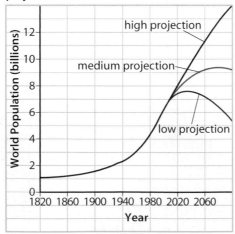

Figure 20.24 In 2005, the per capita growth rate of the global human population was 0.012. Many demographers predict that the population of the world will stabilize at 9 billion people, but not all agree. Depending on how other demographers interpret variables such as birth rate and death rate, predictions vary, as shown in this graph.

produces enough food to feed 10 billion people a vegetarian diet. Not all people are vegetarians, however. Furthermore, cities will have to expand to accommodate people moving from rural areas, and this may reduce the amount of land that is available for agriculture.

To estimate Earth's carrying capacity, many things must be considered. Like the International Space Station, Earth is a closed system. As well as needing resources, we will need effective ways to deal with garbage, sewage, and air pollution. How will the environment be affected by increasing amounts of waste and pollutants entering waterways from larger, denser populations? Will levels of carbon dioxide continue to rise, or will new technologies and habits help us limit the use of fossil fuels? Will countries share their resources to reduce poverty and combat disease? As the density of the human population increases, will we be more susceptible to pandemics, such as influenza?

Perhaps there are too many unanswered questions to be able to determine what the carrying capacity of the world actually is, and whether or not this carrying capacity has been reached. Most likely, different regions will have different limits to growth. No population—human or non-human—can act in isolation, however. We all share, and are connected to, the same biosphere.

Section 20.3 Summary

- Populations and the ecological communities they comprise change over time as a result of natural causes and human activities.
- Climate change, over-harvesting, pollution, and the introduction of invasive species can greatly affect populations.
- Sustainability is the concept of living in a way that meets our needs without compromising the ability of future generations to meet their needs or the health of the biosphere. The practice of

sustainability includes social, economic, and environmental considerations.

- For most of human history, the global human population was stable. Since the Industrial Revolution, improved living conditions have resulted in longer life expectancies and decreased infant mortality. The global human population has grown exponentially as a result.

- Different human populations have different age structures, as shown by age pyramids. Populations with more youth than older people are expected to grow more quickly than populations with fewer youth than older people, or the same number of youth and older people.

- Because people are having fewer children than they used to, the rate of growth in human populations is no longer exponential. Some populations are still growing, however.

- In 2005, the global human population was over 6 billion.

- The carrying capacity of Earth for the human population will be influenced by many factors. Demographers predict that Earth may be able to support from 7 to 14 billion people.

Section 20.3 Review

1. What limiting factor, in your opinion, will have the most influence on slowing down the population growth of the world? Justify your choice.

2. In 2005, the population of Brazil was 184.7 million. The population of Turkey was 72.9 million. If both countries have a per capita growth rate of 1.4 percent, which country would experience the largest impact from a reduction in *cgr*? Justify your answer.

3. Explain why the global human population may be more susceptible to a pandemic, such as avian flu, as the population increases in size.

4. Examine the age pyramids shown below.

   a) Describe the shape of the age pyramid for each country.

   b) For each country, which would be greater—the birth rate or the death rate? Explain your answer.

   c) Explain how the age structure of each population would affect the population's size over time.

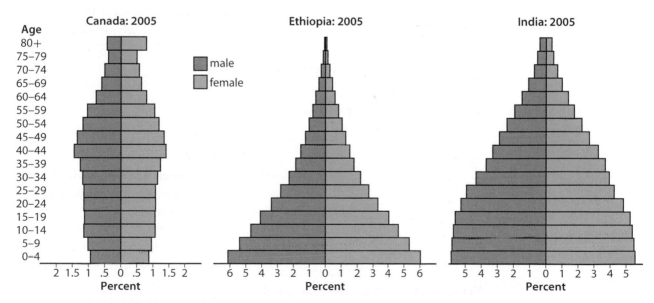

Helping Hippos and Humans

For decades, humans and hippos had been on a collision course along a stretch of the Black Volta River in the Wechiau Traditional Area in Ghana, West Africa. Hippos had long used the winding river system as a place to raise their young, but their grazing grounds had been eroded and depleted as humans encroached upon the banks of the river with farming and fishing. As well, humans were killing hippos, either for the meat or because the hippos were wrecking fishing nets or canoes. The solution to the problem had less to do with technology than with Wechiau residents changing the way they thought about and interacted with their natural environment. They discovered that by accommodating the needs of the hippos and respecting the hippos' habitat, they would be helping to safeguard their own future.

Community-Run Conservation

The Wechiau area along the Black Volta River is home to the second largest hippo population in Ghana. In the early 1990s, the Ghanaian government proposed that a national reserve should be set up to protect the Wechiau hippos. The traditional authority, the local governing body in the area, rejected this idea. They feared that a national reserve, run from outside the community, would alienate their people from the land. Following talks between Wechiau chiefs and sub-chiefs of the traditional authority and representatives from the Nature Conservation Research Centre (a Ghanaian non-governmental organization that manages ecological projects in Ghana), an agreement was made to establish a hippo sanctuary.

According to the agreement, the sanctuary would be community-owned and operated and would encourage *ecotourism*, which incorporates the practice of sustainability into tourism. Profits would flow back to the villages in the area. Wechiau residents would learn about the importance of biodiversity and how biodiversity relates to their own survival. In early 1999, the year the sanctuary was established, the chief of Wechiau and his elders set up a buffer zone between the hippos and humans by declaring that all human activities other than fishing were prohibited within 2 km of the river along the length of the sanctuary area.

Saving Hippos, Sustaining Humans

The Wechiau Community Hippo Sanctuary (WCHS) is unique for several reasons. It is a community initiative with no central government involvement. It protects about 24 hippos, as well as other wildlife, in a core 40 km² area along the Black Volta River. Initially, the sanctuary was completely funded through subsidies and financial support from organizations such as the Calgary Zoo's Conservation Outreach Department. Starting in 2004, however, monthly tourist revenue has paid all operating costs, including local staff salaries and maintenance costs for overnight tourist lodges and a visitors' centre. Proceeds from the WCHS have also significantly benefited the 22 villages in the surrounding area, helping to pay the costs of building new schools and drilling new boreholes for fresh drinking water. Although many Wechiau residents continue to struggle daily to survive, they are committed to the vision of even greater long-term benefits with sustainability. The WCHS has been so successful that other communities in Ghana are looking to it as a model for protecting their endangered species.

• • •

1. Working toward long-term sustainability is not just about protecting the environment. It is also about balancing economic, social, and environmental goals. What are some of the goals that the WCHS helps people meet?

2. Recognizing the legitimacy of the local traditional authority in Wechiau has been the key to the sanctuary's success so far. What are the advantages of involving local communities in conservation projects, instead of handing habitats over to private companies or state governments?

3. The Calgary Zoo continues to support the WCHS in many ways, including providing an on-site wildlife education consultant, who helps to facilitate the sanctuary's progress. What other international conservation projects is the zoo involved in? Why is the zoo's work important to Canadians?

Population density is defined as the number of individuals living in a given area or volume over a specific time frame: $D_p = \dfrac{N}{A}$ or $D_p = \dfrac{N}{V}$. Interspecific and intraspecific interactions, as well as the distribution of resources within a habitat influence how individuals are dispersed within it. Three theoretical distribution patterns of individuals within a habitat are random, uniform, and clumped.

Four major processes that cause changes in population size are the number of births, immigration, the number of deaths, and emigration: $\Delta N = (b + i) - (d + e)$. The rate at which the size of a population changes over a given time interval can be described using the growth rate equation: $gr = \dfrac{\Delta N}{\Delta t}$. Per capita growth rate (cgr) describes the change in the number of individuals of a population over a given time interval in terms of rate of change per individual: $cgr = \dfrac{\Delta N}{N}$ or $cgr = \dfrac{N_{final} - N}{N}$.

Environmental resistance limits the birth rate or increases the death rate in a population. Given unlimited resources and ideal living conditions, the highest possible cgr for a population is its biotic potential (r). The carrying capacity (K) of a habitat is the maximum number of individuals that the habitat can support due to density-dependent limiting factors.

Boom or bust cycles of population growth in a changeable environment are characteristic of populations with r-selected strategies. In contrast, K-selected populations live close to the carrying capacity of their habitats.

Density-dependent and density-independent factors as well as intraspecific and interspecific competition affect a given population. Producer-consumer interactions can affect the growth of the consumer or the producer population, or both. Co-evolution may result in symbiosis. Symbiotic relationships include mutualism, commensalism, and parasitism.

Natural causes and human activities result in changes in populations and, thus, in ecological communities. Communities change over time as a result of ecological succession.

Sustainability involves meeting our social, economic, and environmental needs so that future generations can meet their needs without harming the biosphere.

Chapter 20 Graphic Organizer

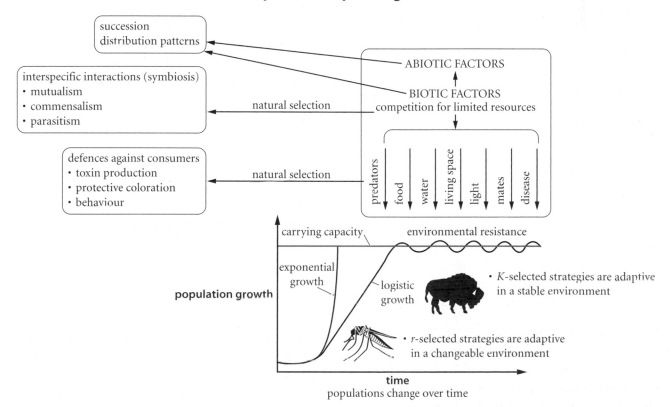

populations change over time

Understanding Concepts

1. Species of grasshopper that belong to the subfamily Melanoplinae are found in vast numbers across North America. About 40 species can be found in the Canadian Prairies. List three factors that might limit the exponential growth rate of populations of these species.

2. Describe a real-life example of a situation in which interspecific competition limits the population size and growth of a species.

3. Identify the four main determinants of population size.

4. Six different one-drop samples in a *Paramecium* sp. population had the following numbers of organisms: 4, 6, 5, 3, 6, and 6. If 20 drops represent 1 mL of solution, and the volume of the solution is 40 mL, calculate the size of the population.

5. For the biotic potential (*r*) of a population to be greater than zero, what has to be true about the birth rate and death rate of the population? Assume that there is no immigration or emigration.

6. *Helicobacter pylori* is a bacterium that lives in the human stomach. Research has shown that this bacterium can cause stomach ulcers. Research has also shown that the presence of this bacterium in the stomach can prevent the development of esophageal cancer and acid reflux in some individuals. Identify the two types of symbiotic relationships that are described here. Explain your reasoning.

7. A population of rattlesnakes contains 1000 individuals. During the year, there are 106 births, 53 deaths, 42 immigrations, and 15 emigrations. Calculate the per capita growth rate for the year.

8. The first species to invade an area and start the process of succession are usually *r*-selected. List the reproductive strategies of *r*-selected species that make them ideal candidates for this role. Explain your reasoning.

9. Identify the three theoretical distribution patterns for populations. What two factors influence the patterns of distribution?

10. In general terms, how does interspecific competition affect the growth of populations?

11. How might predation or parasitism explain why population density does not increase indefinitely?

12. In what way is the relationship between a population of herbivores and the plants they eat similar to the relationship between a predator population and a prey population?

Applying Concepts

13. a) Describe the shape of the age pyramid for a country with fewer young people than seniors.

b) Predict what will happen to the size of the population over time. Justify your prediction.

14. Describe the relationships among biotic potential, environmental resistance, and carrying capacity in a short paragraph.

15. Calculate the size of a population of annual plants five years in the future if the population starts with 100 plants and the growth rate is 10 plants per year. Assume that no immigration or emigration is occurring.

16. Suppose that you have just been hired to teach Grade 6 at a local school. Design an activity you could use to teach your students about factors that affect population growth in different environments.

17. Although all populations eventually face environmental resistance to continued growth, the contribution of abiotic and biotic factors to this resistance may vary from species to species. Compare a bacterium (such as *E. coli*), a plant (such as a type of tree), and a mammal (such as the snowshoe hare or the black bear) with respect to the type of factors that typically limit the growth of their populations.

18. In South Africa, some plants have co-evolved with ants that disperse their seeds. The seeds are produced with a little food package attached. The ants bring the seeds back to their nest, eat the food package and leave the seeds in the nest or discard them with their waste in a manner that protects the seeds from fire and seed-eating organisms. An invasion of another species of ants from Argentina is competing with these ants. They eat the food packages from the larger seeds only and drop the seeds on the ground, where they are exposed to fire and seed-eating organisms.

a) Identify the symbiotic relationship between the plant and the South African ants. Explain.

b) Identify the type of relationship that exists between
  • the Argentine ant and the plant
  • the Argentine ant and the South African ant, with respect to large seeds
  • the Argentine ant and the South African ant, with respect to small seeds

c) If this situation continues, predict how the plant population might evolve. Justify your prediction, with reference to changes in allele frequencies.

19. *Caulerpa taxifolia* is an invasive species of alga that is spreading rapidly along the floor of the Mediterranean Sea. Efforts to reduce or control this species are being researched. The area supports a species of mollusk in low numbers, which feeds slowly on the alga. The plan is to boost the population of this mollusk with the hope that it will reduce the alga population. Scientists believe that there will be less risk in controlling the alga with a natural population of mollusk, rather than bringing in an introduced population. What is the main danger in boosting the numbers of a native species in order to control the alga? Explain your answer.

20. An environment in the early stages of primary succession differs significantly from the same environment in the later stages. In your notebook, prepare a table like the one below. Use the words "low" and "high" to compare the difference expected in both environments.

Comparison of Early and Late Stages of Succession

Characteristic	Early succession	Late succession
amount of available light		
biodiversity		
plant biomass		
interspecific competition		
intraspecific competition		

Making Connections

21. Although China contains only about 7 percent of Earth's arable land, its population was approximately 1.25 billion in 2001—roughly 20 percent of the total human population. Early in the 1970s, the Chinese government realized that the growth rate of China's population was unsustainable and took measures to reduce it. The Chinese government instituted a policy that limited the vast majority of families to only one child and strictly enforced the policy. Describe the benefits and drawbacks of the one-child policy.

22. Forest tent caterpillars (*Malacosoma disstria*) are common throughout North America. In Alberta, they are found mainly in the boreal forest, aspen parkland, and Rocky Mountains. While they feed on a variety of host plants, they most commonly consume leaves of the trembling aspen. A study of the forest tent caterpillar population was conducted in an Alberta forest. Two areas, a fragmented forest and a continuous forest, were sampled at five different sites. The data obtained is presented in the table below.

Caterpillar Population Density in Two Areas of a Forest

Site	Population density in fragmented forest (caterpillars per leaf)	Population density in continuous forest (caterpillars per leaf)
A	5	8
B	12	6
C	8	10
D	4	9
E	11	3

a) Calculate the average density (caterpillars per leaf) of the caterpillar population in both areas.

b) If a tree has about 2000 leaves, determine the size of the caterpillar population on a tree in both forest samples.

c) What assumption did you make regarding the distribution of caterpillars in a tree to calculate the answer to part (b)?

d) Some of the caterpillars that were collected were brought back to the laboratory. Upon analysis, scientists discovered that flies of the families Tachinidae and Sarchophagidae had infected the caterpillars. Identify the population interaction taking place between the flies and the caterpillars.

e) The table below indicates the number of infected caterpillars in samples from each area. Calculate the average infection rate of the caterpillars for each area.

Numbers of Infected Caterpillars in Two Areas of a Forest

Sample size	Number infected in fragmented forest samples	Sample size	Number infected in continuous forest samples
10	3	6	2
12	2	8	3
8	2	8	4
12	4	12	6

f) Based on your answer to part (b), what reasonable conclusion can you make about the effect of the flies on the caterpillar populations in both areas?

g) Is this the only possible explanation for the size differences between the caterpillar populations in the two areas? Justify your answer.

h) Forest tent caterpillars have been present in forested areas for a long time. A heavy infestation tends to occur every 6 to 16 years, and severe infestations can last from 2 to 4 years. These infestations can cause an ecological disturbance in a forested area. What type of succession would take place after a disturbance caused by an infestation of forest tent caterpillars?

Career Focus: Ask a Science Journalist

Science journalist Cheryl Croucher has a passion for helping Albertans understand scientific and environmental issues that require public decisions. In the 1990s, she was CBC Radio's first-ever environment commentator. In 2001, she started her Innovation Alberta Omnimedia Web site, where she has made available hundreds of science-related radio programs, broadcast on CKUA, as both audio files and transcripts. Based in Edmonton, she interviews scientists across Alberta.

Q **What do you, as a science communicator, see as the biggest obstacle to the public's understanding of science?**

People think, "Let's see what the scientists say, because they'll help us make the decisions." Because we don't really understand the scientific method, we get confused when they don't have a black-and-white answer. They're asking more *questions*! One of my objectives is to help people become informed decision-makers so that when we do face issues, we have a better understanding of the bigger picture, and then scientists can help us make decisions.

Q **How did you become a science journalist?**

I was never a science student or keenly interested in science. However, when I started doing my consumer commentaries on CBC, by about 1987, probably half were dealing with environmental issues. Then I met people through the stories I was doing who were taking the scientific and technological approach to finding solutions.

Q **Why did you found Innovation Alberta? What audience are you trying to reach?**

I want to help people become informed decision-makers. Let's not make scientists gods; let's understand where they fit into the scheme of things.

Q **You sometimes present your audience with tough issues. For example, one of your programs addressed the diminishing woodland caribou population. You reported that some herds had decreased by forty percent. It seems that in the new forests that grow following deforestation, caribou populations are reduced, while deer populations explode. Scientists have recommended killing deer, whose populations have exploded, to restore a diverse balance.**

People will say, "Oh, you can't kill those deer, they're so *cute*!" But if you can take people through the process, it's easier for them to come to terms with what has to be done. It's a balancing act. You're dealing with trade-offs.

Q **An additional tough issue is that scientists think that conservation efforts should focus on healthy caribou herds. But concerned listeners might be more motivated to help the most distressed herds. Won't many listeners find this a hard choice?**

If you can take people through the process, it's easier for them to come to terms with what has to be done and the implications. A lot of it is getting rid of the myths and making an *informed* decision.

Q **In the past, there has been a lot of contention between the forestry industry and Aboriginal peoples. Have you seen any growth in mutual respect over the years?**

There has actually been tremendous progress. First of all, there is now recognition that traditional knowledge is legitimate; it's something we can also incorporate into Western science. The Aboriginal people are becoming very vocal and involved, saying "You have to pay attention; we *do* have something to contribute. If you're a hunter and gatherer, you need to *know about* the animals you are hunting." I have watched the change over time from "We're better than you" (on both sides) to an understanding that we each have something to contribute.

Q **Overall, have you seen any change over time in public attitudes on environmental issues?**

I think people are much more aware now. A lot of programs have become just part of our daily life, like recycling and water conservation. These things change public attitudes bit by bit.

Q **If a young person wanted to go into science journalism, what advice would you give?**

The key to being a good science journalist is really being a good journalist. As a journalist, you ask questions, you observe, you gather information, and you help put it into perspective for people.

742 MHR • Unit 8 Population and Community Dynamics

Other Careers Related to Science Communications

Radio/TV Broadcaster Journalists who work in electronic media develop personal presentation skills, as well as research and writing skills. In addition to higher education, they learn on the job by volunteering at university radio stations and cable television programs. Journalism schools look for applicants, for both print and broadcast media training, who have already shown an interest in journalism. There is a growing demand for broadcasters who can present science issues effectively.

Web Site Designer/Developer Graphic artists build web sites that inform and entertain, using a variety of techniques. Courses in graphic arts and web design are offered at universities and community colleges across Canada. Students often begin by developing a portfolio of artwork or web sites in high school. The portfolio enables a university or college to assess the student's potential. Many cutting-edge web sites focus on presenting science to the public.

Science Teacher Science teachers usually begin their careers by choosing mathematics and science subjects in high school, and majoring in a science subject at a university. Then they take teacher training courses, which include theoretical and practical components. Helping students understand science issues can be a very rewarding career.

Wildlife Biologist Wildlife biologists play a critical role in conservation policy by determining the facts about changes in native animal populations, and by linking these facts to either natural cycles or newly introduced causes. Usually, a wildlife biologist focusses on sciences in high school and continues to study sciences at university, with a focus on animal biology.

Forest Science Biologist The management of valuable forest resources requires a forest science biologist to have an extensive knowledge of trees and their habitats. Usually, a forest science biologist focusses on sciences in high school, and then continues to study sciences at university, with a focus on plant biology.

Go Further...

1. Are decisions about animal population management based strictly on numbers? What other factors might play a role in public decision making?

2. How might traditional Aboriginal knowledge of Alberta's forest ecology help scientists understand it better?

3. Why does the public need to understand the scientific method in order to make informed decisions about environmental policy?

Understanding Concepts

1. In a population of grey and white pigeons (*Columba* sp.), the phenotype frequency for white feather colour is the same as the genotype frequency for the *bb* genotype. This is because white feather colour is a recessive trait. The genotype frequencies for the population are 81.0 percent *BB*, 18.0 percent *Bb*, and 1.00 percent *bb*. Determine the phenotype frequency (as a percentage) for grey feathers.

2. If 16 percent of individuals in a population have attached ear lobes, a recessive trait in humans, calculate the frequency of the dominant allele. Assume the population is at genetic equilibrium.

3. Is a population that is at genetic equilibrium evolving? Given reasons to support your answer.

4. Define intraspecific competition. Explain how insects reduce intraspecific competition between adults and offspring.

5. Distinguish between the variables q and q^2 in the Hardy-Weinberg equation.

6. Explain why the effects of genetic drift are more significant in small populations than in large ones.

7. Ethion is an insecticide that kills leaf-eating insects such as mites. A species of mite develops a mutation over time that allows it to survive in the presence of ethion. Is this mutation an example of microevolution? Explain your answer.

8. Describe the relationship between mutation and natural selection.

9. The elaborate tail of the peacock (*Pavo cristatus*) is approximately 120 cm to 150 cm long, while the tail of the peahen is quite short. The long tail reduces the male bird's ability to maneuver and fly and makes him more conspicuous to predators. Suggest at least one reason why this cumbersome structure has not been eliminated by natural selection.

10. The yield of a field of wheat or canola increases when herbicides are used to control the growth of weeds.
   a) Identify the population interaction between the crop and the weeds.
   b) Explain why the yield increases when the weed population is controlled.

11. In studying a population of lizards, scientists sampled 47 sections of a habitat. Each section was 29 km². It was found that the density of the lizards was $\frac{1}{3.8 \text{ km}^2}$.
   a) Calculate the size of the lizard population living in the area.
   b) What assumption did you make regarding the distribution of this population throughout its habitat when calculating your results?

12. Identify the distribution pattern illustrated in the following examples:
   a) an apple orchard
   b) plants that reproduce asexually by sending out runners from the parent
   c) territorial birds of prey
   d) an adult mosquito population
   e) *Homo sapiens*

13. Identify the population interaction in each of the following examples.
   a) The Nile crocodile (*Crocodylus niloticus*) opens its mouth, and the crocodile bird (*Pluvianus aegyptius*) eats the leeches that are attached to its gums and tongue.
   b) Spanish moss (*Tillandsia usneoides*) is an epiphyte, a plant that lacks roots and attaches to the branches of trees for support. The epiphyte obtains all its needs for photosynthesis from the air. The supporting plant is unharmed.
   c) Tiny hookworm larvae penetrate the skin between the toes of a human and migrate to the lungs where they mature. The adults then are coughed up and enter the digestive tract where they drill tiny holes in the intestine and digest human blood for nutrition.
   d) Some insects have shapes that resemble bird droppings. Some have swellings on their legs that look like seeds stuck in the bird droppings.
   e) African sleeping sickness is caused by a unicellular organism, *Trypansoma* sp., which obtains nutrients from its host's blood. It is transferred to humans when they are bitten by an infected Tsetse fly (*Glossina* sp.).
   f) The Torsalo fly (*Dermatobia hominis*) catches insects such as mosquitoes and glues their eggs to the underside of their bodies. When the mosquitoes bite a human or other mammal, the heat from the skin causes rapid development of the eggs into larvae. The larvae penetrate the skin where they form a cyst or boil and feast on the mammal's blood as they mature.

14. The monarch butterfly is tolerant to the bitter chemicals found in the milkweed plant. Monarch caterpillars feed on the milkweed leaves, storing bitter chemicals from the host plant, which causes them to taste terrible and provides monarch butterflies with protection from predators, such as birds. The viceroy butterfly has the same coloration as the monarch butterfly. What kind of mimicry would the viceroy butterfly be exhibiting if it were
a) poisonous?
b) not poisonous?

15. Some species of sponges secrete chemicals that inhibit the growth of other sponges in the immediate area. What type of distribution would you expect to find in areas where this process is occurring? Explain.

16. How can you account for the fact that, in North America, populations of large animals such as bears, moose, and deer are more affected by a loss of habitat than smaller animals such as gophers and squirrels?

17. Give an example of succession and describe two biotic and abiotic factors that change during this process.

18. Describe the age pyramid representing a stable population where there is roughly the same proportion of people in each stage of development.

Applying Concepts

19. If a population has two alleles for a particular locus, *B* and *b*, and if the allele frequency of *B* is 0.70, what percentage of the next generation is expected to be heterozygous for this trait, if the population is at genetic equilibrium?

20. If 1 in 10 000 babies is born with albinism, a recessive trait in humans, calculate the frequency of:
a) the recessive allele
b) the dominant allele
c) the heterozygotes in the population

21. The presence of freckles is a dominant trait in humans. Scientists were studying a population in which half of the individuals had the recessive trait. Calculate the frequency of the freckle allele (*F*) that would lead to these results.

22. A student sampled 100 domestic cats (*Felis catus*) from a population of which 84 had black fur and 16 had white fur. In this species, black fur colour is dominant to white fur.
a) Determine the frequency of each allele in the population.
b) What percentage of the population is expected to be heterozygous for this trait?

23. Tay-Sachs disease causes severe developmental and mental disabilities that occur four to eight months after birth. The disease is due to inheritance of a recessive allele and is especially prevalent in the Ashkenazi (European) Jewish community, affecting 1 out of every 2500 babies.
a) Determine the frequency of this allele in the Ashkenazi Jewish population.
b) What proportion of the Ashkenazi Jewish population is expected to be a carrier for this trait?

24. In a class of 36 students tested for the ability to roll their tongues, 12 were found to be non-rollers, a recessive trait.
a) Determine the frequency of each allele in this population.
b) How many of the 24 tongue rollers would you expect to be heterozygous?

25. In grey squirrels, dark coat colour is dominant to light coat colour. The study of a population of squirrels in a city over a five-year period produced the following results:

Year	Number of dark-coloured squirrels	Number of light-coloured squirrels
1	152	24
2	132	20
3	177	27
4	98	14
5	49	7

a) Calculate the frequency of each allele and genotype in the population for year 1 and year 5 of the study.
b) Is this population evolving? Explain.
c) Identify three environmental conditions that could favour the selection of one genotype or phenotype in the squirrel population.
d) Would the data for this study have been any different if light-coloured fur was dominant to black? Explain.

26. The following table provides estimations of the global population from 1970 to 2000.

Estimated Global Population 1970–2000

Year	Estimated global population (in millions)
1970	3699
1980	4440
1990	5280
2000	6068

   a) Calculate the per capita growth rate for each of the decades.

   b) Describe the trend in the per capita growth rate of the human population during this time period.

   c) In 2005, the per capita growth rate for the human population was 0.012. Why might the population still increase substantially even though the per capita growth rate has decreased?

   d) Identify three limiting factors that you think might slow down the growth of the human population.

27. The Loggerhead Shrike (*Lanius ludovicianus*) is considered by the Committee on the Status of Endangered Wildlife in Canada to be of "special concern" in Alberta. Within a study area in 1998, 232 shrikes were observed at 144 locations. Over the next five years, 52 new shrikes were born and 116 died or left the area.

   a) Calculate the growth rate of this shrike population during the study period.

   b) How large was the shrike population in 2003?

28. A field has an area of 1 ha (100 m × 100 m). If sunflower plants (*Helianthus annuus*) produce the highest number of seeds at a density of 9 plants/m², calculate the maximum number of plants that can grow in this field to allow production of the most seeds. Identify four limiting factors that could cause decreased production in the plants, should the density increase.

29. A population of 812 gophers is growing exponentially in a field. The population has a per capita growth rate of 0.30.

   a) What will the size of this population be after one year?

   b) After two years?

   c) Identify four factors that would limit the growth rate of this population as it reaches the carrying capacity of the environment.

   d) Classify these factors as density-dependent or density-independent.

30. A study of a population of snails in a 5 m² area produced the following results over a seven-year period.

Comparison of Snail Density over a Seven-year Period

Year of Study	Density (snails/m²)
1	17.5
2	70.2
3	108.9
4	115.7
5	129
6	143.8
7	87.7

   a) Graph the results for density versus time.

   b) Calculate the per capita growth rate between year 1 and year 3 of the study.

   c) Determine the size of the population in year six.

   d) List and explain three factors that might have caused a decrease in the population density in the last year.

Making Connections

31. The common fruit fly, *Drosophilia melanogaster*, has a life cycle of 14 days. In this species, long wing (*L*) is dominant to vestigial or short wing (*l*). Individuals with short wings are unable to fly. In culture, they are found walking on the medium at the bottom of the container where the larvae grow. Equal numbers of homozygous long and short wing flies were placed in a large container with an adequate food supply to start a population. Flies were counted every two weeks for a period of three months, and the frequency of each allele in the population was determined. The following data were obtained.

Change in frequency over time of the long wing (*L*) and short wing (*l*) alleles in *Drosophila melanogaster*

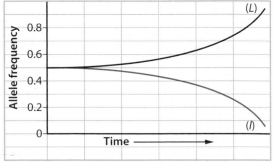

   a) Describe what is happening to the frequency of each allele in the population during this time.

   b) Use your understanding of the Hardy-Weinberg model to explain the data.

c) If this experiment were to continue for a full year, do you think the frequency of the short wing allele (*l*) will ever become 0? Explain your reasoning.

32. The graph below shows the relationship between net productivity (A), biomass (B), and species diversity (C) as succession in an area takes place over time. The net productivity is the amount of energy available to the next trophic level.

Relationship between net productivity (A), biomass (B), and diversity (C) during stages of succession

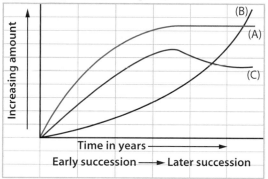

a) Describe how each factor changes as succession occurs.

b) Explain these results.

33. Populations of many of the species that are considered to be at risk (threatened or endangered) are *K*-selected compared to other populations. Give two reasons why such species might be more at risk, explaining your reasoning.

34. As habitats around the world are lost, many species become extinct before we have even discovered them. What advantages are provided by high levels of species diversity, genetic diversity, and ecosystem diversity? In other words, what is the value of biodiversity? How might ecologists or the citizens of countries with high levels of biodiversity that are rapidly being lost use this "value" to preserve habitats and species? Answer this question in the form of a short essay, perhaps focussing on one province, country, or region of the world.

35. Examine the age pyramids shown below.
a) Predict which population will grow the fastest over time. Justify your response.
b) How much would a decrease in the birth rate affect the growth rate of each of the populations? Explain your answer.
c) Suggest how the age structure of each population could affect the economic well-being of each country.
d) Explain how the spread of HIV could affect the growth rate of Nigeria's population (compared to your prediction in part (a)).

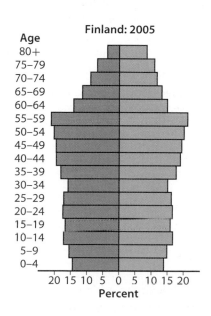

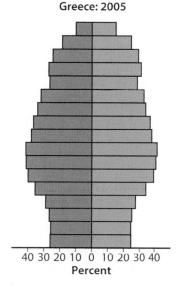

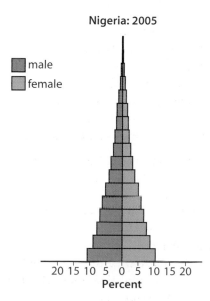

Measurement in Science

Measurements are so much a part of your life that you likely take them for granted. Your clothing is sized, the mass of your food is determined by the gram, the liquids you drink are sold in litres, and many of the items you use every day are made according to detailed specifications. The money you use to pay for any of these items is itself a measurement. The measurements for clothing, amounts of food, and currency are not standard throughout the world, however. While this inconsistency does not make it impossible to buy clothing in Asia, use European tools, or pay in South American currency, the same inconsistency in science would make it almost impossible for scientists to share information, replicate findings, and collaborate on research. In order to avoid this problem, scientists have developed globally agreed-upon standards for measurement, and for recording and calculating data. These are the standards that you will use throughout this science program. This appendix reviews units of measurement, significant digits, and scientific notation so you can use these standard tools for designing and performing scientific experiments and communicating your findings.

Is the Measurement Accurate or Is It Precise?

Before you review the standard conventions used in this text, consider how scientists characterize the measurements they take. In everyday speech, it is acceptable to use the terms "accuracy" and "precision" to mean the same thing. In science, however, these terms have distinctly different meanings.

Scientific *accuracy* refers to how close a given quantity is to an accepted or expected value. For example, under standard (defined) conditions of temperature and pressure, 5 mL of water has a mass of 5 g. When you measure the mass of 5 mL of water under the same conditions, you should, if you are accurate, find the mass is 5 g. Accuracy in science, therefore, involves a comparison.

Scientific *precision* refers to the exactness of your measurements. The precision of your measurements is directly related to the instruments you use to make them. While faulty instruments (for example, a balance that is not working properly) will obviously affect the precision of your measurements, the calibration of the instruments you use is the most influential factor. For example, a ruler calibrated in millimetres will allow you to make more precise measurements than one that shows only centimetres.

Precision can also refer to the closeness of a series of data points. Data that are close to one another are said to be precise. There is no guarantee, however, that the data are accurate until a comparison with an accepted value is made.

Units of Measurement

When you take measurements for scientific purposes, you use the International System of Measurement (commonly know as SI, from the French for *Système international d'unités*). SI includes the metric system and other standard units, symbols, and prefixes reviewed below.

In SI, the base units include the metre, the kilogram, and the second. The size of any particular unit can be determined by the prefix used with the base unit. Larger and smaller units of measurement can be obtained by either dividing or multiplying the base unit by a multiple of 10.

For example, the prefix *kilo-* means multiplied by 1000. So, one kilogram is equivalent to 1000 grams:

$$1 \text{ kg} = 1000 \text{ g}$$

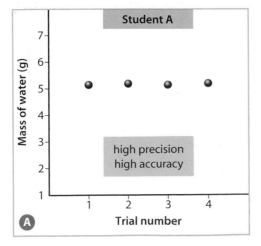

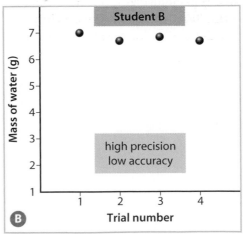

The prefix *milli-* means divided by 1000. So, one milligram is equivalent to one thousandth of a gram:

$$1 \text{ mg} = \frac{1}{1000} \text{ g}$$

Table A.1 shows the most commonly used metric prefixes. Table A.2 shows some common metric quantities, units, and symbols.

Table A.1 Metric Prefixes

Prefix	Symbol	Relationship to the base unit
giga-	G	$10^9 = 1\ 000\ 000\ 000$
mega-	M	$10^6 = 1\ 000\ 000$
kilo-	k	$10^3 = 1\ 000$
hecto-	h	$10^2 = 100$
deca-	da	$10^1 = 10$
–	–	$10^0 = 1$
deci-	d	$10^{-1} = 0.1$
centi-	c	$10^{-2} = 0.01$
milli-	m	$10^{-3} = 0.001$
micro-	μ	$10^{-6} = 0.000\ 001$
nano-	n	$10^{-9} = 0.000\ 000\ 001$

Significant Digits

In many of the biology experiments that you conduct, you will be making measurements. All measurements involve uncertainty. One source of this uncertainty is the measuring device itself. Another source is your ability to perceive and interpret a reading. You cannot, in fact, measure anything with complete certainty. The last (farthest-right) digit in any measurement is always an estimate.

The digits that you record when you measure something are significant digits. *Significant digits* include the digits that you are certain about and a final uncertain digit that you estimate. For example, 4.28 g has three significant digits. The first two digits, the 4 and the 2, are certain. The last digit, the 8, is an estimate. Therefore, it is uncertain. The value 1.2 has two significant digits. The 1 is certain, and the 2 is uncertain. Table A.3 lists some rules to help you identify the number of significant digits in any value.

Table A.2 Commonly Used Metric Quantities, Units, and Symbols

Quantity	Unit	Symbol
length	nanometre	nm
	micrometre	μm
	millimetre	mm
	centimetre	cm
	metre	m
	kilometre	km
mass	gram	g
	kilogram	kg
	tonne	t
area	square metre	m^2
	square centimetre	cm^2
	hectare	ha ($10\ 000\ m^2$)
volume	cubic centimetre	cm^3
	cubic metre	m^3
	millilitre	mL
	litre	L
time	second	s
temperature	degree Celsius	°C
force	newton	N
energy	joule	J
	kilojoule*	kJ
pressure	pascal	Pa
	kilopascal**	kPa
electric current	ampere	A
quantity of electric charge	coulomb	C
frequency	hertz	Hz
power	watt	W

* Many dieticians in North America continue to measure nutritional energy in Calories, also known as kilocalories or dietetic Calories. In SI units, 1 Calorie = 4.186 kJ.

** In current North American medical practice, blood pressure is measured in millimetres of mercury, symbol mm Hg. In SI units, 1 mmHg = 0.133 kPa.

Table A.3 Rules for Determining Significant Digits

Rules	Examples
1. All non-zero numbers are significant.	7.886 has four significant digits. 19.4 has three significant digits. 527.226 992 has nine significant digits
2. All zeros that are located between two non-zero numbers are significant.	408 has three significant digits. 25 074 has five significant digits.
3. Zeros that are located to the left of a value are not significant.	0.0907 has three significant digits. They are the 9, the third zero to the right, and the 7. The function of the 0.0 at the beginning is only to locate the decimal. 0.000 000 06 has one significant digit.
4. Zeros that are located to the right of a value may or may not be significant.	22 700 may have three significant digits, or it may have five significant digits. See the box below for an explanation why.

Rule 4: Explaining Three Significant Digits

The Great Lakes contain 22 700 km^3 of water. Is there exactly this amount of water in the Great Lakes? No—22 700 km^3 is an approximate value. The actual volume could be anywhere from 22 659 km^3 to 22 749 km^3. You can use scientific notation to rewrite 22 700 as 2.270020 $\times$ 10^4 km^3. This notation shows that only three digits are significant. (See opposite for a review of scientific notation.)

Rule 4: Explaining Five Significant Digits

What if you were able to measure the volume of water in the Great Lakes? You could then verify the value of 22 700 km^3. Then all five digits (including the zeros) would be significant. Again, scientific notation enables you to show clearly the five significant digits: 2.2700 $\times$ 10^4 km^3.

Scientific Notation

Scientific notation is a method of expressing numbers that are very large or very small as exponents of the power 10. An exponent is the symbol or number denoting the power to which another number or symbol is to be raised. The exponent shows the number of repeated multiplications of the base. In 10^2, the exponent is 2 and the base is 10. Table A.4 shows the powers of 10 as numbers in standard form and in exponential form.

Table A.4 Powers of Ten in Standard and Exponential Form

	Standard form	Exponential form
ten thousands	10 000	10^4
thousands	1000	10^3
hundreds	100	10^2
tens	10	10^1
ones	1	10^0
tenths	0.1	$\frac{1}{10^1} = 10^{-1}$
hundredths	0.01	$\frac{1}{10^2} = 10^{-2}$
thousandths	0.001	$\frac{1}{10^3} = 10^{-3}$
ten thousandths	0.0001	$\frac{1}{10^4} = 10^{-4}$

Why use exponents? Consider a very large number, such as the distance between Mercury and the Sun (which is 58 000 000 km). If a zero were accidentally added to or left off this number, the distance would appear to be either 10 times larger or smaller than it really is. To avoid making these kinds of mistakes, scientists express numbers in scientific notation.

A Quick Chemistry Reference for the Biology Student

Matter is anything that takes up space and has mass. Overwhelming evidence shows that the matter in living organisms is made up of atoms and that changes in the organic matter in living systems take place at the atomic level. An ordinary chemical or biochemical reaction cannot destroy, create, or split an atom. Current research also reveals a remarkable array of subatomic particles—particles smaller than an atom.

The Structure of Atoms

To understand and explain chemical reactions, you need to know about the subatomic particles called *protons*, *neutrons*, and *electrons*. Their properties are summarized in the following table.

Table B.1 Protons, neutrons, and electrons

Subatomic particle	Symbol	Charge	Amount of charge	Approximate relative mass (in atomic mass units)
proton	p^+	positive	+1	1
neutron	n^0	neutral	0	1
electron	e^-	negative	−1	$\frac{1}{2000}$

In atoms, these subatomic particles are arranged in a characteristic structure (Figure B.1). The protons and neutrons are clustered together in the nucleus, which contains over 99% of an atom's mass but makes up less than 1% of its volume. The electrons surround the nucleus in regions called shells. Electrons make up less than 1% of an atom's mass, although the shells they occupy make up over 99% of its volume.

Different elements, such as hydrogen and oxygen, are distinguished from one another by the number of protons their atoms contain. All atoms of the same element contain the same number of protons. The number of electrons in an atom always equals the number of protons it contains. This means that, overall, an atom has a neutral charge. The

periodic table lists and provides information about all the known elements. For a given element, the number of neutrons may vary from one atom to another.

The Covalent Bond

Atoms group together, often forming very strong bonds. The following example will help you understand how and why one type of bond, the *covalent bond*, forms.

Figure B.2 illustrates the forces that come into play as two hydrogen atoms approach each other. Four interactions develop between the two atoms, as follows:

1. a force of repulsion between the two electrons;
2. a force of repulsion between the two protons;
3. a force of attraction between the electron of hydrogen atom A and the proton of hydrogen atom B; and
4. a force of attraction between the electron of hydrogen atom B and the proton of hydrogen atom A.

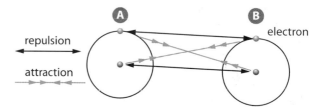

Figure B.2 The forces between two hydrogen atoms.

As the atoms continue to approach each other, the forces of both repulsion and attraction increase. The maximum force of attraction occurs when the nuclei of the two atoms are about 1.05×10^{-4} µm apart. At this point, the electron shells of the two atoms merge. Now each nucleus has access to both of the electrons. The two positive hydrogen nuclei share the same electron shell and are held together (bonded) by the shell's negative charge. The type of chemical bond that involves shared electrons is called a covalent bond.

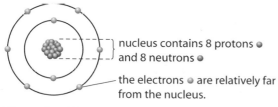

nucleus contains 8 protons and 8 neutrons

the electrons are relatively far from the nucleus.

Figure B.1 This model of oxygen shows the arrangement of subatomic particles in the atom. Fixed numbers of electrons occupy regions called shells. The outermost shell is called the valence shell.

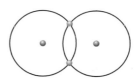

Figure B.3 Two hydrogen atoms that share a pair of electrons have formed a molecule (H_2) with a single covalent bond. The structural formula to show the single covalent bond between the hydrogen atoms is H — H.

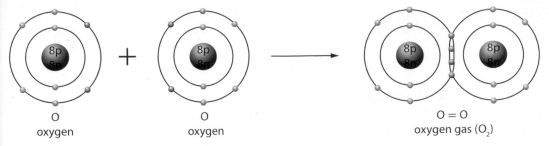

oxygen

oxygen

O = O
oxygen gas (O₂)

Figure B.4 Notice that by sharing two pairs of electrons (in a double bond), each of the oxygen atoms has access to eight electrons in its valence shell. This gives it the same stable valence-shell arrangement as the noble gas closest to it in the periodic table, neon.

Tendency Toward Stability

The noble gases (Group 18 on the periodic table) are known to be so chemically stable that they are unlikely to take part in chemical reactions. When atoms bond, they share, give up, or gain electrons to achieve the same arrangement of valence electrons as that of the noble gas to which they are closest in the periodic table.

You may recall from previous studies that the maximum number of electrons that can occupy the first valence shell outside a nucleus is two (the valence shell arrangement of the noble gas helium). By sharing a valence electron with another hydrogen atom, each of the hydrogen atoms in the new molecule achieves a stable valence shell arrangement. This is shown in Figure B.3.

Double and Triple Bonds

Atoms can also share two pairs of electrons or three pairs of electrons in a covalent bond. In a double covalent bond, two atoms share two pairs of electrons. This is illustrated using two oxygen atoms in Figure B.4.

The electron-dot diagram of carbon dioxide (Figure B.5) shows an example of a three-atom molecule held together by double covalent bonds. The maximum number of electrons that can occupy the valence shell of elements with atomic numbers 3 to 20 is eight. This is a stable electron shell configuration. Examine the CO_2 molecule in Figure B.5. Look for evidence that each atom in the molecule has

access to a stable valence shell arrangement. In a triple covalent bond, two atoms share three pairs of electrons.

$$:\ddot{O}:\ :C:\ :\ddot{O}:$$

Figure B.5 An electron-dot diagram of carbon dioxide. Its structural formula is, thus, O = C = O.

The Polar Covalent Bond

Most of the biochemical reactions in a living cell take place in a water solution. The chemical bonds binding together the atoms in a water molecule have to be strong enough to keep the molecule intact even when heat added to the water makes it evaporate.

$$\begin{matrix} H \\ :\ddot{O}:\ H \end{matrix}$$

Figure B.6 An electron-dot model of a water molecule

The electron-dot diagram in Figure B.6 suggests that a water molecule is held together by ordinary covalent bonds. What this type of diagram cannot show is the relative importance of the protons in the nuclei of the three atoms. The O nucleus has eight positive protons; the hydrogen nuclei have only one proton each. The oxygen nuclei exert a greater attractive force on electrons than do hydrogen nuclei. As a result, the shared valence electrons spend more of their time around the O nucleus than they

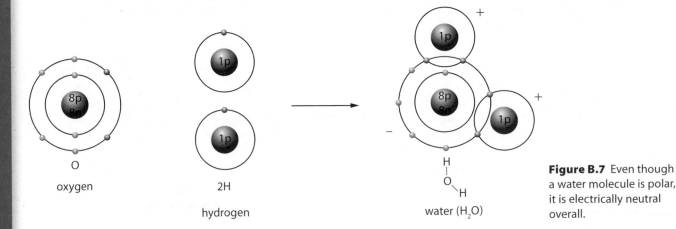

oxygen

2H

hydrogen

water (H₂O)

Figure B.7 Even though a water molecule is polar, it is electrically neutral overall.

do around the H nuclei. This gives the O end, or pole, of a water molecule a partially negative charge. The H ends, or poles, have partial positive charges. The model in Figure B.7 provides a useful representation of the polarity in a water molecule.

To reflect the unequal sharing of electrons within a water molecule, the special type of covalent bond holding it together is called a *polar covalent bond*. In a polar covalent bond, the valence electrons of the atoms are tightly bound, and no electrons are available to carry an electric current.

The Hydrogen Bond

When two water molecules collide, the polar nature of each molecule has an effect on what happens. If the two negative poles (O) meet "head to head," the molecules will repel each other because like charges repel. The two molecules will also repel each other if their positive poles (H) collide. However, in most collisions the negative pole of one molecule will be attracted by a positive pole of the other, and the two molecules will attract each other strongly enough to remain close together. Other water molecules in the vicinity will be attracted to each other in the same way. This type of electrostatic attraction between polar molecules containing a positive hydrogen pole is called a *hydrogen bond*. Figure B.8 shows the pattern of attractions that forms between liquid water molecules as a result of hydrogen bonding.

The Ionic Bond

Atoms can also form ionic bonds. From earlier studies, you may recall that when an atom or group of atoms gains or loses electrons, it acquires an electric charge and becomes an *ion*. The ions formed in this kind of electron transfer are chemically stable because each ion has a valence shell arrangement like that of a noble gas. When the number of electrons is less than the number of protons, the ion is positive (a cation). When the number of electrons exceeds the number of protons, the ion is negative (an anion). Ions can be composed of only one element, such as the hydrogen ion (H^+), or of several elements, such as the bicarbonate ion (HCO_3^-). The attraction between oppositely charged ions is called an *ionic bond*.

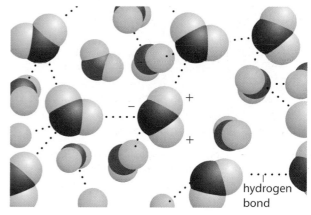

Figure B.8 The polarity of water molecules allows attractions called hydrogen bonds to form between the water molecules. A dotted line is used to represent a hydrogen bond; it indicates the hydrogen bond's weakness relative to covalent or ionic bonds.

Forming Ionic Compounds

If a large number of chlorine atoms are brought together, they pair up to form covalently bonded Cl_2 molecules. The shared electrons are strongly attracted by the two nuclei. In contrast, a sodium atom's single valence electron is only weakly attracted to its nucleus. If a large number of sodium atoms are brought together, a solid does form, but the valence electrons in the solid are so loosely attached to each nucleus that they can easily flow to conduct an electrical current.

However, if a piece of solid sodium is exposed to chlorine gas (Cl_2) there is an explosive reaction that releases both heat and light. In this reaction, electrons are actually transferred from the sodium atoms to the chlorine atoms. Thus, two ions are formed simultaneously: Na^+ and Cl^-. You can follow what happens in Figure B.9.

All that remains after the reaction are tiny cubic crystals of sodium chloride (table salt). The ions have aligned themselves in a pattern that reduces repulsion and maximizes attraction. For the ionic compound NaCl, the cubical ion arrangement shown in Figure B.10 is most stable. Ionic compounds bond into regular, repeating patterns that are determined by the size of the individual ions, the amount of charge they carry, and the kind of charge they carry.

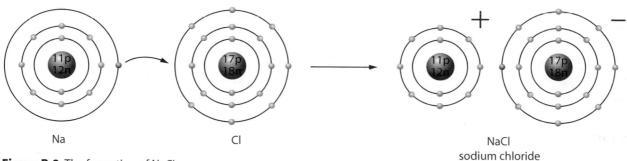

Na   Cl   NaCl
sodium chloride

Figure B.9 The formation of NaCl

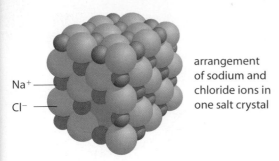

Na$^+$ ———

Cl$^-$ ———

arrangement of sodium and chloride ions in one salt crystal

Figure B.10 An ionic compound such as NaCl (salt) has a characteristic crystalline shape. Like sodium chloride, most ionic compounds involve bonds between metal cations and non-metal anions.

Ionic Solids

The hundreds of different ionic compounds all have these two things in common:

1. They are solids at room temperature.

2. The total charge on the positive ions equals the total charge on the negative ions. Therefore, every ionic solid is electrically neutral even though it is composed of strongly charged particles.

The ionic bonds holding ionic solids (salts) together are extremely strong and stable. For example, sodium chloride melts only at a very high temperature (801 °C) and can safely be kept in a cupboard for years with no danger of decomposition.

Even though it contains millions of charged particles (ions), a crystal of sodium chloride cannot conduct an electrical current. Immobilized by their close-packed solid state, the ions cannot carry a current from one side of a crystal to the other.

Ionic Compounds in Solution

You know that table salt dissolves in water. Many other ionic compounds are also water soluble. What happens to the ions in sodium chloride when it dissolves in water? Attraction by the charged poles of the surrounding water molecules pulls the ions away from the crystal and into solution. Figure B.11 shows how the polar water molecules interact with and surround the sodium and chloride ions.

Figure B.11 Notice the orientation of the water molecules around the sodium ion and the chloride ion.

Once dissolved in water, the sodium and chloride ions are free to move about and collide with other particles. This makes the ions mobile enough to carry an electric current from one location to another. It also allows chemical reactions to occur. So, like many ionic compounds, sodium chloride is an electrolyte. An *electrolyte* is a substance that, when dissolved in water, enables the solution to carry an electric current.

The Biological Significance of Ions

Ions play a vital role in the chemistry of living cells and body systems. For example, modern athletes pay close attention to the level of electrolytes in their body. Intense physical activity causes the loss of NaCl (in sweat). If the lost sodium ions are not replaced, nerve cells cannot send signals to the muscles. Table B.2 identifies the significance of the important ions in your body.

Table B.2 Significant ions in the body

Name	Symbol	Special significance
sodium	Na$^+$	found in body fluids; important in muscle contraction and nerve conduction
chloride	Cl$^-$	found in body fluids
potassium	K$^+$	found primarily inside cells; important in muscle contraction and nerve conduction
phosphate	PO$_4^{3-}$	found in bones, teeth, and the high-energy molecule ATP
calcium	Ca^{2+}	found in bones and teeth; important in muscle contraction
bicarbonate	HCO$_3^-$	important in acid-base balance
hydrogen	H$^+$	important in acid-base balance
hydroxide	OH$^-$	important in acid-base balance

Understanding pH

Biological processes take place within specific limits of acidity and alkalinity. If an environment becomes too acidic or too alkaline for a process to continue at optimum levels, the organism that depends on that process may suffer and die. Fresh-water fish, for example, cannot survive in water that is too acid. Pitcher plants, sundews, and many other plants that grow in acidic soils cannot tolerate alkaline conditions.

Whether an environment is acidic or alkaline depends on the concentration of hydrogen ions (H$^+$(aq)) found in solution. Pure water at 25 °C ionizes very slightly to produce an equal number of hydrogen and hydroxide ions:

$$H_2O(\ell) \rightleftharpoons H^+(aq) + OH^-(aq)$$

Because the hydrogen and hydroxide ions are in balance (that is, equal in number), pure water is said to be neutral.

This neutral point is used as a reference in understanding how acidic or alkaline other solutions are. As solutions become increasingly acid from this point, the concentration of hydrogen ions in them increases. As they become increasingly alkaline, the concentration of hydrogen ions in them decreases. These relationships are summed up very neatly on the pH scale shown in Figure B.12. Each change in number up or down the scale represents a tenfold increase or decrease in the concentration of hydrogen ions.

Measuring pH

For a relative indication of the pH level, a sample can be tested with litmus paper. This simple test will determine whether a solution is either acidic or alkaline. It can also be tested by adding an acid-base indicator such as bromothymol blue. The resulting colour is then compared to a colour chart that indicates relative pH. More precise readings can be determined using a pH meter or probe, such as the one shown in Figure B.13. pH meters and probes use a pair of electrodes to measure the electrical potential of the solution being tested. When used to test a solution whose pH is unknown, the difference in potential between the two electrodes is measured and displayed as a pH value.

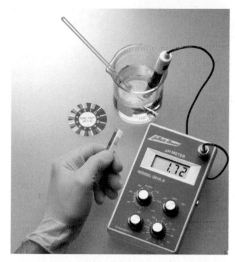

Figure B.13 Both pH paper and a pH meter can be used to determine the pH of a solution. The meter will give the more precise reading.

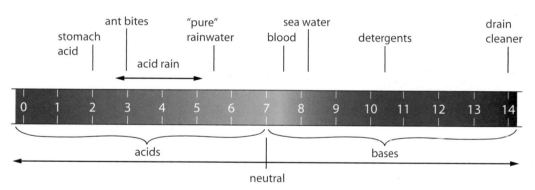

Figure B.12 The average pH values for various substances are indicated on this pH scale.

Microscopy Review

Part 1: Care of a Microscope

A *light microscope* is an optical instrument that greatly magnifies objects too small to be seen with the unaided eye. The figure on the next page shows a compound light microscope. This kind of microscope has a series of lenses (rather than only one, as in a hand lens) and requires a light source to view an object. Study the compound light microscope shown in Figure C.2 and review the major parts and their functions.

To keep your microscope in good operating condition, the following points should be observed.

1. To carry a microscope, always use one hand to hold the arm and your other hand to support the base.

2. Do not touch the lens surfaces with your fingers.

3. Use only lens tissue to clean the lens surfaces.

4. Do not adjust any of the focussing knobs until you are ready to use the microscope.

5. Always focus first using the coarse adjustment knob, with the low-power objective lens in position.

6. Do not use the coarse adjustment knob when either the medium-power or high-power objective lens is in position.

7. Cover the microscope when it is not in use.

Part 2: Using a Microscope

Here, you will use the microscope to view a prepared slide. You will determine the area that can be seen through the eyepiece, called the *field of view*, and calculate the magnification. Finally, you will make a scale drawing, and estimate the actual size of the object you are viewing.

CAUTION: Be sure your hands are dry when handling electrical equipment. Handle microscope slides carefully, since they can break easily and cause cuts.

Materials

- microscope
- prepared microscope slide
- mathematical compass
- clear plastic ruler
- blank sheet of paper
- pencil

Procedure

1. Place the microscope on a flat surface.

2. The microscope should always be stored with the low-power objective in position. If your microscope has not been stored that way, look from the side and rotate the revolving nosepiece until the low-power objective clicks into place.

3. Use the coarse-adjustment knob to lower the low-power objective until the lens is about 1 cm above the stage.

4. Look through the eyepiece and adjust the diaphragm until the view is as bright as possible.

Total Magnification and Field of View

5. To calculate the total magnification of an object, multiply the power of the eyepiece by the power of the objective. For example, if the eyepiece magnification is 10×, the low-power objective is 4×, and the high-power objective is 40×, then:

   a) The total magnification using the low-power objective is $10 \times 4 = 40\times$.

   b) The total magnification using the high-power objective is $10 \times 40 = 400\times$.

6. To determine the field of view, place the clear plastic ruler on the stage.

7. Using the coarse-adjustment knob, focus on the ruler. Position the ruler so that one of the millimetre markings is at the left edge of the field of view, as shown in Figure C.1.

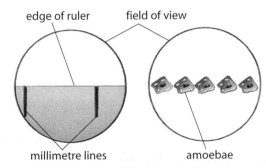

Figure C.1 The diameter of the field of view under low power illustrated here is about 1.5 mm.

8. Measure and record the diameter of the field of view in millimetres (mm) for the low-power objective.

9. Use the following formula to calculate the field of view for the medium-power objective:

$$\text{Medium-power field of view} = \text{Low-power field of view}$$
$$\times \frac{\text{Magnification of low-power objective}}{\text{Magnification of medium-power objective}}$$

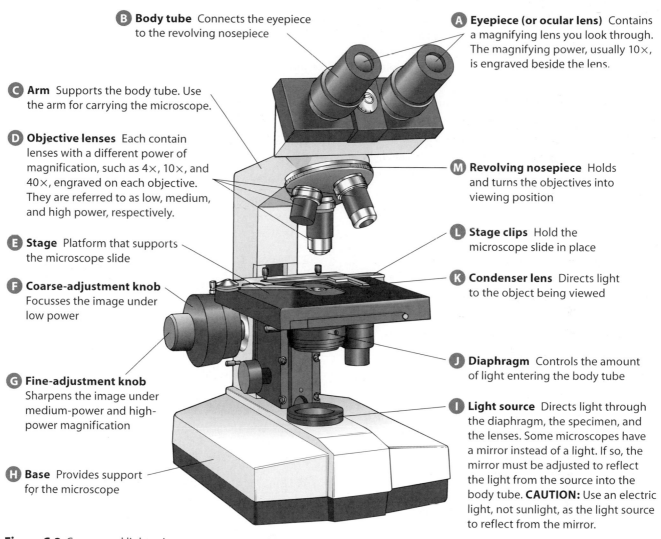

B **Body tube** Connects the eyepiece to the revolving nosepiece

A **Eyepiece (or ocular lens)** Contains a magnifying lens you look through. The magnifying power, usually 10×, is engraved beside the lens.

C **Arm** Supports the body tube. Use the arm for carrying the microscope.

D **Objective lenses** Each contain lenses with a different power of magnification, such as 4×, 10×, and 40×, engraved on each objective. They are referred to as low, medium, and high power, respectively.

M **Revolving nosepiece** Holds and turns the objectives into viewing position

E **Stage** Platform that supports the microscope slide

L **Stage clips** Hold the microscope slide in place

F **Coarse-adjustment knob** Focusses the image under low power

K **Condenser lens** Directs light to the object being viewed

G **Fine-adjustment knob** Sharpens the image under medium-power and high-power magnification

J **Diaphragm** Controls the amount of light entering the body tube

I **Light source** Directs light through the diaphragm, the specimen, and the lenses. Some microscopes have a mirror instead of a light. If so, the mirror must be adjusted to reflect the light from the source into the body tube. **CAUTION:** Use an electric light, not sunlight, as the light source to reflect from the mirror.

H **Base** Provides support for the microscope

Figure C.2 Compound light microscope

For example, if the low-power objective is 4× with a field of view of 2 mm, and the medium-power objective is 10×, then:

Medium-power field of view = 2 mm × $\frac{4}{10}$

= 2 mm × 0.4

= 0.8 mm

Similarly, calculate the field of view for the high-power objective and record the value.

10. Objects in the field of view of a microscope are usually measured in micrometres (μm). One micrometre equals 0.001 mm; or 1000 μm equals one millimetre.

a) In the example in step 9, the field of view under the medium-power objective would be 0.8 mm × 1000 = 800 μm.

b) Calculate the field of view in μm under the high-power objective.

11. You can determine the size of a specimen (such as an amoeba) by estimating how many could fit end to end across the field of view. See Figure C.1 on the previous

page. To do this, divide the field of view by the number of specimens. If the field of view in the illustration is 1500 μm, what is the diameter of each amoeba?

Viewing a Prepared Slide

12. Place a prepared slide on the stage and secure it in place with the stage clips. The low-power objective should be in position. Make sure the object you intend to view is centred over the opening in the stage.

a) Look through the eyepiece. Slowly turn the coarse-adjustment knob until the object is in focus.

b) Use the fine-adjustment knob to sharpen the focus.

13. Once the object is in focus using low power, carefully rotate the revolving nosepiece to the medium-power objective. Look at the side of the objective as you rotate the nosepiece to be sure the objective lens does not strike the surface of the slide.

a) Adjust the focus using *only* the fine-adjustment knob.

b) Next, view the object using the high-power objective. Carefully rotate the nosepiece until the high-power objective clicks into position. Again, be sure the objective does not strike the surface of the slide as you rotate the nosepiece. Adjust the focus using *only* the fine-adjustment knob.

14. Once you have finished viewing the slide, carefully rotate the nosepiece until the low-power objective is in position. If you do not proceed to step 15, making a scale drawing, remove the slide from the stage and return it to its proper container. Unplug the light source and return the microscope to its cabinet. **CAUTION:** Never tug on the electrical cord to unplug it.

Making a Scale Drawing

15. With a mathematical compass, draw a circle (the size does not matter) on blank paper. The circle represents the microscope's field of view.

16. Use the ruler and pencil to divide the circle into four equal sections, as shown in the illustration.

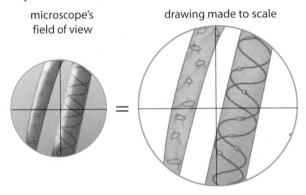

microscope's field of view   drawing made to scale

17. Using the low or medium-power objective, find an area of interest on the prepared slide. Imagine that the field of view is also divided into four equal sections.

18. Notice how much space each part of the object occupies in the field of view.

19. Draw the object to scale in the circle. Draw each part of the object so it is in the same part of the circle as it appears in the field of view. This means the object should occupy the same proportion of space in the circle as it does in the field of view. Label your drawing. Indicate the total magnification and calculate the actual size of the object.

Part 3: Preparing a Wet Mount

Now prepare and view slides of a variety of specimens.

CAUTION: Be careful when using sharp objects such as tweezers. Handle microscope slides and cover slips carefully, since they can break easily.

Materials

- microscope
- cover slips
- tweezers
- tap water
- microscope slides
- medicine dropper
- cotton fibres
- lens paper
- small piece of newspaper and other samples

Procedure

1. To prepare a wet mount, begin with a clean slide and cover slip. Hold the slide and cover slip by their edges to avoid getting your fingerprints on their surfaces.

2. Tear out a small piece of newspaper containing a single letter. Use an *e*, *f*, *g*, or *h*. Using the tweezers, position the letter in the centre of the slide.

3. Using the medicine dropper, place one drop of water on the sample. Hold a cover slip over the sample at a 45 ° angle. One edge of the cover slip should touch the surface of the slide near the newspaper letter sample.

4. Slowly lower the opposite edge of the cover slip over the sample. Be sure no bubbles form beneath the cover slip. This type of sample preparation is called a *wet mount*.

5. With the low-power objective of the microscope in position, place the slide on the stage and secure it with the stage clips. Centre the sample over the opening.

a) Look though the eyepiece. Reposition the slide, if necessary, until you can see the letter. Using the coarse-adjustment knob, focus on the letter. Then, adjust the focus with the fine-adjustment knob.

b) Examine the letter using medium power. Note that it is composed of many small dots.

6. To reveal the structure of small objects, the microscope must do more than magnify—it must also reveal detail. The capacity to distinguish detail is called *resolution*, and the measure of resolution is known as *resolving power*. The resolving power of a microscope is defined as the minimum distance that two objects can be apart and still be seen as separate objects. Prepare another wet mount using several fibres from a cotton ball. Using the low-power objective, locate a part of the slide where two fibres cross each other. Change to the high-power objective. Use the fine-adjustment knob to focus on the fibres. Can both strands of cotton be seen clearly at the same time under high power? How might you explain this result?

APPENDIX D

Review of Biological Drawings

A clear, concise drawing can often replace words in a scientific description. Drawings are especially important when you are trying to explain difficult concepts or describe complex structures. Follow these steps to make a good scientific drawing:

1. Use an unlined (blank) sheet of paper and a sharp lead pencil, ideally 2H, for the drawing, title, and all labels.

2. Make sure your drawing will be large enough to show all the necessary details; a drawing about half a page in size is usually sufficient. Also allow space for the labels, which identify parts of the object you are drawing. Place all labels to the right of your drawing.

3. Make your drawing as simple as is possible, using clean-cut pencil lines (do not sketch). Draw only what you observe. Do not draw parts of the object that are not visible from the angle of view you are observing. If you must show another part of the object, make a second drawing. Indicate the angle of view on each drawing.

4. Most animal and plant tissues are composed of many cells. If you are drawing a representative cell of such tissue, include the boundaries of the other cells surrounding it. This approach will provide context for your drawing.

5. Shading is not usually used in scientific drawings. To indicate darker areas in your drawing, use stippling (a series of dots) as shown in Figure AE.2. Also, use double lines to indicate thicker parts of an object, such as the wall of a plant cell.

6. Label your drawing carefully and completely. All labels should be horizontal, printed in lower-case, and placed in a column to the right of your drawing. Imagine for a moment that you know nothing about the object you are drawing. Think about what structures you would like identified if you were seeing the drawing for the first time.

7. Use a ruler to draw a horizontal line from each label to the structure you are identifying. Make sure that none of these label lines cross each other.

8. Give your drawing a title. The title should appear immediately above the drawing. The title should be printed and underlined. Indicate the magnification of the drawing in parentheses. **Note:** The drawing shown of onion skin cells is from a student's notebook. The student used stippling to show darker areas, horizontal labels and label lines for each structure observed, gave the drawing a title, and indicated the magnification—all elements of a complete scientific drawing. The student has also included the microscope's field of view to give definition to the drawing.

Buccal Mucosal Cells

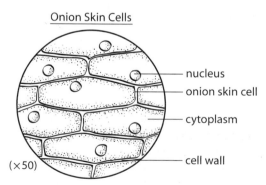

Onion Skin Cells

(×50)

Figure AE.2 The stippling on this drawing of onion skin cells, as observed under a microscope, shows that some areas are darker in appearance than others.

Figure AE.1 Buccal mucosal (cheek lining) cells

Tips for Writing Diploma Exam Written Response Questions

The Diploma Exam Preparation feature at *www. albertabiology.ca* shows examples of the different types of questions that require a written response, although the tips here will assist you in answering any type of question.

Your answers will be assessed on the basis of how well you communicate both your understanding of the information presented and your understanding of the applicable science. Evaluators will be looking for examples of your understanding of scientific principles and techniques. For more information about the Diploma Exams, visit the Alberta Education Diploma Exam web site at **http://www.education.gov.ab.ca/k%5F12/testing/ diploma/**

Key Diploma Exam Skills

In order to successfully answer the questions, you must be able to:

1. Read critically and identify
   - key words, phrases, and data that deliver useful information
   - distractor information and data that can be ignored because it does not have any bearing on the answer to the question
   - if the question is an open-response style that requires a unified response, or if it is a closed-response style that requires a more analytical approach
   - precisely what the question is asking
     - pay close attention to the process words (see list below)
     - pay close attention to the directing words (see list opposite) to determine how you should answer the question. The directing words are always highlighted in boldface type.
   - the scientific concept(s) that you should include in your answer
   - any formula(s) that you will have to use
   - the information in your Data Booklet that you will need

2. Interpret and Analyze
   - process words and directing words
   - information including the key words, phrases, and data presented in the information box
   - information that is presented in charts, tables, and graphs

3. Communicate
   - conclusions by making a formal statement
   - results in the form of charts, graphs, or diagrams
   - ideas or answers to questions in the form of complete sentences, paragraphs, or short essays

4. If you are asked to perform an experiment, you must write the experimental design as follows:
   - state the problem or question to be answered
   - formulate a hypothesis or make a prediction
   - identify the manipulated and responding variable(s) if required
   - provide a method for controlling variables
   - identify the required materials clearly
   - describe any applicable safety procedures
   - list the steps in the experimental procedure
   - provide a sketch(es) of the apparatus to help make the set-up clear
   - provide a method for collecting and recording pertinent data—include the units for the data being collected

Guidelines

The Diploma Exam feature includes guidelines that direct you in the skills and knowledge you need to use to answer the questions successfully. This type of information will *not* appear on the exam.

Assess the type of question and the guidelines that are provided to help you answer it. Use the information provided here to develop your own technique for answering each type of question.

Alberta Science Process and Directing Words

The following "process" and "directing" words have specific meanings when they are used in the Diploma Exam questions. Study this list so you will understand exactly what you are being asked to do in the questions. The success of your answer depends not only on your interpretation of the information in the question but also on your understanding of the wording of the questions.

Process Words

Hypothesis: A single proposition intended as a possible explanation for an observed phenomenon; e.g., a possible cause for a specific effect

Conclusion: A proposition that summarizes the extent to which a hypothesis and/or a theory has been supported or contradicted by the evidence

Experiment: A set of manipulations and/or specific observations of nature that allow the testing of hypotheses and/or generalizations

Variables: Conditions that can change in an experiment. Variables in experiments are categorized as:

- *manipulated variables* (independent variables): conditions that were deliberately changed by the experimenter
- *controlled variables* (fixed or restrained variables): conditions that could have changed but did not, because of the intervention of the experimenter
- *responding variables* (dependent variables): conditions that changed in response to the change in the manipulated variables

Directing Words

Discuss	The word "discuss" **will not** be used as a directing word on math and science diploma examinations because it is not used consistently to mean a single activity.

The following words are specific in meaning.

Algebraically	Using mathematical procedures that involve letters or symbols to represent numbers
Analyze	To make a mathematical, chemical, or methodical examination of parts to determine the nature, proportion, function, interrelationship, etc. of the whole
Compare	Examine the character or qualities of two things by providing characteristics of both that point out their *similarities* and *differences*
Conclude	State a logical end based on reasoning and/or evidence
Contrast/ Distinguish	Point out the *differences* between two things that have similar or comparable natures
Criticize	Point out the *demerits* of an item or issue
Define	Provide the essential qualities or meaning of a word or concept; make distinct and clear by marking out the limits
Describe	Give a written account or represent the characteristics of something by a figure, model, or picture
Design/Plan	Construct a plan; i.e, a detailed sequence of actions for a specific purpose
Determine	Find a solution, to a specified degree of accuracy, to a problem by showing appropriate formulas, procedures, and calculations
Enumerate	Specify one by one or list in concise form and according to some order
Evaluate	Give the significance or worth of something by identifying the good and bad points or the advantages and disadvantages
Explain	Make clear what is not immediately obvious or entirely known; give the cause of or reason for; make known in detail

Graphically	Using a drawing that is produced electronically or by hand and that shows a relation between certain sets of numbers
How	Show in what manner or way, with what meaning
Hypothesize	Form a tentative proposition intended as a possible explanation for an observed phenomenon; i.e., a possible cause for a specific effect. The proposition should be testable logically and/or empirically
Identify	Recognize and select as having the characteristics of something
Illustrate	Make clear by giving an example. The form of the example must be specified in the question; i.e., word description, sketch, or diagram
Infer	Form a generalization from sample data; arrive at a conclusion by reasoning from evidence
Interpret	Tell the meaning of something; present information in a new form that adds meaning to the original data
Justify/ Show How	Show reasons for or give facts that support a position
Model	Find a model (in mathematics, a model of a situation is a pattern that is supposed to represent or set a standard for a real situation) that does a good job of representing a situation
Outline	Give, in an organized fashion, the essential parts of something. The form of the outline must be specified in the question; eg., list, flow chart, concept map
Predict	Tell in advance on the basis of empirical evidence and/or logic
Prove	Establish the truth of validity of a statement for the general case by giving factual evidence or logical argument
Relate	Show logical or causal connection between things
Sketch	Provide a drawing that represents the key features of an object or graph
Solve	Give a solution for a problem; i.e., explanation in words and/or numbers
Summarize	Give a brief account of the main points
Trace	Give a step-by-step description of the development
Verify	Establish, by substitution for a particular case or by geometric comparison, the truth of a statement
Why	Show the cause, reason, or purpose

The Dissection of a Fetal Pig

Note: Illustrations used in this dissection are also available electronically. If you do not dissect a fetal pig or other organism in your course, many virtual dissections are available to enhance your learning.

Pigs are members of the class mammalia. Before birth, the young are nourished by the placenta in the mother's womb. For this reason, pigs (like humans) are known as placental mammals. The structure and organization of the internal organs of the pig are representative of those of all placental mammals. Although the fetal pig is not yet born, its internal systems are complete. In this investigation you will dissect a fetal pig to study its internal organs. This dissection will give you a sense of how internal systems are arranged within your own body.

Dissection involves the careful and systematic examination of the internal structures of an organism. A good dissection will reveal not only the location and structure of individual organs, but also how different organs relate to one another in the various systems of the body. To carry out a successful dissection, you should be familiar with the terms listed in Table A10.1. These are the terms used to describe the location of the various features of the animal and to direct incisions.

This dissection is divided into four parts. In the first part, you will investigate the external anatomy of your specimen and identify its age and sex. In the second part, you will examine the organs of the digestive system. In the third part, you will examine the organs of the circulatory system. Finally, in the fourth part, you will examine the organs of the respiratory system. In between each investigation you will store your specimen. Remember to wrap and store your specimen properly, and to label it so you can identify it again.

Table A10.1 The anatomical terms used to locate organs or incisions during this dissection.

Term	Meaning
Dorsal	Upper or back surface
Ventral	Under or belly surface
Lateral	Side
Anterior	Toward the front (head) end
Posterior	Toward the back end
Superficial	Near the surface
Proximal	Close to
Distal	Far from

Safety Precautions

Extreme care must be taken when using dissecting instruments, particularly scalpels. To the extent possible, make cuts away from your body. The pigs are preserved in a chemical solution. Wear plastic gloves, goggles and an apron at all times, and work in a well-ventilated area. If some of the chemical comes into contact with your skin, wash it off. At the end of each lesson, wash your hands thoroughly. Dispose of all materials as instructed by your teacher, and clean your work area.

Materials

- preserved fetal pig
- dissecting instruments
- plastic bag and tie (to store your specimen)
- disposable plastic gloves
- large tongs
- newspapers and/or paper towelling
- dissecting tray
- string or strong thread
- water-proof tags (to identify your specimen)
- apron
- T pins

Procedure

Part 1 External Anatomy

1. Rinse your specimen and place it on its side in the dissecting tray.

2. Measure your specimen from the snout to the base of the tail. Use Figure A10.1 to estimate the gestational age of your specimen.

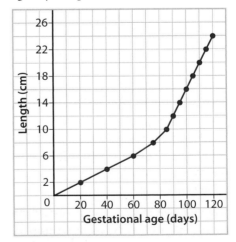

Figure A10.1 The gestation period of the pig is about 115 days. About how old is your specimen?

3. Identify the external features of your specimen using Figure A10.2. Make your own drawing of the lateral view of your specimen, labelling the features. Record the age of your specimen with this drawing.

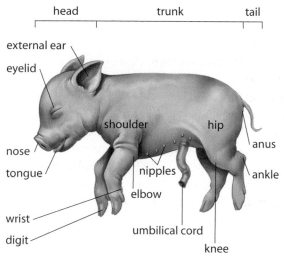

Figure A10.2 A lateral view of a fetal pig.

4. Turn your specimen onto its back. Using Figures A10.3 and A10.4, determine the sex of your specimen. Examine a specimen of each sex.

5. Make your own drawing of the external reproductive organs of specimens of both sexes. Label the structures.

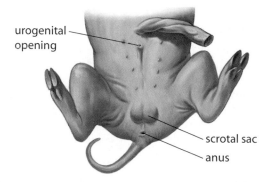

Figure A10.3 The external reproductive organs of a male fetal pig.

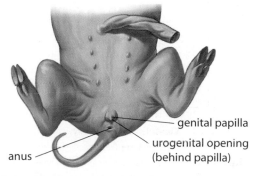

Figure A10.4 The external reproductive organs of a female fetal pig.

Part 2 The Digestive System

A. The mouth

1. Using a strong pair of dissecting scissors, make a cut in the corner of the mouth, cutting toward the posterior of the specimen. Repeat on the other side.

2. Pry the mouth open. Using Figure A10.5, locate and identify the features of the oral cavity.

3. Make your own drawing of the mouth of your specimen, labelling the features.

Analysis

1. Explain how the appearance of the following structures relates to their function as part of the digestive system. Give as much detail as possible, including size, texture, external structure, and internal structure.

   a) the teeth

   b) the tongue

   c) the epiglottis

2. What differences can you see between the pig's mouth structures and your own? Suggest a reason for these differences.

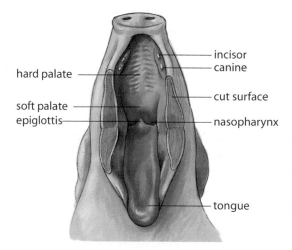

Figure A10.5 The oral cavity of the fetal pig.

B. Exposing the abdominal organs

1. Place the pig in the dissecting tray with its ventral surface uppermost. Spread out the limbs. Tie a piece of string to one of the forelimbs near the ankle. Pass the string under the tray and securely tie the other forelimb. Repeat the process with the hind limbs.

2. Select a point just anterior to the umbilical cord on the specimen's ventral surface. Using forceps, pinch the skin of the abdomen along the midventral line and pull it slightly away from the animal. With your scissors, make an incision in the skin. The incision should be just large enough to pass the point of your scissors through. Now make a midventral cut ending just posterior to the midline of the animal (shown as #1 in Figure A10.6). To avoid damaging the organs as you cut, keep the tips of the scissors pointing up. Be careful not to damage the umbilical cord.

3. From the same starting point, make a second incision around the base of the umbilical cord extending back to just anterior to the anus (shown as #2 on Figure A10.6). You may wish to turn your specimen around so you can cut away from you. Repeat on the other side.

4. Locate the base of the sternum (breast bone), situated in the centre of the chest. The ribs are attached to the sternum. Select a point slightly posterior to the sternum and cut across the ventral surface (shown as #3 in Figure A10.6). The incision should be posterior to the diaphragm, which you will be able to see as a dome-shaped layer of muscle separating the abdominal and thoracic cavities.

5. Make two final incisions, one on each side of the cuts bordering the umbilical cord and just anterior to the hind limbs (shown as #4 in Figure A10.6). Use T pins to pin back the skins to expose the internal organs of the abdominal cavity. The T pins should point away from the specimen so they will not interfere with your work.

6. The organs of the abdomen are covered and protected by a membrane called the peritoneum. The double-layered sheets of peritoneum are called mesenteries. Using forceps or a dissecting probe, gently move the mesenteries aside to reveal the underlying organs.

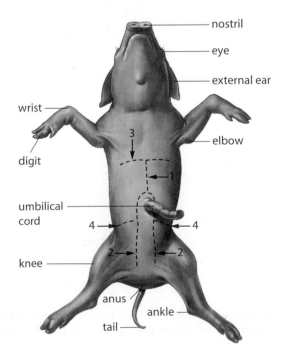

Figure A10.6 A ventral view of a fetal pig showing the pattern of incisions that expose the organs of the abdominal cavity.

7. Using Figure A10.7 below and Figure A10.8, locate and identify the organs of the abdominal cavity. Make a drawing of your specimen showing the location of the internal organs and labelling them.

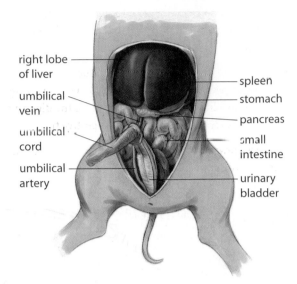

Figure A10.7 The major organs found in the abdominal cavity of the fetal pig.

C. Examining the abdominal organs

1. Locate the liver, the largest organ of the abdominal cavity. Describe its appearance in your own words. Note its different lobes.

2. Locate and describe the esophagus. Note how it passes through the diaphragm just before it enters the stomach.

3. Locate and describe the stomach. Carefully cut open the stomach and describe the inner surface.

4. Locate and describe the pancreas, situated below the stomach and between the stomach and the small intestine. It is usually lighter in colour than the surrounding organs.

5. Locate and describe the small intestine. See if you can identify the separate portions of the duodenum, ileum, and jejunum.

6. Using forceps or a probe, gently lift the connective tissue that links the liver and the duodenum. Locate the bile duct in this mesentery and trace it back to its source at the gall bladder. The gall bladder is embedded on the surface of the liver.

7. Move to the distal end of the small intestine and locate the point on the left side of the abdominal cavity where the large intestine begins.

8. The main part of the large intestine is called the colon. Identify the path the colon takes in the abdomen.

9. Toward the end of the large intestine is the rectum. Note where the tract terminates at the anus.

10. Cut the esophagus as close to the top of the abdominal cavity as you can. Make a second cut as close as you can to the end of the digestive tract near the anus. Carefully remove the entire digestive tract, in one piece, from the specimen.

11. Carefully cut away the connective tissue around the digestive tract. Unravel the tract and make a drawing of it, identifying the different sections of the digestive tract. Measure each section of the digestive tract.

12. Make a drawing of the unravelled digestive tract and describe the appearance of this tissue in your own words.

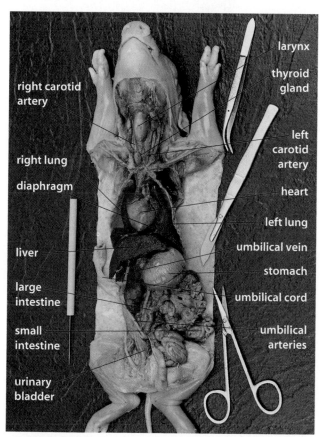

Figure A10.8 The internal abdominal and thoracic organs. (Note: the pancreas is not visible in this photograph.)

Analysis

1. Explain how the appearance of the following structures relates to their function as part of the digestive system. Give as much detail as possible, including size, texture, external structure, and internal structure.

   a) liver
   b) pancreas
   c) esophagus
   d) stomach
   e) small intestine
   f) large intestine
   g) gall bladder

2. Using your own drawings of the abdominal organs, trace the path of food from the mouth to the rectum. Identify the major steps in the digestive process that take place along the way.

Part 3 The Circulatory System

A. Exposing the organs of the thoracic cavity

1. Locate the base of the sternum (breast bone), situated in the centre of the chest. The ribs are attached to the sternum. Use this as the starting point for your incision. With forceps, pinch the skin of the abdomen along the midventral line and draw it slightly away from the animal. With your scissors, make an incision in the skin. The incision should be just large enough to pass the point of your scissors through. Now make a midventral cut (shown as #1 in Figure A10.9). This cut should extend as far forward as the hairs near the base of the throat. Be careful not to damage the underlying body wall as you cut. Remember to keep the tips of your scissors pointing up, not down, to avoid damaging the internal organs.

2. Next, make two cuts (shown as cuts #2 and #3 in Figure A10.9) from the midventral line in the region of the thoracic cavity. Carefully lift the skin and pin it to the sides of the specimen using T pins. The T pins should point away from the specimen so they will not interfere with your work.

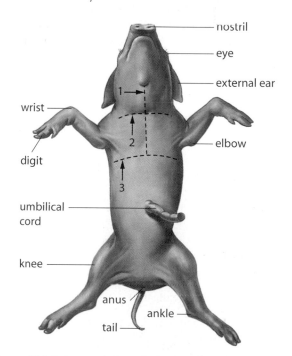

Figure A10.9 A ventral view of a fetal pig showing the pattern of incisions that will expose the organs of the thoracic cavity.

3. Using a sturdy pair of dissecting scissors, cut the ribs along the sternum, and pry them apart to reveal the organs of the thoracic cavity.

4. Using forceps or a dissecting probe, remove the connective tissues and membranes that surround the lungs and heart.

5. Using Figure A10.8 and Figure A10.9, identify the internal organs of the thoracic cavity. Make a drawing of your specimen.

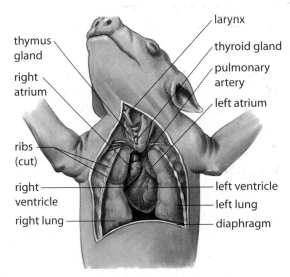

Figure A10.10 The organs of the thoracic cavity.

B. Examining the organs of the circulatory system

1. Using Figure A10.10 and A10.12 for reference, identify and compare the sizes of the following major blood vessels.

   a) the aorta, including the aortic arch;

   b) the superior vena cava;

   c) the pulmonary artery;

   d) the pulmonary vein;

   e) the inferior vena cava;

2. Your specimen may have a small blood vessel connecting the pulmonary artery to the aorta. This vessel is called the ductus arteriosis. Try to locate this vessel on your own specimen. If you cannot find it, examine another specimen in which this vessel is visible.

3. Locate and describe the heart.

4. Make a drawing of your specimen showing the location of the circulatory organs.

5. Carefully cut through the blood vessels a short distance from the heart. Remove the heart. Make an incision in the ventral surface of the heart as shown in Figure A10.11. Your incision should expose all four chambers of the heart.

6. Using Figure A10.12 for reference, identify the internal features of the heart. Try to locate and identify the heart valves at the opening to the blood vessels.

7. Compare the structure of the different chambers of the heart. Make a labelled drawing and describe the structures in your own words.

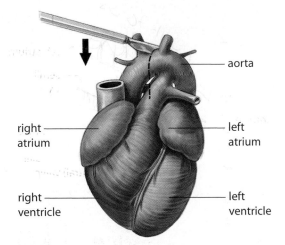

Figure A10.11 With the heart on its dorsal surface, make your incision beginning at the aortic arch and continuing straight to the base of the ventricles.

Analysis

1. Explain how the appearance of the following structures relates to their function as part of the circulatory system. Give as much detail as possible, including size, texture, external structure, and internal structure.

   a) right atrium   **e)** arteries

   b) left atrium   **f)** veins

   c) right ventricle   **g)** ductus arteriosis

   d) left ventricle   **h)** heart valves

2. Using your own drawings, trace the passage of blood from the body through the heart and back to the body.

Part 4 The Respiratory System

Examining the respiratory organs

1. Using Figure A10.10 for reference, identify the major organs of the respiratory system.

2. Note the difference in structure between the right and left lung. In your own words, describe the structure and texture of the lungs.

3. Locate and describe the pleural membranes encasing each lung.

4. Using a probe, move aside the layers of muscle to work deeper into the neck. If necessary, carefully cut the muscle tissue. Locate the larynx, trachea, and esophagus. Describe the difference in structure between the trachea and esophagus.

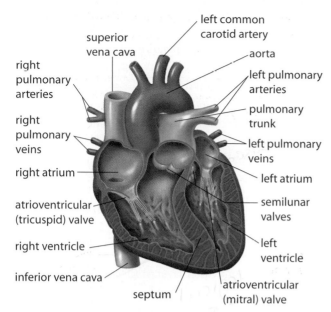

left common
carotid artery

superior
vena cava

aorta

right
pulmonary
arteries

left pulmonary
arteries

pulmonary
trunk

right
pulmonary
veins

left pulmonary
veins

right atrium

left atrium

atrioventricular
(tricuspid) valve

semilunar
valves

right ventricle

left
ventricle

inferior vena cava

septum

atrioventricular
(mitral) valve

Figure A10.12 A ventral cross section of the heart.

5. Examine the rib cage and try to identify the external and internal intercostal muscles.

6. Open the mouth and describe the relationship between the glottis, esophagus, and pharynx.

7. Trace the passage of the trachea through the throat. Try to identify the two branches of the bronchi.

8. Make a drawing of your specimen showing the location of the organs of the respiratory system.

9. Using a small syringe or dropper, push a small amount of air into the trachea. Note the inflation of the lungs.

Analysis

1. Explain how the appearance of the following structures relates to their function as part of the circulatory system. Give as much detail as possible, including size, texture, external structure, and internal structure.

    a) trachea   **e)** larynx

    b) right lung   **f)** glottis

    c) left lung   **g)** diaphragm

    d) pleural membrane   **h)** rib cage

2. Using your own drawings, trace the path of air from the mouth to the lungs.

Glossary

A

abiotic non-living; refers to non-living things in the environment, such as sunlight, water, soil, air, or minerals (3.1)

ABO system classification system for human blood antigens in which the presence or absence of type A or type B antigens on red blood cells determines blood type as A, B, AB, or O. (8.3)

absorbance spectrum a graph showing the relative amounts of light of different colours (wavelengths) absorbed by various compounds (5.2)

abstinence avoidance of sexual intercourse (15.3)

accessory organ term often used to refer to the pancreas, liver, and gall bladder, because their role in the process of digestion is vital, but they are not physically part of the digestive tract (6.2)

accommodation in the eye, adjustment that the ciliary muscles make to the shape of the lens to focus on objects at varying distances (12.2)

acetylcholine the primary neurotransmitter of both the somatic nervous system and the parasympathetic nervous system (11.1)

acid deposition process by which sulfur and nitrogen emissions undergo chemical change in the atmosphere and are deposited in the environment as dry particles and gases, or as wet acid precipitation, including rain, snow, and fog (2.2)

actin protein that, along with myosin, is the chief component of muscle; makes up the thin filament of a muscle fibre; also a main component of the cellular cytoskeleton; *also see actin myofilament* (10.1)

actin myofilament thin myofilament consisting of two strands of actin molecules wrapped around each other; works with myosin myofilament to produce muscle contractions (10.1)

action potential in an axon, the change in charge that occurs when the gates of the K^+ channels close and the gates of the Na^+ channels open after a wave of depolarization is triggered (11.1)

adaptation a structure, behaviour, or physiological process that helps an organism survive and reproduce in a particular environment. (4.1) In vision, the process by which the iris adjusts the size of the pupil based on the light conditions, thereby controlling the amount of light that enters (12.2)

adaptive radiation diversification of a common ancestral species into a variety of species, all of which are differently adapted (4.3)

Addison's disease condition resulting from a damaged adrenal cortex; body secretes inadequate amounts of mineralocorticoids and glucocorticoids; symptoms include hypoglycemia (low blood sugar), sodium and potassium imbalances, rapid weight loss, and general weakness (13.3)

adhesion molecular attraction between two substances or bodies; for example, the attraction between water and the inner surface of a glass tube (2.1)

adrenal cortex the outer layer of the adrenal glands that produces glucocorticoids and mineralcorticoids, hormones that regulate the long-term stress response; also secretes a small amount of gonadocorticoids, female and male sex hormones that supplement the hormones produced by the gonads (testes and ovaries) (13.3)

adrenal gland one of a pair of organs located on top of the kidneys; composed of two layers: an outer cortex and an inner medulla; each layer produces different hormones and functions as an independent organ (13.3)

adrenal medulla the inner layer of the adrenal glands that produces epinephrine and norepinephrine, hormones that regulate the short-term stress response (13.3)

adrenaline *see epinephrine* (13.2, 13.3)

adrenocorticotropic hormone (ACTH) hormone synthesized by the anterior pituitary gland to target the adrenal cortex and regulate the production of glucocorticoids (13.3)

aerobic involving oxygen; see also *oxic* (5.3)

aerobic cellular respiration respiration carried out using oxygen to produce ATP; compare *anaerobic cellular respiration* (5.3)

afterbirth term for the extra-embryonic membranes, placenta, and umbilical cord when expelled from the uterus after birth (15.1)

age pyramid representation of the age structure of a population to show the proportion of individuals in the population in each age class; used by demographers to assess a population's potential for growth (20.3)

agglutination clumping together; for example clumping of red blood cells that occurs when incompatible blood types are mixed (8.3)

AIDS Acquired Immunodeficiency Syndrome; a disease that compromises the body's capacity for immunity; caused by a group of related viruses collectively called human immunodeficiency virus, or HIV, which are transmitted through body fluids; results in susceptibility to other diseases, often resulting in death (14.2)

albedo percentage of incoming solar radiation reflected by a surface (1.1)

aldosterone a type of mineralocorticoid hormone secreted by the adrenal cortex; stimulates the distal tubule and collecting duct of the kidneys to increase the absorption of sodium into the bloodstream, which is followed by the passive absorption of water and chloride (9.3, 13.3)

algal bloom rapid overgrowth of algae in a body of water, usually resulting from high concentrations of nitrate and/or phosphate; can result in deoxygenation of water when algae die, causing death of aquatic plants and animals (2.2)

allantois extra-embryonic membrane that forms the foundation for the umbilical cord (15.1)

allele different form of the same gene occurring on homologous chromosomes (16.1, 17.1, 19.1)

allele frequency rate of occurrence of a particular allele in a population, with respect to a particular gene; usually expressed as a decimal (19.1)

alpha cell cell of the pancreas which secretes glucagon to increase the level of blood glucose; compare *beta cell* (13.4)

alternation of generations term describing the life cycle of a plant that alternates between a diploid sporophyte generation and a haploid gametophyte generation (16.4)

alveolus (alveoli) gas exchange structure within mammalian lungs; tiny air pocket with walls made of a membrane that is a single cell thick, allowing for exchange of respiratory gases (7.1)

amino acid an organic compound consisting of a carboxylic acid group (COOH), an amino group (NH_2), and any of various side groups, linked together by peptide bonds to form proteins (18.2)

ammonification production of ammonia or ammonium products via break down of organic matter by decomposers (2.2)

amniocentesis procedure by which a needle is used to withdraw a small sample of amniotic fluid from the uterus in order to perform a genetic analysis; for safety, cannot be performed before the 14th week of pregnancy (18.4)

amnion extra-embryonic membrane that forms a transparent sac that encloses and protects the embryo and fetus (15.1)

amylase enzyme in saliva that breaks down starch into simpler sugars (6.2)

anabolic compound-synthesizing metabolic reaction (5.1)

anaerobic absence of oxygen (5.3)

anaerobic cellular respiration respiration carried out without using oxygen to produce ATP; compare *aerobic cellular respiration* (5.3)

analogous structures body parts in different species that have a similar function but evolved separately; for example insect and bird wings; compare *homologous structures* (4.2)

anaphase a late stage of cell division (mitosis) during which the centromere splits apart and chromosomes move to opposite poles of the cell; by the end of the phase, one complete diploid set of chromosomes has been gathered at each pole (16.2)

androgen male sex hormone (14.3)

andropause in men, a gradual decline in their testosterone level beginning around age 40; symptoms include fatigue, depression, loss of muscle and bone mass, and a drop in sperm production (14.3)

anemia a condition in which there is a deficiency of red blood cells or too little hemoglobin inside the red blood cells in the bloodstream; results in a deficiency of oxygen in the body tissues (8.2)

anorexia nervosa eating disorder characterized by a morbid fear of gaining weight and a misconception of body image; sufferers starve themselves and typically have a body mass less than 85% of their normal mass (6.3)

anoxic non-oxygen containing; compare *oxic* (5.3)

anterior pituitary anterior lobe of the pituitary gland; an endocrine gland that synthesizes and secretes six major hormones: human growth hormone (hGH), prolactin (PRL), thyroid-stimulating hormone (TSH), adrenocorticotropic hormone (ACTH), follicle-stimulating hormone (FSH), and luteinizing hormone (LH); compare *posterior pituitary* (13.2)

antibody proteins that recognize foreign substances in the body and neutralize or destroy them (8.3)

antibody-mediated immunity component of the immune system that involves the activation of lymphocytes and the secretion of antibodies specific to a specific antigen; also known as *specific defence*; compare *cell-mediated immunity* (8.3)

anticodon specialized base triplet located on one lobe of a transfer RNA (tRNA) molecule that recognizes its complementary codon on a messenger RNA (mRNA) molecule (18.2)

antidiuretic hormone (ADH) hormone regulated by the hyphothalamus and released by the pituitary gland that increases the permeability of the distal tubule and the collecting duct in the nephrons of the kidneys, allowing more water to be reabsorbed into the blood from the filtrate (9.3, 13.1)

antigen molecule found on the surface of cells and pathogens; can be recognized by the body's immune system (8.3)

antiparallel describes the property by which the 5' to 3' phosphate bridges run in opposite directions on each strand of nucleotides in a double-stranded DNA molecule (18.1)

anti-sense strand strand of nucleotides in a double-stranded DNA molecule that is complementary to the sense strand and is *not* transcribed; compare *sense strand* (18.2)

aorta major artery that carries oxygenated blood away from the heart to all regions of the body except the lungs (8.1)

aqueous humour clear, watery fluid in the anterior chamber of the eye; maintains the shape of the cornea and provides oxygen and nutrients for the surrounding cells, including those of the lens and cornea (12.2)

arteriosclerosis general term used to describe several conditions in which the walls of the arteries thicken and lose some of their elastic properties, thus becoming harder; the most common type is called atherosclerosis (8.1)

artery blood vessel that carries oxygen-rich blood away from the heart (8.1)

artificial insemination process by which sperm is collected, concentrated, and placed in the female's vagina (15.3)

asexual reproduction reproduction that requires only one parent and does not involve gametes; produces genetically identical offspring (16.4)

asthma chronic, obstructive lung disease that affects the bronchi and bronchioles, making breathing difficult or impossible because of reduced air flow (7.3)

astigmatism uneven curvature of part of the cornea or lens that results in uneven focus and therefore blurry vision (12.2)

asymmetrical cytokinesis unequal division of the cytoplasm that occurs during cell division to form an egg cell during oogenesis (16.3)

ATP adenosine triphosphate; high-energy phosphate molecule that provides and stores energy required for chemical functions (5.1)

atrioventricular (AV) node bundle of specialized muscle tissue located in the wall of the right atrium; receives electrical stimulus from the sinoatrial node and transmits this impulse over the walls of the ventricles to start their contraction; compare *sinoatrial node* (8.1)

atrium (atria) one of the two upper chambers of the heart that collects blood flowing into the heart; right atrium receives blood from systemic circulation, and the left from pulmonary circulation (8.1)

atrophy reduction in the size, tone, and power of a muscle (10.2)

auditory canal tube that conducts sound waves from the outer ear to the tympanum (eardrum) of the middle ear; amplifies sound waves, effectively making sounds louder (12.3)

autoimmune disorder condition in which T cells or antibodies mistakenly attack the body's own cells as if they had foreign antigens (8.3)

autonomic system in vertebrates, the division of the peripheral nervous system that is under involuntary control; regulates glandular secretions and the function of smooth and cardiac muscle; compare *somatic system* (11.1, 11.3)

autosomal inheritance refers to traits—dominant and recessive—that are coded for by genes on autosomes (non-sex chromosomes) (17.3)

autosome chromosome other than a sex chromosome; human somatic cells have 22 pairs of these (16.1)

autotroph *see producer* (1.1)

axon long, cylindrical extension of a neuron's cell body that can range from 1 mm to 1 m in length; transmits impulses away from the cell body along its length to the next neuron (11.1)

B cell lymphocyte that is activated by a specific antigen to produce memory B cells and plasma cells; plasma cells produce antigen specific antibodies; also known as *B lymphocyte*; compare *T cell* (8.3)

B lymphocyte *see B cell* (8.3)

back mutation mutation that reverses the effects of former mutations (19.2)

Barr body structure formed when the inactive X chromosome condenses tightly (17.2)

basilar membrane one of two parallel membranes that comprise the organ of Corti in the inner ear (the other is the tectorial membrane); lies along the base of the organ of Corti; attached to it are sensory mechanoreceptors known as hair cells (12.3)

Batesian mimicry form of mimicry in which an organism resembles another organism with a defense mechanism, but doesn't itself have the defence mechanism; compare *Müllerian mimicry* (20.2)

beta cell cell of the pancreas which secretes insulin to decrease the level of blood glucose; compare *alpha cell* (13.4)

binary fission asexual reproductive process of cell division in bacteria; produces genetically identical populations (16.4)

binocular vision type of vision in humans (and other primates) with forward-facing eyes; both eyes are used to look at and collect visual information about an object, enabling the brain to perceive depth and three-dimensional images (12.2)

binomial nomenclature a system in which a two-word name (genus plus species) is used to identify an organism (3.2)

bioavailability the amount of a nutrient that a person absorbs from a source, rather than the total amount actually in the source (6.2)

biodiversity the variety of species in an area and their range of behavioural, ecological, physiological, and other adaptations (3.3)

biogeochemical cycle the cyclical route taken by water and other chemical nutrients through all biotic and abiotic components of the biosphere (2.1)

biogeography the study of the past and present geographical distribution of species (4.2)

biological barrier factor such as behaviour that keeps species reproductively isolated even when they exist in the same region (4.3)

biological species *see species* (4.1)

biomass total dry mass of all the living, or once-living, organisms in a given population, area, or other unit being measured (1.2)

biome ecosystem or group of ecosystems in a specific region on Earth that has a particular combination of biotic and abiotic factors; for example, tundra, tropical rainforest, hot desert (3.3)

bioremediation use of living cells to perform environmental clean-up tasks, such as using bacteria to degrade PCBs into harmless compounds (18.4)

biosphere all of the areas on Earth (in the air, land, and water) that are inhabited by and that support life (1.1, 3.1)

biotechnology the use of natural biological systems to create useful new technologies and products (18.4)

biotic living; refers to living things in the environment, such as humans, trees, fish, or bacteria (3.1)

biotic potential (r) highest possible per capita growth rate for a population, given unlimited resources and ideal living conditions (20.1)

blastocyst mammalian embryo at the stage in which it is implanted in the wall of the uterus and consists of a nearly hollow ball of cells; is made up of two groups of cells: the trophoblast and the inner cell mass; this stage follows the morula (15.1)

blind spot region of the retina lacking photoreceptors (rods or cones) where the optic nerve leaves the eye; is incapable of detecting light (12.2)

blood pressure pressure exerted against blood vessel walls as circulating blood passes though the vessels (8.1)

blood transfusion introduction of blood or blood products into an artery or vein (8.3)

blood-brain barrier protective barrier formed by glial cells and blood vessels that separates the blood from the central nervous system; selectively controls the entrance of substances into the brain from the blood (11.2)

bolus smooth, lump-like mass of food rolled by the tongue to aid swallowing (6.2)

bottleneck effect gene pool change that results from a rapid decrease in population size (19.2)

Bowman's capsule in the kidney, cap-like formation at the top of each nephron that serves as a filtration structure; surrounds the glomerulus (9.1)

breathing inspiration and expiration; inspiration moves air from the external environment into the lungs, and expiration moves air from the lungs back to the external environment (7.1)

Broca's area one of two important areas on the left side of the cerebral cortex; coordinates the muscles for speaking and translates thought into speech; damage to this area results in an inability to speak but does not affect the understanding of language; compare *Wernicke's area* (11.2)

bronchiole in a mammal, the passageway that branches from the bronchi into the separate lobes of the lungs; divides into smaller and smaller passageways that carry air into all portions of the lungs (7.1)

bronchitis inflammation of the bronchi; can be acute or chronic (7.3)

bronchus (bronchi) in a mammal, the passageway that branches from the trachea into the lungs, with one bronchus carrying air into each lung (7.1)

budding asexual form of reproduction whereby a new organism develops as an outgrowth of the body of the parent (16.4)

bundle of His a bundle of specialized fibres through which an electrical signal is transmitted from the atrioventricular (AV) node, initiating the contraction of the right and left ventricles (8.1)

calcitonin hormone that regulates calcium levels in the blood; stimulates the uptake of calcium into bones when the concentration of calcium in the blood rises too high (13.2)

Calvin-Benson cycle the light-independent process in which photosynthetic organisms fix carbon from atmospheric carbon dioxide to produce carbohydrates (5.2)

cancer group of diseases associated with uncontrolled, rapid cell division (16.2)

capillary the smallest blood vessel; gases and other substances are exchanged between the circulatory system and body tissues across the capillary wall, which is only a single cell thick (8.1)

carbohydrase enzyme that catalyses the hydrolysis of carbohydrates (6.2)

carbohydrate organic macromolecule that contains carbon, hydrogen, and oxygen in a 1:2:1 ratio; examples include monosaccharides, disaccharides, and polysaccharides (6.1)

carbon dioxide fixation the first stage in the synthesis of carbohydrates through the Calvin-Benson cycle; a carbon atom in carbon dioxide is chemically bonded to a pre-existing 5-carbon compound (ribulose bisphosphate or RuBP) in the stroma of a chloroplast (5.2)

carcinogen cancer-causing agent (7.3)

carcinogenic cancer-causing; describes a factor, such as a chemical mutagen, that is associated with one or more forms of cancer (18.3)

carcinoma malignant tumour (7.3)

cardiac muscle striated, involuntary muscle found only in the heart (10.1)

carnivore an animal that eats other animals; compare *herbivore* (1.1)

carrying capacity (K) theoretical maximum population size that the environment can sustain over an extended period of time; may change over time as the habitat changes (20.1)

catabolic compound-decomposing metabolic reaction (5.1)

catalyst chemical that speeds up a chemical reaction but is not used up in the reaction (6.1)

cataract cloudy, or opaque, grey-white area on the lens of the eye caused by the degeneration of the protein structure of the lens; prevents the passing of light; increases in size over time and can lead to blindness if not medically treated (12.2)

CCK cholecystokinin; one of three enzymes (including secretin and GIP) secreted into the bloodstream by the duodenum, causing inhibition of stomach movement and secretions, and enabling fatty meals to remain in the stomach longer than non-fatty meals; also stimulates increased pancreatic secretions of digestive enzymes and gall bladder contractions (6.2)

cell body the main part of a neuron, containing the nucleus and other organelles and serving as the site of the cell's metabolic reactions; processes input from the dendrites and, if the input received is large enough, relays it to the axon, where an impulse is initiated (11.1)

cell cycle a continuous sequence of cell growth and division; the life cycle of a cell (16.1)

cell plate structure across a dividing plant cell that signals the location of new plasma membranes and cell walls (16.2)

cell-mediated immunity non-specific component of the immune system that involves the activation of white blood cells, specifically macrophages, neutrophils and monocytes, rather than the production of antibodies; also known as *non-specific defence*; compare *antibody-mediated immunity* (8.3)

cellular respiration process in which, mitochondria in the cells of plants, animals, and other multicellular organisms break down carbohydrates and other energy-rich products derived from them, such as fats, to generate molecules of ATP (1.1, 5.1)

central nervous system network of nerves that includes the brain and spinal cord; integrates and processes information sent by nerves (11.1)

centriole one of a pair of cylindrical organelles that moves to opposite poles of the cell during prophase of mitosis; provides an attachment for the spindle apparatus (16.2)

centromere the point at which two sister chromatids of a chromosome are joined and to which the spindle fibres are attached during mitosis (16.1)

cerebellum the part of the hindbrain involved in the unconscious coordination of posture, reflexes, and body movements, as well as fine, voluntary motor skills (11.2)

cerebral cortex thin outer covering of grey matter that covers each cerebral hemisphere of the brain; responsible for language, memory, personality, conscious thought, and other activities that are associated with thinking and feeling (11.2)

cerebrospinal fluid dense, clear liquid derived from blood plasma, found in the ventricles of the brain, in the central canal of the spinal cord, and in association with the meninges; transports hormones, white blood cells, and nutrients across the blood-brain barrier to the cells of the brain and spinal cord; acts as a shock absorber to cushion the brain (11.2)

cerebrum the largest part of the brain, divided into right and left cerebral hemispheres, which contains the centres for intellect, memory, consciousness, and language; interprets and controls the response to sensory information (11.2)

cervix in females, the narrow opening of the uterus that connects to the vagina (14.1)

Chargaff's rule in any sample of DNA, a constant relationship in which the amount of adenine is always approximately equal to the amount of thymine, and the amount of cytosine is always approximately equal to the amount of guanine (18.1)

chemical mutagen molecule that can enter the cell nucleus and induce a permanent change in the genetic material of the cell by reacting chemically with DNA; e.g., nitrites (18.3)

chemiosmosis process through which ATP is generated across the inner membrane of mitochondria and the thylakoid membrane of chloroplasts; couples the movement of hydrogen ions down a concentration gradient to the synthesis of ATP from ADP and phosphate (5.2, 5.3)

chemoreceptor sensory receptor that is sensitive to chemical stimulation; e.g., taste, smell, and blood pH (12.1)

chemosynthesis the process by which certain fungi and bacteria use the energy from chemical nutrients to chemically convert carbon (inorganic) into carbohydrates (organic) such as sugars and starches in the absence of sunlight (1.1)

chlamydia a sexually transmitted infection caused by the bacterium *Chlamydia trachomatis*; symptoms may include discharge from the penis or vagina, burning pain while urinating, or fever; left untreated, the disease can lead to pelvic inflammatory disease (PID) (14.2)

chlorophyll photosynthetic pigment located in the thylakoid membranes within chloroplasts (5.1)

chloroplast organelle within photosynthetic plants, algae, and some bacteria that uses the Sun's light energy to chemically convert carbon (inorganic) into carbohydrates (organic) such as sugars and starches; contains the photosynthetic pigment chlorophyll (5.1)

cholinesterase enzyme that breaks down the neurotransmitter acetylcholine in a synapse (11.1)

chorion in humans, membrane developed from the trophoblast layer of the blastocyst; develops into the fetal part of the placenta; is the outermost of the extra-embryonic membranes which encloses all the other membranes, as well as the embryo (15.1)

chorionic villi sampling procedure where fetal cells are removed from the chorion (a tissue that surrounds the amniotic sac and makes up the fetal placenta) to perform a genetic analysis; can be performed around the 9th week of pregnancy (18.4)

choroid vascular membrane of the eye that lies between the retina and the sclera; absorbs stray light rays that are not detected by the photoreceptors in the retina (12.2)

chromatin long fibres that form chromosomes and contain DNA, a small amount of RNA, and various proteins; non-condensed form of genetic material that predominates for most of the cell cycle (16.1)

chromosomal sex genetic sex of an individual, as determined by the type of sex chromosomes within the gametes at fertilization (14.3)

chromosome a length of DNA and its associated proteins (16.1)

chromosome mapping process for determining the relative position of genes on a chromosome (17.2)

chromosome theory of inheritance theory proposed by Walter Sutton that genes are carried on chromosomes (17.1)

chyme thick liquid formed by mixing food with gastric juice in the stomach (6.2)

circadian rhythm internal signal or 'clock' that tells your body when to sleep and wake (13.1)

circulatory system in animals, the system of vessels that transports blood, and the cells and substances suspended and dissolved in blood, throughout the body (8.1)

circumcision surgical removal of the foreskin of the penis (14.1)

cirrhosis a disorder of the liver in which scar tissue replaces healthy liver tissue and prevents the liver from functioning properly (6.3)

cleavage the process of cell division without cell growth; after fertilization, the zygote undergoes repeated cleavage without increasing in overall size (15.1)

climate average weather conditions in a particular region over a period of time, usually 30 years or more (3.3)

climax community the last or final stage of succession in an area; may remain relatively stable if there are no major environmental changes (20.2)

clone one of a pair of organisms (or more) that are genetically identical (18.4)

clumped distribution distribution of individuals in close proximity to each other throughout a suitable habitat; occurs when individuals tend to congregate where food, water, or shelter is most abundant (20.1)

cochlea one of the three components of the inner ear (cochlea, vestibule, and semicircular canals); involved in hearing; within the cochlea, the mechanical energy of sound is converted into electrochemical impulses that are transmitted to the brain (12.3)

co-dominance describes a situation in which two alleles may be expressed equally; occurs when two different alleles for a trait are both dominant (17.1)

codon in a gene, each set of three bases (for example, ACC or GAA) that code for an amino acid or a termination signal (18.2)

coenzyme chemical needed to make enzymes function (6.1)

co-evolve to evolve (change in traits over time) together, as occurs with two species that are closely associated with one another (20.2)

cohesion intermolecular force that holds molecules of a liquid or a solid together; for example, the attraction of water molecules to each other, resulting in surface tension (2.1)

collecting duct in the kidneys, large, pipe-like channel arising from the tubule connected to the Bowman's capsule in the nephron; functions as a water-conservation device, reabsorbing water from the filtrate in the nephron (9.1)

colour blindness inability to distinguish between or recognize some colours, typically shades of red and green; an inherited condition that occurs more frequently in males than in females; caused by a lack of particular cones, usually red and green (12.2)

commensalism a type of symbiotic relationship in which one individual lives close to or on another and benefits, and the host neither benefits, nor is harmed; compare *mutualism* and *parasitism* (20.2)

community all of the organisms in all the interacting populations in a given area (3.1)

competitive inhibitor *molecule that is able to bind with the active site of an enzyme, thus competing with the substrate to occupy this active site*; if the inhibitor is plentiful, it will occupy the active site, blocking the substrate from binding and stopping enzyme activity; compare *non-competitive inhibitor* (6.1)

complementary base pairs refers to the hydrogen-bonded, nitrogenous base pairs of adenosine and thymine, and of cytosine and guanine in the DNA double helix, or to the base pairs of adenosine and uracil, and of cytosine and guanine in hybrid molecules that link complementary strands of RNA and DNA (18.1)

complete dominance a condition in which the dominant allele of a gene completely conceals the presence of the recessive allele of a gene; an individual with one recessive and one dominant allele has the same observable physical characteristic as an individual with two dominant alleles; compare *incomplete dominance* (17.1)

cone a type of photoreceptor in the eye that is sensitive to different colours; compare *rod* (12.2)

conjugation in micro-organisms, a process of reproduction that involves the transfer of genetic material from one cell to another by cell-to-cell contact through a bridging structure; creates cells with new genetic combinations (16.4)

consumer an organism that cannot synthesize its own food through photosynthesis or chemosynthesis, and must derive some of its nutrients from organic molecules formed by producers (autotrophs); also known as a *heterotroph* (1.1)

continuous trait a trait for which the phenotypes vary smoothly from one extreme to another (17.2)

contraceptive technology any technology that reduces reproductive potential (15.3)

copy DNA (cDNA) artificial form of DNA synthesized from the mRNA of cell samples during a DNA microarray experiment (18.4)

cornea the transparent part of the sclera at the front of the eye, through which light enters (12.2)

corona radiata several jelly-like layers of follicle cells that loosely adhere to one another and surround the egg (15.1)

coronary pathway in animals, the circulatory pathway that supplies oxygen-rich blood to and carries deoxygenated blood from the muscle tissue of the heart (8.1)

corpus callosum bundle of white matter that joins the two cerebral hemispheres of the cerebrum of the brain; sends messages from one cerebral hemisphere to the other, telling each half of the brain what the other half is doing (11.2)

corpus luteum yellowish, gland-like structure that develops from a follicle that has matured and released its egg (ovum); it produces progesterone and some estrogen; if pregnancy doesn't occur, it degenerates (14.3)

cortisol a type of glucocorticoid hormone released by the adrenal cortex of the adrenal gland in a long-term stress response; triggers an increase in blood glucose levels and reduces inflammation (13.3)

Cowper's gland gland in human males that secretes mucus-like fluids into the urethra (14.1)

creatine phosphate a high-energy compound that regenerates ATP in muscle cells (10.1)

cretinism condition in which the thyroid fails to develop properly during childhood; individual has severe hyperthyroidism; characterized by a short, stocky figure, as well as developmental delays if not treated early in life (13.2)

crista (cristae) short, fingerlike projection formed by the folding of the inner membrane of a mitochondrion; provides a large surface area for the production of ATP (5.1)

crossing over the process by which non-sister chromatids exchange genes during prophase I of meiosis, allowing for the recombination of genes (16.3, 17.2)

cryptic coloration type of camouflage that makes potential prey difficult to spot (20.2)

cystic fibrosis a genetic condition that disrupts the function of the cells lining the passageways of the lungs; causes the usually thin mucus and liquid coating on the insides of the lungs to becomes very thick and sticky, leading to breathing problems (7.3)

cytokinesis one of the two main processes in cell division; consists of separation of cytoplasm and organelles and the formation of two daughter cells; *see also asymmetrical cytokinesis* (16.1)

daughter cell any one of two cells produced from the division of a parent cell (16.1)

decomposer organism, usually a bacterium, fungus, earthworm, or insect, that obtains energy by consuming dead plant and animal matter, or waste (1.1)

dehydration synthesis chemical reaction that results in the formation of a covalent bond between two subunit molecules by the removal of an −OH (hydroxyl) group from one subunit and a hydrogen atom from the other subunit; essentially, a molecule of water (H_2O) is removed; compare *hydrolysis* (6.1)

denature to alter the natural structural state of molecules such as nucleic acids and proteins, thereby disrupting their biological activity (6.1)

dendrite short, branching terminal on a nerve cell (neuron) that receives signals from other neurons or sensory receptors and relays the impulse to the cell body; numerous and highly branched (11.1)

denitrification conversion of nitrate or nitrite to nitrogen gas by bacteria in soil (2.2)

density in population dynamics, the number of individuals per unit of area or volume in a population (3.3)

density-dependent factor biotic factor that limits a habitat's carrying capacity (e.g., parasites, disease); the impact increases with the density of the population; compare *density-independent factor* (20.1)

density-independent factor abiotic factor that limits a habitat's carrying capacity (e.g., fire, flood); the impact is not affected by the density of the population; compare *density-dependent factor* (20.1)

deoxyribonucleic acid (DNA) a double-stranded nucleic acid molecule that governs the processes of heredity in the cells of organisms; composed of nucleotides containing a phosphate group, a nitrogenous base (adenine, guanine, cytosine, or thymine), and deoxyribose (16.1, 18.1)

depolarization in a neuronal membrane, reducing a membrane potential to less than the resting potential of −70 mV (11.1)

diabetes insipidus a disorder characterized by excessive thirst, weakness, and heavy and frequent urination due to insufficient levels of anti-diuretic hormone (ADH) (9.3)

diabetes mellitus a serious chronic condition that results when the pancreas does not make enough insulin or the body does not respond properly to insulin; levels of blood glucose tend to rise sharply after meals (hyperglycemia) and remain at significantly elevated levels (13.4)

dialysis procedure that removes wastes and excess fluid from the blood when kidney function is lost due to renal failure; based on the principle of diffusion of dissolved substances along a concentration gradient through a semipermeable membrane (9.3)

diaphragm in mammals, a muscle layer that separates the region of the lungs (thoracic cavity) from the region of the stomach and liver (abdominal cavity); contraction contributes to inspiration by increasing the volume of the thoracic cavity (7.2)

diastolic pressure the lowest blood pressure exerted before the ventricles contract; compare *systolic pressure* (8.1)

dichotomous key identification key that uses a series of paired comparisons to sort organisms into smaller and smaller groups (3.2)

differentiation cellular process that enables a cell to develop a particular shape and to perform specific functions that are different from the functions of other cells (15.1)

digestive system in animals, the system into which food is taken and broken down so that useful substances can be absorbed into and transported by the circulatory (blood) system to individual cells (6.2)

digestive tract in animals, a long tube that extends from the mouth to the anus, through which food moves and is broken down into simpler compounds that are used for energy, growth, and cell repair (6.2)

dihybrid cross cross of two individuals that differ in two traits (17.1)

diploid describing a cell that contains two pairs of every chromosome, designated as 2n; e.g., somatic cells; compare *haploid* (16.1)

disaccharide sugar that can be hydrolysized into two monosaccharide subunits; examples include maltose and sucrose (6.1)

distal tubule in the kidney, tubular portion of the nephron that lies between the loop of Henle and the proximal tubule; main function is reabsorption of water and solutes, and secretion of various substances (9.2)

distribution pattern pattern in which a population is distributed or spread in an area; three types are uniform, random, and clumped (20.1)

divergence the development of one or more new species from a parent species as a result of mutation and adaptation to changing environmental conditions; the parent species continues to exist; compare *transformation* (4.3)

DNA fingerprint the pattern of bands into which DNA fragments sort during gel electrophoresis (18.3)

DNA ligase enzyme that splices together Okazaki fragments during DNA replication on the lagging strand or sticky ends that have been cut by a restriction endonuclease; catalyzes the formation of phosphate bonds between nucleotides (18.1, 18.3)

DNA microarray a chip (usually a glass microscope slide or polymer membrane) that contains a grid of thousands of microscopic cells; each cell contains a nucleic acid sequence that can bind with one of the mRNA molecules transcribed during gene expression; allows scientists to analyze the activity of thousands of genes at once (18.4)

DNA polymerase during DNA replication, an enzyme that slips into the space between two strands, uses the parent strands as a template, and adds nucleotides to make complementary strands (18.1)

DNA probe molecule of DNA with a nucleic acid sequence that is labelled with a radioactive or fluorescent chemical tag; binds to a complementary DNA sequence and can be used to locate a specific genetic marker (18.4)

DNA sequencing the process of identifying the precise nucleotide sequence of a DNA fragment (18.1)

DNA vector in gene therapy, something (commonly, a modified form of virus) that carries recombinant DNA containing a desired gene into a host cell in order to incorporate the gene into a patient's genome (18.4)

domain highest level of classification of living things (above kingdom); the three domains are Bacteria, Archaea, and Eukarya (3.2)

dominant describes a trait which always appears (is expressed) in an individual that is either heterozygous (*Aa*) or homozygous (*AA*) for that trait (17.1)

double helix spiral shape most commonly associated with DNA, made up of two long strands of nucleotides bound together and twisted (18.1)

ductus deferens (ductus deferentia) a storage duct from the epididymis leading to the penis via the ejaculatory duct; formerly known as *vas deferens* (14.1)

duodenum the first 25 cm of the small intestine; important site of chemical digestion of chyme from the stomach (6.2)

ecological community an association of interacting populations that inhabit a defined area (20.2)

ecological disturbance event that changes the structure of a community, sometimes destroying all actively growing organisms (20.2)

ecological niche the role that members of a population play in a community, including the resources that members need and the way in which members interact with other members of the population and the community (3.3)

ecological pyramid a pyramid-shaped model depicting patterns in distribution of energy, biomass and/or numbers of organisms among trophic levels (1.2)

ecology the study of the relationships between living things (organisms) and their non-living surroundings, the environment (1.1)

ecosystem a community of populations, together with the abiotic factors that surround and affect it (1.2, 3.1)

ecotourism form of tourism which incorporates the practice of sustainability (20.3)

ectoderm outermost germ layer formed during animal embryogenesis (15.1)

ejaculation release of semen from the penis (14.1)

ejaculatory duct tube connecting the ductus deferens to the penis (14.1)

electron transport system in mitochondria and chloroplasts, a system of electron-carrying molecules that transfer electrons to generate a hydrogen ion gradient across a thylakoid or inner mitochondrial membrane to produce ATP (5.2, 5.3)

elongation the process of joining nucleotides to extend a new strand of DNA; relies on the action of DNA polymerase (18.1)

embryonic disk flattened, disk-shaped structure formed from the inner cell mass of the blastocyst during the second week after fertilization (15.1)

embryonic period of development the first of two main periods of prenatal development, taking place over the first eight weeks of the first trimester; during this time, cells divide and become redistributed, and tissues and organs form, as do structures that support and nourish the developing embryo; compare *fetal period of development* (15.1)

emigration migration of individuals out of a population; compare *immigration* (20.1)

emphysema obstructive respiratory disorder in which the walls of the alveoli break down and lose their elasticity; reduces the surface area for gas exchange and causes oxygen shortages in the tissues (7.3)

endocrine glands ductless glands that secrete hormones directly into the bloodstream (13.1)

endocrine system in vertebrates, system that works in parallel with the nervous system to maintain homeostasis by releasing chemical hormones from various glands; composed of the hormone-producing glands and tissues of the body (13.1)

endoderm the innermost germ layer formed during animal embryogenesis (15.1)

endometrium the mucous membrane that lines the uterus and increases in thickness in the latter part of the menstrual cycle; is richly supplied with blood vessels to provide nutrients for the fetus (14.1)

endosymbiont theory theory proposing that eukaryotic cells arose through a process in which one species of prokaryote was engulfed by another, thereby creating organelles (18.3)

environmental resistance combined effects of various interacting factors that limit population growth; prevents a population from growing at its biotic potential and determines the carrying capacity of the habitat (20.1)

enzyme protein molecule that acts as a catalyst to increase the rate of a reaction (6.1)

epididymis (epididymides) in human males, a narrow, tightly coiled tube connecting the seminiferous tubules to the ductus deferens; within, the sperm mature and become motile (14.1)

epiglottis in mammals, flap of cartilage located over the entrance to the trachea (called the glottis); closes during swallowing to prevent food from entering the respiratory tract (7.1)

epinephrine hormone produced by the adrenal cortex hormones that helps regulate the short-term stress response; also known as *adrenaline* (13.2, 13.3)

equilibrium state of balance in a system in which there is no net change over time (2.3)

erythrocyte blood cell that contains the respiratory protein hemoglobin and is specialized for oxygen transport; also known as *red blood cell* (8.2)

esophageal sphincter a muscular ring between the esophagus and the stomach that controls the movement of food into and out of the stomach (6.2)

esophagus muscular portion of the digestive tract that directs food from the mouth to the stomach (6.2)

essential amino acid refers to the any of the nine of twenty amino acids that must come from the diet because the human body cannot synthesize them (6.1)

estrogen female sex hormone produced in the ovary; helps maintain sexual organs and secondary sexual characteristics (14.3)

ethanol fermentation type of fermentation in which yeasts and some kinds of bacteria convert pyruvate to ethanol and carbon dioxide when low oxygen conditions inhibit aerobic respiration; compare *lactate fermentation* (5.3)

eukaryote organism characterized by cells that contain membrane-bound, structurally distinct nuclei and other membrane-bound organelles; compare *prokaryote* (3.2)

Eustachian tube bony passage extending from the middle ear to the throat; plays a role in equalizing air pressure on both sides of the eardrum (12.3)

evapotranspiration combined evaporation and transpiration of plants from a terrestrial area (2.1)

excretion process of separating wastes from body fluids and eliminating them from the body; performed by several body systems, including respiratory (excretes carbon dioxide and small amounts of other gases, including water vapour), skin (excretes water, salts, and some urea in perspiration), digestive (excretes water, salts, lipids, and a variety of pigments and other cellular chemicals), and excretory (excretes metabolic wastes that are dissolved or suspended in solution) systems (9.1)

excretory system in animals, the system that regulates the volume and composition of body fluids by excreting metabolic wastes and recycling some substances for reuse; main organs include the kidneys, ureters, bladder, and urethra; also known as the *urinary system* (9.1)

exhalation movement of air out of the lungs during breathing; also known as *expiration* (7.2)

exocrine gland gland which secretes hormones via ducts (13.4)

expiratory reserve volume additional volume of air that can be forced out of the lungs, beyond a regular, or tidal, exhalation (7.2)

exponential growth growth, particularly of a population, in which the increase occurs by a repeated doubling in number (16.4)

exponential growth pattern pattern exhibited by a population which is increasing exponentially (i.e., doubles repeatedly); results in a J-shaped curve showing a brief lag phase, followed by a steep increase in the growth curve (20.1)

exponential growth phase stage in the growth of a population at which birth rate is much higher than death rate because competition for resources is not yet a limiting factor; compare *lag phase* and *stationary phase* (20.1)

external respiration exchange of oxygen and carbon dioxide between the air and the blood; takes place in the lungs; compare *internal respiration* (7.2)

extra-embryonic membrane any in an intricate system of membranes external to the embryo; responsible for the protection, nutrition, respiration, and excretion of the embryo and fetus (15.1)

FAD flavin adenine dinucleotide; coenzyme that functions as a carrier of electrons and hydrogen ions; important coenzyme in electron transport in the Krebs cycle (5.3)

FADH$_2$ reduced form of FAD that can act as an electron donor; important coenzyme in electron transport in the Krebs cycle (5.3)

Fallopian tube see *oviduct* (14.1)

fast-twitch fibre muscle fibre that produces most of its energy anaerobically; adapted for the rapid generation of power, but dependence on anaerobically produced energy results in vulnerability to accumulation of lactate, causing rapid fatigue; also called *Type II fibre*; compare *slow-twitch fibre* (10.2)

fat lipid that is usually of animal origin and solid at room temperature (6.1)

fermentation energy-yielding metabolic pathway in which carbohydrates are anaerobically broken down into simpler components; includes glycolysis and is widely occurring in yeast and bacteria (5.3)

fertilization in humans, the joining of male and female gametes (sperm and egg) to form a single cell that contains 23 chromosomes from each parent, for a total of 46 chromosomes (15.1)

fetal alcohol spectrum disorder (FASD) term used to describe all the disorders related to alcohol consumption during pregnancy; includes the more commonly known clinical disorder called fetal alcohol syndrome (FAS) (15.2)

fetal period of development the second of two main periods of prenatal development, taking place from the start of the ninth week through to birth; during this time, the fetus grows rapidly and organs begin to function and coordinate to form organ systems; compare *embryonic period of development* (15.1)

fight-or-flight response see *short-term stress response* (13.3)

filial generation in breeding, the offspring of a cross; first filial (F_1) generation is the offspring of a cross of the parental generation, second filial (F_2) generation is the offspring of a cross between two organisms in the F_1 generation, and so forth (17.1)

filtrate in the kidney, filtered fluid that proceeds from the glomerulus into the Bowman's capsule of the nephron (9.1)

fimbria (fimbriae) thread-like projections that sweep the released ovum from the ovary into the cilia-lined oviduct (14.1)

first law of thermodynamics law stating that energy cannot be created or destroyed but can only change form (1.1)

first polar body cell that receives the smaller portion of cytoplasm when a primary oocyte undergoes asymmetrical cytokinesis during meiosis I; is not functional and soon degenerates; compare *secondary oocyte* (16.3)

fixation (carbon dioxide) see *carbon dioxide fixation* (5.2)

follicle in the female reproductive system, specialized cell structure within the ovaries; each one contains an ovum (egg) that will be released (14.1)

follicle-stimulating hormone (FSH) reproductive hormone produced by the anterior pituitary gland; stimulates the development of the sex organs and gamete production in males and females (14.3)

follicular stage the first stage of the ovarian cycle (part of the menstrual cycle), during which increased levels of FSH stimulate the follicles to release increased quantities of estrogen and some progesterone into the bloodstream, leading to the release of an egg (ovum) from the follicle (14.3)

food chain model showing the linear pathways through which food (energy) is transferred from producers to primary consumers and to higher trophic levels (1.2)

food web model of food (energy) transfer in an ecosystem that shows the connections among food chains (1.2)

formed portion solid portion of the blood consisting of red blood cells, white blood cells, and platelets (8.2)

fossil record remains and traces of past life found in sedimentary rock, which reveals the history of life on Earth and the kinds of organisms that were alive in the past (4.2)

founder effect gene pool change that occurs when a few individuals start a new, isolated population; for example, on islands (19.2)

founders individuals forming a new population (19.2)

fovea centralis concentration of cones on the retina; located directly behind the centre of the lens (12.2)

fragmentation form of asexual reproduction in which a new organism is created from a fragment (portion) of a parent organism (16.4)

frameshift mutation permanent change in the genetic material of a cell caused by the insertion or deletion of one or two nucleotides so that the entire reading frame of the gene is altered; usually results in a nonsense mutation (18.3)

fraternal twins twins resulting from the simultaneous fertilization and implantation of two eggs; no more genetically alike than other siblings; compare *identical twins* (16.3)

frontal lobe one of four lobes into which each hemisphere of the cerebral cortex is divided; integrates information from other parts of the brain and controls reasoning, critical thinking, memory, and personality; the Broca's area of the frontal lobes is associated with language use; as well, contains motor areas control various aspects of precise, voluntary movement (11.2)

G1 phase the first part of interphase, a somatic cell's growth stage, during which cells carry out rapid growth and metabolic activity; also known as *Growth 1* or *Gap 1* (16.1)

G2 phase the last part of interphase, a somatic cell's growth stage, during which the cell rebuilds its reserves of energy and manufactures proteins and other molecules to prepare for division; also known as *Growth 2* or *Gap 2* (16.1)

gall bladder organ that stores bile produced by the liver (6.2)

gallstone small, hard mass that forms in the gall bladder when cholesterol precipitates out of the bile and forms crystals that grow in size (6.3)

gamete male or female haploid reproductive cell; e.g., egg (ovum) and sperm (14.1, 16.1)

gametophyte haploid generation of a plant; produces male and female gametes that fuse at fertilization to form a diploid sporophyte; also see *alternation of generations* (16.4)

gastrin stomach hormone that stimulates the secretion of hydrochloric acid and the inactive precursor molecule of pepsin from glands in the stomach (6.2)

gastrula term used for the developing embryo after the formation of the three primary germ layers (15.1)

gastrulation the formation of the three primary germ layers in embryogenesis (15.1)

gel electrophoresis tool used to separate molecules according to their mass and charge; can be used to separate fragments of DNA (18.3)

gene the basic unit of heredity; a specific sequence of DNA that encodes a protein, tRNA, rRNA molecule, or regulates the transcription of such a sequence; governs the expression of a particular trait and can be passed to an offspring (16.1, 18.1, 19.1)

gene expression the transfer of genetic information from DNA to RNA to protein (18.2)

gene flow net movement of alleles from one population to another due to the migration of individuals and subsequent interbreeding (19.2)

gene pool total of all the alleles for all the genes of all the individuals in a population (19.1)

gene therapy the process of changing the function of genes to treat or prevent genetic disorders (18.4)

gene-chromosome theory theory stating that genes exist at specific sites arranged in a linear manner along chromosomes; an amendment to the chromosome theory of inheritance (17.2)

genetic code the order of base pairs in a DNA molecule (18.2)

genetic counsellor person who uses an understanding of genetics to predict and explain traits in children (17.3)

genetic diversity degree of genetic variation within a species or population (19.2)

genetic drift change in allele frequencies due to chance events in a small breeding population; see also *founder effect* and *bottleneck effect* (19.2)

genetic engineering manipulation of genetic material to alter genes and blend plant, animal, and bacterial DNA (18.3)

genetic equilibrium condition of a gene pool in which allele frequencies remain constant over time; a population at genetic equilibrium is not changing or evolving; also known as *Hardy-Weinberg equilibrium* (19.1)

genetic marker a characteristic that provides information about the genotype of an individual (18.4)

genetic screening any of several methods of identifying people who are at risk of developing particular genetic conditions or of passing these conditions on to their children (17.3)

genital herpes a sexually transmitted infection caused by one of two herpes viruses: herpes simplex 1 (HSV 1) or herpes simplex 2 (HSV 2); symptoms include painful, fluid-filled blisters on the genitalia that may be accompanied by flu-like symptoms (14.2)

genital wart flat or raised warts around the genital area, caused by human papilloma virus (HPV) (14.2)

genome the sum of all the DNA carried in an organism's cells (18.1)

genomics the study of genomes as opposed to individual genes (18.2)

genotype the combination of alleles for any given trait; compare *phenotype* (17.1)

genotype frequency proportion of members of a population with a particular genotype; usually expressed as a decimal (19.1)

geographical barrier feature such as a river or mountain that prohibits interbreeding and results in speciation by physically separating populations (4.3)

germ cell gamete-producing cell in the male and female gonads (16.3)

germ layers see *primary germ layers* (15.1)

germ line mutation permanent change in the genetic material of a reproductive cell during the lifetime of an organism that is passed on to future generations; compare *somatic cell mutation* (18.3)

germ-line therapy gene therapy used to modify the genetic information carried in egg and sperm cells; see also *gene therapy* (18.4)

GIP gastric inhibitory peptide; one of three enzymes (including secretin and CCK) secreted into the bloodstream by the duodenum, causing inhibition of stomach movement and secretions, and enabling fatty meals to remain in the stomach longer than non-fatty meals (6.2)

glaucoma condition caused when ducts that drain the aqueous humour in the eye are blocked; resulting pressure ruptures delicate blood vessels in the eye and causes deterioration of the cells due to a lack of oxygen and nutrients; can lead to blindness if untreated (12.2)

glial cell support cell of the nervous system that nourishes neurons (nerve-impulse conducting cells), removes their wastes, defends against infection, and provides a supporting framework for all the nervous system tissue (11.1)

glomerular filtration in the kidney, process that results in the movement of water and solutes, except proteins, from the blood plasma into the nephron down a pressure gradient (9.2)

glomerulus in the kidney, a fine network of capillaries within the Bowman's capsule of the nephron; arising from the renal artery, the walls of the glomerulus act as a filtration device (9.1)

glottis in mammals, the opening of the trachea through which air enters the larynx (7.1)

glucagon hormone produced by the alpha cells of the islets of Langerhans in the pancreas to stimulate the liver to convert glycogen back into glucose, which is released into the blood (13.4)

glucocorticoid hormone produced by the adrenal cortex to stimulate tissues to raise blood glucose; e.g., cortisol (13.3)

glycolysis energy-yielding metabolic pathway in which one glucose molecule (with six carbons) is broken down to form two pyruvate molecules (with three carbons each), as well as a small amount of ATP; the first step in both aerobic and anaerobic respiration (5.3)

goitre enlargement of the thyroid gland characterized by a large swelling in the throat, often associated with a deficiency of iodine; occurs when the thyroid gland is constantly stimulated by thyroxine-stimulating hormone (TSH), but is unable to synthesize thyroxine to create a negative feedback loop (13.2)

gonad organ that produces reproductive cells (gametes); the ovary produces eggs (ova), and the testis produces sperm (14.1)

gonadocorticoid hormone produced by the adrenal cortex which supplements the sex hormones produced by the gonads (testes and ovaries) (13.3)

gonadotropin releasing hormone (GnRH) hormone produced by the hypothalamus; acts on the anterior pituitary gland to cause it to release two different sex hormones: luteinizing hormone (LH) and follicle-stimulating hormone (FSH) (14.3)

gonorrhea a sexually transmitted infection caused by the bacterium *Neisseria gonorrhoeae*; can result in infection of the urethra, cervix, rectum, and throat; left untreated, the disease can lead to PID and may spread through the bloodstream to the joints, heart, or brain (14.2)

gradualism in evolution, the theory that change occurs slowly and steadily in a linear fashion, and that large changes occur through the accumulation of many small changes (4.3)

granulocyte a type of white blood cell containing granules in its cytoplasm; the three types of granulocytes are neutrophils, basophils, and eosinophils (8.2)

granum (grana) stack of chlorophyll-containing thylakoids within a chloroplast (5.1)

Graves' disease a severe state of hyperthyroidism that results when the body's immune system attacks the thyroid; antibodies attach to TSH receptors on thyroid cells, causing the thyroid gland to produce too much thyroxine (13.2)

gravitational equilibrium balance required while moving the head forward and backward (12.3)

grey matter part of the nervous system that contains mostly cell bodies, dendrites, and short, unmyelinated nerve fibres; brownish-grey in colour; forms the outer areas of the brain and the H-shaped core of the spinal cord; compare *white matter* (11.1, 11.2)

growth rate (gr) change in population size (N) over a specific time frame (t); N is equivalent to the number of births plus immigration *minus* the number of deaths plus emigration; expressed as $gr = \dfrac{N}{t}$ (20.1)

H

habitat place or area with a particular set of characteristics, both biotic and abiotic, in which an organism lives and is able to survive and reproduce because of particular physical, physiological, and behavioural adaptations (3.3)

hair cell sensory mechanoreceptor attached to the basilar membrane in the organ of Corti within the inner ear (12.3)

haploid describing a cell containing half the number of chromosomes (n) that the diploid (2n) parent cell contains; condition occurring in gametes, either egg (ovum) or sperm; compare *diploid* (16.1)

Hardy-Weinberg equation mathematical description of the Hardy-Weinberg principle; used to predict allele and genotype frequencies in a population; usually stated: if the frequency of allele *A* is p and the frequency of allele *a* is q, then the genotype frequencies after one generation of random mating will always be $p^2 + 2pq + q^2 = 1.00$ (19.1)

Hardy-Weinberg principle principle that states that allele and genotype frequencies remain constant from one generation to the next, as long as five conditions are met: (1) the population is large enough that chance events will not alter allele frequencies, (2) mates are chosen on a random basis, (3) there are no net mutations, (4) there is no migration, and (5) there is no natural selection against any of the phenotypes (19.1)

heat capacity a measure of the amount of heat a substance can absorb or release for a given change in temperature (2.1)

helicase set of enzymes that cleave and unravel short segments of DNA just ahead of the replicating fork during DNA replication (18.1)

helper T cell lymphocyte that, upon recognizing an antigen, gives off chemical signals that stimulate certain immune cells (macrophages, B cells, and other T cells) to perform their respective functions (8.3)

hemodialysis type of renal (kidney) dialysis that utilizes an artificial membrane in an external device and is connected to an artery and a vein in a person's arm to remove waste and excess fluid from the blood when kidney function is lost due to renal failure (9.3)

hemoglobin iron-containing respiratory pigment found in red blood cells that transports oxygen from the lungs to body tissues (8.2)

hemolysis the bursting of red blood cells (8.3)

hemophilia inherited, life-threatening disorder resulting from insufficient clotting proteins in the blood (8.2)

hepatitis inflammation of the liver tissue; the three types are hepatitis A, B, and C (6.3, 14.2)

herbivore organism that eats plants; compare *carnivore* (1.1)

heterotroph see *consumer* (1.1)

heterozygote advantage a survival benefit for those individuals who inherit two different alleles for the same trait (*Aa*), compared to those who are homozygous dominant or homozygous recessive; for example, the allele for cystic fibrosis may help carriers better resist diarrheal diseases such as cholera (17.1, 19.2)

heterozygous describes an individual with two different alleles for a trait (*Aa*); compare *homozygous* (17.1)

histone protein found in chromosomes; acts as scaffold around which DNA winds, enabling it to fit within the small space of the nucleus (16.1)

HIV human immunodeficiency virus; a group of related viruses that destroy the body's capacity for immunity, and so cause AIDS (14.2)

homeostasis the tendency of the body to maintain a relatively constant internal environment (6.0, 11.1)

homologous chromosome chromosome that contains the same gene sequence as another, but that may not be made up of the same alleles; human somatic cells have 22 pairs of these, known as autosomes, and females also have a homologous pair of X sex chromosomes; males have an X and a Y sex chromosome which are not homologous (16.1)

homologous structures body parts in different species that have the same evolutionary origin and structural elements but may have a different function (e.g., bat wing, human arm, dolphin flipper); compare *analogous structures* (4.2)

homozygous describes an individual with two identical alleles for a trait (*AA* or *aa*); compare *heterozygous* (17.1)

hormone chemical messenger sent to many parts of the body to produce a specific effect on a target cell or organ; examples are epinephrine and norepinephrine released from the neurons of the adrenal gland (13.1)

hormone replacement therapy administration of low levels of estrogen and/or progesterone to alleviate symptoms of menopause in females (14.3)

human chorionic gonadotropin (hCG) hormone secreted by the trophoblast at the time of implantation of the embryo; prevents degeneration of the corpus luteum (15.1)

Human Genome Project joint effort of thousands of researchers from laboratories worldwide that determined the sequence of the three billion base pairs making up the human genome (18.1)

human growth hormone (hGH) hormone that ultimately affects almost every body tissue, by direct stimulation or via tropic effects; stimulates the liver to secrete hormones called growth factors, which, along with hGH, influence many physiological processes, such as protein synthesis, cell division and growth, and metabolic breakdown and release of fats (13.2)

human papilloma virus (HPV) virus responsible for a condition known as genital warts; transmitted by skin-to-skin contact (14.2)

hybrid offspring of a cross between two parent organisms with different inheritable traits (17.1)

hydrogen bond weak bond that involves sharing an electron between a slightly positive hydrogen atom and a slightly negative atom, such as oxygen or nitrogen, typically in another molecule (2.1)

hydrologic cycle cycle of evaporation and condensation of water that determines the circulation of water through the atmosphere and biosphere; also known as the *water cycle* (2.1)

hydrolysis chemical reaction in which the addition of a water molecule cleaves a macromolecule into subunits; one hydrogen atom from water is attached to one subunit and a hydroxyl group is bonded to the other subunit, breaking a covalent bond in the macromolecule; compare *dehydration synthesis* (6.1)

hyperglycemia condition resulting from high levels of blood glucose; occurs in individuals with diabetes mellitus (13.4)

hyperopia fair-sightedness, or difficulty seeing things that are nearby; caused by weak ciliary muscles or an eyeball that is too short; compare *myopia* (12.2)

hyperthyroidism condition resulting when the thyroid produces extremely high levels of thyroxine (13.2)

hypertrophy exercise-induced increase in muscle mass due to an increase in the size, not number, of individual skeletal muscle fibres (10.2)

hypothalamus region of the forebrain just below the cerebral hemispheres, under the thalamus; a centre of the autonomic nervous system responsible for the integration and correlation of many neural and endocrine functions; helps to regulate the body's internal environment, as well as certain aspects of behaviour; coordinates the actions of the pituitary gland by producing and regulating the release of certain hormones (11.2)

hypothesis statement that provides one possible answer to a question, or one possible explanation for an observation; also known as *scientific hypothesis* (4.2)

hypothyroidism condition resulting when the thyroid produces extremely low levels of thyroxine (13.2)

identical twins twins resulting when a single zygote divides into two separate cell masses during embryonic development; are genetically identical; compare *fraternal twins* (16.3)

immigration migration of individuals into a population; compare *emigration* (20.1)

immunity ability of the body to protect itself from foreign, disease-causing agents through a specific defence mechanism that uses antibody proteins to recognize, neutralize, and destroy foreign substances (8.3)

implantation the process of attachment of the embryo to the endometrium; occurs within the first week after fertilization in humans (15.1)

in vitro fertilization (IVF) technique in which egg cells are fertilized outside the female's body (15.3)

incomplete dominance a condition in which neither of two alleles for the same gene can completely conceal the presence of the other; compare *complete dominance* (17.1)

induced mutation permanent change in genetic material caused by a mutagen outside the cell (18.3)

infertile condition in which a man or a woman has been trying to conceive children for a year or more unsuccessfully; compare *sterile* (15.3)

inflammatory bowel disease general name for a disease that causes inflammation in the intestines (bowels); examples are Crohn's disease and colitis (6.3)

inhalation movement of air into the lungs during breathing; also known as *inspiration* (7.2)

inheritance of acquired characteristics theory that characteristics acquired during an organism's lifetime could be passed to its offspring (4.2)

inhibin hormone released from the seminiferous tubules; acts on the anterior pituitary to inhibit the production of follicle-stimulating hormone (FSH);

produces a negative feedback loop that controls the rate of sperm formation (14.3)

inhibitor molecule that attaches to an enzyme and reduces its ability to bind substrate; two classes are competitive and non-competitive inhibitors (6.1)

inner cell mass the inner cells of the blastocyst; will develop into the embryo; also known as *embryoblast*; compare *trophoblast* (15.1)

inner ear one of the three separate segments of the ear (outer ear, middle ear, and inner ear); consists of three components: semicircular canals, vestibule (utricle and saccule), and cochlea (12.3)

inspiratory reserve volume additional volume of air that can be taken in by the lungs, beyond a regular, or tidal, inhalation (7.2)

insulin a hormone secreted by the alpha cells of the islets of Langerhans in the pancreas to make target cells more permeable to glucose; enables the body to use sugar and other carbohydrates (13.4)

internal respiration exchange of oxygen and carbon dioxide between the body's tissue cells and the blood (7.2)

interphase growth stage of a somatic cell; there are 3 phases: G1, S, and G2; ends when the cell begins the process of nuclear division (mitosis) (16.1)

interspecific competition competition for limited resources among members of different species; compare *intraspecific competition* (20.2)

interstitial fluid fluid that surrounds all cells in the body; also known as *extracellular fluid* or *tissue fluid* (8.2)

intraspecific competition competition between members of the same population (species) for a limited resource (3.3)

intraspecific competition competition for limited resources among members of the same species; compare *interspecific competition* (20.2)

iris the doughnut-shaped, coloured muscle formed from the choroid at the front of the eye; adjusts the central dark pupil to regulate the amount of light that enters the eye (12.2)

islet of Langerhans cluster of endocrine cells found throughout the pancreas, consisting of glucagon-producing alpha cells and insulin-producing beta cells (13.4)

karyotype the particular set of chromosomes that an individual possesses (16.1)

kidney in vertebrates, one of a pair of organs that filters waste from the blood (which is excreted in urine) and adjusts the concentrations of salts in the blood (9.1)

killer T cell cytotoxic lymphocyte that binds with infected cells and destroys them by puncturing a hole in their membrane; may be activated indirectly by chemical signals from a helper T cell or directly by the presence of the invading pathogen and associated antigens (8.3)

kingdom the second highest taxonomic classification of all living things (below domain); the six kingdoms recognized in biology are Archaea, Bacteria, Protista, Fungi, Plantae, and Animalia. (3.2)

Krebs cycle in cellular respiration, a metabolic pathway consisting of a series of reactions that break down the end products of glycolysis, producing carbon dioxide and generating a large amount of ATP; also known as *citric acid cycle* or *tricarboxylic acid (TCA) cycle* (5.3)

K-selected strategy a life strategy designed to take advantage of stable environmental conditions; characterized by the production of a few offspring with much attention given to offspring survival; organisms that exhibit this strategy include mammals and species that live close to the carrying capacity (K) of their habitats, also known as *K-selection*; compare *r-selected strategy* (20.1)

labia majora along with the labia minora, one of two pairs of external skin folds that protect the vaginal opening (14.1)

labia minora along with the labia majora, one of two pairs of external skin folds that protect the vaginal opening (14.1)

labour all the events associated with parturition (the birthing process) (15.2)

lacation the secretion and formation of breast milk by the mammary glands (15.2)

lactate fermentation type of fermentation in which NADH is used to convert pyruvate to lactate (lactic acid); the resulting NAD+ is recycled to continue the process; carried out by some bacteria, as well as animal muscle cells when demand for energy exceeds aerobic production; compare *ethanol fermentation* (5.3)

lag phase stage at the beginning of growth in a small population in which the rate of growth is slow, since there are only a few individuals to reproduce;

compare *exponential growth phase* and *stationary phase* (20.1)

lagging strand in DNA replication, the strand that is replicated in short segments rather than continuously; compare *leading strand* (18.1)

large intestine final portion of the digestive system; about 1.5 m long, and wider in diameter than the small intestine; comprised of the caecum, colon, rectum, and anal canal; main function is to concentrate and eliminate waste materials (6.2)

laryngitis inflammation of the larynx (7.3)

larynx in mammals, a structure within the upper respiratory tract that contains the vocal cords; also commonly known as *voice box* (7.1)

law of independent assortment Mendel's second law of inheritance, stating that the two alleles for one gene segregate (assort) independently of the alleles for other genes during gamete formation (17.1)

law of segregation Mendel's first law of inheritance, stating that all individuals have two copies of each factor (gene); these copies segregate (separate) randomly during gamete formation, and each gamete receives one copy of every factor (gene) (17.1)

leading strand in DNA replication, the strand that is replicated continuously; compare *lagging strand* (18.1)

lens clear, flexible part of the eye that focusses images on the retina (12.2)

leucocyte see *white blood cell* (8.2)

leukemia cancer of the white blood cells; two main types are myeloid and lymphoid (8.2)

life strategies strategies for reproduction exhibited by organisms; bacteria and species that reproduce close to their biotic potential (r) are considered to have r-selected strategies, and mammals, birds, and species that live close to the carrying capacity (K) of their habitat are considered to have K-selected strategies (20.1)

light-dependent reactions the part of the process of photosynthesis in which reactions dependent on the presence of light convert solar energy into chemical energy, generating two high-energy compounds: ATP and NADPH; compare *light-independent reaction* (5.2)

light-independent reactions the part of the process of photosynthesis in which reactions not dependent on the presence of light use the products of the light-dependent reactions (ATP and NADPH) to reduce carbon dioxide to a carbohydrate; compare *light-dependent reaction* (5.2)

limiting factor any abiotic or biotic condition that limits the number of individuals in a population (3.3)

linked genes genes found on the same chromosome (17.2)

lipase enzyme that catalyzes the hydrolysis of triglycerides into glycerol and fatty acids (6.2)

lipid group of organic macromolecules, including fats, oils, phospholipids, and steroids, that is insoluble in water, but soluble in a non-polar, organic substance (6.1)

liver organ found in the abdomen that performs hundreds of functions as an accessory organ of the digestive system, including the secretion of bile to digest fats; other functions include plasma protein production, blood detoxification, and glycogen storage (6.2)

locus specific location on a chromosome (16.1)

logistic growth pattern population increase that results in an S-shaped curve; growth is slow at first, steepens in an exponential pattern, and then levels off due to environmental resistance such as competition (20.1)

long-term stress response sustained physiological response to stressors, characterized by increases in blood glucose and blood pressure, and decrease in inflammatory response; regulated by hormones produced by the adrenal cortex (13.3)

loop of Henle in the kidney, tubular portion of the nephron that lies between the proximal tubule and the distal tubule; main function is reabsorption of water and ions (9.2)

lung cancer uncontrolled and invasive growth of abnormal cells in the lungs (7.3)

luteal stage the second stage of the ovarian cycle (part of the menstrual cycle), beginning with ovulation; during this stage, luteinizing hormone (LH) stimulates the formation of the corpus luteum, which secretes progesterone and some estrogen, which stimulate in the thickening of the endometrium for implantation of the embryo (14.3)

luteinizing hormone (LH) reproductive hormone produced by the anterior pituitary; in the ovaries, triggers ovulation, stimulates the formation of the corpus luteum, and (with follicle-stimulating hormone) stimulates estrogen production; in the testes, stimulates the release of testosterone (14.3)

lymph interstitial fluid carried throughout the body in the lymphatic circulatory system; is either colourless or pale yellow, with a composition much like the plasma of blood (8.3)

lymphatic circulatory system network of glands and vessels that carry lymph throughout the mammalian body; helps to maintain the balance of fluids in the body (8.3)

lymphocyte type of white blood cell involved in both cell-mediated and antibody-mediated immunity; types include B and T cells (8.2)

macromolecule a large, complex assembly of organic molecules; four categories of macromolecules are carbohydrates, lipids, proteins, and nucleic acids (6.1)

macrophage phagocytic white blood cell that develops from a monocyte; acts as a scavenger, ingesting dead cells and foreign material, and killing micro-organisms; macrophages also stimulate other cells in the immune system (8.3)

map distance distance between genes on a single chromosome (17.2)

map unit distance between points on a chromosome where a crossover is likely to occur in 1% of all meiotic events (17.2)

matrix fluid-filled space within the inner membrane of a mitochondrion; contains proteins and other chemicals needed to break down carbohydrates and other high energy molecules (5.1)

mechanoreceptor sensory receptor that responds to mechanical stimuli, such as that from pressure, sound waves, and gravity; e.g., proprioceptor (12.1)

medulla oblongata part of the hindbrain attached to the spinal cord at the base of the brainstem; controls automatic, involuntary responses, such as heart rate, constriction or dilation of blood vessels to control blood pressure, and the rate and depth of breathing, swallowing, and coughing (11.2)

medusa free-swimming adult form of organisms in the phylum Cnidaria; is an example in animals that exhibit alternation between asexually reproducing and sexually reproducing phases; compare *polyp* (16.4)

meiosis the cellular process that produces haploid gametes from diploid cells in the ovaries and testes (16.3)

meiosis I the first of two sequences in meiotic cell division in which the chromosomes are reduced from diploid to haploid (2n to n) (16.3)

meiosis II the second of two sequences in meiotic cell division in which each of the haploid cells created

during meiosis I undergoes mitosis (without an interphase) (16.3)

membrane potential electrical charge separation across a cell membrane; a form of potential energy (11.1)

memory T cell lymphocyte that carries receptors for a specific foreign antigen that was encountered in an earlier infection or through vaccination; memory T cells quickly promote an immune response if the same antigen is re-encountered in a subsequent infection (8.3)

meninges three layers of tough, elastic tissue within the skull and spinal column which directly enclose the brain and spinal cord (11.2)

menopause period in a woman's life during which a decrease in estrogen and progesterone results in an end of menstrual cycles, usually occurring around age 50 (14.3)

menstrual cycle in a human female, period of 20–45 days during which hormones stimulate the development of the uterine lining, and an egg (ovum) is developed and released from an ovary; if the egg is not fertilized, the uterine lining is shed as the cycle begins again; can be divided into the ovarian cycle and the uterine cycle (14.3)

menstruation initial phase in the menstrual cycle, in which the endometrium disintegrates and is expelled from the uterus of females who are not pregnant (14.1)

mesoderm the middle germ layer formed during animal embryogenesis (15.1)

messenger RNA (mRNA) strand of RNA that carries genetic information from DNA to the protein synthesis machinery of the cell during transcription (18.2)

metabolic pathway a controlled, step-by-step sequence of reactions that is catalyzed by enzymes in living cells to support and sustain life functions (5.1)

metabolism refers to all the chemical reactions that occur within a cell to support and sustain its life functions (5.1)

metaphase the second stage of cell division (mitosis) during which chromosomes line up at the cell's equator in preparation for separation (16.2)

microevolution gradual change in allele frequencies in a population over time (19.1)

microvillus (microvilli) microscopic projection found along exposed cell surfaces that greatly increases the surface area of the cell; found on the villi of the small intestine and on the membranes of certain cells (6.2)

midbrain part of the brain found above the pons in the brainstem; relays visual and auditory information between areas of the hindbrain and forebrain, and plays an important role in eye movement and control of skeletal muscles (11.2)

middle ear one of the three separate segments of the ear (outer ear, middle ear, and inner ear); begins at the tympanum (eardrum) and ends at two small openings in the wall of the inner ear called the round window and the oval window (12.3)

mineral inorganic compound required in trace amounts for normal metabolism (6.1)

mineralocorticoid hormone produced by the adrenal cortex that regulates the balance of electrolytes, such as sodium and potassium, and water in the body; e.g., aldosterone (13.3)

mis-sense mutation permanent change in the genetic material of a cell that results in a slightly altered but still functional protein (18.3)

mitochondrial DNA (mtDNA) DNA within the mitochondria; is genetically identical to that of the female parent because the cytoplasm of offspring is derived from the egg (ovum) (18.3)

mitochondrion (mitochondria) organelle that breaks down organic molecules, usually carbohydrates, to release energy (5.1)

mitosis one of the two main processes in cell division: division of the genetic material and the contents of the cell's nucleus into two complete and separate sets; results in a daughter cell receiving the exact number of chromosomes and genetic make-up as the parent cell; see also *cytokinesis* (16.1, 16.2)

monocyte type of white blood cell that leaves the bloodstream and become further specialized as a macrophage (8.2)

monohybrid cross cross of two individuals that differ in one trait (17.1)

monosaccharide simple sugar that cannot be hydrolyzed into simpler sugars; for example glucose, fructose, and galactose (6.1)

monosomy loss of a chromosome as a result of nondisjunction (16.3)

morphogenesis the series of events that form distinct structures of a developing organism; gastrulation marks the beginning of the process (15.1)

morphology physical structure and form of an organism (3.1)

morula term used to describe a zygote when it becomes a 16-cell sphere (15.1)

mouth opening through which an animal takes in food and water (6.2)

Müllerian mimicry form of mimicry where an organism resembles another organism with a defence mechanism, and also has the defence mechanism; believed to be a form of co-evolution; compare *Batesian mimicry* (20.2)

multiple alleles pattern of inheritance in which a gene has more than two alleles for any given trait (17.2)

muscle fibre skeletal muscle cell (10.1)

muscle twitch muscular contraction that lasts a fraction of a second (10.2)

muscular system in animals, system made up of tissues specialized for movement (10.1)

mutagen substance or event that increases the rate of mutation in an organism; may be physical or chemical (18.3)

mutation a permanent change in a cell's DNA; includes changes in nucleotide sequence, alteration of gene position, gene loss, or duplication and insertion of foreign sequences; an inheritable mutation has the potential to affect an entire gene pool (4.1, 18.3, 19.2)

mutualism a type of symbiotic relationship in which both partners benefit from the relationship, or depend on it in order to survive; compare *commensalism* and *parasitism* (20.2)

myelin sheath the fatty, insulating layer around the axon of a nerve cell, composed of Schwann cells; protects myelinated neurons and speeds the rate of nerve impulse transmission (11.1)

myofibril one of hundreds of thousands of cylindrical subunits that make up a skeletal muscle cell (fibre) (10.1)

myofilament one of many microscopic, string-like structures, composed of actin and myosin, that make up myofibrils; responsible for muscle contraction (10.1)

myoglobin protein in muscle tissue that stores and transports oxygen (10.1)

myopia near-sightedness, or difficulty seeing things that are far away; caused by ciliary muscles that are too strong or an eyeball that is too long; compare *hyperopia* (12.2)

myosin protein that, along with actin, is the chief component of muscle; makes up the thick filament of a muscle fibre; also see *myosin myofilament* (10.1)

myosin myofilament thick myofilament consisting of two strands of mysosin molecules wound around each other; one end consists of a long rod, while the other end consists of a double-headed globular region; works with actin myofilament to produce muscle contractions (10.1)

N

NAD⁺ nicotinamide adenine dinucleotide; coenzyme that functions as a carrier of electrons and hydrogen ions; important coenzyme in electron transport in the Krebs cycle (5.2)

NADH reduced form of the coenzyme nicotinamide adenine dinucleotide (NAD^+) that can act as an electron donor; important coenzyme in electron transport in the Krebs cycle (5.2)

nasal passage passage from the nostrils to the back of the throat through which air enters the body; serves to warm, moisten, and clean incoming air; lined with ciliated cells and mucus-secreting cells; also called the *nasal cavity* (7.2)

natural selection process whereby the characteristics of a population of organisms change over time because individuals with certain heritable traits survive specific local environmental conditions and, through reproduction, pass on their traits to their offspring (4.1, 19.2)

negative feedback mechanism mechanism of homeostatic response by which the output of a system suppresses or inhibits activity of the system; e.g., when a certain blood concentration of a hormone is reached, the endocrine gland releasing the hormone is inhibited by the presence of the hormone (13.1)

nephron microscopic tube-like filtration unit found in the kidneys that filters and reabsorbs various substances from the blood; produces urine (9.1)

nerve message pathway of the nervous system; made up of many neurons grouped into bundles and surrounded by protective connective tissue (11.1)

nervous system in animals, system made up of cells and organs that let an animal detect changes and respond to them; made up of the brain and spinal cord, as well as the nerves that emerge from them and connect them to the rest of the body (11.1)

neuromuscular junction synapse between a motor neuron and a muscle cell (11.1)

neuron nerve cell; the structural and functional unit of the nervous system, consisting of a nucleus, cell body, dendrites, axons, and a myelin sheath; specialized to respond to physical and chemical stimuli, to conduct electrochemical signals, and to release chemicals that regulate various body processes (11.1)

neurotransmitter chemical messenger secreted by neurons to carry a neural signal from one neuron to another, or from a neuron to an effector, such as a gland or muscle fibre (11.1)

neurulation in embryogenesis, process of forming the neural tube, which develops into the brain and spinal cord (15.1)

nitrogen fixation process whereby free atmospheric nitrogen (nitrogen gas) is converted, usually by bacteria, into compounds such as ammonium and nitrates that can be used by other organisms (2.2)

nociceptor pain receptor found throughout the skin and internal organs (12.3)

node of Ranvier gap in the myelin sheath insulating the axon of a myelinated nerve cell; the membrane of the axon is exposed and action potentials occur only at these nodes; nerve impulses jump from one node of Ranvier to the next (11.1)

non-competitive inhibitor a molecule that, upon binding with an enzyme, prevents the enzyme from binding to a substrate by changing the three-dimensional structure of the enzyme and its active site; does not bind with the active site directly; compare *competitive inhibitor* (6.1)

nondisjunction failure of homologous chromosomes pairs or sister chromatids to separate during meiosis I and meiosis II, respectively (16.3)

non-random mating mating among individuals on the basis of mate selection for a particular phenotype or due to inbreeding, rather than mating on a random basis (19.2)

nonsense mutation permanent change in the genetic material of a cell that renders a gene unable to code for a functional protein (18.3)

non-sister chromatids in a tetrad, those chromatids that do not belong to the same chromosome; undergo crossing over during prophase I of meiosis (16.3)

non-specific defence see *cell-mediated immunity* (8.3)

noradrenaline see *norepinephrine* (11.3, 13.3)

norepinephrine neurotransmitter released by sympathetic neurons of the autonomic system to produce an excitatory effect on target muscles; also a hormone produced by the adrenal medulla along with epinephrine to function in the short-term stress response; also known as *noradrenaline* (11.3, 13.3)

nuclease enzyme that hydrolyses the bonds between nucleotides in nucleic acids (6.2)

nucleic acid macromolecule formed from a long chain of nucleotide subunits, each consisting of a five-carbon simple sugar, a nitrogen-containing base, and a phosphate group; two types include DNA and RNA (6.1)

nucleotide units making up nucleic acids (e.g., DNA, RNA), composed of a five-carbon sugar, a phosphate group, and one of five nitrogen-containing bases (adenine, cytosine, guanine, and either thymine or uracil) (18.1)

O

obesity condition in which body mass is 20 percent or more above what is considered to be an ideal body mass for a person's height (6.3)

occipital lobe one of four lobes into which each hemisphere of the cerebral cortex is divided; receives and analyzes visual information, and is needed for recognition of what is being seen (11.2)

Okazaki fragments short nucleotide fragments synthesized during DNA replication of the lagging strand (18.1)

olfactory bulb region of forebrain where ends of sensory nerve fibres from nose terminate and transmit olfactory information to other areas of the brain (12.3)

olfactory cell chemoreceptor for the sense of smell; lines the upper nasal cavity (12.3)

oogenesis the process of female gamete (ova or egg) production in animals (14.1, 16.3)

oogonium the diploid germ cell from which eggs are produced in the ovaries (16.3)

optic nerve a nerve that carries messages from the photoreceptors in the retina to the brain (12.2)

order of dominance sequence indicating which alleles are dominant to other alleles (17.2)

organ of Corti organ of hearing found within the cochlea of the inner ear; contains hair cells that detect vibrations in the inner ear and transmit this information to auditory nerves (12.3)

osmoreceptor cell that is sensitive to osmotic pressure; most are located in the hypothalamus of the brain (9.3)

ossicles the group of three small bones (malleus, incus, and stapes) between the tympanum (eardrum) and the oval window of the middle ear; transmit sound waves from the eardrum to the inner ear (12.3)

otolith calcium carbonate granule associated with sensory receptors for detecting movement of the head; in vertebrates, located in the utricle and saccule in the vestibule of the inner ear (12.3)

outer ear one of the three separate segments of the ear (outer ear, middle ear, and inner ear); consists of the pinna and the auditory canal (12.3)

oval window membrane-covered opening in the wall of the inner ear; receives vibrations from the stapes (one of the ossicles) (12.3)

ovarian cycle the part of the menstrual cycle that takes place in the ovaries (14.3)

ovary in mammals, one of a pair of female reproductive organs (gonads); is suspended in the abdominal cavity and produces eggs (ova) (14.1)

oviduct one of a pair of cilia-lined tubes in the body that transport an egg (ovum) from the ovary to the uterus; also known as Fallopian tube (14.1)

ovulation in females, the process by which a single follicle in an ovary matures and then ruptures, releasing the ovum (egg) into the oviduct; usually occurs at the midpoint (day 14) of a 28-day menstrual cycle (14.1)

ovum (ova) female reproductive cell (gamete) (14.1)

oxic oxygen-containing; compare *anoxic* (5.3)

oxidation process by which an atom or molecule loses an electron (5.1)

P

paleontology the study of ancient life through the examination of fossils (4.2)

pancreas small gland in the abdomen that secretes digestive enzymes into the small intestine, as well as bicarbonate to neutralize hydrochloric acid from the stomach; also secretes the hormone insulin (6.2, 13.4)

pangenesis theory of inheritance proposed by Aristotle that egg and sperm consist of particles, called pangenes, that come from all parts of the body; upon fertilization of the egg by a sperm, the pangenes develop into the parts of the body from which they were derived (17.1)

parasitism a type of symbiotic relationship in which an organism benefits by living on or in an organism of a different species that is harmed by the association; compare *mutualism* and *commensalism* (20.2)

parasympathetic nervous system division of the autonomic system that regulates involuntary processes in the body; works in opposition to the sympathetic nervous system; typically activated when the body is calm and at rest (11.1, 11.3)

parathyroid hormone hormone produced by the parathyroid glands in response to falling concentrations of calcium in the blood; stimulates bone cells to break down bone material (calcium phosphate) and reabsorb calcium into the blood; stimulates the kidneys to reabsorb calcium from the urine; activates vitamin D, which stimulates the absorption of calcium from food in the intestine (13.2)

parent cell original cell that divides to produce two new daughter cells during cell division (16.1)

parental (P) generation in breeding, the organisms that are being crossed; compare *filial generation* (17.1)

parental type describes offspring that have chromosomes that are identical to those of their parents; compare *recombinant type* (17.2)

parietal lobe one of four lobes into which each hemisphere of the cerebral cortex is divided; receives and processes sensory information from the skin, and helps to process information about the body's position and orientation (11.2)

parthenogenesis form of asexual reproduction in which an unfertilized egg develops into an adult (16.4)

parturition the act or process of giving birth to young (15.2)

pedigree diagram that uses symbols to illustrate the patterns of relationships and traits among a family over many generations (17.3)

pelvic inflammatory disease (PID) infection of the female uterus, oviducts, and/or ovaries; can result in a build-up of scar tissue causing infertility; may occur as a result of undetected chlamydia or gonnerhea infection (14.2)

penis male copulatory organ; in humans, the male organ of sexual intercourse; its primary reproductive function is to transfer sperm from the male to the female reproductive tract (14.1)

pepsin protein-digesting enzyme secreted in the stomach; remains inactive until hydrochloric acid is present (6.2)

peptide bond bond between the amino group of one amino acid and the carboxyl group of another in a protein (6.1)

per capita growth rate (cgr) change in population size per individual over a given time frame; expressed as $cgr = \frac{N}{N}$ or $cgr = \frac{N_{final} - N}{N}$ (20.1)

perception interpretation of sensory information by the cerebral cortex (12.1)

peripheral nervous system network of nerves that carry sensory messages to the central nervous system (CNS) and send information from the CNS to the muscles and glands; consists of the autonomic and somatic system (11.1)

peristalsis wave-like series of muscular contractions and relaxations of the circular and longitudinal muscles that surround the various parts of the digestive tract; aids the movement of food through the digestive tract (6.2)

peritoneal dialysis type of renal (kidney) dialysis that utilizes the lining of the intestines, called the peritoneum, as the dialysis membrane to remove waste and excess fluid from the blood when kidney function is lost due to renal failure (9.3)

phagocytosis process by which a cell ingests another cell, bacterium, or particle of organic matter (8.3)

pharynx structure located just behind the mouth that connects the mouth and nasal cavity to the larynx and esophagus; serves as the passageway for air into the respiratory system and for food and water into the digestive system; also known as *throat* (7.1)

phenotype the visible physical and physiological traits of an organism; compare *genotype* (17.1)

phenotype frequency proportion of members of a population with a particular phenotype; usually expressed as a decimal (19.1)

photoreceptor sensory receptor that responds to light stimuli and allows us to sense different levels of light and shades of colour (12.1)

photosynthesis the process by which plants, algae, and some kinds of bacteria use the Sun's light energy to chemically convert carbon (inorganic) into carbohydrates (organic) such as sugars and starches (1.1, 5.1)

photosynthetic pigment compound that traps light energy and passes it on to other chemicals that use the energy to synthesize high-energy compounds; the main photosynthetic pigment is chlorophyll (5.2)

photosystem cluster of light-absorbing pigment molecules within thylakoid membranes in chloroplasts (5.2)

physical mutagen agent that can forcibly break a nucleotide sequence, causing random changes in one or both strands of a DNA molecule; (e.g., X rays) (18.3)

pigment compound that absorbs specific wavelengths of visible light and therefore has colour; see also *photosynthetic pigment* (5.2)

pilus (pili) extensions of a bacterial cell enabling it to transfer genetic materials from one individual to another through the process of conjugation (16.4)

pinna the outside flap of the ear; made of skin and cartilage and shaped in a way that enhances sound vibrations and focusses them into the ear (12.3)

pioneer community first species to colonize a barren or disturbed habitat and initiate primary succession (20.2)

pituitary gland small gland that lies just inferior to the hypothalamus; consists of the anterior and posterior pituitary, both of which produce hormones that influence metabolism, growth, development, reproduction, and other critical life functions (13.2)

placenta in most pregnant mammals, a disk-shaped organ within the uterus that is rich in blood vessels; attaches the embryo or fetus to the uterine wall and facilitates metabolic exchange (15.1)

plasma fluid portion of the blood, made up of water plus dissolved gases, proteins, sugars, vitamins, minerals, hormones, and waste products (8.2)

plasmid small self-duplication loop of DNA in a prokaryotic cell that is separate from the main chromosome and contains from one to a few genes (18.3)

platelet component of the formed portion of the blood, consisting of fragments of cells that are created when larger cells in the bone marrow break apart; contains no nucleus and plays a key role in blood clotting (8.2)

pleural membrane double-layered membrane that encloses the lungs; also referred to as *pleura* (7.1)

pleurisy inflammation of the pleural membranes that surround the lungs (7.3)

pneumonia inflammation of the alveoli (air sacs) in the lungs (7.3)

point mutation permanent change in the genetic material of a cell that affects one or just a few nucleotides; may involve the substitution of one nucleotide for another, or the insertion or deletion of one or more nucleotides (18.3)

polar refers to a molecule with uneven charge distribution (2.1)

polarization lowering the membrane potential of the cell below its equilibrium value; in nerves, the process of generating a resting membrane potential of −70 mV (11.1)

polygene group of genes that all contribute to the same trait (17.2)

polygenic trait trait that is controlled by many genes (17.2)

polyp non-motile adult form of organisms in the phylum Cnidaria; is an example in animals exhibiting alternation between asexually reproducing and sexually reproducing phases; compare *medusa* (16.4)

polyploid describing a cell which contains sets of more than two homologous chromosomes (16.1)

polysaccharide complex carbohydrate consisting of many simple sugars linked together; examples include starch, cellulose, and glycogen (6.1)

pons part of the hindbrain found above and in front of the medulla oblongata in the brainstem; serves as a relay centre between the neurons of the right and left halves of the cerebrum, the cerebellum, and the rest of the brain (11.2)

population any group of individuals of the same species living in the same geographical area at the same time (3.1, 19.1)

population crash a dramatic decrease in the size of a population over a short period of time; compare *population explosion* (20.1)

population density (D_P) the number of individual organisms (N) in a given area (A) or volume (V); expressed as $D_p = \dfrac{N}{A}$ or $D_p = \dfrac{N}{V}$ (20.1)

population explosion a dramatic increase in the size of a population over a short period of time; compare *population crash* (20.1)

posterior pituitary posterior lobe of the pituitary gland; an endocrine gland that stores and releases antidiuretic hormone (ADH) and oxytocin, which are produced in the hypothalamus and transferred to the posterior pituitary by neuronal axons; compare *anterior pituitary* (13.2)

potential difference the difference in the potential energy per unit of charge of an object due to its position or condition; potential difference is like an 'electrical pressure' that pushes charges along a circuit; also referred to as *voltage* (11.1)

precautionary principle the principle stating that governments should act in advance, as a precaution, to prevent potential harm from new technologies, and should act even when neither the danger nor the effectiveness of the preventive measures have been demonstrated scientifically (18.4)

predator organism that kills and consumes other organisms (20.2)

prey organism that is killed and consumed by another organism (20.2)

primary consumer organism that obtains energy by eating plants; also known as a *herbivore* (1.1)

primary germ layers first layers of cells formed during animal embryogenesis, mainly in the vertebrates; consist of ectoderm (outer layer), mesoderm (middle layer), and endoderm (inner layer) (15.1)

primary oocyte each of two cells formed when an oogonium undergoes mitosis (16.3)

primary sex characteristic any structure (organ, duct, or gland) that plays a direct role in reproduction; compare *secondary sex characteristic* (14.1)

primary spermatocyte one of two daughter cells formed by division of the spermatogonia; the other daughter cell replenishes the spermatogonia population (16.3)

primary succession the development of a new community in a previously barren area where there is no soil present, such as on a hardened lava bed, or on a bare rock mountaintop; compare *secondary succession* (20.2)

primase in DNA replication, enzyme that forms a primer used as a starting point for the attachment of new nucleotides (18.1)

primer in DNA replication, short strand of RNA that is complementary to a DNA template and serves as a starting point for the attachment of new nucleotides (18.1)

producer organism that synthesizes its own food from inorganic molecules by using light or chemical energy; also known as *autotroph* (1.1)

productivity the rate at which organisms produce new biomass (2.3)

progesterone female sex hormone produced first by the corpus luteum of the ovary to prepare the uterus for the fertilized egg (ovum), and later by the placenta to maintain pregnancy (14.3)

prokaryote organism characterized by cells that do not contain membrane-bound, structurally distinct nuclei or other membrane-bound organelles; compare eukaryote (3.2)

promoter during transcription, a sequence of nucleotides on the DNA molecule that tells the RNA polymerase complex where to bind (18.2)

prophase the first of the four phases in cell division (mitosis), when chromatin condenses and can be seen as tightly packed chromosomes; the nuclear membrane breaks down, centrioles move to opposite poles of the cell, and the spindle apparatus forms (16.2)

proprioceptor type of mechanoreceptor found in muscles, tendons, and joints; senses the body's position and movements to send information about body position to the brain (12.1, 12.3)

prostate gland in male mammals, a mass of glandular tissue at the base of the urethra that secretes mucus-like, alkaline fluid that neutralizes the acids from urine in the urethra (14.1)

protease enzyme that hydrolyzes the peptide bonds that link amino acids in proteins and peptides (6.2)

protective coloration adaptation that helps individuals avoid predation; includes camouflage, mimicry, and using body colours as a warning signal (20.2)

protein organic macromolecule assembled from subunits of amino acids (6.1)

proteomics the study of all proteins that are produced by a given genome (18.2)

proximal tubule in the kidney, tubular portion of the nephron that lies between the Bowman's capsule and the loop of Henle; main function is reabsorption of water and solutes, as well as secretion of hydrogen ions (9.2)

puberty period in which the reproductive system completes its development and becomes fully functional, and reproductive hormones begin to be formed (14.3)

pulmonary artery blood vessel that carries blood from the heart to the lungs (8.1)

pulmonary pathway in animals, the circulatory pathway that carries oxygen-poor blood from the heart to the lungs and oxygen-rich blood from the lungs to the heart (8.1)

pulmonary vein blood vessel that carries blood from the lungs to the heart (8.1)

punctuated equilibrium model that suggests that evolutionary history consists of long periods of stasis (stable equilibrium), punctuated by periods of divergence (4.3)

Punnett square simple grid used to illustrate all possible combinations of simple genetic crosses (17.1)

pupil aperture in the middle of the iris of the eye, the size of which can be adjusted to control the amount of light entering the eye (12.2)

purines nitrogenous compounds that have a double-ring structure; the nucleotide bases adenine and guanine are derived from purines and always bond with pyrimidines in DNA (18.1)

Purkinje fibre in the heart, a fast-conducting muscle fibre that initiates the almost simultaneous contraction of all cells of the right and left ventricles; signal for this contraction is initiated by the sinoatrial (SA) node and is relayed through the atrioventricular (AV) node and the bundle of His (8.1)

pyloric sphincter muscular ring that acts as a valve between the stomach and the first part of the small intestine (duodenum), controlling the passage of food out of the stomach (6.2)

pyramid of biomass schematic representation of the relative amount of biomass at each trophic level (1.2)

pyramid of energy schematic representation of the relative amount of energy at each trophic level (1.2)

pyramid of numbers schematic representation of the relative numbers of organisms at each trophic level (1.2)

pyrimidines nitrogenous compounds that have a single-ring structure; the nucleotide bases thymine, cytosine, and uracil are derived from pyrimidines and always bond with purines in DNA (18.1)

quadrat area of determined size that is marked out for the purpose of sampling a population; often used to sample plants and other organisms that tend to stay in one spot all their lives (3.3)

R

random distribution distribution of individuals throughout a suitable habitat with no identifiable pattern; occurs when resources are very abundant and population members do not have to compete with one another or group together for survival (20.1)

random sample sample in which all of the individuals in the population have an equal chance of being represented (3.3)

range geographical area in which a population or species is found (3.3)

rapid cycling (of nutrients) relatively quick movement of nutrients through nutrient reservoirs, such as organisms, soil, air, and water (2.2)

reaction centre a specialized, electron-accepting chlorophyll *a* molecule that receives light energy of various wavelengths from pigment molecules found in the photosystems of chloroplasts; transfers electrons to an electron acceptor during the light-independent reactions of photosynthesis (5.2)

receptor protein protein within the membrane of a target cell; circulating hormones bind to specific receptor proteins to produce an effect on the target cell (13.1)

recessive refers to a type of trait which does not appear (is not expressed) in an individual that is heterozygous (*Aa*) for that trait (17.1)

recombinant DNA a molecule of DNA that includes genetic material from different sources (18.3)

recombinant type describes offspring that have a different combination of alleles than the chromosomes of their parents; also known as *recombinants*; compare *parental type* (17.2)

recombination one of the outcomes of meiosis: cell division that produces daughter cells with different combinations of genes than the parent cells; gives rise to offspring that are genetically distinct from one another and from their parents; see also *reduction division* (16.3)

recombination frequency percentage of times that a crossover occurs as gametes are formed (17.1)

red blood cell see *erythrocyte* (8.2)

reducing power the chemical potential energy available in molecules that are in their reduced form (5.1)

reduction process by which an atom or molecule gains an electron (5.1)

reduction division one of the outcomes of meiosis: cell division that produces daughter cells with fewer chromosomes than the parent cells; see also *recombination* (16.3)

reflex arc simple connection of neurons that results in a reflex action in response to a stimulus (11.1)

refractory period the brief time (a few milliseconds) between the triggering of an impulse along an axon and the axon's readiness for the next impulse; during this time, the axon cannot transmit an impulse (11.1)

regulatory sequence strand of DNA that helps determine when various genetic processes are activated (18.3)

renal artery blood vessel that originates from the aorta and delivers blood to the kidneys; splits into a fine network of capillaries (the glomerulus) within the Bowman's capsule of the nephron (9.1)

renal insufficiency general term used to describe the state in which the kidneys cannot maintain homeostasis due to nephron damage (9.3)

renal vein blood vessel that drains from the kidney; returns to the body the solutes and water reabsorbed by the kidney (9.1)

replicate in biology, refers to the reproduction of an exact copy of genetic material, a cell, or an organism (16.1)

replication in genetics, process of creating an exact copy of a molecule of DNA (18.1)

replication bubble oval-shaped unwound area within a DNA molecule that is being replicated (18.1)

replication fork during DNA replication, Y-shaped points at which the DNA helix is unwound and new strands develop (18.1)

replication machine complex involving dozens of different enzymes and other proteins that work closely together in the process of DNA replication and interact at the replication fork (18.1)

replication origin specific nucleotide sequence where replication begins; ranges from a single replication origin in prokaryotes to thousands in eukaryotes (18.1)

repolarization return of a nerve to its resting potential following depolarization (11.1)

reproductive technology any technology that enhances or reduces reproductive potential (15.3)

residual volume amount of gas that remains in the lungs and the passageways of the respiratory system even after a full exhalation (7.2)

respiratory system in animals, system responsible for gas exchange (bringing oxygen into the body and removing carbon dioxide from the body) (7.1)

resting membrane potential potential difference across the membrane in a resting neuron (11.1)

restriction endonuclease type of restriction enzyme that recognizes a specific short sequence of nucleotides within, rather than at the ends of, a strand of DNA and cuts the strand at that particular point within the sequence (18.3)

restriction enzyme enzyme in prokaryotes that catalyzes the cleavage of DNA at specific nucleotide sequences (18.3)

restriction fragment small segments of DNA cut from a DNA molecule by a restriction endonuclease (18.3)

restriction site specific location within a short sequence of nucleotides in a strand of DNA at which a restriction endonuclease will cut (18.3)

retina the innermost layer of the eye, containing the photoreceptors (rods and cones) (12.2)

revolution term used by Georges Cuvier to describe the idea that Earth experienced many destructive natural events, such as floods and volcanic eruptions, in the past that were violent enough to have killed numerous species each time they occurred (4.2)

Rh factor group of antigens found in most red blood cells; people with the Rh factor on their red blood cells are termed Rh positive (Rh$^+$) and people without it are Rh negative (Rh$^-$) (8.3)

rib muscle one of several muscles found between and along the inside surface of the ribs, extending down to the diaphragm; as a group, work with the diaphragm to move air in and out of the lungs; also known as *intercostal muscle* (7.2)

ribonucleic acid (RNA) a nucleic acid molecule that plays a role in gene expression and protein synthesis, composed of a phosphate group, a nitrogenous base (adenine, guanine, cytosine, or uracil), and the five-carbon sugar ribose; structure is similar to DNA (18.1)

ribosomal RNA (rRNA) linear strand of RNA that remains associated with the ribosomes (18.2)

ribosome organelle involved in protein synthesis; brings together the mRNA strand, the tRNA molecules carrying amino acids, and the enzymes involved in building polypeptides (18.2)

RNA polymerase main enzyme that catalyzes the formation of RNA from the DNA template (18.2)

rod type of photoreceptor in the eye that is more sensitive to light intensity (level of brightness) than is a cone, but is unable to distinguish colour (12.2)

rotational equilibrium balance required while rotating the head and body (12.3)

r-selected strategy a life strategy designed to take advantage of favourable conditions; characterized by a high reproductive rate with little or no attention given to offspring survival; organisms that exhibit this strategy include bacteria and species that reproduce close to their biotic potential (*r*); also known as *r-selection*; compare *K-selected strategy* (20.1)

S phase the middle part of interphase, a somatic cell's growth stage, during which the cell's DNA is replicated (16.1)

saccule saclike cavity in the vestibule of the inner ear; contains sensory receptors for gravitational equilibrium (12.3)

saliva watery secretion of the salivary glands; in addition to containing a starch-digesting enzyme, helps lubricate food for easier swallowing (6.2)

saltatory conduction refers to the 'jumping' of action potentials from one node of Ranvier to the next due to the myelin sheath (11.1)

sample small portion of an entire population; samples are counted or estimated and the results are averaged and then applied, or extrapolated, to the entire area occupied by the population (3.3)

Schwann cell a type of insulating glial cell that wraps around the axon of a neuron, creating a myelin sheath (11.1)

scientific hypothesis see *hypothesis* (4.2)

scientific theory general statement that explains and makes successful predictions about a broad range of observations; usually based on hypotheses that consistently lead to successful predictions and explanations (4.2)

sclera the white, tough, fibrous protective outer layer that gives the eye its shape (12.2)

scrotum pouch that contains the testes in most mammals (14.1)

second law of thermodynamics law stating that all energy transformations are inefficient because some usable energy is always dissipated to the environment as unusable heat (1.1)

second polar body one of a pair of cells that results when when a secondary oocyte undergoes asymmetrical cytokinesis during meiosis II; is not a viable gamete; also used to refer to the products of a second division that may occur in the first polar body (16.3)

secondary consumer organism that eats primary consumers (herbivores) (1.1)

secondary oocyte cell that receives the larger portion of cytoplasm when a primary oocyte undergoes asymmetrical cytokinesis during meiosis I; becomes the egg; compare *first polar body* (16.3)

secondary sex characteristic any of the physical manifestations that distinguish male from female but are not required for reproduction, such as distribution of body fat, female breasts, change of voice pitch in adolescent males, differences in muscularity, etc.; compare *primary sex characteristic* (14.1)

secondary spermatocyte each of two cells produced as a result of a primary spermatocyte undergoing meiosis I (16.3)

secondary succession the regrowth of a previously existing community after an ecological disturbance, such as a forest fire, flood, or agricultural activity; differs from primary succession in the presence of soil, which is not usually destroyed in an ecological disturbance (20.2)

secretin one of three enzymes (including CCK and GIP) secreted into the bloodstream by the duodenum, causing inhibition of stomach movement and secretions, and enabling fatty meals to remain in the stomach longer than non-fatty meals; also stimulates the pancreas to release more bicarbonate to neutralize acidic chime (6.2)

segmentation a process by which some physical digestion occurs in the small intestine; chyme sloshes back and forth between segments of the small intestine that form when bands of circular muscle briefly contract (6.2)

selective advantage characteristic that improves an organism's chance of survival, usually in a changing environment; the result of mutations (4.1, 19.2)

selective breeding process of choosing and breeding specific organisms for particular physical features or behaviours (17.1)

selective pressure environmental condition or conditions that select for certain characteristics of individuals, and select against others (4.1)

semen fluid released from the penis during ejaculation; combination of sperm and glandular secretions (14.1)

semicircular canal one of the three components of the inner ear (cochlea, vestibule, and semicircular canals); consists of three fluid-filled loops, arranged in three different planes; contains mechanoreceptors that detect head and body rotation (rotational equilibrium) (12.3)

semi-conservative term used to describe replication: each new molecule of DNA contains one strand of the original complementary DNA and one new strand, thus conserving half of the original molecule (18.1)

seminal vesicle in human males, gland behind the bladder that is connected to the ductus deferens; produces a mucus-like fluid containing the sugar fructose, which provides energy for the sperm (14.1)

seminiferous tubule long, coiled tube inside the testes in which sperm are produced (14.1)

sensation receiving and processing by the brain of neural impulses from the sensory receptors; e.g., sensory receptors on the skin detect heat, and when the brain processes the impulses, the sensation of warmth is felt on that part of the skin (12.1)

sense strand the one strand of nucleotides from the double-stranded DNA molecule that is transcribed; compare *anti-sense strand* (18.2)

sensory adaptation the filtering by the brain of redundant, insignificant sensory information (12.1)

sensory receptor cell or group of cells scattered throughout the body that works continually to receive information about the body's external conditions (through sight, hearing, taste, smell, and touch) and internal conditions (such as temperature, pH, glucose levels, and blood pressure), and then initiates neural impulses in response (12.1)

septum in the heart, the muscular wall that separates the two ventricles and the two atria (8.1)

Sertoli cells cells within the seminiferous tubules that support and nourish developing sperm (14.1)

sessile does not move (3.2)

sex chromosome X or Y chromosome that carries the genes involved in determining the genetic sex of an individual (16.1)

sex hormone one of several chemical compounds that control the development and function of the reproductive system or secondary sex characteristics (14.1)

sex-linked trait trait controlled by genes on either the X or Y chromosome (17.2)

sexual reproduction reproduction involving meiosis, gamete formation, and fertilization; produces genetically distinct offspring (16.4)

sexual selection a type of natural selection that results from non-random mating; e.g., if a male organism can attract more mates as a result of physical traits, his phenotype gives him a reproductive advantage over the other males in his population (19.2)

sexually transmitted infection (STI) infection such as AIDS, chlamydia, or genital herpes that is normally passed from one person to another through sexual activity; also known as *sexually transmitted disease (STD)* (14.2)

short-term stress response the body's acute reaction to stress in which the sympathetic nervous system is stimulated; also known as *flight-or-flight response* (13.3)

silent mutation permanent change in the genetic material of a cell that has no effect on the function of the cell (18.3)

sinoatrial (SA) node bundle of specialized muscle tissue located in the wall of the right atrium of the mammalian heart; generates an electrical impulse that stimulates cardiac muscle fibres to contract and relax rhythmically, producing a regular heartbeat; also known as *pacemaker*; compare *atrioventricular node* (8.1)

sister chromatids two chromatids in a chromosome that are genetically identical and are held together by a centromere (16.1)

skeletal muscle striated, voluntary muscle tissue that comprises skeletal muscles; also called *striated muscle* (10.1)

sliding filament model an explanation for muscle contraction based on the movement (sliding) of actin filaments in relation to myosin filaments (10.1)

slow cycling (of nutrients) long-term storage of nutrients in nutrient reservoirs, such as fossil fuel deposits; nutrients stored in these reservoirs are unavailable for long periods of time (2.2)

slow-twitch fibre muscle fibre that produces most of its energy aerobically; contracts slowly, but can maintain a steady, prolonged production of ATP when oxygen is available; also called *Type I fibre*; compare *fast-twitch fibre* (10.2)

small intestine length of the digestive tract between the stomach and the large intestine; narrower in diameter than the large intestine, it is comprised of the duodenum, jejunum, and ileum; main function is to complete the digestion of macromolecules and to absorb their component subunits (6.2)

smooth muscle nonstriated, involuntary muscle tissue found in the walls of internal organs (10.1)

sodium-potassium exchange pump system involving a carrier protein in the plasma membrane that uses the energy of ATP to transport sodium ions out of and potassium ions into animal cells; important in nerve and muscle cells (11.1)

somatic cell any of the cells of a multicellular organism except those that form gametes (16.1)

somatic cell mutation permanent change in the genetic material of a body cell, *not* including germ cells, during the lifetime of an organism; is copied during DNA replication and passed on to daughter cells, but not passed on to future generations; compare *germ line mutation* (18.3)

somatic gene therapy therapy that is aimed at correcting genetic disorders in somatic (body) cells; see also *gene therapy* (18.4)

somatic system in vertebrates, division of the peripheral nervous system that controls voluntary movement of skeletal muscle; conducts signals form the central nervous sytem to the skeletal muscles and signals from the sensory recptors in the body to the central nervous system; compare *autonomic system* (11.1, 11.3)

sound wave small fluctuation in air pressure resulting from sound, which causes particles around the source to vibrate and move; the auditory system (sense of hearing) detects these movements and the brain perceives them as sound (12.3)

speciation the formation of new species (4.3)

species population of organisms capable of interbreeding and producing fertile offspring (3.1)

specific defence see *antibody-mediated immunity* (8.3)

sperm cell male reproductive cell (gamete) (14.1)

spermatid each of four haploid cells that result when a secondary spermatocyte undergoes meiosis II; each spermatid differentiates into a sperm cell (16.3)

spermatogenesis the process of male gamete (sperm) production in animals (14.1, 16.3)

spermatogonium the diploid germ cell from which sperm are produced in the testes (16.3)

spindle apparatus assembly that carries out the separation of chromosomes during cell division (mitosis); composed of spindle fibres and assembled during prophase (16.2)

spindle fibre one of a network of fibres that forms the spindle apparatus during cell division (mitosis); made of microtubules, hollow tubes of protein that facilitate movement of chromosomes within a cell (16.2)

spirograph graph representing the amount of air that moves into and out of the lungs with each breath (7.2)

spontaneous generation a theory, accepted until the mid-1800s, stating that living organisms could arise from nonliving matter (16.1)

spontaneous mutation permanent change in the genetic material of a cell as a result of the molecular interactions that occur naturally within the cell (18.3)

spore reproductive cell capable of developing into a new organism without fusion with another cell, in contrast to a gamete; contains genetic material and cytoplasm surrounded by a protective sheath or wall (16.4)

sporophyte diploid generation of a plant that produces haploid spores (through the process of meiosis) that develop without fertilization into a gametophyte; also see *alternation of generations* (16.4)

stable equilibrium maintenance of population size around carrying capacity, with only slight fluctuations above and below this capacity (20.1)

stationary phase stage in the growth of a population at which birth rate and death rate are equivalent as competition for resources and other limiting factors slow the rate of growth; compare *exponential growth phase* and *lag phase* (20.1)

sterile condition in which a man or a woman is unable to have children; compare *infertile* (15.3)

sticky end short sequence of unpaired nucleotides remaining on a single strand of DNA at each end of a restriction fragment, after an endonuclease makes a staggered cut at the restriction site (18.3)

stomach "J"-shaped sac lying between the esophagus and the small intestine whose muscles and secretions work to physically and chemically break down food and push it into the small intestine; also stores food (6.2)

striated muscle see *skeletal muscle* (10.1)

stroma fluid in the inner space of a chloroplast, which contains a concentrated mixture of proteins and other chemicals that are used in the synthesis of carbohydrates during photosynthesis (5.1)

stromatolite fossilized sedimentary structure formed from ancient bacteria; iron bands present in some stromatolites provide evidence of oxygen formation in Earth's past (2.3)

substrate substance upon which an enzyme acts (6.1)

succession sequence of invasion and replacement of species in an ecosystem over time (20.2)

superovulation production of multiple eggs as a result of hormone treatment (15.3)

suppressor T cell lymphocyte that slows and suppresses the cell-mediated immune response to an antigen to ensure that healthy tissues are not destroyed (8.3)

surrogate mother woman who becomes impregnated and carries a baby for another; baby may be conceived through artificial insemination or *in vitro* fertilization (15.3)

sustainability concept of living in a way that meets our needs without compromising the health of future generations or of the planet (20.3)

symbiosis direct or close relationship between individuals of different species that live together; usually involves an organism that lives or feeds in or on another organism (host); three forms are *mutualism*, *commensalism*, and *parasitism* (20.2)

sympathetic nervous system division of the autonomic system that regulates involuntary processes in the body; works in opposition to the parasympathetic nervous system; typically activated in stress related situations; compare *parasympathetic nervous system* (11.1, 11.3)

synapse junction between two neurons or between a neuron and an effector (muscle or gland) (11.1)

synapsis aligning of homologous chromosomes side-by-side during prophase I in meiosis (16.3)

syphilis a sexually transmitted infection caused by the bacterium *Treponema pallidum*; if untreated, can cause bones, muscles, and nerve tissue to degenerate (14.2)

systemic pathway in animals, the circulatory pathway that carries oxygen-rich blood from the heart to the body tissues, and oxygen-poor blood from the tissues back to the heart (8.1)

systolic pressure maximum blood pressure exerted during ventricular contraction; compare *diastolic pressure* (8.1)

T cell lymphocyte that is primarily responsible for cell-mediated immunity; roles include activation of certain immune cells, destruction of invading pathogens, suppression of cellular immunity, and promotion of immune response upon reinfection; types include helper, killer, suppressor, and memory T cells; compare *B cell* (8.3)

T lymphocyte see *T cell* (8.3)

target sequence in DNA replication, short sequence of nucleotides within a strand of DNA recognized and cut by restriction endonucleases (18.3)

taste bud sensory receptor in the bumps (papillae) on the tongue (12.3)

taxonomy practice of classifying organisms based on common fundamental characteristics (3.2)

tectorial membrane one of two parallel membranes that comprise the organ of Corti in the inner ear (the other is the basilar membrane); during the transmission of sound waves, the basilar membrane vibrates, causing the sensory hairs to flex against the tectorial membrane (12.3)

telophase the final stage of cell division (mitosis) in which a nucleolus forms around chromosomes at opposite ends of the dividing parent cell; this stage is followed by cytokinesis to form two daughter cells (16.2)

temporal lobe one of four lobes into which each hemisphere of the cerebral cortex is divided; shares in the processing of visual information but its main function is auditory reception; also linked to understanding speech and retrieving visual and verbal memories (11.2)

tendon fibrous connective tissue that connects skeletal muscle to bone (10.1)

teratogen any agent that causes a structural abnormality of the developing fetus due to exposure during pregnancy; e.g., smoking (15.2)

termination in DNA replication, the completion of the new DNA strands and the dismantling of the replication machine (18.1)

tertiary consumer organism that eats secondary consumers (1.1)

test cross cross of an individual of unknown genotype with a homozygous recessive individual; used as a method to determine the unknown genotype (17.1)

testis (testes) in mammals, one of a pair of male reproductive organs (gonads) that produces sperm (14.1)

testis-determining factor gene carried on the Y chromosome that triggers the production of male sex hormones (14.3)

testosterone reproductive hormone produced in the testes; stimulates the development of the male reproductive tract and secondary sex characteristics; only minor effects in females (14.3)

tetrad a homologous pair formed during prophase I of meiosis, so named because it contains four chromatids (16.3)

thalamus sensory relay centre at the base of the forebrain that governs the flow of information from all other parts of the nervous system, mainly between the forebrain and hindbrain, and between areas of the sensory system (except for the sense of smell) and cerebellum (11.2)

theory of evolution by natural selection a well-supported, widely accepted explanation of how species have changed, and continue to change, during Earth's history as a result of natural selection (4.2)

thermoreceptor sensory receptor that detects heat and cold (12.1)

threshold potential in a neuronal membrane, the minimum change in the membrane potential required to generate an action potential; usually −55 mV (11.1)

thylakoid interconnected flattened sac within the stroma of a chloroplast; membranes contain chlorophyll; may occur in a stack called a granum (5.1)

thylakoid space in chloroplasts, the area inside a thylakoid that is completely sealed off from the surrounding stroma (5.2)

thyroid gland butterfly-shaped gland located below the larynx in the neck; produces the hormone thyroxine; helps regulate metabolism and growth (13.2)

thyroid-stimulating hormone (TSH) a hormone released by the anterior pituitary which causes the thyroid gland to secrete thyroxine; controlled by a negative feedback mechanism: rising thyroxine levels in the blood detected by the hypothalamus and anterior pituitary suppress the secretion of TSH and, therefore, thyroxine (13.2)

thyroxine (T_4) hormone produced by the thyroid and released into the bloodstream; controls the rate at which the body metabolizes fats, proteins, and carbohydrates for energy (13.2)

tidal volume volume of air that is inhaled and exhaled in a normal breathing movement when the body is at rest (7.2)

tonsillitis infection of the tonsils, which are located in the pharynx (7.3)

trachea (tracheae) in vertebrates, tube that carries air from the nasal passages or mouth to the lungs; also known as *windpipe* (7.1)

transcription the first stage of gene expression, in which a strand of messenger RNA (mRNA) is produced that is complementary to a segment of DNA (18.2)

transect a long, relatively narrow rectangular area marked out in a study area for the purpose of sampling a population (3.3)

transfer RNA (tRNA) type of RNA that works with messenger RNA (mRNA) to direct the synthesis of a polypeptide in a process known as translation (18.2)

transformation the evolution of one species into another as a result of mutation and adaptation to changing environmental conditions, resulting in the replacement of the old species; compare *divergence* (4.3)

transforming principle ability of dead pathogenic bacteria to pass on their disease-causing properties to live, non-pathogenic bacteria; phenomenon described by Frederick Griffith in 1928 (18.1)

transgenic genetically engineered; a transgenic organism is produced by incorporating the DNA from one organism into another to create a new genetic combination (18.4)

transitional fossil the remains or impression of a prehistoric organism that shows intermediary links between groups of organisms and shares characteristics common to these groups (4.2)

translation the second stage of gene expression, in which the mRNA nucleotide sequence directs the synthesis of a polypeptide (a chain of amino acids) with the aid of another RNA molecule, transfer RNA (tRNA) (18.2)

transposon short strand of DNA capable of moving randomly from one chromosome to another; also called *transposable element* or *jumping gene* (18.3)

triglyceride high-energy organic molecule composed of one glycerol molecule and three fatty acid molecules; main component of fats and oils (6.1)

trimester one of the three three-month periods into which pregnancy is divided (15.1)

trisomy gain of an extra chromosome as a result of nondisjunction (16.3)

trophic level in an ecosystem, a feeding level through which energy and matter are transferred; indicates an organism's position in the food chain and is determined by the number of energy transfer steps required to reach each level (1.2)

trophoblast the outer cell layer of the blastocyst; will develop into the chorion membrane; compare *inner cell mass* (15.1)

tropic hormone hormone that targets endocrine glands and stimulates them to release other hormones (13.1)

true breeding organisms that are homozygous for a particular trait or set of traits and produce offspring that exhibit the same characteristics generation after generation (17.1)

tubal ligation a surgical sterilzation procedure in women that involves cutting the oviducts and tying off the cut ends to ensure that the ovum does not encounter sperm or reach the uterus (15.3)

tubular reabsorption in the kidney, process in which water and useful solutes are reabsorbed from the filtrate in the nephron and transported into capillaries for reuse by the body (9.2)

tubular secretion in the kidney, process that moves additional wastes and excess substances from the blood into the filtrate in the nephron; uses mainly active transport (9.2)

tympanum round, elastic structure within the middle ear that vibrates in response to sound waves; also known as *eardrum* or *tympanic membrane* (12.3)

type 1 diabetes a condition in which the immune system produces antibodies that attack and destroy the beta cells of the pancreas so they are unable to produce insulin; is usually diagnosed in childhood, and patients require daily insulin injections; also known as *juvenile diabetes* and *insulin-dependent diabetes* (13.4)

type 2 diabetes a condition that develops slowly over time either because the insulin receptors on the body's cells stop responding to insulin or because the beta cells of the pancreas produce less and less insulin over time; condition often appears in overweight adults; also known as *adult-onset diabetes* and *non-insulin-dependent diabetes* (13.4)

ulcer slow-healing sore that forms when the thick layer of mucus that protects the lining of the stomach from the acids in digestive juices is eroded (6.3)

ultrasound sound with a frequency greater than the upper limit of human hearing; used in a procedure by which sound waves sent through the body provide information about internal structures, such as a developing fetus (18.4)

umbilical cord flexible, often spirally twisted, tube that connects the abdomen of a fetus to the mother's placenta in the uterus, and through which nutrients are delivered and waste is expelled (15.1)

uniform distribution distribution of individuals in an evenly spaced pattern over a defined area; seen in artificial populations, such as an orchard, or in birds of prey and other territorial organisms (20.1)

ureter in mammals, a pair of muscular tubes that carry urine from the kidneys to the bladder (9.1)

urethra the tube through which urine exits the bladder and the body (9.1, 14.1)

urinary bladder organ where urine is stored before being discharged by way of the urethra (9.1)

urine in the kidneys, filtrate of the nephron upon leaving the collecting duct; exits the body through the urethra (9.2)

uterine cycle the part of the menstrual cycle that takes place in the uterus (14.3)

uterus in mammals, expanded muscular organ in the female reproductive tract through which eggs pass to the environment or in which an embryo develops and is nourished before birth (14.1)

utricle saclike cavity in the vestibule of the inner ear; contains sensory receptors for gravitational equilibrium (12.3)

vagina a muscular tube that leads from outside the female's body to the uterus; serves as an entrance for the erect penis to deposit sperm during sexual intercourse and as an exit for the fetus during childbirth (14.1)

valve membranous extension of a vessel or the heart wall that opens and closes, ensuring one-way fluid flow (8.1)

variation a visible or invisible difference between one individual and other members of a population (4.1)

vas deferens (vasa deferentia) former name for the storage duct from the epididymis leading to the penis via the ejaculatory duct; now known as *ductus deferens* (14.1)

vasectomy a sterilization procedure in men; involves cutting and tying the ductus deferens (15.3)

vasoconstriction decrease in the diameter of blood vessels; vasoconstriction near the skin conserves body heat (8.2)

vasodilation expansion in the diameter of blood vessels; vasodilation near the skin brings more blood to the surface to help reduce body temperature (8.2)

vegetative reproduction a form of asexual reproduction in which a new plant grows from a modified stem (16.4)

vein blood vessel that carries oxygen-poor blood to the heart (8.1)

vena cava (vena cavae) one of two large vessels, the superior and inferior vena cavae, that open into the right atrium of the heart (8.1)

ventricle one of the two lower chambers of the heart; each ventricle receives blood from one of the atria and pumps it into systemic or pulmonary circulation (8.1)

villus (villi) finger-like projection along the ridges of the small intestine; increases surface area to aid in the absorption of nutrients (6.2)

vital capacity the total volume of gas that can be moved in or out of the lungs; equal to tidal volume + inspiratory reserve volume + expiratory reserve volume; also known as *total lung volume capacity* (7.2)

vitamin organic compound required in trace amounts for normal metabolism (6.1)

vitreous humour a clear, jelly-like fluid inside the posterior chamber of the eye; helps to maintain the shape of the eyeball and support the surrounding cells (12.2)

vulva the external parts of the genital organs of female mammals; includes the labia majora and labia minora, as well as the glans clitoris (14.1)

water reabsorption in the kidney, process which removes water from the filtrate in the nephron and returns it to the blood for reuse by body systems (9.2)

Wernicke's area one of two important areas on the left side of the cerebral cortex; stores the information involved in language comprehension; the ability to utter words is not affected if this area is damaged, but the words make little sense; compare *Broca's area* (11.2)

white blood cell colourless blood cell that protects the body from infection by way of the immune response, and also plays a role in allergic reactions and inflammation; three types include granulocytes, monocytes, and lymphocytes; also known as *leucocyte* (8.2)

white matter part of the nervous system that made up of tracts of myelinated nerve fibres; whitish in colour; forms the inner region of some areas of the brain, and the outer area of the spinal cord; compare *grey matter* (11.1, 11.2)

Y

yolk sac one of the extra-embryonic membranes suspended from the abdominal area of the embryo; in humans, serves no nutritive function, but contributes to the formation of the digestive tract and produces the first blood cells and the future egg (ova) or sperm cells (15.1)

Z

zona pellucida thin, clear layer of protein and carbohydrates surrounding the plasma membrane of the egg (ovum) (15.1)

zygote cell formed by the union of two gametes; the product of fertilization; has 23 pairs of chromosomes for a total of 46 chromosomes (diploid) (15.1)

Index

Numbers in bold font indicate page(s) where the term is defined; **t** indicates the term is in a Table; **f** indicates the term is in a Figure; *Illus* indicates the term is in an unnumbered illustration; *Rev* indicates the term is discussed in a Review question.

exchange in the lungs, 250, 252
exchange in the umbilical cord, 517
in cellular respiration, **9f**, 182, 183, 188
in diffusion, 157
in muscle, 339–341
in photosynthesis, **9f**, 162
in respiration, 244, 252
in the brain, 388
in the circulatory system, 276, 277, 281, 282, 288
in water molecule, **35f**
Oxygen cycle, 43
Oxygen deficit, 341, 342
Oxytocin, 437, 444, **445f**, 525
Ozone, 54

Pain, 427, 430
Paleoartist, 147
Paleoclimatologist, 147
Paleontologist, 146, 147
Paleontology, **122**
Paleotechnician, 147
Paleozoic era, **128f**
Pancreas, **217f**, **218f**, **223**, 231, **436f**, **456**
hormones of, 456, 457
Pancreatic amylase, 223, **225t**
Pancreatic lipase, **225t**, 227
Pancreatitis, 235, 238*Rev*
Pangenesis, 586
Papillae, 426
Parasites, **103**, 108, 725
Parasitism, 103, **724**, 725
Parasympathetic autonomic system, 367
Parasympathetic nervous system, **397**, **398f**
Parathyroid gland, **439f**, 449
Parathyroid hormone (PTH), 449
Parent cell, 74, **551**
Parental (P) generation, 588, 589, 600, 607
Parental type, **600**
Parietal lobes, **390**, **391t**
Parthenogenesis, **575**
Parturition, **523–526**
Pascal (Pa), **749t**
Passive diffusion in respiration, 252, 254
Passive transport, 156, 157
Patellar reflex, 371
Paternal chromosomes, **563f**, 565, 566
Pathogens, **293–300**
Pedigree, **611**, **612f**, 613
Peer Education Counsellor, 539
Pelvic inflammatory disease (PID), **489**
Penfield, Wilder, 392
Penis, **479f**, **480**, 481
Penylketonuria (PKU), 612, 613
Pepsin, 220, **225t**

Peptide, **209**
Peptide bond, 209, **211f**
Per capita growth rate (*cgr*), **709**, 735
Perception, **406**
Peripheral nervous system, **367**, 396–399
autonomic system, **397**, **398f**
somatic system, **396**, 397
Peristalsis, 219, 222, 367
Peritoneal dialysis, **319**, **322f**, 359*Rev*
Peroxisome, **154f**, 155
Persistent organic pollutants (POPs), **59**
Pesticide resistance, 121*Rev*
Petroleum hydrocarbons, 62
in the carbon cycle, 46
pH,
and enzyme action, 215
general principles of, **754**, 755
in Calgary tap water, **51t**
measuring of, 755
of blood, 314
regulation in the body, 317
scale, 755
Phagocytosis, **159**, **293**, 300
Pharmacist/Pharmacy Assistant, 467
Pharynx, **245f**, **246**
Phenotype, **590**, 591, 675
Phenotype frequency, **679**
Phenylalanine, 613
Pheromones, 426
Philosophie Zoologique, 123
Phosphate ion (PO_4^{3-}), 50, **754t**
in Calgary tap water, **51t**
in nucleotides, **626f**, **627f**
Phospholipid, 208
Phospholipid bilayer, **156f**
Phosphorus, 63
cycle, 49, 50
Photopsin, 415
Photoreception, 408, 410–418
Photoreceptors, 408, 410, 414, 415
Photosynthesis, 8, 10, 12, 28, **43f**, **44f**, 86, **162–180**
by *Euglena*, 86
light-dependent reactions, **170**, 171, 177
light-independent reactions, **170**, 176, 177
Photosynthetic pigment, **170**, 177
Photosystems I & II, 171, 173, 174, 177
Phylum, **88t**, 92
Physical mutagens, **645**
Physiotherapist, 354
Phytoplankton blooms, 160
Phytoremediation, **62**
Pig (dissection of), 762–767
Pigment, **170**
Piikani, 59, 60
Pilus (*pl.* pili), **573**
Pineal gland, **439f**, 443

Pinna, **419**
Pinocytosis, **159**
Pioneer community, **726**
Pitch, 246
Pituitary gland, **387f**, **436f**, 441, **444**, **445f**, 526
Placenta, 510, 511, 515, **516**, **517f**
Plaeoclimatologist, 147
Plant cells, **154f**, 155–159, 558, 559
Plantae kingdom, 86, 92
Plants, 85, 571
breeding, 610, 611
classification of, 85–87
geologic time scale of, **128f**
human uses, **169f**
in ecology, 4
in phytoremediation, 62
photosynthesis in, 8, 10
reproduction in, 574–577
solar energy storage in, 10
transgenic, 655
UV radiation effects on, **54t**
Plaque (in heart disease), 277, 279
Plasma, **282**, **284**, 291
osmotic pressure in, 316
Platelets, **283**, 284
Plato, 122
Pleural membrane, **246**, 247
Pleurisy, **258**
Pleurisy root (*Asclepias tuberose*), 255
Pneomothrorax, 253
Pneumonia, **257**, 258
Pneumothorax, 250
Point mutation, **643**
Polar, **35**
Polar covalent bond, 752, **753**
Polar ice, **94f**
Polarization, 373
Pollution, 58
Polychlorinated biphenyls, 655
Polydactyly, 612
Polygene, 607
Polygenic inheritance, 605, 607
Polygenic traits, **607**
Polygraphs, 397, **399f**
Polymers, **206**
Polypeptide, **209**
Polyploid, **552**
Polyploidy, 571
Polysaccharide, **207**, 208, 216
Polysaccharides, **225f**
Ponds (boundary of), 4
Pons, **387**, **391t**
Population crash, 708
Population density (D_P), **704**, 705
Population distribution, 705–707
Population explosion, 708
Population growth, 707–714
of humans, 733–736
Populations, **79**, 84, 109, **678**

Photo Credits

131 (center), © Jonathan Blair/CORBIS; 131 (center), © Martin Harvey/Peter Arnold Inc.; 131 (center), © Nigel J. Dennis/ Firstlight; 131 (center), © Thomas Kitchin & Victoria Hurst/Firstlight; 135 (center left), © Tribune Media Services, Inc. All Rights Reserved. Reprinted with Permission; 136 (top center), © Joseph T. & Suzanne L. Collins/Photo Researchers Inc.; 136 (top right), © Michael Redmer/Visuals Unlimited; 139 (top right), © K. G. Vock/Okapia/Photo Researchers, Inc.; 143 (top center), © Photo by Jo McCulty, courtesy of Ohio State University; 144 (top center), © Photo by Jo McCulty, courtesy of Ohio State University; 144 (center left), © SuperStock. Inc/SuperStock; 145 (top center), © Joseph T. Collins/Photo Researchers, Inc; 145 (top right), © BEATTY, BILL-maXximages.com; 146–147 (spread), © Rob & Ann Simpson/Visuals Unlimited; 148 (top center), © University of Calgary; 152–153 (spread), © CP PHOTO/Larry Mac Dougal; 154 (top center), © CP PHOTO/Larry Mac Dougal; 157 (top center), © Ian Crysler; 160–161 (spread), © NASA/SPL/PUBLIPHOTO; 161 (bottom left), © Jeremy Woodhouse/Getty Images; 161 (top right), © Dr. David Newman/Visuals Unlimited; 162 (top center), © Bob Gibbons/SPL/PUBLIPHOTO; 162 (top right), © Rob Howard/CORBIS; 163 (top left), © VEER Michael Kevin Daly/Photonica/Getty Images; 163 (top left), © Dr. David M. Phillips/Visuals Unlimited; 163 (top right), © Science Source/Photo Researchers, Inc.; 163 (top right), © EYE OF SCIENCE/SPL/ PUBLIPHOTO; 164 (bottom right), © George Chapman/Visuals Unlimited; 165 (top right), © Dr. Donald Fawcett & Dr. Porter/ Visuals Unlimited; 165 (bottom right), © Joel Sartore/National Geographic/Getty Images; 171 (center left), © Royalty-Free/ CORBIS; 176 (top left), © f1 online/Alamy; 178 (bottom left), © Pixtal/age fotostock; 178 (bottom center), © H. Wiesenhofer/ PhotoLink/Getty Images; 178 (bottom right), © S. Alden/PhotoLink/Getty Images; 182 (top right), © Blaslus Erlinger/Zafa/ Corbis; 191 (bottom right), © Courtesy Dr. Ken Preston/Bread Wheat Studies and Baking Research/Grain Research Laboratory/ Canadian Grain Commission; 191 (bottom center), © Courtesy Dr. Ken Preston/Bread Wheat Studies and Baking Research/ Grain Research Laboratory/Canadian Grain Commission; 192 (bottom right), © LARRY LEFEVER/Grant Heilman Photography; 193 (bottom right), © John Maier, Jr./The Image Works; 195 (top center), © NASA/SPL/PUBLIPHOTO; 198 (top center), © CP PHOTO/Larry Mac Dougal; 200–201 (spread), © Tim Tadder/New Sport/Corbis; 202 (top center), © Tim Tadder/Corbis; 204–205 (spread), © DR RAY CLACK (FRPS) & MERVYN DE CALCINA- GOFF (FRPS)/ SPL/PUBLIPHOTO; 205 (bottom left), © Image provided courtesy of Given Imaging; 205 (center right), © DU CANE MEDICAL IMAGING LTD/SPL/PUBLIPHOTO; 210 (bottom right), © Artbase Inc.; 211 (bottom left), © Jean Claude Revy-ISM/PhototakeUSA.com; 223 (top left), © M. Kage/ SPL/PUBLIPHOTO; 223 (top center), ©Ron Boardman/Stone/Getty Images; 232 (bottom right), © Royalty-Free/Corbis; 233 (top right), © Royalty-Free/Corbis; 234 (bottom left), © Artbase Inc.; 235 (top right), © CNRI/SPL/PUBLIPHOTO; 236 (bottom left), © Alison Wright/CORBIS; 239 (top center), © DR RAY CLARK (FRPS) & MERVYN DE CALCINA-GOFF (FRPS)/SPL/ PUBLIPHOTO; 240 (top center), © DR RAY CLARK (FRPS) & MERVYN DE CALCINA-GOFF (FRPS)/SPL/PUBLIPHOTO; 242 (bottom left), © Dr. Fred Hossier/Visuals Unlimited; 242–243 (spread), © Jake Norton/MountainWorld Photography; 244 (top center), © Kennan Harvey/Getty Images; 245 (bottom right), From Mader Inquiry Into Life 9th ed. © 2000, 1997 by McGraw-Hill Companies, Inc.; 255 (bottom right), © Barrett & Mackay Photography Inc.; 259 (bottom right), 2005 D2 Production Inc.; 260 (top center), From Mader Inquiry Into Life 9th ed. © 2000, 1997 by McGraw-Hill Companies, Inc.; 263 (top center), © Jake Norton/MountainWorld Photography; 264 (top center), © Jake Norton/Mountain World Photography; 266–267 (spread), © Vince Michaels/Stone/Getty Images; 267 (bottom left), © Firstlight.ca; 269 (top right), © Klaus Guldbrandsen/ Photo Researchers, Inc; 272 (top center), © Ed Reschke/Peter Arnold, Inc; 277 (bottom center), © Zephyr/SPL/PUBLIPHOTO; 280 (bottom right), © Alix/Photo Researchers, Inc; 281 (top left), © Simon Fraser/SPL/PUBLIPHOTO; 282 (bottom right), © A. Syred/SPL/PUBLIPHOTO; 283 (bottom right), © Dennis Kunkel Microscopy, Inc.; 284 (top left), © Dr. David M. Phillips/Visuals Unlimited; 285 (center), © Dr. R. King/SPL/PUBLIPHOTO; 285 (center right), ©Ed Reschke/ Peter Arnold, Inc; 285 (center), © Dr. Fred Hossler/Visuals Unlimited; 285 (center right), © Ed Reschke/Peter Arnold, Inc; 285 (center), © Ed Reschke/Peter Arnold, Inc; 285 (center right), © Ed Reschke/ Peter Arnold, Inc; 289 (top left), © John Forsythe/Visual Unlimited/ Getty Images; 289 (top center), © John Forsythe/Visual Unlimited; 290 (bottom right), © Mike Powell/Getty Images; 295 (bottom center), From Mader Inquiry Into Life 9th ed. © 2000, 1997 by McGraw-Hill Companies, Inc; 298 (top right), © J. Stevenson/SPL/PUBILIPHOTO; 301 (top center), © Vince Michaels/Stone/Getty Images; 302 (top center), © Vince Michaels/Stone/Getty Images; 304–305 (spread), © Erich Lessing/Art Resource, NY; 305 (center right), © Lawrence E. Armstrong; 305 (bottom left), © Wellcome Library, London; 319 (top right), © Dr. E. Walker/Photo Researchers, Inc; 322 (top right), © PHOTOTAKE Inc./Alamy; 322 (center right), © Dr. P. Marazzi/Photo Researchers, Inc; 323 (top left), © Tom McCarthy/PhotoEdit, Inc.; 324 (bottom right), © Peter Menzel/SPL/ PUBLIPHOTO; 325 (top left), © Ron Chapple/Getty Images; 325 (top center), © Richard Hutchings/PhotoEdit, Inc.; 325 (top right), © Stuart Westmorland/First Light; 327 (top center), © Erich Lessing/Art Resource, NY; 328 (top center), © Erich Lessing/Art Resource, NY; 330–331 (spread), © Tom G. Lynn/Time Life Pictures/Getty Images; 331 (bottom left), © STAR TRIBUNE-MINNEAPOLIS/ST. PAUL 2006; 332 (center left), © Ed Reschke/Peter Arnold, Inc; 332 (bottom left), © Ed Reschke/ Peter Arnold, Inc; 332 (bottom left), © Ed Reschke/Peter Arnold, Inc; 340 (center right), © PROFESSORS P. MOTTA & T. NAGURO/SPL/PUBLIPHOTO; 341 (bottom center), © SuperStock; 341 (center right), © Ian Crysler; 343 (bottom right), © Ryan McVay/Getty Images; 349 (top left), © Nancy Sheehan/PhotoEdit Inc.; 349 (top center), © Alistair Berg/Getty Images; 349 (top right), © Rayman/Digital Vision/Getty Images; 349 (center right), © Altrendo Images/Getty Images; 349 (center left), © George Shelley/Masterfile; 351 (top center), © Tom G. Lynn/Time Life Pictures/Getty Images; 352 (top center), © Tom G. Lynn/Time Life

Pictures/Getty Images; **352** (top left), © Ed Reschke/Peter Arnold, Inc.; **352** (top left), © Ed Reschke/Peter Arnold, Inc.; **352** (center left), © Ed Reschke/Peter Arnold, Inc.; **355** (bottom), © Royalty Free/Digital Vision/Getty Images; **356** (top center), © Tim Tadder/ New Sport/Corbis; **360** (top right), © Bill Stormont/Corbis; **360–361** (spread), © Frans Lanting/Corbis; **362** (top center), © Frans Lanting/Corbis; **364–365** (spread), © Scott Camazine/Photo Researchers, Inc; **365** (bottom left), © Wolfgang Rattay/Reuters/ Corbis; **366** (top), © Hans Blohm/Masterfile; **366** (bottom right), © Image courtesy of the Still National Osteopathic Museum, Kirksville, MO [AS 49]; **368** (top right), © Dr. Dennis Kunkel/Visuals Unlimited; **368** (bottom center), © SPL/Photo Researchers, Inc; **372** (center left), © Ed Reschke/Peter Arnold, Inc; **372** (center left), © MPI Biochemistry/Vilker Steger/Photo Researchers, Inc; **372** (center), © G. Gschmeissner/SPL/Publiphoto; **373** (center right), © Tom McHugh/Photo Researchers, Inc; **378** (bottom right), © James Stevenson/Photo Researchers, Inc; **379** (center left), © Copyright Dennis Kunkel Microscopy, Inc.; **380** (center left), © Don W. Fawcett/Photo Researchers. Inc; **381** (bottom left), © A, Paseika/SPL/Publiphoto; **381** (bottom center), © Alvin Telser/ Visuals Unlimited; **381** (bottom right), © Robert Calentine/Visuals Unlimited; **381** (bottom left), © Dr. John D. Cunningham/ Visuals Unlimited; **381** (bottom center), © Innerspace Imaging/SPL/Publiphoto; **381** (bottom right), © Dr. Fred Hossler/Visuals Unlimited; **383** (center left), © WireImage Stock/Masterfile; **383** (center left), © Earl Clendennen/Alamy; **383** (bottom left), © Scott Houston/Corbis; **383** (bottom left), © Wesley Bocxe/Photo Researchers, Inc; **383** (bottom left), © C. Molloy/SPL/Publiphoto; **385** (top right), © Kevin P. Casey/CORBIS; **386** (top center), © Anatomical Travelogue/Photo Researchers, Inc; **386** (top right), © Manfred Kage/SPL/Publiphoto; **388** (top right), © Biophoto Associates/Photo Researchers, Inc; **389** (top center), © M. Kulyk/ Photo Researchers, Inc; **393** (bottom left), © J. Timothy Cannon, Ph. D.; **393** (bottom right), © J. Timothy Cannon, Ph. D.; **394** (bottom center), © Courtesy of Washington University in St. Louis Magazine 58(2), Summer, 1988; **395** (top left), © Gca/SPL/ PUBLIPHOTO; **395** (top center), © Simon Fraser/SPL/Puliphoto; **395** (bottom left), © Ralph Hutchings/Visuals Unlimited; **396** (top center), © Peter Griffith/Masterfile; **399** (top left), © Peter Dazeley/Getty Images; **400** (top right), © Garyroberts/ Worldwidefeatures; **401** (center), © Scott Camazine/Photo Researchers, Inc.; **402** (center left), McGraw-Hill Higer Education/ Rebecca Gray, photographer/Don Kincaid, dissections; **402** (center), © Scott Camazine/Photo Researchers, Inc; **403** (bottom left), © Motor Lab- University of Pittsburgh; **404–405** (spread), © PM Images/Getty Images; **405** (bottom left), © Jerry Shuiman/ SuperStock; **406** (top center), © Design Pics Inc./Alamy; **407** (top left), © DR M. PHELPS & DR J. MAZZIOTTA ET AL/ NEUROLOGY/SPL/PUBLIPHOTO; **407** (bottom left), © Kathleen Finlay/ Masterfile; **407** (bottom center), © Deborah Davis/ Alamy; **407** (bottom right), © Jutta Klee/Getty Images; **408** (top center), © Copyright IllusionWorks, L.L.C.; **408** (top center), © Copyright IllusionWorks, L.L.C.; **408** (top right), © Copyright IllusionWorks, L.L.C.; **408** (bottom right), © Najlah Feanny/Corbis; **410** (top center), © Darwin Wiggett/First Light; **411** (top left), © Bruce Rowell/Masterfile; **411** (bottom left), © Adam Hart-Davis/ Photo Researchers, Inc.; **411** (bottom left), © Adam Hart-Davis/Photo Researchers, Inc.; **413** (bottom left), © Leonard Lessin/Peter Arnold, Inc; **413** (bottom left), © Leonard Lessin/Peter Arnold, Inc; **414** (bottom left), © SPL/Photo Researchers, Inc.; **414** (top right), Ishihara's Test for Colour Blindness, published by KANEHARA & CO., LTD, Tokyo, Japan. For accurate testing the original plate should be used. From p. 499 Figure 24.11 Inquiry Into Life 9th ed. by Sylvia Mader © 2000, 1997 by the McGraw-Hill Companies, Inc. All rights; **415** (top center), © Lennart Nilsson/Albert Bonniers Förlag AB; **415** (bottom right), © Ralph C. Eagle Jr./Photo Researchers, Inc.; **419** (top right), © Bob Daemmrich/ Photo Edit; **421** (bottom left), © Susumu Nishimaga/SPL/ Publiphoto; **421** (bottom center), © Dr. Goran Bredbory/SPL/Publiphoto; **423** (bottom left), © Photo by Gary Zajic, Auditory Biochemistry Laboratory (director: Dr. Jochen Schacht), Kresge Hearing Research Institute, The University of Michgan; **426** (top left), © Omikron/Photo Researchers, Inc.; **430** (top right), © Dante Fenolio/Photo Researchers, Inc.; **430** (bottom left), © Ken Lucas/Visuals Unlimited; **431** (top center), © PM Images/Getty Images; **432** (top center), © PM Images/Getty Images; **434–435** (spread), © BAUER, ERWIN & PEGGY/Animals Animals/Earth Scenes; **435** (bottom left), © Royalty-Free/Corbis; **436** (center), © Harley Soltes/Time Life Pictures/Getty Images; **437** (bottom left), © Prof. P. Motta/SPL/Publiphoto; **438** (top center), © Jean-Francois RIVIERE/TOP/Imagestate; **438** (top left), © SALMAIMONE/Grant Heilman Photography; **438** (bottom left), © Dee Breger/Photo Researchers, Inc; **438** (bottom center), © Dr. L. Orci/University of Geneva/SPL/PUBLIPHOTO; **438** (bottom right), © Chris Priest/SPL/PUBLIPHOTO; **439** (bottom center), © CORBIS; **443** (bottom left), © The Litebook Company Ltd. An Alberta Corporation www.litebook.com; **446** (top center), © Bettmann/CORBIS; **446** (top right), © Peter Dench/CORBIS; **448** (top right), © Micheal Ross/Photo Researchers, Inc.; **449** (bottom right), © Richard A. Miller, M.D., Ph.D., University of Michigan Medical School; **451** (top right), © Jeremy Maude/Masterfile; **452** (bottom left), © Carlos Davila/Alamy; **453** (top center), © ED RESCHKE/PeterArnold, Inc; **458** (bottom right), © Michael P. Gadomski/Photo Researchers, Inc.; **459** (top right), © Anne Clack/Wellcome Photo Library; **459** (top center), © Kevin Winter/Getty Images; **459** (center right), © SPL/ PUBLIPHOTO; **462** (top left), © Russ Curtis/Photo Researchers, Inc; **463** (top center), © BAUER, ERWIN & PEGGY/Animals Animals/Earth Scenes; **464** (top center), © BAUER, ERWIN & PEGGY/Animals Animals/Earth Scenes; **467** (bottom left), © Dr. Ray Rajotte, Scientific Director of the Alberta Diabetes Institute; **468** (top center), © Bill Stormont/Corbis; **472–473** (spread), © David P. Hall/Masterfile; **474** (top center), © David P. Hall/Masterfile; **476–477** (spread), © David M. Phillips/Photo Researchers, Inc.; **477** (bottom left), © 2003 Getty Images; **480** (center right), © A. Syred/SPL/PUBLIPHOTO; **485** (bottom right), © Ed Reschke/Peter Arnold, Inc; **486** (bottom left), © Dr. David M. Phillips/Visuals Unlimited; **486** (bottom right), © A. Pasieka/SPL/ PUBLIPHOTO; **487** (bottom right), © George Musil/Visuals Unlimited; **488** (bottom left), © Dr. Linda Stannard, UCT/Photo

Morgan/Peter Arnold, Inc.; **723** (bottom right), © Scott Camazine/Photo Researchers, Inc.; **724** (bottom left), © Mark Moffett/Minden Pictures; **724** (top right), © Jim Brandenburg/Minden Pictures; **725** (bottom left), © B. RUNK/S.SCHOENBERGER/Grant Heilman Photography; **725** (bottom), © Science VU/E.White/Visuals Unlimited; **725** (bottom right), © Scott Camazine/Photo Researchers, Inc.; **738** (top right), © Pat Bennett/Alamy; **739** (top center), © Byron Jorjorian/Alamy; **740** (top center), © Byron Jorjorian/Alamy; **743** (bottom left), © Douglas Faulkner/Photo Researchers, Inc.; **744** (top center), © Lynda Richardson/CORBIS

Illustration Credits

132 (bottom left) Victoria Roswell, **156** (bottom center) John Harvey, **159** (top center) John Harvey, **180** (bottom left) John Harvey, **240** (bottom left) John Harvey, **262** (center left) Dave Mazierski, **273** (bottom left) Bart Vallecoccia, **273** (bottom center) Bart Vallecoccia, **273** (bottom right) Bart Vallecoccia, **296** (bottom left) Theresa Sakno, **297** (top center) Bart Vallecoccia, **309** (bottom left) Bart Vallecoccia, **309** (bottom center) Bart Vallecoccia, **309** (bottom right) Bart Vallecoccia, **367** (center right) Victoria Rowsell, **370** (top left) Theresa Sakno, **376** (top center) Theresa Sakno, **376** (bottom center) Theresa Sakno, **378** (top center) Theresa Sakno, **379** (bottom center) Victoria Rowsell, **388** (top left) Victoria Rowsell, **388** (bottom left) Victoria Rowsell, **391** (top center) John Harvey, **397** (top right) John Harvey, **411** (top right) Bart Vallecoccia, **412** (center left) Bart Vallecoccia, **412** (bottom left) Bart Vallecoccia, **417** (bottom left) John Harvey, **417** (bottom center) John Harvey, **417** (bottom center) John Harvey, **417** (bottom right) John Harvey, **436** (bottom right) Bart Vallecoccia, **437** (top center) John Harvey, **437** (bottom right) John Harvey, **444** (bottom right) John Harvey, **446** (bottom left) Bart Vallecoccia, **448** (top center) Victoria Rowsell, **448** (bottom left) Victoria Rowsell, **451** (bottom right) Victoria Rowsell, **452** (bottom right) Bart Vallecoccia, **456** (bottom right) John Harvey, **468** (center left) Dave Mazierski, **497** (center left) Dave Mazierski, **512** (top center) Bart Vallecoccia, **513** (top center) Theresa Sakno, **513** (bottom left) Bart Vallecoccia, **516** (top left) John Harvey, **517** (bottom center) John Harvey, **535** (bottom center) Victoria Rowsell, **537** (top center) Theresa Sakno, **537** (bottom center) Victoria Rowsell, **546** (bottom center) Jane Whitney, **553** (top left) Theresa Sakno, **565** (top center) Theresa Sakno, **569** (bottom center) Theresa Sakno, **576** (top center) Jane Whitney, **579** (top center) Jane Whitney, **601** (top right) Theresa Sakno, **604** (bottom left) Bart Vallecoccia, **631** (bottom center) Victoria Rowsell, **690** (bottom center) John Harvey, **712** (top left) Dave Mazierski